K. HATCH

UNITED STATES HISTORY

RICHARD N. CURRENT • ALEXANDER DE CONDE • HARRIS L. DANTE

SCOTT, FORESMAN PROGRAM

IN UNITED STATES HISTORY

UNITED STATES HISTORY
TESTS
RESOURCE BOOK
UNITED STATES HISTORY: IDEAS IN CONFLICT

SCOTT FORESMAN PROBLEMS IN AMERICAN HISTORY
THE CAUSES OF WAR
THE NEGRO IN AMERICA
LABOR IN AMERICAN SOCIETY
THE SUPREME COURT IN AMERICAN LIFE
AMERICAN FOREIGN POLICY
THE SOCIAL SETTING OF INTOLERANCE
REFORM IN AMERICA
GREAT DEPRESSIONS
POLITICAL LEADERSHIP IN AMERICA

UNITED STATES HISTORY

Richard N. Current   University of North Carolina at Greensboro

Alexander DeConde   University of California, Santa Barbara

Harris L. Dante   Kent State University, Kent, Ohio

SCOTT, FORESMAN AND COMPANY

Richard N. Current is Distinguished Professor of American History at the University of North Carolina at Greensboro. Formerly he was William F. Allen Professor of American History at the University of Wisconsin. He has taught at colleges and universities in nine states and also at the University of Munich, Germany, and the University of Oxford, England. Dr. Current received his A.B. degree from Oberlin College, his M.A. degree from Fletcher School of Law and Diplomacy at Tufts University, and his Ph.D. degree from the University of Wisconsin. He has written many historical books, including *Daniel Webster and the Rise of National Conservatism, The Lincoln Nobody Knows,* and *John C. Calhoun.* Dr. Current is a past member of the board of editors of the American Historical Review and is at present a councilor of the Society of American Historians, Inc.

Alexander DeConde is Professor of History and chairman of the history department at the University of California, Santa Barbara. He has also taught at Stanford University, Whittier College, Duke University, and the University of Michigan. He received a B.A. degree from San Francisco State College and M.A. and Ph.D. degrees from Stanford University. Dr. DeConde has written extensively in the field of American diplomatic and political history, and his titles include *Herbert Hoover's Latin American Policy; The American Secretary of State: An Interpretation; Entangling Alliance: Politics and Diplomacy Under George Washington;* and *The Quasi-War: The Politics and Diplomacy of the Undeclared War with France.* Dr. DeConde has received numerous awards and grants, including a Guggenheim Fellowship and a Fulbright Award in American studies.

Harris L. Dante is Professor of History and Education at Kent State University, Ohio, where he teaches courses in social studies education and the history of United States education. He holds B.A. and M.A. degrees from the University of Illinois and a Ph.D. degree from the University of Chicago. Dr. Dante gained both high school and college teaching experience in Burlington, Iowa, and has taught at the University of Chicago. Active in the National Council for the Social Studies, he has served two terms on that organization's board of directors, and currently is chairman of its Committee on Teacher Education and Certification. Dr. Dante has written articles for many historical and educational publications, including the *Journal of the Illinois State Historical Society* and *Social Education.*

EDUCATIONAL CONSULTANTS:

I. James Quillen, Professor of Education, Stanford University
Daniel Powell, Nicholas Senn High School, Chicago,
                and Northwestern University

EDITORIAL ASSISTANCE:

Jordon Levin, Taft High School, Chicago

Thomas J. Gorman   Designer
Nina Page   Picture Editor
Edward Vebell   Illustrator: "Men in History"

The business activity charts were adapted from material supplied by the Cleveland Trust Company.

Poem on p. 758: "Song of the Open Road" by Ogden Nash. Copyright 1932 by Ogden Nash. Originally appeared in the "New Yorker." From "Verses from 1929 On" by Ogden Nash, by permission of Little, Brown and Co.

Table of Contents

Instructional Visuals

Illustrative elements such as maps, charts, graphs, photographs, and paintings, along with extended captions, are systematically coördinated to explain and clarify major ideas and themes in *United States History*.

Picture Essays

The entire history of mankind, after "prehistoric" times, is commonly divided into three main periods—Ancient, to about the year 500 A.D.; Medieval, from 500 to about 1500; and Modern, from 1500 to the present. American history had its background and its beginnings in European history during the early Modern period. The Modern period began with a number of new developments—the discovery and colonization of America, the Protestant Reformation, the growth of trade and town life, the rise of capitalism, and the emergence of strong nation-states, or nations.

The Path to Independence

While these changes were going on, Europe exerted its influence upon America, but America also had a great impact upon Europe.

America provided an opportunity for many people to start their lives anew if they were discontented with European conditions. Some made the long voyage to distant colonies because they thought they could be more prosperous there, some because they hoped to have more freedom to think or worship as they pleased, and others for both reasons. The very existence of this opportunity affected the attitude of many Europeans, even those who remained at home. They became more restless, more insistent that the lot of ordinary men and women be improved in Europe itself. Thus America had a psychological effect that would be hard to measure.

The possibility of finding refuge in America for unpopular faiths encouraged some people to break away from the Roman Catholic Church or from one of the Protestant denominations and to form new sects. At the same time, both Roman Catholics and Protestants looked to America as a place where they could strengthen their own church by founding colonies of their cobelievers or by sending out missionaries to convert the Indians. Thus the religious diversity and the religious controversies of Europe were intensified.

Even before the discovery of America, Europeans had begun to carry on a profitable trade with distant lands in Asia. After the founding of American colonies, the volume of trade greatly increased. From America, Europeans obtained large quantities of familiar items such as fish, furs, timber, pitch, turpentine, sugar, molasses, and rum, besides new commodities such as potatoes, tobacco, cocoa, and corn. Europeans also secured, from Mexico and Peru, greater quantities of gold and silver than they had ever known.

With the increase in commerce, new methods of carrying on business were introduced in Europe. Joint-stock companies were formed. These were owned by investors who bought shares of stock and thus provided funds for trading activities. The stockholders divided the profits (or the losses, when a venture failed), and some made great fortunes from their investments. Stock exchanges were established for the buying and selling of shares. Insurance companies were organized to insure ships and cargoes against losses from shipwreck, piracy, and other dangers.

The increased supply of precious metals also affected business. Much of the gold and silver was coined, and so the amount of money in circulation grew. This had a twofold effect: the prices of most goods rose, and the cost of borrowing money, the interest rate, fell. Both the rising price level and the falling interest rate stimulated business by making possible larger and larger profits.

Moneylenders became bankers who provided means for the safekeeping of money and who made loans not only of cash but also of credit. Bankers found that they could lend larger sums (that is, promise to pay their borrowers larger sums) than the amount of actual coin they had on hand. This was possible because a borrower usually did not draw out, all at once, the full amount that he had borrowed from the bank. He could pay some of his debts by drawing a *draft* on the bank, ordering the bank to pay one of his creditors. Merchants also discovered that they could pay some of their debts by means of their own private credit. For example, Mr. A could sell a consignment of goods to Mr. B, then draw a draft on Mr. B. (up to the value of the goods he had sold him) and use this draft to pay a debt to Mr. C. Drafts and similar forms of paper (or *bills of exchange*) came to be used even more than cash in the payment of large debts.

The new business system—with privately owned, profit-making companies (corporations) and with extensive use of money and credit—is known as *capitalism.* It gradually replaced feudalism. Under feudalism, the people had been divided into two main classes. At the top were the comparatively few feudal lords who owned the land, and at the bottom were the great mass of serfs who tilled it. The rise of capitalism brought into existence a new "middle class" consisting of the *bourgeoisie,* the wealthy townsmen who made their fortunes from banking and trade.

Along with the changes in economic life went changes in political organization. During the Medieval period, each of the great feudal lords had been pretty much a law unto himself, and disorders had been frequent. The rising bourgeoisie, however, desired a strong, orderly government which could make conditions safe for business. Hence, in every country where a strong king arose and tried to establish his authority over the feudal lords, the great merchants generally gave their support to the king. Thus they helped to create large and powerful kingdoms, or nations (nation-states). The rise of strong nations in Europe—England, France, Spain, and others—was both a cause and a result of the colonization of America.

Competing for power and wealth, the nations developed new principles of international politics. One of these was the theory of *mercantilism.* According to mercantilism, the king's government should control the economic life of all the people. The theory held that a nation would be prosperous and powerful if it had a large amount of gold and silver (so as to stimulate business) and if it did not need to rely on other nations for important materials, especially war materials. Following a mercantilist policy, a nation tried to maintain a "favorable" balance of trade. That is, it attempted to export as much as possible and import as little as possible, so that money would be drawn into the country rather than drained out. Hence a nation also sought colonies. These, it was hoped, would provide materials that could not be produced at home (above all, gold and silver) and would serve as markets to which to send goods that could not be profitably sold at home.

Another new principle of international politics was the *balance of power*. Each nation sought to increase its own power by acquiring territory and allies and thus maintaining a balance (preferably an overbalance) against its enemies or potential enemies. At the same time, each hoped to weaken its enemies by depriving them of territory or allies.

In search of wealth and power, the European nations engaged in continual wars from the beginning of the Modern period. From the sixteenth century through the eighteenth, the control of America (or of portions of it) was one of the main objects of European warfare and diplomacy.

At first, Spain was the most powerful of the nations and claimed the whole of the New World. All the others had to contend against the Spanish claim. England became the leading sea power, however, after destroying the Armada which, in 1588, the Spaniards had sent out to invade and conquer her. Henceforth, England's great rival was France. Between 1688 and 1783, England and her allies fought a series of five wars with France and France's allies. The first three of these Anglo-French wars began in Europe and spread to America, involving the French

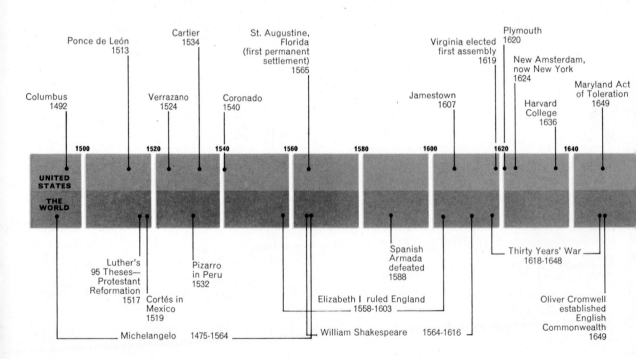

colonists and the English colonists. The fourth one, the French and Indian War (1754-1763), started in America and later became practically a global conflict, with fighting in Europe and in Asia. The fifth one, the Revolutionary War (1775-1783), also had its origins in America and also broadened into something of a world war, with Great Britain facing the hostility of France, Spain, and the Netherlands as well as the United States.

American independence was largely a product of the European system of international politics. Resentment against British policies of mercantilism caused the American colonists to revolt in the first place. Then the principle of the balance of power led France to support the Americans in order to weaken Great Britain by depriving her of her colonies and to strengthen France by gaining a future ally in the form of the United States.

Thus, by 1783, a new republic of thirteen states had arisen from the thirteen colonies that England had founded along the Atlantic coast of North America, beginning in 1607. The people of these states kept most of the ideas and customs that they or their ancestors had brought from the British Isles and from western Europe. American civilization remained a branch of European civilization. Yet, in the course of 176 years, a distinctively "American" character had appeared. The development of this character and the achievement of independence provide the main themes of American history during these formative years.

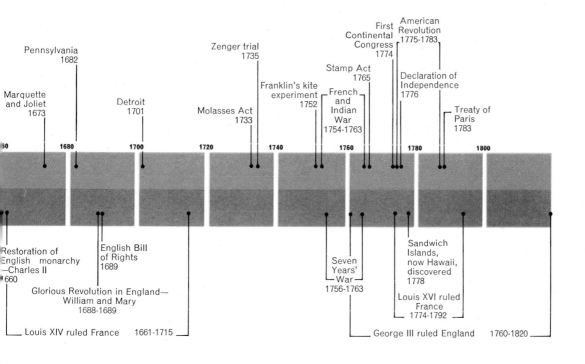

1

The Beginnings of United States History

One day in May in 1607, after sailing in three ships up a broad river, about a hundred men and a few boys landed in a thickly wooded wilderness far from home. The place was swampy and full of mosquitoes, yet fairly easy to fortify and defend. Here the men began to cut down trees and build a town, which they named for their king, James I of England. All kinds of troubles lay ahead—disease, starvation, Indian attacks—but the town itself survived.

That spring day in 1607, when Englishmen first arrived at Jamestown, might be considered as the day when the history of the United States began. From the Jamestown settlement, the colony of Virginia grew, and from other settlements a total of thirteen English colonies later developed along the Atlantic coast of North America. In time these became independent states, and others were added until a great nation of fifty states stretched from the Atlantic Ocean across the North American continent and beyond to a cluster of islands far out in the Pacific.

The year 1607 seems like a long time ago. Yet the lives of only a half dozen men, one after another, would easily cover the whole period from that time to the present. Viewed as merely the equivalent of six lifetimes, the whole span of American history seems really rather brief.

Of course, American history had its beginnings much earlier than 1607. The first Americans, except for the native Indians, were Europeans. They came from the British Isles and from western Europe, and they brought European civilization with them to the wilds of North America. That civilization already had a history reaching back through many centuries and many lands to the very first settled communities, in dim and distant antiquity.

United States history, then, is an extension of European history. In the beginning it was a continuation of English history in particular. The earliest colonists thought of themselves simply as Englishmen who happened to be living in North America, and the Englishmen who stayed at home looked upon the colonists in the same way. As time passed, however, the colonists began to feel that they had become different, as indeed they had. By 1750, they usually considered the people of Britain and other European nations as foreigners, and those people often referred to the colonists as "Americans." New ways of life were developing in the New World.

For this, there were two main reasons. One was that the Americans were a mixture of nationalities. To the English colonies came not only English people but also Scotch-Irish, German, French, Swiss, and others. Each group brought its own customs, and each borrowed from the rest. Many men married women of nationalities other than their own.

"What is the American, this new man?" asked a young French nobleman, Michel Guillaume Jean de Crèvecoeur, who lived and traveled in the colonies for a number of years. He answered his own question in his book, *Letters from an American Farmer,* published in 1782. He noted that in America a man might have an English grandfather, a Dutch wife, and a French daughter-in-law. "Here individuals of all nations are melted into a new race of men," Crèvecoeur said, "whose labor and posterity will one day cause great changes in the world."

One significant group in the colonies consisted not of Europeans but of Africans, practically all of whom came to North America as slaves. By their labor, they contributed much to the development of American civilization. But the conditions of slavery prevented them from keeping up many of their old customs. The Negroes came from a number of African tribes, with distinct languages and cultures. When brought to America, the people of the different tribes were mixed together. Since they usually were unable to speak the same language, it was difficult for them to communicate with one another and thus coöperate in resisting enslavement. On the plantations they were forced to give up many of their old customs and to adopt the white man's ways. Naturally, then,

much from their native cultures was lost, and their descendants had little opportunity to learn about it.

The native peoples, the American Indians, also played an important role in American history. They were helpful to the first Europeans who arrived in the New World. In some cases, they gave food to the starving colonists. They also showed the colonists how to raise a number of new plants—including potatoes, tomatoes, cocoa, and tobacco. As the colonists began to take more and more land from the Indians, however, the Indians resisted. American history has derived much of its drama and color from the Indian resistance to the advance of white settlement.

The second principal reason for the development of a civilization that was distinctively American in character was the physical environment of the colonies. Here lay a vast wilderness to be cleared and an abundance of land to be cultivated. The first settlers along the coast faced many difficulties and dangers, but having overcome these, they found new opportunities to acquire land and other property. They developed farms and villages and later mills and towns and cities, with many of the social, religious, and political institutions common to the European communities from which they had come. As more colonists arrived and people moved farther and farther inland, the same process of taming the wilderness and re-creating civilization was repeated (and it was to be repeated over and over until most of the continent had been settled).

Thus, from the outset, Americans continually underwent a "frontier" experience. Historians have treated the frontier as an imaginary line, as an area, and as a process. It was the line, moving unevenly westward as the country gradually filled up, that divided the settled from the unsettled part of the country. It was the area of new settlements along that line. It was also the process by which life gradually became more civilized within that area.

"American social development has been continually beginning over again on the frontier," wrote the great historian Frederick Jackson Turner in 1893.

This perennial rebirth, this fluidity of American life, this expansion westward with its new opportunities, its continuous touch with the simplicity of primitive society, furnish the forces dominating American character.

According to Turner, this experience made Americans more restless, enterprising, materialistic, individualistic, lawless, and democratic than Europeans. It accounted for the differences between American and European history.

Turner exaggerated the importance of the frontier. Nevertheless, if we take the term to mean the whole influence of the physical environment together with the mixing of various nationalities within that environment, it does provide the basic explanation for the growth of distinctively American ways of life.

ENGLAND BECAME A COLONIZING POWER

Almost five hundred years before the famous voyage of Christopher Columbus in 1492, the Norse explorer Leif Ericson touched upon the northeastern coast of North America. Yet Columbus, not Ericson, is considered as the effective discoverer of the New World. The explorations of Ericson led to no great and lasting consequences, for Europe was not yet ready to respond. During the next five centuries, however, Europe underwent remarkable changes, and the return of Columbus in 1493 touched off one of the greatest colonization movements in all history.

The changes going on in Europe amounted to a kind of reawakening. People had begun to take more and more interest in the world about them. Increasingly they tried to control natural forces by means of science and invention rather than prayer or magic. Among the new inventions were guns, windmills and water mills, the printing press, and the mechanical clock. Especially important for

overseas exploration were the compass and the *astrolabe,* a device for finding the latitude by sighting a star.

Well-organized nations with strong kings were coming into existence. The kings had the support of businessmen, who began to form a new "middle class" between the nobles, who held the land, and the serfs who worked it. Towns increased in size and number as centers of trade. Commerce reached out from Europe to distant places in the Far East. Costly items of trade—jewels, glass and chinaware, silks and other fine cloths, drugs, perfumes, spices—were brought all the way from Japan, China, India, and neighboring islands.

The trade routes lay partly over seas and partly over land. They were controlled at certain points by Arab, Italian, or other merchants. These middlemen took such a large profit that prices were excessively high by the time the goods reached the British Isles and other parts of western Europe. Both the merchants and the rulers of these nations hoped to find new routes, entirely by sea, which the merchants and the rulers themselves could control.

Columbus was looking for such a route when, with the backing of Spain, he sailed westward over the uncharted Atlantic Ocean. When he sighted land, he thought he had reached one of the islands of the Far East. On three later voyages he looked for a passage by water through the islands and land masses he found. For more than a hundred years, other explorers sailing under the flags of various nations kept up the search. They never discovered the kind of passage they were seeking, but they revealed most of the outlines and much of the interior of the North and South American continents.

On the basis of Columbus' discoveries, Spain at first claimed the whole of the New World (Line of Demarcation, 1493) but soon agreed to share the part of it now known as Brazil with Portugal (Treaty of Tordesillas, 1494). In the sixteenth century, Spain began founding colonies and building an empire in both North and South America.

Some of the Spanish settlements lay inside the present boundaries of Florida, New Mexico, and California. Thus Spanish colonization formed part of the background for the civilization of the United States.

Meanwhile other nations, among them England, had challenged the Spanish claim to a monopoly of the New World. Because of her success, England rather than Spain was to be the "mother country" of the United States.

England challenged Spain for power

England based her claim to a share of the New World on the explorations she had sponsored, particularly those of John Cabot, who had sailed from England to North America as early as 1497. For many years, however, England was too weak to make good her claim against the opposition of Spain, which in the sixteenth century was the greatest power in the world.

The Spanish kings ruled a vast empire in Europe as well as in the New World. They became the champions of the Roman Catholics against the Protestants after the Protestant movement began. This movement was led by men like Martin Luther, a German, and John Calvin, a Frenchman, who protested against and undertook to reform certain church practices which they considered wrong. Roman Catholic leaders started to institute their own reforms and tried to win back the people who had left the Roman Catholic Church to join Protestant churches. Bitter religious wars were fought, but Europe remained divided between Roman Catholic and Protestant nations.

King Henry VIII of England broke away from the Church of Rome and set up the Church of England, or the Anglican Church, and declared himself the head of it. His daughter, Elizabeth I (who ruled from 1558 to 1603), had to defend her church and her government against the Roman Catholics both at home and abroad. At home the Roman Catholics plotted to put Mary "Queen of Scots" on the throne. Abroad, the Spanish King

Philip II encouraged the plotters and threatened to attack England. Elizabeth I had Mary put to death and kept up an undeclared war against Spain.

Bold English seamen, with the encouragement of the queen, roved the waters of Spanish America, capturing treasure ships and plundering coastal towns. The greatest of the "sea dogs," Sir Francis Drake, made his way along the coasts of South and North America and on around the world. He brought rich loot to Elizabeth, who secretly had backed his expedition. She made him a knight and thus showed both her gratitude to him and her open defiance of Spain.

Elizabeth made an alliance with the Dutch, who were revolting against Spanish rule, and Philip II now declared war on her nation. He sent (1588) a tremendous fleet, the "Invincible Armada," to invade and conquer England. The English were ready with a large number of ships which, though smaller than the enemy's, were faster and more maneuverable. After the Armada arrived, a terrible storm arose. The storm helped the English for it sank or scattered most of the Spanish fleet. England, now the strongest sea power in the world, could proceed to set up colonies of her own in North America.

Colonization appealed to many Englishmen

In his book *Utopia* (1516) the Englishman Sir Thomas More described life on an imaginary island in the New World. Here there were no poor and no rich. All the people lived comfortably, but they had only contempt for wealth itself. Everyone worked but no one had to work too hard. Peace and happiness prevailed. (Hence, the term *utopia* has come to mean any dream of an ideal society.)

The imaginary life in *Utopia* contrasted sharply with the actual life of England in Sir Thomas More's time. Many landowners were converting their farms into sheep pastures because more money could be made from wool than from grain. The farm tenants were in effect forced from the land,

Greenland

ERIC THE RED, 982

ERICSON, 1000

JOHN CABOT, 1498

HUDSON, 1610

Hudson Strait

Labrador

CARTIER, 1534-36

Hudson Bay

Newfoundland

JOHN CABOT, 1497

Hudson cast adrift

St. Lawrence R.

Stadacona (Quebec)

Columbia R.

L. Superior

CHAMPLAIN, 1603-09

Hochelaga (Montreal)

L. Champlain

JOLIET AND MARQUETTE, 1673

L. Huron

L. Michigan

L. Erie

L. Ont.

LA SALLE, 1681-82

HUDSON, 1609

Missouri R.

Ohio R.

ATLANTIC OCEAN

Arkansas R.

Mississippi R.

DE SOTO, 1539-41

VERRAZANO, 1524

Colorado R.

CORONADO, 1540-42

Death of De Soto

Death of Narvaez

PONCE DE LEON, 1513

COLUMBUS, 1492

CABRILLO AND FERRELO, 1542-43

Rio Grande

MOSCOSO DE ALVARADO, 1542-43

CABEZA DE VACA, 1536

San Salvador

Cullacán

Gulf of Mexico

Cuba

Hispaniola

Compostela

NARVAEZ, 1528

"NORTH SEA" (CARIBBEAN SEA)

982–1513
1514–1602
1603–1682

DRAKE, 1577-80

"SOUTH SEA" (PACIFIC OCEAN)

PREF
UNIVERS

note: Present-day place names are used in these descriptions to help locate the areas of exploration.

25

DISCOVERY AND EXPLORATION OF
NORTH AMERICA: 982-1682

Eric the Red, a Norseman traveling from Iceland, discovered Greenland in 982 and set up a colony there. The saga of his exploits was narrated by several generations of Scandinavians before being written down.

Leif Ericson ventured west from his father's colony in Greenland and sailed along the Atlantic coast of North America in 1000. He landed three times: at *Helluland,* or land of flat stones; *Markland,* or woodland; and *Vinland,* or vineland. Some scholars identify these locations as Newfoundland, Nova Scotia, and Massachusetts.

Christopher Columbus, first modern explorer of the New World, sailed August 3, 1492, from Palos, Spain. Land (the Bahamas) was sighted on October 12, and after island-hopping in the Caribbean Sea, Columbus returned with the news that he had reached Asia. Even after three additional trips across the Atlantic Ocean, he persisted in that belief.

John Cabot (Giovanni Caboto), hoping to eliminate the Arab middlemen in the spice trade, got financial backing from English merchants for a westward voyage. His single ship reached "newfounde land" in June 1497. With his son Sebastian, he made another voyage the next year, exploring the New England coastline.

Giovanni da Verrazano was the first modern navigator to explore New York harbor. A member of a Florence banking family, he was commissioned by Francis I of France to seek a strait to China through the New World. His search, in 1524, led him along the Atlantic coast from South Carolina to Newfoundland.

Henry Hudson, an Englishman, had first tried to sail northeast through Russia to the Orient, but decided to cross the Atlantic Ocean in 1609. He rediscovered New York harbor for his Dutch sponsors and sailed 150 miles north on the river that now bears his name. Voyaging under the English flag in 1610, he found a great bay (later named for him), where his mutinous sailors left him to die.

Juan Ponce de León tried to explore Florida in 1513, but his expedition was foiled by hostile Indians. The Spanish king then promised him he could be governor of Florida if he conquered it. Returning in 1521 with 200 well-armed soldiers, Ponce de León again failed to subdue the Indians; he himself died of an arrow wound.

Pánfilo de Narváez led another futile Spanish expedition to Florida in 1528. A combination of disease, starvation, and Indian fighting reduced his army of four hundred to four. The survivors crossed the Gulf of Mexico to Texas. Two of them, **Alvar Núñez Cabeza da Vaca,** and Estabanico, a Negro, adventured their way across the Southwest to join other Spaniards in California in 1536.

Hernando De Soto and 600 Spanish nobles in 1539 successfully invaded Florida. Searching for Indian treasure, they traveled north to the Carolinas and then west across the Mississippi River to Texas. The search was futile, but De Soto did claim for Spain a vast area of the Southeast. After he died of a fever in 1542, about 300 of his men, led by **Luis de Moscoso de Alvarado,** managed to reach Mexico to report their explorations.

Francisco Vásquez de Coronado, a Spanish nobleman, spent his entire fortune searching for the legendary Seven Cities of Gold in the Southwest. He was led on by a wily Indian who hoped to exhaust the Spanish plunderers and get revenge for the murder of his people. Coronado's expedition (1540-1542) reached as far inland as Kansas.

Juan Rodriguez Cabrillo, a Portuguese navigator sailing for Spain, and his pilot, **Bartolomeo Ferrelo,** explored the west coast for the mouth of a transcontinental river. The failure of their voyage (1542-1543) convinced the Spanish to give up their search for such a passage.

Sir Francis Drake was looking for an escape route for his pirate ship when he landed on the California coast in 1579. He brazenly planted the English flag, although the Spanish held many prior claims to California. Failing to find his escape route, he returned to England by sailing west across the Pacific Ocean.

Jacques Cartier, searching for the Northwest Passage, opened up the vast northeast interior for French settlement. On two voyages, in 1534 and 1535, he explored the St. Lawrence River valley and befriended the Indians living there.

Samuel de Champlain first came to Canada in 1603. He returned twice as official geographer for French King Henry IV, the second time remaining to govern the fur-trading posts he had established. He explored northern New York (Lake Champlain) and the St. Lawrence river valley, founding Quebec in 1608.

Louis Joliet, a Frenchman born in the New World, and **Jacques Marquette,** a Jesuit priest, first sighted the Mississippi River at the mouth of the Wisconsin River in 1673. They traveled down the Mississippi as far as Arkansas, where they were turned back by unfriendly Indians. They had long since realized that the "great river" was not a route to the Pacific.

La Salle (the French nobleman Robert René Cavalier) gave the name Louisiana, after Louis XIV of France, to the land he explored. In January 1682, with 23 Frenchmen and 18 Indian warriors, he traveled down the Illinois and Mississippi rivers to the Gulf of Mexico.

and many roamed around in gangs begging and stealing. The villagers' fear of them is recalled in the nursery rhyme: "Hark, hark! The dogs do bark: the beggars are coming to town."

While the masses were poor and in many cases growing poorer, the wool growers, dealers, and manufacturers prospered. Great merchants exported woolens and other goods to foreign nations. Some of the merchants formed companies so as to share the expenses, risks, and profits in large trading ventures. Often the shareholders in a company made fantastic profits from a single voyage.

The merchants adopted a theory of trade which held that their trading activities were good for the nation as a whole. This theory eventually came to be known as *mercantilism*. It maintained that a country was strongest and most prosperous when exports were greater in value than imports. Then gold and silver would flow into the country to make up for the difference in value. The increase of money in circulation would stimulate business and create new jobs. Hence, according to the mercantilist theory, the government ought to encourage sales to foreign nations and discourage purchases from them.

The idea of acquiring colonies in North America fitted well into the mercantilist theory. Colonies would become places to send the poor and the unemployed, to sell manufactured goods, and to obtain raw materials which otherwise would have to be bought from foreign lands. The colonial trade would provide additional business for shipowners, and it would furnish additional revenue for the government, which could tax the trade.

Colonies would also provide places of refuge for religious and political minorities. Not all the English people were satisfied with the Church of England. Roman Catholics objected to it, as did many Protestants. The Puritans wished to simplify the services, that is, to "purify" them. The Quakers and other dissenting groups wanted complete independence of worship. According to the laws, however, everyone, regardless of belief, was required to conform with the established church, the Church of England, and had to pay taxes to support it.

During the seventeenth century, there was a continual struggle between the Parliament and the king. Under King James I, the government persecuted the Puritans and other Protestant dissenters. These groups got control of Parliament and, in the 1640's, fought a civil war, executed King Charles I, and set up a dictatorship under their leader Oliver Cromwell. In 1660, the kingship was restored, with Charles II on the throne. Finally, in the Glorious Revolution (1688-1689), Parliament asserted its supremacy by deposing King James II, who had become an ardent Roman Catholic, and bringing in the Protestants William and Mary as sovereigns.

During those years of religious and political disturbance, first one group and then another, when it was out of power, looked to North America as a place to find safety. At the same time, the men who were in power looked to North America for lands with which to reward their friends and followers. Thus the religious and political as well as the economic conditions in England accounted for the interest in colonies in the New World.

The English founded thirteen colonies

According to English law, the monarch was both the owner and the sovereign of all new lands that Englishmen discovered or settled. The government itself did not, however, undertake colonizing projects. These were left to private individuals, partnerships, or companies.

By promoting colonies, men generally hoped to serve patriotic or religious ends and at the same time to make profits for themselves. This they expected to do by selling or renting land to settlers and by engaging in colonial trade. First, the promoters had to obtain from the king a grant of land and a charter giving them the right to start a colony and the right to govern the colonists. Next, the promoters had to get together ships, supplies, and people and send them to North America. This was a very expensive business.

The kings awarded land grants and colonial charters one after another. Sometimes the boundaries of a new grant conflicted with those of a previous one, and sometimes the men receiving the land transferred parts of it to other men. Sometimes charters, after having been awarded, were revised or revoked. Consequently there was a good deal of quarreling and confusion about the promotion of colonies.

Nevertheless, companies and "proprietors," either individuals or groups, succeeded in establishing colonies which were to last. Grants made to two groups of merchants, known as the London Company and the Plymouth Company, led to the beginnings of Virginia and Massachusetts. Grants to various proprietors—the Calvert family, Lord Ashley and seven partners, the Duke of York, and William Penn and others—resulted in the founding of Maryland, the Carolinas, New York, and the Quaker colonies (Pennsylvania, Delaware, and New Jersey). Settlers moving out from Massachusetts formed other New England colonies (Rhode Island, Connecticut, and New Hampshire), which eventually managed to get separate charters from the king. A grant to a group of trustees who acted as a charity rather than a business resulted in the establishment of the last of the mainland colonies, Georgia.

Thus, over the long period from 1607 to 1733, a total of thirteen English colonies were established on the North American continent. (Still others appeared on various islands in and near the Caribbean Sea.) The promoters did not make as much money as they had expected, and so colonization proved more or less a failure as a business enterprise. Still, it was a great success as an experiment in the making of new societies.

REVIEWING THE SECTION

1. During the reign of Elizabeth I, what political and military events enabled England to become the world's greatest sea power?

2. Why were the English interested in establishing colonies?

3. Explain how the thirteen English colonies were established on the North American continent.

THE ENGLISH COLONIES PROSPERED

The early arrivals from England, where the countryside was rapidly being stripped of its trees, were much impressed by the vast and almost unbroken forest they found in North America. With the animals and birds it sheltered, this forest furnished abundant food, fuel, and building material. Yet it stood as an obstacle to the cultivation of the soil, and before they could begin to farm, the settlers had to turn to the laborious task of clearing fields.

The newcomers were also struck by the abundance of land. The Old World had seemed crowded, but there was plenty of room in the New World. Some of the soil was poor, however, and some of the good land was hard to get at. Hostile Indian tribes as well as the forest were barriers, and transportation was difficult except on navigable streams. Hence the population moved rather slowly into the interior from the original settlements along the coast.

Differences in physical environment from north to south led to the development of three fairly distinct regions, each with its own characteristic form of economic life. In New England the farms were small and fairly self-sufficient, and shipbuilding and shipping became important industries. In the middle colonies, or "bread colonies" (New York, New Jersey, Pennsylvania, and Delaware), farms were larger and more productive, and much grain, flour, and meat was exported to other colonies and to overseas markets. In the South, extensive plantations as well as modest-sized farms appeared, and tobacco, rice, and indigo were produced for export.

As the colonies grew, they prospered. Only a comparative few of the colonists got rich, but on the whole the people in North America were better off than their contemporaries in England and in every other part of the world.

The population grew rapidly and became diverse

The colonies needed labor to develop their economic resources. The Old World contained multitudes who were eager to get a new start in life in the colonies, but most of these people were too poor to pay their own passage across the ocean.

To bring laborers to the colonies, a system of "indentured" servitude developed. According to this arrangement, men and women signed contracts to work as servants for a period of years, varying from four to seven. The contracts were sold to landholders who needed workers, and thus money was provided to pay for the ocean passage. (Originally a contract was written twice on a large sheet of paper, which was cut in two; one piece was kept by the servant and the other given to his master. The cut was made with special indentations or indentures, so that the two pieces could be identified as parts of the same contract, and hence the expression "indentured" servant.) A master was required to care for his servants during their terms of servitude. At the end of their terms they were free, and if they could make enough money, they might obtain land and servants of their own.

Most of the indentured servants went to the middle colonies, especially to Pennsylvania, where labor was needed on the large farms. At first, many also went to the colonies in the South. In 1619, however, a Dutch ship docked at Jamestown and left twenty Negroes there. For a time these and additional Negroes who were brought in were held only in temporary servitude, much like white servants, but gradually the Negroes began to be kept as permanent slaves.

Indentured servants continued to arrive in the colonies, some even after the Revolutionary War, but after 1700, slaves rapidly replaced indentured servants on the tobacco plantations. In the rice fields of South Carolina and Georgia, Negro slavery, which had been brought in from the West Indies, prevailed from the outset. In New England and the middle colonies, some Negro slaves were used as household servants or as farm hands, but they were much less numerous in those regions than in the South.

During the eighteenth century many colonists came from France, Germany, and Ireland, some as indentured servants, others paying their own way. Those from France were chiefly Huguenots, Protestants who had been denied freedom of worship at home. Those from Germany were Roman Catholics and Protestants who had suffered from French invasions of their nation. Those from Ireland, the so-called Scotch-Irish, were Presbyterians whose ancestors had been sent from the Scottish lowlands to northern Ireland to help hold that country for the king of England. When the English government prohibited the export of their woolen goods and insisted on conformity to the Church of England, and at the same time absentee English landlords raised rents, the Scotch-Irish began to leave Ireland by the thousands.

The colonial population grew fast, partly because of the large immigration from abroad and partly because of a high birth rate in the colonies themselves. By 1775, the total population was more than two million, nearly ten times as many as in 1700. About a third of the total number of people were themselves immigrants or were descendants of immigrants from nations other than Britain. There were more than 750,000 Negroes (59,000 of them free) included in this figure.

Most colonists farmed the land

Throughout the colonial period, at least nine tenths of the people made their living chiefly by cultivating the soil. Some depended also on various industries, and these, too, were closely related to the land, to the natural resources.

Farming methods were generally crude. The colonial farmer, like the European farmer, used a hoe, mattock, or wooden plow drawn by oxen to break the ground. He sowed by hand and harvested with a sickle or scythe. He threshed grain by flailing it or having oxen trample it; he then tossed it up and let the wind blow away the chaff.

British Possessions in North America, 1763

Thirteen Original Colonies

All Others

TYPE OF COLONY AND DATE

1642	1691	1715
CORPORATE	ROYAL	PROPRIETARY

COLONY	TYPE			FIRST SETTLEMENT	DATE
VIRGINIA	1606	1624		JAMESTOWN	1607
NEW HAMPSHIRE	1622	1679		DOVER	1623
MASSACHUSETTS	1629	1691		PLYMOUTH	1620
MARYLAND	1632	1691	1715	ST MARY'S	1634
RHODE ISLAND	1644			PROVIDENCE	1636
CONNECTICUT	1662			HOUSE OF HOPE	1633
NORTH CAROLINA	1663	1729		ALBEMARLE SOUND	1660
SOUTH CAROLINA	1663	1729		ALBEMARLE POINT	1670
DELAWARE	1664			FORT CHRISTINA	1638
NEW JERSEY	1664	1702		FORT NASSAU	1623
NEW YORK	1664	1685		FORT ORANGE / FORT AMSTERDAM	1624
PENNSYLVANIA	1681	1693	1694	PHILADELPHIA	1682
GEORGIA	1732	1753		SAVANNAH	1733

Map labels: POSSESSIONS OF HUDSON'S BAY COMPANY, L. St. John, INDIAN RESERVE, NOVA SCOTIA, L. Superior, L. Nipissing, QUEBEC, MASS., L. Huron, L. Michigan, L. Ontario, L. Erie, N.H., Albany, MASS., Boston, N.Y., CONN., Providence, Hartford, R.I., PA., N.J., New York, Philadelphia, Wilmington, MD., DEL., INDIAN RESERVE, Baltimore, VA., SPANISH POSSESSIONS, Ohio R., Williamsburg, Norfolk, PROCLAMATION LINE OF 1763, N.C., Mississippi R., INDIAN RESERVE, S.C., GA., Charleston, Savannah, ATLANTIC OCEAN, WEST FLORIDA, EAST FLORIDA, Gulf of Mexico

PREPARED BY RSAL MAP, INC.

The colonial farmer gave less attention than the European farmer did to fertilizing and conserving the soil. In North America, much of the land was both rich and plentiful, but labor was comparatively scarce; so it paid to economize on labor rather than land. Despite his more careless methods, the colonial farmer as a rule enjoyed greater abundance than did his European counterpart.

In New England the typical farm was so small that the owner and his sons could take care of it themselves. They produced milk, meat, fruits, vegetables, hay, and corn for their own use. They were discouraged from growing wheat because of the spread of a plant disease, the "blast" or black-stem rust. New England came to depend on the middle colonies for its wheat supply.

In the middle colonies, especially in Pennsylvania, the typical farm was larger and better tilled than in New England. It yielded not only crops for home consumption but also wheat and meat for export. Many of the Pennsylvania Germans used the careful methods of farming they had learned in Germany. With their extensive holdings, they needed all the labor they could get, and they resorted to the use of indentured servants, women as well as men. Often the farmers' wives and daughters also worked in the fields.

In Virginia, Maryland, and North Carolina tobacco was the leading export crop. Intensive cultivation of tobacco quickly depleted the soil, and growers acquired larger and larger plantations so as to have a reserve supply of fresh land. On the plantations the labor was simple and repetitive, the kind that slave gangs could easily be taught to perform.

In South Carolina and Georgia, too, where the most important products were rice and indigo, slaves were profitably employed. During part of the year they waded in flooded fields along the river bottoms to cultivate the rice. The rest of the time they tended to the indigo plants, which grew on higher ground, and assisted in the manufacture of blue indigo dye.

On farms and plantations everywhere a good deal of manufacturing was carried on. Families generally made their own yarn, cloth, clothes, shoes, candles, soap, and the like, as well as bread, butter, cheese, and other foodstuffs. In addition, farmers often engaged in industries such as fishing and the operation of sawmills.

Lumbering, fishing, fur-trading, iron-making, and shipbuilding developed into large and specialized industries, especially in the middle colonies and New England. These industries, particularly shipbuilding, became big businesses for that time, and in many cases required the investment of considerable capital and the employment of large numbers of workers.

In the cities various kinds of skilled craftsmen appeared, such as carpenters, cobblers, *chandlers* (candle makers), *coopers* (barrel makers), weavers, tailors, wheelwrights, tinsmiths, and blacksmiths. The master craftsman was much like the owner of a small business. He himself worked, but he also hired journeymen and apprentices to help him. These men aspired to become master craftsmen themselves, with shops of their own.

Overseas trade was necessary

Before the end of the colonial period, Americans were producing more than half of the manufactured goods they used. They had to obtain from Britain, however, high-quality manufactures such as heavy machinery, fine tools, and fancy furniture and cloth.

The colonists had to find the means to pay for these imports. Gold and silver coins were scarce. In dealing among themselves, the people often resorted to barter, or they made payments with beaver skins, warehouse certificates for tobacco in storage, or paper currency. These did not, however, circulate as money outside the colonies. The colonists had to sell goods abroad in order to get the foreign money or credit with which to pay for imports.

In trying to sell abroad, the colonists were somewhat limited by British law. They had to send their tobacco and certain other "enumerated items" —such as furs, timber, and naval stores—only to Britain. They could not export to the British Isles or to the British West Indies, however, any fish, flour, wheat, or meat, since these would compete with similar products of Britain itself.

A large direct trade in the enumerated items, especially tobacco, developed between the colonies and Britain. To dispose of the rest of the products, colonial merchants looked to other markets, especially in the French, Dutch, and Spanish islands of the Caribbean. There the products were exchanged for coins and for sugar, molasses, and other West Indian produce. Some of this was taken to Britain and used, along with foreign money, to help pay for goods that the mainland colonies imported from Britain.

Another pattern of indirect or "triangular" trade was developed with southern Europe. Colonial ships with cargoes of fish and other products would go to southern Europe, exchange their cargoes for wine and money, take these to Britain, and then return home with British manufactured goods.

The slave trade also often took a triangular

form. Colonial vessels carried rum and other trading supplies from New England ports to the Guinea coast of Africa. From Africa the ships took slaves to the West Indies, and from there they returned to their home ports with sugar, molasses, and cash. On the "middle passage," from Africa to the West Indies, many of the captives, closely packed in the holds of the ships, died of disease and were thrown overboard. After the survivors had reached the West Indies and had been "seasoned" for a time, some of them were shipped on to the North American mainland, to be sold to the tobacco and rice planters.

REVIEWING THE SECTION

1. For what reasons and under what conditions did the various nationality groups migrate to the colonies?

2. How did the methods of farming and the crops raised differ among the colonies?

3. Why did the colonies find it necessary to develop foreign trade? What patterns of foreign trade developed?

SOCIAL AND INTELLECTUAL LIFE DEVELOPED

The colonists derived most of their social and intellectual habits from England. From England came their language, of course, and also their system of weights and measures—foot, yard, ounce, pound, pint, quart, and so on—and their money calculations in pounds, shillings, and pence. With the language came most of their folklore, literary and scientific knowledge, and concepts of education and law.

Most of the colonists read the King James version of the Bible in English, first published in 1611. They acquired their religious concepts very largely, though not entirely, from English interpretations of the Christian faith.

The colonists brought from England most of their ideas of the proper relation of man to man in society. In the colonies, as in England, few people believed in complete social equality. Most of them took for granted the existence of distinct social classes, with an upper class of landholding country gentlemen and a titled aristocracy or nobility at the top.

In the colonies, however, social classes developed along lines somewhat different from those of England. So did the churches, the schools, and many of the habits of speech and thought. Distinctive patterns of social and intellectual life arose in the colonies because of the American environment and the mixture of English and other European influences within that environment.

Social mobility existed in the colonies

Though some English aristocrats were promoters of colonies, almost none of them settled in North America as colonists. A few country gentlemen became settlers, but the vast majority of the colonists were originally of the middle or lower classes.

In North America those who managed to become great landholders or wealthy merchants formed a kind of colonial aristocracy, though they were not descended from English aristocrats. Beneath them in the social structure was a large middle class, proportionately much larger than in England. This middle class was made up of merchants, shopkeepers, craftsmen, and farm owners. Lower yet was a class which included indentured servants, other farm laborers, and unskilled town workers such as dockhands. At the very bottom of the social structure were the Negro slaves.

The colonists were quite conscious of belonging to one class or another, and the differences were clearly marked by clothing and personal appearance. A farmer, for example, wore plain homemade clothes and shoes. A wealthy planter or merchant dressed himself up in buckle shoes, knee breeches, colorful waistcoat, ruffled shirt, and powdered wig.

Nevertheless, except for the slaves, people in the colonies had many opportunities to improve their economic and social status, more opportunities than people in England or other European nations had at that time. Once a man had gained wealth, he was likely to be accepted as a social equal by those who were already rich. His children and grandchildren were inclined to look upon themselves as trueborn aristocrats.

The story of the Byrds, one of the great families of Virginia, provides an outstanding example of *social mobility* (movement up and down in society) in the colonies. William Byrd I arrived in the colony about 1670 and proceeded to make a fortune by selling slaves and by trading with the Indians for furs and hides. He began the building of an impressive mansion, "Westover," not far from Jamestown, on the James River. His son William Byrd II added to the fortune by land speculation and other enterprises; by the time he died (in 1744) he owned 179,440 acres. However, a grandson, William Byrd III, lost a large part of the fortune, including the Westover estate, and found himself in approximately the same position his grandfather had been in soon after he started building his fortune.

Women were more highly respected and had greater freedom in the colonies than in England. In the colonies they were outnumbered by men and were valued partly because of their relative scarcity. In 1704, a woman named Sarah Knight traveled alone all the way from Boston to New York. Such a trip seemed natural enough in the colonies, but it would have been almost unthinkable in England, where a respectable woman dared not go far without a female companion or a male escort.

Various religious groups existed in the colonies

Though the religions were brought from England and other nations of Europe, they formed a new and different pattern in North America. In each of the European nations there was a state church, usually Roman Catholic or Protestant, and the people were required to conform to its practices and contribute to its support, whether they agreed with it or not. In England the Church of England was the state church. In the colonies, by contrast, a great variety of churches existed, none of them completely dominant over the others.

True, the Church of England was, by law, the established church of several of the colonies, and the people in them were supposed to pay taxes to support it. In fact, however, the Church of England managed to maintain a privileged position only in Virginia, Maryland, and certain parts of a few other colonies, and even in these places other denominations were permitted to worship as they pleased. It is true also that the Puritan, or Congregational, church was established in Massachusetts, Connecticut, and New Hampshire, but in these colonies, too, other religious groups, except in the early years, were allowed to set up churches of their own.

To visitors from abroad the variety of religious groups in the colonies of the New World seemed strange and bewildering. Besides Anglicans and Congregationalists, there were Presbyterians, several different kinds of Baptists, Quakers, Moravians, Lutherans, Dutch Reformed, and other Protestants. The Roman Catholics were comparatively few in number, and Jews even fewer.

Many of the Protestants—the Congregationalists, Presbyterians, Dutch Reformed, French Huguenots, and some of the Baptists—were Calvinists. That is, they held beliefs which had come directly or indirectly from the teachings of John Calvin. He had preached the doctrine of *predestination,* the doctrine that, from birth, each soul is predestined for either salvation or damnation. He had also insisted upon hard work and strict morality.

Such Calvinist or Puritan attitudes dominated the lives of most New Englanders in the early days. As life gradually became easier, however, many of the Puritans began to take their religion less and less seriously. So did other Protestants.

The trend away from religion was reversed by the Great Awakening, a series of revivals during the 1730's and 1740's. The outstanding revivalist of the time was Jonathan Edwards, a remarkable

MEN IN HISTORY

FRANKLIN AND EDWARDS

In the last years of the 1730's, a religious revival swept Great Britain's colonies on the North American continent. The strong convictions of the American colonists surfaced and became the main social movement of the day. The concern of that movement was the nature of man and his salvation.

This upsurge of religious fervor was marked by the "preaching of terror with accompanied bodily effects." Among the congregations there was "Swooning away and Falling to the ground . . . bitter Shriekings and Screamings; convulsion-like Tremblings and Agitations, Strugglings and Tumblings." This great religious revival was known as the "Great Awakening," and was to last ten years.

While the mass of the people were swept up in the movement, many theologians were opposed to it. They thought it appealed merely to men's emotions. They believed that "an enlightened mind, and not raised affections, ought always to be the guide of . . . men." To them reason was the one reliable element that governed men's minds.

The most prominent defender and promoter of the Great Awakening was the New England clergyman, Jonathan Edwards, who had played an important part in all the major philosophical and theological controversies of his time. He believed the current enthusiasm among people and clergy was "a surprising work of God." It was necessary to scare people into heaven, and emotions had to be catered to because they were the prime movers in human life.

Standing aloof from the Great Awakening were the humanists, who had been unable to find in the religion of the time a satisfaction of their needs. These people were convinced that current worldly problems should be the chief concern of man. Foremost among them was Benjamin Franklin of Philadelphia. Franklin believed that the true Great Awakening was to come not in the field of religion, but in the expanding knowledge of the physical world; that it was man's duty to concentrate on this expansion of knowledge.

By his own admission Franklin was a deist, a believer in a Supreme Being, though not certain how to approach Him.

While the orthodox religious people believed that deism meant a disbelief in God, there were some clergymen who were not disturbed over Franklin's belief, nor he over theirs.

In contrast to Franklin's beliefs, Edwards' whole philosophy centered about a deep conviction in an all-encompassing divine power. His chief purpose in life was to proclaim that power. He believed a supernatural sense had been granted arbitrarily to men like himself who had been chosen for salvation.

Franklin believed that the theological arguments advanced by Jonathan Edwards were a waste of time, since no practical benefit could be derived from them. And as he advanced in age and experience, Franklin developed a humanist philosophy that "occupied itself with what was before it, with the present rather than with the past or the future, with the best of possible rather than with the best of conceivable worlds." A better world, Franklin thought, could be achieved only through skepticism, freedom, compassion, and the use of reason to solve human problems.

Jonathan Edwards believed that men were basically evil. He thought it impossible for anyone to control his own mind, since the behavior of all men was directed by divine power, and only divine power could remold men into truly worthwhile human beings.

Franklin's worldly philosophy made him the leader in many movements for the direct benefit of man. One of his chief concerns was for the advancement of education, which he considered the surest foundation of happiness for both the family and the state. Students should be taught what is most useful and most beautiful. Through the study of history, tradition, and customs, youth could learn morality, religion, good citizenship, logic, and reasoning.

Jonathan Edwards is remembered for his theological writings, which have affected American religious thought for many generations. Benjamin Franklin is revered for his humanity, humor, and scientific achievements. Thus in different ways, both men made lasting contributions to the heritage of the United States of America.

theologian who had written a pamphlet on the soul at the age of ten and who later wrote a brilliant treatise on the freedom of the will. As a Massachusetts minister, Edwards preached a number of terrifying sermons. Addressing the sinners in his audience, he once declared: "The God that holds you over the pit of hell, much as one holds a spider, or some loathsome insect, abhors you, and is dreadfully provoked." Edwards was trying to turn people back to the strict Puritan faith of their forefathers.

The Great Awakening spread throughout the colonies, but it had its greatest effect in the back country of the South. On the whole, the movement failed to revive old-fashioned Calvinist doctrines, but it succeeded in adding tens of thousands of new members to Baptist and "New Light" Presbyterian churches which abandoned the doctrine of predestination and proclaimed that man could be saved through conversion, through the exercise of his own free will.

In the colonies more than anywhere else in the world at the time, there developed a tolerant attitude toward religious differences. Tolerance seldom was extended to Roman Catholics, but Protestants were more and more inclined to let one another worship as they pleased. This came about not because many Protestants had deliberately sought tolerance as an end in itself. It came about, rather, because conditions in the colonies happened to favor it. With so many religious groups around them, people gradually began to doubt whether any church, even their own, could possibly have a monopoly of righteousness and truth.

Some colonists tried to keep learning alive

The great English lexicographer Samuel Johnson referred, in 1756, to the existence of an "American dialect." To Johnson and to other Englishmen as well, the accent and even many of the words of the colonists had begun to sound strange. The Americans adapted words from many languages, such as *squash* from an Indian language,

prairie from the French, and *boss* from the Dutch. They formed new words by combining old ones, such as *snow-plow* and *bull-frog*. They also kept a number of expressions, such as *cater-corner* and *fall* (for *autumn*), which were going out of use in England.

To Dr. Johnson the Americans seemed like barbarians. Actually they took great pains to educate their children and keep learning alive. Massachusetts adopted a law in 1647, requiring each town to see that at least reading and writing were taught. Every town of a hundred or more families was also expected to provide a Latin grammar school (high school). In other colonies many children learned to read and write in private or church schools or at home from tutors or parents. By the end of the colonial period, probably a higher proportion of Americans than of Englishmen could read.

By 1763, there were three thousand college graduates living in America. Six colonial colleges were functioning: Harvard, William and Mary, Yale, the College of New Jersey (Princeton), King's College (Columbia), and the College of Philadelphia (the University of Pennsylvania). All but the last two of these had been founded primarily for the training of ministers.

Though most books and magazines continued to be imported from England, hundreds of books were published in the colonies, especially in Boston and Cambridge. Weekly newspapers appeared in all the colonies except New Jersey and Delaware, which were well enough supplied from New York City and Philadelphia. At any given time after 1750, several monthly magazines were available in the colonies, though none of them had a very long career. Yearly almanacs contained a variety of reading matter in addition to weather data.

The most famous of these was *Poor Richard's Almanack,* which was full of popular sayings, such as "Early to bed and early to rise makes a man healthy, wealthy, and wise." Its publisher, Benjamin Franklin, was the most versatile American of his time, if not all time. Franklin was not only a printer and newspaperman but also a scientist, inventor, philosopher, educator, essayist, civic leader, and diplomat. His kite experiment in 1752, by which he showed that lightning was a flash of electricity, made him known throughout the world. Human and practical as well as brilliant and profound, Franklin represented the developing American national character at its very best.

REVIEWING THE SECTION

1. How did the social structure in the thirteen colonies differ from that in England and other parts of Europe?

2. What conditions in the English colonies led to a greater degree of religious freedom and religious tolerance than existed in England and elsewhere in Europe? What were the effects of the Great Awakening?

3. In what ways did the colonists foster education and learning?

THE COLONIES LARGELY GOVERNED THEMSELVES

The government of England was both *constitutional* and *representative*. The English constitution was embodied in various unwritten customs and written documents. These limited the powers of the king and guaranteed certain rights to the people—for example, the right to a jury trial.

One of the most famous of the constitutional documents was Magna Charta (1215). Originally this great charter, which a group of nobles had forced the king to grant, did no more than assure special privileges to the nobility. In the course of time, however, Magna Charta had come to symbolize the conviction that the people as a whole, not just the nobles, possessed rights which the king was bound to respect.

The representative part of the English government was the Parliament, consisting of the House of Lords and the House of Commons. The House of Lords, not an elective body, included certain church officials as well as titled nobles. The House of Commons was elected by a comparatively small number of Englishmen who were allowed to vote. Together, the two houses were supposed to represent the interests of the whole nation and indeed the whole empire.

Laws for England and the colonies were made, according to ancient custom, by the king and the Parliament or, as the expression went, by "the King in Parliament," that is, in consultation with the two houses. After about 1720, however, the actual initiative both in making and carrying out laws fell to a group of parliamentary leaders, who formed a cabinet with a prime minister at the head. The prime minister, rather than the king, was beginning to act as the real head of the government.

The American colonists accepted and endorsed the constitutional and representative principles of the mother country. As time passed, however, the Americans began to put new interpretations upon those principles. The thirteen colonies, acquiring separate representative institutions of their own, sometimes claimed more rights of self-government than the British authorities were willing to allow.

The British government was lax

In making laws for the colonies, the British government was concerned chiefly with achieving mercantilist aims. Mercantilism required the colonies to concentrate upon producing those goods which the mother country could not produce. Thus she would be freed from dependence on foreign countries.

To carry out these aims, Parliament, from 1660 on, passed a series of laws on shipping, trade, manufactures, and money. The shipping laws, or the Navigation Acts, provided that all goods must be carried to or from the colonies either in English or in colonial ships, not in foreign ships. The trade laws were those requiring that tobacco and other enumerated items be sent only to Britain and prohibiting other products, such as meat, grain, and flour, from being sent there. The Hat Act (1732), the Iron Act (1750), and other manufacturing laws were intended to restrict the development of hat-making, iron-working, and other colonial industries. The currency laws prohibited the issuance of paper money in the colonies.

For a time, the English government made efforts to tighten its control over the colonies and improve the enforcement of the laws. In the 1680's, King James II combined New England, New York, and New Jersey into one colony, which he called the Dominion of New England. He appointed a governor, Sir Edmund Andros, with absolute powers to rule the combined colony. With the Glorious Revolution (1688-1689), King James II was driven from the throne, and his attempt to unify the colonies came to an end.

Meanwhile, the English government succeeded in increasing its authority over some of the individual colonies. Originally, all of them either had been *corporate* (that is, founded and largely governed by companies) or *proprietary* (founded and largely governed by proprietors). Gradually most were converted into *royal* colonies, supervised directly by the king and Parliament without having to act through a company or a proprietor. After 1752, only Pennsylvania, Delaware, and Maryland remained as proprietary colonies, and only Connecticut and Rhode Island as corporate ones.

In the royal colonies, the British government appointed governors and other colonial officials, and in all the colonies it appointed royal officials such as customs collectors. These men were usually appointed for political reasons; many of them were incompetent. The British government did not supervise them very well. There was, in Britain, no single office in charge of colonial affairs. Various departments, the treasury and others, administered laws in the colonies as well as in Britain. As a result of the administrative confusion and inefficiency, it would have been difficult to enforce the laws effectively in the colonies, even if the British government had consistently wished to do so.

From about 1713 on, the government made no very serious effort to enforce the laws. The first prime minister, Sir Robert Walpole, and other government leaders believed that Britain would be better off if colonial affairs were not very strictly regulated. By increasing their own business, Walpole reasoned, the colonists could afford to buy more from British merchants. Hence, the government followed a policy which Walpole called *salutary neglect,* that is, the government purposely neglected to enforce the laws fully.

Representative assemblies met in the colonies

To the companies and proprietors who founded colonies, the colonial charters had given certain powers of government. To the colonists themselves, the charters had guaranteed the rights of Englishmen. Acting on the basis of the charters, the founders of colonies sooner or later authorized the people to elect representatives to assist in colonial government.

The first of the elected assemblies appeared in Virginia, in 1619. At that time the stockholders of the Virginia Company, who had been making laws in England for the colony, authorized the election of a general assembly, later called the House of Burgesses, which met in Jamestown. The next assembly appeared in Massachusetts, in 1630. By then, a majority of the stockholders of the Massachusetts Bay Company lived in the colony itself, and as "freemen" they met four times a year in a so-called General Court to approve laws for Massachusetts. Later, some of the nonstockholders were made freemen, and the freemen began to send representatives to the General Court instead of going in person.

In Virginia, Massachusetts, and the rest of the colonies the same overall pattern of government arose. In each, there came to be a governor and a two-house legislature. In the royal colonies the governor was appointed by the English authorities, and in the proprietary colonies by the colonial proprietors with the approval of the king. In the corporate colonies he was chosen by the colonial legislature. Generally, the governor's council served as the upper house, and its members were chosen in the same way as the governor himself.

Governing the Colonies. Although legally ruled by the British Parliament, American colonists developed their own practical means of self-government. One was the town meeting (most common in New England), where individuals could vote directly on all the issues. Each person present had the right to make his views heard, and tempers occasionally flared over the more controversial issues. The town meeting is an important part of the American democratic heritage.

Though, in all cases the lower house was elected by the people, not all the people had the right to vote or hold office. In some of the colonies, only those belonging to the established church could do so, and in all of the colonies, only those who owned a specified amount of property could vote or hold office. Property owners were numerous, however, especially in New England. Hence, in the colonies, a much larger proportion of the people enjoyed political rights than in England.

In the colonies it early became the rule that an elected representative must be a resident of the district from which he was elected. This was quite different from the practice in England, where a member of Parliament might or might not live in the town or borough that he represented. The difference still persists. Today, United States senators and representatives must reside in their respective states or districts. Members of the British Parliament may live in any part of the nation.

Gradually, each of the colonial assemblies assumed the power to pass tax bills, appropriations bills, and other laws for its colony. The governor could veto the laws, and the London authorities could disallow them. Sometimes, to keep the governor from using his veto power, the assembly threatened to withhold the appropriation for his salary. Sometimes, to get around the London authorities, the assembly repassed a disallowed law in a slightly altered form. More and more, each of the colonial legislatures came to consider itself as a kind of little parliament which was as supreme within its own colony as Parliament itself was in England.

The colonies remained disunited

In each colony the people and their representatives were unwilling to give up any of their powers, either to England or to the other colonies. The thirteen were reluctant to coöperate with one another, even when they faced common problems. The greatest problem was that of defense. Along the edge of settlement, there was a continual danger of attack by Indians, who often received aid and encouragement from European allies—Spanish, Dutch, or French.

For their "mutual safety and welfare," the people of Massachusetts, Plymouth, New Haven, and Connecticut formed the New England Confederation, a kind of military alliance, in 1643. Massachusetts refused to admit to the confederation the settlements of Maine, New Hampshire, and Rhode Island, since Massachusetts claimed their territory as its own. The confederation proved ineffective when, in 1675, the worst Indian conflict of colonial times, King Philip's War, broke out. In three years of fighting, King Philip, sachem of the Wampanoag tribe, and his followers brought death and destruction to much of New England.

In later years, as population increased and settlements spread, the people of the various colonies were brought into closer and closer contact. Roads were improved and intercolonial trade grew. The postal service was extended and speeded up. By about 1750, postriders carried the mails all the way from Maine to Georgia. It now took only three weeks, instead of six as it had formerly, for a letter to go from Boston to Philadelphia. Nevertheless, each of the colonies continued to act as though it were quite independent of the rest. "Fire and water are not more heterogeneous than the different colonies in North America," an Englishman wrote after visiting them in 1759-1760. "Nothing can exceed the jealousy and emulation which they possess in regard to each other."

In 1754, even though a war with the French and the Indians was about to begin, the colonies refused to act together for their common defense.

At the call of the British government, delegates from seven colonies met in Albany, New York. Here, one of the delegates, Benjamin Franklin, proposed what became known as the Albany Plan of Union. According to this plan, "one general government" would be set up for the colonies. A president general would be appointed by the king, and a grand council would be elected by the colonial assemblies. The colonies would keep their existing separate governments but would allow the new general government to take charge of war-making and relations with the Indians.

The colonial assemblies disapproved of Franklin's plan, and it never went into effect. The colonists would not be ready for any real confederation until after the great war with the French and Indians had been fought and won.

REVIEWING THE SECTION

1. How did the English Parliament govern the colonies so as to achieve its mercantilist aims? What did its policy of "salutary neglect" attempt to achieve?

2. What conditions enabled the colonists to obtain a great deal of self-government? What governmental institutions did they establish?

3. What conditions in colonial America pointed up the need for more coöperation among the colonies?

THE FRENCH THREAT WAS ELIMINATED

From the beginning, England and the English colonies had to contend with other European rivals in North America. The Dutch, after founding New Netherland in the Hudson Valley, remained a continual threat to New England for half a century. After defeating the Dutch in three wars, the English finally took New Netherland (1664), and renamed it New York. The Spaniards continued to endanger the southern frontier, and from time to time the English fought with them. The French, however, provided the most serious and lasting threat to British America.

The French empire in North America was almost as old as the British, the French having started their first settlement in 1608, at Quebec, only a year after the founding of Jamestown. Eventually, French forts, towns, and trading posts were scattered along the St. Lawrence Valley, around the Great Lakes, and down the Mississippi Valley to the Gulf of Mexico.

However, the vast North American continent hardly seemed large enough to accommodate the British and the French in peace. By 1750, the British in America had fought three wars against the French and their Indian allies. Yet the French and the Indians remained a threat to the British colonists.

This danger was, oddly enough, an advantage to the British government in its dealings with the colonies. As a Swedish professor, Peter Kalm, wrote after a tour of the colonies in 1748-1749:

I have been told by Englishmen...that the English colonies in North America, in the space of thirty or fifty years, would be able to form a state by themselves, entirely independent of Old England. But as the whole country which lies along the seashore is unguarded and on the land side is harassed by the French, in times of war these dangerous neighbors are sufficient to prevent the connection of the colonies with their mother country from being quite broken off. The English government has therefore sufficient reason to consider the French in North America as the best means of keeping their colonies in due submission.

After the fourth and final war against the French and the Indians (1754-1763), the British and the Americans succeeded in eliminating France as a colonial power on the continent. The British government, as predicted, then faced the problem of keeping its colonies "in due submission."

The British and the French came into conflict

Trouble arose between the British and the French in North America for several reasons. The French were Roman Catholics and the British predominantly Protestants; zealots on both sides feared for the future of their religion. The French and the British competed fiercely for the fur trade of the Indians, and they disputed the ownership of the Ohio country, the territory between the Great Lakes and the Ohio River. This territory was important to the French, for it provided the shortest route between their colonies of New France (Canada) and Louisiana. It was equally important to the British, who looked to the land as a potential home for their growing colonial population. Indeed, both the British and the French began to feel that their very survival in North America depended on the destruction of the other's power.

Still another reason for conflict in America was the fact that Britain and France were rivals for power in Europe and throughout the world. Whenever France and Britain went to war, their colonies became involved in it. The first three wars between the French and the English colonies (King William's War, 1689-1697; Queen Anne's War, 1702-1713; and King George's War, 1744-1748) began in Europe and spread to North America.

The fourth and final war was different. It began in the wilds of North America and then spread to Europe and even around the world to India. To Americans, this war seemed much more important than the earlier three, and they thought of it as their own war rather than the king's or queen's. They called it *the* French and Indian War (1754-1763). Europeans remembered it as the Seven Years' War (1756-1763).

The French and Indian War was fought

To enforce their claim to the Ohio country, the French began to build a line of forts from Lake Erie to the point where the Allegheny and Monongahela rivers join to form the Ohio River. The British government instructed the colonial governors to stop the French. The acting governor of Virginia (which claimed the Ohio country as part of the colony) sent a force of Virginians to head off the French by erecting a fort of their own. The French drove off the Virginians, completed the fort themselves, and named it Fort Duquesne. When the twenty-two-year-old George Washington arrived with a small relief force from Virginia, the more numerous French fell upon him and compelled him to surrender (July 4, 1754). Thus began the French and Indian War.

The next year an army of British regulars and colonial troops under General Edward Braddock set out to retake Fort Duquesne. Though experienced in European methods of warfare, General Braddock was unfamiliar with the techniques of Indian-fighting on the American frontier. He had his men cut a road through the forest, and then he marched them in regular formation over the road. Near the fort he ran into a French and Indian ambush (July 9, 1755). Braddock himself and many of his men were killed, and the rest fled.

The war was going badly for the British and the Americans. The population of the British colonies was about fifteen times as large as that of the French, but the British colonists soon lost their enthusiasm for the war, except when their own homes were actually endangered. The colonies often acted as if they were independent of one another and of Britain. When the British government called upon them for soldiers and supplies, the assemblies seldom responded quickly or adequately. Many of the New England merchants made money out of the war by selling supplies to the French in New France and the French West Indies.

At first the British government was further handicapped by poor generalship, such as that of the unfortunate General Braddock, and by incompetent direction of the war as a whole. Then (1757) Prime Minister William Pitt was given special war powers. With Pitt organizing the war effort, a turning point came when the British and the Americans succeeded in capturing Fort Duquesne (1758).

The decisive battle of the war was fought at Quebec (1759). The English general James Wolfe brought an army up the St. Lawrence River, led the men up a hidden ravine to the heights above the town, and surprised a larger French force led by the Marquis de Montcalm. Wolfe attacked and quickly won the victory. Both he and Montcalm lost their lives in the battle.

It was not until 1763, however, that a peace treaty was signed. The French then ceded New France and practically all their claims east of the Mississippi River to Britain. They yielded the rest of their claims on the continent to Spain. Nothing was left of the former French empire in North America except for a few islands in the West Indies and in the Gulf of St. Lawrence.

Peace brought problems to the British Empire

The war left Britain with more than twice as much territory as she formerly had possessed in North America. To govern and defend all this territory would be a complicated and expensive task. The war also left Britain with a very large national debt. To meet this debt would be difficult enough even without the added cost of administering the empire.

British landlords and merchants, who were influential in Parliament, objected to new taxation which would fall upon them. They thought it only fair that the colonists themselves should bear at least a part of the burden of their own defense. Government leaders agreed. They remembered the half-hearted support that most of the colonists had given to the war, as well as the illegal trade that some had carried on with the enemy.

The government leaders concluded that the policy of salutary neglect had been a mistake. Control over the colonies, these men thought, now ought to be tightened up. Smuggling ought to be stopped and all customs duties collected. To help enforce the laws and at the same time defend the colonies, regular military and naval forces ought to be stationed there permanently, even in peacetime. To raise additional revenue, taxes ought to be imposed directly on the colonists. Such were the lessons that the British government leaders learned from the French and Indian War.

Quite different, however, were the lessons that leading colonists learned from it. From their war experiences they had gained confidence in themselves as soldiers. They had acquired a low opinion of British military ability as illustrated by officers like General Braddock. Now that the French were no longer dangerous neighbors, the Americans felt little need for British protection. Certainly they were in no mood to submit quietly to new taxes and new controls.

The postwar problems of the empire, once the British government attempted their solutions, were bound to lead to serious trouble between the mother country and the colonists.

REVIEWING THE SECTION

1. Why did the British and the French come into conflict in North America?

2. What events precipitated the French and Indian War? What led to the British victory?

3. How did the defeat of the French lead to disputes between Britain and the thirteen colonies?

CHAPTER 1 CONCLUSION

The history of the American people began with the expansion of Europe in general and England in particular. It began with the founding of the thirteen English colonies on the mainland of North America, the first of them in 1607, the last in 1733. This history was a continuation of European and especially English history in a new environment. From the beginning, American civilization was a branch of the civilization of Europe, the roots of which stretched back to ancient times.

Nevertheless, American history and civilization developed somewhat differently from that of England and Europe. There were two major reasons for this. One was the mixture of English and other European nationalities in America, and the other was the experience of living in the new environment. Before the end of the colonial period, which lasted for more than a century and a half, from 1607 to 1776, American life had acquired distinctive characteristics.

The population of British America became much more diverse than that of Britain or of any other European country. A few Swedes and Finns had lived along the Delaware River and a number of Dutch had settled along the Hudson even before English colonies —Pennsylvania and New York—were established in those areas. In addition to the English colonists, many French, Scotch-Irish, German, and Swiss, as well as African slaves, came to the New World.

The great majority of the people in the colonies, farmed the land on which they lived, as they had in their homelands. In some of the colonies, however, they engaged in economic activities that they had not known in Europe, activities such as the production of tobacco, rice, and indigo. In all of the colonies the white people, as a whole, made a better living from the land than they or their ancestors had done in the Old World. And the Americans had many more opportunities to acquire land of their own.

A system of social classes grew up in the colonies but it differed from that of England or Europe. In America, there existed no real aristocracy consisting of families that had inherited special privileges and titles of nobility, such as earl, marquis, and duke. The middle class was large, proportionately much larger than in the old countries. With the exception of the slaves, even the poorest people believed that they or at least their children might get ahead by hard work and good luck. Then they could join the middle class or even join the upper class, which was made up of very wealthy families who thought of themselves as the colonial aristocracy. In North America at that time, there were a great many more chances to rise, economically and socially, than anywhere else in the world.

There was also greater freedom of religion in North America than anywhere else. Though official churches existed—the Anglican in a few colonies and the Congregational in a few others—they had to face the competition of a great many other churches. A large measure of religious toleration, unusual for those days, arose as an unplanned result of the great variety of religious sects.

The colonists tried to preserve their heritage of English thought. In proportion to their numbers, more of the colonists learned to read than did Englishmen, and more of them went to college. Without intending to do so, however, the colonists acquired peculiarities of speech and vocabulary which caused Englishmen to say that a corrupt form of English, an American dialect, had grown up in the colonies.

The colonists claimed the political and legal rights of Englishmen, but gradually and unconsciously they adopted a new conception of those rights. After representative assemblies had come into existence in the colonies, the people began to assume that these assemblies as well as Parliament possessed the power to make laws. Indeed, the colonists often maintained that their assemblies had the exclusive right to legislate for the individual colonies and that Parliament could legislate only for the British Empire as a whole.

Often the colonists disobeyed the laws that Parliament passed to regulate the colonies' shipping, trade, manufacturing, and currency. For a time, under the policy of salutary neglect, the British government made no very serious or consistent effort to enforce all the laws.

Then came the French and Indian War, which resulted in the elimination of France as a rival to Britain in America. Except when their own immediate borders were in danger, the colonists sustained the war effort rather half-heartedly. Many traded with the enemy. When the war ended, Britain was left with an increased burden of debt and with greatly enlarged territory in America to govern and protect.

Government leaders in Britain concluded that they must tighten their control over the colonies and make them pay some of the costs of imperial defense. The government made plans to keep regular military and naval units permanently in North America, for both defense and law enforcement, and it also made plans to impose new taxes directly upon the colonists.

The colonists, however, now felt that, with the French danger removed from the interior of the continent, they could take care of themselves. They were less willing than ever to obey parliamentary regulations or to pay taxes not authorized by their own assemblies.

Thus the French and Indian War had one effect on British attitudes and just the opposite effect on colonial attitudes. Peace was to be followed by a dozen years of controversy and then another war, this one between the colonies and the mother country. There was at last to be not only a distinctive American character but also a separate American nation.

In concluding this chapter, two observations should be made.

First, emphasis has been given to *differences* between the English colonies, on the one hand, and England and the rest of Europe on the other. This has been done to show developments that were unique in North America, to reveal part of the background for the creation of a new nation, the United States. Yet *similarities* between European and American civilization remained and still remain, and these similarities are more numerous and more important than the differences.

Second, the chapter has covered the colonial period to the 1760's. In other words, it has covered about two and a half centuries. The rest of American history, from that time to this, has lasted about two centuries. Nevertheless, the remainder of the book will be devoted to this later period, beginning with the achievement of national independence. This first chapter, then, should be considered an introduction to the main subject of the book, which is *United States History*.

FOCUSING ON SPECIFICS

1. What important changes were taking place in Europe about the time Columbus discovered America?

2. Why was Columbus searching for a new route to the Far East?

3. List the ideas which were basic to mercantilism.

4. Describe the system of indentured servitude.

5. How did the social status of colonial women differ from that of English women?

6. How did religion in the colonies differ from religion in England and other parts of Europe?

7. How did Jonathan Edwards influence Protestantism in the colonies?

8. What was the purpose of the Navigation Acts, the Hat Act, and the Iron Act?

9. How did the colonial legislatures exercise control over the colonial governors and avoid control by the London authorities?

10. Which European countries rivaled England for control of North America? Which of England's rivals were eliminated during the colonial period?

REVIEWING MAIN THEMES

1. What events in England and the rest of Europe led to England's colonization of North America?

2. How did the colonists earn a livelihood? How were they affected by the British mercantilist system?

3. How did the American colonies differ from England in social structure, religion, and education?

4. How did self-government in the various colonies develop under British rule?

5. How did the rivalries between Britain and other European nations affect the thirteen colonies? How did the French and Indian War affect the relationship between Britain and the colonies?

EVALUATING THE ISSUES

1. Some historians have suggested that in the United States, the abundance of land was a major factor in the growth of democracy and the development of a nation of small farms. Considering the experience of other frontier populations, such as the Australians, Argentinians, or Cossacks in tsarist Russia, do you believe this thesis is sound? Explain your answer.

2. A well-known modern historian said, "In a number of ways what Americans would be for generations to come was settled in the course of those first hundred years." Discuss this statement.

3. Compare the political institutions which developed in the English, French, and Spanish colonies of North America in the mid-eighteenth century. Which country permitted its colonists to achieve the greatest degree of self-government? Why?

4. How do you account for the fact that the thirteen English colonies, in spite of the different circumstances under which they were founded, had developed similar governments by 1750?

CHAPTER **2** 1763-1783

The American Revolution

The American Revolution was the first of the great movements by which a colonial people broke away from imperial rule and formed an independent nation. Since that time, colonial peoples in Latin America and more recently in Asia and Africa have done the same thing.

It might seem strange that the colonists in British America should have revolted before those in Spanish or French America. On the whole, the people in the English colonies, enjoying greater economic opportunity and wider political freedom, had been better off than the people in the Spanish or the French colonies. For the English colonists, there had been many advantages in belonging to the British Empire. There had been, for example, the profits of shipping and trade which, though restricted in some respects, were encouraged in others. There had been the protection of the British army and navy in times of danger, such as the period of the French and Indian War. And there had been the pride of being members of the greatest and most powerful aggregation of peoples in the world.

Throughout modern history, however, revolutions have usually occurred among people who were relatively well off rather than among those who were the most miserable and oppressed. Gen-

erally, it is not misery in itself that brings about revolt. Rather, it is the contrast between actual and ideal conditions. When the experiences of a people cause them to expect more than they have been given—or to fear the loss of what they already possess—they are ripe for revolutionary discontent. If they have enough energy, education, resources, and political skill, they may act upon their discontent by organizing themselves and launching a revolution.

After the French and Indian War, the British government began to impose unaccustomed controls upon the colonies. Henceforth, the westward movement of population was to be limited. Trade and other economic regulations were to be strictly enforced. Units of the British army and navy were to be stationed in North America to assist in enforcing the laws. Taxes were to be levied on the colonists to help pay the costs of imperial government, including the cost of maintaining the army and navy.

If the new policy were successfully carried out, the colonists feared they would lose many economic opportunities and some of their political liberties. Colonial prosperity had been based largely upon illegal trade, the exploitation of western lands, the development of manufactures, and the use of paper money, all of which were now to be discouraged or prevented. The high degree of self-government in the colonies had depended on the power of the colonial assemblies to levy taxes on their own people and to appropriate money for paying the salaries of colonial governors and certain other officials. These officials would become independent of the assemblies—and of the voters who elected the assemblies—if the British government should succeed in taxing the people to pay the officials' salaries.

Hence the new policy led to a dozen years (1763-1775) of colonial discontent and resistance, and finally to war. In resisting the British measures, the colonists at first claimed only the rights of Englishmen, especially the right to be free from "taxation without representation." The colonists later stood upon the natural rights of man, the rights to "Life, Liberty and the pursuit of Happiness," as expressed in the Declaration of Independence. A struggle to correct wrongs within the British Empire had turned into a war for separate nationhood.

Though the Americans had broadened their theories and enlarged their aims, they continued to see themselves as fighting not so much for something new and different as for old and familiar values, which they feared they were about to lose. Thus, in essence, the American Revolution was both conservative and democratic, a movement to conserve the liberties that the people already possessed.

THE COLONISTS RESISTED NEW BRITISH LAWS

George III was only twenty-two when, in 1760, he became king of England. His mother had advised him again and again: "George, be a king." For nearly a half century his great-grandfather George I and then his grandfather George II, both of whom were more German than English, had sat upon the throne without exercising real power. The Whig party, made up of wealthy landowners and merchants, had governed Great Britain and the empire through Parliament and the cabinet.

The new king proceeded to follow his mother's advice. Although he did not attempt to abolish the system of parliamentary government that had grown up, he undertook to control it, appointing and dismissing one cabinet minister after another. Disputes often arose between the king and Parliament, and the treatment of the colonies became changeable and inconsistent.

This is not to say that George III alone was to blame for the conflict with the colonies. Most members of Parliament agreed with him that the colonies ought to be more strictly controlled and ought to pay a larger share of the costs of imperial government. All the important laws to carry the new policy into effect were passed by large majorities, though a few members of Parliament sided with the colonists and spoke out in their support when the Americans undertook to resist the laws.

Great Britain began a new imperial policy

The British government began its new policy with a royal proclamation to limit settlement in the west. By acts of Parliament the colonies were prohibited from issuing paper money, and were required to support British troops in America. In addition, stricter laws were enacted to prevent smuggling.

The Royal Proclamation of 1763 was a response to Pontiac's Rebellion, which occurred that same year. After the close of the French and Indian War, Indians under the Ottawa chief Pontiac had attacked settlers all along the frontier, from Detroit to Pennsylvania. During the rebellion, the king issued the proclamation, forbidding settlement west of the Appalachian Mountains or, to be more exact, west of a line that divided the rivers flowing into the Atlantic Ocean from those flowing into the Gulf of Mexico. By keeping settlers out of the Indian country, the king intended to prevent further troubles with the Indians. To the colonists, however, the proclamation seemed an attempt to deprive them of western lands, for which, among

1763   *Royal Proclamation of 1763* forbade settlement west of the Appalachian Mountains.
Colonists continued to settle in the forbidden territory.

1764   *Sugar Act* increased duties on refined sugar, reduced duties on imported molasses, and imposed new or higher duties on coffee and certain other imports.
Several colonial merchants pledged a general boycott of certain British products through nonimportation, which was to become an effective colonial weapon.

Currency Act prohibited the issue of paper money by any of the colonies.
Merchants wrote to England in protest. Colonists evaded the law when possible.

1765   *Stamp Act* levied a tax on legal documents, newspapers, almanacs, and other items, and required that they bear stamps showing the tax had been paid.
The Stamp Act Congress was called to protest to the king against the taxes. Sons of Liberty were organized to oppose the law. Some colonists terrorized tax collectors and attacked houses of British officials in Boston.

Quartering Act required colonists to furnish lodging and supplies for British troops.
Colonists refused to provide all of the supplies called for in the act.

1767   *Townshend Acts* imposed duties on specified colonial imports.
Colonial boycotts continued and became more widespread.

Suspension of New York Assembly by Parliament was precipitated by that state's refusal to comply with the Quartering Act.
Fear that all assemblies might be suspended spread throughout the colonies. Many of them rallied to support New York; Massachusetts colonists were most aggressive in defying British law. Numerous protest demonstrations were held; one such incident resulted in the slaying of several colonists by British soldiers (*Boston Massacre*, 1770).

BRITISH LEGISLATION AND COLONIAL REACTION

other things, they had gone to war against the French and Indians.

The Sugar Act of 1764 was designed to stop an illegal trade and to raise money from customs duties. According to an earlier law—the Molasses Act of 1733—a duty of sixpence a gallon was supposed to be collected on molasses brought from the French West Indies to the mainland colonies. Colonial merchants seldom paid the duty. They usually gave the British customs officials a bribe, averaging about a penny a gallon, to overlook the requirements of the Molasses Act. At this rate, molasses from the French West Indies was cheaper than that from the British West Indies, even though the latter could be imported duty free. Smuggling was so common that the British government was spending about four times as much on operating the customs service as it was collecting in customs revenues.

The Sugar Act reduced the duty on imported molasses from six to three pennies, and it also imposed new or higher duties on coffee and certain other imports. Presumably, the colonial merchants would be willing to pay the lower molasses tax. The British government did not depend solely on the merchants' willingness to pay, however. It made provisions for the strict enforcement of the Sugar Act. Ships of the royal navy were now to be stationed permanently in North American waters to watch out for smugglers. When caught, lawbreakers were to be tried in admiralty courts by judges appointed and paid by the British government, rather than by juries in local courts; in the past, juries in the local courts usually had sym-

1770 *Repeal of the Townshend Acts,* except the tax on tea, was secured.
Nonimportation was dropped, and good feeling prevailed among the colonists.

1773 *Tea Act* granted the British East India Company a monopoly on colonial tea trade.
Colonists boarded ships in Boston harbor and dumped the cargoes of tea overboard (*Boston Tea Party*); in other colonies the company's ships either were not allowed to unload or the tea was confiscated and stored.

1774 *The Intolerable Acts* were passed by Parliament as reprisal for the destruction of the East India Company's property. The *Boston Port Act* closed the port until the colonists would pay for damage caused by the Boston Tea Party. The *Massachusetts Government Act* reorganized the government and restricted the right of the people to hold town meetings. The *Quartering Act* provided that British troops might be lodged among the people as well as in barracks. The *Administration of Justice Act* provided that British officials charged with murder could be returned to England for trial.
All of the colonies except Georgia sent delegates to the *Continental Congress,* organized to devise means of united colonial resistance. The congress advised the colonies to make preparations for defense against possible British attack.

The Quebec Act set up a civil government in the province of Quebec, recognized certain French laws as valid there, and extended the boundaries of Quebec southwestward to the Ohio and Mississippi rivers. It also granted religious freedom to Roman Catholics in Quebec.
Colonists interpreted this law as evidence that Britain intended to nullify colonial claims to western land. Protestants were alarmed over religious provisions of the act.

1775 *First battle of the Revolutionary War* was fought at Lexington, Massachusetts, when British redcoats, on their way to seize military stores collected in Concord by colonists, were stopped by Massachusetts minutemen.

pathized with the defendants. With good reason, colonial merchants feared the destruction of their profitable trade with the French West Indies.

The Currency Act of 1764 prohibited all of the colonies from issuing paper money; previous laws had prohibited it only in New England. Its purpose was to keep colonial debtors from trying to pay English creditors in paper currency, which was worth less than silver coin. Its effect would be to discourage business of all kinds in the colonies, since they suffered from a chronic shortage of coin and needed paper money to carry on their business.

Under the terms of the Quartering Act of 1765, when British troops were stationed within a colony, that colony was required to provide the troops with living quarters and certain supplies. This law was designed to do directly what the Sugar

Act was designed to do indirectly, that is, to compel the colonists to support the soldiers who were being sent among them. The colonists could see no justification for the presence of the army, now that the French and Indian War and Pontiac's Rebellion were over. Troops had not been maintained in North America before 1754, when there was constant danger from the French and their Indian allies. Why should troops be kept in North America now that the danger had been eliminated?

Suspicious colonists could see no reason for the new policy except to deprive them of their rights as Englishmen, their right to be taxed only by their own elected representatives, their right to be tried only by a jury of their peers. The colonists also saw, as a consequence of the new policy, the end of their prosperity. When a business depression came, in the 1760's, they blamed it on the Sugar Act and the Currency Act.

At first, discontented though they were, the colonists only grumbled about the recent laws and evaded them as best they could. After the passage of an even more unpopular law, however, they resorted to strong words and violent deeds.

The Stamp Act led to violence

The Stamp Act (1765) levied a tax on legal documents and on newspapers, almanacs, and other items. All of these had to bear stamps to show that the tax had been paid. The law was designed to raise money for the defense of the colonies; it was not intended to provoke those colonial leaders—the lawyers and the newspapermen—who could most effectively arouse their fellow colonists. Yet this was the actual effect of the law. It met such violent opposition that enforcing it was hopeless from the start.

Members of the colonial assemblies promptly met to discuss and denounce the Stamp Act. The Virginia House of Burgesses adopted resolutions which the young lawyer Patrick Henry had introduced and which declared:

The General Assembly of this Colony have the only and *sole exclusive* Right and Power to lay Taxes and Impositions upon the Inhabitants of this Colony.

The Massachusetts assembly proposed that all of the colonies send delegates to a congress, or convention, to agree upon joint action.

Nine of the colonies responded and were represented at the Stamp Act Congress, which met in New York (September 1765). This congress drew up resolutions yielding "all due subordination" to Parliament but denying its right to tax the colonies. The congress sent to the king and to Parliament a petition for the repeal of both the Stamp Act and the Sugar Act. The congress also called upon the people to back up these demands by boycotting British goods.

While merchants in New York, Philadelphia, and Boston refused to import from Great Britain, mobs in these and other places took more forceful steps. The mobs attacked stamp collectors and compelled them to resign before they had succeeded in selling any stamps. Groups known as Sons of Liberty, with Samuel Adams and Patrick Henry among the leaders, were formed to organize the resistance to the hated law.

In justifying their opposition, the colonists argued that the law was contrary to the English constitution. One of the rights guaranteed by the constitution, they said, was "That no man can justly take the Property of another without his Consent." To tax a man would be to take some of his property, so he must not be taxed except by his own consent, and this he could give only through his elected representatives. Since the colonists elected no representative to Parliament, its members had no right to tax them.

All this talk of "taxation without representation" made little sense to most Englishmen, who took a different view of their constitution. True, the colonies sent no representatives to Parliament but, Englishmen pointed out, neither did Ireland nor even certain areas of England itself. This did not mean that these places were unrepresented. They were "virtually" represented by members from other places, who looked out for the interests of the individual parts of the empire as well as for the empire as a whole.

The doctrine of "virtual" representation seemed like nonsense to most Americans, who were accustomed to actual representation by men elected from the particular localities which they were supposed to represent. Few of the colonists really wanted to elect their own members of Parliament, however, for such members would be too few to prevent undesirable legislation, and yet their presence would justify Parliament in legislating for the colonies.

More impressed by the colonists' boycott than by their constitutional argument, Parliament, in 1766, decided to abandon the Stamp Act but at the same time to insist upon the right to impose such a tax. First, the Declaratory Act was passed, declaring simply that Parliament had full power to make laws "to bind the colonies and people of America ... in all cases whatsoever." Then the Stamp Act was repealed. During the same year, the Sugar Act was amended to make the molasses duty only one penny a gallon.

The feelings of many colonists were expressed by George Mason of Virginia, who wrote in criticism of the British:

We rarely see anything from your side of the water free from the authoritative style of a master to a school boy: "We have with infinite difficulty and fatigue got you excused this one time; pray be a good boy for the future, do what your papa and mama bid you."

Parliament tried "external taxes"

The British authorities in London assumed, incorrectly, that the Americans, in resisting the Stamp Act, had been objecting to "internal" taxes but would be willing to accept "external" taxes. Accordingly, Parliament imposed (1767) the so-called Townshend duties on colonial imports of lead, paint, paper, glass, and tea. Like the stamp duties, these were intended to raise revenue but, unlike the stamp taxes, were to be collected before the taxed goods entered the colonies. In that sense, they were to be external.

Although the Townshend duties provoked no such uproar as the Stamp Act, they seemed equally unconstitutional to the colonists. As one of them, John Dickinson, explained in his *Letters from a Farmer in Pennsylvania* (1768), Parliament had the right to levy external duties, but only for regulating trade, not for raising revenue. Again, merchants agreed to import no goods from Great Britain, and the Sons of Liberty threatened violence to all who hesitated to join the boycott.

Soon the British government further aroused the colonists. The colonial assemblies had not fully complied with the Quartering Act, and Parliament singled out the New York assembly for punishment (1767), refusing to recognize any of the assembly's actions until full support should be provided for the British troops quartered in the colony. Parliament had hoped to divide the American colonies by thus punishing only one of them, but the others quickly expressed their sympathy with New York.

To assure the collection of duties and in order to deal with smuggling at its very center, the British government appointed a special board of customs commissioners (1767), to be located in Boston instead of London. The Boston commissioners soon made themselves unpopular, ordering sudden raids and seizing many ships on mere technicalities. Every seizure meant money for the commissioners, since they received one third of the value of the cargo.

To protect the commissioners, troops were sent to Boston. The local Sons of Liberty, under Samuel Adams, made life miserable for the soldiers standing guard in front of the custom house. On March 5, 1770, a jeering crowd threw rocks and snowballs at the ten men on duty, as crowds often had done before. This time, the soldiers were goaded into firing. Several in the crowd were killed, in what Americans afterward remembered as the Boston Massacre.

Already, merchants in Great Britain had been demanding repeal of the Townshend duties because of the renewed boycott, which again hurt the merchants' business. In 1770, Parliament repealed all the duties except the one on tea. This one, Parliament hoped, not only would raise a small revenue, but also would serve as a reminder of the powers which already had been asserted in the Declaratory Act.

REVIEWING THE SECTION

1. What were the purposes of the Royal Proclamation of 1763, the Sugar and Currency Acts (1764), and the Quartering Act (1765)? Why did the colonists resent these laws?

2. What action was taken by the colonists against the Stamp Act (1765)? How did they justify their opposition to the Stamp Act? How did the British respond to this opposition?

3. Why did colonists oppose the Townshend duties (1767)? How did Great Britain attempt to enforce the Quartering Act and the Townshend duties?

THE COLONIES COOPERATED MORE CLOSELY

For about three years (1770-1773) after the repeal of all but one of the Townshend duties, good feelings prevailed between the colonies and the mother country. True, there were occasional incidents, as when Rhode Islanders burned the British patrol vessel *Gaspee* after it had run aground near Providence (1772). Also, the more radical of the colonial leaders, such as Samuel Adams, continued to insist on the rights of the colonists and to denounce the tyranny of Parliament. Most of the people, however, were content to enjoy the prosperity which had come with the reopening of British trade.

Now that the colonies were less preoccupied with grievances against Great Britain, they began to give more attention to their complaints against one another. Connecticut, for example, claimed land in northeastern Pennsylvania. While resisting the Connecticut claim, Pennsylvania quarreled with Virginia over territory in the Ohio Valley to the west of the Proclamation Line of 1763.

The most serious troubles occurred within the colony of North Carolina. Settlers in the Carolina Piedmont area (between the coastal plain and the Appalachian Mountains) objected to the tyranny not of Parliament but of their own colonial assembly. They charged that the assembly was dominated by eastern planters who levied unfair taxes and denied the rights of local self-government. The frontiersmen, who in 1768 had organized themselves as Regulators, refused to pay taxes, and demanded government reforms. A brief, small-scale civil war ensued, with militiamen from the east

defeating the Regulators in the Battle of Alamance (1771). This left the westerners so bitter that many of them continued to oppose the easterners even after the colonial struggle against Great Britain had been renewed. On the whole, however, the renewal of the dispute with the British (1773-1774) brought about closer coöperation and greater unity among the colonies than had ever before existed.

The Tea Act revived the quarrel

By 1773, the East India Company, a great corporation which largely monopolized both the commerce and the government of the British possessions in India, found itself in serious financial difficulties. The Tea Act was passed to help the company.

This law authorized the company to sell tea directly to retailers in North America, without paying any taxes except the tea tax left over from the Townshend duties. In the past, the company had been required to pay various taxes in Great Britain and had been allowed to sell its tea only to British merchants, who in turn sold it to American merchants, who then distributed it among retailers in the colonies. Under the new law, with the middlemen's profits and most of the taxes eliminated, the company would be able to undersell all competitors. The colonists, who had a reputation as inveterate tea drinkers, were expected to swallow the Townshend tax along with the cheap tea and, in doing so, to provide large profits for the East India Company.

The reaction in North America surprised the British authorities. American tea dealers, of course, protested against the unfair competition from a giant corporation, but tea drinkers also resented the new law, for they considered it an attempt to trick them into accepting taxation by Parliament. The colonists took oaths to use none of the company's tea. When its tea ships arrived in colonial ports, angry crowds compelled them either to turn back or to leave their cargo, unsold, in warehouses. In Boston harbor, the followers of Samuel Adams,

Angry Colonists continually protested Britain's attempts to limit their growing economy. This cartoon, published in 1774, satirized the worsening relations between the colonies and the mother country after passage of the hated Tea Act of 1773. Two rowdy colonists, having tarred and feathered an unfortunate royal customs agent, "offer" him some tea.

disguised as Indians, boarded the ships and threw the tea into the harbor.

As punishment for the "Boston Tea Party," the British government struck at the Bostonians with four measures which became known as the Intolerable Acts (1774). One of these closed the port of Boston to all shipping except for military stores and shipments of food and fuel cleared by customs officials. Another reorganized the Massachusetts government so as to lessen the power of the assembly and restrict the right of the people to hold town meetings. A third limited the jurisdiction of the colony's courts by providing that customs officers and other royal officials, when accused of murder while carrying out their duties, could be tried in Great Britain. The other authorized the quartering of troops among the people as well as in the barracks which the colony had provided.

Still another British measure, the Quebec Act (1774), seemed to Americans like a serious threat to their interests. This act set up a permanent civil government and drew definite boundaries for the province of Quebec, which had been ruled by a military governor since its acquisition by the British in 1763. The new Quebec government was to have no elected assembly; it was to recognize the validity of certain features of French law; and it was to favor the Roman Catholic Church. The new boundaries were to include the whole area west of the Appalachian Mountains and north of the Ohio River. The act was intended merely to provide for Quebec an efficient government that would be satisfactory to the French settlers of the province, but the British colonists looked upon it as one more scheme to check representative government in North America and discourage people from taking up land in the west.

By the Intolerable Acts, Parliament had hoped to isolate Massachusetts from the other colonies by singling it out, just as Parliament earlier had hoped to isolate New York. After the passage of these laws and then the Quebec Act, however, the other colonies rallied to the support of Massachusetts. In their resistance to British authority, all were now more determined, and they were soon to be better united than ever.

The first Continental Congress met

Revolutions do not just happen; they must be led and organized. In the colonies, men like Patrick Henry and Samuel Adams, extreme opponents of British policy, were responsible for the early leadership and organization of what was soon to become the American Revolution. At first, the colonial assemblies served as centers of resistance. Then delegates from nine of the assemblies were brought together in the Stamp Act Congress, and people enrolled in local groups such as the Sons of Liberty. Still later, committees of correspondence were formed, and the Continental Congress met, with representatives from all but one of the thirteen colonies.

Local committees of correspondence had appeared in 1772, when Samuel Adams induced the towns of Massachusetts to appoint men to keep in touch with one another and agree upon united action. These committees, drawing up statements of rights and grievances, kept alive the anti-British feeling in New England.

Intercolonial committees of correspondence began in 1773, when Patrick Henry and other Virginians established a committee for their whole colony and proposed that each of the other colonies do the same. Thereafter, the colonies had a network of committees through which to coördinate their plans. After the passage of the Intolerable Acts and the Quebec Act, these committees arranged for an intercolonial congress to be held.

The Continental Congress, with delegates from all the thirteen colonies except Georgia, met in Philadelphia for its first session in September 1774. From the outset, the delegates were divided. Moderates were still willing to let Parliament regulate colonial trade, so long as no effort was made to raise revenue by taxation. The more extreme members, however, had moved beyond that position. They now wished to deny Parliament any power of legislating for the colonies.

On behalf of the moderates, Joseph Galloway of Pennsylvania proposed a plan for reforming the empire. Galloway's proposal was something like the one that Benjamin Franklin had presented at Albany twenty years earlier. A council, to represent all the colonies, was to have a veto over acts of Parliament, and Parliament was to have a veto over the actions of the colonial council. The Galloway plan was defeated by one vote.

Moderates and extremists compromised on a statement of grievances, to be embodied in a petition to the king. This denied that Parliament had any real authority over the colonies, but it went on to say that the colonists would nevertheless abide by Parliament's acts if these were confined to legitimate regulations of trade. The statement assured the king of the Americans' "allegiance to his majesty" and their "affection" for their "fellow subjects" in Great Britain.

Responding to the demands of the extremists, the majority approved a set of resolutions which a convention in Suffolk County, Massachusetts, had passed and which Samuel Adams had introduced at the Philadelphia congress. These Suffolk Resolves called upon the people to make military preparations for defense against a possible attack by the British troops in Boston.

The majority decided, moreover, that all trade with Great Britain should be stopped. They adopted a nonimportation, nonexportation, and nonconsumption agreement, to apply to all goods to or from Great Britain, and they formed the Continental Association, with members in each of the colonies, to see that the agreement was enforced.

Finally, when the delegates adjourned, they did so with the understanding that they would meet again the following spring. Thus they viewed the Continental Congress as a continuing body, not merely a temporary organization.

Great Britain yielded too little

"The New England Governments are in a State of Rebellion," George III exclaimed (November 1774). "Blows must decide whether they are to be subject to this Country or Independent." Not only New England but also the Middle and Southern colonies, at the Continental Congress, had defied the mother country and, in the latest boycott agreement, had declared what amounted to economic war.

The British policy-makers faced a dilemma. On the one hand, they could yield to the demands of the Continental Congress, but if they did so, they would have to recognize the colonies as practically independent. On the other hand, the British could reject the petition from the colonists, but in that case they would probably have a full-scale war to fight.

During the winter of 1774-1775, Parliament debated the question of what to do about the colonies. Some members favored giving in to them. Lord Chatham (William Pitt), for example, urged that the troops be withdrawn from Boston, and Edmund Burke argued eloquently that the Intolerable Acts ought to be repealed. Other members, however, insisted that if the colonies were to be kept subordinate within the empire, Samuel Adams and others of his kind would have to be taught a lesson.

Twice before, Parliament had backed down after its measures had brought on crises in relations with the colonies. It had repealed the Stamp Act and, with one exception, the Townshend duties. This time, however, it did not back down; it refused to repeal the Intolerable Acts.

Instead, Parliament proposed a compromise by passing the so-called Conciliatory Propositions. These proposed that the colonies avoid parliamentary taxation by taxing themselves "for contributing their proportion to the common defence." The propositions failed to say how much the "proportion" of each colony would be; presumably, this would be left for Parliament to decide.

The Conciliatory Propositions did not go far enough to suit the discontented colonists, who could see little difference between being taxed by Parliament and being forced to tax themselves at Parliament's behest. The propositions said nothing about the Intolerable Acts and the other laws against which the colonists had been protesting. In any case, the British offer came too late. By the time it was received in North America, the first shots of the Revolutionary War already had been fired.

REVIEWING THE SECTION

1. What was the purpose of the Tea Act (1773)? the Intolerable Acts (1774)? the Quebec Act (1774)? What was the colonists' response to each of these British measures?

2. What was accomplished by the first Continental Congress?

3. In what way did the British try to compromise with the American colonies? Why did the colonists reject the British proposals?

AMERICANS MADE INDEPENDENCE THEIR AIM

Time and again, throughout the history of the modern world, a war undertaken for one purpose had been carried on for other and quite different purposes. This was true of the Revolutionary War. The aim of the American colonists, at the beginning of the war, was only to uphold their concept of the British Empire. After the first year of fighting, however, the aim was changed to independence.

The American concept of the empire was well expressed by the Philadelphia lawyer James Wilson in his pamphlet *Considerations on the Authority of Parliament* (1774). Parliament, Wilson said, represented only the people of Great Britain. "And have those, whom we have hitherto been accustomed to consider as our fellow-subjects, an absolute and unlimited power over us?" Wilson asked. "Have they a natural right to make laws by which we may be deprived of our properties, of our liberties, of our lives?" He replied that, just as the British Parliament could make laws for Great Britain, so the colonial assemblies and they alone could make laws for the colonies. Great Britain and the American colonies were "different members of the British Empire"; they were "independent of each other, but connected together under the same sovereign."

Thus, by 1775, Americans had come to look upon the British Empire as a kind of federation of peoples with each group having its own legislative body, and with all groups tied together by allegiance to the king. For the colonists to assert their complete independence, they now had only to announce that they were breaking the connection with the British crown. This they did with the Declaration of Independence in 1776.

They were not unanimous, however, in making the final break. All along, some Americans had hesitated even to resist the powers of Parliament, and at the end these people could not bring themselves to give up their loyalty to the king. How many Americans, in their hearts, disliked the War for Independence, no one can say with certainty. One of the greatest of the Revolutionary leaders, Samuel Adams' cousin John Adams, estimated that about a third of the people actively supported the war, another third secretly or openly opposed it, and the rest were indifferent.

Revolutions usually are carried out by a determined minority, and apparently the American Revolution was no exception.

Fighting began at Lexington

During the winter of 1774-1775, in accordance with the Suffolk Resolves, which the first Continental Congress had approved, New Englanders began to prepare for a possible attack from the British troops in Boston. "Minutemen," ready to fight on a minute's notice, drilled in militia companies. Guns and gunpowder were collected and stored for emergency use.

On April 18, 1775, a force of seven hundred British redcoats left Boston to march the eighteen miles to Concord, intending to seize the arms and ammunition which had been accumulated there. During the night, the hard-riding horsemen William Dawes, Paul Revere, and Dr. Samuel Prescott had warned the people in the villages and on the farms. When the redcoats reached Lexington, on the way to Concord, colonial militiamen were waiting for them on the village green. A British officer ordered the militiamen to disperse, when suddenly shots rang out. Who fired the first shot, nobody knows, but eight of the militiamen were killed and ten were wounded.

The British moved on to Concord and found that the Americans already had taken away most of the powder supply. After burning what was left and fighting off an attack from Americans, the British started to march back to Boston. All along the way, they had to brave the gunfire of Americans who were hiding behind trees, rocks, and stone fences. Before the day was over, the British had suffered 273 casualties (killed, wounded, or missing), about three times as many as the Americans had suffered.

During the weeks that followed, militiamen arrived from all over New England to surround the enemy in Boston. In the Battle of Bunker Hill, which actually was fought on Breed's Hill (June 17, 1775), the British attempted to break the siege. The Americans waited in their entrenchments on top of the hill and held their fire as the redcoats, their guns blazing, advanced toward them. When, at close range, the Americans fired back, the enemy ranks were mowed down. The British tried again, and the same thing happened. When the British attacked a third time, the Americans, their ammunition almost gone, were forced off the hill in bitter hand-to-hand fighting.

For the British, this victory was both costly and incomplete. Their losses were 226 killed and 828 wounded, compared with the Americans' 100 killed, 267 wounded, and 30 captured. The siege had not been broken. Both sides now realized that they had a hard and bloody war on their hands.

Independence was declared

Meanwhile (May 1775), the second Continental Congress met in Philadelphia, with delegates again from twelve of the colonies (delegates from Georgia did not arrive until the following September). This congress, unlike the previous one, did not confine itself to adopting resolutions. It also acted as a central governing body for the colonies.

Within the various colonies, the assemblies took charge of government. They defied the governors and other royal officials, who sooner or later gave up attempts to reëstablish British authority. Many of the officials took refuge on British warships.

Even though both the congress and the assemblies were behaving like independent governments, most Americans still hesitated to declare independence. In July 1775, the congress sent another petition to King George III and issued the "Declaration of the Causes and Necessity of Taking up Arms." This blamed the troubles on the king's ministers rather than on the king himself. It explained that the Americans had been "reduced to the alternative of choosing an unconditional submission to the tyranny of irritated ministers, or resistance by force." In choosing resistance, they had no "ambitious designs of separating from Great Britain, and establishing independent states."

Nevertheless, just one year later, the congress adopted a very different declaration. This one concluded that "these United Colonies are, and of Right ought to be Free and Independent States." What accounted for the change in war aims?

First, the Americans had received no satisfaction from the British government. The king did not even answer their petition. Instead, he issued a proclamation declaring that the colonies were in rebellion. Parliament voted to send 25,000 additional troops to North America and passed an act prohibiting all trade with the colonies.

Second, the Americans desperately needed foreign aid if they were to win even a limited war, one waged only for a redress of grievances within the empire. To get all the aid they needed, they would have to act as an independent people, with full power to make treaties and alliances with foreign countries. Thus the requirements of the war itself seemed to necessitate a change in war aims.

Third, the Americans found that they had to make terrible sacrifices, as in the Battle of Breed's Hill (Bunker Hill), in order to carry on the struggle. The costs would be out of proportion to the benefits unless some grand objective was to be achieved.

Fourth, a powerful pamphlet helped many wavering Americans to make up their minds. This was *Common Sense,* first published in January 1776. Its author was Thomas Paine, an Englishman who had come to North America less than two years earlier. Paine argued that it was plain common sense for this great continent to cut itself loose from a small island which was no more fit to govern it than a satellite was to rule the sun.

After much debate, the congress appointed a committee to draft the Declaration of Independence. The committee, which included Benjamin Franklin and John Adams, left the actual writing primarily to one member, Thomas Jefferson.

Jefferson based the declaration on the political theory of John Locke, an English philosopher who had written two treatises on government (1690) to justify the English revolution of 1688-1689, which had overthrown King James II. According to Locke, men had originally created government in order to protect their rights to life, liberty, and property, and whenever the existing government ceased to do so, the people could abolish it and create a new one. Jefferson changed the emphasis of Locke's theory by stressing human rights rather than property rights. He wrote:

We hold these truths to be self-evident; that all men are created equal, that they are endowed by their Creator with certain unalienable Rights, that among these are Life, Liberty and the Pursuit of Happiness.

Thus he stated the basic faith which was to guide future generations of Americans in their effort to make democracy more and more a reality for all.

1775-1776

April 19, 1775
Battles of Lexington and Concord. British victories. The British sent an expedition to seize and destroy rebel military stores at Concord. The expedition was met by a small force of minutemen at Lexington. Fighting began and the minutemen retreated. The British went on to Concord and destroyed the Patriot military stores they found there. On their return march to Boston, they suffered heavy casualties.

May 10 and 12, 1775
Capture of Fort Ticonderoga and Crown Point. United States victories. The capture of these forts in New York gave the Patriots two strategic bases plus artillery and other military stores needed for the siege of Boston.

June 17, 1775
Battle of Bunker Hill (Breed's Hill). British victory. The British tried to dislodge Patriot troops entrenched on a hill overlooking Boston. The Patriots were forced to withdraw, but the British suffered heavy casualties.

September 12-December 31, 1775
Invasion of Quebec. British victory. The Patriots launched an assault against Quebec in an effort to get Quebec to join the rebellious thirteen colonies and to prevent the British from using the city as a base for an attack on the colonies. The assault failed.

February 27, 1776
Battle of Moore's Creek Bridge, North Carolina. United States victory. The British planned to join forces with the Loyalists in the Southern colonies but the Patriots defeated the Loyalists.

March 17, 1776
Siege of Boston. United States victory. With the help of the guns captured at Fort Ticonderoga, the Patriots forced the British to evacuate the port of Boston.

June 28, 1776
Battle of Charleston, South Carolina. United States victory. When the British were unable to unite with the Loyalists, they decided to establish at Charleston a base for operations in the Southern colonies. They were unsuccessful.

August 27, 1776
Battle of Long Island. British victory. Both the British and the Patriots wished to occupy the strategic city of New York. The British routed the Americans, who retreated through New Jersey.

December 26, 1776
Battle of Trenton, New Jersey. United States victory. The Patriots needed a spectacular victory to raise the morale in the colonies. They surprised and captured the British garrison.

Map labels

L. Superior
L. Michigan
L. Huron
L. Ontario
L. Erie
QUEBEC (By Quebec Act of 1774)
QUEBEC
Montreal
St. Lawrence
L. Champlain
CROWN POINT
FT. TICONDEROGA
MASS.
N.H.
BUNKER HILL
CONCORD
LEXINGTON
BOSTON
MASS.
N.Y.
Hudson R.
CONN.
R.I.
LONG ISLAND
New York
PA.
TRENTON
N.J.
MD.
DEL.
VA.
N.C.
MOORE'S CREEK BRIDGE
S.C.
CHARLESTON
GA.
INDIAN RESERVE
WEST FLORIDA
EAST FLORIDA
Gulf of Mexico
ATLANTIC OCEAN
Mississippi River

PREPARED BY
UNIVERSAL MAP, INC.

American Revolution

→ British moves

→ U.S. moves

× Battles

Thirteen Original Colonies

Other British Possessions

The Battle of Lexington, by Amos Doolittle, 1775

The Battle of Lexington, by Pendleton, 1830

"The Dawn of Liberty," by Henry Sandham, 1886

The Battle of Lexington was the first skirmish of the American Revolution. On the morning of April 19, 1775, a band of forty minutemen met a column of seven hundred British soldiers on the Lexington, Massachusetts, village green. The battle was of no military significance, but the spirit of Lexington became a symbol of the Revolution.

Over the years, as the details of the event became hazy, patriotic artists began to glorify the stand of the minutemen. Notice that each of these three illustrations depicts the same landscape. A few months after the battle, artist Amos Doolittle showed the minutemen breaking ranks and running from the fire of the superior British force. No shots were returned by the colonists.

Fifty-five years later, in 1830, an artist showed several minutemen returning the redcoats' fire, and only a few Patriots fled the battle. But in 1886, 111 years later, Henry Sandham painted "The Dawn of Liberty" with a steadfast line of minutemen firing away at the royal troops.

1777-1779

January 3, 1777
Battle of Princeton. United States victory. The Patriots defeated the British and cleared most of New Jersey.

July 5, 1777
Fort Ticonderoga. British victory. The British, on their way from Quebec to Albany, New York, recaptured the fort.

August 6, 1777
Battle of Oriskany. United States victory. A second British force heading for Albany, besieged Fort Stanwix. Patriots, on the way to help the garrison, managed to fight off an attack.

August 16, 1777
Battle of Bennington. United States victory. The British went to Bennington, Vermont, for supplies but were forced to leave without them.

September 11, 1777
Battle of Brandywine. British victory. The British, on their way to Philadelphia, were merely slowed down by the Patriots at Brandywine.

October 4, 1777
Battle of Germantown. British victory. The Patriots were repulsed by the British near Philadelphia.

October 17, 1777
Battle of Saratoga. United States victory. The Patriot victory at Saratoga, New York, finally halted the invasion from Quebec.

June 18, 1778
Evacuation of Philadelphia. The British, concerned about reports of a French fleet in the vicinity, left Philadelphia and headed for New York City.

June 28, 1778
Battle of Monmouth, New Jersey. Drawn battle. The Patriots attacked the British. After some initial successes, they were forced on the defensive. The British withdrew and reached New York safely.

July 4, 1778
Capture of Kaskaskia. United States victory. To stop raids in the west, the Patriots sent troops to occupy several posts, including Kaskaskia and Vincennes on the Mississippi River.

December 29, 1778
Battle of Savannah, Georgia. British victory. The British defeated a force of local militia and occupied the city.

February 23, 1779
Battle of Vincennes. United States victory. The British had recaptured Vincennes but were forced to surrender it again.

Map labels: L. Superior, L. Michigan, L. Huron, L. Ontario, L. Erie, Quebec, St. Lawrence, Montreal, L. Champlain, N.H., MASS., FT. TICONDEROGA, BENNINGTON, ORISKANY, SARATOGA, FT. STANWIX, Albany, N.Y., MASS., CONN., R.I., Detroit, Ft. Pitt, QUEBEC, PA., PRINCETON, GERMANTOWN, BRANDYWINE, MONMOUTH, Philadelphia, New York, N.J., MD., DEL., Ohio R., VINCENNES, KASKASKIA, VA., N.C., INDIAN RESERVE, S.C., GA., SAVANNAH, ATLANTIC OCEAN, WEST FLORIDA, EAST FLORIDA, Gulf of Mexico

PREPARED BY
UNIVERSAL MAP, INC.

American Revolution

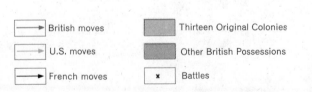

→ British moves

→ U.S. moves

→ French moves

☐ Thirteen Original Colonies

☐ Other British Possessions

× Battles

1780-1781

May 12, 1780
Siege of Charleston, South Carolina. British victory. The Patriots were besieged and finally forced to surrender to the British.

August 16, 1780
Battle of Camden. British victory. The Patriots tried to go on the offensive in the South but were routed by the British.

October 7, 1780
Battle of King's Mountain. United States victory. The tide turned in the South when the Patriots decisively defeated the Loyalists.

January 17, 1781
Battle of Cowpens. United States victory. The British sent a force to attack the Southern Patriots but the British were defeated after suffering heavy casualties.

March 15, 1781
Battle of Guilford Courthouse, North Carolina. British victory. The Patriots were defeated, but the British suffered such heavy losses they finally had to withdraw.

May 21-October 19, 1781
Yorktown campaign. United States victory. The Patriots (General George Washington) and the French (Comte de Rochambeau) planned a joint attack against the British in New York supported by the French West Indian fleet (Comte de Grasse). But when de Grasse notified Washington that the fleet was leaving the West Indies (Aug. 13) for Chesapeake Bay, Washington decided to attack the British in that area. The French and Patriot troops crossed the Hudson River (Aug. 20-26), feinted toward Staten Island, and then went southward through New Jersey.

De Grasse arrived off Yorktown (Aug. 30), set up a naval blockade, and landed his troops to join the French (Marquis de Lafayette) who were blockading the British (Lord Cornwallis) from the land side. The British fleet (Admiral Thomas Graves) appeared and a sharp action followed. The French fleet was reinforced (Sept. 9) and the British fleet withdrew to New York for repairs (Sept. 10).

De Grasse sent ships up Chesapeake Bay and transported the bulk of the troops of Washington and Rochambeau to Yorktown (Sept. 14-24). The combined forces began the siege of Yorktown. Cornwallis was forced to surrender (Oct. 19) when the British fleet failed to return in time with reinforcements.

Then he listed the actions by which King George III had infringed upon the rights of the colonists and thus had given them grounds for abolishing British rule and setting up independent governments.

On July 2, 1776, the congress passed a resolution to the effect that "all political connexion" between the colonies and Great Britain was "dissolved." On July 4, 1776, the congress adopted the Declaration of Independence to reëmphasize and justify the resolution that already had been passed. Henceforth, the United Colonies were known as the United States.

In Philadelphia and in other places throughout the new nation, cannon were fired and church bells were rung to celebrate the news that independence had been declared. Not all the people rejoiced, however, not the large minority who remained loyal to the king. These people called themselves Loyalists, but the Patriots called them Tories.

Congress took charge of war-making

The second Continental Congress assumed the overall direction of the American war effort—the raising of supplies, money, and soldiers, and the planning of military campaigns. Yet the congress had no power to impose taxes or to draft men; it could only make requests to the states and leave the taxing and the drafting up to them. Hence the congress was handicapped as it dealt with tasks that would have been difficult at best.

From the beginning of the war, there was a shortage of war materials in America. There were many gunsmiths, but not enough to meet the sudden demand for guns. Some of the states offered bounties to encourage the manufacture of arms and ammunition, and the congress set up a government arsenal for manufacturing them at Springfield, Massachusetts. American troops occasionally captured equipment from the British. For most of its military supplies, however, the United States had to rely on importations from abroad, especially from France.

Even when materials were available, it was hard for Americans to find the means to pay for them. Cash was scarce, and the states were reluctant to tax their own people. Hence the congress often requisitioned supplies directly from farmers or manufacturers and made payment with certificates of indebtedness—promises to pay later—or with paper money. This Continental currency was issued in such large quantities that it became practically worthless. To meet the costs of war, the congress had to turn more and more to borrowing from foreign countries.

When it came to raising troops, the Revolutionary leaders could not count upon the whole man power of America. Many of the Tories, avoiding service in the Patriot ranks, aided and even fought alongside the British. The Patriots themselves generally disliked regular military service, though willing enough to take up arms and oppose the enemy whenever he approached their homes. Fortunately, the United States was to receive military and naval support, as well as loans and supplies, from abroad.

To induce men to enlist, the states offered bounties, usually in the form of gifts of land, and several of the states resorted to conscription. The men thus recruited served in militia units which remained under state control. In addition, the congress raised a regular force of volunteers, the Continental Army, and (June 1775) appointed George Washington as commander in chief of this army and of all the state militia.

Washington, then forty-three, had been an early advocate of independence, and he had gained a great deal of military experience in the French and Indian War. He also possessed remarkable qualities of character—courage, steadiness, sound judgment, and devotion to the cause—which made him a natural leader. During the Revolutionary War, he did not have a completely free hand in devising strategy, since the congress often interfered with his plans. Nevertheless, more than any other one man, he was responsible for keeping the Patriot armies in the field and leading them to the final victory.

REVIEWING THE SECTION

1. What events led to the fighting at Lexington? at Breed's Hill?

2. Why did the colonists decide, a year after the fighting began, to declare independence? What philosophy did Thomas Jefferson express in the Declaration of Independence?

3. What problems did the second Continental Congress face in conducting the war? How did the congress obtain men and supplies?

THE PATRIOTS GAINED IMPORTANT VICTORIES

In waging war against Great Britain, the United States faced serious disadvantages. The population of the United States was less than a third as large as the British, and many of the Americans opposed the war effort. The economic resources of the Americans were even smaller in proportion to those of the British. The governing bodies in the United States were newly organized, and authority was divided among the thirteen states and between the states and the congress. The United States had no navy except what it could hastily improvise, while Great Britain was much the most formidable sea power in the world.

Yet the Americans had the advantage of fighting on their own soil. The British were compelled to carry the war to them, at a distance of three thousand miles and more. Moreover, the people of Great Britain themselves were divided, and most of them showed little enthusiasm for the war. The British were reluctant to join the army, so the government turned to hiring mercenaries from Germany. A total of thirty thousand mercenaries, more than half of whom were Hessians, so called because they came from the area known as Hesse-Cassel, fought in the colonies.

Before the end of the war, the Americans obtained another advantage, an alliance with France, the most powerful nation on the European continent. The loans and supplies and the military and naval forces which the French provided were indispensable to the success of the United States.

Saratoga was the turning point of the war

During the first year of the fighting (1775-1776), the Patriots took the initiative on several fronts. After driving the enemy back from Concord and inflicting heavy losses at Breed's Hill, they tightened their siege of the city of Boston. In northern New York, they captured the British strongholds at Fort Ticonderoga and Crown Point. The Patriots pressed on northward to threaten Quebec in the hope of bringing Quebec and the other provinces into the union as the fourteenth state. They had to turn back, however, when the Canadians failed to rise and assist them. Far to the south, Patriots drove out the royal governor of North Carolina by crushing his Loyalist supporters in the Battle of Moore's Creek Bridge (February 27, 1776). In South Carolina, Patriots drove a British fleet and army out of Charleston harbor.

When the British forces sailed away from Boston (March 17, 1776), they abandoned their last foothold on American soil. Before long, however, they reappeared. In the summer of 1776, hundreds of ships and an army of 32,000 men—the largest war-making expedition that Great Britain ever had sent abroad—arrived in New York harbor. Henceforth, the Patriots were to be on the defensive.

The commander of the newly arrived British army, General William Howe, offered the American rebels a choice of surrendering with a royal pardon or facing what he thought was an invincible force. Certainly, Washington's army was no match for Howe's army in numbers, training, or equipment. Nevertheless, commissioners from the congress rejected Howe's offer.

When Howe's troops landed, Washington and his men were driven off Long Island and Manhattan Island. Slowly and stubbornly, they retreated through New York and New Jersey, across the Delaware River, and into Pennsylvania. On Christmas night, 1776, Washington daringly recrossed the Delaware and surprised and scattered the Hessians at Trenton. Later he drove off the redcoats at Princeton. By the year's end, though the

Patriots had given up a great deal of ground, Howe was a long way from the grand triumph that he had expected.

The next year, Howe sailed from New York City with part of his army to occupy the American capital, Philadelphia. In the Battle of Brandywine (September 11, 1777), Washington failed to check Howe's army after it had landed at the head of Chesapeake Bay. Howe marched on into Philadelphia, and after an unsuccessful attempt to drive Howe out, Washington camped for the winter at Valley Forge, nearby. The congress took refuge in York, Pennsylvania.

Although Howe now held both New York and Philadelphia, the two largest cities in the United States, he nevertheless controlled only a small part of the country as a whole. Although he had won additional battles, he was as far as ever from a decisive victory. Another British general, however, on a distant field, was about to suffer a decisive defeat.

General John Burgoyne, with an army of British regulars, Canadians, German mercenaries, and Indian allies, had invaded the United States from the province of Quebec. Advancing rapidly at first, Burgoyne easily retook Fort Ticonderoga. Then he began to run into trouble. At Bennington (August 16, 1777), New Hampshire militiamen caught one of his detachments and cut it to pieces. In other engagements he lost more and more troops. Finally, he was surrounded at Saratoga (October 17, 1777) and had no choice but to surrender all that was left of his army, about five thousand men.

The victory at Saratoga was a great turning point in the war. It led to an alliance between the United States and France.

France came to the support of the United States

From the beginning of the controversy between the colonies and Great Britain, the French government had closely watched events in North America. The French remembered their defeat at the hands of Great Britain in 1763, and they were eager to see her humbled. They assumed that Great Britain, their traditional enemy, would be weakened if she should lose a part of her empire. Accordingly, they were glad to help the Americans.

The Revolutionary leaders were well aware of the French point of view. Even before the Declaration of Independence, the congress had appointed a secret committee to seek foreign aid, and the committee had sent an agent, Silas Deane, to France. The French king and also the Spanish king were willing to furnish supplies but insisted on doing it secretly, so as to keep the British from learning about it. Hence a fictitious trading company was set up, and it sent millions of dollars worth of munitions to the Americans.

After the Declaration of Independence, the Americans hoped that the French would recognize the United States officially and provide additional aid, including outright military support. Benjamin Franklin went to France to help in making a treaty for these purposes. Franklin received an enthusiastic welcome from the French people. They looked upon him as one of nature's noblemen, a "natural man" from the wilds of romantic America, and he lived up to the image by wearing a backwoodsman's fur cap. The French government, however, was cautious. It gave new grants and loans to the United States but delayed the making of a treaty. The French leaders wanted to wait and see whether the Americans actually had a chance of winning the war.

Then came the news of the victory at Saratoga. In London, the news induced Parliament to make another peace offer, this one conceding practically all of the American demands, including the abandonment of parliamentary taxation and the repeal of the Intolerable Acts. In Paris, the French leaders feared that, unless they acted promptly, the Americans and the British might be reconciled, and then the chance to disrupt the empire would be lost. In 1778, Franklin and Deane signed two treaties with France, a treaty of amity and commerce and a treaty of alliance. Soon France was at war with Great Britain.

The French alliance brought indispensable naval as well as military aid to the Americans. The congress had managed to get together only a few warships, though it commissioned hundreds of *privateers,* privately owned vessels, to prey on British commerce. One of the warships, with John Paul Jones in command, raided towns along the British coast, and Jones engaged in other daring exploits. By himself, however, he could hardly threaten the British control of the seas. The French navy itself was no match for the British navy as a whole, yet a French fleet was to gain a temporary and local advantage in American waters, thus enabling the Americans and their French allies to win the final battle, at Yorktown.

The enemy was trapped at Yorktown

After the surrender at Saratoga, the British adopted a more cautious war plan than that of Burgoyne. Sir Henry Clinton, who replaced General Howe in the spring of 1778, abandoned Philadelphia and marched the occupation force back to New York. Washington followed with his army and remained at White Plains, near New York City, to keep an eye on Clinton. Soon Clinton launched a sea-borne invasion of the Southern states. He assumed that Loyalists were numerous in the South and that they would welcome and assist the British.

Approaching from the sea, the British succeeded in taking Savannah (December 29, 1778) and Charleston (May 12, 1780). A number of Loyalists joined the invaders, whom Clinton had left under the command of Lord Cornwallis, and the combined forces advanced far into the back country. The farther they went, however, the more resistance they encountered from Patriot militiamen. At King's Mountain, on the northern border of South Carolina, the Patriots killed, wounded, or captured a whole force of more than a thousand Loyalists (October 7, 1780).

To deal with Cornwallis and his redcoat and Loyalist followers, Washington sent General Na-thanael Greene to the Carolinas. Greene, a blacksmith from Rhode Island, was probably the finest of the American officers, next to Washington himself. At first, while accumulating reinforcements, Greene tried hit-and-run tactics and avoided a pitched battle. Finally, when he thought his army was ready, he took up a position at Guilford Courthouse, North Carolina, and awaited Cornwallis' attack (March 15, 1781). Cornwallis managed to drive Greene from the field but lost so many men that he decided to abandon his effort to conquer and hold the Carolinas.

After this battle, Greene and Cornwallis moved off in opposite directions. Greene headed south, to try and retake Charleston and Savannah. Cornwallis left for Virginia, in the hope of conquering it. He soon gave up this attempt also and retreated to the relative safety of the seacoast. At Yorktown, Virginia, he began to build fortifications while waiting for the British navy to reinforce or rescue him.

Washington, still watching Clinton's army in New York City, learned that a French fleet under Admiral de Grasse was sailing for Chesapeake Bay. After conferring with General de Rochambeau, the commander of the French army in the United States, Washington decided to try and trap Cornwallis at Yorktown. Washington and Rochambeau hastily marched a large part of their forces to the head of Chesapeake Bay and then transported them by ship to the James River. This army of more than 15,000, nearly half of whom were Frenchmen, hemmed in Cornwallis on the land side. De Grasse's fleet, larger than any the British could send to the scene in time, prevented escape by sea. Cornwallis with his more than 7000 men was helpless as the much larger French and American forces began to close in. On October 19, 1781, he surrendered.

REVIEWING THE SECTION

1. Why was the victory at Saratoga the turning point of the war?

2. Why did France join in an alliance with the

American revolutionaries? How did the alliance with the French help the United States win the war?

3. How did the French army contribute to the United States victory at the Battle of Yorktown? the French navy?

THE UNITED STATES WON THE PEACE

Despite the capture of Cornwallis' army, the United States had not yet definitely won the war in 1781. Other British forces remained, unbeaten, on United States soil. They continued to occupy the seaports of New York, Wilmington (North Carolina), Charleston, and Savannah. The British soon recovered complete control of American waters, and after one of their fleets caught and crushed the fleet of Admiral de Grasse in the West Indies (1782), the French were in no position to challenge the British naval superiority. Great Britain was far from beaten, and she could have gone on fighting, had she wished to do so.

After Yorktown, King Geoge III wanted to continue the war, but other government leaders were ready to consider peace. The war had become more and more unpopular with the British people. Besides, it had driven the former colonies into an alliance with Great Britain's dangerous rival, France. By letting the colonies go and granting them generous terms, perhaps Great Britain could draw them—as independent states—back to friendly relations with the mother country.

Peacemaking, however, was no longer a simple matter of negotiations between the British and the Americans. The American Revolution had broadened into a general war. Before it was over, not only the United States and France but also Spain and the Netherlands were arrayed against Great Britain. There was a danger that, at the peace conference, France and Spain might induce Great Britain to be less generous to the United States. They might sacrifice the interests of this new nation in order to get what they wanted for themselves. Thus, when it came to making peace, many

Americans thought the United States had almost as much to fear from their ally, France, as from their enemy, Great Britain.

Nevertheless, when the final treaty was signed at Paris in 1783, its terms were highly favorable to the United States. The American diplomats—Benjamin Franklin, John Adams, John Jay—had proved themselves at least as shrewd and able as the Europeans with whom they dealt.

The Americans grew suspicious of France

As early as 1779, the congress had appointed John Adams to represent the United States at a peace conference, if and when such a conference should meet. Adams was bound by the treaty of alliance with France (1778), which stipulated that neither of the two countries would "conclude either truce or peace with Great Britain without the formal consent of the other first obtained." He also had instructions from the congress to enter into no negotiations unless Great Britain first recognized the United States as "sovereign, free, and independent." He was told, moreover, to insist upon boundaries which would give the United States a broad expanse of territory between the Appalachian Mountains and the Mississippi River.

After arriving in France, Adams got into arguments with the French leaders. They wanted to control American policy, and they found that they could not control Adams. Through the French minister in the United States, they, therefore, used their influence in the congress to get a new peace delegation with a new set of instructions. They were successful and Adams left France for the Netherlands, where he served as the American minister.

The congress appointed a commission which included Adams, Benjamin Franklin, and John Jay, the American minister to Spain. They were directed, as Adams had been before, to demand the recognition of independence, but no longer were they to insist upon any particular boundaries. Instead, they were to proceed "as circumstances may direct." Moreover, members of the commission were to keep in close touch with the French government and follow its advice.

In the spring of 1782, before Jay or Adams had joined Franklin, the British government sent a man to Paris to talk informally with him. To the British agent, Franklin suggested "necessary" and "desirable" terms. His necessary terms included both independence and the Mississippi boundary, and his desirable ones included the cession of the remaining British possessions in North America to the United States as a means of bringing about true "reconciliation" with Great Britain.

When Jay arrived from Spain, he objected to continuing the conversations with the British agents, because the communications from the British government were addressed merely to "persons" from "colonies or plantations" and not to official representatives of an independent nation, the United States. Franklin agreed to discontinue the conversations.

He had kept the French government informed of what was going on, but Jay was growing more and more suspicious of both France and Spain. His experiences in Spain had not been reassuring. The Spanish government had refused to receive him officially as the minister from the United States, to say nothing of negotiating any kind of treaty with him.

True, Spain had gone to war, but for reasons of her own, not for American independence. She hoped to recover some of her former possessions, which in earlier wars had been lost to Great Britain. These included West Florida and, far more important, the Rock of Gibraltar. By 1782, a Spanish army in North America had conquered West Florida, but Gibraltar remained securely in British hands.

Though Spain had no alliance with the United States, she had one with France. In this treaty (1779), the two powers agreed to make no separate peace. Thus France was bound to Spain, while the United States was bound to France.

Jay feared that, to persuade Spain to make peace, France might try to get concessions for her from Great Britain. The three powers might agree to an arrangement for dividing, between Great Britain and Spain, the territory stretching from the Appalachians to the Mississippi. When Jay learned that a secret mission was leaving Paris for London, he thought his suspicions were confirmed. Franklin was much less worried than Jay. Actually, though Jay was mistaken about some of the details, he was correct in thinking that the French government was considering separate negotiations with Great Britain—negotiations which would have violated the terms of the American alliance and would have lessened the bargaining power of the United States.

The Americans negotiated separately with Britain

On his own initiative, Jay sent word to Great Britain suggesting that separate negotiations be opened between the British and the Americans, even though the British had not yet recognized them as representatives of a sovereign nation. When Adams returned to Paris from the Netherlands, he approved what Jay had done, and Franklin was willing to go along with the idea. The British were pleased at what seemed to them a good chance to break up the alliance between France and the United States.

Secret negotiations soon began between British representatives and the three Americans in France. The Americans no longer told the French government what they were doing. Before the end of 1782, a preliminary treaty had been drawn up between the United States and Great Britain.

In proceeding along these lines, the diplomats of the United States of course had disregarded their instructions from the congress, but technically they had not violated the terms of the alliance with France. According to those terms, the United States was to make no peace without France, but the preliminary treaty did not in itself provide for peace. The preliminary treaty, by its own words, was not to take effect until a final treaty, with the approval of France, had been made.

When the French foreign minister protested to Franklin about what the Americans had done, Franklin admitted that they had perhaps seemed a bit disrespectful, but he gave assurances that they actually held the French king and his government in high regard. He said:

The English, I just now learn, flatter themselves they have already divided us. I hope this little misunderstanding will therefore be kept a secret, and that they will find themselves totally mistaken.

After thus cleverly playing upon French fears of losing the United States as an ally, Franklin coolly asked for a new loan for the United States from the French government.

Despite his protest, the French foreign minister was probably as much pleased as annoyed by the action of the Americans in negotiating separately with Great Britain. He was getting tired of Spain's reluctance to make peace, and he now had an excuse to go ahead with the final negotiations, whether Spain got what she wanted or not. He was eager to keep the friendship of the United States, and France promptly granted the new loan which Franklin had requested.

Spain as well as France at last agreed to a general settlement, and in Paris, on September 3, 1783, a final treaty was signed between Great Britain and the United States. The terms of the Treaty of Paris were essentially the same as those of the preliminary treaty. Great Britain recognized the independence of the United States, and though she did not cede her remaining possessions in North America as Franklin once had suggested, she agreed to boundaries which gave the United States all the territory southward from present-day Canada to present-day Florida and from the Appalachian Mountains westward to the Mississippi River.

From the American point of view, the treaty had certain defects. Some of its boundary descriptions were vague, and it contained unpopular articles concerning the collection of debts owed to British creditors and the restitution of property which the states had confiscated from Loyalists. Worst of all, the treaty included no provision for American trade with the British Empire. During the years ahead, there was to be continual controversy between the two nations over trading rights and over the interpretation of parts of the treaty.

For the time being, however, the American people had good cause to rejoice. Before the end of 1783, the British forces sailed away from New York City, thus giving up the last of the ports in the United States which they had been occupying. George Washington rode into the city at the head of a column of United States soldiers. The whole country—and it was a vast country—now clearly belonged to the Americans.

REVIEWING THE SECTION

1. Why did John Jay grow suspicious of France, an ally of the United States? Why was he suspicious of Spain?

2. What were the terms of the peace treaty between Great Britain and the United States? What were the defects of the treaty?

CHAPTER **2** CONCLUSION

After 1763, the British government began to carry out a new policy with regard to the British colonies. The colonists were to be compelled to obey trade regulations which for many years had not been strictly enforced. The colonists were also to be restricted in other ways, and they were to be taxed to help pay the costs of imperial defense, including the cost of maintaining troops which, for the first time, were to be permanently stationed among them.

From the view of British leaders, the new policy

was both necessary and wise. The colonies provided a market for the goods produced in Great Britain and could be a source of supply for materials that could not be produced in the mother country. The colonies were supposed to supplement and not compete with the business of the mother country. They would not fulfill their primary purpose unless the trade regulations were enforced. Moreover, according to the British argument, the colonies themselves benefited from their connection with the empire and especially from the protection which the empire afforded them. Hence it was only fair that they share the costs of providing these benefits.

From the view of leaders in the colonies, however, the British Parliament had no right to tax the colonists or even, as many of the leaders came to believe, to pass any kind of laws for governing them. Only their own little parliaments, their colonial assemblies, could do this. Otherwise, the colonists would lose the political liberties to which they had long been accustomed. They also would lose much of their economic prosperity, for this depended largely on various economic activities—trade with the French West Indies, development of manufactures, use of paper money, and exploitation of western lands—which the new policy threatened.

Thus there were both political and economic issues at stake in the quarrel that raged off and on from 1763 to 1775. Possibly, Great Britain could have kept the colonies within the empire if she had been willing to accept their concept of the empire. They conceived of it as a federation of peoples, with each group having its own separate legislative body and with one king reigning over all of them. Possibly, the continued membership of the colonies in the empire might have proved beneficial for both sides, despite the theory of mercantilism. The British government refused to make any serious concessions to the aggrieved colonists, however, until it was too late—until three years after the Revolutionary War had begun.

During the prewar years, from 1763 to 1775, the British government provoked three waves of angry discontent in the colonies. The first two times, the government partially backed down, and good feelings were restored. The third time, the government refused to give in, and soon the shooting started. The first wave of discontent (1765-1766) resulted from the Stamp Act, which quickly was repealed, but only after

the passage of the Declaratory Act, which asserted the absolute power of Parliament to legislate for the colonies as it saw fit. The second wave (1767-1770) was caused by the effort to collect the Townshend duties, which, except for the duty on tea, finally were removed. The final wave (1773-1775) arose with the news of the Tea Act and was heightened by the Intolerable Acts, which Parliament refused to consider repealing (until the peace offer of 1778).

While the colonial leaders were developing a philosophy of revolt—based at first on the rights of Englishmen and then on the natural rights of man—they were also forming organizations for coöperation and for self-government. Finally, they established the Continental Congress, which met in 1774, and the second Continental Congress, which continued as the central governing body.

By the time the second Continental Congress began its sessions, the first battle of the war already had been fought, at Lexington. The congress soon declared that the colonies were fighting only for their rights within the empire and not for independence. In a little more than a year, however, the experiences and the necessities of the war brought the majority around to adopting independence as the war aim. From then on, the Americans were divided between Patriots, who supported the War for Independence, and Loyalists or Tories, who opposed it.

In carrying on the war, the congress was handicapped because it had to depend largely on the various states for troops and supplies, and the states often found it difficult to raise their quotas. (In carrying on the French and Indian War, the British government had been similarly handicapped by its dependence on the colonial assemblies.) Nevertheless, with the assistance of France, the congress and the states scraped together enough men and materials to keep the war going. Although France gave secret aid from the beginning, she hesitated to commit herself completely to the American cause until the Americans had declared their independence and had shown their ability to fight.

After about a year of fighting (1775-1776), the Patriots compelled the British temporarily to abandon their military foothold in the colonies, but the British soon returned, in greater force than ever. After the enemy landings at New York City, the Patriots lost a number of battles and spent most of their time retreating (1776-1777). Then, at Saratoga, they finally won an important victory. The news from Saratoga led the British government to make a peace offer, and this in turn induced the French to join the Americans as allies (1778).

Up to that time, most of the important battles had taken place in the North. For the rest of the war, all the important fighting occurred in the South. The British expected, with the aid of Loyalists, to conquer the South easily and then to use it as a base for conquering the rest of the country. The Patriots proved more than a match for the redcoats and their Tory allies, however, and Cornwallis' army withdrew from the interior to Yorktown. There, with the aid of a French army and a French fleet, the Patriots trapped Cornwallis.

Only with French aid, economic and military, had the United States been able to win the second decisive victory, the one at Yorktown. France was an indispensable ally in the war. Peace was yet to be made, however, and when it came to peacemaking, France was more a hindrance than a help to the United States. By the terms of their alliance, neither of the two nations was to make a separate peace. But France also had promised not to make peace without her other ally, Spain. The Spaniards had gone to war against Great Britain for the sole purpose of regaining territory. There was now (1781-1782) a danger that, to persuade the Spaniards to make peace, France might induce Great Britain to give Spain territory west of the Appalachian Mountains—territory that the Americans wanted for themselves.

In this dangerous situation, the American peacemakers shrewdly played off France against Great Britain and Great Britain against France, each of which desired the friendship of the United States as a possible future ally against the other. When it appeared that the French and Spaniards were going to leave the United States in the lurch and negotiate separately with Great Britain, the Americans themselves opened separate and secret negotiations with her. These led to a preliminary treaty, which, with some changes, became the final treaty (1783). Though the final terms were unsatisfactory in some respects, they were, on the whole, highly favorable to the United States. This nation had scored one of the greatest diplomatic triumphs it was ever to achieve in all its history.

FOCUSING ON SPECIFICS

1. What advantages did the colonists enjoy as members of the British Empire?

2. The duty on molasses was greater under the Molasses Act of 1733 than under the Sugar Act of 1764. Why, then, did the Sugar Act cause more resentment than the Molasses Act?

3. What was the purpose of the Stamp Act (1765)?

4. Why were the Sons of Liberty organized? the committees of correspondence?

5. How did Americans differ from Englishmen in their interpretation of the right of representation in government?

6. Why did the British believe the Townshend duties would be accepted by the colonists? Why did John Dickinson believe they were unconstitutional?

7. What measures did the British adopt in response to the Boston Tea Party? What effect did these measures have on the colonies?

8. How did members of the British Parliament feel about the colonists' response to the Intolerable Acts?

9. How many people were estimated by John Adams to have supported the American Revolution? How many people opposed it?

10. Why is *Common Sense* by Thomas Paine considered to have been an important document?

11. How did the ideas of John Locke contribute to Jefferson's political thought? How did Jefferson change the emphasis of Locke's ideas?

12. Why was Great Britain willing to let the colonies become independent even though it was not yet defeated militarily?

REVIEWING MAIN THEMES

1. How did the British attempt to tighten their control over the thirteen colonies between 1763 and 1774? Why? What was the basis of the colonists' opposition to the measures taken by the British?

2. What attempts did the British make to compromise with the colonists? Why did the colonists refuse to accept the British compromise proposals?

3. What events precipitated the colonies' declaration of independence from Great Britain?

4. What advantages and disadvantages did the United States have in waging war against Great Britain?

5. In spite of their difficulties with France and Spain, how were the colonies able to negotiate a favorable peace treaty with Great Britain?

EVALUATING THE ISSUES

1. In the Declaration of Independence, Thomas Jefferson wrote that governments long established should not be changed for light and transient causes. Considering the nature of the colonists' grievances against Great Britain and the British willingness to compromise, were the colonists justified in declaring independence from Great Britain? Explain your answer.

2. Why were the thirteen colonies not joined by the British West Indies and the remaining British-held possessions in North America in the rebellion against British rule?

3. To what extent did the Patriots and Loyalists differ in occupation and social status?

EXAMINING THE TIMES

1. How did the rivalries between Great Britain and other European nations affect the development of the thirteen colonies? the establishment of the United States of America?

2. How did British rule affect the colonies before 1763? after 1763?

3. What led to the rebellion of the thirteen colonies? How did the colonists justify their rebellion against British rule?

The Trading Post and the Mission

While Europeans came to the New World for many different reasons, all of them faced the same initial problems: finding food and shelter and protecting themselves from the Indians. What the settlers built was determined by the purpose for which they came, the country from which they came, the area to which they came, the skills they possessed, and the building materials available to them. The settlers progressed from primitive huts in the wilderness to cities that rivaled many in Europe. In the process, they altered the land they found and

added something to it; they built the United States landscape.

The Dutch, eager to expand their commerce, established (1624) a trading post in the New World, called New Amsterdam. It was located on the tip of Manhattan Island, a site ideal for defense as well as trade. To protect themselves, they based the plan for their settlement on a 17th-century method of colonization—the building of a fort surrounded by a village.

The fort, called a battery, contained a church, the governor's house, soldiers' barracks, and a guardhouse. It was fortified

Redraft of the Castello Plan, New Amsterdam, 1660

The Stadthuys of New York in 1679, Corner of Pearl St. and Coentijs Slip

by artillery mounted on platforms at the corners of the fortress. The village, with its market place, houses, public buildings, tenant farms, and private farms, grew out from and around the fort. Both the village and the fort were surrounded by a wooden stockade. As trade flourished and the need for protection lessened, the settlement spread rapidly beyond the stockade. Like old Amsterdam, New Amsterdam had its canal and glazed tile and brick houses with stepped gable ends facing the street.

The Spanish, unlike the colonists along the eastern coast, had no desire to eliminate the Indians; in fact, the Spanish planned to train the Indians for citizenship and economic self-sufficiency. They tried, therefore, to educate the Indians and convert them to Christianity. For that purpose, they founded many missions in the New World, including twenty-

one in California. Because most of the Indian tribes the Spanish met were friendly, each mission needed only one or two padres, a handful of soldiers, and a load of supplies. Generally, the structure of a completed mission was a rambling, four-sided building, formed around a square. The inner arcade, typical of Spanish architecture, served as an outdoor hallway connecting various parts of the mission. The outside of the building had only one or two doors which were locked at night against hostile tribes.

The early wooden and thatched roof buildings were soon replaced with ones of stone, adobe, and brick. The largest and most imposing part of the mission was the church, designed in massive scale and decorated with the best that could be gotten from New Spain or that could be improvised by the padres and the mission Indians.

View of the Convent, Church, and Indian dwellings at Mission San Carlos Borromeo, Carmel, by Jose Cardero, 1791

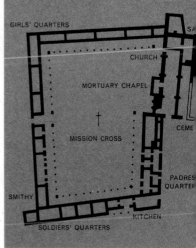

Representation of the layout of Mission San Carlos Borromeo Carmel from the Sunset Book, The California Missions

The New England Village Plan

The early New Englanders, like their neighbors in New Amsterdam, were concerned about protection. They settled, therefore, in compact communities (which resembled medieval English villages) surrounded by open fields.

A New England community like Wethersfield, Connecticut, was divided into village lots and field lots. The village lot was large enough to include a house and several outbuildings; the field lots consisted of strips of upland, meadowland, wood, and marsh so that each farmer had both good and bad land. Streets and lanes were laid out primarily to provide access from the village to the strip farms and were therefore arbitrary and not necessarily related to property divisions.

There was a plot in the center of the village reserved for grazing purposes and referred to as the "common." Facing the common were the church or meeting house, the minister's house, the burial grounds, the market place, and the school.

All the streets and lanes converged on the common. Most villages had at least one blockhouse, a fortress-like structure of logs with an overhanging second story. Sometimes the meeting house was used as the blockhouse The compactness of the village kept the settlers close to the blockhouse where they could take refuge in case of attack, and to the meeting house, the center of civil and religious community life.

The houses built by the New Englanders were similar to the English houses, even to the overhanging second story, the casement windows, the steep-pitched shingle roofs, the gables, and the central chimney for heating the entire house. Because of severity of the climate, clapboards (overlapping boards) were added to the outside of the house.

As fear of the Indians lessened, some isolated farm units appeared. New England, however, remained an area of compact communities rather than individual farms.

A drawing of the original town plan of Wethersfield, Connecticut, 1641

The New Haven Public Square, by William Giles Munson, c. 1780

View of Windham, Connecticut, 1815

Whipple House, Ipswich, Massachusetts, c. 1640

View of Canaan, between the Green Woods and Salisbury, Connecticut, 1789

Section and Plan of a Blockhouse, 1789

The Plantation

A plat of Taylor's Mount, Maryland, 1779

1. Dwelling Houses
2. Free-Mens Lodge
3. Negro Quarters
4. Brick Milk House
5. Meat Houses
6. Poultry House
7. Corn Houses
8. Stables
9. Smoke House
10. Servants Lodge
11. Dry Well House
12. Smiths Shop

The Plantation, by an unknown artist, c. 1825

Hampton, the Seat of General Charles Ridgley, Maryland, by William Birch, 1799

Although the earliest Southern settlements were compact villages like those of New England, the Indians were soon pushed out and ceased to be a major threat. Individual planters were able to occupy large tracts of land, and the South became an area of widely scattered, virtually self-contained estates. The fertile soil of the tidewater area made it possible for the Southerner to raise staple crops such as tobacco, rice, and indigo for export; the plantation, therefore, became a commercial agricultural venture. In addition to land, the planter needed a large labor force and a way to ship his crop to market. The many navigable streams made it possible for some planters to build their own docks and deal directly with colonial as well as English merchants; the importation of Negro slaves provided the labor.

The plantations which dotted the Southern countryside varied from the grand (Hampton, in Md.) to the modest (Colonel Blackburn's house in Va.). The layouts of all of them, however, were similar. As in the drawing of a typical tidewater plantation, each consisted of a main house (living quarters for the planter and his family) and several separate buildings (for cooking, housing servants, etc.).

The main house was made of brick or frame, had anywhere from one and a half to three stories, and had two chimneys, one at each end. Some, like the Brabants near Charleston, had high hipped roofs and a single veranda, not too unlike the houses in the French provinces. Others, like Blackburn's, had the steep-pitched roofs of English houses. Still others had spectacular entrances.

By the 18th century, it was the magnificent plantation houses, the aristocratic, almost feudal life on the plantation that set the pattern for all of the South.

Brabants near Charleston, South Carolina, by Charles Fraser, 1800

Rippon Lodge, Colonel Blackburn's house in Virginia, by Benjamin Henry Latrobe, 1796

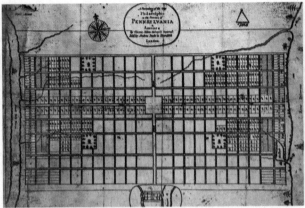

Plan of Philadelphia, by Thomas Holme, 1683

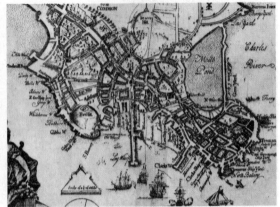

Map of Boston, by Will Burgiss, 1728

The Colonial City

Fourth of July in Centre Square, by John Lewis Krimmel, c. 1810-12

While agriculture dominated the Southern economy, the New England and Middle colonies were developing commercial interests as adjuncts to agriculture. Boston grew haphazardly from a compact New England village to a thriving port with a tangled network of narrow curving streets. By 1774, Philadelphia (population 40,000) was the largest city in the colonies; it, too, was a busy port.

Unlike Boston, Philadelphia was carefully planned. The pattern, which had a long tradition in Europe, was based on a gridiron of streets, intersecting at right angles and forming square or rectangular blocks of approximately equal size.

High and Broad streets bisected the center of town from east to west and from north to south respectively. Ten acres in the center of town were designated for the market and the town hall; eight acres were set aside for city commons. East-west streets were named for native trees, and north-south streets were numbered. The simple red brick houses had, according to one writer, the same "serene, almost self-conscious respectability . . . found in street after street of 18th-century London." And, by the end of the 18th century, Philadelphia had the first underground water supply system in the country and a medical center in Pennsylvania Hospital; it claimed to be the cultural and political center of the continent.

Second Street North from Market Street, with Christ Church, Philadelphia, 1799, by William Birch & Son

Pennsylvania Hospital, by Paul Svinin, c. 1812

During the years from 1783 to 1815, European and United States history continued to be closely interrelated.

The most important European developments of this period had their origin in France. (One historian wrote, "when France sneezed, Europe caught a cold.") There, during the 1780's, people became more and more discontented with the *Ancien Régime* (Old Regime), the existing government and society, which the royal family (the Bourbons) and a comparatively small number of wealthy, land-holding nobles dominated. The discontent led to the French Revolution. This began, in 1789, with the calling of a representative assembly, the Estates General, which imposed limitations on the king and thus established a constitutional monarchy. However, the revolution went on to greater and greater extremes. A republic was proclaimed in 1792, and a reign of terror followed, with the king, the queen, and hundreds of other men and women being put to death. Finally, in 1795, the revolutionary violence came to an end, when a remarkable young soldier of only twenty-six, Napoleon Bonaparte, took charge of French affairs. Napoleon made himself dictator and later, in 1800, emperor of France. Then he tried to make himself master of all Europe.

Already, from 1791 on, France had been almost continuously involved in wars abroad as well as disorders at home. France's chief enemy at this time, as for many years before, was Britain. Britain fought, at first, to prevent the spread of French revolutionary doctrines and, later, to check Napoleon's schemes for dominating the European continent and the British Isles. At last, in 1815, Britain and her allies eliminated the Napoleonic threat by defeating the French in the Battle of Waterloo.

The Establishment of a New Nation

The French Revolution could be considered, in part, as an outgrowth of the American Revolution. For one thing, the French government had spent so much money to aid the Americans in their War for Independence that, afterwards, the government found itself practically bankrupt. The financial crisis in France led to the calling of the Estates General, which proved to be the first step in the French Revolution. For another thing, the leaders of this revolution, at least in its early stages, were largely inspired by the principles of the American Declaration of Independence. The French, in 1791, adopted their own Declaration of the Rights of Man, which embodied similar principles. "Men are born and remain equal in rights," the French declaration said. "The aim of every political association is the protection of the natural and imprescriptible rights of man."

A better way of looking at the American and French Revolutions, however, would be to view them both as manifestations of a single broad movement which affected, in one way or another, not only the Americans and the French but also people in many other countries of the world. The democratic ideals of the time, which were spelled out in the Declaration of Independence and the Declaration of the Rights of Man, were briefly summed up in the slogan of the French Revolution—*liberté, egalité, fraternité* (liberty, equality, and fraternity, or brotherhood).

Not all the advocates of democracy proposed, as yet, that the right to vote be given to every man. But they all felt that no group of men, merely because of privileges of birth, should be allowed to lord it over the rest of mankind. The democrats believed that the people should form a real community, a society to which all fully belonged and in which all had an interest in the welfare of others and an opportunity for their own advancement.

Originally, the word *fraternité* implied the ideal of community, but soon the word came to mean more than that. During the French Revolutionary wars and the ensuing Napoleonic wars, the French government emphasized the need for all the people to be loyal to the nation. *Fraternité* began to signify this kind of loyalty, that is, *nationalism.*

**unit II
1783-1815**

Of course, nations (or nation-states) had existed before, and the people of each of them had been expected to obey their king. The new type of nationalism, however, aroused and involved the whole people in a way that the old-fashioned patriotism had never done. To illustrate the difference, European kings had fought their wars with relatively small bands of hired, professional troops. The American states and the Continental Congress, in their War for Independence, relied upon citizen-soldiers rather than specially trained mercenaries, but succeeded in enlisting only a small proportion of the citizens for active service. The French revolutionary leaders, going much further, passed a law known as the *Levée en Masse* (1794), which declared that all Frenchmen were "in permanent requisition for the service of the armies." This, the first national draft in Modern history, proved highly effective. Henceforth, all Frenchmen owed their highest loyalty to the nation and were obliged, if called upon, to die for it.

From France, the new kind of nationalism spread to other countries, especially to some of those that Napoleon had conquered. Leaders in those countries—in Prussia, for example—imitated the French by adopting conscription and arousing a national spirit in order to drive out the French invaders and regain national independence. Thus the idea of *fraternité,* in the form of nationalism, served as a unifying force in a number of countries besides France.

The ideas of *liberté* and *egalité,* however, led to divisions within countries, including France herself. People who advocated these ideas, and who called themselves "democrats," faced opposition from defenders of the old order, who were known as "aristocrats."

The French Revolution and the European wars accompanying and following it provide a background for United States history from 1783 to 1815. In the United States, the major developments during this period were the adoption of the

Constitution, the further strengthening of the national government, the rise of political parties, the beginning of United States neutrality, the purchase of the Louisiana Territory, and the fighting of two wars—an undeclared war with France (1798-1800) and the War of 1812 (to 1815) with Britain. All these events occurred in response, wholly or partly, to events in Europe, and all of them reflected the new spirit of the times.

The influence of nationalism—the trend toward national unification—can be seen in several developments in the United States. The Constitution of 1787, replacing the Articles of Confederation, gave the United States a much stronger central government. This was further strengthened, during the 1790's, by the economic policies of Alexander Hamilton. The wars with France and Great Britain helped to stimulate American nationalism, even though both wars also produced serious divisions of opinion within the United States.

Differences of opinion over foreign policy, as well as over Hamilton's economic program, helped to create political parties in this country. In the 1790's the followers of Hamilton favored Britain against France in the European war and opposed the social and political reforms of the French Revolution. The followers of Hamilton's rival, Thomas Jefferson, took the side of France and sympathized with the French revolutionaries. Now, for the first time (1791), the word "democrat" began to appear in the United States. Jeffersonians looked upon themselves as democrats and upon the Hamiltonians as aristocrats, and the Jeffersonian party became known as the Democratic-Republican party. The Hamiltonians did not call themselves aristocrats but did think of themselves as nationalists, and their party

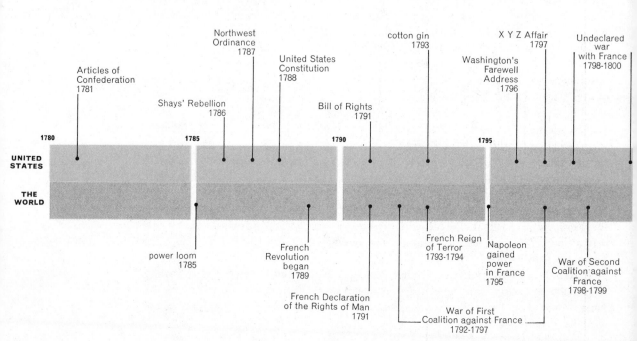

took the name of Federalist (which to them really meant Nationalist).

The leaders of both parties agreed, at first, that the United States ought to stay out of the wars that raged in Europe. Hence the United States government adopted a policy of neutrality (1793), and President George Washington, in his Farewell Address (1796), justified at some length the principle of noninvolvement in European quarrels. The policy failed to work perfectly, as is shown by the fact that the United States went to war in 1798 and again in 1812. Nevertheless, neutrality was, on the whole, fairly well maintained, and it proved advantageous to the American people. During most of the time from 1783 to 1815, they enjoyed peace and prosperity, as American ships carried on a thriving trade overseas.

The conflicts among the European nations provided opportunities for the United States to grow and prosper. This country was enabled to enlarge not only its commerce but also its territory. For years after 1783, Britain continued to occupy United States soil in the Northwest, and Spain disputed the claim of the United States to land in the Southwest. Because of the war in Europe, Britain (1794) and Spain (1795) made treaties with the United States and recognized American claims to full sovereignty over territory as far west as the Mississippi. Again because of the requirements of war in Europe, France (1803) sold to the United States the vast territory known as Louisiana, thus doubling the total area of this country and preparing the way for its eventual growth as a great continental power. An historian (Samuel F. Bemis) has observed that, during the early years of American independence, while the United States was weak in comparison with European powers, "Europe's distresses" made possible America's successes.

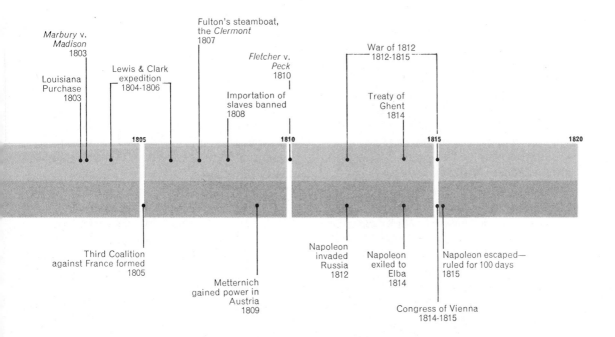

CHAPTER **3** 1781-1787

The Experiment in Confederation

With the coming of peace the American people faced challenges almost as great as those presented by the Revolutionary War. Old political institutions had to be modified or new ones had been created to replace them. Colonies had to be changed into states, and the states, in turn, had to be bound into a new nation. The people had to adjust to new social and economic conditions and prepare their country for a respected place in a world of jealous and often warring nations.

Few Europeans thought the Americans could succeed. Now that the pressure for coöperation against Great Britain was removed, even friendly critics predicted the collapse of the wartime union of the thirteen colonies.

Despite such gloomy predictions, Americans resolutely proceeded to accept the challenges of independence. They immediately began to exercise the power that had formerly been in the hands of the British. Since no other people ever had tried to build a large, independent nation out of colonies, Americans had no historical pattern to guide them in using the power they had won. Confronted with a new situation, they made use of their earlier, somewhat limited experiences with government, and they experimented with new ideas for the governing of a new nation.

The Americans were now faced with a problem which had troubled the British. Before the Revolution, the British had been unable to find a satisfactory balance between a strong central government and local units of government in the colonies. In the period 1781 to 1789, Americans tried to deal with this challenge. They experimented with a constitution, called the Articles of Confederation, which later proved to be inadequate.

Even though the first American national government did not endure, the new nation survived. Equally important, the American experiment in nation-making established a pattern that was later used by other peoples as they strove for self-government and national independence.

In the process of this experiment, Americans created a new social order in which they eliminated some of the obvious evils of the past and laid the foundations for future democratic practices. They passed laws to effect redistribution of property so that the many could own land. They separated church and state so that the many ultimately could enjoy religious freedom. They tried to restrict slavery and to end the slave trade so that ultimately the many would know personal liberty. They broke down inherited class differences so that the many at least would have the opportunity to advance socially and economically. They laid the basis for a system of public education so that the many could have the means of bettering themselves and of governing themselves intelligently.

This period of the Confederation, then, was a time of experiments. Most important was the testing of democracy—government by the people. Democracy had roots in the American past, but it did not become fully developed even in these years. Nonetheless, the democratic philosophy early began to affect the structure of American politics and has been a part of American politics and government ever since.

AMERICANS ESTABLISHED A NEW SOCIAL ORDER

So important were the social consequences of the American Revolution that some scholars have talked about *two* revolutions. One gained freedom from Britain, and the other, an internal revolution, struck at the social system that had been established in the colonies. In a strict sense, the term *revolution* is too strong to describe reforms in the period of the Confederation. Neither the political nor the social revolution marked a complete overthrow of what had previously existed. Widespread reforms rather than radical or violent social changes, were felt in every state. It is only in this sense of widespread change that the term *revolution* can properly be used.

No political revolution the size of the one in America could avoid some social upheaval. Many Americans had fought more against status and privilege, as represented by the British crown and its officials, than for abstract ideals. It was logical, therefore, that these Americans would demand change in the social order and would resist the reëstablishment of a privileged class, even a privileged class made up of native Americans.

During and immediately after the Revolution, many Americans for the first time experienced freedom from social restraint—from numerous small obligations that in the past had seemed to fix their status for life. These Americans were determined to retain their personal freedom and were willing to experiment with a new order where social and economic advancement were open to all—at least to all white males, regardless of birth. In such a society a man could go up or down the social ladder on the basis of his own merits. This kind of movement, making for a "fluid" society, became a distinguishing characteristic of American life.

Symbols of an aristocratic order were abolished

The use and ownership of land often determined a man's political rights and his place in the society of the colonial period. For example, his right to vote and to hold office usually depended upon the amount of property he owned. Therefore, those Americans who wanted to build a social democracy immediately directed some of their reforming zeal against the system of privilege based upon ownership of property.

In colonial times, large property holdings had been encouraged and protected by the old English laws regarding primogeniture and entail. Under the principle of *primogeniture*, the oldest son inherited all of his father's estate even if the father died without leaving a will. By *entail* a landowner could prevent his descendants from giving or selling his property to anyone outside the family. These practices had the effect of confining ownership of land somewhat, but did not perpetuate an extensive landed aristocracy as in western Europe. If a family were guaranteed wealth generation after generation, its members could get a good education, maintain a high social position, and perhaps acquire political influence. To prevent the growth of such a privileged class, American reformers attacked the laws of primogeniture and entail and succeeded in eliminating them.

Other symbols of the old order, such as hereditary titles and honors, also were attacked by the reformers. Some of the Patriots had resented the few titled nobles of the colonial period, and they wanted to prevent the growth of a nobility in the new nation. As a result, many of the state constitutions expressly forbade the creating, the bestowing, or the accepting of titles. The Articles of Confederation prohibited the granting of any title of nobility and forbade state and federal government officials to accept such titles from foreign governments.

Loyalists lost wealth and status

Many colonists remained loyal to Britain during the Revolution, and therefore were called Loyalists or Tories. A number of them claimed hereditary privileges; these men formed the backbone of the aristocracy. Most Loyalists, however, were not aristocrats. In wealth, education, and social status they differed little from the average Patriot. Although no one knows exactly how many Loyalists there were during the Revolution, historians have estimated that they comprised from one fourth to one third of the population of the thirteen colonies.

From the British point of view the Loyalists had been faithful subjects and valuable allies. Some fifty thousand of them had fought alongside the British armies, and others had aided the British cause by providing them with food, supplies, and information. The Patriots regarded the Loyalists as traitors and particularly dangerous enemies because they had turned against former friends and neighbors.

During the Revolution, Patriots had dealt harshly with Loyalists. In 1777, the Continental Congress had urged the states to confiscate and sell Loyalist property to help finance the war. The states needed no prodding. All of them seized Loyalist land, as well as other forms of Loyalist wealth. Some states had hounded their Loyalists into exile. Some eighty thousand Loyalists left the country to avoid persecution and discrimination at the hands of irate Patriots.

British authorities wanted to help the Loyalists regain their lost property or receive compensation for it. The peace treaty of 1783 said, therefore, that congress should ask the states to make restitution to the Loyalists. Congress made the recommendation, but the states virtually ignored it. Many landless Patriots had purchased former Loyalist property at low cost and, in turn, they had become landowners and supporters of the new order. Because of the influence of these new landowners in state legislatures, the Loyalists were not allowed to recover lost property and no payment was made to them. Some Americans even suggested that the Loyalists should not be allowed to return to their homes.

Nonetheless, a number of Loyalists did return. These people, as well as the Loyalists who had remained in the country throughout the Revolution, gradually accepted the verdict of the Revolution as final; they, too, began to profit from the social changes it brought. Before the end of the Confederation period, these former Loyalists became indistinguishable from other Americans.

Status of slavery in the nation was weakened

About half a million Negro slaves, another large segment of the American population, were also affected by the limited social upheaval of the Revolution. Many Patriots found it embarrassing to talk about and fight for personal liberty while Negroes were held in bondage. By pointing out this inconsistency, British and Loyalist propaganda added to the embarrassment of the Patriots. As a result, and because many Americans considered slavery a vicious institution, the Patriots attacked the slave trade.

This traffic in human beings, usually from tropical Africa and the West Indies to American ports, had aroused indignation in the colonies. When colonial legislatures had tried to stop the slave trade, however, their laws had been vetoed in England because the British were unwilling to give up the profits from the traffic. After independence was achieved, states began prohibiting the trade, and within a decade all states except Georgia and South Carolina passed laws against it. This legislation did not end the traffic, which continued on an illegal basis, but it did cut down the trade and deprive it of governmental support.

The campaign against slavery itself was more difficult. In the Northern states, where slaves were few, defenders of slavery were scarce. Vermont abolished slavery in 1777, and Pennsylvania did so gradually, beginning in 1780. Massachusetts outlawed the practice three years later, as a result of a court decision based on a constitutional statement that "All men are born free and equal." In the era of the Confederation, slavery lost ground everywhere in the North.

In the South the situation was different. There slavery flourished. Many prominent Southerners, including George Washington and Thomas Jefferson, were opposed to it, but most Southern whites considered slavery profitable and necessary and favored its continuance. James Madison said that slave labor allowed him the leisure to pursue his public career. Some Southern states, such as Virginia and Maryland, where slavery was considered unprofitable, permitted manumission, or the freeing of a slave by his master. This practice was later curtailed, and slavery remained entrenched throughout the South.

Both Northerners and Southerners were concerned about social problems connected with the freeing of Negroes. A year after slavery had been outlawed in Massachusetts, men agitated to keep free Negroes out of Boston. They alleged that if Negro labor came into the city, it would threaten the livelihood of lower-class whites. Some progress had been made—the status of slavery in the new nation had been weakened—but for the Negro the important social consequences of the Revolution would not be fully realized for many years to come.

The church–state relationship was altered

Religious discrimination was practiced in every colony, though more strongly in some than in others. None of the colonies had denied freedom of worship, but this freedom had been largely for the benefit of the Protestants rather than for the small number of Catholics and Jews. All the colonies gave favored treatment to Protestants, or to Protestants of a particular sect.

This favoritism reflected the relationship between church and state. In most colonies there had been state churches—churches established by law and supported by taxes paid by all the people, regardless of individual religious beliefs. In all New England, except Rhode Island, the established Church was Congregational. In the South, government supported the Anglican church—the Church of England.

Some Patriots, including Thomas Paine, Benjamin Franklin, John Adams, and Thomas Jefferson, accepted a form of religion called deism. This religion was based on belief in God as experienced through reason and nature. Such men, tied to no established sect, wanted to separate church and state. They favored freedom of religion and believed that worship should be a private matter. They wanted to go even further, however. To them religious freedom also included a man's right to deny support to any church, as well as the right to be a nonbeliever.

Many Americans who opposed the union of church and state did so not only because of religious beliefs, but also because they saw this as an important step toward social democracy. Soon after the Revolution, a number of states severed the bond between church and state. In some places, such as Massachusetts, Connecticut, and New Hampshire, however, the last ties were not cut until years later.

The Anglican church, which became the Protestant Episcopal Church of America, lost support from public funds in Virginia as early as 1776. For years it tried to regain its privileged position but was opposed by other religious and political groups. Finally, in December 1785, seven years after Jefferson had introduced the bill, the Virginia legislature passed a noteworthy law, the Statute of Religious Liberty. This statute declared that "no man shall be compelled to frequent or support any religious worship, place, or ministry whatsoever," and that all men were free to think as they desired in matters of religion. Although the leaders of the new nation did not end discrimination, or allow full freedom of religion, this law which they had sponsored reflected one of the important social changes of the Revolution.

Plans were made to expand public education

Education required special attention because the Revolutionary War had injured many of the existing schools. Some were abandoned, others lost students and financial support, and many were purged of teachers with Loyalist leanings. Schools at all levels suffered in one way or another.

After the war, prominent Patriot leaders realized that if all men were to participate intelligently in public affairs, the new government must provide educational opportunities for the poor as well as for the rich. They urged a system of public education. One of these men, John Adams, said:

laws for the liberal education of youth, especially of the lower class people, are so extremely wise and useful, that, to a humane and generous mind, no expence for this purpose would be thought extravagant.

Three years later, in the "Bill for the More General Diffusion of Knowledge," Jefferson urged the state of Virginia to establish a public school system. He favored elementary education for the masses, secondary schooling for those able to profit from it, and a liberal university education for the most gifted, primarily for the few who gave promise of becoming leaders in society. It was better, he believed, to educate the people to become useful citizens "at the common expence of all, than that the happiness of all should be confined to the weak or wicked." Despite its good intention, the bill failed to pass the legislature.

In constitutions, laws, and legislative resolutions, various states expressed support for the idea of expanding education at public expense. The number of private colleges, usually church-supported, increased, and a few public schools were constructed; some actually opened their doors in the 1780's. Unfortunately, most states did not get beyond the talking or planning stage because Americans of the Confederation era lacked the money to finance a vast expansion in public schools. A beginning had been made, however, in the movement that was later to make public education a significant part of the American way of life.

REVIEWING THE SECTION

1. What practices of Old World society were abolished in the new nation?

2. How did the Revolution affect the lives of Loyalists?

3. What effects did the Revolution have on the institution of slavery?

4. How did freedom of religion become an established tradition in American life?

5. Discuss the advances made toward the ideal of widespread public education.

THE STATES FORMED A LOOSE ASSOCIATION

While fighting Britain, Americans were forced to decide quickly how they could conduct the Revolutionary War most effectively, and then how they would govern themselves. They had to decide what kind of government would take over the authority that had been exercised by Britain and her officials.

In the second Continental Congress, which directed the war, Americans had created a functioning political institution. But this was a body designed only to meet an emergency. It had no legal basis, that is, it had not been created by a constituted authority, such as a king or a parliament. In June 1776, therefore, at the same time that the Declaration of Independence was under consideration, congress appointed a committee to frame a constitution for a national government. Americans believed that such a national government could fight the war more effectively than could thirteen separate governments. Later, a national government would be better able to maintain total independence.

The first national constitution, the Articles of Confederation, formed the legal basis for a loose association of thirteen states and for a national government that would not weaken the sovereignty of the states. This protection of the independent authority of the states reflected a popular fear of concentrated authority, a fear characteristic of American political philosophy, particularly in the 1780's.

States set a pattern for the new nation

While the Continental Congress worked on a government for the nation, the governing bodies in the thirteen colonies made plans for new governments of their own. These state governments resembled the colonial governments that they succeeded; and all were based on written constitutions. By 1777, within a year after independence had been declared, every state but three had framed constitutions.

The first state constitutions were written and adopted in various ways. Provisional legislatures, entirely on their own and while busy with numerous wartime problems, quickly drew up these constitutions and put them into effect. Some Patriot leaders, among whom was Thomas Jefferson, objected. They argued that the constitutions should be written by special conventions whose members were elected by the people for that specific purpose. The finished constitution should then be sub-

mitted to the voters and should go into effect only when the voters approved. Although only Massachusetts in 1780 and New Hampshire in 1783 adopted such a procedure, this became the pattern for constitution-making in the United States.

Since these constitutions grew out of a common heritage in English law and history and a common colonial and revolutionary experience, they had a number of similar features. All sought to protect personal liberties, such as freedom from arrest without a warrant or the right to trial by jury, by listing them in declarations of rights. All included provisions which sought to protect the people against executive tyranny.

Nonetheless, all the states had an elected governor, with clearly limited powers. This deliberately planned weakness in the executive branch revealed that even though Americans of the Confederation era spoke of a government with powers separated and balanced among the legislative, executive, and judicial bodies, in practice they created governments where the legislature had the greatest power. These legislatures, often composed of two houses, were elected by the people.

Despite this emphasis on elected legislatures, the new state governments were generally conservative; they did not establish complete democracy. None granted every free man the right to vote. All imposed property qualifications for voting, and higher ones for holding office. Yet in some states the property qualifications were so light that energetic free men could meet them with relative ease. Some retained religious qualifications, usually designed to exclude Catholics or non-Christians. Every state granted the right to vote on terms more generous than in the colonial period. In brief, the new state constitutions, despite their limitations, took the people well along on the road to local self-government.

A plan for a national government was drafted

Most important in the new nation's pattern of constitution-making were the Articles of Confederation, the plan of union drafted by a committee under the chairmanship of John Dickinson of Pennsylvania. This draft went to the second Continental Congress in July 1776, where it was debated and amended. Finally, in November 1777, it was sent to the states for approval.

This amended constitution attempted to establish a national government without impinging upon the sovereignty, or basic independence, of the states. In other words, its framers deliberately created a weak national government which they called a firm league of friendship. Like the state constitution-makers, they feared and distrusted centralized power.

The Articles would provide the national government with a congress consisting of one house composed of delegates appointed by the states. That congress would perform all of the national government's functions. It would maintain an army and navy, conduct foreign relations, make treaties, declare war, issue currency, and handle Indian affairs. Each state delegation, regardless of the state's size, would have one vote. In minor matters congress would govern through simple majority vote. In larger issues, such as those affecting war and peace, it could act only if nine out of thirteen states voted approval.

The Articles guaranteed the independence and sovereignty of the states, and the states retained all powers except those expressly delegated to the national government. Congress had no power to tax; only the states could do that. To obtain money, congress could requisition it from the states. The states were obligated to supply money in proportion to the value of their improved lands.

Congress would have a president, but he would not, in the strictest sense, be an executive officer. His power would not exceed that of any other delegate, except that he would preside over congress. The Articles made no provision for national courts, except for those to deal with specific disputes between states. Each state was obligated to honor the laws and judicial decisions of every other state.

This loose union of states, the Articles said, was to be perpetual. To change this constitution would be almost impossible, for any amendment required approval of all thirteen states. (Yet later some state legislatures were quick to suggest changes.)

The second Continental Congress refused to consider any changes. It insisted on ratification of the Articles as written. Within a few months most of the states accepted the Articles as congress presented them. However, several states still refused to ratify without some modification.

Concessions led to adoption of the Articles

The source of difficulty over ratification was a clause in the Articles which said, "No state shall be deprived of territory for the benefit of the United States." Seven states claimed ownership of lands between the Appalachian Mountains and the Mississippi River. Of these, Virginia and New York had the largest claims. They based them on colonial charters, laws, and Indian treaties. The Articles would protect those claims.

Maryland, one of the six states without western lands, refused to accept the Articles unless the clause protecting the landed states were removed. With the support of other landless states, Maryland argued that the territory beyond the mountains should belong to all Americans rather than to individual states. All had fought to retain this territory; therefore, all should profit from it.

Several of the landless states, such as Delaware and New Jersey, were small. They did not wish to see their neighbors grow even larger and more powerful than they now were.

Despite the arguments, the need for union during the war was so great that, by February 1779, all the states except Maryland had ratified the Articles. Maryland's stand was a bitter disappointment to many Americans for most thought that union without her was undesirable.

In October 1780, New York and Virginia accepted a momentous resolution that satisfied the landless states. In this resolution congress declared that all unappropriated lands should be sold for the benefit of the whole nation. The resolution also said that the western territory should be formed into states "which shall become members of the Federal Union, and have the same rights of sovereignty, freedom, and independence, as the other states."

Several months later, led by Virginia, the landed states gave life to the resolution by surrendering, with some lands withheld, their western claims. On March 1, 1781, therefore, Maryland ratified the Articles, and the nation's first constitution went into effect.

Americans thus created a central government with a national domain. This western territory, which belonged to all Americans, helped bring some strength to a weak confederation.

REVIEWING THE SECTION

1. What features did the new state governments have in common?

2. Describe the national government under the Articles of Confederation and its relationship to the state governments.

3. Of what importance was the victory of the landless states in the dispute over unappropriated lands?

CONGRESS PROVIDED FOR ORDERLY GROWTH

Congress' resolution of October 1780 had established a land policy that affected the growth of the nation for the next hundred years. Up to that time, most nations had treated settlements beyond national boundaries as colonies, with status inferior to that of the mother country. These colonies, according to the political thought of the time, should exist for the benefit of the mother country.

Americans of the Confederation era, many of whom were streaming over the mountains to settle in the West, rejected this colonial doctrine of in-

Western Land Claims and Cessions, 1776-1802

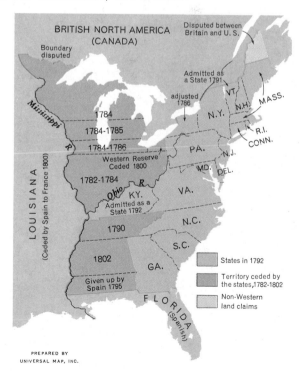

equality. They decided that their rapidly expanding western settlements should not be governed as colonies, but as territories which would ultimately enter the Union as states on an equal footing with the original thirteen.

This principle of equality lay at the heart of the land system which the Confederation Congress created for the winning, the settling, and the governing of the western lands. This principle and the means of carrying it out in an orderly manner solved the problem of expansion for what was already a basically democratic society that wished to spread its evolving democratic political institutions. This land system was the outstanding success of the Confederation government.

Jefferson suggested a plan of government

When the Revolutionary War began, only a few thousand colonists lived west of the Appalachian Mountains. During and after the war, Americans swarmed into the virgin lands. By 1790, some 120,000 settlers were living there. Many of these settlers had crossed the mountains under the leadership of land speculators. These speculators bought raw land with the idea of selling it to settlers at a considerable profit.

One such speculator was John Sevier, known as the "lion of the border" because of his bold courage. From North Carolina he led settlers into the region that would become the state of Tennessee. Daniel Boone, the most famous of pioneers, worked for the land speculator Judge Richard Henderson of North Carolina, who stimulated the growth of Kentucky. The men who bought land from the speculators were usually the frontiersmen who with their families tamed the wilderness, farmed the land, and built the towns.

To profit from this rapid western settlement, the national government had to find a way to keep the frontiersman loyal to the Union. This meant that the government had to be made attractive to him by recognizing and meeting some of his political needs. Among other things, the western settler

needed a system of law and order that would allow him local self-government. The national government needed a system that would give it a bond with the frontiersman, a claim to his allegiance without denying him local self-government.

The early pattern of settlement in the Southwest had lacked plan or order, so it could offer no solution to the problem. In 1784, when the landed states began giving their land to the United States, the Confederation Congress tried to deal with the problem of the territory in the Northwest. It appointed a committee headed by Thomas Jefferson to make a plan for governing that territory.

Jefferson devised a plan that would have divided the Northwest into ten districts. In each district the settlers would choose their own form of government, adopt a constitution, and send a delegate to the congress. Later, when a district's population equaled that of the free inhabitants of the smallest of the original thirteen states, it would be admitted into the Union as a state equal to all the others.

With only a few changes the congress adopted Jefferson's plan, which became known as the Ordinance of 1784. This ordinance was never put into effect because within three years it was replaced by another law, but its principles became the basis for the new nation's land policy.

Congress provided for the survey and sale of land

Another committee headed by Jefferson worked out a plan for the survey and sale of western lands, known as the Land Ordinance of 1785. This ordinance, which followed the practice of New England towns, provided for six-mile-square townships in the Northwest. A township would contain thirty-six sections, each one-mile square. Four sections in every township were to be set aside for the federal government and one for the support of public schools. The other sections were to be sold for not less than a dollar an acre at public auction at land offices in the West.

This ordinance was designed more to bring money to the national government, which had few sources of revenue, than to make settlement easy for the pioneers. It did not permit the sale of less than one section. Since a section contained 640 acres, a frontiersman had to have at least $640 if he were to buy directly from the government land offices. Few frontiersmen could bring together that much money. Thus, these terms favored speculators, who often formed private land companies to buy government lands.

Several of these land companies wanted even greater advantages than allowed under the Ordinance of 1785. They sent to the congress lobbyists who, for private profit, sought virtual suspension of the ordinance. Eager for immediate large income the congress gave in to the speculators.

The most successful of the speculative groups was one formed in Boston in 1786 by veterans of the Revolutionary War. This group, called the Ohio Company, sent a former army chaplain, Dr. Manasseh Cutler, to lobby in the congress in the summer of 1787. He persuaded the congress to sell to the Ohio Company at bargain prices a vast tract of land bordering the banks of the Ohio and Muskingum rivers. Although congress reserved some sections for educational and other purposes, 1.5 million acres went to the Ohio Company for less than nine cents an acre.

Once the men of the Ohio Company had claim to the land, they wanted assurance that they could exploit it in an orderly and profitable manner. Without government support this would be difficult. Squatters already had taken some choice pieces of land, both north and south of the Ohio River. They had held the land against Indian attacks and had refused to move at the request of either the speculators or the government.

This defiance by squatters convinced many members of the Confederation Congress that the western settlers were not worthy of the kind of self-government that Jefferson had proposed in 1784. Congress decided, therefore, to put aside Jefferson's earlier plan, the Ordinance of 1784, and replace it with a new one, the Ordinance of 1787, better known as the Northwest Ordinance.

The Northwest Ordinance listed steps to statehood

The new law, passed in July 1787, established the Northwest Territory and provided for its later division into no more than five and no fewer than three states. By using a system of limited self-government within the territory, statehood could be reached in three stages. In the first stage, officials chosen by the Confederation Congress—a governor, a secretary, and three judges—would rule the entire territory. They would put into effect those laws from the thirteen states which they thought suitable for the Northwest Territory.

In the second stage, when the Northwest Territory gained a population of five thousand free adult males, its people could elect a legislature which would share power with appointed officials. The legislature could, at this stage, send a nonvoting delegate to the congress. Neither the legislature nor the territorial officials could interfere with the personal freedoms of the people, which were protected by a bill of rights. But not all would have the right to vote. Only those who owned at least fifty acres of land could vote.

When any part of the territory acquired 60,000 or more free people, it could frame a constitution and apply for statehood. Congress would then admit that part to the Union as a state on an equal footing with the original thirteen states. This comprised the third stage of development.

The Northwest Ordinance prohibited slavery and involuntary servitude in the entire region. This provision had the ultimate effect of keeping slavery south of the Ohio River.

Westerners disliked the Northwest Ordinance because it embodied the views of Easterners. In its limitations on self-government, the ordinance did reflect the determination of Eastern speculators to obtain and retain control over the distribution of western lands. Yet the ordinance was a noteworthy achievement for the Confederation government. Although those who moved into the Northwest Territory did not immediately gain the privileges of Jefferson's more democratic plan,

Boundaries indefinite

BRITISH NORTH
AMERICA
(CANADA)

L. Superior

L. Huron

L. Michigan

Mississippi River

LOUISIANA
(Spanish)

L. Erie

L. Conn.
Reserve to
1800

TERRITORY NORTHWEST
OF THE
RIVER OHIO 1787

Ohio River

VA.

KENTUCKY
(Part of Virginia to 1792)

PREPARED BY
UNIVERSAL MAP, INC.

An American Log-House

THE LAND ORDINANCES
1785 AND 1787

The Territory Northwest of the River Ohio (commonly known as the Northwest Territory) was established by Congress in 1787 under the Northwest Ordinance. The ordinance determined how the territory would be governed and outlined the steps through which a proposed area could become a state. Even before the Northwest Ordinance was passed, squatters, hungry for land, had moved west and had begun to make clearings and to build crude log houses for their families. Two years earlier, the Land Ordinance of 1785 had provided for the survey and sale of western lands as a source of immediate income for the Confederation government. This public land was divided into townships six miles square. Section 16 of each township was set aside for support of education, and four additional sections were set aside for the government.

The Northwest Territory existed only until 1800 when it was subdivided. The two ordinances set precedents for further territorial development. Later land laws modified some of the procedures established under these ordinances, such as the system for numbering the sections.

These plats show how townships and sections of townships were described, as provided in the Land Ordinance of 1785. Plat A shows townships in relation to the base line and principal meridian. The township shown in dark green is described as Township 3 North, Range 3 East. Plat B is an enlargement of Township 3 North, Range 3 East, showing how the 36 sections of a township were numbered. (A section is a square mile, or 640 acres.) Plat C is an enlargement of Section 32, showing how the section might be subdivided.

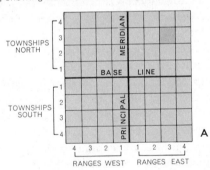

TOWNSHIPS
NORTH

MERIDIAN

BASE LINE

TOWNSHIPS
SOUTH

PRINCIPAL

A

4 3 2 1 | 1 2 3 4
RANGES WEST | RANGES EAST

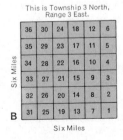

This is Township 3 North, Range 3 East.

Six Miles

36	30	24	18	12	6
35	29	23	17	11	5
34	28	22	16	10	4
33	27	21	15	9	3
32	26	20	14	8	2
31	25	19	13	7	1

B

Six Miles

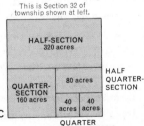

This is Section 32 of township shown at left.

HALF-SECTION
320 acres

QUARTER-
SECTION
160 acres

80 acres

HALF
QUARTER-
SECTION

40
acres | 40
acres

C

QUARTER
QUARTER-SECTIONS

the Ordinance of 1784, nonetheless, they had assurance that they could take with them, and eventually exercise, their American right of self-government. They would also retain their personal liberties, and eventually they would regain equality with the people in the thirteen original states.

The Northwest Ordinance thus solved the problem of how the United States could govern a vast territory without creating second-class citizens. This system of orderly expansion enabled the country to grow through the admission of new states.

REVIEWING THE SECTION

1. In what way was the Ordinance of 1784 an important foundation for a United States land policy?
2. What problems arose from the administration of the Land Ordinance of 1785?
3. How was the Northwest Ordinance a successful solution to the problem of continuous national expansion?

CONGRESS TRIED TO HANDLE FOREIGN AFFAIRS

Under the Articles of Confederation, only the national government could conduct official relations with foreign governments. It could send and receive ambassadors and negotiate treaties and alliances. But it could not be sure that all the states would comply with the commercial treaties it made. For this and other reasons, the national government lacked effective power in foreign relations. Yet the United States had entered the world of independent nations and could not avoid participating in that world. It sought a place in world trade and tried to gain the respect of other nations. These goals proved difficult to attain.

Foreign nations such as Britain, France, and Spain were aware of the weakness of the Confederation government. Since they doubted that the loose union truly comprised a nation, they showed little respect for the new government. They interfered in American politics and tried to manipulate the new government.

The Confederation government was not even able to exercise full authority in the national domain west of the Appalachian Mountains. In the north of that territory the British flag still flew, and in the south Spain's flag fluttered over soil Americans called their own. These matters made the whole problem of foreign relations one of the most difficult confronting the new nation.

Britain refused to grant trade privileges to the U.S.

The Confederation government's most serious diplomatic problems were with Great Britain. One of the most pressing was the problem of trade. Americans wanted the advantages of being independent and, at the same time, the commercial benefits which, as members of the British Empire, they had enjoyed before the Revolution. British leaders, on the other hand, demanded harsh treatment of the former colonies. They saw in the United States a future commercial rival. The British government, therefore, prohibited Americans from engaging in trade in the British West Indies. By law, the British required most products going to their ports to be carried in English ships. These restrictions caused economic suffering in New England towns where shipbuilding and trade had to be curtailed.

British restrictions did not end trade with the United States. Britain continued to buy raw materials, such as cotton, tobacco, and lumber, but not manufactured goods, from the United States. Through smuggling, New Englanders, among others, overcame some of the British restrictions. At the end of the Confederation period, about seventy-five per cent of all American exports went to Britain. About ninety per cent of America's imports came from Britain.

Americans traded with Britain because they needed manufactured goods, such as fine cloth, pots, pans, tools, lanterns, and various kinds of hardware. Britain offered an established market for American raw materials, such as cotton. British merchants also offered long-term credit. Thus, economic dependence on Britain was almost as great as it had been before the Revolution.

Many Americans were dissatisfied with the one-sided nature of this trade. They believed, with some justification, that Britain was carrying on a trade war against them. They demanded retaliation. But the states would not follow a common policy against Britain, and the Confederation government had no weapons with which to force Britain to change her policy. Having nothing to fear from reprisals, Britain saw no reason to extend generous trading privileges to Americans.

The Confederation government hoped to overcome some of the British restrictions through negotiation of a commercial treaty. To obtain such a treaty, John Adams went to London in 1785 as the new nation's first minister to Britain. The British would make no treaty. They also refused to send a minister of their own to the United States. Since Britain treated the United States with contempt, Adams ended his fruitless mission in 1788.

The British violated terms of the peace treaty

Adams also had tried to obtain satisfaction for British violations of the peace treaty of 1783. That treaty said that when British soldiers left American soil, they should not carry away Negro slaves or other American property. In spite of the treaty, the soldiers did take away slaves, perhaps as many as several thousand. American slave owners demanded payment for their losses. The British refused. Americans used this violation to justify their own violation of the treaty.

Before the Revolution, British merchants had loaned millions of dollars to Americans; for the most part, these loans were made to Southern planters. American lawyers argued that the Revolution had in effect canceled the debts. The British creditors insisted that the debts were still legal and had to be paid. Their demands resulted in a provision in the peace treaty which said creditors should meet no lawful impediment in seeking payment.

Southerners defied the treaty terms. Maryland, Virginia, and other states passed laws that forbade state courts to aid in the collection of the debts. Congress pointed out that the peace treaty had become the law of the land, binding on the states, and the states had no right to pass laws in conflict with the treaty. This argument had no effect, for the Confederation Congress could not force payment of the debts. It was equally helpless in trying to carry out the two treaty articles dealing with Loyalists.

The unpaid debts and the persecution of the Loyalists gave the British an excuse for retaining a chain of military and trading posts in the Northwest. These posts, or forts, were strung out along the southern shores of the Great Lakes in territory belonging to the United States. In the peace treaty Britain had promised to give up the posts quickly. When powerful Canadian fur traders and British merchants heard of this, they protested and demanded retention of the posts. These traders, who had a lucrative business in the region, wanted British protection until they could bring to a close their affairs south of the Great Lakes.

Some Englishmen believed that their government had been foolishly generous by ceding the Northwest to the United States. Others argued that the cession violated Britain's obligations to their Indian allies who lived in the territory. British commanders in the region feared an uprising if the Indians there were to come under American control. They wanted to keep the posts and retain the good will of the Indians.

The British government, therefore, instructed its officials in British North America (Canada) not to deliver the posts to the Americans. This decision to retain the posts had come before the United States had itself clearly violated the treaty. The continued presence of British soldiers on American soil angered many Americans, particularly Westerners who wanted to settle in the region. They were also convinced that British agents from the posts supplied Indians with arms and encouraged raids on established frontier settlements.

The Confederation government seemed unable to find a diplomatic solution to any of its problems with Great Britain.

Congress signed an agreement with France

Since France was an ally, the Confederation government expected better treatment from her than from Britain. In 1784, France relaxed some of her commercial restrictions. She granted Americans a limited right to trade in some ports of her Caribbean colonies. Americans were disappointed, however, because they had expected larger concessions, such as freedom to trade in France's home ports.

Jefferson, who became minister to France in 1784, wanted to strengthen friendship with France through trade. He thought that commerce with France would do well because most of it would be in goods that would supplement rather than compete with each other. The United States could exchange raw materials, like tobacco, for French manufactures, such as textiles. This type of exchange appealed to French leaders, who wanted to break Britain's economic hold on the United States.

Under liberal French decrees, American commerce did reasonably well, but it had no firm foundations. The thirteen separate states competed with each other for French trade. They violated parts of the commercial treaty of 1778 with France, and manipulated duties, to the annoyance of French merchants. Congress did not have the power to enforce uniform treatment of French commerce.

The French used their consuls in the United States to solicit trade. The commercial treaty of 1778, which provided for the consuls, said nothing about their privileges and immunities. In 1784, therefore, French and American negotiators agreed to a consular convention. It called for French consuls to deliver their credentials to state authorities, rather than to the congress. This procedure implied that the thirteen separate states were

sovereign. Congress, therefore, rejected the convention. That convention, the most important diplomatic agreement of the Confederation period, was revised and finally accepted in 1788. Although it recognized the sovereignty of the national government, some of its provisions did impinge on that sovereignty.

Despite the efforts of Jefferson and the French consuls to stimulate commerce, American trade did not go to France in any significant volume. Some Americans did profit from the newly opened channels of trade by selling more to France than they bought from her. To the dismay of the French, however, the trade was one-sided, primarily because Americans preferred British goods.

The United States also defaulted on repayment of money it had borrowed from France during the Revolution. Although the congress tried to pay installments on the principal, it could not even keep up interest payments. The states turned down requests from congress for money. Fortunately, the French government, anxious to retain close ties with the United States, did not exert pressure for payment and even assumed some of the payments.

Trade negotiations with Spain broke down

Relations with Spain were about as bad as those with Britain. The difficulties stemmed from three issues: navigation of the Mississippi River, the southwestern boundary, and trade policy.

In the peace treaty of 1783, the United States and Britain agreed that their citizens could navigate the Mississippi to the sea. Since Spain owned Louisiana and the Floridas, two separate provinces at that time, she controlled both banks of the river for its last two hundred miles. And, because she was not a party to the peace treaty, Spain properly denied that Americans had any right to use the river within her territory. In 1784, she closed the river to Americans.

Westerners protested against closure of the Mississippi. They insisted that their livelihood depended on use of the river to get their produce, such as tobacco and wheat, to eastern markets, and they demanded that the congress force Spain to reopen the river.

At the same time, friction over the southwestern boundary also arose from the peace treaty. That treaty had fixed the boundary between the United States and Spain's West Florida at the thirty-first parallel. In the preliminary peace treaty in 1782, Britain and the United States had agreed secretly that if West Florida remained in British hands, its boundary would be some one hundred miles farther north, to the latitude of 32°25′.

During the Revolutionary War, however, Spain had conquered the Floridas and territory north of the thirty-first parallel. Britain ceded the Floridas to Spain with indefinite boundaries. The Spaniards argued, rightly, that they were not bound by the terms of the final Anglo-American peace treaty. They claimed territory far beyond the thirty-first parallel and established military posts there. They also supplied the Indians in that area with arms and encouraged them to raid American settlements in the region. In 1785, therefore, part of the Southwest lay under a foreign flag, and seethed with intrigue and Indian warfare.

Delegates from the Northeast, representing trading interests, were not greatly concerned about the problems of the western settlers. What they wanted most was a commercial treaty that would allow Americans to trade in Spanish ports.

Since she feared that the Westerners might try to gain control of the Mississippi by force, Spain, unlike Britain, was willing to negotiate with the new nation. To do so, she sent a special envoy, Don Diego de Gardoqui, to the United States in 1785. In the following year, he agreed to a commercial treaty with John Jay, the United States secretary for foreign affairs.

The Jay-Gardoqui Treaty was a compromise. Spain offered trading privileges in some of her homeland ports and conceded a boundary at the thirty-first parallel. In return, Jay agreed that the United States would not insist on use of the lower Mississippi for thirty years.

To Southerners in the congress it seemed that Jay had sacrificed the welfare of the Southwest to the interests of Northeastern merchants. As a result, the Southerners voted against the treaty, and it failed to obtain the nine votes necessary for ratification. This uncompleted treaty—another failure in foreign relations—aroused such strong sectional differences that they appeared to endanger the continuance of the loose confederation.

REVIEWING THE SECTION

1. How did postwar Anglo-American trade relations irritate Americans?

2. What terms of the peace treaty of 1783 were violated by the United States and Britain?

3. Why was the United States unable to achieve successful trade relations with France?

4. What were the main areas of conflict between Spain and the United States? Why did attempts at settlement fail?

CRITICISM OF THE CONFEDERATION INCREASED

The failures in foreign policy affected the Confederation government in two ways. In the 1780's, many Americans came to believe that the gravest threats to the existence of the new republic came from foreign countries. The failures in foreign policy had aroused sectional antagonisms and loosened some of the bonds of union. At the same time, the hostility of countries such as Britain and Spain had the surprising effect of strengthening some of the existing bonds of union. Regardless of their attitude on these points, most Americans came to feel that survival as a nation depended on an effective foreign policy, and that they could have an effective foreign policy only if the national government acquired more power.

Internal problems also contributed to a desire for a stronger national government. Wealthy merchants and planters, generally considered to be conservatives, from the first had favored a strong national government. They had lent money to the United States. As the government floundered in

SOME SOCIAL, ECONOMIC, AND POLITICAL ACHIEVEMENTS DURING THE CONFEDERATION PERIOD, 1781-1789

1. The laws of primogeniture and entail and the custom of conferring titles were eliminated.
2. Steps were taken toward personal as well as religious freedom. Most of the states outlawed the slave trade, and some gains were made in separation of church and state.
3. Criminal codes were revised in many states to make the punishment more nearly fit the crime.
4. States laid the basis for a system of public education.
5. The Revolutionary War ended, and the Treaty of Paris was signed.
6. The departments of war, foreign affairs, finance, Indian relations, and post office were established.
7. A national domain was created when the landed states surrendered their claims to western lands. This was accomplished under a resolution which provided that the western

territory should be formed into states "which shall become members of the Federal Union, and have the same rights of sovereignty, freedom, and independence, as the other states."
8. Through the adoption of the land ordinances, provision was made for orderly land expansion and governing of the territories.
9. Commercial treaties were made with France, the Netherlands, Sweden, Prussia, and Morocco.
10. The government acquired some revenue in the form of cash requisitioned from the states.
11. Some of the interest was paid on the foreign war debt, and progress was made in reducing the principal; sound credit was established and maintained with some foreign bankers.
12. Through the sale of western lands, some of the principal as well as some of the interest was paid on the domestic debt.

financial difficulties, conservatives became convinced that they stood a better chance of being repaid by a national government that had more power than the one established under the Articles of Confederation. As much as anything else, these conservatives desired a unified control over commerce. They started a movement that finally led to a new constitution to replace the Articles of Confederation.

The government failed to solve financial problems

When Americans became independent, they did not enter the era of prosperity and well-being that many had anticipated. Instead they encountered years of financial stress and strain. From 1783 to 1787, the United States suffered from an economic depression. It struck New England with special severity. There was some business expansion and economic growth, but the new nation seemed unable to cope with its financial problems. In

financing the Revolutionary War, congress had incurred a large public debt. It had also tried to pay some of the war costs by issuing paper money that was not backed by gold or other forms of tangible wealth. Between 1775 and 1780, congress issued more than $200 million of this money, called Continental currency.

The states also issued uncounted sums of paper money. This paper currency declined rapidly in value, became virtually worthless, and was repudiated. At the end of the war, most states said the paper currency was not legal tender, and they refused to accept it in payment of taxes. Yet the congress and the states had paid for services and goods with the paper money. In effect, because they now refused to redeem it, congress and the states had used paper money as though it were a tax designed to help finance the war. Repudiation injured the credit of the new nation.

After the war, congress tried to raise money to pay its remaining debts, foreign and domestic, by requisitioning it from the states. Between 1781 and 1786, the average annual payments sent by the states to the federal treasury could not even pay the government's running expenses, to say nothing of its debts.

The states, like the federal government, had come out of the war with large debts. Like the federal government, they had also stopped issuing paper money. They attempted to raise funds for payment of wartime debts by levying heavier taxes.

Taxable resources varied from state to state. Most states levied a direct tax on land and buildings. Some states raised money with import duties, others with inland or excise taxes. The kind of tax adopted affected various groups of people differently. Taxes on imports affected merchants most directly. Excise taxes, such as those imposed on the sale of food, usually had a severe impact on farmers. The distribution of these taxes, and the means of paying them, created conflict between economic groups of Americans in the 1780's.

Farmers, who were often debtors and who seldom saw much *hard money* (metallic money), had the most difficulty in paying their taxes. When they did not pay, they became subject to court action, to loss of property, and even to imprisonment. They demanded the right to pay taxes in kind —with produce—or with paper money. By 1786, at the depth of the depression, seven states had responded to the demands of the farmers by once again issuing paper money. As before, this money depreciated in value.

Nonetheless, legislators in some states passed laws making this money legal tender. In Rhode Island, considered an extreme example, merchants and creditors refused to accept payment in paper money. The Rhode Island legislature then passed a law imposing penalites on anyone who refused such payment. People of all states—particularly the conservatives, who often were creditors—found the situation intolerable. They wanted to strengthen the power of the federal government in financial matters so as to curb what they considered radical control of many of the state legislatures.

Attempts to amend the Articles were unsuccessful

The desire to increase the financial power of the national government was not a new one. Even before all of the states had adopted the Articles of Confederation, the congress had struggled with this problem. In February 1781, the congress itself proposed an amendment which would give it the power to levy a tax of five per cent of the value of all goods coming into the United States. The money from this import tax would pay the wartime debts. This amendment, the Impost of 1781, was sent to the states for ratification.

Twelve states quickly ratified. Rhode Island, opposed to strengthening the national government at the expense of the states, refused to do so. While the other states put pressure on Rhode Island to reconsider, Virginia, also concerned about state sovereignty, withdrew her approval. Therefore, the amendment failed.

Two years later, those who wanted to give the congress an independent income proposed a modified version of this scheme. The congress adopted it, but New York refused to ratify it on terms acceptable to congress.

Other amendments failed to gain adoption, even by the Confederation Congress. None of the amendments would have changed the basic character of the first constitution, but for the first time, they would have given congress power over taxation. This was a political as well as a financial power; therefore, the amendments ran into opposition by those who feared any consolidation in the power of the central government.

The failure to amend the Articles of Confederation strikingly pointed up its major defect—the need for unanimous consent by the states for any amendment. This requirement became an almost insuperable obstacle to change in the Articles.

Shays' Rebellion frightened many Americans

While the amendments were under consideration, farmers who could not pay their taxes or their private debts saw sheriffs seize their property and sell it. The situation was particularly bad in New England, where farmers believed that their welfare was being sacrificed to add to the wealth of creditors in Boston and other towns. Mobs of poor farmers in several areas rioted in protest. In western Massachusetts in 1786, protesting farmers organized an uprising under the leadership of Daniel Shays, a former captain in the Continental Army. Their revolt became known as Shays' Rebellion.

Shays organized his followers, many of them war veterans armed only with sticks and pitchforks, into disciplined groups. He also announced a program that demanded cheap paper money, tax relief for the distressed, a *moratorium* (legal delay on payment of debts), and the abolition of imprisonment for debt.

During the summer, Shays and armed bands of farmers used force or threats of violence to prevent collection of debts, whether public or private. They invaded country courts and broke up sheriffs' sales of seized property.

Men of property sought the aid of congress, but it had no money available to pay for troops. Neither did the state. Finally, wealthy merchants of Boston agreed to provide the necessary funds, and they persuaded Governor James Bowdoin to call out the state militia. In January 1787, this militia confronted Shays' poorly armed farmers with cannon and cavalry. In several skirmishes, the militiamen killed three farmers, wounded one, captured about 150 of them, including Daniel Shays, and chased the others into the hills.

Although Massachusetts effectively crushed the rebellion, conservatives continued to fear for the safety of their property. In March, Shays and other rebel leaders were tried and sentenced to death, but they were later pardoned. The state yielded to some of the farmers' demands by granting tax relief and allowing postponement of debt payments More important in the long run, Shays' Rebellion convinced conservatives in various parts of the country that only a strong national government could prevent anarchy or keep discontented mobs from gaining control of state governments. Despite the obstacle of unanimous state consent, these men decided to try to change the Articles.

Congress called a special convention

The events that brought decisive action in the movement for change in the first constitution grew out of efforts by several states to coöperate on problems they could not handle alone. Men from Maryland and Virginia met in Alexandria in 1785 to try to settle a quarrel over the use of the Potomac River, which formed a boundary between their states. Washington, who owned considerable land beyond the mountains, had a special interest in the development of the Potomac as a western waterway flowing into Chesapeake Bay, so he invited the group to meet at nearby Mount Vernon, his home. After making a limited agreement on use of the Potomac, the men decided to discuss the larger problem of interstate commerce with spokesmen from other states. Led by James Madison, the Virginia representatives invited all the states to a conference at Annapolis, in September 1786, to deal with the interstate issues.

Only five states sent delegates to the Annapolis conference. With this meager representation, the meeting failed to achieve its announced purpose. Yet, bold men, such as Alexander Hamilton, a young lawyer from New York who had been a military aide to Washington, persuaded the delegates to try again for wider coöperation.

Hamilton, who desired a strong national government, had long been dissatisfied with the Articles. He prepared and gained support for a report criticizing the Articles. More important, the report also asked the Confederation Congress to call a special convention of delegates from all the states to discuss amendments to the federal constitution that would make it "adequate to the exigencies of the Union." The convention would meet in Philadelphia, in May 1787, and would report its results to congress.

At first, it seemed that the Philadelphia convention would fail, as had the Annapolis meeting. To be successful, the new convention needed the active support of respected leaders such as Washington. He did not offer his support until he heard of the riots and bloodshed in Massachusetts. Like other men of property, he expressed alarm over the apparent anarchy. As a result, he supported the idea of the convention.

Congress itself had accepted Hamilton's proposal reluctantly. In February 1787, it issued invitations to all the states explaining that the sole purpose of the Philadelphia convention was to revise the Articles. All the states but Rhode Island responded favorably and chose delegates. Virginia selected George Washington as one of her delegates. He borrowed cash for the trip and in May, like other prominent men of property, set out for Philadelphia.

REVIEWING THE SECTION

1. What financial problems was the Confederation government unable to handle?

2. How did uprisings such as Shays' Rebellion indicate weaknesses in the Confederation government?

3. What were the first steps taken toward changing the Articles of Confederation?

CHAPTER 3 CONCLUSION

In the 1780's, even before the Revolutionary War had ended, colonists became Americans and created a federal government for a new nation. They built upon their own colonial experience in local government, the recorded experience of others, and some ideas of their own. Their common experience as colonists under Britain is reflected in the similarity of the governments they established in the various states. Ultimately, they all possessed written constitutions, a feature unique to American government. The loose union of states also followed this pattern. Its written constitution was the Articles of Confederation.

In many respects, all of the constitutions were conservative; all showed respect for human rights. In one way or another, each state, as well as the entire nation, took part in a limited social as well as political revolution. The foundations of the landed aristocracy of colonial days were destroyed, and the right to vote was extended to more people than had had that right in the colonial period. These were important steps toward social and political democracy.

At the end of the nineteenth century some historians writing about the Confederation period said that the Americans' first experiment in constitutional government was a dismal failure. They called this the critical period in American history, implying that the decade of the 1780's could have determined whether or not the new nation would survive. They suggested that if it had continued under the Articles, it would have failed. It was saved, according to the thinking of these earlier historians, by bold and far-sighted men who were willing to abandon the first constitutional experiment and try another.

None could deny that in the 1780's there were years of turmoil, economic distress, and social unrest. Yet, all was not black despair; the Confederation government did work. Through its great ordinances of 1785 and 1787, it solved the problems of unorganized territories more effectively than had any other nation.

Twentieth-century historians, studying the period in depth, have revised the older concept of the critical period. They have shown that many Americans in this period prospered, as well as suffered, and that toward the end of the 1780's, most of them were beginning to recover from the depression that had hampered governmental and economic activity. By the end of the decade, the Americans were looking to the future with hope.

In relations with other nations the United States had not been completely ineffective. After all, Spain had negotiated with the Confederation government and had even offered concessions. Foreign enemies did not destroy the new nation, nor did civil war.

The nation not only survived, but the leaders had enough wisdom to examine the weaknesses and to try to correct them.

Most informed Americans realized that the federal government was not strong enough to protect American commerce when dealing with foreign countries. Its power was not sufficient to remove barriers to the free flow of trade within the nation, win international respect for the nation and its people, provide adequately for defense, or gain an economic stability of its own. Many Americans were willing to eliminate these weaknesses and give the federal government more power. However, change was almost impossible because of the first constitution's most glaring weakness—the right of any state to veto an amendment.

In balancing various historical interpretations, it is fair to conclude that the Confederation government was not a total failure. It established a new nation and held it together for nearly a decade. This, in itself, was a noteworthy accomplishment. In this sense, and in that of being the foundation for an even greater and longer-lasting democratic experiment, the experiment in confederation can be considered a success.

FOCUSING ON SPECIFICS

1. Describe the practices of primogeniture and entail. Why did American reformers eliminate them?

2. How did the Virginia Statute of Religious Liberty mark a change in church-state relations?

3. Explain how a territory could advance to statehood under provisions of the Northwest Ordinance.

4. What major problem did the government face in its dealings with new western settlements?

5. What conflict between debtors and creditors arose over the use of paper money?

6. How did the unsuccessful attempt of congress to get ratification of the Impost of 1781 reveal a basic weakness in the requirement for amendment of the Articles?

7. What economic conditions in New England led to Shays' Rebellion?

8. How did some Patriots' acceptance of deism contribute to the separation of church and state?

9. Why was the Confederation Congress unable to help the Loyalists regain confiscated lands?

10. What interstate problem led to the Mount Vernon conference?

11. Why did a crisis arise over Spanish control of the southern part of the Mississippi River?

12. How did the British justify their retention of military and trading posts in the Northwest?

13. Give reasons why Americans continued to trade with Britain in spite of British restrictions on American commerce.

REVIEWING MAIN THEMES

1. What were some of the achievements of the United States under the Articles of Confederation?

2. Discuss the ways in which the Revolution brought about social changes in the United States.

3. What major features characterized the government set up under the Articles of Confederation?

4. Explain how the congressional land ordinances provided for the orderly expansion of the United States in accordance with the principles of democracy.

5. What difficulties did the Confederation government experience in its dealings with foreign powers?

6. What domestic difficulties which confronted the Confederation government led to agitation for reform of the Articles?

EVALUATING THE ISSUES

1. Do people who favor a strong central government today do so for the same reasons as did people of the 1780's? Explain.

2. In your opinion, was government under the Articles of Confederation a success or failure? Give reasons for your answer.

3. Some historians maintain that an economic struggle between different classes of society is present in every period of history. What indications are there that a class struggle took place during the years of the Confederation?

CHAPTER 4 1787-1789

The Making of the Constitution

Robert Morris, known as the financier of the American Revolution, once said that some people boasted of the Constitution "as a work from Heaven," but he saw it as "the work of plain honest men." His was a sensible judgment. Yet the makers of the Constitution were not ordinary Americans. They created a superb instrument of government that has become the oldest written Constitution still in use. Under this Constitution the United States has prospered and has become one of the greatest democracies of all times.

The success of the United States Constitution has prompted men everywhere to study it. Throughout the world, people seeking to establish new governments have used this Constitution as a pattern.

The Americans who framed the Constitution did not have such a pattern to guide them. When the delegates gathered in Philadelphia, they did not even have in mind a specific goal that was acceptable to all. George Washington summed up what he considered to be the general purpose of

the meeting, and he probably expressed the attitude of most of the delegates when he wrote on June 6, 1787, to the Marquis de Lafayette that the convention hoped to establish "a Government of respectability under which life, liberty, and property will be secured to us."

The men at the Philadelphia convention, however, did not agree on the best method for achieving this general goal. Some of the delegates believed that only minor revisions of the Articles of Confederation were needed to make them effective. Others thought their objectives, as outlined by Washington, could be reached most directly through a strong central government based on a new constitution. Even within this latter group there were differences of opinion. There were delegates who wanted to abolish the states, while others wanted to allow the states to exercise limited power within the larger structure of government.

It was a distinguished group which gathered at Philadelphia. A great number were learned men who had read widely and had studied law, history, and philosophy extensively. They were familiar with the works of ancient political theorists and philosophers, and they had kept themselves well-informed regarding current political thinking. In addition, most of them were practical men of affairs. They were able to combine their practical experience with their learning to create a workable plan for government, one which could be changed as needed. As a result, the rules of political behavior which were established by the men at the Philadelphia convention proved to be applicable not only in their own time but also in the years that followed.

This was the fundamental reason for the success of the Constitution. However, this document, which was the result of many compromises by the delegates, did not please all of them, nor did it please all other Americans in 1787.

DELEGATES STUDIED THE NATION'S PROBLEMS

Some Americans had been so satisfied with the existing state of affairs that they doubted the need for the convention. In addition, a large number of Americans, later known as Antifederalists, distrusted the convention delegates. They were afraid that these men would establish a strong central government and that such a government would place an aristocracy in power. They had observed that the men most critical of the Articles of Confederation were also critical of democracy.

In spite of the doubts and fears of many Americans, the state legislatures or governors had appointed seventy-four delegates to the convention at Philadelphia. Of the seventy-four, nineteen failed to appear. Those who did attend made up one of the most outstanding groups of Americans ever brought together at one time.

The delegates represented twelve of the thirteen states, and practically every geographic subdivision and important political faction within the states. Economic groups did not receive such broad representation. None of the delegates came from the poor, the debtors, or the workingmen; most owned property of some kind. The constitution-makers were lawyers, merchants, bankers, professors, plantation owners, and land speculators, but this pattern of representation was not the result of plan or of any plot. These men were chosen as delegates because they were leaders within their own states. A few of the delegates probably were motivated by a desire to gain economic benefits for themselves and their friends in the making of a new constitution, but the majority did not seek personal profit. In their actions most of the delegates reflected the interests and attitudes of the states or regions they represented.

Even in their own attitudes toward democracy the delegates reflected attitudes of their time. In 1787, many Americans identified "democracy" with rule by turbulent, undisciplined mobs, not with government by the freely expressed will of the majority of the people. Therefore, none of the delegates explicitly favored democracy, yet they wanted a government that would represent the people and the various political, geographic, and economic interests that existed in the nation.

The delegates were unusual men in many respects. Forty-two of them had served in the Continental Congress, and nearly all had held some important public position or had served in the legislatures of their states. About one half of them had graduated from college—a remarkable achievement in the America of the 1780's.

Not all of America's eminent leaders were present, however. John Adams, Thomas Jefferson, and Thomas Paine were out of the country and could not attend. Some of the popular leaders of the Revolution, such as Samuel Adams and Patrick Henry, either were not chosen as delegates or refused the appointment.

Nationalists took command early in the convention

Poor weather and bad roads made travel difficult, especially for the delegates from the New England states. On May 14, 1787, the day set for the opening of the convention, only the delegations from Virginia and Pennsylvania were present at Philadelphia's State House, known to later generations of Americans as Independence Hall, where independence had been declared and where the sessions would be held. By May 25, twelve days after the convention opened, the delegations from seven states finally had arrived, and the necessary quorum was present.

Some delegates did not arrive until two months later. In nearby Maryland local political conflicts delayed the final appointment of deputies so that the Maryland delegation did not appear until June 2. New Hampshire had felt it could not afford the expense of a delegation. Not until John Langford, a wealthy merchant from Portsmouth, offered to pay his own way as well as that of another delegate was that state represented at the convention. The New Hampshire delegation finally arrived at Independence Hall in July.

The South had the largest representation at the convention, and Southern delegates were most regular in attendance and most influential in debate. Fourteen of them worked throughout the convention and signed the constitution. New England's representation was smaller. Only six New Englanders signed the constitution. A few others from the area, such as Elbridge Gerry of Massachusetts, stayed to the end of the convention but disapproved of the completed document and refused to sign it.

Some of the delegates, who were to become known to Americans as "The Founding Fathers," began work before the formal sessions opened. Delegates who favored a strong central government—called nationalists at first but later known as Federalists—held private meetings to make plans for replacing the Articles with a new constitution. For instance, between May 14 and May 25, the Virginia delegates met for two or three hours every day. Therefore, when the convention opened, the nationalists took command immediately.

First, the nationalists arranged for Washington's unanimous election as presiding officer. Though a moderate in most of his views, Washing-ton generally supported the nationalists' cause. Then, to encourage free and unbiased debate, the nationalists obtained passage of a motion pledging the convention to keep its proceedings secret. The delegates agreed "that nothing spoken in the House be printed, or otherwise published or communicated without leave." To prevent the intrusion of public pressure, or criticism from the press, the constitution-makers closed the doors and stationed armed sentries outside and inside the hall.

Vital decisions were made by only a few men

Committees did most of the work at the convention, and debate on the floor of the hall most often revolved around the committee reports. The convention itself resembled a large committee more than it did a national assembly, since the average daily attendance was only about thirty. No more than eleven states were represented in the deliberations at any one time. In the committees and in the convention itself, about a dozen men had key roles and made the vital decisions.

In this group was James Madison, later known as the "Father of the Constitution" because he provided steady leadership, combined with industry, intelligence, and learning. Madison, a nationalist, was a quiet, unimposing, scholarly man rather than a dynamic statesman. During the convention, he kept careful notes of the proceedings. These notes were not published until after his death and more than fifty years after the convention. Only then were historians able to learn a more nearly complete story of the convention.

One of the two most famous men at the meeting in Philadelphia was Benjamin Franklin, who had gained world renown as a statesman and scientist. People looked with respect at anything to which he gave his name. Although Franklin was too old to be as active as Madison, he brought prestige and dignity to Independence Hall. His influence for stability and compromise was second only to that of George Washington, the most noted man at the convention.

HOW THE CONSTITUTION OVERCAME WEAKNESSES UNDER THE ARTICLES

ARTICLES OF CONFEDERATION OF THE UNITED STATES OF AMERICA	CONSTITUTION OF THE UNITED STATES OF AMERICA
The Articles of Confederation established a loose confederation of states.	WE THE PEOPLE of the United States, in Order to form a more perfect Union . . . do ordain and establish this Constitution for the United States of America. **Preamble**
The central government was not given authority to act directly on individuals and states.	This Constitution, and the Laws of the United States which shall be made in pursuance thereof; and all Treaties made or which shall be made, under the Authority of the United States, shall be the supreme Law of the Land; and the Judges in every State shall be bound thereby. (Kingpin clause) **VI:(2)**
The enforcement of federal laws and treaties was left to the states.	The Congress shall have the Power To provide for calling forth the Militia to execute the Laws of the Union, suppress Insurrections and repel Invasions. **I:8(15)**
Unanimous consent of the states was required for amendment of the Articles of Confederation.	Amendments shall be valid as Part of this Constitution, when ratified by the Legislatures of three fourths of the several States, or by Conventions in three fourths thereof. **V**
Each state was given one vote in Congress.	Representatives shall be apportioned among the several States according to their respective Numbers. **I:2(3)** The Senate of the United States shall be composed of two Senators from each State. **I:3(1)**
Congress was not authorized to raise money by taxation.	The Congress shall have the Power To lay and collect Taxes. **I:8(1)**
The federal government was not given sole power to coin money; states also kept that right.	The Congress shall have the Power To coin Money and regulate the Value thereof. **I:8(5)** No State shall coin Money. **I:10(1)**
Congress was not empowered to regulate trade among the states.	The Congress shall have the Power To regulate Commerce with foreign Nations, and among the several States. **I:8(3)**
No provision was made for federal courts in which to try individuals who broke federal laws.	The judicial Power of the United States, shall be vested in one supreme Court, and in such inferior Courts as the Congress may from time to time ordain and establish. **III:1**
No provision was made for a federal executive. Laws were executed by committees of Congress.	The executive Power shall be vested in a President of the United States of America. **II:1(1)**

Note: The abridged paragraphs from the Constitution may be identified as follows: I:2(3) refers to **Article I**, section 2, paragraph 3.

The men who had planned the convention had relied heavily on Washington's prestige and his presence at the sessions to contribute to the success of the venture. In addition, they hoped his participation in it would reassure those Americans who feared the results of the convention. When Washington had been hesitant about attending, Madison and others had explained to him that he was destined for a key role. Washington seldom spoke or took a direct part in the proceedings, but as presiding officer he was almost always present. Like Franklin, he took a moderate, conciliatory position on most issues. Without Washington's presence the convention might have failed.

The delegates decided to draw up a new constitution

On May 29, when the convention at last was ready for its main business, Governor Edmund Randolph of Virginia addressed the group. He analyzed the defects of the Articles of Confederation and then proposed fifteen resolutions as remedies. Those resolutions outlined a new plan of government, known as the Virginia plan.

Randolph's first resolution, which called for the establishment of a national government, went directly to the core of the issue. He proposed that the delegates disregard their instructions concerning the revision of the Articles and, instead, draw up a new constitution. The delegates reacted to this startling proposal with complete silence at first; then, heated debate broke out.

Because they realized that public sentiment was against them, the nationalists sought quick action to reduce the power of the states and to establish a strong central government, one which could act directly on the people. They also realized that they might not have another chance, such as the one now offered by the convention, to make a new constitution. Their problem, therefore, was to frame a government so superior to the one under the Articles that the people would recognize the need for a new constitution and would be willing to adopt it.

Washington recognized the difficulties in this problem, but he urged the delegates to rely on their own views and proceed with the work of the convention, even if their plans should later prove to be unacceptable to the people. "If to please the people," Washington said, "we offer what we ourselves disapprove, how can we afterwards defend our work? Let us raise a standard to which the wise and honest can repair," he advised. "The event is in the hands of God."

Many of the delegates, particularly the ones who were nationalists, apparently were impressed with such advice. Since the nationalists were in a majority at the convention and were well organized beforehand, Randolph's resolution for establishing a new government was adopted. Only Connecticut opposed it, though the New York delegation was divided on the question. It was after the adoption of Randolph's first resolution that the gathering in Independence Hall became a constitutional convention. The delegates themselves, not the people or their elected representatives, made the vital decision to draw up a new constitution.

REVIEWING THE SECTION

1. What steps did the nationalists take to gain control of the convention?

2. What were the roles of Washington, Madison, and Franklin at the convention?

3. Why did the delegates decide to draw up a new constitution instead of revising the Articles of Confederation?

DELEGATES AGREED ON A PLAN OF GOVERNMENT

As soon as the delegates decided to draft a new constitution rather than repair the Articles of Confederation, they were faced with the problem of working out a plan of government which they, themselves, could accept. This problem focused attention on the chief element of conflict at the convention—antagonism between the large and the small states. The large states wanted a national government with a legislature for which representatives would be chosen on the basis of population. The small states wanted one representative for each state, regardless of size or population.

Randolph's Virginia plan favored the large states; therefore, delegates from the small states opposed it. Then the small states proposed a plan. Since William Paterson of New Jersey brought the counterproposal before the convention, it became known as the New Jersey plan. These two plans differed so widely in their objectives that for a time it seemed probable that the delegates from the large and small states would never agree and the convention would be a failure.

The large states favored the Virginia plan

In the Virginia plan, the nationalists proposed a strong, unified central government. Unlike the government of the Confederation, it would operate directly upon individuals rather than upon the states; therefore, it would truly be a national government. This government would also have its own officers and agencies such as marshals and courts, to carry out its laws and its other functions.

The source of government power, under the Virginia plan, was a national legislature. Like the legislatures of several of the states, this body would have an upper house and a lower house. The people in the states would elect the members of the lower house. The lower house, then, would choose the members of the upper house from persons nominated by the state legislatures. The number of representatives in each house would be in proportion to the free population in the state. This meant that the American people, not the states as units, would be represented. This also would be true in the voting within the legislature, because the members would vote as individuals, not as part of a state unit, which had been the procedure for voting in the Confederation Congress.

The national legislature would have far greater power than the Congress of the Confederation. The legislature could nullify state laws if it thought they conflicted with the constitution. It could also use force against any state that did not meet its obligations to the central government.

Even the executive officer and the courts would be dependent on the legislature. The national executive would be chosen by the legislature for a fixed term but would not be eligible for reëlection. The legislature would also set up a national judiciary, consisting of supreme and inferior courts. The national executive and part of the national judiciary would comprise a council of revision. This council could examine and set aside state and national laws.

Under the Virginia plan, the states with the largest population and greatest wealth would control the national legislature. That legislature would have the power to define the extent of its own authority, as well as the authority of the states. The large states, therefore, favored the plan. Delegates from the small states feared the plan would destroy state independence.

The small states preferred the New Jersey plan

Delegates from the small states insisted that any central government must preserve the equality of the states. In this way the small states would have a voice in national affairs. Equality also would imply that sovereignty lay in the states rather than in the nation as a whole. In other words, the men from the small states asked that the states be represented as equal units in any national legislature; furthermore, they wanted the states to control the central government.

These ideas were the basis of the New Jersey plan, which William Paterson submitted to the convention on June 15, 1787. He had waited to present the new proposal until additional delegates had arrived in Philadelphia to increase the strength of the small-state group.

With some modification, the New Jersey plan would retain the main features of the Articles of Confederation. It would strengthen the Confederation government by giving more power to the congress, which would remain a single-house legislature. The congress could regulate commerce among the states and raise money with taxes. It would elect a federal executive body consisting of several persons—essentially a council subject to state control. The executive council would have a fixed term and could not be reëlected. It would appoint the judges in a federal system of courts, which would have less power than the national judiciary under the Virginia plan.

The outstanding feature of the New Jersey plan was what scholars call the kingpin clause—the bolt designed to hold the whole structure together. This clause would make the acts of congress and all treaties the supreme law of the land, regardless of laws within the states.

The Virginia and New Jersey plans presented the convention with alternatives of major importance—a strong, centralized union or another loose association of states tied together more firmly than before. Both plans would retain republican government—rule through representatives of the people. In both plans the power of the legislature, or the congress, was fundamental. Under the Virginia plan, the legislature would have the power to pass laws on all matters affecting the national welfare. Under the New Jersey plan, the congress would have only enumerated powers.

Opponents were willing to compromise

Faced with well-defined alternatives, the delegates debated heatedly. Luther Martin of Maryland argued for the small states. "The General Government," he claimed, "was meant merely to preserve the State Governments and not to govern individuals, and . . . its powers should be kept within narrow limits."

James Wilson of Pennsylvania upheld the position of the large states. He thought it was unfair for states with a minority of the population to gain control over states containing a majority. "Can we forget for whom we are forming a Government?" he asked. "Is it for men, or for the imaginary beings called States?" Since neither side would give way, the convention deadlocked.

This stalemate alarmed Benjamin Franklin. If this convention failed, the old statesman warned, "mankind may hereafter, for this unfortunate instance, despair of establishing Governments by human wisdom and leave it to chance, war and conquest." Franklin's plea for moderation influenced the delegates, and they acknowledged the importance of compromising their differences.

Oliver Ellsworth and other representatives from the state of Connecticut advanced the plan that brought the opponents together. These compromisers suggested that the states could be represented in the lower body of the legislature, or house of representatives, according to their populations. In the upper house, or senate, the states would be represented as equal political units. Regardless of population or wealth, each state would have two senators. This combination of features from the two plans, which was adopted by the convention, is known as the Connecticut Compromise or the Great Compromise.

Next, the delegates tried to resolve sectional differences. Northerners wanted the slaves included in a count of population for determining a state's share of direct taxes. But the North did not want the slaves counted when determining the number of representatives that state would have in the house. They also wanted the congress to have the power to make tariffs and regulate trade. Southerners, who owned most of the slaves, wanted the slaves counted for purposes of representation, but not for direct taxation. Southerners also feared that the congress might place export duties on their crops, interfere with the slave trade, and make commercial treaties similar to the Jay-Gardoqui Treaty, which they thought favored the North and injured the South.

These differences, too, were resolved by compromise. It was decided that three fifths of the slaves would be counted for purposes of representation and direct taxation. The congress was allowed to regulate commerce, but not to levy export duties. The congress was prohibited for a period of twenty years from bringing an end to the foreign slave trade. The new constitution gave the president the power to make treaties of all kinds, but approval of two thirds of the senate, rather than a simple majority, was required. As a group, the Southern states could, therefore, veto a commercial treaty which they did not favor.

New powers were given to the central government

As more compromises were reached, the constitution took shape as a document with features from both the Virginia and New Jersey plans. The Great Compromise, however, conceded more to the Virginia plan than to the New Jersey plan, and as a result, the constitution became more national than federal in character.

The kingpin clause in the new constitution (*Article VI, para. 2*) was a basic element for holding the Union together. Although proposed by the supporters of the New Jersey, or small state plan, it was an important concession to the advocates of a strong, central government. It stated that the constitution and the laws and treaties made under it would be the "supreme Law of the Land." This revised kingpin clause enabled the central government to act directly on the people through state and federal officials who were bound to enforce federal laws regardless of conflicting state laws.

The newly framed constitution granted other important powers to the central government. Among these powers was exclusive control over foreign relations, particularly over matters of war and peace. In addition, the congress was given the power to levy taxes, regulate commerce, fully control money, and pass laws "necessary and proper" to carry out its responsibilities (*Article I, sec. 8*). The constitution took from the states some of the powers which they had exercised under the Articles of Confederation, such as the right to issue money and to pass laws that prevented creditors from collecting their debts.

The new constitution contained concessions to the principle of state sovereignty, such as equality of state representation in the senate, but nowhere did it recognize the claim of the states to individual sovereignty. Despite its many compromises, the constitution which was developed at the convention laid the foundation for a nation, not for a loose association of states.

A government with checks and balances was formed

Some of the delegates did not like the way the constitution was taking shape, and they left the convention. The remaining delegates worked through the hot, humid days of late summer to complete the document. They created a government with checks and balances wherein the powers of the legislative, executive, and judicial branches would be separated. Each branch would have enough power of its own to check excesses or abuses in the use of power in the other branches. When power was used properly, the whole government would be in balance and would function in an orderly manner.

The delegates worked out this system of checks and balances because they feared the abuse of power. For example, since they equated democracy with mob rule and believed it would lead to tyrannical government controlled by demagogues, they tried to devise a system of checks and balances which would safeguard the government against such tyranny. At the same time, they wanted to prevent the growth of aristocracy, or government by a privileged class.

This fear of concentrated power was reflected in several of the features of the new government. For instance, only in the election of representatives to the house did the constitution give the people a direct part in selecting those who governed them. The state legislatures, not the people themselves, would choose the senators.

Fear of demagogues led the makers of the constitution to remove the selection of the executive, or president, even further from the people. The

THE STRUCTURE AND POWERS OF THE GOVERNMENT

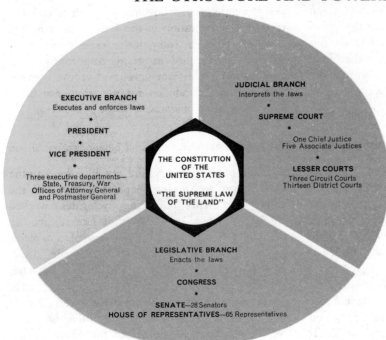

EXECUTIVE BRANCH
Executes and enforces laws
*
PRESIDENT
*
VICE PRESIDENT
*
Three executive departments—
State, Treasury, War
Offices of Attorney General
and Postmaster General

THE CONSTITUTION
OF THE
UNITED STATES

"THE SUPREME LAW
OF THE LAND"

JUDICIAL BRANCH
Interprets the laws
*
SUPREME COURT
*
One Chief Justice
Five Associate Justices
*
LESSER COURTS
Three Circuit Courts
Thirteen District Courts

LEGISLATIVE BRANCH
Enacts the laws
*
CONGRESS
*
SENATE—28 Senators
HOUSE OF REPRESENTATIVES—65 Representatives

The Constitution of the United States provides for three separate and distinct branches of the national government and delegates certain broad powers to each. The abuse of power by any one branch of government is controlled by a system of checks and balances.

SEPARATION OF POWERS

The chart on this page shows how each branch of the new government was organized in 1789 to implement the powers granted in the Constitution. Each branch has grown, but the basic structure remains unchanged.

Legislative. Congress is empowered to tax; to regulate commerce; to declare war; and to make all the laws necessary to carry out its specified powers and duties.

Executive. As chief executive, the President serves as commander in chief of the armed forces. He makes treaties, suggests

president was to be elected by a complicated system of electors appointed by the state legislatures. This elaborate procedure was a compromise between various views as to how the president should be chosen and what his role should be. Some of the people at the convention wanted a virtual monarch, others desired only an administrative figurehead. Yet the office of president, while removed from the direct choice of the people and held in restraint by checks, emerged as a position of considerable power, with the president responsible only to the people, not to congress. This office stood out as one of the most striking features of the constitution.

The judiciary, or supreme court, was even more distant from the people than was the president. With the consent of the senate, the president would appoint the justices to the supreme court; they would hold office for life. Practically all of the delegates agreed upon the need for a supreme national court, but not all agreed on its powers. Some

delegates believed that the supreme court could veto laws it considered unconstitutional; others did not. The constitution itself did not say the court could exercise such a veto, primarily because strong objections had arisen against anything similar to the council of revision as included in the Virginia plan.

After all of the compromises had been agreed upon, a committee of style polished the legal language. When this final draft went to the convention, only forty-two delegates were still in attendance. Few of them were fully satisfied with the package of compromises, but only three of the delegates refused to sign. On September 17, 1787, therefore, thirty-nine men signed the constitution.

REVIEWING THE SECTION

1. On what points did the Virginia plan differ from the New Jersey plan? What was the Great Compromise?

measures to Congress, signs or vetoes bills, executes laws, and appoints many national officials.

Judicial. The Supreme Court and lesser courts interpret the laws and try cases which come under their jurisdiction. These federal courts determine the constitutionality of federal, state, or local laws.

CHECKS AND BALANCES

The chart on this page shows how the system of checks and balances allows for considerable participation in and checking of the affairs of each branch by the other two.

Many examples of checks and balances may be traced to specific clauses in the Constitution; others have developed through interpretation. For example, the precedent for determining the constitutionality of federal laws by the Supreme Court was established in the *Marbury* v. *Madison* case (1803).

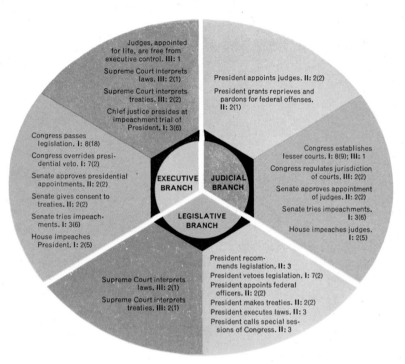

2. What new powers were given to the central government by the Constitution?

3. Why was a government with checks and balances devised? Why did the Constitution remove the selection of senators, the executive, and the judiciary from the people?

A FIGHT DEVELOPED OVER RATIFICATION

Early in the convention the delegates had decided to ignore the Articles because they had realized they would have difficulty gaining approval for their plan of government. It would have been especially difficult because unanimous consent of the states was required for amending the Articles. The delegates had agreed to ask the Congress of the Confederation to call special conventions to be elected by the people, for the purpose of ratifying the new constitution. They further agreed that ratification by only nine states, instead of thirteen as required by the Articles, would be enough to put the new constitution into effect.

As soon as the plan for ratification became known, the struggle began. Inconsistencies confused the issues. Although the basis of argument was whether or not the government would be federal or national, the constitution was a skillful fusion of both and, therefore, offered no clear choice between such alternatives. Moreover, the terminology used in the debates was puzzling. The Federalists, who favored ratification, realized that the idea of a strong national government, such as the constitution would establish, was unpopular. They called themselves Federalists in order to overcome the stigma which might have been attached to the name Nationalists. The true federalists, who believed that the constitution would establish a government that was more national than federal, were left with no choice other than the name of Antifederalists.

Three delegates to the Philadelphia convention who were also members of the Confederation Congress immediately brought the new constitution to that congress. Ten days after the convention had been adjourned, the Congress of the Confederation, without recommending either approval or disapproval, sent the constitution to the states.

Rhode Island, whose people were opposed to a stronger union, refused to call a convention. Therefore, that state did not participate directly in the struggle over ratification. In the other states the legislatures held elections for delegates to the ratifying conventions. These elections, as well as the voting in the conventions themselves, were contests for or against the constitution, for the delegates were chosen on the basis of their attitudes toward the new document.

In these contests local issues sometimes divided Federalists from Antifederalists. More often, however, economic, class, and sectional differences divided the two groups. Most merchants, owners of large plantations, professional men, men of property and education, and, in general, those who lived in the coastal or tidewater areas were Federalists. Owners of small farms, frontiersmen, debtors, the uneducated and the poor, and those who lived in the interior or back country were generally Antifederalists.

Federalists had many advantages in their efforts to promote ratification. They had a positive program, designed to overcome some of the difficulties facing the nation, and they had better organization, greater resources, and more effective leadership than did the Antifederalists. Most of the newspapers and many men of prestige favored the Federalist position. The knowledge that men like Washington and Franklin supported the constitution probably persuaded many to favor ratification.

Even the method of electing men to the state conventions favored the Federalists. These delegates were to be elected on the same basis as were the representatives to the state legislatures, which meant that the people from the tidewater areas would be overrepresented. Property qualifications for voting also assured Federalists of heavy representation in the ratifying conventions.

The Federalists needed every advantage, for at first most Americans seemed to sympathize with the Antifederalists. The settlers of the back country, in particular, distrusted the men who made and fought for the constitution more than they distrusted the document.

Federalists urged ratification

Knowing they had to overcome considerable opposition, the Federalists promptly began a campaign of persuasion through newspapers and pamphlets. Through these media, the Federalists admitted that the constitution had flaws, but they also pointed out that it was the best frame of government which the nation's finest minds could produce. They argued that if the constitution were rejected, financial chaos, national bankruptcy, civil war, and disunion might follow.

For ten months, Federalists battled for ratification. They and the Antifederalists published quantities of political literature, pleading for public support. Alexander Hamilton, in collaboration with James Madison and John Jay, published a series of essays examining and explaining the new constitution from the Federalist point of view. Under the pen name "Publius" the three men wrote eighty-five articles for New York newspapers between October 1787 and July 1788.

These essays, later published as a book called *The Federalist*, comprise one of the great treatises on the American constitutional system. Thomas Jefferson called it "the best commentary on the principles of government which ever was written."

The Federalist was a partisan, not an objective, analysis of the constitution. It defended the principle of a national government as outlined in the constitution, but the authors were careful to point out that the constitution was federal as well as national. To overcome popular fears of centralized authority, they tried to show that under the new constitution the powers of the government would not be extensive enough to be dangerous. They insisted, however, that the government had to be strong enough to insure survival as a nation. The Federalists also believed that national unity through a uniform interpretation of the constitution was necessary. Hamilton said that the supreme court had the right to declare acts of the congress void. Madison even argued that the "necessary and proper" clause (*Art. I, sec. 8, para. 18*) would give the congress the power to make laws not specifically denied to it by the constitution. The Federalists argued for a strong government with independent powers to tax and to act directly on the people.

Antifederalists opposed ratification

Nearly all of the Antifederalists believed that the new constitution would establish a central government which would be too powerful. George Mason of Virginia pointed out that "it is a national government and no longer a Confederation." Antifederalists called the constitution illegal, which in a technical sense it was, because the men at Philadelphia had by-passed the amending procedure under the Articles of Confederation. Critics said the constitution would cripple good government, destroy state sovereignty, and take away the rights of the people. They considered it dangerous and unnecessary to give a national government as much power as was given by the constitution.

Antifederalists argued, for example, that the "necessary and proper" clause would allow the central government to take away the powers of the states. They also insisted that the government's independent powers of taxation could be used to drain the states of their sources of revenue, thereby reducing them to impotence. Of all the Antifederalist arguments, the strongest, the most effective, and the one repeated most often was the simple statement that the new constitution had no bill of rights. The makers of the constitution had discussed such a bill but had decided it was unnecessary because most of the state constitutions themselves either included such bills of rights or in other ways guaranteed personal liberties. This defense did not reassure the Antifederalists who replied that the central government would have a sphere of sovereignty of its own and would operate directly on the people. Without a bill of rights to restrain that government, it might someday encroach on basic human freedoms.

The Antifederalists, as well as the Federalists, produced political literature in defense of their ideas. The *Letters of a Federal Farmer,* by Richard Henry Lee of Virginia, published in October 1787, was one of the most influential of the works which presented the position of the Antifederalists. Lee advanced most of the standard Antifederalist arguments. He said that the constitution was undemocratic because it would place the majority under minority control. This reflected the common fear of the Antifederalists that the new government would be controlled by the rich—the upper classes. Lee's essays, "written with art" and moderate in tone, won a wide audience.

The Antifederalists had strong arguments, greater concerns about democracy than their opponents and, probably, slight majority sentiment on their side; moreover, their leaders were learned and eloquent men, such as Governor George Clinton of New York and Patrick Henry of Virginia. However, they were not as effective as the Federalists in swaying public opinion. At a time when the nation wanted a positive program, their stand was defensive and their arguments largely negative.

All thirteen states ratified the Constitution

Several states, large and small, acted promptly. Delaware, Pennsylvania, and New Jersey ratified the constitution in December 1787; Georgia and Connecticut followed in January 1788; Maryland ratified in April of the same year. South Carolina became the second of the large states to approve, in May 1788.

Elsewhere, Federalists and Antifederalists fought closer battles, and the issue was long in doubt. In

Massachusetts, distrust of the constitution was widespread, but after a hard struggle, the Federalists won, and in February 1788, that state became the sixth to ratify. On June 21, 1788, New Hampshire gained the distinction of making official the adoption of the constitution, when it became the ninth state to ratify. Nonetheless, the fate of the constitution was still in doubt. Four states, where about forty per cent of all Americans lived, still had not ratified it. Without at least two of those states, Virginia and New York, it seemed unlikely that the new Union could succeed.

Virginia—the home of Washington, Jefferson, Madison, and other distinguished leaders—at the time had the largest population and the greatest influence in the Union. The Antifederalists, led by able men such as Patrick Henry and Richard Henry Lee, fought their best battle in Virginia, but they lost. On June 25, 1788, Virginia became the tenth state to ratify.

On July 4, many people celebrated the new Union with parades and bonfires. However, in Providence, Rhode Island, mobs of farmers attacked the merrymakers, and rioting between Federalists and Antifederalists in New York indicated that rejoicing was premature. New York was a key state; the Antifederalist forces there, led by Governor George Clinton, comprised a heavy majority in the ratifying convention. New York City threatened to secede if the state did not ratify the constitution. Finally, under the excellent leadership of Alexander Hamilton, the balance shifted in favor of ratification. On July 26, New York's convention approved the constitution by a narrow margin. It was the eleventh to do so.

Although the Constitution had become official with ratification by the ninth state, it had needed the prestige and authority of the major states before it could really go into effect. With ratification by New York and Virginia, the Constitution had that prestige and authority.

North Carolina and Rhode Island, where Antifederalist majorities at first had defeated ratification, did not ratify the Constitution until after the new government had gone into effect. North Carolina gave approval in November 1789, but Rhode Island delayed doing so until May 1790.

Some recent scholars, analyzing the struggle for ratification, have concluded that the adoption of the Constitution represented the will of a minority, not a majority of the people. It is true that only a small percentage of Americans voted for delegates to the state conventions, and that the method for electing the delegates was not entirely democratic. However, this does not mean that only a minority favored the Constitution. It has been estimated that almost half of the free population favored ratification. Moreover, the method for securing ratification was a democratic one for that time.

Friends of the Constitution led the new government

After the Confederation Congress, which was still in session in New York, declared the Constitution duly ratified, the people turned their attention to the election of representatives to the new Congress. The old Confederation Congress decided that the House of Representatives and Senate of the new Congress should convene on the first Wednesday of March, which that year fell on the fourth day of the month. As a result, for many years new administrations began on March 4. It was also decided that the states should select presidential electors in January 1789 and that the electors should cast their ballots in February.

As critics of the Constitution had foreseen, few, if any, of the representatives or senators elected to the first Congress came from the ranks of committed Antifederalists. Many of the new legislators had served as delegates to the Philadelphia convention. The prestige they had acquired by sponsoring the Constitution contributed, at least in part, to their success. When the first Congress convened, almost a month late, many friends of the Constitution were among its members.

The presidency, too, was entrusted to a man who was a friend of the Constitution. Many people had supported the Constitution primarily because they had assumed that George Washington would be the first President and would lead the new government through its first years. In accordance with the Constitution, the electors voted for two men for President. As expected, they unanimously chose Washington. John Adams of Massachusetts, who received the second highest number of electoral votes, became Vice President.

At noon on April 30, 1789, Washington, accompanied by a military escort, rode alone in a four-horse carriage to Federal Hall at the corner of Wall and Nassau streets in New York City. There, on a balcony facing Wall Street, he stood tall and austere, dressed in a dark brown suit, white silk stockings, and shoes with silver buckles, and wearing a dress sword. He saw below him a mass of excited people who had gathered to observe the ceremony. The secretary of the Senate held forth the Bible on a velvet cushion. The general placed his left hand on the book and raised his right hand. Chancellor Robert Livingston of New York, the state's highest judge, administered the oath of office; then, he cried, "Long live George Washington, President of the United States!" The crowds shouted the same words, and the cannon roared. The new government was in existence.

REVIEWING THE SECTION

1. What were some of the arguments used by the Federalists in support of ratification of the Constitution?

2. Why did the Antifederalists oppose the Constitution?

3. Why was it vital to secure ratification of the Constitution by New York and Virginia even though nine states already had ratified it?

THE CONSTITUTION BECAME A LIVING DOCUMENT

The American Constitution has withstood more tests and trials than any other written constitution. Since it has survived when all over the world constitutions, both republican and monarchical, have been cast aside, many Americans have come to venerate their Constitution as though it were a sacred relic. They have resented efforts to change it.

This attitude reflects a misunderstanding of why the Constitution has survived and the basic reason for its greatness. Instead of being a relic, it has continued to be a living force and a growing document. It has grown and changed with growth and change in the nation.

The makers of the Constitution created a stronger Union than had existed under the Articles of Confederation, yet they preserved the states. They granted broad power to the national government, yet they placed limitations on its use. They gave only certain specified powers to Congress, yet they authorized Congress to make laws that were necessary to carry them out. They thought that this kind of balanced government would survive better than an unlimited democracy or a monarchy.

Almost all the delegates at Philadelphia had assumed that later changes would make the Constitution a better instrument of government. Because they realized that the difficulty of changing the Articles of Confederation had been an almost insurmountable handicap, they fashioned the Constitution so that the means for changing it would be less rigid. With considerable wisdom they provided that future amendments would become integral parts of the Constitution itself. They made it possible for future generations to make lawful changes without destroying the Constitution.

Provisions were made for amending the Constitution

The constitution-makers deliberately wrote a brief, general document—one which did not attempt to spell out detailed functions of government. They decided that precise language would not allow enough elasticity to meet new needs. Therefore, the framers left it to Congress, the President, and the courts to add to what they had written and to interpret what was not entirely clear.

For example, the national government was given certain enumerated powers and certain powers were to be retained by the state governments. Still other

AMENDING THE CONSTITUTION OF THE UNITED STATES
(as provided in Article V)

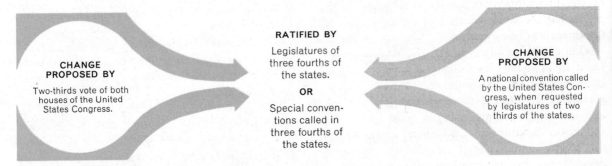

CHANGE PROPOSED BY
Two-thirds vote of both houses of the United States Congress.

RATIFIED BY
Legislatures of three fourths of the states.

OR

Special conventions called in three fourths of the states.

CHANGE PROPOSED BY
A national convention called by the United States Congress, when requested by legislatures of two thirds of the states.

The Constitution provides for its own flexibility by setting up a process for making amendments which become a part of the Constitution itself. The formal process of amendment is divided into two parts—proposal and ratification. The method of ratification for a particular amendment is selected by Congress. The Twenty-first Amendment is the only one which has been ratified by special convention. Thus far, all amendments have been proposed by Congress.

powers were to be shared by both federal and state governments. The division of these powers was not clearly stated and was subject to interpretation by the courts. In theory, the Constitution separated the powers of Congress, the President, and the courts. In practice, these three branches of government overlapped in their use of power, were dependent on one another, and were uncertain what powers belonged exclusively to each one.

Because it was written in less than precise language, future generations were able to expand the Constitution through interpretation, particularly when the chances for the adoption of a formal amendment seemed poor. Two ways of proposing amendments and two methods of ratifying them were provided. Amendments could be proposed by Congress, with the approval of two thirds of both houses, or by a national convention called by Congress at the request of the legislatures of two thirds of the states. Then the amendment had to be ratified either by the legislatures in three fourths of the states or by special conventions in three fourths of the states. It is interesting to note that no amendment ever has been proposed through a national convention.

These provisions made amendment difficult but not impossible. They gave a minority the power to block change, but they placed virtually no restrictions on what an amendment might do. The Constitution itself forbade the passage of only two kinds of amendments—any amendment to abolish the slave trade before 1808 and any amendment which deprived a state of equal representation in the Senate without the state's consent.

Since the process of amendment is difficult, Americans often have had to take advantage of the broad wording of the Constitution to effect change. Within the design of the original Constitution, modified by a few amendments, the people of the United States have taken a republican government with limited democratic features and made it into a government which is basically democratic.

Washington's administration set some precedents

President Washington and the members of the first Congress knew that the Constitution had been drawn as a general, not a specific, plan of action. They realized that what they did might set lasting precedents which would in themselves help to shape the development and future of the Constitution. As the first Congress applied the principles of the Constitution to specific situations, it implemented the work which had begun when the document was being framed.

One of the problems which the first Congress faced in applying the Constitution was that the document did not clearly provide for executive departments. It referred to them ambiguously and said nothing about how many or what kinds they should be. Assuming that it had freedom to act in this area, Congress quickly created three executive departments—the departments of state, treasury, and war. It also established the offices of the attorney general and the postmaster general. This was one of many ways in which the first Congress set a precedent for interpreting the meaning and intent of the Constitution.

The judicial system, too, required action by Congress before it could function. The Constitution said:

The judicial power of the United States, shall be vested in one supreme Court, and in such inferior Courts as the Congress may from time to time ordain and establish.

In September, Congress passed the Judiciary Act of 1789, creating a supreme court of six members, three circuit courts, and thirteen district courts—the lowest ones in the federal judicial system. This act also outlined the jurisdiction of the various courts. By giving the state courts original jurisdiction in cases involving the Constitution, the laws, and the treaties of the United States, it made the state courts part of the judicial system of the national government. In effect, this act distributed the nation's judicial power between the federal government and the states.

The Constitution did not say that a case could be appealed from a state court to the Supreme Court. Federalists in Congress assumed that, in limited instances, this right was implied in the Constitution. In the Judiciary Act, therefore, the principle of judicial review of state legislation was established. In this way the act set a precedent for the supremacy of federal authority in the national judicial system.

The Bill of Rights was added

During the struggle over ratification, even the Federalists realized that the most conspicuous weakness in the Constitution was the lack of a bill of rights. The men who had framed the document had not been opposed to such a bill. They had thought it unnecessary because the national government would have only enumerated powers that would not endanger the rights of the people. However, the outcome of the fight for ratification had hinged on the issue of a bill of rights in several states, including Virginia and New York. Federalists won to their side some of the waverers by promising amendments to the Constitution that would clearly protect personal liberties.

In the state ratifying conventions, men had proposed dozens of amendments to protect individual rights. Under the leadership of James Madison, Congress went through the various proposals and reduced them to twelve amendments, in the form of a bill of rights. In September 1789, the bill was submitted to the states. Three fourths of the states ratified ten of the amendments; two were rejected. In December 1791, after the state of Virginia had approved, the ten amendments became part of the Constitution.

Since the Bill of Rights imposed limitations on the central government, and not on the states, it strengthened the federal features of the Constitution. The first eight amendments enumerated individual rights, such as freedom of religion, speech, and press, and the right to trial by jury. These eight amendments could properly be considered a bill of rights, but the Ninth and Tenth Amendments could not.

The Ninth Amendment stated that the listing of rights in the Constitution was not complete or exclusive. The Tenth Amendment said that

The powers not delegated to the United States by the Constitution, nor prohibited by it to the States, are reserved to the States respectively, or to the people.

Some of the lingering distrust between the nationalists and the supporters of state rights could be seen in the debate over the Tenth Amendment, which was taken from the Articles of Confederation. Some of the supporters of state rights wanted to place the word *expressly* before the word *delegated* in order to shift the emphasis of the Constitution away from nationalism. Their effort failed; yet the Tenth Amendment marked a retreat, though a small one, from the strong nationalism of the Philadelphia convention.

The original Constitution established the new government. The Bill of Rights was made an integral, second part of that Constitution. Without depriving the federal government of sovereign power, the Bill of Rights placed restraints on that government.

REVIEWING THE SECTION

1. How has the vague terminology of the Constitution enabled it to meet the changing needs of the nation? What provisions did the Founding Fathers make for adding formal amendments to the Constitution?

2. What important precedents in the executive and judicial branches of the government were established by the first Congress?

3. Why was the Bill of Rights added to the Constitution? What restraints did the first ten amendments place on the federal government?

CHAPTER CONCLUSION

Since the Constitution was designed to place barriers between persons in control of political power and the people at large, it may seem to be undemocratic. The separation of powers, the system of checks and balances, the indirect election of the President, the indirect election of senators, the appointment of judges for life, and the presidential veto, all were deliberate barriers against majority rule. The Founding Fathers did not try to set up a popular democracy. They endeavored to establish a mixed government, wherein democratic, aristocratic, and authoritarian elements would be balanced. They believed that this kind of government would be best for all of the people; it was the kind favored by respected political philosophers.

The framers of the Constitution gave the advocates of democracy an important share in this mixed government. Through the House of Representatives, they gave the people direct representation in the national legislature in proportion to their numbers in each state. This was an unusual and farsighted feature and assured representative government for the whole country.

Federalists and Antifederalists alike were confident that the principle of separation of powers would benefit the people and agreed that it belonged in the Constitution. In *The Federalist,* Madison referred to the separation of powers as "this essential precaution in favor of liberty" and as "the sacred maxim of free government."

The actual division of power between the central government and the states was another unique feature of the Constitution. Although it was more national than federal, the central government was a skillful and workable combination of both concepts, a result of compromise between nationalists and advocates of state rights. That central government did not acquire complete sovereign power. The states, for example, remained self-governing units with exclusive power over local matters.

Despite the restraints placed on the power of the federal government, it could act directly on the individual citizens of the states. This principle, the kingpin clause, has been considered a major factor in the success of the Constitution. The kingpin clause bound state officers to the Constitution by oath and required the police forces in every state to enforce federal as well as state laws.

The Constitution of the United States was workable, and it has endured. This is a tribute to the wisdom of the Founding Fathers. Yet, they did more than build a workable government. In an age of monarchy it was unusual that a constitution should have been based on the consent of the people—at least of those who could and would vote. The Constitution guaranteed a republican form of government for each state, as well as for the nation, and limited the powers of both the federal government and the states. Establishment of a republican, representative government on a scale greater than had ever before been tried was a remarkable achievement. Equally remarkable was the idea of a federal union of states, each of which retained considerable sovereignty. As incorporated in the Constitution, these were original contributions to the history of self-government.

FOCUSING ON SPECIFICS

1. How did the delegates to the Philadelphia convention differ in their viewpoints on the best method for improving the government?

2. What was the purpose of the kingpin clause?

3. Which groups tended to be Federalists? Antifederalists?

4. What were some of the major arguments for ratification of the Constitution presented in *The Federalist*?

5. What were the major arguments against ratification used by Antifederalists?

6. What did the Judiciary Act of 1789 accomplish? What principle did it establish?

7. In what respects was the Tenth Amendment to the Constitution a concession to supporters of state rights?

8. What sectional conflicts were reflected in the drafting of the Constitution?

9. Describe the amending process established by the Constitution.

10. How did the procedure for ratifying the Constitution differ from that required to amend the Articles of Confederation?

REVIEWING MAIN THEMES

1. In what ways did the backgrounds and attitudes of the delegates to the convention contribute to the development of the Constitution?

2. What major compromises led to a constitution acceptable to the majority of delegates?

3. In what ways was the central government under the Constitution more powerful than it was under the Articles of Confederation?

4. What advantages did the Federalists have over the Antifederalists in the struggle over ratification?

5. How did the work of the first Congress help shape the development of the Constitution?

EVALUATING THE ISSUES

1. How did the Constitution emerge as a balance between state and national sovereignty?

2. Although the United States has become a great power under a written constitution, Britain has attained greatness without such a document; instead, it has a body of laws and traditions which serve as legal sanctions for government action. Do you see any advantages in a written constitution? any disadvantages?

3. The eighteenth century is sometimes called the Age of Reason because the influential philosophers and political thinkers of the time maintained that the power of reason could be used to reconcile differences of opinion. How did the delegates to the constitutional convention express this philosophy in their work on the Constitution?

CHAPTER **5** 1789-1801

The Rise of
Political Parties

In 1789, when George Washington became President, the United States was a nation of less than four million people; most of them were free, but some were slaves. The bulk of the population lived along the Atlantic seaboard. About five per cent of the people lived across the mountains in the interior, most of them in areas that soon would become the states of Kentucky, Tennessee, and Ohio. Only a few Americans lived in towns or cities. In 1790, only six cities had populations of 8000 or more—Philadelphia, New York, Boston, Charleston, Baltimore, and Salem. The combined population of these cities comprised only three per cent of all Americans.

Although cities were growing, the greater part of the nation continued to be rural. Most Americans lived on farms or in farm communities and earned their living from the land. By European standards the living they earned was good. The sea and the rivers teemed with fish, the forests abounded with game, and the rich soil yielded abundant crops. Americans ate regularly and well, but they were far from being rich. They had not yet begun to exploit the country's vast natural resources, such as coal and iron.

With the establishment of their new national government, the people of the United States looked forward to a period of political stability and economic expansion during which they could reap the benefits from their land of plenty. This was a reasonable hope, for the Antifederalists had accepted the Constitution, and the nation had emerged from the economic depression of the 1780's. Indications were that the new government was capable of solid growth, particularly since its leaders did not have to fight an entrenched political opposition. There were no powerful political figures of national stature who could or would block government measures.

This was the kind of situation Washington desired. He felt that he should be a nonpolitical President, a government leader who was above party. Many of his contemporaries considered his attitude the proper one for him to assume. Like

Washington, they considered political opposition as "faction," as something disloyal. In his first inaugural address Washington spoke out against "party animosities." Later, he often referred to himself as "one who is of no party," and urged his countrymen to "drive far away the demon of party spirit."

Washington's thinking reflected contemporary political ideas. The Constitution itself made no provision for political parties. Yet Americans had had considerable experience with group action in politics. Groups with opposing views had long existed within the colonies and, later, within the states. But these had been local and temporary groupings of people brought together to deal with a single issue; they were not permanently organized parties, nor were they national in membership or activity.

Washington at first tried to organize a nonpolitical administration, but this plan never really worked, for he appointed men who had been Federalists to most of the government posts. Led by Alexander Hamilton, the first secretary of the treasury, these men became the nucleus of a new Federalist coalition, the first national political party.

Hamilton's policies stimulated political opposition, particularly from Thomas Jefferson, the first secretary of state. Jefferson and James Madison, who was a member of the House of Representatives, coöperated to establish the second national political party, the Democratic-Republican party. This party differed from the former Antifederalist coalition.

These two parties, Federalist and Democratic-Republican, began to take shape late in 1790 and early in 1791. By 1792, as Washington's first term drew to a close, they were clearly established. Although he may not have realized it himself, Washington, by this time, had become a party President. As he came more and more under the influence of Hamilton, his government became a party government, dependent on Federalist support.

The Democratic-Republicans attacked government policy and ran rival candidates for office.

Washington found it difficult to reconcile himself to such political opposition. As he looked forward to retirement at the end of his presidency, he defended what he thought had been his nonpolitical administration. "I was no party man myself," he declared, "and the first wish of my heart was, if parties did exist, to reconcile them." His wish was never realized.

During Washington's presidency, national political parties became part of American society. They helped make the new government work and, most important of all, they provided the means by which the people could organize themselves and bring about changes in government through peaceful agitation rather than through violence.

FEDERALISTS STRENGTHENED THE GOVERNMENT

Much of the political philosophy of Washington's government came from the ideas of Alexander Hamilton. When Hamilton became secretary of the treasury, he was in his early thirties—young, brilliant, and with a thirst for power. He not only had definite views on political philosophy, economic policy, and foreign policy; he also had plans for putting his ideas into practice.

Hamilton had been born in the British West Indies, the son of Scottish and French parents. His tastes and ideas were aristocratic. Through his marriage to Elizabeth Schuyler, the second daughter of General Philip Schuyler, one of New York's wealthiest landowners, he had become a member of the aristocracy of wealth which he had long admired. He also admired the British form of aristocracy based on an hereditary nobility and frequently had insisted that the British system of government was the best in the world. At the Philadelphia convention, Hamilton had asserted that Americans could do no better than to model their new government after the British system.

Hamilton believed that the common people were ignorant and incapable of governing wisely. He wanted to entrust political power to men of intelligence, education, and wealth. Hamilton reasoned that such men would have a selfish interest in the new government, since their property would need government protection. To protect that interest, they would defend the Constitution. He believed that the new system of government could survive only if men of property profited from it and, thus, were willing to support it. Hamilton wanted to use the self-interest of such men to build and maintain a strong central government.

With Washington's support, Hamilton developed and carried out a bold program designed to gain the respect of foreign nations for the new government. His immediate objectives were to establish the nation's credit at home and abroad and to build up the strength of the national government at the expense of the states. He believed that whatever contributed to a strong union was good policy for the government.

•

Hamilton developed a broad economic program

Much of Hamilton's program required the enactment of financial legislation. It often has been considered as chiefly economic in nature; actually, it was far more than that. It was a program designed to strengthen the nation's economy, its political system, its foreign policy, and its Constitution.

Hamilton was given the opportunity to explain his program soon after he assumed the office of secretary of the treasury. In September 1789, the House of Representatives asked him to prepare a plan for improving the nation's credit. Using Britain's experience as a guide, Hamilton prepared a report which embodied the principles of his program and presented it in January 1790.

Hamilton pointed out that the United States would need credit if it were to increase its commerce and operate its government properly. Its credit standing would depend on how faithfully it paid its existing debts. He recommended that the national debt be *funded* at face value. This meant that the national government should take in the various certificates of indebtedness, many of them worth little, which Congress had issued during and after the Revolution and should replace them with government bonds bearing a uniform and dependable rate of interest. The money for this funding would come from import duties and *excise* taxes, taxes on goods produced within the country.

The secretary of the treasury also recommended that the national government *assume,* or take over the payment of, the debts which the states had acquired during the Revolutionary War. There was some justice in Hamilton's proposal, for the debts represented a contribution to the common cause of independence. Yet Hamilton's suggestion was not made entirely in the interests of justice. He hoped to make the states financially dependent upon the national government, thereby strengthening that government. In addition, he wanted holders of both state and national bonds to become strong supporters of the national government. Therefore, he wanted them to look to that government for payment. Obviously, his program was designed to implement political as well as economic policy.

The problem of the public debt was settled

Most members of Congress liked the idea of funding the public debt so that the nation's credit would be improved. They felt that the foreign debt, owed primarily to the French and Dutch, should be paid in full. But many objected to payment of the domestic debt at face value, that is, they objected to the replacement of the old certificates with new bonds promising to pay the same amount in dollars.

Hamilton and his friends argued that rightfully the foreign and domestic debts could not be divided. These men insisted that national honor required payment of the entire public debt at face value. When the debate subsided, Congress passed the funding bill Hamilton had proposed.

Unfortunately, greedy speculators were rewarded. The people who knew beforehand of the plans to fund the debt were able to buy up at low prices the outstanding certificates; they took advantage of the people who were unaware of the potential worth of those certificates.

Stiffer opposition greeted Hamilton's assumption bill. States with large or unpaid debts, such as Massachusetts and Connecticut, liked the idea of having the national government take over their payment. States with small debts, such as Georgia, or those which had repaid most of their debts, such as Virginia, opposed the plan. They saw no valid reason why they should pay federal taxes to help states that had not taken care of their own debts. With Virginia leading the opposition, the struggle over federal assumption of states' debts increased the distrust between Northern and Southern states.

To avoid a sectional split, Hamilton asked Jefferson, who was opposed to assumption, to persuade fellow Virginians to accept a political deal. The Virginians were eager for the new permanent national capital to be located in the South. In exchange for votes from the South in support of assumption, Hamilton offered Northern votes in Congress for support of a capital on the Potomac River. Jefferson agreed to the bargain; Hamilton's assumption bill passed in July 1790, and the problem of the public debt was settled.

A national bank was established

Another feature of Hamilton's program was the creation of a national bank, modeled after the Bank of England. Hamilton's bank was to be called the Bank of the United States, and it was to be privately controlled. Private individuals would own four fifths of its stock and the national government would own one fifth. The bank would be national because it would operate under a charter from the central government and would be given a monopoly of the government's banking business. The government would deposit in the bank the money collected from taxes and other sources, and the bank could issue banknotes (which would circulate as paper money) on the basis of funds it held.

At that time there were few banks in the nation and most of them were unstable. Hamilton argued that a national bank was needed to provide businessmen with banknotes that had a fixed value and with loans. He explained that the bank would help the government by providing a safe place for the deposit of federal funds, by increasing income through the payment of a fee for its charter, and by keeping up the price of government bonds through its own purchases at proper times.

Hamilton wanted to establish the bank for political and constitutional, as well as economic, reasons. He had three basic considerations. First, the bank would benefit the merchants and bankers who, for the most part, would control it, and it would serve as another tie between the wealthy class and the national government. Second, by accepting the principle that the Constitution permitted the government to engage in the banking business, Congress would broaden the power of the national government. Third, this enlarging of the powers of Congress would weaken the power of the states.

Nothing in the Constitution specifically authorized Congress to create a bank. The basis for such action could be found only in the "elastic" clause (*Article I, sec. 8*) which allowed Congress to enact such laws as were "necessary and proper" for carrying out the powers of government as laid down by the Constitution. When the bank bill reached Congress, James Madison and others opposed it on the grounds that it was unconstitutional and that it would benefit only the wealthy. Nonetheless, Congress passed the bill, and it went to the President.

Washington, too, was puzzled as to the constitutionality of the bank bill. He asked his department heads for their opinions on the bill. Hamilton, of course, argued for the bank; Jefferson opposed it. Washington accepted Hamilton's advice and, in February 1791, signed the bank bill. The Bank of the United States began operating that year under a charter that ran for twenty years.

The national government raised money by taxation

When the new government began to operate, its main source of money came from the sale of public lands. To pay for funding and assumption, the national government needed more money than such sales could produce. Hamilton favored two kinds of federal taxes to raise more money, a tariff on imports and an excise tax on distilled liquors.

Through the tariff Hamilton hoped to do far more than merely raise money. When applied with discrimination, he believed the tariff would raise the price of foreign manufactured goods. If these prices were high enough, American manufacturers could afford to compete with goods of their own. By protecting goods made in the United States against competition from low-priced foreign manufactures, the tariff would stimulate industry in the United States and, ultimately, would increase the general prosperity. In the summer of 1789, Hamilton's supporters managed to get a tariff through Congress, but its rates were lower than Hamilton desired. Nonetheless, this tariff produced some of the revenue the government required, and it established a policy of limited protection for goods produced in the United States.

Later, in December 1791, Hamilton explained his ideas for the stimulation and protection of industry in his Report on Manufactures. He argued that if the United States were to survive in a world where other nations protected their own industries and discriminated against foreign goods, it must adopt a policy similar to theirs. America's new industries, he pointed out, suffered from shortages in experienced labor and in capital. Without the protection of a tariff and other forms of government aid, they could not be expected to compete with the established industries of Europe.

Hamilton's report urged Congress to set up protective tariffs and establish bounties for new industries. He maintained that Congress should give bonuses for improvements in the quality of goods, promise rewards to encourage inventions, and exempt from taxation essential raw materials that came from abroad. According to Hamilton's plan, the North would handle the manufacturing and shipping, and the South would do the farming and provide the raw materials. Theoretically, the entire nation would prosper.

Southerners did not like the plan. It seemed too much like the old British colonial system which had exploited the farmer. Congress would not accept all of Hamilton's proposals but, in May 1792, it passed a tariff act that included some of his recommendations.

Earlier, in March 1791, Congress had passed another part of Hamilton's program, the tax on distilled liquors. He intended this excise tax, also, to have a political as well as an economic impact. He wanted to use this tax to assert the power of the national government directly over individuals, as well as to raise money. Such power previously had belonged to and had been exercised by the states.

The power of the government was tested

Almost from the day it was passed, the excise tax on distilled liquors aroused opposition. The owners of small farms in the back country of Pennsylvania, Virginia, and North Carolina were particularly affected by the tax. These frontier farmers, who seldom saw hard cash and who had difficulty moving their crops to market, commonly converted part of their corn and rye crops into whiskey. On the backs of mules or horses they transported this whiskey over rugged mountain trails to country towns where they sold it or bartered it for dry goods. To many farmers, Monongahela rye whiskey was as good as money. The excise tax went as high as twenty-five per cent of the price of a gallon of whiskey, and it hit the western distillers hardest; it became known as the whiskey tax.

In 1794, farmers in four counties of western Pennsylvania refused to pay the tax, attacked the tax collectors, and touched off the Whiskey Rebellion. The uprising frightened some of Hamilton's friends who thought it was part of a plot to destroy the national government. Hamilton saw the rebellion as an opportunity to test the power of the national government.

Under the Constitution, Congress had the authority to use the militia "to execute the laws of the union" and to "suppress insurrections." Congress, therefore, authorized the President to call out state militia to enforce the law and end the uprising. In this first open defiance of federal law, no one knew whether or not the states would remain loyal to the Union and send their troops to act against a sister state. When four states, including Pennsylvania, answered Washington's call for troops, Hamilton knew that the national government had successfully met its first test of power.

An army of some 13,000 men, headed by Hamilton and accompanied part of the way by President Washington, marched on Pennsylvania's western counties. Before this overwhelming force, opposition vanished. The troops captured a few of the rebel leaders, whom Washington later pardoned.

The national government had triumphed against its first rebels. The whiskey distillers now paid the excise tax. As Hamilton had foreseen, few now doubted the power or willingness of the federal government to compel the people to obey its laws.

Hamilton and the Federalists paid a price for this triumph. Many Americans, particularly Westerners, condemned the government's use of such great force to crush a handful of farmers. These critics turned to political action to oppose the government and Hamilton's policies.

Jefferson and Madison opposed Hamilton's program

Several years before the outbreak of the Whiskey Rebellion, it was apparent that Hamilton's program was dividing the nation. Men within government and elsewhere were grouping into two national parties. The men who followed the leadership of Hamilton and Washington formed the Federalist party. Opponents of the government joined the Democratic-Republican party, led by Thomas Jefferson and James Madison.

Although Federalists and Democratic-Republicans differed over many issues, such as economic policy and the interpretation of the Constitution, nowhere did they divide with greater bitterness than over the issue of foreign policy. Federalists believed that the nation's welfare would be advanced best if the government tied itself closely to Britain. The Democratic-Republicans, on the other hand, generally favored a policy of close political and economic coöperation with France as the best means of serving the nation's interest.

The course of the French Revolution, which had broken out in 1789, intensified party passions in the United States. At first, most Americans were in sympathy with the revolution in France, and many even hailed it with enthusiasm. In April 1793, news that was alarming to some Americans reached the United States. The revolutionaries had beheaded King Louis XVI, and France had declared war on Britain, the Netherlands, and Spain.

Democratic-Republicans rejoiced because France, like the United States, now had become a republic and was fighting Britain, America's old enemy. The Federalists recoiled in horror from what they considered unrestrained violence in the French Revolution. Democratic-Republicans celebrated French victories and wore the tricolored cockade, a symbol of French Republicanism. Federalists defended Britain and denounced France. Vice President John Adams, for example, wrote that "Dragon's teeth have been sown in France and come up monsters." Foreign policy had thus become an important, even violent, part of United States political life.

REVIEWING THE SECTION

1. How did Hamilton propose to improve the nation's credit? What effects did he hope to achieve through his plan?

2. What objections were raised to Hamilton's funding bill and assumption bill? How did Hamilton manage to get the assumption bill passed?

3. What were Hamilton's reasons for proposing

JEFFERSONIANS
VERSUS
HAMILTONIANS

**JEFFERSONIANS:
DEMOCRATIC-REPUBLICANS**

**HAMILTONIANS:
FEDERALISTS**

SOCIAL COMPOSITION OF PARTIES

Jeffersonians, for the most part, were artisans, shopkeepers, frontier settlers, or owners of small farms in the interior regions of the South and West.

Hamiltonians, for the most part, were merchants, bankers, manufacturers, or professional men from New England and the Atlantic seaboard, along with some wealthy farmers and Southern planters.

ATTITUDES TOWARD GOVERNMENT

Jeffersonians favored a form of government which was more democratic than that of Britain.

Hamiltonians admired the British aristocracy and British system of government and wished to see it used as a model.

Jeffersonians thought that the common people were capable of self-government. They wanted to establish a small property owners' democracy.

Hamiltonians considered the common people ignorant and incapable of self-government. They wanted men of wealth and property to rule.

Jeffersonians desired to increase the opportunities for the common people to participate in government by lowering voting qualifications.

Hamiltonians desired high voting qualifications, claiming that unfettered democracy was anarchy.

Jeffersonians favored a strict interpretation of the Constitution to limit the powers of the central government and conserve state rights.

Hamiltonians favored a broad interpretation of the Constitution to strengthen the central government at the expense of state rights.

Jeffersonians wanted to reduce the number of federal officeholders.

Hamiltonians wanted an expanding bureaucracy.

Jeffersonians favored freedom of speech and press.

Hamiltonians, under certain circumstances, favored restrictions on speech and the press.

VIEWS ON ECONOMIC CONCERNS

Jeffersonians preferred an agrarian society, but with some industry subordinate to agriculture.

Hamiltonians preferred an industrial society with a balanced economy.

Jeffersonians believed that the government should offer no special favors to business.

Hamiltonians believed that the government should foster business and contribute to the growth of capitalistic enterprise.

Jeffersonians felt that no special favors should be given to manufacturers.

Hamiltonians favored a protective tariff to aid manufacturers.

Jeffersonians opposed Hamilton's bank bill as unconstitutional and wanted to encourage state banks.

Hamiltonians proposed a powerful national bank, modeled after the Bank of England.

Jeffersonians felt that the national debt was harmful to the nation, that the debt should be paid as quickly as possible, and that the nation should remain out of debt.

Hamiltonians considered the national debt a blessing, to be used to advantage in the establishment of credit.

POSITIONS ON FOREIGN POLICY

Jeffersonians distrusted Britain and wanted the United States to establish a policy favorable to France.

Hamiltonians wanted the United States to break official bonds with France and tie itself closely to Britain.

the establishment of a national bank? What was the constitutional basis for establishing a national bank?

4. What did Hamilton hope to accomplish by his plan for tariffs and taxes? What was the reaction in Congress to Hamilton's proposals?

5. In what way was the Whiskey Rebellion a test of the strength of the federal government?

FEDERALIST DIPLOMACY WAS SUCCESSFUL

The political differences over foreign policy intensified the feud between Hamilton and Jefferson. Hamilton believed that Jefferson and Madison had "a womanish attachment to France and a womanish resentment against Great Britain." If these men were left to pursue their own course in foreign policy, Hamilton feared they would drive the country to war against Britain. Determined to prevent this, the secretary of the treasury interfered with the conduct of foreign affairs. He tried to persuade Washington to follow his, not Jefferson's, ideas in dealing with France and Britain. At times he negotiated privately with the British.

As a result of Hamilton's agitation, Jefferson decided, in 1792, to resign as secretary of state. He said he could not stand Hamilton's tampering with foreign affairs, his own area of responsibility. Hamilton also spoke about leaving. Washington asked both men to stay so that his government could retain the unity he considered essential. Both men agreed to remain in the official family, which from that time was known as the President's cabinet.

As the end of his term approached in 1792, Washington himself planned to retire to Mount Vernon. Fearing that party strife might disrupt the Union if Washington did not seek a second term, both Hamilton and Jefferson begged him to reconsider. Jefferson told Washington that "North & South will hang together, if they have you to hang on."

When others also pleaded with him, Washington did reconsider. Since no one would run against him, his decision postponed a party battle over the presidency. He easily won reëlection, but Democratic-Republicans made a party contest out of the balloting for Vice President. John Adams, nonetheless, won reëlection without great difficulty.

The administration chose a policy of neutrality

In his second term, Washington had to devote most of his attention to stormy events in foreign relations. One of Washington's first decisions in the new term concerned American policy toward the war between France and Britain. Since both nations had colonies in the Caribbean and their armed ships fought there, Americans easily could have become involved. By the terms of the French alliance of 1778, the United States was committed to defend France's colonies in the Caribbean. If France asked for such aid, the United States could have been dragged into the war.

As was his practice when faced with such a "delicate situation," Washington turned to his cabinet members for advice. He asked to what extent good faith would compel the United States to honor its treaty obligations. He wanted to know what he should do in the crisis.

All the advisers agreed that the President should adopt a policy of neutrality, but Hamilton and Jefferson disagreed on how it should be carried out. Hamilton urged a policy of neutrality which would favor Britain, thus calling for an impartial interpretation of American obligations to France under the treaties of 1778. Jefferson wanted a neutrality favorable to France. His view was based on a benevolent interpretation of American obligations.

Washington himself wanted "to maintain a strict neutrality" so as to prevent his own people "from embroiling us" with France or Britain. He made this idea the official policy in a proclamation of neutrality which he issued on April 22, 1793. The proclamation declared the United States at peace with both France and Britain and warned Americans against hostile acts toward either country.

Washington also had asked his advisers if the

French treaties remained in effect after the French monarchy had been overthrown. He also asked if he should receive a minister from the French Republic. Again Hamilton and Jefferson differed. Hamilton wanted to suspend the treaties and not recognize the republican government of France. He sought to use the French Revolution as an excuse for getting rid of the French alliance and drawing the United States closer to Britain.

Jefferson argued that the treaties were still legally binding and that the President should recognize the French republican government and receive its minister. In this instance, Washington followed Jefferson's advice.

The new French minister was a rash young man of thirty known as "Citizen" Edmond C. Genêt. As soon as he arrived in the United States, Genêt began to meddle in American politics. He insulted Washington and infuriated the Federalists. He did not ask for military aid under the terms of the French alliance, but he did demand assistance, assistance that would have violated American neutrality and perhaps have driven the nation to war against Britain. His defiance of American neutrality became so intolerable that Washington demanded the recall of the French minister. Genêt's misconduct forced Washington's government to define neutral obligations with greater clarity than before. The Neutrality Act of June 1794, which prohibited foreign warships from fitting themselves out in United States ports, was the result.

Jay arranged a treaty with Britain

At the same time that American neutrality was being endangered by Genêt's activities, the United States was brought to the verge of war with Britain because of problems of trade, lack of agreement on neutral rights, and British-instigated trouble in the Northwest. When France went to war against Britain, she opened to American shipping, ports in her colonies in the Caribbean which had previously been closed to foreigners. This was done because the British were sweeping most French shipping from the seas, and only neutral ships could supply France.

Since the profits were good, Americans quickly built up a flourishing trade in the French Caribbean ports. This trade aided France, so the British decided to stop it. Beginning in June 1793, Britain issued three orders-in-council, essentially executive decrees which reaffirmed the principle that Britain would not allow in time of war a trade that was prohibited during peace. In enforcing this dictum, known as the Rule of 1756 (because Britain had applied it during the Seven Years' War), British naval officers confiscated United States ships and cargoes, and imprisoned the seamen.

Newspapers in the United States played up these captures. Anti-British sentiment became so strong that it made Washington's policy of neutrality difficult to maintain. The difficulty increased when word of renewed British hostility in the Northwest reached Philadelphia, the capital city at that time.

Troubles in the Northwest stemmed from Washington's efforts to subdue the Indians in that region by use of federal troops. Two military expeditions, one in 1790 and another in 1791, failed. In the summer of 1794, in the Northwest Territory, a third expedition, under General "Mad Anthony" Wayne, crushed the Indians in the Battle of Fallen Timbers.

Before the battle, officials of the British possessions to the north of the United States were providing the Indians with supplies and had promised them they could recover lands settled by Americans at the time of the Revolutionary War. This promise enraged Americans. They also had other grievances, such as the presence of British troops in the northwest posts on American soil and the persistent refusal of the British government to make a commercial treaty. Together these grievances brought on a crisis between the United States and Britain.

Americans rushed into preparations for war, much to the alarm of Hamilton and other Federalists. To avert war, Hamiltonians persuaded the President to send John Jay, the chief justice of the United States Supreme Court, on a special mission to London. Despite secret dealings between Hamilton and the British, dealings which weakened Jay's bargaining position, Jay succeeded in obtaining a commercial treaty, which he signed in November 1794. When details of the treaty reached the United States, Democratic-Republicans condemned it as a sellout to Britain, because the treaty conceded few of the things Jay had been instructed to obtain from Britain, such as payment for the Caribbean captures and generous trade privileges. Jay became so unpopular that mobs throughout the country burned him in effigy. No other treaty ever aroused such violent public reaction in the United States.

Democratic-Republicans tried desperately to defeat Jay's Treaty, first in the Senate and then in the House of Representatives, where they attempted to withhold funds necessary to carry it out. Although the treaty had shortcomings, it served the nation well. Because of it, the British finally evacuated the northwest posts. More important, it kept the peace at a time when war might have split the Union. In addition, the willingness of Britain to make a treaty with its former colonies was a small victory for American diplomacy.

Spain granted concessions to the United States

While Jay was negotiating in London, Spanish foreign policy was becoming more favorable to the United States. Spain decided to withdraw support from Britain and join France as an ally in the European war. Spain feared the change would bring British reprisals. Because Jay's mission seemed to have drawn the United States closer to Britain, Spain even feared an attack by Anglo-American forces on her colonies in North America, such as Louisiana and Florida. Spain was also worried about aggressive action against her colonies by restless American frontiersmen, so her ministers decided to forestall such attacks by purchasing American good will.

In the summer of 1794, Spain invited the United States to send a minister to Madrid to negotiate over American grievances. Washington sent Thomas Pinckney, who had been serving as the minister in London. In October 1795, the Spaniards signed the Treaty of San Lorenzo, usually called Pinckney's Treaty. It gave to the United States many of the things Americans had been seeking in the past ten years. The United States obtained unrestricted navigation of the Mississippi, the right to deposit goods in warehouses at New Orleans for reloading on ocean-going vessels, a settlement of the Southwest boundary at the thirty-first parallel (which meant Spanish troops had to retreat southward), and a promise that Spain would not incite Indians against Americans. The United States promised to keep Indians in its territory from striking at Spanish lands.

So pleased were Americans with Pinckney's Treaty that the Senate approved it unanimously. This agreement appeared to compensate for the dissatisfactions with the treaty Jay had negotiated with Great Britain.

The new national government had achieved noteworthy diplomatic gains, though not entirely on its own. Spain and Britain made concessions because they were more concerned with their policies in Europe than with those in America. Yet few could deny that Federalist diplomacy had made possible the Jay and Pinckney treaties. These treaties freed American soil from the British in the Northwest and the Spanish in the Southwest, for the first time since independence. At last the United States could fly its flag over all the territory granted to it in the peace treaty of 1783.

France interfered in United States politics

Federalist diplomacy was not as successful with France as it was with Britain and Spain. When the French learned of Jay's Treaty, they became angry. They considered it virtually an alliance with Britain. The French contended that one of the treaty's provisions, which allowed the British to seize provisions from United States ships destined for French ports, violated the French-American treaties of 1778. Therefore, the French interfered in American politics to try and prevent Jay's Treaty from going into effect.

To justify their meddling, the French made a distinction between the American people and their Federalist government. They portrayed Washington's administration as a captive of British policy, and the majority of the American people as desirous of French friendship. Genêt's successors as French ministers to the United States publicly supported Democratic-Republicans in elections, put pressure on senators to defeat Jay's Treaty, and tried to prejudice the American people against that agreement.

This interference in American politics by the French infuriated Washington. It made him all the more determined to support the treaty with the British. The increasing tensions arising over matters of foreign policy also prompted Washington to announce his decision to retire. For some time, he had been weary and disappointed with the personal abuse leveled at those engaged in politics. French meddling in the affairs of the United States convinced Washington, however, that his nation needed a warning, which he decided to give in the form of a farewell statement. Hamilton asked him to withhold the announcement until three months before the electors would choose a President. So, through the newspapers, Washington offered his Farewell Address to the people, in September 1796.

This address, which came to be one of the most influential statements on foreign policy ever made by an American, dealt with both foreign and domestic affairs. Washington opened with the announcement that he would not be a candidate for a third term. He warned against "the insidious wiles of foreign influence," stressed faithfulness to existing agreements, and said "'tis our true policy to steer clear of permanent alliances with any portion of the foreign world." He defended his own policies and denounced French meddling and the French alliance, which had become embarrassing.

Federalists praised the Farewell Address, Democratic-Republicans denounced it as political propaganda, and the French were quite displeased with it. Pierre A. Adet, the French minister, openly threw the weight of his influence into the presidential campaign on the side of Thomas Jefferson, the Democratic-Republican candidate. Adet said that only a victory by Jefferson would eliminate the possibility of war with France. The French minister tried by every possible means to defeat John Adams, the Federalist candidate.

Adet's interference did Jefferson more harm than good. Adams won the election of 1796, the nation's first contested presidential election, but Jefferson gained the vice presidency. Federalists retained control of the government, and it seemed likely that there would be no basic change in American policies.

REVIEWING THE SECTION

1. What problems confronted Washington in his efforts to maintain neutrality in the war between France and Britain?

2. What issues led to increased antagonism between the United States and Britain? In what respects was Jay's Treaty a diplomatic success?

3. Why was Pinckney's Treaty an important victory for the United States?

ADAMS AVOIDED ALL-OUT WAR WITH FRANCE

In the period between Adams' election and his inauguration, tension with France increased. The French government had recalled Adet and had refused to appoint a successor. When Washington sent Charles Cotesworth Pinckney, a South Carolina Federalist, as America's new minister to France, the French refused to receive him, threatened him with arrest, and forced him to leave the country. In February 1797, Pinckney retreated to Amsterdam to await instructions from Adams.

On March 2, 1797, two days before Adams was to take office, the French government published a decree saying its navy would seize United States ships and would treat as pirates all Americans

MAJOR EVENTS IN UNITED STATES FOREIGN AFFAIRS: 1776-1815

1776-1789 (From the Declaration of Independence to the end of the Confederation period)

STATEMENTS OF POLICY

1776   *Declaration of Independence* enabled U.S. to establish formal diplomatic relations and negotiate treaties.
Treaty Plan of 1776, a model for future commercial treaties, included principles of neutral rights.

WARS AND PEACE TREATIES

1776-
1783   *Revolutionary War* was ended with *Treaty of Paris of 1783.* In that treaty Great Britain recognized the independence of the U.S.

MILITARY ALLIANCES

1778   *Treaty of Alliance* with France brought invaluable military aid to U.S. in the Revolutionary War.

BOUNDARY SETTLEMENTS AND ACQUISITIONS

1783   *Treaty of Paris.* Great Britain ceded territory to the U.S. south of the Great Lakes to the Floridas and west of the Appalachians to the Mississippi River.

ECONOMIC POLICY AND COMMERCIAL TREATIES

1778   *Treaty of Amity and Commerce* with France.
1782   *A treaty of amity and commerce* with the Netherlands.
1783-
1786   *Commercial treaties* were signed with Sweden (1783), Prussia (1785), and Morocco (1786).
1786   *Jay-Gardoqui Treaty* (unsigned). An unsuccessful attempt to settle southern boundary dispute with Spain.
1788   *A consular convention* with France established privileges and immunities to be accorded consuls.

In 1799, the United States frigate, *Constellation,* captured the French frigate, *Insurgente.* This engagement, which took place in the French West Indies, was the first important naval battle in the undeclared war with France, fought primarily to protect the growing American commerce.

American Frigate Constellation Capturing the French National Frigate L'Insurgente, Feb. 9, 1799

1789-1815 (From the beginning of government under the Constitution to the end of the War of 1812)

STATEMENTS OF POLICY

1793   *Proclamation of Neutrality* made by Washington in an effort to avoid involvement in the European war.
1794   *Neutrality Act* made neutrality the law of the land.
1796   *Washington's Farewell Address,* which had a lasting influence on U.S. foreign policy, urged avoidance of permanent alliances with other nations.

WARS AND PEACE TREATIES

1798-
1800   *Undeclared naval war* with France, intensified by the XYZ affair in 1798, was ended with the *Convention of 1800* (Treaty of Mortefontaine).
1812-
1814   *War of 1812* with Britain was ended with the *Treaty of Ghent* in 1814, which mentioned none of the issues over which the nations had fought. The treaty returned relations with Britain to the prewar status quo.

BOUNDARY SETTLEMENTS AND ACQUISITIONS

1794   *Jay's Treaty* with Great Britain provided for commissions of arbitration to settle northern boundary disputes. Great Britain withdrew from Northwest trading posts.
1795   *Pinckney's Treaty* with Spain recognized U.S. boundary claims in the Southwest. Spain surrendered claims north of the 31st parallel.
1803   *Louisiana Territory,* purchased from France for $15 million, doubled U.S. land area.

ECONOMIC POLICY AND COMMERCIAL TREATIES

1794   *Jay's Treaty.* U.S. gained limited trading privileges and made concessions to Great Britain on neutral rights.
1795   *Pinckney's Treaty* (Treaty of San Lorenzo) with Spain gave U.S. unrestricted navigation of the Mississippi and the right of deposit at New Orleans.

found serving on British ships. The decree also said that France would no longer recognize the principle of "free ships free goods," that is, the principle that goods on a neutral ship should not usually be subject to capture by a warring nation. France justified this action, which amounted to limited war against United States shipping, with the argument that Jay's Treaty had violated the French alliance. But the full impact of the French actions was not felt until Adams took over as President.

The mission to France failed

As soon as Adams became President, he called Congress into special session to deal with the crisis between the United States and France. At his request, Congress approved a special mission to France, consisting of Charles C. Pinckney, John Marshall, a prominent Virginia Federalist, and Elbridge Gerry, a personal friend with Democratic-Republican leanings. The commissioners were to offer maritime and trade concessions similar to those in Jay's Treaty. In return, Adams expected France to resume normal diplomatic relations, respect United States rights at sea, and release the United States from the treaties of 1778.

Pinckney, Marshall, and Gerry met in Paris in October 1797, but Charles Maurice de Talleyrand-Périgord, the French minister of foreign relations, refused to receive them officially. Through secret agents, he demanded a bribe of $250,000 merely for the privilege of negotiating. Bribery itself did not shock the United States emissaries, but they had no money to pay a bribe. They rejected Talleyrand's proposals.

When one of Talleyrand's agents threatened war, Marshall answered that his country would protect herself. "You do not speak to the point," the agent shouted, "it is expected that you will offer money.... What is your answer?"

"It is no! No!" Pinckney exclaimed, "not a sixpence!" Legend later changed this to "Millions for defense, but not one cent for tribute."

After months of waiting, the commissioners finally ended their mission. Their dispatches telling of their shameful treatment reached Philadelphia before they arrived home. The story shocked Adams and convinced him he could not deal with the French government except through force. In March 1798, he explained the failure of his peace mission, and asked Congress for authority to arm merchant ships and take other defensive measures.

Refusing to believe the President's charges, the Democratic-Republicans accused him of seeking war and demanded to see the commissioners' dispatches. Adams then sent the dispatches to Congress, substituting the letters X, Y, and Z for the names of Talleyrand's agents. A short time later the dispatches were published. Now even some Democratic-Republicans turned against France, and Federalists talked openly of war.

The United States fought an undeclared naval war

The reaction to the "X Y Z" dispatches made Adams a genuinely popular President. Congress responded to his leadership by authorizing naval retaliation against French sea raiders and by passing other defensive measures. It created the navy department, voted money for new warships, authorized increases in the regular army, and, in July 1798, abrogated the French treaties. Washington came out of retirement to take command of a new army that was to be organized by Hamilton, the second in command. As war fever spread over the nation, some Americans feared a French invasion.

Since Democratic-Republicans in Congress were not in favor of an immediate declaration of war against France, Adams placed the nation in a state of half war. Neither France nor the United States declared war, and neither authorized offensive hostilities or the capture of private property by warships. The United States Navy, fighting primarily to protect commerce, attacked only French warships and *privateers,* privately owned vessels armed for raiding commerce. The United States waged a limited, undeclared war.

The infant United States Navy performed well.

By the winter of 1798, it had forced French corsairs to stop their attacks in American coastal waters and to fall back on their bases in the West Indies. At some risk, the navy then expanded operations. It based most of its ships in the enemy's waters in the Caribbean, where most of the undeclared war subsequently was fought.

The first important engagement of the war between a regular warship of the French navy and one from the United States Navy occurred in February 1799, off the island of Nevis in the French West Indies. In this battle the more heavily armed United States frigate *Constellation*, under the command of Thomas Truxton, captured the French frigate *Insurgente.*

Under orders not to fire on the United States flag, the French captain had tried to avoid battle. When captured, he asked, "Why have you fired on the national flag? Our two nations are at peace." Truxton merely replied, "You are my prisoner." This exchange illustrates the puzzling, and sometimes frustrating, nature of relations with the French, relations which could be called neither war nor peace.

The Federalists passed repressive laws

This state of half war disturbed many Federalists. The extremists among them, such as Secretary of State Timothy Pickering, were violently anti-French. They thought that a full-scale war against France would give them an excuse for expanding the nation's frontiers at the expense of Spain, France's ally, and for drawing the United States closer to Britain. In addition, these extremists believed that a full-scale war would provide the opportunity to crush the Democratic-Republican party and other political opposition. Hamilton wanted to lead an army of conquest into Louisiana and Mexico.

Federalists tried to destroy the Democratic-Republicans and force conformity to their own war aims with four laws known collectively as the Alien and Sedition Acts. These laws were based on the supposition that a French faction within the country threatened the nation's survival. President Adams signed the first of these laws, the Naturalization Act, in June 1798.

Prior to this, five years of residence had been required before an alien could qualify for citizenship. The Naturalization Act raised this period to fourteen years and placed limitations on the freedom of action of aliens. Since most immigrants, who were from the middle and lower classes, became Democratic-Republicans, this law struck at one source of Democratic-Republican strength.

The next law, the Alien Friends Act, gave the President the power to deport aliens whom he considered dangerous. This was designed to deal with the problem of alleged French agents in the United States. A third law, the Alien Enemies Act, would apply only in case of declared war or invasion. It permitted the President to arrest or deport enemy aliens as he saw fit, in order to preserve public safety.

As the capstone for their repressive program, the Federalists passed the Sedition Act, which Democratic-Republicans called a "gag law." It provided punishment, by fine and imprisonment, for conspiracies against the government and for scandalous statements uttered against it, the Congress, or the President. This law struck at native-born Americans as well as at foreigners.

Although mainly the work of extreme Federalists, the Alien and Sedition Acts won broad support in the party. Not one prominent Federalist—neither Adams, Washington, nor Hamilton—opposed their enactment. Adams did not deport any foreigners under the alien laws, but his administration did enforce the Sedition Act.

Jefferson, Madison, and other Democratic-Republican leaders saw in the Alien and Sedition Acts a trend toward tyranny, which they felt they had to resist and expose. Late in 1798, Jefferson expressed his opposition in a set of resolutions adopted by Kentucky's state legislature. Madison wrote a set of similar resolutions which the Virginia legislature approved. These Kentucky and Virginia resolutions declared the Alien and Sedition Acts void and unconstitutional because the federal government had exercised powers not specifically delegated to it, and demanded their repeal. The resolutions advanced the doctrine that a state could judge for itself when the national government exceeded its constitutional power. When the central government went too far, this doctrine said, the states could rightfully *nullify,* or declare illegal, all offending laws. The resolutions called on all the states to take similar action against the laws. None did so. As a strong expression of the state-rights view of the Union, these resolutions achieved an importance, especially among Southerners, that lasted long after the Federalist era.

Adams made peace with France

Most Americans did not want full-scale hostilities. Democratic-Republicans were as opposed to all-out war with France as they were to the Alien and Sedition Acts. Extreme Federalists, who hoped for an expanded war to solve some of their problems, were unable to gain majority support for it, even within their own party.

Yet the naval battles and the news of widespread anti-French sentiment in the United States alarmed Talleyrand. He did not want an enlarged war with the United States. It would offer no direct benefits to France and would ruin the plans of French statesmen to reacquire Louisiana. Therefore, through William Vans Murray, the American minister at The Hague, Talleyrand made peaceful overtures to the United States. The French government repealed decrees against United States shipping, restrained its privateers in the West Indies, and told some Americans that it wanted peace.

President Adams had broken with the extreme Federalists, as a result of a quarrel over Hamilton's rank in the new army and, consequently, he had lost much of his own enthusiasm for war. He accepted Talleyrand's offer to negotiate a peace with honor, and in 1799, he sent a second mission to Paris. This commission was composed of three reliable Federalists—Murray, Chief Justice Oliver Ellsworth, and William R. Davie, a former governor of North Carolina. The sending of this peace mission deepened the split in the Federalist party, for the extremists, men such as Pickering and Hamilton, had insisted that the French overtures were meaningless and had urged their rejection.

Murray, Ellsworth, and Davie met in Paris in March 1800. They were received by Talleyrand, now minister of foreign relations for a new French government headed by Napoleon Bonaparte. The American envoys demanded from the French their official abrogation of the treaties of 1778 and payment for the ships and cargoes that French raiders had seized. After prolonged negotiations with a French commission headed by Napoleon's brother Joseph, the Americans agreed to a compromise treaty that dropped the claims for damages and suspended the old treaties. The Treaty of Mortefontaine, often known as the Convention of 1800, was signed in September 1800. Despite strong resistance by extreme Federalists, the Senate finally approved the treaty after Adams left office.

That convention ended the undeclared war, freed the United States from its first entangling alliance, cleared the way for Napoleon Bonaparte to reacquire Louisiana, and helped weaken the influence of the Federalist party. Adams always defended his decision for peace and his missions to France. "They were," he later wrote, "the most disinterested and meritorious actions of my life."

REVIEWING THE SECTION

1. How did the failure of the first Adams-appointed mission to France bring the United States to the brink of war?

2. Why did the United States fight an undeclared naval war against France?

3. Why did the Federalists enact the Alien and Sedition Acts? How did the Democratic-Republicans respond to these laws?

4. How did the Adams administration negotiate a settlement of hostilities between France and the United States? What were the terms?

PRESIDENTIAL ELECTIONS: 1796-1812

In the charts illustrating presidential elections, the winning candidate is always listed first. Beginning with the election of 1880, candidates of minor parties are listed separately when they receive electoral votes. Otherwise, they are grouped together under the heading, "MINOR PARTIES." Because political parties were not well developed prior to 1796, the elections of 1789 and 1792 are not included.

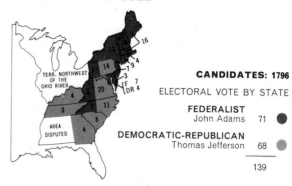

CANDIDATES: 1796

ELECTORAL VOTE BY STATE

FEDERALIST
John Adams   71

DEMOCRATIC-REPUBLICAN
Thomas Jefferson   68

139

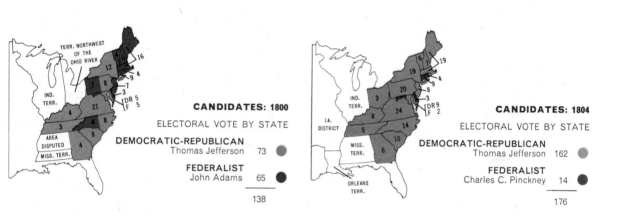

CANDIDATES: 1800

ELECTORAL VOTE BY STATE

DEMOCRATIC-REPUBLICAN
Thomas Jefferson   73

FEDERALIST
John Adams   65

138

CANDIDATES: 1804

ELECTORAL VOTE BY STATE

DEMOCRATIC-REPUBLICAN
Thomas Jefferson   162

FEDERALIST
Charles C. Pinckney   14

176

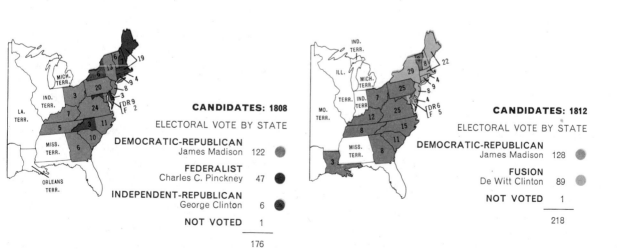

CANDIDATES: 1808

ELECTORAL VOTE BY STATE

DEMOCRATIC-REPUBLICAN
James Madison   122

FEDERALIST
Charles C. Pinckney   47

INDEPENDENT-REPUBLICAN
George Clinton   6

NOT VOTED   1

176

CANDIDATES: 1812

ELECTORAL VOTE BY STATE

DEMOCRATIC-REPUBLICAN
James Madison   128

FUSION
De Witt Clinton   89

NOT VOTED   1

218

THE DEMOCRATIC-REPUBLICANS WERE ELECTED

Although foreign relations dominated the administration of John Adams, that administration is also notable as marking the end of the Federalist party as an effective national political organization. Under Adams, the Federalist party split into two wings, one wing following his leadership, and the other looking to Alexander Hamilton for guidance.

Difficulties within his own party began for Adams almost as soon as he became President. In his inaugural address he committed himself to a continuation of Washington's policies. He also retained Washington's cabinet, a decision which proved to be a mistake, for the cabinet officers gave their loyalty to Washington and Hamilton, not to Adams. Most of the men in the cabinet were committed to Hamilton's program and resented any departure from it. They secretly went to Hamilton for advice on almost all matters of policy.

When Adams became fully aware of the extent of Hamilton's control over the cabinet officers, he reacted against the war program of the extreme wing of his own party. In defiance of his department heads, including Secretary of State Timothy Pickering, Adams sent a second mission to Paris. Extreme Federalists and others who thought that full-scale war was the solution to the problems with France were furious. They predicted that the Federalist party would be divided so deeply by Adams' action that the Democratic-Republicans would win the presidency in the coming election.

Hamilton turned against Adams

Despite the split in their ranks, John Adams was the Federalist choice for President in 1800. As they had done four years earlier, the Democratic-Republicans gave their nomination to Jefferson.

Dissatisfied with his party's choice, Hamilton decided to work secretly against Adams. In the state elections of April 1800, Hamilton tried to fill the seats in New York's state legislature with men who were loyal to him personally. Since the legislators would choose New York's presidential electors, Hamilton, in this way, could influence the presidential election. The plan failed because Aaron Burr, the Democratic-Republican leader in New York City, ran a ticket that defeated Hamilton's Federalist candidates.

The Federalist defeat in New York had several important political consequences. It assured Jefferson of the state's twelve electoral votes, made Burr the Democratic-Republican choice for the vice presidency, and prompted Adams to rid his official family of what he now called "Hamilton's spies." Adams quickly forced Secretary of War James McHenry and Secretary of State Pickering out of his cabinet.

Hamiltonians now became so angry with Adams that some of them thought his reëlection might be as great a misfortune as a victory by Jefferson. Moderate Federalists, on the other hand, wanted to strengthen the party in the South in order to offset the loss of New York. Therefore, the Federalists chose Charles C. Pinckney of South Carolina to run with Adams.

Unreconciled Hamiltonians worked out a plan to give Pinckney rather than Adams the presidency. Their plan was based on the expectation that Adams and Pinckney would receive an equal number of electoral votes in all the states except South Carolina, where Pinckney would get more. This would give Pinckney a larger majority of the electoral votes than Adams, and would make Pinckney President.

Adams found out about the scheme, and so bitter did strife within the Federalist party become that Hamilton decided to attack the President directly. In autumn 1800, Hamilton wrote a long letter intended for private circulation among Federalists in which he tried to show that Adams was unfit for the presidency. A copy fell into Burr's hands, and he had it published as a pamphlet so as to embarrass the Federalists.

Most Federalists were shocked. Friends of Adams rushed out with pamphlets of their own striking at Hamilton. These attacks merely aggravated the discord within the Federalist party. Federalist chances for victory now seemed lost. "I cannot describe . . . how broken and scattered your Federal friends are!" one Federalist wrote.

Federalists lost the election

While the Federalists fought among themselves, the Democratic-Republicans never let up in their attacks on Adams. Jefferson, who was conducting his campaign from his Virginia estate at Monticello, hailed the Federalist strife as "wonderful." He conferred with Madison as to the best means of using it to the advantage of their party. Democratic-Republicans denounced Adams as an aristocrat and a monarchist. They attacked unpopular administration measures, such as the Alien and Sedition Acts, and tried to make the most of the fact that the war fever had subsided. They stressed the peace issue, claiming that they had forced Adams to send his second mission to Paris, thus suggesting that they, not he, had "saved the country from war."

Adams and the moderate Federalists also emphasized the peace issue, but the extremists' desire for war was too well known to be denied. Federalists, therefore, condemned Democratic-Republicans as men who would disrupt the Union through the nullification doctrine as stated in the Kentucky and Virginia resolutions. They attacked Jefferson as a radical and an atheist, one who would force French doctrines on Americans. A vote for Jefferson, the people were told by the Federalists, would be a vote against God.

Despite the split in their ranks, Federalists fought hard to regain the ground lost in the New York elections, and they did well. In December 1800, as the electoral returns from each state became known, the vote from South Carolina was awaited anxiously. With eight electoral votes, South Carolina was the pivotal state. Her votes went to Jefferson and Burr. The Democratic-Republicans won the presidency and gained majorities in both houses of Congress. Federalist

leadership in national affairs had been overthrown.

Nonetheless, Adams had come close to victory. In states other than New York, he ran stronger in 1800 than he had run four years earlier. The switch of a few hundred votes in New York City could have secured Adams' reëlection.

Later, in thinking over the causes of his defeat, Adams concluded that his decision to send the second mission to France had been a decisive factor. In seizing a proper moment for peace negotiations Adams had disregarded political consequences. Although he had been willing to fight a full-scale war with France if it were necessary, he had refused to lead the nation into an unnecessary war so as to keep the Federalist party in power.

The House chose Jefferson over Burr

Accustomed to power, the Federalists were bewildered and alarmed by their loss. A number of them were convinced that a revolution similar to the one in France would follow and would destroy the nation. One thing consoled them. Jefferson and Burr had received the same number of electoral votes. In 1800, electors did not distinguish by their vote between candidates for the presidency and vice presidency. The candidate who received the highest number of votes became President, and the one with the second highest total became Vice President.

According to the Constitution, in the case of a tie the election would be decided by the House of Representatives. The representatives would vote not as individuals but as part of a state unit. Each state would have one vote, and the balloting by states would decide who would be President. The decision was not to be made in the newly elected House where the Democratic-Republicans would have a clear majority, but by the existing legislature, where the Federalists held control.

Everyone knew that the Democratic-Republicans had intended Jefferson to have the presidency. Nonetheless, the Federalist leaders in the House had two alternatives. They could choose either

Jefferson or Burr, and thereby gain substantial favors from either man for their support. Or they could create a stalemate in which neither man would be elected. In this way their party, through complicated maneuvers, might stay in power.

When it became clear to Federalists that they did not control enough votes in the House to elect a President, or retain power, but could influence the choice of a Democratic-Republican, the idea of placing Burr ahead of Jefferson and making Burr President, spread rapidly among them. Hamilton, who considered Burr "the most unfit and dangerous man of the community," opposed this scheme, but his advice and exhortations were disregarded.

In February 1801, when the balloting in the House took place, the Federalists almost succeeded in giving the presidency to Burr. Finally, a Federalist from Delaware, James Bayard, broke the stalemate. After thirty-six ballots, Jefferson was chosen President. With control of both the Congress and the presidency, but not of the judiciary, the Democratic-Republicans had consolidated their victory. The Twelfth Amendment, adopted in 1804, made impossible another tie vote for the presidency. It required separate ballots for President and Vice President.

REVIEWING THE SECTION

1. What was the effect of the Hamilton-Adams feud on the Federalist party?

2. What were the chief issues in the presidential campaign of 1800?

3. What factors enabled Jefferson to become President?

CHAPTER CONCLUSION

The Federalist era, as the twelve years under Washington and Adams are called, was a time of precedent-making in government and in politics. When Washington took over the presidency, there were no national political parties and no rules for the conduct of the government. He and his supporters, particularly Hamilton, interpreted and applied the Constitution as they thought necessary and made it the heart of a workable system of government.

In dealing with crises such as the people's reactions to the French Revolution, the Whiskey Rebellion, and Jay's Treaty and its consequences, Washington's government set precedents in politics and foreign policy. In supporting and carrying out Hamilton's program, the government changed the character of American politics, primarily by stimulating the rise of political parties. At the beginning of the 1790's, men often gained office solely because of their personal qualifications. By the end of the decade, men more often gained office because they were members of an organized party.

Issues such as payment of the public debt, the establishment of a national bank, and the conduct of foreign policy became party issues and were fought out on a national basis. A number of explanations for the origin and growth of political parties have been advanced by historians. According to recent studies, the Federalist and Democratic-Republican parties were the products of national rather than state politics. It is no longer believed that they were built on earlier local or state foundations. They sprang from divisions within Washington's own government and within Congress over issues of national concern, such as Hamilton's program and Jay's Treaty.

When Adams took office, party division over national issues continued. In addition, the Federalist party itself split over the issue of war or peace with France. Extreme Federalists wanted a war so they could crush political opposition. Ultimately, John Adams himself had to decide between peace, at the risk of worsening the split in his party, and a war which might have assured a Federalist victory in 1800. He decided on peace. Democratic-Republicans profited from his dilemma. Jefferson gained the presidency; the Federalists ceased to be the party in power; and the Federalist era ended.

Many Federalists considered the Democratic-Republican victory a tragedy and their own years in office a failure. The tragedy lay not in the loss of an election but in the Federalists' own concept of government. Their idea of a government by a wealthy and talented elite had already become outmoded, and they failed to realize it. They openly expressed distrust of the people at a time when the people wanted more, not less, participation in government. Democratic-Republicans, on the other hand, praised the wisdom of the people, and thereby they gained votes.

The Federalists, whose leadership was as intelligent as that of any party in the nation's history, had failed as politicians but not as statesmen. They had given life to the Constitution; they had given honest, efficient government to the nation. They had established the precedent of using the national government to promote the general welfare, and they had guided the nation through years of internal turbulence and foreign danger. They had placed the United States flag, in the Northwest and Southwest, over all territory that rightfully or technically belonged to the United States. When they left the national scene, the national government was strong and the nation prosperous, and the country was at peace. These were significant accomplishments for the nation's first political party.

FOCUSING ON SPECIFICS

1. Why did Hamilton prefer to entrust political power to men of property?

2. What ideas did Hamilton promote in his Report on Manufactures?

3. Why did the whiskey tax arouse strong opposition from frontier farmers?

4. How did Hamilton and Jefferson differ in their attitudes toward American obligations to France under the treaties of 1778?

5. What effect did Citizen Genêt's conduct have on Washington's policy of neutrality?

6. Why was Spain willing to negotiate a treaty with the United States in 1794?

7. What concessions did Spain make to the United States in Pinckney's Treaty?

8. What advice did Washington give to the nation in his Farewell Address?

9. How did Congress respond to the publication of the "X Y Z" dispatches?

10. What economic, social, and sectional differences tended to distinguish Federalists from Democratic-Republicans?

11. Why did the extreme Federalists want an all-out war with France?

12. What were the provisions of the Virginia and Kentucky resolutions?

REVIEWING MAIN THEMES

1. What conditions led to the formation of political parties during Washington's administration?

2. How did Hamilton's legislative program improve the nation's economy and strengthen the national government? Why did many people criticize his program?

3. Explain how the Federalist and Democratic-Republican parties differed in economic policy, constitutional interpretation, political philosophy, and foreign policy.

4. Describe the diplomatic accomplishments of Washington's administration.

5. How did the Adams administration avoid an all-out war with France and still uphold the honor of the United States?

6. What political developments brought about the end of the Federalist era?

7. What contributions to the nation were made by the Federalists?

EVALUATING THE ISSUES

1. The historian, Carl N. Degler, has said that "almost all of the Hamiltonian program was enacted in the early 1790's and, from the vantage point of retrospect, this was most fortunate; for of the two contending economic programs, the Federalists' was the more far-sighted. The laissez-faire . . . [society] of Jefferson would have been neither a strong nor a prosperous nation for long." Do you agree with this statement? Give reasons for your answer.

2. Is the advice given in Washington's Farewell Address as applicable today as it was in 1796? Explain.

3. In general, Hamilton's broad interpretation of the Constitution has gained greater acceptance than has Jefferson's strict interpretation. What reasons can you suggest to explain this development?

4. Could the need for maintaining a strong national defense ever justify the passage of such laws as the Alien and Sedition Acts? Explain your answer.

CHAPTER **6** 1801-1815

The Jeffersonians in Power

Thomas Jefferson believed that his victory marked the beginning of great changes in ideas regarding government. "The revolution of 1800," he said later, "was as real a revolution in the principles of government as that of 1776 was in its form." Jefferson's followers and, later, many historians accepted this view, added details to it, and gave it the force of legend. According to the legend, Jefferson had overthrown the aristocratic Federalist system within the federal government and replaced it with his own democratic system. Later generations of Americans looked upon him as the father of democracy.

Jefferson, a landed, slaveholding aristocrat, scarcely could have been considered a democratic man of the people. Since his narrow victory in the election of 1800 did not lead to radical changes, it cannot be considered a real revolution. Yet, there was no doubt that the Jeffersonians did bring to Washington, the new national capital, some changes in ideas about how the American federal system was to operate.

Unlike the Federalists, the Democratic-Republicans believed in democracy, in majority rule. They wanted to bring the government as close to the people as possible so that it would be responsive to the people's wishes. They wanted to develop a nation of many small property owners, mainly farmers, since they believed that such people were the best equipped to be both rulers and citizens in a democracy. Jefferson conceded that in Europe, with its exploited masses of poor and landless people, democracy might be dangerous. But he did not believe that democracy posed any threat in the United States, where the great majority of the people owned some property. This concept of a small property owners' democracy, therefore, had great political appeal. Jeffersonian democracy reflected a realistic knowledge of society as it existed.

Jeffersonians distrusted government. They believed that, for the most part, its power should be negative rather than positive. They were convinced that power corrupted and that anyone who had power was potentially dangerous. In contrast to

Hamiltonians, Jeffersonians wanted to keep the government from intervening in economic matters. They believed that such intervention usually led to the granting of some form of economic privilege to a favored few. To Jeffersonians, the greatest threat to democratic freedom lay in the use of political power by an aristocracy or some other minority group, for the purpose of increasing the wealth of that group.

From the beginning, Jefferson's actions were in keeping with his democratic philosophy. Instead of riding to his inauguration in a fancy carriage flanked by a mounted military escort, he walked. The ceremony itself was simple. But Jefferson's inaugural address was not a simple speech; it was a work of lasting literary quality as befitted the talents of the most intellectual of American Presidents.

Jefferson tried to heal some of the wounds of the campaign by being conciliatory in his inaugural address. He appealed to the Federalists for unity, saying that "every difference of opinion is not a difference of principle. . . . We are all Republicans, we are all Federalists." This appeal did not suggest that any revolution in government was taking place. Jefferson also expressed his view of what constituted good government. He said that his would be a "wise and frugal government" and would leave men "free to regulate their own pursuits of industry and improvement." In foreign policy, Jefferson pledged "honest friendship with all nations, entangling alliances with none." Few Federalists could take issue with this pledge, for it appeared to be a continuation of the foreign policies of Washington and Adams.

Having presented his program to the people, Jefferson assumed the office of President. For the first time, the government of the United States passed from the hands of one political party into those of a rival party. This transition was especially important because it had not come about through a violent revolution. It demonstrated to the world that by peaceable means it was possible to bring about changes within government.

JEFFERSONIANS TOOK CONTROL OF GOVERNMENT

When the Jeffersonians assumed control of the government, they were fortunate. The Federalists had handed them the machinery of government in good working order. The nation was at peace; the people were prosperous. Both political parties, despite their differences, were committed to the support of the Constitution. This state of affairs gave the new President time to think about what he should do before taking any action.

Unlike George Washington, Jefferson did not consider himself a nonpolitical President. Although he sought national unity, his was a party government, and he acted quickly to appoint loyal Jeffersonians to positions of power. He filled his cabinet posts with Democratic-Republicans whose views on government and society were similar to his own. For example, he appointed as secretary of state his close friend, neighbor, and political collaborator, James Madison. Few men in high office have been able to work together with such an intimate understanding of each other's views as did Jefferson and Madison. Jefferson chose Albert Gallatin, a Democratic-Republican from Pennsylvania, as secretary of the treasury. Gallatin had gained fame as a defender of the men who participated in the Whiskey Rebellion (1794) and as a member of the House of Representatives who opposed Alexander Hamilton's program.

In lower level appointments, Jefferson moved slowly. He did not remove Federalists who were in office when he took command. But he did not appoint any of his political opponents to an office when a vacancy occurred. Whenever he could, he filled federal offices with loyal Democratic-Republicans. By the end of his first term, he had replaced about half of the Federalists in government offices with men of his own party. Four years later the government was completely in Democratic-Republican hands. While the laws had not changed, men with a different philosophy of government had taken control and they would interpret and administer the laws as they saw fit.

Jeffersonians modified the Hamiltonian program

Despite the bitterness of the campaign of 1800 and the intensity of their opposition to Federalist policies, Jefferson and Madison did not attempt to destroy the Hamiltonian system. Although they were determined to purge the government of supposed abuses by their predecessors, they generally accepted the Hamiltonian program. They modified what the Federalists had done and built their own program on that framework.

The Democratic-Republican program was based on the idea that the federal government should do as little as possible in matters concerning the domestic life of the nation. "Let the general government be reduced to foreign concerns only," Jefferson had said shortly before taking office. He wanted the federal government to "be reduced to a very simple organization and a very inexpensive one; a few plain duties to be performed by a few servants." If Jefferson, as President, continued to hold this point of view, he would not try to guide Congress, except in a negative way. This was the course Jefferson followed during the first years of Democratic-Republican rule.

In keeping with their philosophy of government, the Jeffersonians wished to relieve the people of the whole system of internal taxation and to reduce the public debt. The only way they could pay off the public debt and, at the same time, reduce taxes, was by cutting government services and by practicing economies in running the government. Jefferson and his fellow Democratic-Republicans believed that the public debt, wars, armies, and navies were sources of corruption. They were convinced that debts incurred to finance wasteful spending would endanger freedom.

The Jeffersonians eliminated the need for a large number of government employees when Congress repealed all of the internal taxes. This action left the national government dependent, to a large extent, on import and export duties for revenue to carry on its operations.

Since the Federalists had spent most of the nation's money on the navy and army during the half war with France, it was logical for Albert Gallatin, the secretary of the treasury, to look for ways to economize in the armed forces. The army was reduced, the manpower of the navy was cut, and only a few ships were kept in commission.

As a result, Gallatin was able to bring annual expenditures for the armed forces to within $1.9 million. Despite the repeal of the internal taxes, his economies were so successful that within eight years he had lowered the public debt from $83 million to $57 million, in addition to paying the expenses of running the government during that time.

Jefferson's reductions in the armed forces reflected his desire to economize. They also showed his fear that a large standing army would threaten civilian government. Although he thought a navy would not pose such a threat, Jefferson saw no reason why Democratic-Republican farmers should pay taxes for a navy used chiefly for the protection of a few Federalist shippers. Besides, he believed that trade and commerce should be kept subordinate to agriculture.

The Louisiana Purchase doubled the nation's area

One of Jefferson's most pressing problems was the fate of Louisiana, the vast region stretching westward from the Mississippi River to the Rocky Mountains. France once had controlled the province but had ceded it to Spain in 1763, at the close of the Seven Years' War. During the Federalist era, there were frequent rumors that France had regained Louisiana. These rumors alarmed American statesmen, who preferred to have weak Spain as a neighbor rather than powerful France. On October 1, 1800, the rumors became a fact, when the ministers of Napoleon Bonaparte, ruler of France, signed a secret agreement with Spain, in which Spain ceded Louisiana to France in return for a kingdom in Italy. The Louisiana cession included New Orleans, east of the Mississippi, but not the territory known as East and West Florida.

A few months after he became President, Jefferson heard rumors of the cession, and he soon took steps to prepare for any possible change in the status of Louisiana. In an open letter to Robert R. Livingston, the United States minister in Paris, in April 1802, Jefferson said, "There is on the globe one single spot, the possessor of which is our natural and habitual enemy. It is New Orleans...." If France took possession of New Orleans, friendship would end. From that moment, according to Jefferson, the United States must marry itself "to the British fleet and nation."

Several months later, Jefferson's alarm increased. On October 16, 1802, the day after the Spanish king gave the final order transferring Louisiana to France, the Spanish official still in charge of New Orleans withdrew the American right of deposit there. Westerners assumed that the order had come from Napoleon. Actually, it was the Spaniards, not the French, who, on their own initiative, had suspended the right of deposit. Later, when the United States protested, the Spanish government revoked the suspension.

Jefferson realized that he might bring on a war if he took strong measures against France and Spain. If he did nothing, however, he would play into the hands of Federalists who were demanding forcible seizure of New Orleans. His government might even be overthrown and the Union disrupted. Jefferson decided that the United States should try to purchase New Orleans and the Floridas, at that time thought to be part of the Louisiana cession.

In January 1803, the President appointed James Monroe as a special envoy to France to work with Livingston in attempting to buy New Orleans and the Floridas. The men were authorized to offer as much as $10 million for the land. In return, Jefferson was willing to guarantee to France the free navigation of the Mississippi as well as the ownership of Louisiana west of the river. Monroe and Livingston were instructed to cross the channel to London and seek an alliance with Britain if the negotiations with France should fail.

Even before Monroe arrived in Paris, Napoleon approached Livingston and offered to sell all of Louisiana. Since Napoleon could have kept both the territory and American good will by making small concessions to the United States, historians always have been interested in his reasons for making the offer. Those reasons were complex, but understandable.

Napoleon's plan for a French empire in North America had gone wrong. Some fifty thousand French troops had died in the fight to suppress a rebellion of former slaves in Saint Domingue, a French colony on the island of Santo Domingo (now called Hispaniola). This fighting had delayed the French occupation of Louisiana. In addition, Napoleon expected to go to war again against England in the spring of 1803. The reversals in Santo Domingo and the developments in Europe led Napoleon to give up his plan for an empire in North America.

To keep Louisiana out of British hands and possibly to realize some profit from it before American frontiersmen claimed it for their own, Napoleon offered to sell Louisiana to the United States for $25 million. Although Livingston and Monroe had no authority to buy the entire province, they quickly recognized a bargain and decided to act on their own without delay. After haggling over the price, they signed a treaty for the purchase of Louisiana, dated April 30, 1803, in which the United States agreed to pay $15 million, or about three cents an acre, for this vast land of incalculable value in the heart of North America.

The proposal freed Jefferson from his political dilemma but raised another problem: he thought he lacked the constitutional power to buy Louisiana and to bring its people into the Union. He believed this could be done only through a constitutional amendment. However, Jefferson recognized the need for a quick decision to take advantage of the great bargain offered by France. His advisers insisted that a constitutional amendment was unnecessary and in gaining it he would lose valuable time. He could accomplish all that was necessary

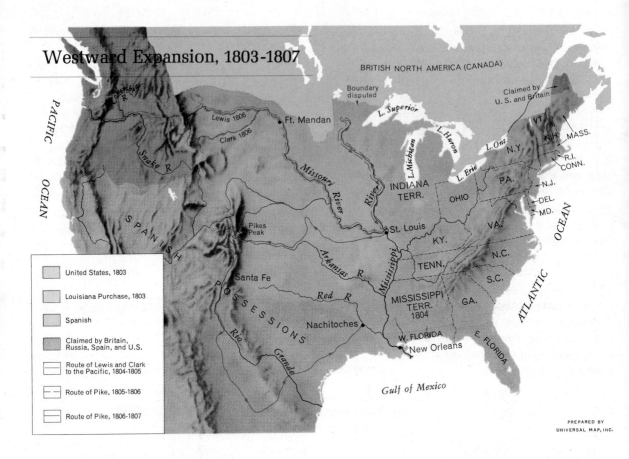

Westward Expansion, 1803-1807

BRITISH NORTH AMERICA (CANADA)

PACIFIC OCEAN

Boundary disputed

Claimed by U. S. and Britain

L. Superior

L. Michigan

L. Huron

L.Ont.

L. Erie

Lewis 1806

Clark 1806

Ft. Mandan

Snake R.

Missouri River

River

INDIANA TERR.

OHIO

PA.

N.Y.

VT.

N.H.

MASS.

R.I.

CONN.

N.J.

DEL.

MD.

St. Louis

KY.

VA.

Pikes Peak

Santa Fe

Arkansas R.

Red R.

Mississippi

TENN.

N.C.

S.C.

MISSISSIPPI TERR. 1804

GA.

Nachitoches

W. FLORIDA

E. FLORIDA

New Orleans

Rio Grande

ATLANTIC OCEAN

SPANISH POSSESSIONS

Gulf of Mexico

	United States, 1803
	Louisiana Purchase, 1803
	Spanish
	Claimed by Britain, Russia, Spain, and U.S.
	Route of Lewis and Clark to the Pacific, 1804-1805
	Route of Pike, 1805-1806
	Route of Pike, 1806-1807

PREPARED BY
UNIVERSAL MAP, INC.

in the matter, both legally and quickly, they said, through the President's power to make treaties. Jefferson finally accepted their advice.

In October 1803, the Senate approved the treaty for the purchase of Louisiana. On December 20, France transferred the province to the United States. Through good fortune and the shrewd statesmanship of Jefferson and his advisers, the United States had doubled its territory.

Jefferson sent explorers into the wilderness

Through several daring explorations, Americans learned more regarding the vast extent of the Louisiana Territory. The President named two army officers, both familiar with the wilderness and the ways of Indians, to lead the expedition. The first

was Jefferson's twenty-eight-year-old private secretary and fellow Virginian, Captain Meriwether Lewis. The second was thirty-two-year-old Lieutenant William Clark, another Virginian and a former Indian fighter.

Lewis and Clark carefully chose and trained the men for their expedition. They started up the Missouri River in May 1804, after the United States had taken formal possession of the Louisiana Territory. Cutting through the Rocky Mountains, the expedition moved westward along the Snake and Columbia rivers and their tributaries. Finally, in November 1805, the explorers sighted, as Clark described it, "this great Pacific Ocean which we have been so long anxious to see." The expedition camped on the Pacific shore. In September 1806, they returned to St. Louis with a careful record of what they had seen and done. The Lewis and Clark expedition had strengthened the claim of the United States to the Oregon country and had marked land and river routes westward for settlers who were to come later.

The most noted American explorer of the southern part of the Louisiana Territory was another young army officer in his late twenties, Lieutenant Zebulon Montgomery Pike. In the fall of 1805, Pike and a party of about twenty men set out to find the true source of the Mississippi River. Although Pike did not find the source of the river, he brought back much useful information about the area he had explored.

In the summer of 1806, Pike went on another expedition, seeking the headwaters of the Arkansas and Red rivers. He and his men explored what is now Colorado and New Mexico. In Colorado, Pike discovered the peak that now bears his name, but he failed in his effort to climb it. On his return, Pike described the Great Plains as desert, unsuitable for farming.

Burr's conspiracy led to a trial for treason

Most Americans were pleased with the purchase of Louisiana. Some New England Federalists, however, believed the annexation would upset the balance of power within the Union and feared that New England's national influence would diminish. Extremists among them preferred to have New England secede from the Union and form a separate northern confederacy rather than face a future of shrinking political power.

Leaders of the extremists believed that a northern confederacy would have to include New York as well as the New England states, if such a confederacy were to succeed. Alexander Hamilton, still powerful in New York, rejected the secessionist scheme. The plotters turned to Aaron Burr, whose future in the Democratic-Republican party appeared bleak. Jefferson disliked Burr and had seen to it that he was dropped from the presidential ticket in 1804. In the same year, therefore, Burr

agreed to run with Federalist support for governor of New York. Many people assumed that, if elected, Burr would lead New York into the northern confederacy.

Hamilton urged friends to vote against Burr, whom he denounced as a dangerous man, one who could not be trusted in high office. Burr lost the election, blamed Hamilton for the defeat, and challenged Hamilton to a duel. Although Hamilton was opposed to dueling, he felt his political career would be ruined if he refused the challenge; so he accepted. The great Federalist fell before Burr's bullet at Weehawken, New Jersey, on July 11, 1804, and died the next day.

With the loss of New York, the scheme for a northern confederacy had collapsed and the power of the Federalist party had been weakened. In the presidential election of 1804, Jefferson carried every state but Connecticut and Delaware.

Burr spent most of the following year in the Southwest, where he engaged in mysterious activities which finally led to his being suspected of plotting against the government of the United States. He was arrested and brought to trial on the charge of treason before the United States Circuit Court at Richmond, Virginia, in August 1807, with Chief Justice John Marshall presiding.

High drama marked the trial. Jefferson was eager for Burr's conviction, but Marshall rigidly applied the constitutional provision that no one shall be convicted of treason "until there be proof of the overt act by two witnesses." Since not even one person could testify that Burr himself had waged war against the United States or aided its enemies, he was acquitted. Marshall's ruling set a precedent that made conviction for treason difficult.

A free but ruined man, Burr went into exile in France. No one has ever known precisely what he had plotted. Some historians have believed that he wished to detach the Southwest from the Union and become its ruler. Others have thought that he wanted to drive the Spaniards from North America and carve an empire from Spanish lands beyond Louisiana, in Mexico.

MEN
IN
HISTORY

HAMILTON AND BURR

Aaron Burr, who challenged, shot, and mortally wounded the great Federalist Alexander Hamilton in a duel, has been portrayed as an ambitious, unprincipled villain—one who used an uncivilized method to settle an old political rivalry. Hamilton has been considered the innocent man of principle, forced into combat for having performed his patriotic duty. Yet the paths of the two men had often crossed, and the relationship between them had begun to develop long before their famous duel.

Early in their careers both men fought and worked together. They served gallantly in the Revolutionary Army, and following the war, the two men became members of the same profession. Both passed the law examination of New York, after a few months of concentrated study. Hamilton quickly became the leader of the state bar, but Burr gained a reputation as the better trial lawyer. The two men collaborated on many cases, forming an unbeatable team. When in opposition to each other, Hamilton would address the court with technical, sophisticated, and lengthy arguments. Burr, seeking out his opponent's weak arguments, would attack briefly and to the point.

Appointed secretary of the treasury by President Washington, Hamilton, the admirer of British government, advocated a financially responsible government, a strong national bank, and an industrial society. He backed up his conception of government financial policy with proposals to fund the foreign and the domestic debt, establish American credit, and stabilize American securities. Congress proved eager to coöperate with Hamilton. His personal standards of integrity and honesty in office were of immeasurable aid to the young nation in establishing its financial system. But he had no sympathy with democracy, feeling that the "rich and well-born" ought to control America and that the "mass of the people" could "seldom judge or determine right."

Burr entered politics in New York. He became the state's attorney general and later, with the support of such elements of the population as the Tammany Society, an organization of Revolutionary War veterans which he converted into a political machine, he became a United States senator. He tied with Jefferson in the presidential election of 1800, and when the House of Representatives, after thirty-six ballots, chose Jefferson, Burr became the third Vice President of the United States. Four years later, ignored by Jefferson, Burr decided to run for the governorship of New York. Hamilton, hearing that Burr had engaged in political intrigue, worked to defeat him.

Becoming more and more fearful of Burr, Hamilton began to attack Burr's moral character. An attack of this kind was a recognized offense under the "Code Duello," a way of settling personal disputes which was accepted by many aristocratic Americans during this period. (The custom died in the somewhat less than aristocratic gunfights of the wild West.) Some of Hamilton's caustic words found their way into print and came to the attention of Burr, who now demanded "satisfaction" under the "Code." Hamilton entered the contest with misgivings.

The duel ended with Hamilton dying and Burr's political future ruined. Although charged with murder both in New Jersey and in New York, as Vice President of the United States Burr continued to preside over the Senate the following winter. When his term of office had expired, he could not return to his law practice in New York, where he was under indictment. In fact, it would have been unpleasant for him to remain anywhere in the East. He fled to the Southwest, where he talked and schemed with prominent men. Even today there remains a mystery about his activities there. Some historians believe that he wished to detach the Southwest from the Union and make himself ruler of a new empire.

President Jefferson ordered Burr's arrest, and he was brought to Richmond, Virginia, for trial on the charge of treason. After a sensational trial, Burr was acquitted. The presiding judge, Chief Justice John Marshall, upheld the exact wording of the Constitution: "No Person shall be convicted of Treason unless on the Testimony of two Witnesses to the same overt Act, or on Confession in open Court." Since the prosecution could not produce witnesses to prove Burr had actually committed a treasonable act, he became a free man. Burr went into exile in Europe, but soon returned to New York where he practiced law until his death in 1836.

REVIEWING THE SECTION

1. What changes did the Jeffersonians make in the Hamiltonian program?

2. Why did Napoleon offer to sell all of Louisiana to the United States? How did Jefferson resolve the constitutional problems of making this vast territory part of the United States?

3. What was the purpose and achievement of the Lewis and Clark expedition? of Zebulon Pike's explorations?

4. What attempts were made during Jefferson's administration to dismember the Union? How were Aaron Burr and Alexander Hamilton involved in these attempts?

NEUTRAL RIGHTS BECAME AN ISSUE

Thomas Jefferson could look back on the results of his first administration (1801-1805) with considerable satisfaction. The American people were contented, the Democratic-Republican party was stronger than it had been four years earlier, and the Louisiana Purchase was a crowning achievement. Jefferson told a friend that smoother relations with Britain and France had come with peace between the two nations, and bickering without war marked the relationship with Spain. "Other nations," he said, "view our course with respect and anxiety."

In Jefferson's second administration, which began in March 1805, all this changed. Foreign affairs produced bitter divisions among the people and again brought the nation to the verge of war. Many of the difficulties arose from the war between Britain and France, which, after a period of peace, had been renewed in May 1803. For two years after the start of the war, American traders prospered from it. They sold goods and delivered them to the ports of the belligerents, particularly to French and Spanish colonies in the Caribbean. This commerce led to the rapid growth of the United States merchant marine, and the United States became the world's foremost neutral trading nation.

In 1805, the British attacked this trade. They said they would not allow neutral ships, meaning those of the United States, to trade with Britain's enemies. British naval cruisers thereupon began the capture of scores of United States ships which were carrying goods to French or to Spanish ports. At the time, Spain was France's ally. In October of that year, the British admiral Horatio Nelson smashed the combined French and Spanish fleets at the Battle of Trafalgar. This victory insured Britain's control of the seas.

In the Battle of Austerlitz a month later, Napoleon crushed the armies of Russia and Austria—Britain's allies—and made himself the master of the continent. After this, France ruled on land, and Britain on the sea, but neither could directly injure the other.

Britain blockaded territory under French control. Napoleon retaliated by throwing a "paper" blockade—one which he could only proclaim and not really enforce—around the British Isles. In a scheme known as the Continental System, Napoleon tried to keep British goods out of Europe. Britain struck back with a series of orders-in-council which were wartime decrees virtually prohibiting neutral trade with Europe. This was a serious blow to the United States.

Jefferson believed Britain and France urgently needed trade with the United States and reasoned that they would respect the neutral rights of his nation if they were faced with the loss of its trade. He hoped to protect the rights of the United States through a policy of economic pressure, which he called peaceful coercion.

Impressment of American sailors brought protests

With British orders prohibiting neutral trade with Europe, and with the British fleet in control of the seas, most of America's trade went to British ports and most of America's grievances were against Britain. Most bitter of all grievances was that of *impressment*—naval recruiting by force. The British used "press" gangs to force men into their navy. Life aboard British warships, where floggings were brutal and the payment for services low, did not entice men to enlist. Sailors who were impressed often deserted. Many British deserters took service aboard United States merchant ships, where the pay was higher and the living conditions better.

In their search for deserters, British naval officers examined neutral ships in British ports and stopped them at sea. Although the British government never claimed the right to impress any but British sailors, in practice United States citizens as well as British subjects were impressed from the ships searched by the British navy. Jefferson's government protested the impressment of Americans. However, Britain would not retreat on the impressment issue, nor on the issue of neutral trade. So Jefferson decided to retaliate. In April 1806, Congress passed the Nonimportation Act to keep certain British goods out of the United States, unless Britain's government settled American grievances.

At the same time, Jefferson sent two men, James Monroe, the regular minister to Britain, and William Pinkney, a Baltimore lawyer, on a special mission to London to negotiate the grievances. To give Monroe and Pinkney more bargaining power, the President decided to delay enforcing the Nonimportation Act. In December 1806, Monroe and Pinkney concluded a treaty which included concessions from both sides, but the British offered no concession on the impressment issue. This disturbed Jefferson, and he refused to send the treaty to the Senate. Further efforts to negotiate failed. Despite the failure of the Monroe-Pinkney Treaty, Jefferson still refrained from putting the Nonimportation Act into effect.

A clash at sea a short time later made Americans angrier than ever. In June 1807, the British frigate *Leopard* hailed the United States frigate *Chesapeake* off the coast of Virginia and demanded that she submit to a search for deserters. When permission was refused, the British fired upon the *Chesapeake,* killing three United States sailors and wounding others. A British search party boarded the *Chesapeake,* which was unprepared for action,

and took off four alleged deserters. Only one of them proved to be a British deserter, and the British hanged him. The other three were citizens of the United States. This outrage infuriated Americans; some clamored for war. In negotiations later over the *Chesapeake* affair, the British apologized for the *Leopard's* violence and offered to make amends, but they refused to give up impressment. During the negotiations, Americans' fervor for war subsided but the bitterness over the *Chesapeake* affair lingered on for years.

The policy of peaceful coercion failed

Even during the heat of the *Chesapeake* crisis, Jefferson retained faith in his idea that economic pressure would force Britain and France to respect United States rights. In December 1807, the Nonimportation Act finally was allowed to go into effect, but it was not strong enough to suit the President. He wanted to shut off all United States trade with Britain and France. Jefferson believed that once the belligerent powers realized they would no longer get American raw materials and food, they would come to terms on the issue of neutral rights.

In that same month, at Jefferson's urging, Congress passed the Embargo Act which prohibited United States ships from leaving for foreign ports. Later laws gave the federal government broad power for enforcing this policy of self-blockade. On the surface the Embargo Act was impartial, but in practice it helped Napoleon's Continental System. Since Britain controlled the seas and had already destroyed France's overseas commerce, the embargo had the effect of denying United States supplies only to Britain.

The embargo misfired despite the injury inflicted on Britain. It caused greater hardships in the United States than in Britain. Seaports, especially those in New England, suffered from a financial depression. Moreover, Napoleon took advantage of the embargo to serve his own needs. He said that since United States ships could not leave port legally, those in continental harbors must be British

THE PRESIDENTS OF THE UNITED STATES

GEORGE WASHINGTON
(1732-1799)
IN OFFICE: 1789-1797

JOHN ADAMS
(1735-1826)
IN OFFICE: 1797-1801

From Virginia. Washington's administration set many precedents for the new government. He established a foreign policy of strict neutrality, followed Hamilton's fiscal policies, and demonstrated the power of the federal government by suppressing the Whiskey Rebellion. Though Washington felt himself to be above party politics, he generally followed Federalist policies.

Federalist from Massachusetts. The major problem during the Adams administration was the increased hostility with France. When war with France threatened, the Federalists passed the Alien and Sedition Acts (1798) in order to insure unanimity of opinion. These repressive measures resulted in Adams' loss of popularity and were a factor in the subsequent downfall of the party.

THOMAS JEFFERSON
(1743-1826)
IN OFFICE: 1801-1809

JAMES MADISON
(1751-1836)
IN OFFICE: 1809-1817

Democratic-Republican from Virginia. Although Jefferson believed in the theory of a limited central government, his actions often expanded the role of the federal government. During his administration, the Louisiana Territory was purchased (1803), war was fought with the Barbary pirates (1801-1805), and the Embargo Act (1807) was passed in an effort to protect neutral rights.

Democratic-Republican from Virginia. Madison's presidency was dominated by the issues of neutral rights and impressment, culminating in the War of 1812. Mismanagement of the war, as well as economic hardship, led to the threat of secession by a group of Federalists in New England. The second Bank of the United States was chartered (1816) during his administration.

ships in disguise. So he seized the United States merchant ships.

Many Democratic-Republicans, as well as the Federalists, denounced the embargo. Finally, the political pressure against the embargo became too strong for Congress to resist. Congress repealed the Embargo Act on March 1, 1809, three days before Jefferson left office. Jefferson's policy of peaceful coercion had failed.

In a further effort to exert economic pressure on the French and British, Congress next passed the Nonintercourse Act. This act excluded United States ships from British and French ports and closed United States ports to ships from Britain and France. However, it allowed the President to open trade with whichever of these nations would agree to respect United States rights.

Because of strong public reaction against Jefferson's Embargo Act, the Federalists recognized a possible opportunity to regain control of the government in the election of 1808. Their party spirit was revived; they fought unrelentingly and made some gains. But James Madison, Jefferson's secretary of state, was elected President. Madison, too, was committed to the policy of economic pressure established by Jefferson's Democratic-Republican administration.

At first, the policy of nonintercourse appeared to be a success, for President Madison obtained from the British minister in Washington, David M. Erskine, an agreement which would satisfactorily settle United States grievances. Madison then lifted the Nonintercourse Act as it applied to Britain. However, George Canning, the British foreign secretary, repudiated Erskine's agreement, and the embarrassed Madison again put the policy of nonintercourse into effect against Britain.

Like the Embargo Act, the Nonintercourse Act imposed an intolerable burden on United States commerce. So Congress dropped the policy of nonintercourse and replaced it with Macon's Bill No. 2, which reopened United States trade to all the world, but barred British and French warships from United States waters. It, too, permitted the President to apply nonintercourse to one belligerent if the other agreed to respect American rights.

Macon's Bill No. 2 favored Britain. So Napoleon convinced Madison that he was ready to respect United States rights. In February 1811, therefore, Madison applied nonintercourse only against Britain. Many Americans expected that the result would be war.

Frontiersmen grew increasingly anti-British

Other grievances against the British on the Northwest frontier—grievances having nothing to do with freedom of the seas—contributed to the expectation of war. For more than a decade, Westerners, bit by bit, in dubious treaties with individual tribes, had been acquiring Indian land for settlement. Some tribes resisted the advancing frontiersmen. The British had supported such resistance before Jay's Treaty was signed, but British policy did not support Indian resistance to the Americans after the treaty had gone into effect. Unfortunately, after 1807, anti-British sentiment became deeply embedded in the United States. Westerners then began believing rumors that the British in Upper Canada (later known as the Province of Ontario) were encouraging the Indians to attack frontier settlements in the United States territories.

In reality, Indian resistance stemmed more from the land policies of the Westerners themselves than from British policy. In September 1809, William Henry Harrison, governor of the Indiana Territory, had made treaties at Fort Wayne with several tribes. These agreements opened millions of acres of rich farm land to settlement and forced the Indians to move westward to an area along the Wabash River.

Most Indians resented the policy and actions of the United States government for they thereby were denied the use of their traditional hunting grounds. Two of these Indians—a Shawnee chief known as Tecumseh, "The Shooting Star," and his brother, a medicine man called The Prophet—organized a movement to unite all of the tribes against the advancing whites. Tecumseh urged his people to surrender no more land and to resist the advance of the white man. He told Harrison that the whites "have driven us from the sea to the lakes—we can go no farther."

Westerners believed that British plotting was behind Tecumseh's resistance and plan of Indian confederation. On November 7, 1811, they found what they considered to be clear evidence of British intrigue with the Indians, when about a thousand of Harrison's troops clashed with Tecumseh's warriors while the Indian chief himself was away. The encounter took place at The Prophet's village on Tippecanoe Creek, a tributary of the Wabash River. Harrison's men defeated the Indians and in the village found weapons made in Britain. The discovery of these weapons in the Indian camp further crystallized sentiment for war against Britain.

War hawks wanted to fight the British

The leaders of the Twelfth Congress, which met in special session in Washington three days before the Battle of Tippecanoe, were young men, such as Henry Clay of Kentucky and John C. Calhoun of South Carolina. This new group, which had replaced the leaders of the Revolutionary generation came from the West and lower South. They were nationalists and belligerent patriots. Although they did not form a majority in Congress, or even within the Democratic-Republican membership, they controlled important committees. They considered impressment and other maritime restrictions a national disgrace and demanded war against Britain. As a result, they became known as "the war hawks of 1812."

The war hawks' objectives appealed to both the Northwest and the South. Following the Battle of Tippecanoe, Westerners argued that the only way to end the Indian troubles on the Northwest frontier was to conquer Britain's possessions in North America (Upper and Lower Canada). The war hawks pointed out that, since the United States lacked a strong navy, an attack on these possessions would be the most effective way of striking at the British. Southerners, too, wished to expand their nation and at the same time do injury to Britain. Since Spain was now Britain's ally, the Southerners advocated an invasion of Spanish Florida.

President Madison and his new secretary of state, James Monroe, sided with the war hawks. However, Federalists and moderate Democratic-Republicans resisted the pull to war. New England Federalists, in particular, thought that war against Britain would be a national tragedy. They considered Napoleon a tyrant and the nation's true foe.

When the British learned that Americans were seriously preparing for war, they relaxed their restrictions on United States commerce, and on June 23, 1812, suspended the orders-in-council as they applied to the United States.

This concession came five days too late. On June 18, after the war hawks had brought the crisis to a head, Madison had signed a declaration of war against Britain, unaware that the orders-in-council would be suspended. If the major cause for war was British violation of neutral rights, as most Americans believed, except for impressment that cause was removed at the start of the war.

REVIEWING THE SECTION

1. Why did the British policy of impressment become a heated issue between the United States and Britain?

2. What economic measures did Jefferson and Madison use in their attempt to secure the neutral rights of the United States? What was the effect of these measures?

3. How did Indian problems on the Northwest frontier arouse anti-British sentiment in the West?

4. Why did the war hawks demand war against Britain?

MADISON LED A DIVIDED NATION INTO WAR

In his war message to Congress, Madison insisted that the United States must defend its neutral rights against Britain's violations. Impressment was

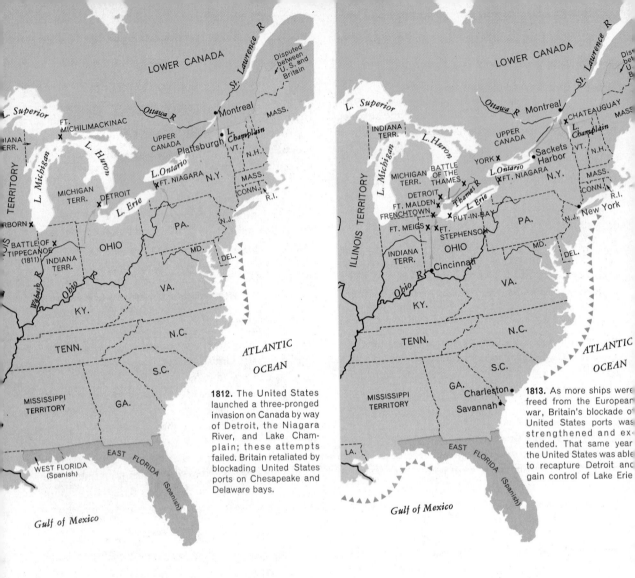

1812. The United States launched a three-pronged invasion on Canada by way of Detroit, the Niagara River, and Lake Champlain; these attempts failed. Britain retaliated by blockading United States ports on Chesapeake and Delaware bays.

1813. As more ships were freed from the European war, Britain's blockade of United States ports was strengthened and extended. That same year the United States was able to recapture Detroit and gain control of Lake Erie.

at the top of the list of United States grievances. Madison did not give much attention to Indian troubles on the frontier, and he said nothing regarding Upper and Lower Canada and the Floridas.

Despite Madison's emphasis on freedom of the seas and the depth of public sentiment on this issue, many of the representatives from the northern seaboard states which had been most injured by long impressments and ship captures, voted against war. While the people from the New England and Middle Atlantic states had suffered, they also had profited from overseas trade. They considered that trade more important than their grievances. War would destroy this source of income. The strong-

hold of the group of Federalists who loved Britain, hated the French, and detested Napoleon was in these states.

The Federalists were convinced that French violations of United States rights were as humiliating as those of the British. Many other Americans shared this view, believing that the United States had good cause for war against France as well as Britain. When the Senate considered the declaration of war, a debate raged for days on the question of whether or not to include France. A proposal for war against France lost by only four votes.

Madison led a divided nation into the conflict against Britain. On the day Madison proclaimed

War of 1812

→ British moves	→ United States moves
▲▲ British blockade	✗ Battles

1814-1815. Britain further extended her blockade of the Atlantic coast and launched a triple thrust against Lake Champlain, Chesapeake Bay, and New Orleans. The United States successfully defended itself in all three battles. The most dramatic U.S. victory of the war, the Battle of New Orleans, had no effect on the outcome of the war; a peace treaty had been signed two weeks earlier.

LOWER CANADA

Disputed between U.S. and Britain

L. Superior

INDIANA TERR.

L. Huron

L. Michigan

MICHIGAN TERRITORY

ILLINOIS TERRITORY

L. Erie

UPPER CANADA

Montreal

BATTLE OF LAKE CHAMPLAIN

Plattsburgh

L. Champlain

MASS.

VT.

N.H.

L. Ontario

BATTLES OF CHIPPAWA AND LUNDY'S LANE

N.Y.

MASS.

CONN.

R.I.

PA.

N.J.

INDIANA TERR.

OHIO

BALTIMORE

FT. McHENRY

MD.

Potomac R

WASHINGTON, D.C.

BLADENSBURG

DEL.

Patuxent R

Chesapeake Bay

KY.

VA.

TENN.

N.C.

Huntsville

S.C.

MISSISSIPPI TERRITORY

BATTLE OF HORSE SHOE BEND

GA.

Mobile

Pensacola

EAST FLORIDA (Spanish)

ORLEANS

Gulf of Mexico

PREPARED BY UNIVERSAL MAP, INC.

Naval Heroes of the United States, by Currier & Ives, 1846

hostilities, the people in maritime New England expressed their opposition by fasting and praying. They considered the war declaration shameful and unnecessary.

New England opposed the war against Britain

The people of the United States were militarily and politically unprepared for war when the fighting started in 1812. Bitter party feelings and jealous sectional loyalties divided the people and weakened the war effort.

New England Federalists were most intense in their opposition to the war. Even though many of them prospered from the wartime stimulation of manufacturing and trade, they looked upon the war as the Democratic-Republican party's fight rather than the nation's. Derisively, they called it "Mr. Madison's War." Some New England Federalists discouraged enlistments in the armed forces, withheld money from the federal government, and supplied British troops with food and other provisions. Some even went so far as to take an oath of allegiance to Britain's King George.

In Congress, too, the Federalists obstructed the war program by refusing to support taxes, loans, and other measures. They implied that the Democratic-Republicans had gone to war to help Napoleon, and to open cities of the northern seaboard to devastation by the British navy while United States troops marched into Upper Canada.

The depth of public sentiment against the war was evident in the presidential election of 1812. Some politicians suggested that the only party division should be between those who wanted peace and those who wanted war. In New York, antiwar Democratic-Republicans nominated DeWitt Clinton; Federalists supported him. Clinton carried every state north of the Potomac River except Vermont and Pennsylvania. Madison, with the solid support of the South and West, won reëlection, but Federalist strength in Congress was doubled.

The most serious large-scale organized opposition to the government came from New England during the closing days of the war. In October 1814, Massachusetts called a convention of New England states to discuss their grievances; the convention met secretly in December in Hartford, Connecticut. Using the arguments of state rights, extreme Federalists wished to threaten secession. But moderate Federalists gained control, so the Hartford Convention merely denounced Madison's conduct of the war and proposed some amendments to the Constitution to safeguard New England's position in the Union. Many Americans considered the convention treasonable and, as a result, the Federalist party suffered.

The war hawks wanted to conquer Canada

Madison and his advisers wanted an early peace because they were aware of the nation's unpreparedness and knew that the nation was divided. However, the war hawks clamored for a swift victory in Upper and Lower Canada before any peace was settled. To these men, it seemed logical to try to capture these British possessions. They believed the conquest would be cheap, "a mere matter of marching."

Canada, with a population of less than a million people, was weak when compared to the United States, and it was vulnerable to direct attack from

the United States. British sea power could not support Upper Canada against an overland thrust. Moreover, Americans expected the French Canadians in Lower Canada (part of which was later known as the Province of Quebec) to aid them rather than to assist the British.

Logically, the United States soldiers should have marched on Montreal in order to stop British reinforcements from coming by way of the St. Lawrence River. Instead, in the summer of 1812, the United States dispersed its inadequate forces in a three-pronged attack, one force striking into Upper Canada by way of Detroit, another moving out across the Niagara River, and the third pushing forward from Lake Champlain.

General William Hull, veteran of the Revolutionary War, crossed into Upper Canada from Detroit with some two thousand men, lost a skirmish, retreated to Detroit and, without firing a shot, surrendered the fort there to the British. The invasion across the Niagara River failed when citizen soldiers of the New York militia refused to fight outside their own state. From across the river they watched while the enemy killed or captured United States regulars. The third group of invaders, ordered to strike at Montreal from Plattsburgh on Lake Champlain, marched north about twenty miles, but they, too, refused to cross into Upper Canada. The commanding general then marched the troops back to Plattsburgh.

The Americans received no assistance from the French Canadians, and nowhere did they make the gains they had expected to make. Before the end of 1812, Americans tried to retake Detroit, but failed. In 1813, Canadians hurled back two more invading armies. During 1812-1813, the United States forces had been on the offensive, but their march on Upper Canada failed.

The small United States Navy had some successes

Americans fought more effectively on water than they did on land during the early part of the war. Yet, in comparison to Britain's battle-tested fleet of more than eight hundred warships, the United States Navy was extremely small. Until the spring of 1813, it had only sixteen ships of various sizes.

When the fighting began, the British could spare only a few warships for duty in United States waters; the bulk of the royal navy was needed in the European war against Napoleon. This made it possible for the United States frigates and sloops-of-war to win a number of individual duels with British warships. In August and December, the frigate *Constitution,* known as "Old Ironsides," won two spectacular battles. These defeats humiliated the British, made Americans happy, and brought consolation for the poor showing of the United States Army, but they had little effect on the outcome of the war.

In the spring of 1813, the British sent more ships to North America and tightened the blockade of United States ports. At first, the British excluded New England from the blockade but, in the spring of 1814, the ports in that section, too, were closed. Most United States warships never again were able to get out of port, and United States commerce was swept from the seas.

The most notable naval victory for the United States in 1813 took place on Lake Erie. There, twenty-eight-year-old Captain Oliver Hazard Perry manned vessels—hastily built on the spot—with inexperienced sailors and Kentucky riflemen and sought out the British. He found the enemy's fleet in October and forced it into submission.

After Perry's victory, which left Lake Erie under United States control, the British forces abandoned Detroit. General William Henry Harrison, now in command of American forces in the Northwest, pursued the British and overtook them on the north bank of the Thames River in what is now Ontario. Here Harrison won the Battle of the Thames. It was here, too, that Tecumseh, who had become a brigadier general in the British army, was killed. The battle led to the breakup of the Indian confederation and freed the Northwest military frontier from immediate danger.

The British invaded the United States

The war took an especially bad turn for the United States in 1814, primarily because of events in Europe. The United States had gone to war just at the time that Napoleon invaded Russia, an invasion which turned into disaster for the French. In April 1814, Napoleon was forced to abdicate his throne and go into exile on the Mediterranean island of Elba. Britain could now concentrate her full might against the United States. That summer Britain tightened her blockade of the Atlantic coast and shipped to her possessions in North America thousands of veteran troops released from service in Europe.

Prior to this time, the British had simply defended their North American colonies against attacks by the United States. Now they planned to invade the United States in three major campaigns. They were going to strike southward from Lake Champlain, raid the area of Chesapeake Bay, and slash at New Orleans.

Late in August the British sent the strongest army yet to meet the Americans in combat—ten thousand disciplined troops—under General Sir George Prevost. His army was supported by a fleet of ships carrying his supplies. Prevost tried to gain control of Lake Champlain before attacking the force of United States regulars and militia facing him at Plattsburgh, New York. A United States naval squadron, commanded by Captain Thomas Macdonough, met the British challenge on the lake and won a decisive victory. Prevost retreated to Montreal, leaving behind quantities of supplies. The Battle of Plattsburgh had saved New England and New York from invasion.

In August, General Robert Ross landed an army of approximately four thousand British soldiers on the banks of the Patuxent River, which empties into Chesapeake Bay, and marched toward Washington. At Bladensburg, Maryland, on the edge of the District of Columbia, about seven thousand hastily summoned and poorly trained United States militiamen made a stand. Unable to resist the disciplined charges of the British redcoats, the militiamen broke and ran. Ross then marched into Washington, and President Madison and his officials fled to Virginia.

To retaliate for the burning of York (later known as Toronto) by United States troops in 1813, and to impress the Americans with the horror of war, the British burned most of the government buildings in Washington. Ross himself supervised the making of a bonfire out of the White House furniture. With the city of Washington partially in ruins, the British army climbed aboard its transports and proceeded up Chesapeake Bay to attack Baltimore.

Guarding the approaches to Baltimore was Fort McHenry, manned by regulars and Maryland militiamen. On September 13, 1814, the British ships stood offshore and bombarded the United States fort. From one of the British ships, Francis Scott Key, a United States lawyer who had gone aboard to obtain release of a prisoner, watched the nighttime cannonading. Key was so impressed by the fort's resistance that on the next day he wrote the words to the "The Star-Spangled Banner." Set to the music of an old ballad, Key's song soon came to be regarded as our national anthem.

After the futile assault on Baltimore, the British withdrew to Jamaica. Except for the burning of Washington, which infuriated the people of the United States, the second offensive thrust accomplished nothing. The third British force had not yet attacked.

REVIEWING THE SECTION

1. Why did the New England Federalists oppose the war against Britain? What actions did they take to obstruct the war effort?

2. Why did the United States fail to conquer Canada?

3. What were the results of Perry's victory on Lake Erie and of Harrison's victory on the Thames River?

4. What was the outcome of the British attacks on the Lake Champlain and Chesapeake Bay areas?

THE WAR HELPED UNIFY THE NEW NATION

While British soldiers were setting fire to Washington, British and United States diplomats were trying to negotiate a peace. In fact, an unusual feature of the War of 1812 was that peace efforts were begun even before the fighting had started. Soon after the United States had declared war, both governments suggested an armistice. These early efforts to make peace failed because neither Britain nor the United States would modify its position on the issue of impressment.

In November 1813, Lord Castlereagh, the British foreign secretary, wrote to Secretary of State James Monroe offering to talk about peace. Madison and Monroe quickly accepted the offer. The President appointed a commission of five Americans to meet with a British commission in the Flemish town of Ghent, then occupied by British troops.

Since it took many weeks for dispatches to cross the Atlantic Ocean, the United States commission was given wide powers. Fortunately, the commission was made up of men of exceptional ability who could use those powers wisely—John Quincy Adams, Albert Gallatin, Henry Clay, James A. Bayard, and Jonathan Russell. In contrast, the three-man British commission was undistinguished and had little power.

Britain regarded the negotiations at Ghent as a side show, so she sent her finest diplomats to the Congress of Vienna where peace negotiations were being conducted which the British considered of far greater import to Europe than the ones at Ghent. Peace talks in Ghent began on August 8, 1814.

American diplomats negotiated a satisfactory peace

One firm condition in the original instructions to the United States commissioners was that they could offer no concession on impressment. Secretary of State Monroe wrote that if Britain would not abolish impressment, "the United States will

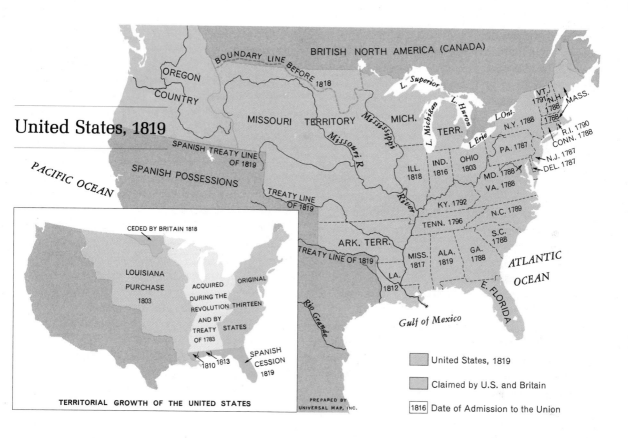

United States, 1819

BRITISH NORTH AMERICA (CANADA)

OREGON COUNTRY

PACIFIC OCEAN

SPANISH POSSESSIONS

SPANISH TREATY LINE OF 1819

MISSOURI TERRITORY

TREATY LINE OF 1819

TREATY LINE OF 1819

L. Superior

L. Huron

L. Michigan

MICH. TERR.

L. Erie

L. Ont.

VT. 1791

N.H. 1788

MASS.

R.I. 1790

CONN. 1788

N.Y. 1788

PA. 1787

N.J. 1787

DEL. 1787

ILL. 1818

IND. 1816

OHIO 1803

MD. 1788

VA. 1788

KY. 1792

N.C. 1789

TENN. 1796

ARK. TERR.

S.C. 1788

MISS. 1817

ALA. 1819

GA. 1788

LA. 1812

E. FLORIDA

Rio Grande

Gulf of Mexico

ATLANTIC OCEAN

Mississippi R.

Missouri R.

TERRITORIAL GROWTH OF THE UNITED STATES

CEDED BY BRITAIN 1818

LOUISIANA PURCHASE 1803

ACQUIRED DURING THE REVOLUTION AND BY TREATY OF 1783

ORIGINAL THIRTEEN STATES

1810 1813

SPANISH CESSION 1819

PREPARED BY UNIVERSAL MAP, INC.

United States, 1819

Claimed by U.S. and Britain

1816 Date of Admission to the Union

have appealed to arms in vain." With Britain victorious in Europe and with her navy free to concentrate on the war with the United States, this was an unrealistic demand. Britain officially refused to give up impressment, but the issue had lost its fire.

With the end of the war in Europe, the royal navy needed less manpower, so it stopped its impressments. As a result, President Madison modified the peacemakers' instructions by putting aside the issue of impressment. The United States representatives then sought a peace treaty that restored territory and relations with Britain to their prewar status.

The British made drastic demands. "Their terms," Bayard said, "were those of a Conqueror to a conquered People." Rejecting the British demands, the Americans threatened to break off negotiations. Finally, in an effort to break the deadlock, the British asked the United States commissioners to draw up terms for a treaty.

The British government accepted the United States treaty outline as the basis for a peace settlement. A month later, on Christmas Eve, 1814, the commissioners signed the Treaty of Ghent.

Basically the peace treaty provided for the restoration of all occupied territory to the status it had before hostilities. It also called for fair treatment to the Indians who fought in the war, and for the settlement of boundary conflicts between Upper and Lower Canada and the United States through commissions composed of Americans and Englishmen.

Militarily, the United States had not done well in the struggle; yet, its diplomats gained a satisfactory peace. Although they were men with considerable diplomatic skill, their success in these negotiations was largely due to the fact that the attention of the British government at that time was focused on problems in Europe. The British wished to be free to deal with European questions and not to be bogged down in a continuing military campaign in North America in search of complete victory.

Jackson's victory made him a national hero

It would have been very difficult for Britain to attain complete victory, as military developments in the Southwest proved. General Andrew Jackson, a politician from Tennessee and a skilled military leader, had campaigned against Britain's Indian allies. In the Battle of Horseshoe Bend in present-day Alabama, the most powerful group of Indians in the South, the Creek Confederacy, was defeated by Jackson in March 1814. That victory deprived Britain of a powerful ally, and the treaty which followed forced the Creeks to surrender large tracts of land in the Mississippi Territory, comprising more than half of the Creek lands. This rich land later became the heart of the cotton country.

Because of his victories against the Indians, Jackson was given command in May of all United States forces in the Southwest and the responsibility for meeting the British thrust against New Orleans. He believed the British might strike at Florida and seek to use Pensacola as a base; on his own authority, he invaded Florida and captured Pensacola. Then, he marched his troops to the region above New Orleans to meet the formidable British threat.

At the very time that the peacemakers were concluding their work at Ghent, the British were landing an army of veterans below New Orleans. On Christmas Day, Sir Edward Pakenham took command at New Orleans. He planned to assault New Orleans, capture it, and use it to gain favorable terms in the peace negotiations. Neither Pakenham nor anyone in the United States knew that a peace treaty had been signed the previous day.

Pakenham was slow in preparing his assault. This gave Jackson, who had originally misjudged the nature of the British thrust, time to throw up defenses. He placed his motley army—made up of about five thousand Tennessee and Kentucky militiamen, Louisiana Creoles, Negroes, and pirates—behind a dry canal situated between the Mississippi River and a cypress swamp. Then, for protection, Jackson's men built high, mud breastworks, reinforced with sugar barrels.

The Battle of New Orleans began at dawn on January 8, 1815. Pakenham foolishly launched a frontal attack, with about eight thousand brave, disciplined troops. Jackson's men held their fire until the redcoats were at close range. Then the United States rifles and cannons mercilessly slaughtered the invaders.

The British were forced to retreat, leaving behind 700 dead—including Pakenham himself—1400 wounded, and 500 to be captured by the Americans. The United States suffered only 8 dead and 13 wounded.

Since the peace treaty already had been signed, Jackson's victory at New Orleans had no effect on the outcome of the war, but it brought joy to Americans. News of the British defeat reached Washington in February 1815, about a week before the word of the peace treaty reached the people. Many Americans incorrectly assumed that the United States had humbled Britain. "In the fulness of our glory," one American wrote, "we grant peace to a worsted enemy." Even though the Battle of New Orleans was not a decisive factor in bringing about peace, it made a national hero of Andrew Jackson.

The war had important consequences

President Madison knew that the United States had not beaten Britain into submission, despite the wild rejoicing over the victory at New Orleans. On the day the Treaty of Ghent arrived, the President quickly sent it to the Senate, where it gained prompt, unanimous approval. The Senate's action reflected the deep desire of the people of the United States for peace. Although the Federalist press criticized the treaty, it was one of the most popular ever negotiated by Americans. Although the United States gained none of its original war objectives, the treaty marked the end of a needless war.

The War of 1812 did, however, have a number of consequences of importance to all Americans. The war ended the Indian menace, both on the Northwest and the Southwest frontier, and opened the way to expansion and settlement. Americans were now free to push into the West. "The continent lay before them," historian Henry Adams said, "like an uncovered ore-bed."

Grumbling and dissatisfaction were voiced in New England and elsewhere, but the war and the peace that followed aroused a spirit of patriotism. New England's influence in national affairs declined, and the South and West gave society a character that was more aggressively American than it ever had been. The people of the United States now shared another common national experience; they seemed to feel a new sense of unity. Albert Gallatin wrote:

[War] has renewed and reinstated the national feelings which the Revolution had given and which were daily lessened. The people have now more general objects of attachment with which their pride and political opinions are connected. They are more American; they feel and act more like a nation.

This nationalism also awakened interest in the growth of United States industry. The long period of restriction on commerce, beginning with the Nonimportation Act and Jefferson's embargo, and the war itself had diverted capital investment from shipbuilding and commercial ventures to the financing of factories. Industrial growth was stimulated to such an extent that the chief increase in national wealth at the end of the war came from expanding manufacturing.

The peace of Ghent and the year 1815 also marked a turning point in the relations of the United States with the other nations of the world. Up to that time, the new nation either had been involved in or had been affected by Europe's rivalries. Even the development of political parties in the United States had been influenced by such external factors. After 1815, Americans began to pay more attention to domestic than to foreign affairs. They soon entered a long period of relative isolation from the international politics of Europe.

REVIEWING THE SECTION

1. How did changing conditions in Europe enable the United States and Britain to negotiate a satisfactory peace?

2. Of what significance was Jackson's victory at New Orleans?

3. What were the consequences of the War of 1812 for the United States?

CHAPTER CONCLUSION

Jeffersonian democracy, as expressed in the spirit of the administrations of Thomas Jefferson and James Madison, stood for the principle that the people themselves, rather than their leaders in government, were the basic source of power. Jeffersonians believed that, under proper conditions, man could be trusted to govern himself. They maintained that under the Federalists the government had wielded too much power. Jefferson, therefore, urged simplicity in gov-

ernment. He wanted all Americans to understand how the government functioned so that they could participate in it. He sought to practice economy and wanted to keep taxation at a minimum so that government would not expand and become a burden to the people.

When faced with practical realities, Jefferson frequently reversed himself and put aside theory to meet a specific problem. He disliked Britain and admired France, yet he was willing to make an alliance with

Britain when he heard that France had regained Louisiana. Jefferson believed in strict construction of the Constitution, yet he purchased the territory of Louisiana under the principle of broad construction.

Jefferson was an agrarian nationalist who wanted to see the United States flag flying over all of the North American continent. He hoped that farmers of small land areas would settle the continent and make his ideal agrarian democracy grow. For this reason, he sponsored the Lewis and Clark expedition as well as the acquisition of Louisiana.

In dealing with the nations of Europe, Jefferson wanted no entangling alliances. When war broke out again in Europe and the belligerents violated United States rights, he tried to force them to respect those rights with a policy of peaceful coercion. With the support of Congress, he carried out this policy, to a large extent, through the Embargo Act, which effected a self-blockade. However, the embargo brought economic difficulties to the country and had to be abandoned.

Madison, who succeeded Jefferson as President in 1809, tried to follow a similar policy with basic modifications, but his policy also failed. His administration not only entangled itself in the rivalries of Europe but also led a divided nation into war. The causes of the War of 1812 are complex, but most historians agree that the basic causes for America's war declaration were maritime grievances against Britain, such as her infringements on neutral rights and her impressment of United States sailors.

The war was poorly managed. At first, it was poorly fought. It almost brought disaster to the United States. Although the Treaty of Ghent gave Americans none of their original war objectives, the people were pleased with it. The treaty ended the war and the only thing of importance which it gave to Britain or to the United States was peace.

The war had important consequences, however, such as the stimulation of industrial manufactures and the awakening of United States nationalism. "The people of the United States constitute one great nation," a Southerner wrote shortly after the peace, and "whether a man be born east, west, north, or south, provided he is born within the limits of the country, he is still an American."

Jeffersonian democracy had survived bitter internal divisions and a war. Under the Jeffersonians, the people of the United States had achieved a greater unity than they had previously known. They also experienced a ripened sense of nationhood that was needed to overcome the still powerful force of sectionalism.

FOCUSING ON SPECIFICS

1. What themes did Jefferson emphasize in his first inaugural address?

2. How did Jefferson's tax program reflect his philosophy of government?

3. Why did Jefferson wish to limit the size of the armed forces?

4. Why were many New England Federalists displeased with the Louisiana Purchase?

5. What important precedent was established by Aaron Burr's trial for treason?

6. What was the purpose of the British orders-in-council?

7. Why were Americans embittered over the *Chesapeake* affair?

8. Why did Jefferson's Embargo Act fail to attain its objective?

9. What was the purpose and effect of the Non-intercourse Act? What was the purpose of Macon's Bill No. 2?

10. Why did the views of the war hawks appeal to both the Northwest and the South?

11. Why was the Hartford Convention called? What did it accomplish?

12. Why did many Americans think it would be easy to conquer Canada?

13. What events in Europe led to Britain's decision to invade the United States?

14. Why was the Battle of Plattsburgh significant?

15. What were the final terms of the Treaty of Ghent?

REVIEWING MAIN THEMES

1. Discuss the basic principles upon which the Jeffersonians built their program.

2. What circumstances led to the purchase of Louisiana?

3. How did the Jefferson and Madison administrations attempt to defend American neutral rights during the war between Britain and France? Why were these attempts unsuccessful?

4. What grievances led the United States to declare war on Britain in 1812? Why was the nation divided over the war?

5. In what respects did the United States become more unified as a result of the war?

EVALUATING THE ISSUES

1. Can the revolution of 1800 correctly be called a revolution? Explain.

2. As secretary of the treasury, who do you think was more attuned to the problems of a growing nation: Alexander Hamilton or Albert Gallatin? Why?

3. Was Jefferson's decision to purchase Louisiana a violation of his own principles? If so, do you think his decision was justifiable? Why?

4. Historians have long noted the role which chance, circumstance, and timing play in history. Give examples from this chapter to show how these forces influenced the course of events.

EXAMINING THE TIMES

1. What circumstances accounted for the rise of the Federalist party? for its decline?

2. What domestic and international problems of the nation under the Articles of Confederation led some leaders to favor a stronger central government? What provisions did the new Constitution make for dealing with these problems?

3. How did Washington and Jefferson use the powers of their office to strengthen the growing nation?

4. How did each of the first four Presidents attempt to avoid all-out war with the British or the French? Why was war eventually declared?

5. What events from 1783 to 1815 tended, in the long run, to strengthen nationalism in the United States?

6. What, if any, developments between 1783 and 1815 tended to discourage nationalism?

The Plan for Washington

Although the building of new towns was resumed after the Revolutionary War, the most ambitious new project was the creation of a national capital. Planned by a group of unusual men, including George Washington and Thomas Jefferson, the new capital would be the greatest effort ever made by the federal government in planning an individual city.

Because of the potential commercial and land speculation opportunities, established communities in the North and the South became bitter rivals for the site of the new federal district. At one point, in desperation, the idea of two capitals was advanced. One man even suggested that the capital be built on a platform and moved between the two sites. A compromise was reached when Southern delegates in Congress supported Secretary of the Treasury Alexander Hamilton's measure for assuming state war debts and, in return, grateful New York delegates approved the choice of a Southern location for the capital.

The location finally chosen was a ten-mile square along the Potomac River where it divides the states of Maryland and Virginia. Washington had once surveyed this region and con-

Map of the City of Washington, by R. King, 1818

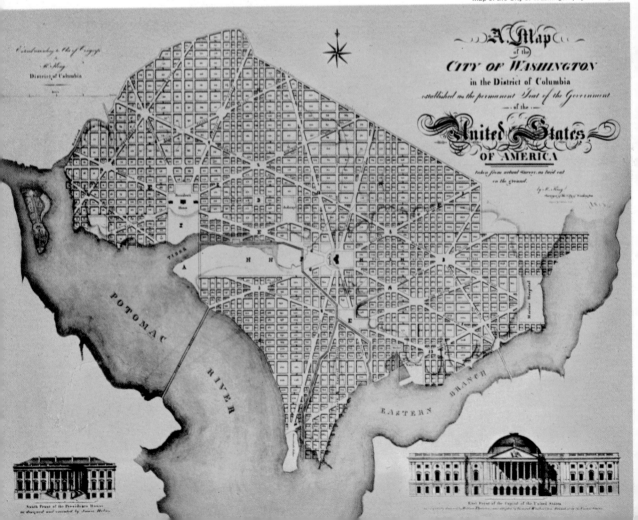

sidered the site ideal for the new national capital.

Major Pierre Charles L'Enfant, a French-born engineer who had served in the Revolution, was chosen to plan the capital city. While a student at the Royal Academy of France, he had been influenced by the men who had tried to create beautiful cities such as Paris and Versailles. They used monuments, public buildings, open spaces, and broad avenues to achieve their goal; L'Enfant planned to do the same.

L'Enfant's design was based on a gridiron superimposed on a radial plan. A hill, known as Jenkins Heights, was chosen as the site for the Capitol. A wide, gardened mall would connect it with the President's House. Broad diagonal avenues, connecting distant points, would intersect right-angled streets. The junctions of these avenues would create open squares for state shrines, a national church, and colleges. Convenient shopping centers were planned. A waterfall, cascading from the base of the Capitol, and five huge spouting fountains would add beauty. Monuments honoring Washington and the navy, and an obelisk, from which all distances on the con-

tinent were to be measured, would be erected.

The two most important buildings in L'Enfant's plan were the President's House and the Capitol. Competitions were held in 1792 for the design of these buildings. The winning design for the Capitol was submitted by an amateur architect, Dr. William Thornton. His plan for a stately building of two wings joined by a domed center won President Washington's praise for its "grandeur, simplicity, and convenience...." James Hoban, an Irish architect working in Charleston, S.C., submitted the winning design for the President's House. Each designer received a gold medal worth ten guineas ($500), a city lot, and the task of constructing his building.

L'Enfant's plan, shown in the map of the city of Washington, by R. King (1818), was ambitious. Washington, however, grew very slowly and L'Enfant's plan was only imperfectly expressed. For long periods, the plan was completely ignored. Finally, in the 1900's, L'Enfant's plan was revived; by 1965, as an aerial view of the city shows, L'Enfant's dream was close to realization.

Aerial view of Washington, D.C., 1965

City of Washington from Beyond the Navy Yard, by W. J. Bennett, 1833

President's House, Washington City, 1820-1821, by Baroness Hyde de Neuville

The Young Capital

Addressing the first joint session of Congress held in the completed Senate wing of the new Capitol, President John Adams prayed that the new "territory be the residence of virtue and happiness...." At the President's House, his wife Abigail saw little cause for happiness; her new home was without water, bathrooms, adequate light, or heat.

Property owners also had little reason for happiness. As lot prices went steadily downward, many regretted that they had given half of their land to the new district. Commercial enterprises did not develop, and government efforts to stimulate land sales failed.

Despite Congress' refusal, after 1801, to spend any money to improve Washington, the presence of the government helped the city expand. By 1812, the population had tripled. During the War of 1812, however, Admiral Sir George Cockburn, leading a force of British marines, captured Washington and put all public buildings to the torch. Only a rainstorm saved the city from complete destruction. Reconstruction began and slowly the scars of the great fire were removed. The President's House was painted white to cover the marks of the fire and it is possible that the term "White House" dates from this period.

When the Marquis de Lafayette visited Washington in 1824, he viewed a city totally unlike that of L'Enfant's dream. The Mall was a series of swamps, sheds, and shacks. Streets were little more than rutted paths and some of the areas of the city were known by such descriptive names as Foggy Bottom, Cabbage Alley, Cow Town, and Louse Alley. A water color of the President's House (by the Baroness Hyde de Neuville), however, proved that there was more to the city than that. By 1820-1821, when the picture was painted, government buildings already erected included the state department building (left front), the treasury building (left rear), the war department building (right front), and the navy department building (right rear).

A view of Washington from beyond the Navy Yard (1833) depicted a quiet, rural town. But the city continued to grow, not only in size, but in dignity. By 1850, the Capitol was an impressive building and broad avenues, like Pennsylvania Avenue, were lined with stately trees.

View of the Capitol at Washington, by W. H. Bartlett, 1850

The U.S. Capitol and the unfinished dome, c. 1861-1862

Washington continued to grow and change. But L'Enfant's plans were all but ignored. A bequest of $500,000 by the Englishman James Smithson for "an establishment for the increase and diffusion of knowledge among men" gave the city the opportunity to become the cultural center as well as the political center of the nation. Despite the classical style already established for important buildings, James Renfrew's "Norman castle" in red sandstone was accepted as the design for the Smithsonian Institution (1849).

Construction went on even during the Civil War. Since Washington was dangerously close to the battle front, a ring of defensive forts was built on the hills surrounding the city. Fort Stevens, one of those forts, is still a tourist attraction as are other temporary buildings erected during the war. President Lincoln, anxious to show that the Union still existed and was functioning effectively, ordered the completion of the new Capitol wings and the new dome (c. 1862).

After the Civil War, the city continued to expand and prosper. Many new buildings, such as the State, War, and Navy departments building, were erected to house government office workers. By 1892, Washington was a thriving city with outstanding landmarks such as the Washington Monument, the Capitol, and the White House.

The Expansion of the Capital

1800. In 1793, George Washington laid the cornerstone of the Capitol and construction began under the direction of Dr. William Thornton. The north wing was completed and Congress met there for the first time in 1800.

1814. Dr. Thornton was unable to get along with Congress and, in 1803, the English-born architect, Benjamin Latrobe, took over as Capitol architect. By 1807, the south wing was completed. The building was burned during the War of 1812 and Latrobe began the work of restoration.

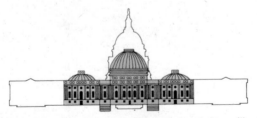

1830. Once again the Capitol architect was unable to get along with Congress, and, in 1817, the American-born architect, Charles Bulfinch, replaced Latrobe. The wings of the building were linked and a central dome was added. By 1830, Bulfinch had added steps, terraces, and the gate house.

1863. The Capitol, as we know it today, was completed when a nine-ton dome, topped by Thomas Crawford's statue of Freedom was added to balance the newly enlarged wings in 1863. (Between 1958 and 1961, the central section was extended eastward 32½ feet for better balance.)

State, War, and Navy Building, c. 1890

The City of Washington, Birds-Eye View from the Potomac—Looking North, by Currier & Ives, 1892

A Return to L'Enfant's Dream

The lack of any effective control over the rapid and haphazard growth of the capital was gradually destroying what remained of L'Enfant's dream. In 1900, therefore, a commission was appointed to study plans for the city. A comprehensive plan, which modified, enlarged, and reëstablished L'Enfant's plan, came from that commission.

In 1902, the firm of McKim, Mead, and White extensively remodeled the White House, removed the conservatories, and added the executive office wing and the East Gallery. In 1949, the White House was found to be structurally unsound and the entire inner structure was replaced. By 1965, the gardens had been changed and the "President's House" had become a building of great historic significance to Americans.

Progress toward fulfilling L'Enfant's dream, however, was slow. As late as 1920, the Mall was still without any order; the vista to the Capitol was filled with trees and temporary buildings from World War I. By 1965, the Mall had been cleared and L'Enfant's plan restored. Some temporary buildings from World War II, however, remain.

In the 1790's, an unusual group of men had planned a national capital for a small, newly independent nation. They had intended this uniquely planned city to express the power that new nation would one day acquire. They had planned and built a President's House which Thomas Jefferson once described as "big enough for two emperors, one Pope and the grand Lama. . . ." And, they had planned and built a capitol which Jefferson called "the first temple dedicated to the sovereignty of the people. . . ." For a time that nation lost sight of the dream of those men but by the middle of the twentieth century that dream had been restored and that capital served a nation of over 190 million people.

Aerial view of the White House, 1965

The Mall in the 1920's

The Mall looking from the Washington Monument to the Capitol, 1965

The ruling classes of Europe were glad to get rid of Napoleon, in 1815. They looked upon his career of aggression as a natural result of the French Revolution, and they viewed the French Revolution as an outbreak of mass insanity. They determined not only to prevent such disturbances in the future but also to change Europe back to what it had been in the past. In other words, they stood for *reaction*—that is, for a movement back toward previous social and political conditions.

Problems of a Growing Nation

The reactionary spirit of Europe at this time was seen in both the foreign and the domestic policies of the leading nations. In making a peace settlement at the Congress of Vienna, in 1815, the five great powers—Russia, Prussia, Austria, Britain, and France—put old ruling families back on the thrones of kingdoms that Napoleon had overturned. Then the powers joined together in an alliance, known as the Concert of Europe, to coöperate in preventing revolutions within nations and wars between nations. Britain soon withdrew from the alliance, but the other members continued to support it for about fifteen years. Meanwhile, all the powers, including Britain, passed laws to stamp out what the rulers considered radical and dangerous ideas. These laws limited or prohibited freedom of speech, of the press, and of political association.

While the governments were trying to maintain the *status quo* (the existing state of affairs), the development of the factory system was making great changes in economic and social conditions. This development (sometimes called, rather inaccurately, the Industrial Revolution) had begun in England in the early 1700's and had spread throughout Europe and to the United States by the early 1800's. New machines, powered by water or by steam, were being used more and more for the manufacture of various goods, particularly cloth. The machines were brought together and placed in factories, which were located where power was available, and workers were drawn from the countryside to tend the machines. A new class of factory workers thus grew up (in addition to the workers who continued to produce hand-made articles at home or in workshops), and a new class of factory owners, or industrial capitalists, grew up also.

Both the workers and the capitalists had grounds for discontent with the *status quo*. The factory laborers, many of them women and children, generally were overworked and underpaid, and they found life hard, dirty, and disagreeable in the growing mill towns. At the same time, the craftsmen who continued to make goods by hand objected to the factory system because it often produced the same goods more cheaply and thus forced the craftsmen to lower their own prices. Though the capitalists were better off, and many of them indeed wealthy, they also had cause for complaint. Their political influence was not equal to their wealth, nor was it equal to the political influence of the great landowners. Most of the mill owners as well as the shopkeepers could not even vote (as of 1815).

In the years immediately after 1815, comparatively few Europeans thought that much could be done to improve society or government. Then, by about 1830, the mood of the people began to change. More and more of them, workers, capitalists, and others, came to believe in social and political as well as economic progress. They began to feel that poverty and suffering could and should be lessened, if not entirely eliminated. They began to think that governments could and should be made more responsive to the will of the people, or even be made completely democratic.

The new faith in progress took various forms, among them humanitarianism, political liberalism, democratic radicalism, and socialism. *Humanitarianism* was simply a strong sympathy with the poor and unfortunate, together with an urgent desire to do something to help them. *Political liberalism* was the belief that governments should regulate life as little as possible, leaving individuals fairly free to pursue their own concerns. *Democratic radicalism* could be summed up in two principles: first, that the purpose of government should be "the greatest good to the greatest number"; and second, that "every man ought to count for one and none for more than one" when it came to influencing government. *Socialism,* in the most common of its several forms, was the idea that the workers themselves should own and operate the factories and other means of production, that each should contribute to production according to his abilities and should share in the output according to his needs, and that the workers should run the government as well as the economic system. Thus there were different kinds of reformers, and the disagreements among them made it hard for them to coöperate effectively.

unit III
1815-1850

In France and other European countries the reformers could make little headway by peaceful means, and so they turned to violence, but they were not much more successful with this. In 1830, the French workers rose up in the July Revolution (a small uprising in comparison with the great Revolution that began in 1789) and overthrew the king, who was soon replaced by another king. In 1848, a revolution in France led to the establishment of a new republic, which proved to be short-lived. That same year, revolutions were attempted also in Italy, Germany, and Austria, but none of these succeeded.

In Britain, meanwhile, the reformers did not undertake a revolution, though they resorted to rioting at times. They accomplished some political reform through essentially peaceful agitation. The radical democrats demanded that Parliament be made thoroughly democratic—with its members elected from districts of approximately equal population (instead of the grossly unequal districts that existed) and by the votes of all men (instead of a comparatively small number of landowning aristocrats). The Reform Bill of 1832 did not go nearly far enough to please the radical democrats, but it did make the districts more nearly equal, and it gave the vote to many of the wealthier businessmen and farmers, thus lessening the power of the landed aristocracy. The radical democrats continued to insist upon more thoroughgoing reform, and in 1848 they presented to Parliament a great "charter"—a petition with thousands of signatures—which demanded, in vain, that all men be allowed to vote.

Social as well as political reformers in Britain gained some of their objects through parliamentary legislation. A law of 1833 abolished slavery throughout the British colonies. By 1850, other laws had eliminated a number of inhumane practices in the British Isles themselves. For instance, the death penalty was no longer imposed for petty crimes, and owners of mills and mines were required to make at least a little provision for the safety of their employees.

In the United States, between 1815 and 1850, there were reform movements somewhat similar to those in Europe. European reformers, especially the British, provided ideas and examples for the Americans. Reform was largely an international cause. Thus, in 1843, the peace societies of the world held a conference in London, and of the 300 delegates, 13 came from the United States. There were some differences, however, between the European and the American problems of reform. In the United States, the government already was comparatively demo-

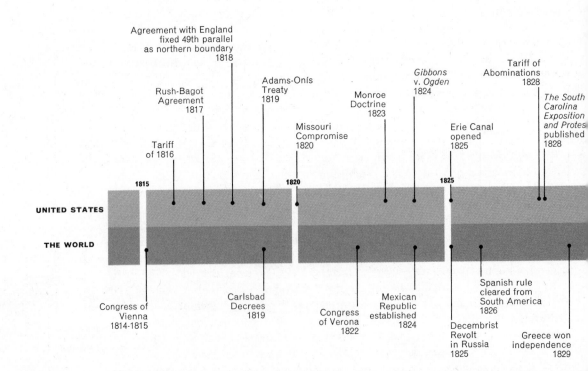

cratic, and political reformers in this country did not have to contend against an entrenched aristocracy. They were able to make considerable progress in extending democracy even further. Though poverty and suffering were less widespread in the United States, there existed here a social evil as bad or worse than any in Europe—slavery—and American social reformers, therefore, had at least as much to do as their European counterparts.

Reform in the United States became largely a sectional matter. Both the factory system and the reform spirit were far more characteristic of the North than of the South, while slavery persisted in the South alone. The economic and social differences resulted in political controversies between the sections. Sectional antagonism was intensified by the spread of antislavery feeling in the North and pro-slavery feeling in the South. It was also intensified by territorial expansion, as the North and the South contended for the control of newly acquired territories in the West.

In the United States, reform did not lead to revolution as it did in several European countries, but by 1850 it was threatening to eventuate in civil war.

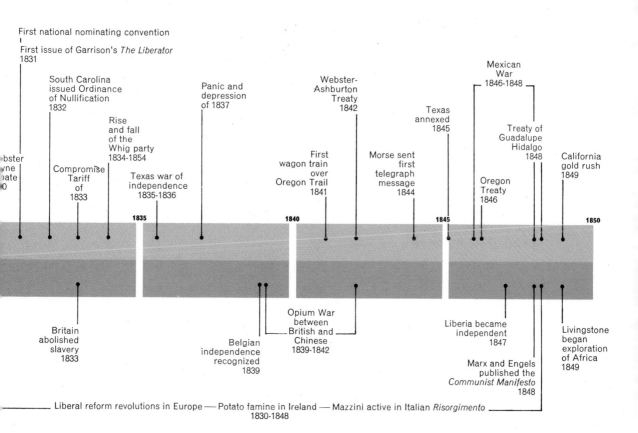

First national nominating convention

First issue of Garrison's *The Liberator*
1831

South Carolina
issued Ordinance
of Nullification
1832

Rise
and fall
of the
Whig party
1834-1854

Panic and
depression
of 1837

Webster-
Ashburton
Treaty
1842

Mexican
War
1846-1848

Texas
annexed
1845

Treaty of
Guadalupe
Hidalgo
1848

California
gold rush
1849

bster
yne
ate
0

Compromise
Tariff
of
1833

Texas war of
independence
1835-1836

First
wagon train
over
Oregon Trail
1841

Morse sent
first
telegraph
message
1844

Oregon
Treaty
1846

1835   1840   1845   1850

Britain
abolished
slavery
1833

Belgian
independence
recognized
1839

Opium War
between
British and
Chinese
1839-1842

Liberia became
independent
1847

Livingstone
began
exploration
of Africa
1849

Marx and Engels
published the
Communist Manifesto
1848

Liberal reform revolutions in Europe — Potato famine in Ireland — Mazzini active in Italian *Risorgimento*
1830-1848

Economic Development of the Nation and the Sections

Abraham Lincoln and Jefferson Davis were born less than a hundred miles apart, and Lincoln less than a year after Davis, in the state of Kentucky when it was still mostly a wilderness. The fathers of both boys were frontier farmers. Shortly before the War of 1812, the Davis family moved southwestward to Louisiana and then to Mississippi. They began to plant cotton and buy slaves. Jefferson Davis eventually became a wealthy slave owner and cotton planter. Shortly after the War of 1812, the Lincoln family moved northwestward to Indiana and then to Illinois. Lincoln's father continued to farm a small piece of land, and Lincoln himself became a successful lawyer.

The lives of Lincoln and Davis illustrate the way in which the nation was dividing into sections which were widely divergent in character. Lincoln grew up with one of the sections, the Northwest; Davis grew up with another, the Southwest.

From the beginning, the history of the United States has been largely a history of different sections and of the relations among them. A *section*

may be defined as a large area within which the people feel that they have important interests in common, interests differing from and at times conflicting with those of people in other parts of the nation. To draw the exact boundaries of a section, as it existed at any particular time, is rather difficult. The boundaries were usually indefinite, and they changed over the years.

During the period from 1815 to 1850, three main sections existed: the Northeast, the Northwest, and the South (which included both the Southeast and the Southwest). The sectional divisions resulted from differences in the economic development of the nation.

The industrial development of the United States started first and proceeded fastest in the Northeast. Most of the shipping and commerce already had been concentrated in that part of the nation, and now most of the manufacturing also came to be located there. Slavery disappeared, and a new class of factory owners and a new class of factory workers came into existence.

The rise of cotton mills both in the Northeast and in Britain created a tremendous demand for raw cotton. Soon, most of the cotton was coming from the South; it took the place of tobacco as the section's chief crop. Cotton-growing spread westward, eventually all the way to Texas. Slaves were useful where cotton was grown, so slavery expanded and became more firmly established than ever.

Before the spread of cotton and slavery, the Northwest and the Southwest had been quite similar in their way of life. Originally, the whole area between the Appalachian Mountains and the Mississippi River was settled by essentially the same kind of people, people like the Lincolns and the Davises. These early settlers were usually owners of small farms. They cleared the fields, built log cabins, and tilled the soil themselves.

With the westward movement of people, this part of the country grew much faster than the country as a whole. In 1790, when the first federal census was taken, only one tenth of the total population lived beyond the Appalachians. By 1830, more than one fourth lived there, and by 1850, almost one half.

While the area was filling up, it was also dividing. To the south of the Ohio River, many of the farmers turned to planting cotton and buying slaves. Others sold their clearings to the more prosperous planters who were moving in from the older states—planters who brought slaves with them to help build new plantations. To the north of the Ohio River, where the Northwest Ordinance (1787) forever prohibited slavery and where the soil and climate were unsuited to cotton cultivation, small farms continued to develop, and the owners of small farms continued to be the predominant group.

No section was completely self-sufficient. The Northeast needed foodstuffs and raw materials, especially cotton; the Northwest needed cotton goods and other manufactures; and the South needed both manufactures and foodstuffs. So it became necessary for the various sections to trade with one another and with other nations. Improvements in transportation and communication made it possible to carry on extensive trading. These improvements enabled the separate sections to develop; they also made it possible for the sections to remain together as parts of a single nation.

AMERICANS MADE TECHNOLOGICAL ADVANCES

As more and more people moved westward, the nation faced serious problems of transportation and communication. People talked constantly of the need for *internal improvements*—the clearing of rivers and harbors, the digging of canals, and the building of roads and eventually railroads.

The question was: Who should pay for and carry out these improvements? Private companies could undertake certain projects, but only those that would not cost too much and would pay a big enough profit. State governments could take responsibility for large and expensive projects, but only those that lay entirely within state borders. The national government had the greatest resources and widest authority, but many people doubted that it had the constitutional power to carry out large-scale improvement plans.

In spite of the opposition it faced, the national government did a great deal to improve transportation. Private companies were active in many ways. Some of the greatest undertakings were carried out by the states; for example, the government of New York was responsible for one of the most ambitious projects of all, the Erie Canal.

Steamboats made transportation faster and cheaper

Robert Fulton had been interested in boats from the time he was a boy in Pennsylvania. At the age of twenty-one (in 1786), he went to England to work as an engineer. There he met James Watt, the inventor of the steam engine. Fulton began to experiment with steam-powered vessels, first in England and then in France. After twenty years abroad, he returned to the United States.

In the summer of 1807, Fulton made a test run

with the *Clermont,* an American sailboat equipped with an English-built engine and a paddle wheel on each side. He went up the Hudson River from New York City to Albany and back, a distance of approximately three hundred miles, at an average speed of nearly five miles an hour. "The power of propelling boats by steam is now fully proved," Fulton boasted to a friend. Other inventors had tried out steamboats before, but no previous vessel had gone so far or so fast.

Soon companies were formed to operate steamboats on the Hudson and on other rivers. In 1811, the *New Orleans,* the first steam-powered vessel to operate west of the Appalachians, made a voyage from Louisville down the Ohio and the Mississippi to the city for which she was named. She then plied back and forth regularly between New Orleans and Natchez.

Eventually, a special kind of steamboat was developed for the Mississippi and its tributaries. These waters were shallow with suddenly changing currents, shifting sand or mud bars, and submerged tree trunks and roots. So the typical Mississippi boat had a flat bottom, a powerful, high-pressure engine, and large paddle wheels on each side of the boat or one paddle wheel which extended the full width of the boat at the stern.

The larger and faster a boat, the more profitable it would be, so both the size and the speed of boats were increased. By 1850, the average size was about five hundred tons, and the fastest of them could make 25 miles an hour in still water. The running time from New Orleans to St. Louis —a distance of 1300 miles—was cut to 3 or 4 days. The first steamboats to make the trip had taken more than 3 weeks; the still earlier flatboats, which were poled upstream, had taken almost 4 months. The emphasis on speed often led to races, and to get up more pressure, the rival captains would order the safety valves held down. As a result, many boats exploded or ran aground. Nevertheless, as a contemporary wrote, "wealth rolls up in the cities as a result of the speedy and cheapened transportation which the steamers have effected."

Turnpikes supplied links between river systems

Turnpikes were toll roads. They got their name from a common type of tollgate—a horizontal pole, or pike, which turned on a post at one end to open or close. Most of these roads were surfaced with crushed rock and laid out as straight and level as possible, crossing streams by means of massive stone bridges; they made traveling easier and faster. Other roads, which skirted around tree stumps and went right through fordable streams, were little more than two tracks, often deeply rutted and dusty when not muddy.

A private company built and operated the first turnpike (beginning in 1792)—from Philadelphia to Lancaster, sixty miles away. Other companies went into the business, and soon toll roads radiated from each of the eastern cities to surrounding towns. Private corporations could afford to construct roads only through populous areas, where traffic would be heavy. If improved highways were to be run long distances through thinly settled country, the national government or state governments would have to finance the construction, or at least a part of it.

Beginning in 1803 with the admission of Ohio to the Union, Congress provided that part of the money from the sale of public land within the western states might be used for building roads. With such money, the federal government constructed (1811-1818) a toll highway, the Cumberland Road. It extended across the Appalachians from Cumberland, Maryland, to Wheeling, in what is now West Virginia, thus connecting the Potomac River with the Ohio River. A few years later, a private corporation, with financial aid from the Pennsylvania government, extended the Philadelphia-Lancaster turnpike to Pittsburgh, thus connecting the Delaware and the Susquehanna with the Ohio. Still later (1825-1838), the federal government extended the Cumberland Road or National Road westward to Illinois. The Illinois and Missouri governments subsequently carried it on across the Mississippi River.

The National Road and other turnpikes were busy and profitable. Over them moved long lines of stagecoaches, freight wagons, and private carriages. Despite the tolls, overland freight rates were the lowest ever. Nevertheless, they remained much higher than steamboat rates, too high for the hauling of bulky commodities, such as grain, flour, or lumber. It was much easier to transport goods by water than by land, and so, to supplement the rivers, the country needed not only new highways but also new waterways.

Canals connected east and west

Before 1800, a sudden flurry of canal-building had spread over England. Some Americans hoped to follow the English example, though distances were greater and the terrain was rougher in the United States. By the early 1800's, a number of short canals, most of them built by private companies, were in use.

But the canal age did not really begin in this country until July 4, 1817, when Governor De Witt Clinton of New York presided over ceremonies at which the first shovelful of earth was dug for the Erie Canal, the greatest construction job that Americans had ever undertaken. The route, comparatively level, ran from the Hudson River up the Mohawk River and on to Lake Erie. Even so, eighty-three locks and many aqueduct bridges and cuts and fills were necessary to carry the canal through hills and across valleys. By October 1825, Clinton's "big ditch"—4 feet deep, 40 feet wide, approximately 350 miles long—was completed.

The Erie Canal proved an immediate success. Its prosperity encouraged the state of New York to build several branches and inspired the states of Ohio and Indiana to construct waterways from Lake Erie to the Ohio River. By the 1830's, canals were in operation from Cleveland to Portsmouth, and from Toledo to Cincinnati. By the 1840's, an Indiana canal, branching off from the Toledo-Cincinnati route, ran to Evansville. Freight and passengers now could go by water, with several boat changes, all the way from New York through the Great Lakes to Chicago, or down the Ohio and Mississippi rivers to New Orleans.

Through the Erie Canal, New York City had much better access to the trade of the interior than did its rival cities of the eastern seaboard. The cities of Baltimore and Washington hoped to compete by means of the Chesapeake and Ohio Canal. Along with the federal government, these cities contributed money to a private company which began construction in 1828 with the intention of tunneling through the mountains. The company never got beyond Cumberland with the ambitious undertaking.

Even at best, canals had serious disadvantages. Steamboats could not be used on canals, for the churning of propellers or paddle wheels would cause the banks to cave in. Canal boats, towed by horses or mules walking on a path along the side, were so slow that passengers could step off and stride ahead. Throughout the North the canals were forced to close during winter freezes.

The canal age had hardly begun when its end was foreshadowed by the appearance of a new means of transportation, one that was much faster, more dependable, and so adaptable that it could be used almost anywhere—the railroad.

Railroads revolutionized transportation

By 1800, railroads of a kind were already quite old. Wooden or iron tracks, along which men or animals pulled cars to haul coal from mines, had been used in England for some time. Inventors in both England and the United States were beginning to experiment with steam-powered vehicles. In 1826, a short rail line began to operate as a public carrier between two towns in England.

This news stirred the interest of businessmen in the United States, especially those in the seaboard cities that were seeking better access to the interior. By 1831, three railroad lines were in operation in this country. The Baltimore and Ohio ran from Baltimore west about 13 miles. The Mohawk

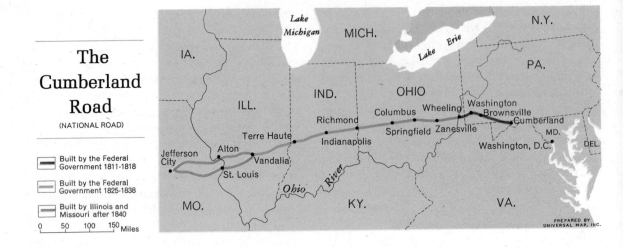

The Cumberland Road
(NATIONAL ROAD)

Built by the Federal Government 1811-1818

Built by the Federal Government 1825-1838

Built by Illinois and Missouri after 1840

0   50   100   150 Miles

PREPARED BY
UNIVERSAL MAP, INC.

and Hudson ran from Albany to Schenectady, New York, a distance of 16 miles. And the Charleston and Hamburg operated over a track in South Carolina which, when completed two years later, was the longest in the world—136 miles. By 1836, the total trackage of American railroads was more than 1000 miles; by 1850, it was more than 9000 miles, with some in almost every state. There remained so many gaps between lines, however, that there was as yet no national railroad network.

Meanwhile, railroad equipment was rapidly improved. A locomotive with two pairs of driving wheels, a cowcatcher, and a huge, flaring smokestack became standard in this country. The American type of passenger car, at first merely a stagecoach on rails, developed into a long, boxy carriage with two rows of seats and a center aisle. The average speed of passenger trains rose to about thirty miles an hour.

These trains were noisy, uncomfortable, and accidents were frequent because of poor roadbeds. A traveling Englishwoman wrote:

One great inconvenience of the American railroads is that, from wood being used for fuel, there is an incessant shower of large sparks, destructive to dress and comfort, unless all the windows are shut, which is impossible in warm weather.

Yet the future belonged to the railroads, not the canals. Though rail travel and transport were somewhat more expensive, they were much quicker. To illustrate, in the 1850's, the travel time from New York to Cleveland, a distance of about 700 miles, was 9 days by water and only 3 days by rail. To an even greater extent than the steamboat, the steam train had begun to revolutionize transportation.

Inventions speeded communication

Samuel F. B. Morse, born in Massachusetts, studied art as a young man in England. He opened a studio upon his return to the United States and soon achieved fame as a portrait painter. Once, on a voyage home from a visit to Europe, he learned in a shipboard dinner conversation that electric batteries could send a current over wire of almost any length. Immediately he thought of the possibility of sending messages long distances by wire. After several years' work on the idea at home, he applied for a patent on an electromagnetic telegraph (1837), but he needed money to develop and test his device. In 1843, Congress appropriated $30,000 to build an experimental telegraph line from Washington, D.C., to Baltimore, more than forty miles away. On May 24, 1844, Morse

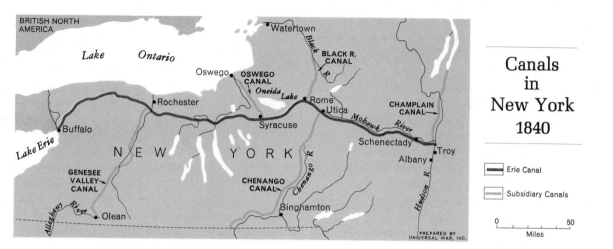

Canals in New York 1840

Erie Canal

Subsidiary Canals

0   50

Miles

PREPARED BY UNIVERSAL MAP, INC.

made a dramatic demonstration by sending from Washington a message which his partner received perfectly in Baltimore: "What hath God wrought!"

By 1846, telegraph wires had been extended to New York City and, within a few years, to Chicago and New Orleans. Soon the wires reached out to most of the larger towns.

The telegraph was of great importance to the railroads, and most of the telegraph poles were put up along the railroads' rights of way. With the new invention, it was much easier than before to control the movement of trains; as a result, the service became more regular and somewhat safer.

The telegraph was also very valuable to the newspaper business. Only weeks after Morse's great demonstration, a news report was sent over the original line to Washington—the report that James K. Polk had been nominated for the presidency at the Democratic convention in Baltimore. Previously, publishers had gathered most of their out-of-town news from out-of-town newspapers which came in the mail. The publishers now could get their information immediately and directly, by wire. A number of large publishing firms joined in 1846 to form the Associated Press, an organization through which the publishers coöperated in the gathering and the distribution of news by telegraph.

That same year a new machine, the Hoe rotary-cylinder press, began to be used in the printing of newspapers. Now, news could be not only collected but also printed much more quickly.

For the first time, people all over the country could, at a given moment, be reading and thinking about the same events, events which had occurred that same day or the day before.

REVIEWING THE SECTION

1. How did the development of steamboats contribute to the nation's system of transportation?

2. How did the building of turnpikes improve the transportation system of the nation?

3. For what purposes were canals built? What were the disadvantages of canals?

4. How was American transportation revolutionized by the railroads?

5. What major effects did the invention of the telegraph have on American life? What changes occurred in the newspaper industry during the 1840's?

THE NORTHEAST BECAME AN INDUSTRIAL CENTER

There were a number of reasons why manufacturing developed fastest in the Northeast. In this area, and especially in New England, many streams with their falls or rapids provided good water power. Even during colonial times, countless water mills had been set up to grind grain, saw lumber, or operate iron forges and triphammers. By the early 1800's, many men already were skilled in the use of machines. There was also a ready supply of unskilled workers, first, from the less prosperous farms of the section, and later, from the immigrant ships which put in at northeastern ports. And there was capital to invest in factories and mills.

The other sections—the Northwest and the South —had some of the same advantages, at least in certain places, and in these places a few industries grew up. But, on the whole, neither the Northwest nor the South possessed all of these advantages to the same degree. As a result, during the period 1815-1850, they did not become so industrialized as the Northeast.

Even in the Northeast during this period, the mills and factories never provided a livelihood for all the people, or even for most of them. The majority continued to live and work on farms. Nevertheless, industry, together with commerce, produced most of the great fortunes of the section and a rapidly increasing proportion of its total wealth. Within the Northeast the industrial interests came to predominate, giving it its special character as a section.

New methods of production were developed

The use of machinery, powered at first by water and then, in many cases, by steam, brought workers together in fairly large mills or factories. Previously, most workers had labored alone or with a few others at home or in small shops. Many continued to do so.

Shoemakers, for example, still made shoes by hand. In shoemaking centers like Lynn, Massachusetts, the work became highly specialized, each person concentrating on cutting out a particular piece or making a particular stitch. Generally, these people did their work at home. A merchant provided them with material, collected the processed pieces, and paid for the labor. He then arranged for finishing and selling the shoes. Such ready-made shoes, without graded sizes or differences between lefts and rights, were used primarily by sailors and by slaves. Most people still made their own shoes or had them made to order.

The arrangement by which a merchant put out materials and collected the work from homes or shops is known as the "putting-out" system. It was used also in the making of cloth. The merchant provided cotton or wool for spinners and yarn and thread for weavers. This system continued, in some instances, to the middle of the nineteenth century.

Most families, especially on the farms, still produced the larger proportion of the goods they needed for their own use—from soap to shoes, from candles to cloth. However, both the putting-out system and the household manufactures gave way to the rising factories and factory-made products.

The factory system developed earliest in cloth manufacturing. The first spinning mill in the United States was set up in 1791, at Pawtucket, Rhode Island, with the aid of Samuel Slater, an English mechanic who had brought over an extensive knowledge of English machinery. By cutting off imports of English textiles, Jefferson's embargo of 1807 and the War of 1812 stimulated the growth of spinning mills in the United States. By 1815, there were more than a hundred such mills, mostly in New England.

Up to this time, thread and yarn had been spun in the mills, and cloth had been woven on hand looms in homes or on crude power looms in separate mills. In 1813, the Boston merchant Francis C. Lowell perfected a new power loom. Organizing the Boston Manufacturing Company, Lowell set up at Waltham, Massachusetts, the first mill in the United States for weaving as well as spinning. This company and other companies soon established many more combination mills. By the 1830's, textile manufactures had gone ahead of overseas commerce as the biggest business in New England.

Meanwhile, a one-time Massachusetts farm boy,

Eli Whitney, originated a system of mass production through the manufacture of standardized and interchangeable parts. In 1798, the government needed thousands of muskets, and it needed them in a hurry, for it expected an all-out war with France. In those days, skilled gunsmiths fashioned weapons one at a time, each a little differently from any other. There were not enough gunsmiths in the entire world to produce quickly the number of muskets the government needed.

Whitney had a plan for making any number of identical guns and producing them with great speed. He designed a separate machine to turn out each part. "One of my primary objects," he wrote,

is to form the tools so the tools themselves shall fashion the work and to give every part its just proportion —which, when once accomplished, will give expedition, uniformity, and exactness to the whole.

He contracted with the government to deliver ten thousand finished muskets in two years. Though he was late in filling his contract, he proved the value of his new technique.

Afterward, other manufacturers began to use the same technique for producing such things as clocks, farm implements, and sewing machines.

Working conditions deteriorated

Most of the early factory workers came from farms. In many of the New England textile mills, whole families were hired, and children as young as four or five years of age helped their parents tend the spindles and looms. Though far from satisfactory, this arrangement was better than the one in some of the mills in old England where orphans were brought together, overworked, and exposed to all kinds of vice.

In Waltham and later in Lowell, Massachusetts, the mill owners were determined to avoid the evils of both the American and the British hiring practices. The companies brought in farm girls in their late teens and early twenties, put them up in boarding houses, paid them reasonably well for their time (about $2.50 a week), and carefully supervised their behavior. After a few years at the mills, girls would return home with their savings to marry and settle down.

Despite long hours—from sunup to sundown six days a week—which then were usual, the Lowell girls found time for many social and educational activities. They even wrote, edited, and published a literary magazine, the *Lowell Offering*. English visitors, such as Charles Dickens, familiar with the horrible conditions in some of the mines and factories in Britain, were very favorably impressed by the clean and cheerful appearance and the pure moral life of the Lowell factory workers.

Most of the industrial workers in the United States were far worse off. The men of the construction gangs performed backbreaking labor on turnpikes, railroads, and canals. These hard-working men, an increasing number of whom were Irish immigrants, got fifty cents to a dollar for a twelve-hour or fourteen-hour day. This was a higher wage than the Lowell girls received, but the men had families to support, the jobs were seasonal and uncertain, and few made enough money in a year to maintain their families adequately.

About 1840, Irish men and women, looking for better jobs, began to go into the textile mills. Soon, these newcomers replaced the native farm families and farm girls, even in Lowell itself. The Lowell companies abandoned their paternalistic attitude, and the boarding houses were converted into overcrowded tenements. As piece rates replaced daily wages, employees had to work harder in order to take home the same pay. Not only in Lowell but also in many other mill towns, working and living conditions were worse in the 1840's than they had been in the 1820's and 1830's.

Workers organized to bargain collectively

Some workers combined their efforts in order to bargain with their employers as a group, rather than as individuals. The worker combinations, which came to be known as unions, demanded shorter hours and higher pay. To back up their demands, the unions threatened to *strike*—that is, to quit work temporarily.

Neither factory workers nor construction gangs were the first to organize themselves and bargain collectively. The first were skilled artisans, such as *cordwainers* (shoemakers), who formed a union in Philadelphia in 1792, printers, carpenters, masons, hatters, and shipbuilders.

In each of the trades there were three levels of craftsmen. A man began as an *apprentice,* or learner. He worked his way up to become a *journeyman* (so-called because originally he journeyed about for a time as an itinerant worker). Finally, if he were able and lucky enough, he could become a *master* craftsman. The master was a businessman as well as a laborer; he owned his own shop, hired apprentices and journeymen, and dealt with customers as a seller of goods or services. Journeymen, as well as masters, often owned farms or city homes, and most of them took pride in their skill and their social position.

As more and more products were mass-produced, however, some of the craftsmen began to feel that they were falling behind in the struggle for income and prestige. The highly skilled cordwainers, for example, feared that they would get less and less money for the shoes they made (each man doing the whole job himself) if people could buy shoes that were made more cheaply by specialized workers under the putting-out system. Printers objected to the introduction of new, labor-saving presses.

From colonial times, the craftsmen had been organized in guilds. These regulated wages, working conditions, methods of production, and the price and quality of the products. Ordinarily, the guilds would not serve very well as organizations for collective bargaining between the worker and the employer, since they included and indeed were dominated by the master craftsmen, who themselves were employers. So, in many cases, the journeymen formed their own unions.

At first, the journeymen of a particular craft in a particular city acted alone. Thus, in 1825, six hundred journeymen carpenters in Boston struck for a ten-hour day. The strike failed, largely because the building contractors refused to deal with master carpenters who accepted the journeymen's demands.

Later, the unions of various crafts coöperated in city-wide federations. In 1835, the Philadelphia General Trades' Union, still seeking a ten-hour day, called a general strike of all the "workies" in the city. Among those who responded were cordwainers, weavers, dock workers, bricklayers, plasterers, masons, and carpenters. Although the strike leader claimed that the city's "blood-sucking aristocracy" was "terror-stricken," this strike also failed.

As transportation improved and both goods and people moved about more freely, conditions of labor in one city depended on conditions in other cities. It would be hard to raise wages or shorten hours in one place without doing the same in others. Hence, labor leaders tried to set up intercity federations of unions. In 1834, the leaders from six cities founded the National Trades Union; and in 1836, the printers and the cordwainers set up their own national craft unions.

The early unions achieved very few successes, though they helped to persuade President Martin Van Buren to proclaim, in 1840, a ten-hour day for employees of the federal government. The unions were handicapped because, whenever an employer took a labor dispute to court, the judge, falling back on English common-law precedents, usually held that unions were illegal conspiracies to interfere with trade. The unions were not strong enough to survive a period of widespread unemployment, and very few of them lasted through the general business depression that began in 1837.

Northeastern farmers adjusted to new conditions

Even before the depression began, farmers in many parts of the Northeast already were suffering from hard times. In many areas the soil was poor in comparison with the fresh lands of the Northwest. On the poorer soils the farmers could not raise crops cheaply enough to compete with those which came in larger and larger amounts from northwestern producers to northeastern consumers, by way of the improved means of transportation. More and more, the production of wheat, corn, cattle, sheep, and hogs was shifting westward to Ohio, Indiana, and Illinois.

To maintain a satisfactory living standard, the disadvantaged farmers of the Northeast could choose between two courses of action. They could leave their unproductive acres and either move westward and take up new lands or go to the mill towns and get factory jobs, or they could remain where they were and turn to producing special crops with which the staples of the Northwest could not compete.

Thousands and thousands of northeastern farmers, especially in New England, abandoned their farms. In Vermont and New Hampshire, many rural areas actually lost population. Whole townships were practically deserted, and the houses and barns were left to fall in ruins.

In the Northeast as a whole, however, the great majority of the farmers stayed on their farms. They took advantage of their nearness to the markets of the growing cities and concentrated on the production of perishable or bulky items which could not easily be shipped in from a distance— milk, butter, cheese, potatoes, apples and other fruits, and hay.

REVIEWING THE SECTION

1. What new manufacturing methods were developed in the early 1800's?

2. What new social problems resulted from the development of the factory system?

3. Why did craftsmen attempt to form unions? What handicaps prevented them from achieving their goals?

4. How did most farmers of the Northeast adjust to the heavy competition from the farms of the Northwest?

THE NORTHWEST WAS A SECTION OF SMALL FARMS

During the period from 1815 to 1850, the Northwest was predominantly, though not exclusively, a land of farms and farmers.

A number of cities developed as centers of industry and commerce, especially on the Great Lakes and on the Ohio and Mississippi rivers. In the 1830's, Cincinnati, on the Ohio, was the largest city, with a population of 40,000. St. Louis, an older river port, on the Mississippi, was the second largest, with 10,000. Chicago, on Lake Michigan, was growing fast, and by 1850, it had surpassed Cincinnati. These and other cities were important centers for the storage, shipment, and processing of the products from the surrounding forests and farms. The leading industries were lumbering, woodworking, flour-milling, meat-packing, whiskey-distilling, and the manufacturing of leather goods and farm implements.

Nevertheless, in the section as a whole, agriculture remained more important than industry. The great majority of the people lived and worked on farms. These farms generally were rather small, averaging about two hundred acres. Though at first many were subsistence farms, producing a variety of things for the use of the owner and his family, most of them developed into commercial operations, specializing in certain crops and producing a surplus of these for sale. The chief products were corn, wheat, pork, mutton, and beef.

Pioneers went west to take up farming

Before the War of 1812, settlers in the Northwest had to brave the Indian danger. Then United States victories, especially in the Battle of the Thames (1813), in which the great Shawnee leader Tecumseh was killed, broke the power of the Indians. After the war, the federal government forced new treaties upon the tribes, compelling them to give up more and more land. There were to be no further Indian troubles in the Northwest, east of the Mississippi River, except for the Black

Hawk War (1832) in Illinois and Wisconsin, and this war was only a minor conflict.

Once the danger had been eliminated, pioneers rushed as never before to take up land. They went west by two main routes. One route led from New York and New England by way of the Erie Canal and the Great Lakes. The other led from Pennsylvania and states farther south by way of the Ohio River and its tributaries. The southern part of Ohio, Indiana, and Illinois—the part that was occupied earliest—was settled primarily by people from Pennsylvania, Maryland, Virginia, North Carolina, Kentucky, and Tennessee. The northern part of Ohio, Indiana, and Illinois, together with Michigan and Wisconsin, was settled originally by New Englanders, New Yorkers, and immigrants who had landed at Boston or New York.

Most of the Northwest was heavily timbered, but in Illinois a large proportion of the land was already treeless. This was the grand prairie, covered with wild grass which in some places grew as tall as a man. The early pioneers had never seen anything quite like this verdant growth, and they avoided it. They found that much of the land was wet and marshy, and where it was dry, the tough sod was hard to break with a wooden plow. Before long, however, determined settlers began to drain and plow the prairie land and to grow rich crops on the fertile black loam.

Government land policy encouraged settlement

When the first settlers arrived in the Northwest, practically all the land belonged to the federal government. In accordance with the Ordinance of 1785 and subsequent land laws, the government, in stages, surveyed the "public domain," opened land offices, and offered lands for sale to the highest bidders.

At the time the great migration began, the minimum price was $2 per acre and the minimum purchase was 160 acres. This meant that a man would have to pay at least $320 for a farm even if there were no competitive bidding. But he could buy on credit, paying one fourth down and the rest in three annual installments. He could get his farm and begin to live on it if he had only $80 in cash.

This seemed easy enough, but after taking over the land, many settlers found that they could not complete the payments. During the depression that began in 1819, many feared the loss of their land if they were held to their debts. So Congress changed the land law in 1820 and passed a relief act in 1821. The new land law eliminated installment purchases but reduced the minimum price to $1.25 and the minimum purchase to 80 acres. Now a buyer would need at least $100 in cash, but with that sum he could make an outright purchase of a small farm. The relief act permitted previous buyers to cut their acreage from 160 to 80 acres, to pay off the balance at the new, low price, and to have more time to make their payments.

In years of prosperity many more people went west and many more acres of the public land were sold than in times of depression. During the boom of the 1830's, annual sales rose to several times the highest previous level. Prices soared, the average rising far above the legal minimum. Only about one fourth of the land sold went directly to actual settlers. Most of it went to speculators who bought large tracts with the intention of dividing them into farms or town lots which they then sold at a profit. Suddenly, in 1837, another depression struck. Sales and prices dropped, and thousands of overly optimistic buyers were left land-poor.

Not all the pioneers had waited for the government to survey lands, open land offices, and hold auctions in the area in which they settled. Some, the "squatters," had gone ahead and occupied lands in the hope that they could later buy them at the minimum price. When bidding finally began, these people often lost out to speculators or other buyers. Many of the squatters appealed to their congressmen, however, and Congress responded by passing special "preëmption" laws that gave specific individuals the right to buy, without any bidding, the lands on which they had settled. Fi-

Changing means of transportation. Cheaper and better means of transportation were needed as people moved inland and developed the western lands. The flatboats, used on canals and rivers, were slow and difficult to handle. With the coming of steamboats, which were faster, easier to maneuver, and capable of carrying greater loads, transportation costs were reduced and river trade expanded. However, steamboats could not be used on canals. Overland transportation was needed to tie the sections of the country together in areas not reached by rivers. The steam train, with its greater speed and accessibility, supplied this need. Transportation by rail, though more costly than transportation by water, contributed more to the growth and commercial expansion of the United States.

Flatboats on the Ohio River

Giant Steamboats, by Hippolyte V. V. Sebron, 1853

View of Pennsylvania Rail Road Bridge, by Herline & Hensel, c. 1850

nally, in 1841, Congress passed a general preëmption act which gave all squatters the same right.

Farmers began using machines

While the use of machinery was swelling the output of factories, it was also beginning to increase the production of farms.

Americans had more incentive to invent and use labor-saving farm implements than did the British or other Europeans. Abroad, land was scarce and labor plentiful, so people tried to economize on land, cultivate carefully and intensively, and produce as much as possible *per acre*. In this country labor was scarce and land plentiful, so people tried to economize on labor, cultivate rapidly even though carelessly, and produce as much as possible *per man*.

The new implements were most widely used in the Northwest. Here a large number of farmers were prosperous enough to afford the equipment, the land generally was flat enough for easy operation of the machines, and the grain fields were broad enough to make their use very economical.

Plowing became easier and faster as wooden plows were replaced (after 1819) by plows made of cast iron. The new ones were made with several parts, which could be replaced individually if broken. By 1830, iron plows were so much in demand that they were being mass-produced. Soon steel plows became available, plows which cut the soil even more cleanly and deeply and were even more durable than the ones made of cast iron. These were especially useful in breaking up the tough prairie sod of Illinois.

Meanwhile, planting was facilitated by the introduction of horse-drawn harrows and grain drills. Harvesting was improved even more by horse-drawn mowing machines and hay rakes; finally reapers were developed which proved to be among the most helpful of all the newly developed farm equipment. Cyrus H. McCormick demonstrated his reaper in Virginia as early as 1831. With the McCormick machine, a crew of six or seven men could harvest as much in a day as fifteen men using the old-fashioned cradle scythe.

REVIEWING THE SECTION

1. How did the federal government promote settlement in the Northwest?
2. What developments in farm equipment helped increase agricultural productivity?

THE SOUTH BEGAN TO SPECIALIZE IN COTTON

In colonial times, the leading Southern crops had been tobacco and rice. After independence, both crops continued to be produced—rice, along the South Carolina and Georgia coast, and tobacco, not only in Maryland, Virginia, and North Carolina, but also in new areas, especially in Kentucky. New crops appeared—hemp in Kentucky, sugar cane in Louisiana. Most important of all, cotton became the leading crop of the majority of the Southern states, though practically no cotton had been grown there before the Revolutionary War.

Cotton-growing gave new life to slavery, which Virginia leaders such as George Washington and Thomas Jefferson once had expected to die out because tobacco-growing had seemed less and less profitable. As cotton cultivation spread throughout the South, slavery spread with it.

Not that the South was ever made up of cotton plantations alone. There were also the tobacco, sugar, and rice plantations, all of them worked by slaves. Countless farms in the region produced still other crops and were tilled not by slaves but by the farmers and their families. Indeed, the great majority of Southerners never owned any slaves. More corn, mules, and oxen were produced on the farms of the South than on the farms of the Northeast and the Northwest together.

Besides its plantations and farms, the South had some industries, and it had a few sizable cities—New Orleans, Charleston, and Baltimore. At one time, shortly after the War of 1812, many Southerners expected cotton mills to spring up in the South, since the section had plenty of water power as well as raw material. And, before 1850, several mills did appear in Georgia and the Carolinas, though only a few compared to the number in New England.

In the South, however, cotton-raising seemed much more profitable than cotton-manufacturing. It made much more money than any other Southern crop. Cotton and slavery, more than anything else, caused the South to become increasingly different from the Northeast and the Northwest during the period from 1815 to 1850.

The "gin" increased cotton production

In the United States, cotton was first grown along the coast and on the offshore islands of Georgia and South Carolina. This was a very fine quality cotton. The long fibers could be easily separated from the smooth black seeds but it required a constantly warm and moist atmosphere and could not be grown successfully at a distance of more than a few miles from the coast.

Besides the "sea-island" cotton, there was another variety, the "upland" cotton. Though this had shorter fibers, it would thrive in almost any place where the growing season was long enough and the autumn rainfall not too heavy. But fuzzy, green seeds stuck to the fibers, making them hard to clean.

By 1793, prospective cotton planters were looking for a "gin" (short for "engine") to clean the upland cotton. The legislature of Georgia even offered a prize for a satisfactory one. Eli Whitney, then a recent Yale graduate, was serving as a tutor on a Georgia plantation. He soon devised a practical machine (1793). It consisted of a bin with slats on one side, a roller with wire teeth, and a revolving brush. As the roller turned, the teeth pulled the fibers between the slats, leaving the seeds behind. The brush, revolving in the opposite direction, swept the fibers off the teeth. Using water power, a gin could clean a thousand pounds of green-seed cotton a day. A slave, doing the work by hand, could clean only a pound or two a day.

Once the cleaning problem had been solved, cotton cultivation spread rapidly over Georgia and the Carolinas, though not over Virginia, Maryland, or Kentucky, where the growing season was too short. Soon it began to spread westward from Georgia. By 1830, the entire annual crop amounted to less than one million bales; during the 1850's, it was to exceed four million.

Soil exhaustion caused Southerners to move west

Both tobacco and cotton were hard on the soil. In the older states along the Atlantic seaboard, repeated croppings exhausted the natural supply of essential soil minerals. Torrential rains washed away much of the original topsoil, exposed the red clay underneath, and cut deep gullies in the hillsides. Many once-prosperous farms and plantations were ruined.

The more enterprising farmers and planters of the seaboard states reacted in one of two ways to the deterioration of the countryside. Either they stayed on and attempted to restore the soil, or they moved west and began all over again.

Southern agricultural reform began in Maryland and Virginia. One of the earliest reformers was John Taylor of Caroline (a Virginia county). In his book *Arator* (1813), Taylor advocated deep plowing, the use of compost as a fertilizer, and the rotation of crops. The greatest advocate of scientific farming was another Virginian, Edmund Ruffin. In his *Essay on Calcareous Manures* (1832) he recommended the application of *marl,* a calcium deposit left by the decomposition of ancient seashells, to neutralize the acidity in exhausted soils.

Ruffin and other scientific farmers published farm journals, formed agricultural societies, and sponsored exhibits and fairs. Thus, they gave wide circulation to new ideas. As a result, some farmers and planters checked erosion, improved the quality of their cotton and livestock, diversified their crops, and adopted more efficient methods of using slave labor. The wasteful ways were continued by others who could not afford or could not appreciate scientific methods. Still other farmers abandoned their worn-out lands.

Migrating Southerners looked first to Alabama and then to territory farther west. *"The Alabama Fever* rages here with great violence," a North Carolina planter wrote in 1817, "and has carried off vast numbers of our citizens. I am apprehensive, if it continues as it has done, it will almost depopulate the country." The westward movement did almost depopulate some parts of the Carolinas, just as it did some parts of New Hampshire and Vermont. By 1850, there were about one fourth as many North Carolinians living in the newer states of the Southwest as in North Carolina itself. The older states gained population slowly, while the newer ones grew with amazing speed.

As a rule, the earliest pioneers in the Southwest, like the ones in the Northwest, owned small farms and were nonslaveholders. Some of them prospered, bought slaves and additional lands, and became large plantation owners themselves. Others sold their original clearings, moved farther west, and pioneered again. From the already settled states also came planters migrating with slaves and money. They either bought up the partially improved lands or bid for large tracts at the government land offices.

By 1850, the Southwest was producing nearly three fourths of the total cotton crop. The cotton planters were located primarily in the "black belt" of central Alabama and Mississippi, a great treeless stretch of land where rotted limestone had left a fertile black soil, and in the bottom lands of the Tennessee, the Alabama, the Mississippi, and other river valleys. When, in the 1840's, levees were built to control floods in the states of Mississippi and Louisiana, the wide, flat delta region of the Mississippi River became an extremely rich cotton-growing area. In the Southwest as a whole, however, there still remained a majority of white men who possessed no slaves, worked their own small farms, and raised crops other than cotton. But their farms generally occupied the hilly places with relatively poor soil.

REVIEWING THE SECTION

1. Why was the invention of the cotton gin of crucial importance in the spread of cotton cultivation?

2. How did farmers in the states of the south Atlantic seaboard deal with the problem of worn-out soil?

TRADE TIED THE SECTIONS TOGETHER

During the period from 1815 to 1850, the rapid economic changes made people throughout the country increasingly dependent on one another, even though the population was more widely distributed than ever before. Manufacturers depended on farmers and planters to buy manufactured goods. Farmers and planters depended on the people in manufacturing towns, both at home and abroad, to buy agricultural products. As transportation improved, domestic and foreign trade flowed faster and faster and related more and more closely the cities to the countryside, the sections to one another, and the United States to Britain and the rest of the world.

Not only specialization but also the increasing complexity of business made people more dependent on one another. As the factory system developed, workers had to look to factory owners for jobs, because the workers had fewer opportunities to make a living on their own. Factory owners had to look to bankers and investors for funds with which to carry on and expand operations. If farmers and planters wished to increase production, they had to look to lenders for money with which to buy land, equipment, and supplies. Thus, many people were interconnected by loans and investments. If one person failed to pay his debts on time, others would be unable to pay theirs, and business failures would multiply. Although the new and complicated methods of production increased the output of all kinds of goods, these methods also made economic depressions much more frequent and much more widespread than they formerly had been.

BUSINESS ACTIVITY   1800-1850

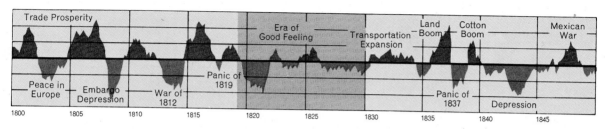

The long-range pattern of business activity in the United States shows that business cycles have shared certain characteristics and have recurred with some regularity, although no cycles have been identical. Many different economic conditions caused the panics preceding sharp declines in business activity. Some depressions were only short, mild recessions. Others were long and severe. The first major depression involving a banking crisis occurred in 1819, following a panic touched off by a decline in foreign demand for American foodstuffs. This depression lasted until 1822, when business began a slow recovery, marked by minor fluctuations. Throughout the years, some recovery periods reached new levels of sustained business activity; others were only short-lived and were followed quickly by new periods of depressed business activity.

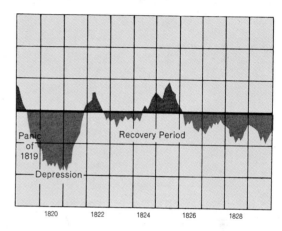

New York became the nation's import-export center

At one time, foreign trade had been divided among a number of seaports, large and small, scattered along the Atlantic coast from Savannah and Charleston northward; these ports were especially numerous in New England. After the War of 1812, however, most of the smaller ports languished, and the larger ones grew bigger and busier than ever. The leading Atlantic ports were Boston, Philadelphia, Baltimore, and above all New York, which, after 1810, rapidly increased its lead as the largest city in the United States. New York possessed a fine natural harbor, and the Erie Canal gave it unrivaled access to the hinterland.

The first line of *packets,* fast sailing ships, between the United States and Britain began operating from New York in 1819. The packets carried passengers, mail, and light freight on a regular schedule, making the transatlantic voyage in three weeks when winds were favorable.

The first steam-powered vessel to cross the ocean (1819) was the *Savannah.* It left from Savannah, Georgia, rather than New York. The *Savannah* took nearly a month to make the crossing, and part of the time she used sails to supplement her paddle wheels. The British steamship *Sirius* was the first to cross (1838) without using her sails (most steamships carried auxiliary sails until the 1880's). The British took the lead in the development of steamships, though a Swedish-American inventor, John Ericsson, contributed to the development of the screw propeller. By 1850, the crossing-time for the best British and American steamers had been reduced to about ten days.

The great bulk of imports from abroad were landed at New York and, from there, distributed throughout the nation. The imports consisted mainly of high-grade cloth, iron and steel products, china and earthenware, wines and liquors, exotic fruits, sugar and molasses, coffee, cocoa, and tea. The larger proportion of exports also went out through New York, but in the export trade New Orleans ran a close second; occasionally New Orleans took first place. This was to be expected, since cotton, tobacco, and other Southern products made up two thirds of all American exports. The remaining third consisted largely of grain, flour, and meat.

The foreign trade of the United States involved most of the nations of the world. Still, as in colonial times, Britain remained much the biggest supplier of foreign goods and much the best customer for American products.

Home markets grew despite inadequate currency

The domestic trade of the United States increased far more rapidly than the foreign trade. A great portion of the domestic trade was really a part of the foreign trade—it arose from the gathering of products to be exported and from the distribution of goods that had been imported. With the improvements in transportation, farmers, planters, and manufacturers could reach a wider home market than ever before. Indeed, by 1850, the United States had become one great market, one great buying and selling area, for most commodities—though, by present-day standards, these still moved slowly and inefficiently. Trade was especially handicapped by the lack of a sound, uniform, and abundant money supply.

In the cities and larger towns, stores began to specialize in groceries, dry goods, hardware, or other lines. In the villages and smaller towns, there were general stores full of miscellaneous merchandise, like the one in which Abraham Lincoln once clerked in New Salem, Illinois. Wandering through the countryside were peddlers. Some traveled on foot and carried a pack containing pins, needles, combs, jewelry, clocks, and other lightweight items of some value. Other peddlers drove wagons.

In dealing with peddlers and country storekeepers, the customers often paid in kind rather than in cash—exchanging their own produce, such as fresh eggs, for their purchases, such as tea or coffee. This custom of bartering persisted for a long time because of the scarcity of money.

Though a mint had been founded (in Philadelphia) as early as 1792, gold and silver coins of the United States were rarely seen for many years thereafter. Until the great discoveries in the Far West, little gold or silver was mined in this country. Most of the cash that Americans used consisted of foreign coins, but there were never enough of these coins to meet the needs of trade.

To supplement the coins, banknotes were circulated as paper money. These amounted to nothing more than promises to pay cash. They had no government backing, and they were not legal tender (that is, they did not have to be accepted in payment of debts). They were issued by banks which sprang up in great numbers after the War of 1812. Often these banks issued more in notes than their cash on hand would safely allow them to do. If too many holders of the notes suddenly presented them for payment, such banks had to close, and their notes became worthless. So varied and bewildering were the state banknotes that it was hard for an uninformed person to know their real value.

For twenty years (1816-1836) there was also a national bank, the second Bank of the United States, which had branches in the principal cities. The second Bank of the United States, like the first one (1791-1811), was chartered by the federal government, held a monopoly of the government's banking business, and served the general public. Its own banknotes were dependable, well known, and accepted everywhere. From 1819 on, it made a practice of accumulating state banknotes and presenting them to the issuing banks for payment. This compelled the state banks to be more careful than they otherwise might have been. Even during the lifetime of the national bank, however, the nation needed, as a medium of exchange, more money and better money than was available.

Corporations were organized to raise capital

The nation also needed money, or capital, for productive purposes—for building and maintaining highways, canals, and railroads and for establishing and operating farms, plantations, and businesses of all kinds. Much of the money for transportation improvements came from the federal and state governments. It was raised mainly by tax collections and the sale of bonds. Much of the money for the first factories came from merchants who already had accumulated profits in shipping and commerce. A large portion of the money for buying land and developing farms and plantations came from the farmers and planters themselves and from individual savings and from bank loans in the form of banknotes.

To make it easier to raise capital, the business *corporation*—a group of persons authorized by law to carry on a business as a single entity—was brought into wider and wider use. At first, it was necessary for the organizers of a company to get a special act from a state legislature in order to incorporate. Eventually, with Connecticut setting the example in 1837, the states passed general incorporation laws, which made it possible for a company to obtain a charter of incorporation by merely conforming to the legal requirements. The corporation had great advantages over individual firms or partnerships: it could raise money by selling shares of stock, and its life did not depend on one or two individuals. It could also raise money by selling bonds. The stockholders were the owners of the company; the bondholders were its creditors, that is, people who had made loans to it, the bonds being the evidence of the debt.

The earliest corporations in the United States were set up for banking, insurance, and the construction and operation of toll bridges and turnpikes. Later, many companies were incorporated for railroad and manufacturing enterprises.

As corporations multiplied, regular markets developed for the purchase and sale of stocks and bonds. By far the largest of the market places was in New York, though there were others in Boston, Philadelphia, and Baltimore.

European and especially British investors furnished much of the capital for the early economic growth of the United States. By 1850, foreigners held nearly half of the federal and state bonds, and they owned a considerable though much smaller part of the corporation bonds and stocks.

Even though governments, banks, and individuals provided large amounts of money, the problem of financing new enterprises remained difficult. In a developing nation, such as the United States of that period, land and other natural resources were plentiful, but capital as well as labor was relatively scarce.

The modern "business cycle" had its beginnings

In most places throughout history, the people have been more prosperous at certain periods than at others. In the American colonies, there were occasional times of economic distress. Before the nineteenth century, hard times were generally due to wars, plagues, bad harvests, or other disasters which caused production or transportation to break down. In certain areas, there would not be enough of the necessities of life to go around. The shortages were usually confined to one region at a time, and they came and went rather irregularly.

During the nineteenth century, however, the periods of depression were essentially different from the earlier ones. The new depressions were periods of overproduction rather than underproduction, of surpluses rather than shortages—though people nevertheless suffered from poverty and hunger, since they could not afford to buy as much as they needed. These depressions spread rapidly not only from one part of the nation to another, but from Europe to the United States, and from the United States to Europe. They soon became general rather than local, and they arrived with almost rhythmic regularity.

The nineteenth-century "business cycle" had a typical pattern, with four phases: panic, depres-

BRITISH NORTH AMERICA
(CANADA)

Bangor
Bath
Portland
Boston
Schenectady
Buffalo Albany
New Haven
New York
Detroit
Toledo
Cleveland
Philadelphia
Sandusky
Columbus Cumberland
Baltimore
Washington, D.C.
Chicago
Springfield
Indianapolis
Cincinnati
Richmond
Norfolk
Louisville
Lexington
Raleigh
Chattanooga
Wilmington
Memphis
Columbia
Charleston
Atlanta
Savannah
Vicksburg
Montgomery
New Orleans

PREPARED BY
UNIVERSAL MAP, INC.

▭ Railroads in use, Dec. 1850

Railroads in Operation, 1850

In 1850, trackage in the United States totaled more than 9000 miles. At that time most of the railroads were concentrated in the Northeast. Although there were some lines operating in other sections, it was many years before the sections of the nation were linked together by railroads.

sion, recovery, and prosperity. The panic started with people rushing to the banks in an effort to convert their banknotes into cash. Many banks closed down. Prices began to fall. With more goods on hand than they could sell at profitable prices, many factories cut back their production or went out of business entirely. Many workers lost their jobs. With the prices of their crops falling, many farmers and planters found themselves unable to pay their debts, and mortgages were foreclosed. Soon the country was in the depths of a depression. After three or four years, recovery began, and eventually the country enjoyed prosperity once more. During the nineteenth century, a panic leading to a depression occurred about every twenty years—the first in 1819 and the second in 1837.

This business cycle from prosperity to depression and back again resulted from the economic developments of the time. Though these developments increased productivity, they also caused instability. The growth of specialization and the widening of the market meant that more and more people were producing not merely for their own use but also for sale to others at a distance. It was hard to predict how much could be profitably sold, and since productivity was increasing, the tendency was to produce too much for the actual demand. The coming of the factory system meant that a longer time elapsed between the start of production and the final selling of the finished product. This made it still more difficult to adjust productive capacity to market demand.

REVIEWING THE SECTION

1. How did improvements in transportation affect domestic trade between 1815 and 1850? What were the monetary problems which hindered trade? What steps were taken to resolve these problems?

2. Why were new ways of raising capital needed? What methods were found?

3. How did depressions in the nineteenth century differ from earlier ones? What conditions brought on these business fluctuations?

CHAPTER **7** CONCLUSION

During the period from 1815 to 1850, transportation and communication were improved by the use of steamboats on the navigable rivers; the construction of turnpikes, canals, and railroad lines; and the introduction of the magnetic telegraph. These improvements made it possible for different parts of the nation to specialize more and more and thus develop into increasingly distinctive sections. The Northeast concentrated primarily on manufacturing, the Northwest on commercial farming, and the South on cotton-planting. Both the improvements in transportation and the specialization in production enabled the nation, as a whole, to become one vast trading area, within which widely scattered people were interdependent, both as producers and as consumers.

Thus the economic changes made for both unity and diversity. On the one hand, they caused people to become more dependent on one another for their livelihood and their prosperity. On the other hand, the changes caused people to feel that they had interests differing from and even conflicting with the interests of other people. More important, the inhabitants of one section often felt that the inhabitants of another were profiting at their expense.

Differences of opinion about economic policy underlay most of the leading political issues of the period. Should the federal government encourage American manufactures by imposing a protective tariff, that is, by placing high duties on competing manufactures imported from abroad? Should the government spend large amounts for internal improvements all over the country? Should the government continue the national bank, with its great power over the state banks and its monopoly of the government's banking business? Should the government sell the public lands cheaply or give them away, in order to stimulate agricultural production in the Northwest?

These were the main questions that the political parties debated year after year. To some extent they were sectional questions. On the whole, the Northeast favored tariff protection, the Northwest demanded internal improvements, and the South opposed both. Yet none of the sections was a solid unit in economic interests or political views. In each of the three sections, there were the same two major parties, so political lines cut across sectional lines.

As time passed sectional feelings were intensified. By 1850, there were indications that they might become much stronger than partisan loyalties, and in the South, even stronger than national patriotism.

FOCUSING ON SPECIFICS

1. How did the federal government aid in the building of turnpikes?

2. Why was the canal era of short duration?

3. Why did industry develop most rapidly in the Northeast?

4. What advantages did the corporation have over individual firms and partnerships?

5. How did the growth of specialization and the widening of markets contribute to the ups and downs of the business cycle?

REVIEWING MAIN THEMES

1. What developments made the sections increasingly dependent upon one another?

2. What social problems arose in the Northeast as a result of economic development during the period from 1815 to 1850?

3. What factors contributed to the growth of the Northwest into a section of small farms?

4. What changes took place in Southern agriculture between 1815 and 1850?

5. Explain how improvements in transportation and communication during the period from 1815 to 1850 both contributed to national unity and increased the specialization of each section.

EVALUATING THE ISSUES

1. Was the invention of the cotton gin essential to the continuation of slavery in the South? Explain.

2. How do you explain the fact that the spread of cotton cultivation in the South was not accompanied by a corresponding development of a Southern textile industry?

3. Explain the paradox that overproduction often causes many people to suffer from poverty and hunger.

The Testing of National Unity

The day was July 4, 1826, exactly half a century after the signing of the Declaration of Independence. On that day Thomas Jefferson, author of the Declaration, died at his home on a hilltop near Charlottesville, Virginia. On the same day John Adams, the Declaration's "ablest advocate and defender," as Jefferson had called him, died at his home near Boston.

Once Jefferson and Adams had been bitter rivals, but in old age they were good friends, and they kept in close touch by mail. It seemed to many Americans that the deaths of Jefferson and Adams on the same day and on such an historic anniversary was something more than a mere coincidence. It seemed almost like a sign from God, telling the people to remember their patriotic past, to rise above their sectional differences, and to strengthen their sense of national unity.

This sense of national unity was based not only on economic developments—not only on transportation improvements, increased specialization, and growing trade. It was based also on memories and

sentiments, the tradition of an historic past, the hope for a great national future. Patriotism was kept alive by familiar symbols: the flag, stories of the exploits of military heroes, and rousing songs like "Hail, Columbia!" written during the undeclared war with France (1798-1800), and "The Star-Spangled Banner," written during the War of 1812. The people were reminded of their Revolutionary heritage especially as they celebrated with parades, picnics, and patriotic speeches on the Fourth of July.

The spirit of national independence and national unity affected many features of American life. It affected, for example, both literature and law. Literary men tried to create works that would be distinctively American, not mere imitations of English or other European models, and some of them were remarkably successful. Justices of the Supreme Court usually interpreted the Constitution in such a way as to increase the powers of the national government and lessen the powers of the state governments.

A similar spirit also affected foreign policy. The Monroe Doctrine, as first announced in 1823, warned the nations of Europe to leave the Americas to the Americans. The great majority of the people of the United States were enthusiastic about the doctrine, which eventually became an additional symbol of American patriotism.

In politics, the national spirit had to contend with sectional and partisan feelings. Political quarrels occasionally threatened to break up the nation. In 1819-1820, congressmen argued over the admission of Missouri as a slave state, and Southerners began to feel that many Northerners were hostile to the South. In 1832-1833, another bitter dispute arose, both in and out of Congress, when a South Carolina convention declared that the federal tariff acts were "null, void, and no law" within that state.

Nevertheless, throughout the period from 1815 to 1850, the unifying forces of national feeling prevailed over the disruptive tendencies of sectionalism. A compromise settled the Missouri question, and another led South Carolina to withdraw its nullification attempt. Thus national unity survived even the worst trials to which it was put. As late as the 1840's, the great majority of the people, no matter where they lived or to what party they belonged, took pride in thinking of themselves as Americans.

AMERICANS SOUGHT CULTURAL INDEPENDENCE

After the United States had won its political independence in the Revolutionary War, many writers and teachers thought the nation should try to achieve its cultural independence as well. They said Americans ought to produce their own art and literature. "America must be as independent in *literature* as she is in *politics,* as famous for *arts* as for *arms.*" Thus wrote a young war veteran and Yale graduate, Noah Webster (1785).

The War of 1812 had brought commercial independence. At least Americans generally thought so, for after this war they ceased to be troubled by British interference with their shipping on the high seas. They still looked to England and other European countries, however, for their standards of literary and artistic excellence and for most of the books they read. Leaders of American thought continued to call upon the people to develop a culture of their own. "We have listened too long to the courtly muses of Europe," the famous author and philosopher Ralph Waldo Emerson told the Phi Beta Kappa society at Harvard College in 1837. "We will walk on our own feet; we will work with our own hands; we will speak our own minds."

The United States was slow to achieve the literary and artistic originality which men like Webster and Emerson desired. Nevertheless, during the period from 1815 to 1850, considerable progress was made toward the development of a distinctively American literature.

Americans were considered culturally backward

As late as 1830, about seventy of every hundred books sold in the United States were published in England. During the next decade, the American book industry grew very fast, and by 1840 the proportions were reversed—about seventy of every hundred books sold in the United States were published in this country. Nevertheless, most of the books continued to be written by British authors. American readers eagerly bought copies of the latest novels by Charles Dickens and Sir Walter Scott. These and other British novelists were as popular in the United States as in Britain.

A number of British visitors to this country returned home and wrote books which upheld the view that this was a land with little culture. These travel accounts pictured life in the United States as crude and dirty. The American people were described as speaking a corrupted form of English, with a nasal twang. They were accused of bolting their food with a "gobble, gulp," chewing tobacco and spitting the juice everywhere, gambling, dueling, beating slaves, and gouging out one another's eyes in free-for-all fights.

British commentators generally believed that Americans were crude and uncultured because of the effects of democracy. These critics were sure there could be no respect or encouragement for artistic creativity in a country where all the people were equal, or thought they were.

A young French visitor, however, took a different view. After touring most of the states in 1831-1832, Alexis de Tocqueville wrote two volumes on *Democracy in America* (1835 and 1840). He, too, believed that Americans lagged behind Englishmen and other Europeans in science, literature, and art, but he did not think that democracy was to blame. Rather, he thought that Americans, because of their history and circumstances, were preoccupied with practical affairs and, therefore, had little time for cultural and scientific pursuits. He explained:

Their strictly Puritanical origin—their exclusively commercial habits—even the country which they inhabit, which seems to divert their minds from the pursuit of science, literature and the arts—the proximity of Europe, which allows them to neglect these pursuits without lapsing into barbarism—a thousand special causes, of which I have only been able to point out the most important—have singularly concurred to fix the mind of the American upon purely practical objects.

American writers began using native themes

At the very time when some people were saying there was no such thing as an American literature, a number of writers in the United States already were beginning to take up native themes and treat them in an original way. Several of these men were hailed, even abroad, as great literary artists. Indeed, this period was later to be considered as a "golden age" of American literature.

The first American to be recognized abroad was the New Yorker, Washington Irving. Irving found material for stories in the Dutch folklore of the Hudson Valley. He made use of this folklore in such stories as "Rip Van Winkle" and "The Legend of Sleepy Hollow," the most widely read of his many writings. Another New Yorker, James Fenimore Cooper, found inspiration for his "Leatherstocking Tales" in his boyhood on the New York frontier. Cooper turned out more than thirty novels in the thirty years between 1820 and 1850, most of them relating the adventures of Indians and pioneers.

Herman Melville, also a New Yorker, based some of his best novels on his experiences as a sailor. His *Moby Dick* (1851) was an adventure story, telling of Captain Ahab's pursuit of the great white whale which had bitten off his leg. It was also a philosophical allegory, full of symbols many readers found difficult to understand. The novel was not very popular in Melville's lifetime, but many years afterward it was praised both abroad and at home as one of the greatest novels in the English language.

Edgar Allan Poe, who spent the last years of his life in New York, invented the detective story, developed his own brand of horror tale, and originated a theory of poetry based on music and mathematics. He put his theory into practice in such poems as "Ulalume," "Annabel Lee," and "The Raven," which made him famous when it was published in a newspaper.

Walt Whitman proclaimed himself the poet of American democracy. The son of a Long Island carpenter, Whitman wrote his first poems while wandering through the countryside, working at odd jobs. He could not persuade any publisher to take the poems, so he paid a printer to put them into a small book, *Leaves of Grass* (1855). These poems, full of enthusiasm for the United States and its people, were rather wordy, and they had no regular meter or rhyme. They struck many people as barbarous. Nevertheless, Whitman wrote more and more of his unusual poems, bigger and bigger editions of *Leaves of Grass* came out, and eventually it was translated into many languages. By the time of his death (1892), Whitman was widely acclaimed as a unique and authentic voice of the American spirit.

PRESIDENTIAL ELECTIONS: 1816-1828

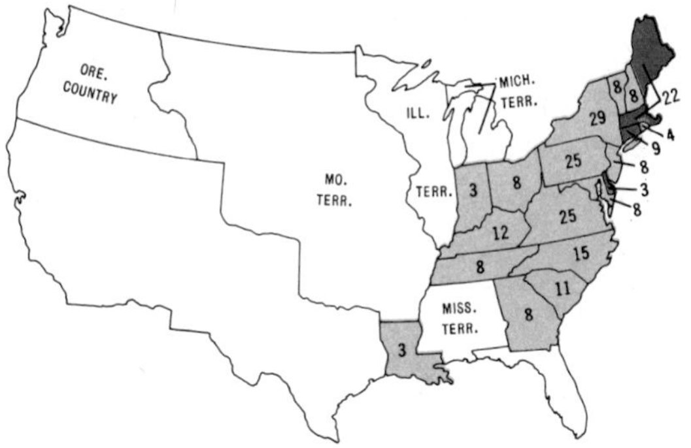

CANDIDATES: 1816

ELECTORAL VOTE BY STATE

REPUBLICAN
James Monroe 183

FEDERALIST
Rufus King 34

NOT VOTED 4
_____
221

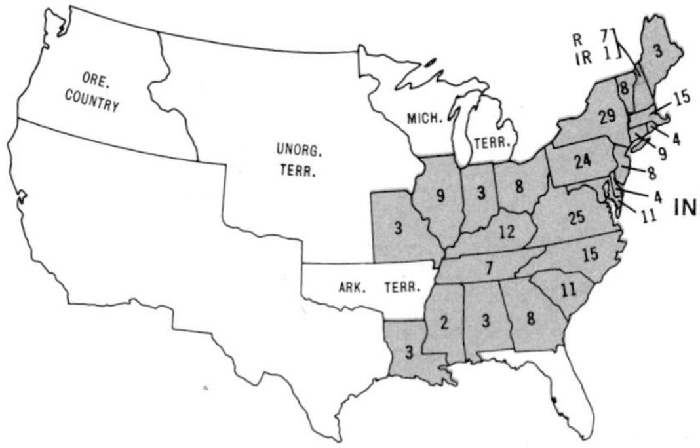

NO POPULAR VOTE
PRIOR TO 1824

CANDIDATES: 1820

ELECTORAL VOTE BY STATE

REPUBLICAN
James Monroe 231

INDEPENDENT-REPUBLICAN
John Q. Adams 1

NOT VOTED 3
_____
235

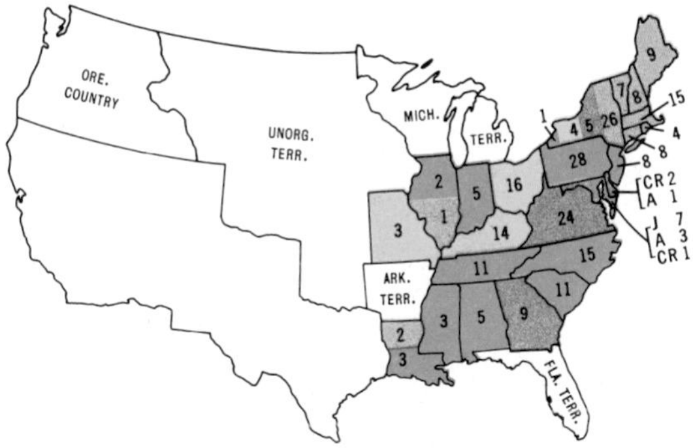

NO POPULAR VOTE
PRIOR TO 1824

CANDIDATES: 1824

ELECTORAL VOTE BY STATE   POPULAR VOTE AND PERCENTAGE

NO PARTY DESIGNATIONS

John Q. Adams*	84	108,740
Andrew Jackson	99	153,544
Henry Clay	37	47,136
William H. Crawford	41	46,618
	261	356,038

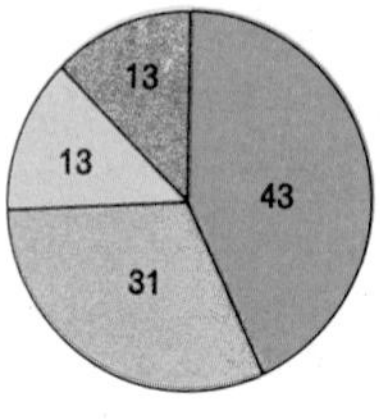

*No candidate having a majority in the electoral college,
Adams was elected by the House of Representatives.

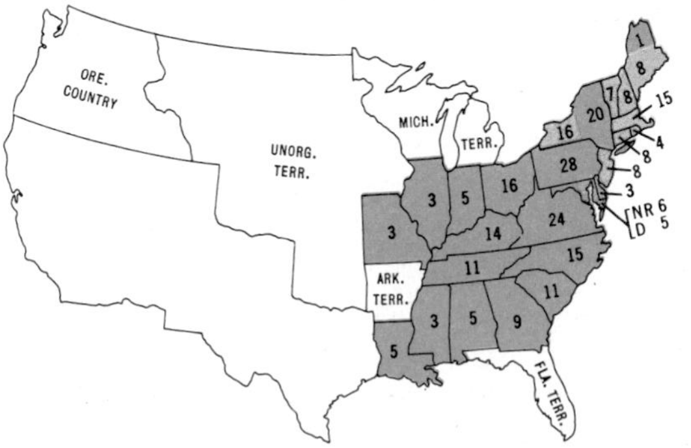

CANDIDATES: 1828

ELECTORAL VOTE BY STATE   POPULAR VOTE AND PERCENTAGE

DEMOCRATIC
Andrew Jackson 178   647,286

NATIONAL REPUBLICAN
John Q. Adams 83   508,064
_____   _____
261   1,155,350

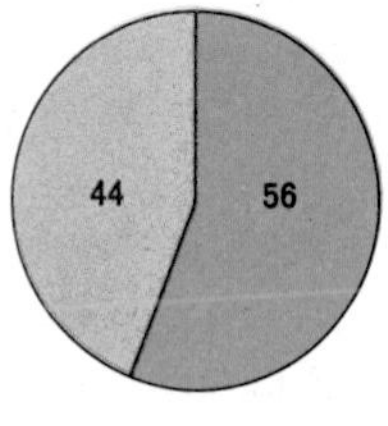

There was a "flowering" of New England

At first, most of the outstanding writers were New Yorkers, and New York, already the largest city in the country, became the literary center as well. In the 1840's, however, there was a "flowering" of literature in New England. One New England village, Concord, Massachusetts, almost outshone New York. Three of the greatest authors of the period lived in Concord, and many others visited there.

The leader of the Concord group was Ralph Waldo Emerson. After resigning as a Unitarian minister in 1832, Emerson developed his own philosophy of "transcendentalism." He believed that each human soul was part of a great "oversoul" which transcended everything else. Some people thought his mystical ideas were rather hard to understand, but many thousands could appreciate the practical part of his teachings. He taught that life was essentially good but could be made better if people would learn to be self-reliant and to recognize the great possibilities they were born with. Though he borrowed ideas from a variety of thinkers, ancient and modern, he put his own stamp upon them. His philosophy was distinctively American in stressing optimism and individualism.

Henry David Thoreau, a friend of Emerson, built a hut in the woods on Emerson's land and lived there for two years. In his book *Walden* (1854), Thoreau explained:

I went to the woods because I wished to live deliberately, to front only the essential facts of life, and see if I could not learn what it had to teach, and not, when I came to die, discover that I had not lived.

During the Mexican War (1846-1848), Thoreau refused to pay taxes because of his opposition to the war. He spent one night in jail, and then his friends paid his taxes for him. To justify his stand, Thoreau wrote *Resistance to Civil Government* (1849). This essay on "passive resistance" later influenced a number of revolutionary thinkers. One of the best known of these was Mohandas K. Gandhi, who led a campaign for passive resistance to British authority in India after World War I.

Another friend and neighbor of Emerson, Nathaniel Hawthorne, found themes for many of his stories in the Puritan past of New England. In *The Scarlet Letter* (1850) he examined the Puritan psychology of sin and evil. This book still is regarded as one of the finest of American novels.

REVIEWING THE SECTION

1. Why did Europeans consider Americans to be lacking in culture? How did Alexis de Tocqueville account for this lack of refinement?

2. Which New York writers contributed to America's "golden age" of literature? What native themes did they use in their works?

3. Which writers contributed to the "flowering" of literature in New England? What ideas did they express in their works?

THE SUPREME COURT EMPHASIZED NATIONAL POWERS

John Marshall, chief justice of the Supreme Court from 1801 to 1835, still is considered as the greatest of all the chief justices. Born in Virginia, Marshall served as a soldier in the Revolutionary War. He was with George Washington's army at Valley Forge during the terrible winter of 1777-1778, when the soldiers, partly because of the weakness of the government, were suffering from the want of adequate supplies. That experience impressed the young Marshall with the need for a strong and efficient national government. After leaving the army, Marshall studied law at the College of William and Mary, and later he became one of the ablest lawyers of his time.

During his thirty-five years on the Court, Marshall delivered hundreds of opinions. In all of them he took a broad view of the Constitution. Like Alexander Hamilton, he found authority for the federal government to do many things which the Constitution did not, in so many words, authorize the federal government to do. In general, the effect of his decisions was to limit the powers of the separate states and enlarge the powers of the federal government.

The Court overruled Congress

The Constitution did not, in so many words, give the Supreme Court the power of *judicial review*, that is, the power to review laws and decide whether or not they were constitutional. The Judiciary Act of 1789 provided that the Court might review laws of the state legislatures, though nothing was said about those of Congress. The Court proceeded, nevertheless, to pass upon national as well as state laws. No one paid much attention when the Court upheld the constitutionality of congressional acts, as it did on a few occasions between 1789 and 1803. The nation took notice, however, when the Court first declared a part of an act of Congress unconstitutional, as it did in the case of *Marbury* v. *Madison* (1803).

The facts of the case were these: Shortly before the end of his presidential term, John Adams signed a paper officially appointing a man named William Marbury as a justice of the peace in the District of Columbia. When Jefferson succeeded Adams as President, this document had not yet been delivered to Marbury, so he could not take office. Marbury asked Secretary of State James Madison to give him the commission, but Madison refused. Then Marbury turned to the Supreme Court and requested a special kind of court order (a writ of mandamus) directing Madison to deliver the appointment paper to him. The Judiciary Act of 1789 had authorized the Court to issue orders of this kind.

Giving the Court's opinion, Marshall said that Marbury was entitled to his commission and that Madison really ought to give it to him. Marshall went on to say, however, that the Court could not compel Madison to do so, for it could not issue the kind of order that Marbury had requested. True, Congress had provided for this in the Judi-

ciary Act of 1789, but, in doing so, Congress had gone beyond the Constitution. The Constitution specified the kinds of cases over which the Court should have jurisdiction *(Article III, sec. 2),* and this was not one of them. Hence the clause of the Judiciary Act of 1789 regarding writs of mandamus was unconstitutional.

By thus rejecting a specific power which Congress had conferred, Marshall seemed to be reducing the authority of the Supreme Court. At the same time, however, he was asserting a general power which was far more important—the general power of overruling Congress.

Not for more than half a century—not until the Dred Scott decision of 1857—was the Supreme Court again to declare unconstitutional any part of an act of Congress. Meanwhile the Court upheld a number of acts of Congress, and it disallowed a number of acts of state legislatures.

The Court declared state laws unconstitutional

The Constitution imposes a variety of restrictions upon the states. It forbids them, among other things, to pass any law "impairing the obligation of contracts," *(Art. I, sec. 10, para. 1).* The Supreme Court had to decide just what these words meant and to what kinds of state laws they applied. The Court did so in the cases of *Fletcher* v. *Peck* (1810) and *Dartmouth College* v. *Woodward* (1819).

The case of *Fletcher* v. *Peck* grew out of certain land grants made by the legislature of Georgia. A later legislature, in 1796, repealed the law that authorized the grants. Some of the grantees, who thus had their land taken away from them, appealed the case to the Supreme Court. Their lawyers claimed that the grant of lands was essentially a contract between the state of Georgia and the grantees; the state, therefore, had violated the Constitution by impairing the obligation of the contract. The attorneys for the state of Georgia argued that some of the legislators had been bribed to pass the law granting the lands, and that the later legislature, therefore, had a perfect right to undo what the previous one had done.

In his decision, Marshall held that a land grant was indeed a contract and therefore, even though there had been corruption, it was unconstitutional for Georgia to repeal the law making the grant. This was the first time the Supreme Court disallowed a state law on the grounds that it was inconsistent with the federal Constitution, though in previous cases the Court had disallowed state laws on the grounds that they were inconsistent with federal laws or treaties.

The Dartmouth College case arose from a quarrel between the president and the trustees of the college. The trustees dismissed the president, and he then obtained from the legislature of New Hampshire a new charter which converted Dartmouth into a state university, with himself as its president. The original charter of Dartmouth had been granted by King George III of Great Britain, before the Revolution. The college trustees, through their attorney, Daniel Webster, maintained that this charter represented a contract which the state had no right to break.

When the case came before the Supreme Court, Webster reminded Marshall and the associate justices that they had already decided, in the case of *Fletcher* v. *Peck* that "a *grant* is a contract." The Dartmouth charter, Webster proceeded to argue, "is embraced within the very terms of that decision," since "a grant of corporate powers and privileges is as much a *contract* as a grant of land." The Court decided in favor of the college.

This decision meant that private colleges and other nonprofit corporations would be safe from the arbitrary interference of state governments. It meant, also, that business corporations would be safe. In this respect, the decision was favorable to the growth of business.

The Court backed the nation against the states

Time and again one state or another asserted powers which came into conflict with powers claimed by the federal government. Whenever a case concerning such a conflict reached the Supreme Court, Marshall and his associates decided in favor of the federal government and against the state.

The case of *McCulloch* v. *Maryland* (1819) involved the second Bank of the United States, which had been founded in 1816, five years after the charter of the first Bank of the United States had expired. Like the first Bank of the United States, the second one was a corporation which received its charter from the federal government by an act of Congress. The Bank had its main office in Philadelphia and branches in other cities throughout the country. The state of Maryland tried to drive the Baltimore branch out of business by imposing a heavy tax upon it. When the head of the Baltimore office refused to pay the tax, the state threatened him with imprisonment, and he appealed the case to the Supreme Court.

Marshall and his colleagues now were faced with two basic questions. Was it constitutional for Congress to charter the Bank? If so, was it constitutional for a state to tax one of the branches? In answering the first of these questions, Marshall followed essentially the same line of reasoning that Alexander Hamilton had used in 1791 to justify the original bank. Marshall pointed out that the Constitution authorized Congress to pass all laws "necessary and proper" for carrying out the specified powers of Congress, such as the power to lay and collect taxes. A bank, he said, was "necessary and proper" for such purposes. In answering the second of the questions, he observed that the power to tax was the "power to destroy." If a state could tax banks or other agencies of the federal government, it could destroy them and thus destroy the Constitution itself. In short, Marshall decided that Congress could set up a bank and that the states could not impose taxes upon it.

The case of *Gibbons* v. *Ogden* (1824) arose from a dispute over the use of steamboats on the Hudson River. The inventor of the steamboat, Robert Fulton, and the promoter, Robert Livingston, had secured from the state of New York a charter which gave them the sole right to carry passengers on the river to and from New York City. Fulton and Livingston authorized Aaron Ogden to operate ferryboats between New York and New Jersey. The federal government, in accordance with an act of Congress, gave a license to another man, Thomas Gibbons, and he went into business in competition with Ogden. When Ogden sued Gibbons in the New York courts, the judges decided in Ogden's favor and ordered Gibbons to quit the business. Gibbons then appealed to the Supreme Court.

In deciding this case, Marshall and his fellow judges had to interpret the clause of the Constitution which says that Congress shall have power to regulate commerce among the states *(Art. I, sec. 8, para. 3)*. The Constitution does not define the word *commerce,* nor does it say whether Congress has the exclusive power to regulate it. The judges had to decide whether "commerce" included navigation and whether congressional laws to regulate it took precedence over state laws. Marshall reasoned that the authors of the Constitution had used the word *commerce* in a broad sense; they had intended to include the operation of boats as well as the buying and selling of goods. The regulatory power of Congress, he concluded, was "complete in itself" and could be "exercised to its utmost extent." Therefore, the law of New York, granting a steamboat monopoly between New York and New Jersey, must give way to the law of Congress authorizing federal licenses for the operation of steamboats between one state and another. This decision, by forbidding the states to restrict interstate commerce, helped to prepare the way for the economic growth of the nation.

REVIEWING THE SECTION

1. In what way did Marshall's decision in *Marbury* v. *Madison* establish the principle of judicial review?

2. How did the Supreme Court decisions in *Fletcher* v. *Peck* and *Dartmouth College* v. *Wood-*

ward establish the principle that no state legislature can pass a law that is inconsistent with the federal Constitution?

3. How did the Supreme Court decisions in the cases of *McCulloch* v. *Maryland* and *Gibbons* v. *Ogden* establish the principle that no state can pass laws that are in conflict with the regulatory powers of Congress?

CONGRESS MADE A SECTIONAL COMPROMISE

Soon after his inauguration in 1817, President James Monroe paid a visit to New England. Monroe was a Virginian, a member of the Republican party (formerly the Democratic-Republican party), and a close friend of Jefferson. The Federalists in New England had been strongly opposed to Monroe's predecessors Jefferson and Madison, yet Monroe was now received with great enthusiasm. A Federalist newspaper of Boston commented that an "era of good feelings" had begun with his inauguration. This phrase was repeated in other parts of the country, and Monroe's presidency (1817-1825) came to be known as the Era of Good Feelings.

Political feelings seemed so good because a strong opposition party no longer existed. The Federalist party had been declining steadily and was on the verge of disappearing altogether. In 1820, the Federalists did not even bother to nominate a presidential candidate to run against Monroe. He was reëlected, receiving 231 of 235 electoral votes.

Despite the appearances of political harmony, there was a good deal of discontent beneath the surface. The discontent was intensified by the Panic of 1819 and the depression that followed. Much of the discontent on the part of Northerners was due to a belief that the South unfairly dominated national politics. After all, three Presidents in succession, each serving two terms, were Virginians: Jefferson, Madison, and then Monroe. Disgruntled Northerners complained that the nation was being ruled by a "Virginia dynasty." They pointed out that the slave states were overrepresented in Con-

Missouri Compromise of 1820

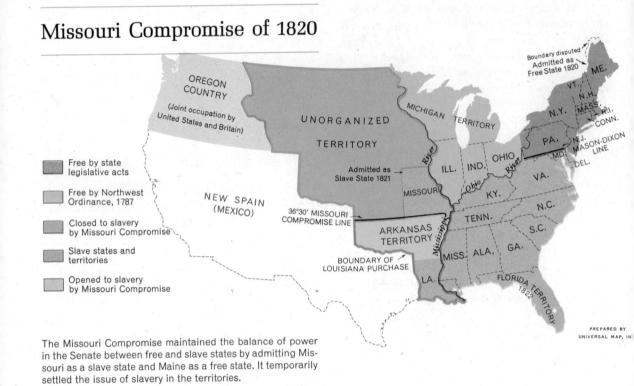

Free by state
legislative acts

Free by Northwest
Ordinance, 1787

Closed to slavery
by Missouri Compromise

Slave states and
territories

Opened to slavery
by Missouri Compromise

The Missouri Compromise maintained the balance of power
in the Senate between free and slave states by admitting Missouri as a slave state and Maine as a free state. It temporarily
settled the issue of slavery in the territories.

gress and in the electoral college because of the
"three-fifths clause" of the Constitution (*Art. I,
sec. 2, para. 3*). This clause provided that three
fifths of the slaves (even though they could not
vote) should be counted in determining the number of congressional representatives and presidential electors a state should have. Hence the vote
of a man in a slave state carried more weight than
the vote of a man in a free state.

Congress argued over the admission of Missouri

Much of the discontent came to the surface in
the Missouri controversy of 1819-1821. Certain
Northern politicians were hoping to revive the
Federalist party and make it a broad Northern
party by playing upon Northern suspicion and
jealousy of the South. An opportunity seemed to

present itself when Missouri applied for admission
to the Union as a slave state. There were, at that
time, eleven free states and eleven slave states. If
Missouri should be admitted with slaves, there
would be twelve slaveholding to eleven nonslave-
holding states. In the Senate the slave states would
have a majority of twenty-four to twenty-two,
though in the House the free states would continue to have a majority, despite the three-fifths
clause. Some Northern congressmen, for reasons
of both politics and principle, violently opposed
the admission of Missouri as a slave state.

When an enabling bill—a bill to enable Missouri to become a state—was being discussed in
Congress, a representative from New York, James
Tallmadge, Jr., proposed an amendment. This
amendment provided that no more slaves should
be brought into Missouri and that those already

there should be gradually set free. After a heated debate, the Tallmadge amendment passed the House, but it failed to pass the Senate.

While the House and the Senate were arguing over Missouri, a bill was brought up for the admission of another state, Maine, as a free state. Maine was a part of Massachusetts, and Massachusetts had given its permission for separate statehood, but only on the condition that Congress should give its approval before March 4, 1820. The Southerners in Congress said, however, that they would refuse to admit Maine as a free state unless the Northerners would agree to admit Missouri as a slave state.

The Missouri advocates contended that Congress had no constitutional right to tell a state, when it applied for admission, whether or not it could have slavery. They said that Missouri would be the equal of any other state once it entered the Union. It could then decide on its own "domestic institutions" just as South Carolina or New York could. So there was no sense in refusing to let Missouri come in with the kind of constitution it wanted. The "anti-Missourians" replied that Congress could impose conditions on the admission of a state and that it had done so in the past. By prohibiting slavery in the Northwest Territory, for example, Congress had imposed freedom as a condition for the admission of any state from that territory.

A compromise settled the Missouri question

A compromise was gradually worked out. The first step was taken when the Senate agreed to combine the bills for admitting Missouri with slaves and Maine without. The second step came when the Senate adopted an amendment proposed by Senator Jesse B. Thomas of Illinois. The Thomas amendment prohibited slavery, not in the state of Missouri itself, but in the rest of the Louisiana Purchase to the north of the southern boundary of Missouri (latitude 36° 30'). By this amendment, Thomas hoped to make the compromise more acceptable to the "anti-Missourians" in the House.

In the House the speaker, Henry Clay, secured the passage of the amended Maine-Missouri bill after dividing it into three separate bills. Some Northern Republicans, voted along with the Southern Republicans in favor of the measures.

Still a third step was necessary, however, before Missouri was finally admitted and the controversy ended. The Missouri constitution, though permitting slaves to be brought in, forbade free Negroes to enter the state. Thus it conflicted with the federal Constitution, for the latter contains the following provision: "The citizens of each state shall be entitled to all privileges and immunities of citizens in the several states," (Art. IV, sec. 2, para. 1). This meant that citizens of New York were entitled to the same privileges as citizens of Missouri, including the privilege of moving to and living in Missouri. Negroes were citizens in New York and a few other states. The Missouri constitution would deprive these Negro citizens of privileges and immunities guaranteed them by the Constitution.

Again Clay took the lead in arranging a settlement. He simply resolved to admit Missouri on the condition that the offending clause should never be construed in such a way as to infringe on the privileges and immunities of citizens of any state. Obviously, the Clay resolution did not mean very much. Yet both houses of Congress passed it and, having done so, agreed to let Missouri in.

Before the Missouri Compromise, the Mason-Dixon Line (the southern boundary line of Pennsylvania established by two English astronomers between 1763 and 1767 to settle a boundary dispute between the proprietors of Pennsylvania and Maryland) and the Ohio River had come to form the boundary between freedom and slavery. The Missouri Compromise extended this boundary westward across the Louisiana Purchase territory.

REVIEWING THE SECTION

1. What were the chief points at issue in the debate over the admission of Missouri?

2. What steps were taken to resolve the conflict over the admission of Missouri?

MONROE APPEALED TO PATRIOTISM

In a message to Congress, December 2, 1823, President Monroe announced an American policy. He said the United States would oppose attempts by European powers to acquire new colonies in either North or South America, to interfere with any independent nation on these continents, or to extend a European system of government and diplomacy to any part of this hemisphere. He added that the United States would make no attempt to interfere in the "internal concerns" of any of the powers of Europe. This, then, was a policy of America for the Americans and Europe for the Europeans. It did not yet have a name, but thirty years later it began to be called the Monroe Doctrine. Monroe deserved to have the policy named for him because he made the first official statement of it. Yet, when he did so, he was expressing ideas which were already widely held.

Monroe's announcement was made in response to certain specific challenges in the international politics of the time. Yet it was more than a statement of foreign policy. It was also an appeal to the patriotism of the people of the United States, an effort to stir in them a sense of their national greatness. This appeal was intended to counteract the spirit of sectional and factional bitterness, which had been aroused by the Panic of 1819 and the Missouri controversy.

Europe seemed to threaten America

Early in 1823, it had looked as if the powers of Europe might send an expedition across the Atlantic to recover for Spain her former colonies in the Americas which had revolted and declared their independence. Four of the powers—Russia, France, Austria, and Prussia—were then coöperating to prevent revolutions and maintain peace. These members of the "Holy Alliance" authorized

France to intervene in Spain, overthrow a revolutionary regime there, and put a Bourbon king back on the Spanish throne. After France had done so, many people in both Europe and America wondered what would happen next. Would the European allies try to intervene in Spanish America?

Among the established nations of the world, only the United States had recognized the independence of any of the new Latin-American nations. In 1822, President Monroe had told Congress that five of the new nations were ready for recognition: Argentina, Chile, Peru, Colombia, and Mexico. Congress then appropriated money for sending ministers to them.

The possible intervention of France in Spanish America seemed a threat to the United States. There appeared to be other threats as well.

One of these came from Russia, which had vast territorial claims in North America. In 1821, the Russian tsar ordered foreign ships to keep away from the northwest coast north of the fifty-first parallel. Monroe's secretary of state, John Quincy Adams, strongly objected to the tsar's order. Not only would it interfere with the activities of United States whalers and fur traders, but it would also strengthen the Russian territorial claims. Adams saw the order as an effort to enlarge Russian America, and he repeatedly protested to the Russian government. He said the United States would oppose Russian attempts at further colonization on this continent.

Another supposed threat came from Britain. Adams feared that the British had designs on Cuba, which still belonged to Spain. Like Jefferson and others before him, Adams did not wish to see Cuba transferred from a weak nation like Spain to a strong nation like Britain. He thought that, eventually, Cuba would free itself from Spanish control and would become part of the United States.

Monroe announced an American policy

Fortunately for the United States, Britain did not quite agree with her European allies on the question of Spanish America. Of course, Britain did not entirely agree with the United States, either. The British did not favor complete independence for the revolted colonies. The British wished to see the reëstablishment of the Spanish empire, provided that the Spaniards would give them special trading privileges with it. Thus the British could keep down the growing competition of the Americans. The British were not willing to permit the French to intervene, for French intervention would probably lead to French domination.

In the summer of 1823, the British prime minister, George Canning, proposed to the United States minister in London, Richard Rush, that their two governments should act together. Canning suggested that the two nations should make a joint statement in which they would warn the Holy Alliance not to intervene, and would promise never to take any additional American territory for themselves. Rush was ready to agree to Canning's proposal on one condition: Britain must first agree to recognize the new Latin-American nations. When Canning refused to promise recognition, Rush wrote home for instructions.

After hearing from Rush, President Monroe turned to former Presidents Jefferson and Madison for advice. Both of them urged him to authorize the joint statement with Britain. Monroe also asked the opinion of his secretary of state, Adams, and Adams disagreed with Jefferson and Madison. Adams opposed the joint statement for two reasons. First, it would pledge the United States not to acquire additional territory, and he hoped eventually to get Cuba, Texas, and other territory. Second, such a joint statement would make it seem to the world as if the United States were only trailing along after Britain, as if "in the wake of the British man-of-war." Adams insisted that it would be more dignified and honorable for the United States to speak out on its own.

When the time came for Monroe to speak out, in his message of December 2, 1823, he no longer had a choice between coöperating with Britain and acting alone. His only alternatives were to act alone or not act at all, for Prime Minister Canning had lost interest in making a joint statement with the United States. The French minister to Britain had assured him that France really did not intend to intervene in Spanish America by force of arms.

Monroe directed his message against all the powers of Europe, including Britain. He intended to head off every scheme for recovering old colonies or acquiring new ones in the Western Hemisphere. He wished to encourage the Latin Americans to provide for their own defense. And he hoped to arouse and unite the people of the United States.

Monroe's message had important consequences

By his bold statement, President Monroe did not frighten off the powers of Europe and thus preserve the independence of Latin America. True, the existing nations of Latin America retained their independence, and others later gained theirs. The United States would not have been strong enough to protect those nations, however, if the powers of Europe had made a combined and determined effort to conquer them. The United States was able to maintain the principles of Monroe, to the extent that it did so, largely because the powers of Europe disagreed among themselves.

After Monroe's announcement, the United States did not immediately establish strong leadership over the nations of this hemisphere. As secretary of state and later as President, Adams was cautious in applying the Monroe Doctrine. He was not enthusiastic about sending delegates from the United States when, in 1825, the Venezuelan liberator, Simon Bolívar, called a conference of all the American nations in Panama. Adams yielded to the advice of his secretary of state, Henry Clay, and appointed two delegates. In Congress, however, the opponents of the Adams administration objected that the conference might result in the formation of an entangling alliance. The congressional debate delayed the departure of the United States delegates. One of them died before he got to Panama,

MAJOR EVENTS IN UNITED STATES FOREIGN AFFAIRS: 1815-1853

1815-1853 (From the end of the War of 1812 to the Gadsden Purchase)

STATEMENTS OF POLICY

1823 *Monroe Doctrine.* Core of the doctrine was the principle that the Eastern and Western hemispheres should be divided, politically. Monroe warned Europeans to stay out of the Americas; he restated the principle of noninterference of the U.S. in the internal affairs of Europe. Later Presidents have applied and added corollaries to the doctrine when the security of the Western Hemisphere seemed endangered. The doctrine has been one of the most enduring foreign policies established by the United States.

EXECUTIVE AGREEMENTS

1817 *Rush-Bagot Agreement.* U.S. and Britain agreed to partial disarmament on the Great Lakes and Lake Champlain—the first reciprocal reduction of naval armaments. Though modified, the agreement is still in force today.

WARS AND PEACE TREATIES

1846-1848 *The Mexican War* was ended with the *Treaty of Guadalupe Hidalgo* in 1848. Since that time, peace has prevailed between the U.S. and Mexico.

With the coming of peace in 1814, settlers began to move westward. In search of new and better lands they soon went beyond the boundary of the U.S. to lands owned or claimed by foreign powers. Along the way, they braved many dangers, such as attacks by Indians. Once the lands were settled, there was agitation for annexation. By 1848, the U.S. had acquired over one million square miles of new land west of the Mississippi River.

Emigrants Attacked by the Comanches, by Seth Eastman, c. 1850

BOUNDARY SETTLEMENTS AND ACQUISITIONS

1818 *The Convention of 1818* with Britain fixed the boundary line between British North America and the U.S. from Lake of the Woods west to the Rockies and provided for 10-year joint occupation of the Oregon country.

1819 *Adams-Onís Treaty.* Spain ceded all of Florida to the U.S. The U.S. gave up claims to Texas, and a definite southwestern boundary for the Louisiana Purchase was set. Spain renounced claims to the Oregon country.

1824 *A treaty with Russia* resolved conflicting claims to the Oregon country. Russia relinquished to the U.S. all claims to that area, which lay south of 54°40′.

1842 *Webster-Ashburton Treaty* with Britain settled the present-day Maine-New Brunswick boundary line, vaguely defined in 1783 in the Treaty of Paris.

1845 *Annexation of Texas.* An independent republic since 1836, Texas was annexed by joint congressional resolution. It was admitted to the Union that same year.

1846 *The Oregon Treaty,* between Britain and the U.S., divided the Oregon country at the 49th parallel. It ended the joint-occupation agreement made in 1818 and renewed in 1827. The entire boundary between the U.S. and British North America at last was fixed.

1848 *Treaty of Guadalupe Hidalgo.* The U.S. paid $15 million to Mexico for ceding California and New Mexico and agreeing to the Rio Grande as the boundary of Texas.

1853 *Gadsden Purchase.* The U.S. paid Mexico $10 million for parts of present-day Arizona and New Mexico.

ECONOMIC POLICY AND COMMERCIAL TREATIES

1815 *A commercial convention* restored trade relations between the U.S. and Britain to prewar status. (The commercial clauses of Jay's Treaty had expired in 1807.) In 1818, the agreement was renewed for a 10-year period.

1832-1849 *Commercial treaties* were signed with Russia (1832), Muscat (1833), and Siam (1833). A treaty with China (1844) gave the U.S. most-favored-nation privileges. In a commercial treaty with Hawaii (1849), the U.S. formally recognized Hawaiian independence.

1846 *A treaty with New Granada* (later Colombia) granted the U.S. transit rights across the Isthmus of Panama. The U.S. agreed to guarantee neutrality of the isthmus and Granada's sovereignty over it.

1850 *Clayton-Bulwer Treaty.* U.S. and Britain agreed never to fortify or exercise exclusive control over any canal route in Central America. Both agreed to guarantee the neutrality of any canal, when constructed.

and the other arrived after the conference was over. Thus the United States did not participate in the first attempt at Pan-American coöperation.

Though the immediate consequences were slight, the long-range effects of Monroe's message were extremely important. Later leaders of the nation repeated and elaborated upon his words. In time, the United States grew strong enough to make it dangerous for hostile powers to seek territory or political influence in the Western Hemisphere. Later generations of Americans could be counted upon to support their government in such a policy, for they had come to believe in the Monroe Doctrine as something almost sacred.

REVIEWING THE SECTION

1. Why did the United States view France, Russia, and Britain as threats to its security and to the security of the Western Hemisphere?

2. Why did Britain want to avoid European intervention in Latin America? Why did the United States act alone when it formulated the Monroe Doctrine?

3. What were the immediate effects of the formulation of the Monroe Doctrine? What were the long-range effects of the doctrine?

JACKSON DEALT WITH NULLIFICATION

As President, John Quincy Adams had a broad conception of the powers and duties of the federal government. He recommended

laws promoting the improvement of agriculture, commerce, and manufactures, the cultivation of the mechanic and of the elegant arts, the advancement of literature, and the progress of the sciences, ornamental and profound.

Adams' successor, Andrew Jackson, who was elected in 1828, had no such definite program to propose to Congress. Yet, far more than Adams, Jackson was a popular representative of the national spirit. He was famous as a military hero, the

victor over the British in the Battle of New Orleans at the close of the War of 1812. He rose to the presidency on the strength of his military fame. The voters had no way of knowing how he would stand on questions of policy, once he was in office.

In some respects, President Jackson proved to be an advocate of state rights rather than national powers. For example, he vetoed a bill to give federal aid for the building of the Maysville road in Kentucky. Even though this route was intended to form a branch of the Cumberland (National) Road, he doubted whether the government could constitutionally finance an improvement lying entirely within a single state. He sided with Georgia when that state defied a decision of the Supreme Court. The Georgians wished to get rid of the Creek and Cherokee Indians and take their lands. The Supreme Court held that Georgia must not violate the treaties which the United States had made with the Indians. Jackson is supposed to have said: "John Marshall has made his decision; now let him enforce it."

Nevertheless, Jackson strongly asserted the national authority when South Carolina declared the tariff laws null and void and threatened to disobey them.

The tariff became a hot issue

After the War of 1812, many Democratic-Republicans began to favor policies of a kind they had opposed earlier, when Alexander Hamilton and the Federalists had advocated them. The Democratic-Republicans now began to favor protective tariffs, a national bank, and federal expenditures for internal improvements. The aim was to create a "home market." Supposedly, tariffs would encourage the growth of industries and industrial towns, which would buy the products of farms and plantations. A national bank would provide credit and currency so payments could be made easily throughout the entire country. Improvements in transportation would make possible the rapid shipment of both farm products and manufactured goods. One of the leading advocates of such measures, Henry Clay, referred to them collectively as the "American System." Clay and other advocates of the system assumed that it would be good for all the people.

In 1816, the protectionists carried through Congress the highest tariff yet passed. This law had the support of many congressmen from both parties and all sections. Some Southerners voted in favor of it. They expected that many cotton factories would be built in the South, where there was plenty of water power and where the cotton supply was close at hand. Some Northerners voted against the tariff of 1816. At that time the biggest business in New England was overseas shipping and trade. The merchants of Boston and other seaports, who made a living by importing and selling foreign products, opposed protective tariffs because these would cut down on imports.

By 1828, the attitudes of many people toward the tariff had changed. Very few cotton mills had been built in the South, while the number of cotton plantations had greatly increased. Even those Southerners who once favored the tariff now saw nothing to be gained from it. Most Southerners considered it positively harmful to them. They could prosper best by selling cotton throughout the world and buying manufactured goods from abroad. They thought the tariff, by making it difficult for Europeans to sell to Americans, would also make it difficult for them to buy from Americans. At the same time, since the tariff would be added to the purchase price of imported goods, these would become more expensive.

Meanwhile, textile manufacturing had grown tremendously in the North, especially in New England. The manufacturing interest was beginning to be more important than the shipping interest. The promoters of new mills believed that these infant industries would have to be protected from foreign competition until they had grown big and strong enough to stand by themselves.

In 1827, Calhoun, now Vice President, used his vote in the Senate to break a tie and defeat a "woolens bill" for raising the tariff on woolen goods. The next year a bill was introduced for raising the tariff not only on woolens but also on many other imports, including raw wool. This bill did not entirely please the New England manufacturers, since it would add to the cost of some of their raw materials. Yet many of the New England representatives and senators, including Daniel Webster (now a senator from Massachusetts), voted for the bill, and it passed.

Southerners denounced the tariff of 1828 as the "tariff of abominations." The cotton growers of South Carolina were especially bitter. The state was not very prosperous, and many of its fields were being abandoned and left to grow up in sedge grass and pine trees. On their eroded and exhausted soil, the South Carolina planters could not compete very well with planters on the newly developed and richer lands of the Southwest. Most of the South Carolinians blamed their troubles on the tariff, however, and certainly the tariff made their troubles even worse.

Calhoun developed his nullification theory

Some of the South Carolinians were so angered by the "tariff of abominations," they demanded that their state secede from the Union. This demand posed a challenge for John C. Calhoun. Already the outstanding leader of his state and the Vice President of the United States, he wished to maintain his leadership at home and eventually to become President. He needed to find a way to satisfy his discontented fellow South Carolinians, and save them from the hated tariff, yet avoid antagonizing the rest of the country. His problem was to discover some legal and constitutional way of doing this.

Calhoun found the solution to his problem in the theory of nullification, which he began to work out in 1828. According to this theory, the separate states were sovereign. That is, the ultimate source of political authority belonged to the *people* of the states. By ratifying the Constitution, they had con-

MEN
IN
HISTORY

WEBSTER, CLAY, AND CALHOUN

Three men—Daniel Webster, Henry Clay, and John Calhoun—dominated the American political scene for more than twenty-five years. These men represented divergent views of the expanding nation. All three sought to serve the nation, yet each fought for the interests of his own section on issues which divided the nation.

The three men were different in temperament and tradition. Webster was "New England and the Northeast." His view of America was largely influenced by his respect for Anglo-Saxon law and society. The United States would do well, he believed, to follow New England's example of imitating industrialized Britain.

Clay was "the West." He represented the creative, vigorous spirit of the young, triumphant United States. His personality embodied the nature and the humor of the frontier. The United States he envisioned was the giant of the future.

One word describes Calhoun—"correct." Always the model gentleman, he was "the South," and he exhibited the manners and morals found in that section of the nation.

Webster, at one time in favor of free trade, after 1830 sought a high tariff to protect New England's industries. Clay's "American System" advocated moderate rates. Clay did not want the United States to be so highly industrialized as Britain, but believed the nation should at least be self-sufficient. When South Carolina, which favored free trade, was ready to resist the high tariff by force, Calhoun advanced the theory of nullification. By this theory, a sovereign state could justify its refusal to obey a federal law which it held to be inconsistent with the Constitution. To dramatize the depth of his feeling, Calhoun said: "Write nullification on my tombstone."

Because he opposed industrialism and feared the power of centralized finance, Calhoun stood against a national bank. "Property is timid," he warned, "and seeks protection, and nothing is more gratifying to government than to become a protector." Wall Street, he prophesied, "is in the ascendant in the councils of the Union. Every measure is controlled by it, and its pleasure—banks, brokers, and stock jobbers sway everything." Henry Clay held no similar fears. A national bank

was part of his American System, although he was willing to compromise on the power given to the institution. Webster contended that what the nation needed was "currency . . . acceptable in . . . every town, village, and hamlet of our extended land."

Although Webster disliked slavery, he was no abolitionist. He believed the evolution of the modern world would eventually destroy slavery. His support of the Fugitive Slave Law in 1850 cost him the backing of the abolitionists. The important thing, he maintained, was to save the Union. Clay also disapproved of slavery, but managed to live with it. Calhoun defended and even praised slavery. "A good—a positive good," he said.

Calhoun, though he denied it, became more and more a sectionalist. He increasingly felt the peril and isolation of the South, the section which he saw as the oppressed area of the nation. He opposed the growth of federal power, looking upon the nation as a confederation in which state rights were supreme. His dislike of extreme democracy and his fear of the despotism of the majority led him to the theory of "concurrent majorities." This theory required a majority within each state, in addition to a majority in the nation as a whole for the adoption of laws that would be binding on all the people.

Webster's legalistic mind saw federal law and administration as supreme. He opposed nullification and regarded secession as revolution. His famous cry from the floor of the Senate, "Liberty and Union, now and forever, one and inseparable," represented a broader outlook than he had held in earlier days.

The noblest fame of the "Great Pacificator" Henry Clay, rested upon his ability to find compromise solutions to divisive questions. The salvation of the Union, which Clay considered necessary for the future of the states and the nation, was the purpose of every compromise. "My sympathies are reserved for the great mass of mankind," Clay declared.

With mutual respect for one another, Webster, Calhoun, and Clay expended their energies in defending their own views. When the three sectional heroes no longer walked the halls of Congress, an era had passed.

ferred certain powers upon the federal government, but they had given up none of their sovereignty. Hence they alone could decide whether or not Congress was exceeding the powers which had been granted to it. According to the Calhoun theory, the Supreme Court could not properly make such a decision, since the Supreme Court was merely one of the three branches of the government which the states had created.

How could the people of the states go about the business of deciding the constitutionality of acts of Congress? Calhoun concluded that they could do this by the same procedure they had used to ratify the Constitution and the amendments to it. That is, if the people of a particular state should feel that an act of Congress was unconstitutional, they could hold a convention and "nullify" the act. So far as this particular state was concerned, the federal law would then be null and void.

If people in other states believed that the law in question should be upheld, they could try to add a constitutional amendment that would specifically give Congress the power to pass such a law. If three fourths of all the states should ratify the amendment, the nullifying state would be overruled. That state then would have to yield unless, as a last resort, it chose to secede. It could secede by a process similar to that of nullification, that is, by holding another convention and repealing the ordinance by which it once had ratified the Constitution. According to Calhoun, secession, like nullification, was a perfectly legal and constitutional process, not a revolutionary one at all.

The legislature of South Carolina published the first statement of Calhoun's theory, together with a denunciation of the tariff, in a document entitled *The South Carolina Exposition and Protest* (1828). Calhoun himself wrote the document, but he kept it anonymous for the time being. He was running for reëlection as Vice President, this time on the ticket with Andrew Jackson, and the nullification theory might prove to be unpopular in the North. Calhoun hoped that Jackson, once he had been elected President, would take the lead in bringing

about a reduction of the tariff. Then it would not be necessary for Calhoun to associate himself publicly with the theory or attempt to put it into practice.

Jackson opposed nullification

In January 1830, a senator from South Carolina, Robert Y. Hayne, denounced the tariff and defended the theory of nullification. Daniel Webster replied to Hayne in an eloquent speech. Webster insisted that the Constitution had made the federal government completely sovereign with respect to those powers which the Constitution conferred upon it. "It is, Sir, the people's Constitution, the people's government, made for the people, made by the people, and answerable to the people," Webster declared. He meant the people of the whole nation, not those of the separate states. He concluded with the words: "Liberty *and* Union, now and forever, one and inseparable!"

Everyone wondered which side President Jackson would take on the question involved in the Webster-Hayne debate. At a Jefferson's birthday banquet in 1831, Jackson gave the following toast: "Our *Federal* Union—*It must be preserved!*" This was taken to mean that the President disapproved of nullification. He differed with Calhoun on personal and political matters as well as this question of principle. Soon the bitter quarrel between the President and the Vice President became public.

Congress had done nothing to get rid of the "tariff of abominations," despite Calhoun's hopes. In 1832, a new tariff law was passed, but it made only slight changes. It did not satisfy Calhoun or his followers in South Carolina so they held a convention and put his theory into effect. They adopted a "nullification ordinance" which declared that all the tariff acts, especially those of 1828 and 1832, were "null, void, and no law, nor binding upon this state."

Calhoun resigned as Vice President and went back to Washington as a senator from South Carolina to defend his theory and his state's application of it. Privately, Jackson threatened to hang him as a traitor. Publicly, Jackson issued a proclamation in which he denounced nullification as both unconstitutional and unpatriotic. "The laws of the United States must be executed," he said. He prepared to execute them by using the army and the navy. His supporters in Congress introduced a "force bill" to give him specific authority to use force, if necessary, against South Carolina.

Congress adopted another compromise

Again, as at the time of the Missouri controversy, Henry Clay took the lead in bringing about a compromise. He sponsored a bill for lowering the tariff by yearly stages, so that after ten years the rates would be back at about the same level as in 1816. When Congress passed the compromise tariff, it also passed the force bill, which was to take effect only if South Carolina persisted in defying federal law.

The South Carolina convention now met again and did two things. First, it repealed the ordinance nullifying the tariff laws. Second, it adopted an ordinance nullifying the recently passed Force Act. Thus the nullifiers appeared to have the last word. Of course, the Force Act would not have taken effect anyhow, once the original nullification ordinance had been repealed. In nullifying this act, South Carolina was nullifying a law which, to all intents and purposes, was already null and void.

Calhoun and his followers claimed a great victory for the principle of nullification. They boasted that this principle had saved their state from both the injustice of the protective tariff and the danger of federal invasion. True, South Carolina had scored a point in bringing about a gradual tariff reduction. Yet Calhoun had failed to get nullification accepted by the rest of the country as a peaceful and constitutional procedure.

From this experience Calhoun learned that no state, by itself, could protect its interests against the will of the majority, as expressed in acts of Congress; but he continued to expound his theory of state rights, including the rights of nullification and secession. Nevertheless, while continuing to defend and elaborate his theory at every opportunity, he turned more and more to developing a sense of solidarity throughout the South.

Meanwhile, the United States had survived the worst sectional crisis it had ever faced. In the minds of most Americans, President Jackson and Senator Webster stood out as great heroes because of their insistence upon maintaining a strong and permanent Union. Thus, temporarily at least, the sense of national unity was strengthened rather than weakened as a result of the nullification attempt.

REVIEWING THE SECTION

1. How did the conflicting interests of New England manufacturers and Southern cotton growers lead to disagreement over tariff policy?

2. What were the tenets of Calhoun's theory of nullification?

3. How did President Jackson respond to South Carolina's ordinance of nullification?

4. How did the tariff compromise of 1833 dispel sectional conflict? How did South Carolina respond to the compromise?

CHAPTER CONCLUSION

One of the main themes of United States history has been the conflict between sectionalism and nationalism, between loyalty to one state or section and loyalty to the nation as a whole.

After the War of 1812 the spirit of nationalism grew stronger than ever before. Evidences of this can be seen in developments in literature, constitutional law, foreign policy, and domestic politics.

An American literature began to appear as a result of the writings of Washington Irving, James Fenimore Cooper, Herman Melville, Edgar Allan Poe, Walt Whitman, Ralph Waldo Emerson, Henry David Thoreau, Nathaniel Hawthorne, and others. These writers turned to American subjects and treated them in an original way. Some of these men were hailed, even in England and elsewhere in Europe, as outstanding literary figures of their time.

Constitutional law, as interpreted and applied by John Marshall and the Supreme Court, stressed the powers of the federal government as opposed to the rights of the states. In his decisions Marshall upheld the powers of Congress to make laws for all the people—for example, to set up a bank with branches throughout the nation and to regulate commerce (in a broad sense) between the states. He denied the right of a state to interfere with the business of the nation as a whole by arbitrarily revoking corporation charters or by setting up monopolies in interstate shipping or trade.

Foreign policy was both a cause and a result of the growing sense of national greatness. Under President James Monroe and Secretary of State John Quincy Adams, the United States dared to challenge the European powers by asserting its leadership in this hemisphere. This nation stood out alone in recognizing and insisting upon Latin-American independence. Though Monroe and Adams did not actually establish the kind of leadership they proclaimed, they put forth in the Monroe Doctrine a policy that was to be extremely important in the future. They also stirred up a general feeling of national pride.

In politics the spirit of nationalism was well expressed by such outstanding leaders as Daniel Webster and Henry Clay. The foremost lawyer in the country, Webster defended national powers against state rights in important cases such as those involving Dartmouth College and the national bank. He also became the most persuasive advocate of tariffs and the most persuasive opponent of nullification. He was called the "Defender of the Constitution." Clay, even more than Monroe or Adams, urged American leadership in the Western Hemisphere. He invented the term "American System" and championed the policies it represented—tariffs, internal improvements, the national bank. He also took the lead in arranging compromises to hold the nation together, such as the Missouri

Compromise of 1820 and the tariff compromise of 1833. Thus he got a reputation as the "Great Pacificator" or the "Great Compromiser."

Both Webster and Clay were political opponents of Andrew Jackson, who disliked the so-called American System and the Marshall court as well. Nevertheless, as the nation's greatest military hero, the "hero of New Orleans," Jackson was a living symbol of American patriotism. As President, he stood up for the powers of the federal government when those powers were challenged by the state of South Carolina.

That challenge was the most serious threat, up to that time, from the opposing spirit of sectionalism and state rights. This divisive spirit had been seen during the War of 1812, when some of the extreme Federalists of New England hinted at secession. Sectionalism broke out again when Federalist politicians aroused Northern opposition to the admission of Missouri as a slave state. Then, on the most dramatic occasion of all, the spirit of sectionalism and state rights erupted when South Carolina threatened to defy and disobey federal laws.

John C. Calhoun, the "Great Nullifier," was the outstanding theorist of state rights. Calhoun and Clay and Webster, at times political friends and at other times political rivals, came to be known as the "Great Triumvirate." During the War of 1812 and immediately after it, Calhoun had been as much a nationalist as Clay and more a nationalist than Webster, who criticized the war and opposed the tariff of 1816. Webster and Calhoun afterwards changed their political views because of the changing economic interests of their constituencies. As manufacturing grew in New England, Webster began to advocate protection for industry. As manufacturing ceased to grow much in South Carolina, Calhoun began to oppose protection.

Calhoun felt that his nullification theory was based upon the same principles as the Kentucky and Virginia resolutions (1798-1799) of Jefferson and Madison. In presenting his theory, Calhoun always insisted that he remained devoted to the federal Union. He contended that nullification would help to preserve the Union by protecting the interests of minorities and keeping all parts of the nation satisfied. His critics argued, however, that nullification would lead to the destruction of the Union.

The challenges from sectionalism and state rights provided a kind of testing of national unity. By the

1830's, the nation appeared to have survived all tests.

In later years, however, even more serious challenges were to come. The economic issues—banking, tariff protection, internal improvements—remained alive. The slavery issue became more divisive than ever as antislavery feeling spread in the North and proslavery feeling in the South. The issue of extending slavery into the West was revived and intensified as new territories were acquired. Eventually many people were inclined to feel that the North and the South even had different civilizations. Sectionalism, especially in the South, developed into a kind of separate nationalism.

Calhoun's theory was not forgotten. When, more than ten years after his death, the Southern states finally seceded, they believed that secession was entirely legal and constitutional. They justified it on the basis of his theory.

FOCUSING ON SPECIFICS

1. What was John Marshall's view of the powers of the central government? What were the main effects of the decisions made by the Supreme Court during the years he served as chief justice?

2. How did Marshall interpret the meaning of the word *commerce* in the clause in the Constitution which gives Congress the power to regulate interstate commerce?

3. Why were the years during Monroe's administration termed the Era of Good Feelings? To what extent is this title inaccurate?

4. Why did many Northern politicians oppose the admission of Missouri as a slave state?

5. What was Henry Clay's role in the settlement of the controversy over the admission of Missouri?

6. What were the main features of the Monroe Doctrine?

7. Why was the United States able to uphold the principles of the Monroe Doctrine in the early nineteenth century?

8. In what respects did President Jackson prove to be an advocate of nationalism? of state rights?

9. Why did Calhoun believe that a state could legally and constitutionally secede from the Union?

10. What was the chief issue in the Webster-Hayne debate?

REVIEWING MAIN THEMES

1. During the years between 1815 and 1850, what progress was made by the United States toward achieving a literature which was distinctively American?

2. How did the major decisions of the Supreme Court under Chief Justice John Marshall strengthen the federal government?

3. What steps were taken to resolve the problems that arose when Missouri sought entrance into the Union?

4. What circumstances led to the formulation of the Monroe Doctrine? What were some of its important consequences?

5. What were the causes of the nullification crisis of 1832? How was the crisis settled?

EVALUATING THE ISSUES

1. European critics of American society, when stating what they believed to be the reasons for the backward state of American culture, often touched upon this question: Does a democratic society tend to inhibit the achievement of artistic excellence by placing too great a value on equality and standardization, or does such a society encourage excellence by giving more people the opportunity to reach their capacities? Discuss.

2. The Missouri Compromise was the first attempt to settle the question of the expansion of slavery into the territories. Do you agree with Jefferson's observation that the drawing of a geographical line would tend to intensify sectional differences, or do you think that the reasoning of the Compromise was sound and conceivably could have settled the matter permanently? Explain.

3. The authors state: "Calhoun felt that his nullification theory was based upon the same principles as the Kentucky and Virginia resolutions (1798-1799) of Jefferson and Madison." Do you think Calhoun was justified in holding this position? Support your view.

4. Before 1823, the United States attempted to keep itself free from entangling alliances. The Monroe Doctrine, however, reflected a willingness to become involved in the affairs of Latin America. Did the doctrine, therefore, indicate a substantial change in foreign policy, or was it a new interpretation of old principles? Explain.

The Growth of Democracy

The democratic ideal is well expressed in the Declaration of Independence. "All men are created equal," not equal in size, strength, intelligence, or skill, but equal in their right to "Life, Liberty and the pursuit of Happiness." Moreover, governments derive their "just powers from the consent of the governed." This means that the majority must rule, though always with due regard for the rights of the minority, especially its right to persuade others and thus convert itself into a majority.

In the early 1800's, the United States was probably the most democratic nation in the world. Nevertheless, many American as well as foreign observers believed that this country was not nearly so democratic as it should be. It fell short of the ideal in several respects. Not all the people were allowed to vote or to hold office. Officeholders sometimes acted as if they owned their offices and had no responsibility to the people. Opportunities to rise in politics, society, and business were limited in various ways. There was much poverty and ignorance and, worst of all, slavery continued to exist in half of the states.

During the 1820's, 1830's, and 1840's, many people in the United States undertook to reform the nation, to get rid of social and political inequities. These reformers were inspired not only by the democratic ideals of the Declaration of Independence but also by the Christian ideals of the New Testament. They were inspired by the teachings of Jesus, who had counseled his followers to deal charitably with one another.

The spirit of reform seems to have been stimulated, at least in part, by the development of industry. The introduction of machines and factories made it possible to produce more goods than ever before. This growing abundance of goods seemed to give promise of a more comfortable life for everybody. At the same time, the industrial changes upset the lives of many people and brought hardships and losses to some, especially to those who depended for their livelihood on occupations which could not compete with the new factory system. Part of the desire to improve society was stimulated by the contrast between the possibilities and the actualities of life in a mechanized society. Certainly the spirit of reform was strongest in those parts of the United States and Europe that were being most rapidly industrialized. In Britain, France, and other nations of western Europe, there were democratic and humanitarian movements comparable to those in the United States. Reformers in Europe and the United States often coöperated with and influenced one another.

STATES REVISED THEIR CONSTITUTIONS

The original state constitutions did not provide for complete political equality. With few exceptions, they did not permit women, Negroes, or white men without a specified amount of taxable property to vote or hold office; they allowed only white men owning a certain amount of taxable property to do so.

At the time these constitutions were adopted, most of the free men throughout the nation were farmers who owned their farms. There were comparatively few workers in towns and cities, and many of them were independent craftsmen who owned some property—shops, homes, even farms. Hence, the great majority of white men could vote or run for office if they wished to do so. There seemed to be no serious contradiction between democratic theory and the property requirement.

With the growth of industry, however, it appeared that a time might come when a large number of people, if not a majority of them, would be factory workers who owned little or no property. Many of these men would have no political rights under the existing constitutions. So reformers began to urge that the constitutions be changed to broaden voting rights.

The newer states in the west set an example for the older states in the east. When Ohio joined the Union in 1803, its constitution enfranchised all white men and, as other new states were formed, their constitutions generally did the same. On the frontier the early settlers were roughly equal in social and economic opportunity. It seemed natural to make them equal in political opportunity as well.

The eastern states became concerned about their loss of population to the western states. If they were to keep people at home, they would have to grant them additional political rights. This was another reason for the demand by reformers that the constitutions of the eastern states be changed.

These states began, one by one, to hold conventions for drawing up new constitutions. The new constitutions were more democratic than the old ones, not only in regard to voting and officeholding, but in other respects as well.

More men were allowed to vote

In some of the state conventions, there was strong opposition to removing the property qualifications, and reforms were made only after long and bitter debates. When the Massachusetts convention met in 1820, for example, Daniel Webster argued that men with property ought to have more influence in government than men without it. He said "power *naturally* and *necessarily* follows property" and "property as such should have its weight and influence in political arrangement." If the poor were given political power, some people believed, they would use it to pass laws depriving the rich of some of their wealth.

In Rhode Island the opposition to change was so strong that, for many years, no constitutional convention was even called. The old colonial charter (granted in 1663 by King Charles II) continued to serve, with only a few alterations, as the state constitution. It imposed property qualifications so high that more than half of the adult men in the state were unable to vote. Discontented Rhode Islanders, led by Thomas W. Dorr, held their own convention, drew up a new constitution, and formed a separate state government with Dorr as governor. The regular state authorities began to arrest the "Dorrites" and put them in prison. Dorr and a band of armed followers then attacked the state arsenal in Providence (1842) in order to get arms and ammunition with which to protect their rebel government. They were unsuccessful, however, and the "Dorr Rebellion" collapsed.

Despite the resistance to change, considerable progress was made. In Massachusetts the new constitution, adopted in 1821, lessened the influence of the rich, though it still restricted the vote to taxpayers. In New York in the same year the property requirement for voting was abolished. Even in Rhode Island the vote eventually (1843) was extended to most men.

In a few of the Northern states the Negroes benefited from the extension of the suffrage to men of modest means, but generally the Negroes were bypassed. In Pennsylvania, the right to vote was taken from the Negroes at the same time it was given to additional white men. The new Pennsylvania constitution, adopted in 1838, included the word "white" as an added qualification for voting.

Voters were given more power

Not only was the number of legal voters increased, but the number of elective offices was increased as well. Thus more government officials were made directly responsible to the people.

Previously, the legislatures in some of the states had not provided equal representation for all of the people of the state. The areas of these states which had been occupied the longest had more representatives in proportion to population than did the newly occupied areas. The western parts of these states had gained population much faster than the eastern parts, but the western parts had not been given a corresponding increase in representation in the state legislatures.

In Virginia, when the constitutional convention met in 1829, the delegates from the western counties demanded representation in proportion to numbers. In the revised constitution (1830) the western counties gained additional seats in the House of Burgesses, though the *tidewater* (coastal) counties continued to be overrepresented.

In a number of states the voters were allowed to elect a larger number of administrative officials than before. Generally, the very first constitutions had provided for the popular election of only the legislature, the governor, and a few other high state officials. The rest of the officials were appointed by the governor or the legislature. The revised constitutions provided, however, that most of the high officials should be elected by the people.

In most of the states, at first, the people had no chance to vote in presidential elections. The legislature simply cast the state's electoral vote. In 1800, this was still true in ten of the states; the voters chose the presidential electors in only six states. Later, one state after another made arrangements for the people to take part. After 1828, there was only one state, South Carolina, in which the legislature still cast the presidential vote.

REVIEWING THE SECTION

1. Why did many people oppose extending the suffrage to all white males? What steps did the states take to extend the suffrage?

2. How were government officials made more responsive to the will of the people? What change was made in the way the President was elected?

THE PEOPLE BECAME MORE ACTIVE IN POLITICS

As both the number of eligible voters and the number of elective offices increased, political parties became more important than ever. It was up to them to bring large masses of people together and provide them with definite political goals. It was up to the parties also to organize the state and national governments and give central direction to the many elected officials. Without strong parties, politics would have been quite chaotic.

So as the states grew more democratic, the political parties became more highly organized and more tightly disciplined. This was especially necessary in states like New York and Pennsylvania, which had large and diverse populations. In these states political machines and party bosses appeared. They had loyal party workers whom they rewarded, when the party was victorious, by appointing them to state jobs. Later this "spoils system" also was applied to the federal government, the victorious party dividing federal as well as state jobs among the loyal party workers. The desire for such jobs motivated and held together the core of the party membership. The common man now had more opportunity to hold public office than he had had in earlier years.

The parties increased their control over nominations and, at the same time, made them more democratic by holding conventions to nominate candidates, including those running for the presidency. In theory at least, the nominating convention represented the party members and gave expression to their will.

In political campaigns, especially presidential campaigns, the parties aroused the voters and brought them out to the polls as never before. Thus the number of people taking part in politics, as voters, increased not only because of the removal of voting restrictions but also because of the activity of politicians.

The people could help nominate candidates

The Constitution does not provide a means for the parties to nominate candidates for the presidency or for other offices. (The Constitution does not even provide for political parties.) From 1796 to 1816, the representatives and senators of each party in Congress got together in two separate *caucuses* (party meetings) and named the presidential candidates. In 1820, when President Monroe ran for reëlection (as a Republican), he did not need a caucus to renominate him because no other Republican was running against him. The Federalist party had no caucus because it had practically ceased to exist.

If the caucus system were to be revived in 1824, the man named by the Republican caucus would win. Since no new party had appeared to take the place of the Federalist party, the Republican candidate would have no opposition, and nomination would amount to election. There were several Republicans with presidential ambitions, however, and to some the idea of a caucus seemed unfair and undemocratic. Members of the House and the Senate were not elected for the purpose of naming a President, and so they would not necessarily represent the wishes of the voters who had elected them. A demand arose for overthrowing "King Caucus."

In 1824, King Caucus was overthrown. A nominating caucus met, but only about a third of the

Republicans in Congress were present. The man they picked, William H. Crawford of Georgia, did not have the field to himself. Three other candidates, Andrew Jackson, Henry Clay, and John Quincy Adams, were nominated in new ways—by the state legislatures or by mass meetings in the various states.

By 1828, there were again two parties. The more conservative Republicans, who had picked up many of the old Federalist doctrines, were now called National Republicans (later to be known as Whigs). They supported President John Quincy Adams for reëlection. The Republicans who upheld the doctrine of state rights and represented the agricultural interests (now called Democrats) offered Andrew Jackson as their candidate. But there was still no regular system for making nominations; they were made by state legislatures or by local mass meetings.

A new system, the national nominating convention, was introduced in time for the election of 1832. It was first used by the earliest third party in United States history—the Anti-Masonic party. This party opposed a fraternal organization called the Society of Freemasons. The society was opposed because it was secret and exclusive and hence, supposedly, undemocratic. Feeling against the Masons had become stronger than ever when (in 1826) a man named William Morgan, who had written a book in which he accused the Masons of horrible deeds, mysteriously disappeared from his home in Batavia, New York. Morgan's friends believed that Masons had kidnaped and murdered him in order to keep the book from being published. The excitement over Morgan's disappearance spread to other states. Some of President Jackson's political opponents saw a chance to use this excitement against him, since he was a member of the society. They organized the Anti-Masonic party and, in 1831, held a national nominating convention in Baltimore to pick a presidential candidate for the election of 1832.

Later, the Whigs and the Democrats began to hold nominating conventions of their own. In theory, the convention system was democratic. Party members in local meetings elected delegates to state conventions, and these, in turn, sent delegates to the national convention. In practice, professional politicians dominated the proceedings. Nevertheless, many more people were able to take part in the nominating process under the new method than had been able to do so under the caucus method.

The common man could get a government job

By the time Thomas Jefferson had left the presidency in 1809, most government officeholders were Democratic-Republicans. Jefferson's successors—Madison, Monroe, and the second Adams—had kept most of the same men in government offices. These officeholders stayed on for years, even though some were inefficient or guilty of corruption.

When Jackson took over the presidency, in 1829, he determined to change all that. "Office is considered as a species of property," he told Congress, "and government rather as a means of promoting individual interests than as an instrument created solely for the service of the people." It seemed to him that the officeholders constituted a privileged group, remote from the people and more concerned with their own welfare than with the people's interests. He thought that the government offices should belong to the people and that most of the people were fit to hold them. Official duties, he said, could be made "so plain and simple that men of intelligence may readily qualify themselves."

Some of Jackson's followers spoke more cynically. These men frankly said that government jobs should be used to reward party members who had helped put the party into power. One of the Jacksonians, William L. Marcy of New York, declared: "To the victors belong the spoils."

If government jobs belonged to the victors, and if the common man was fit to help govern, then no one should hold a particular job very long. Instead, it ought to be passed around among several men.

So the Jacksonians advocated rotation in office as a kind of corollary to the spoils system.

Accordingly, President Jackson, unlike his predecessors, immediately began to remove officeholders and replace them with his followers. He did not remove nearly so many, however, as his opponents accused him of doing. During his two terms he replaced only about one fifth of the total number. Nor did he appoint illiterate backwoodsmen to positions requiring special knowledge, as his critics also charged.

The use of patronage for party purposes—a practice which later Presidents also followed—sometimes led to serious abuses. Eventually a day was to come when reform was demanded, and (after 1883) the spoils system began to give way gradually to the merit system in the civil service.

Despite its evils, the spoils system had desirable and democratic implications, at least in the beginning. It meant that more and more people had a chance to hold government jobs. It meant also that a party could get the support of enthusiastic job seekers at election time. Hence, the party could win elections without depending heavily on wealthy individuals and corporations for campaign funds and thus falling under their control.

More voters went to the polls

Only about 27 in 100 white men voted in the presidential election of 1824, but more than twice as high a proportion—about 55 in 100—did so in 1828. The proportion of voters remained approximately the same in the next two elections, those of 1832 and 1836. Then it jumped again in 1840, with more than 78 in 100 casting their ballots.

This remarkable increase in voting was due only in part to the reduction or removal of property requirements. It was due also to the activity of political parties. Elections became more exciting and aroused more popular interest than in earlier years.

In 1824, there were four presidential candidates, all Republicans: Andrew Jackson, John Quincy Adams, Henry Clay, and William H. Crawford.

PRESIDENTIAL ELECTIONS: 1832-1844

CANDIDATES: 1832

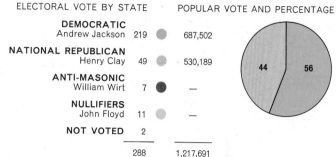

ELECTORAL VOTE BY STATE   POPULAR VOTE AND PERCENTAGE

DEMOCRATIC
Andrew Jackson   219   687,502

NATIONAL REPUBLICAN
Henry Clay   49   530,189

ANTI-MASONIC
William Wirt   7   —

NULLIFIERS
John Floyd   11   —

NOT VOTED   2

288   1,217,691

44   56

CANDIDATES: 1836

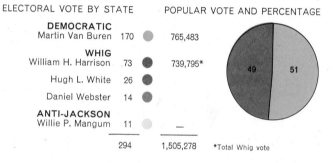

ELECTORAL VOTE BY STATE   POPULAR VOTE AND PERCENTAGE

DEMOCRATIC
Martin Van Buren   170   765,483

WHIG
William H. Harrison   73   739,795*

Hugh L. White   26

Daniel Webster   14

ANTI-JACKSON
Willie P. Mangum   11   —

294   1,505,278   *Total Whig vote

49   51

CANDIDATES: 1840

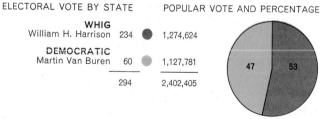

ELECTORAL VOTE BY STATE   POPULAR VOTE AND PERCENTAGE

WHIG
William H. Harrison   234   1,274,624

DEMOCRATIC
Martin Van Buren   60   1,127,781

294   2,402,405

47   53

CANDIDATES: 1844

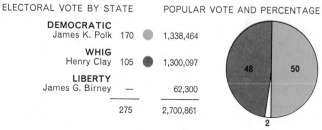

ELECTORAL VOTE BY STATE   POPULAR VOTE AND PERCENTAGE

DEMOCRATIC
James K. Polk   170   1,338,464

WHIG
Henry Clay   105   1,300,097

LIBERTY
James G. Birney   —   62,300

275   2,700,861

48   50

2

None of them won a majority in the electoral college, and so the House of Representatives had to choose between the two highest, Jackson and Adams. The followers of Jackson, the great military hero of the War of 1812, thought the House of Representatives ought to choose him, because he had received more popular votes and more electoral votes than Adams. Nevertheless, Clay threw his support to Adams, and the House chose him.

After his election, Adams named Clay as his secretary of state. In those days the office of secretary of state was looked upon as a stepping stone to the presidency. Since each of the last four Presidents—Jefferson, Madison, Monroe, Adams—had held that office, Clay could expect to succeed Adams. The angry Jacksonians charged that there had been a "corrupt bargain" between the two men, Clay agreeing to make Adams President now, and Adams promising to make Clay President later. No doubt Adams had agreed to support Clay in the future, but there was nothing corrupt about the agreement.

The Jacksonians determined to win the next election, and they immediately began to prepare for it. When the election came, in 1828, with Jackson opposing Adams, it had some of the characteristics of a "grudge fight." Certainly it was a dirty campaign. The Jacksonians accused the conscientious and puritanical Adams of waste, extravagance, and all kinds of misdeeds as President. The Adamsites accused Jackson of even worse crimes, including murder and adultery. They said he had shot some of his own soldiers in cold blood during the War of 1812 and had knowingly lived for a time with another man's wife. The charges and countercharges, false though they were, aroused the interest of the voters and brought them to the polls in unprecedented numbers. Jackson, with 56 per cent of the popular vote, easily defeated Adams.

In 1832, Clay ran against President Jackson. Jackson decisively defeated him as well as the Anti-Masonic candidate, William Wirt, who carried only the state of Vermont. Then, in 1836, Jackson picked his Vice President, Martin Van Buren, to succeed him. The Whigs (formerly the National Republicans) put three candidates in the field—William Henry Harrison, Daniel Webster, and Hugh L. White—but Van Buren, with Jackson's backing, defeated them all.

To most voters, the Whigs seemed to be the party of the rich and the Democrats the party of the common man. The Whig leaders began to realize that they could never elect a President until they changed the image of their party. They did so in 1840.

That year the Whigs nominated only one man for the presidency, William Henry Harrison. He was the victor of the Battle of Tippecanoe (1811), a man whose reputation could be used to offset Jackson's military fame. For the vice presidency they nominated John Tyler, a Virginia Democrat who had turned against Jackson and was expected to bring some of Jackson's former followers along with him. The Democrats renominated Van Buren.

In the campaign the Whigs turned the tables on the Democrats. The Whigs claimed that *they* were the friends and the Democrats were the enemies of the common man. A Democratic newspaper unintentionally helped the Whig propaganda. The editor remarked that Harrison was a simple soul who would have been happy just to live in a log cabin and guzzle hard cider. Immediately the Whigs took up the log cabin and the cider jug as symbols of their campaign. They said their candidate was indeed an unpretentious old soldier, a frontier fighter, a common man. They pictured Van Buren, on the other hand, as an effete Easterner who lived in a mansion and ate with gold-plated spoons.

The Whigs, in 1840, set a new pattern for political campaigns; they introduced the circus atmosphere that has prevailed ever since. Their candidate, Harrison, was the first to go out and make stump speeches for himself. Although such electioneering by a presidential candidate did not become the accepted practice until after the Civil War, other Whig innovations were promptly adopted for the quadrennial circuses—huge mass meetings, parades of shouting marchers, campaign buttons and badges, campaign slogans and songs. The singing Whigs, to the refrain of "Tippecanoe and Tyler too," not only carried the election of 1840, but also stimulated more people to vote than ever before, even more than in the bitter election of 1828.

REVIEWING THE SECTION

1. Why was the caucus replaced by the nominating convention?

2. How did the "spoils system" tend to increase political democracy?

3. How did the activities of political parties increase the number of participating voters?

THE JACKSONIANS FAVORED FREE ENTERPRISE

The movement for political reforms, reforms intended to give a larger role to the common man, is often called Jacksonian Democracy. Actually, the movement was broader than any man or party. Nevertheless, Jackson and his followers did much to further it. They also advocated changes in economic policy, hoping to make economic as well as political life more democratic.

The Whigs and the Democrats had very different philosophies about the proper relationship between the government and economic life. The Whigs advocated essentially the same policies as Alexander Hamilton, the same ones that Henry Clay had called the American System. According to the Whigs, the federal government should regulate and encourage economic activity by means of protective tariffs, a national bank, and expenditures for internal improvements.

The Democrats believed that such policies would help certain manufacturers, bankers, and some businessmen but would hurt other businessmen and nearly all farmers and planters. So the Democrats insisted that the government should keep its hands off economic affairs. They believed that the government should allow free opportunity for all and should give special favors to none. In open competition, according to the Democratic theory,

individuals and companies would get ahead in proportion to their own abilities.

Jackson won the "bank war"

The second Bank of the United States (chartered in 1816) served a number of important purposes. It handled the government's funds, made loans to business firms, and issued banknotes which circulated as a dependable form of currency. But Jackson and his followers disliked the Bank. They looked upon it as a dangerous monopoly, for it had an exclusive right to the federal government's banking business. Some, the "hard money" men, also objected to it because they thought only gold and silver coin should be used as money. Still others, the "soft money" men, objected for a very different reason; they thought there should be even more banknotes in circulation. The "soft money" people favored the state banks (banks chartered by the states rather than the federal government) and wished them to be free to put out large quantities of their own banknotes. But the Bank of the United States indirectly regulated the state banks and prevented them from issuing notes as freely as they would have liked.

The charter of the Bank was to expire in 1836. Fearing Jackson's opposition, the president of the Bank, Nicholas Biddle, made loans to certain politicians and newspapermen to induce them to support the Bank. Henry Clay, a friend of Biddle's, advised him that it would be easier to get the Bank rechartered in 1832 than later on. Clay persuaded him to apply for a new charter immediately.

Congress passed a recharter bill in 1832, but President Jackson vetoed it. He denounced the Bank as undemocratic, unconstitutional, and un-American (since many of the stockholders were foreigners). In the election of 1832, Clay ran as a friend of the Bank, and he was badly defeated. The Bank proved to be much less popular than Clay had thought it was.

Jackson, convinced that the people were behind him, promptly took steps to weaken the Bank. He ordered the secretary of the treasury to deposit no more of the government's money in it and to put the money in a number of state banks instead. When the secretary declined on the grounds that such action would be against the law, Jackson appointed a new secretary, and when this one also hesitated, Jackson appointed still another, Roger B. Taney. Secretary Taney began to put the money in what Jackson's opponents called the administration's "pet banks."

Biddle counterattacked by raising the Bank's interest rates and calling in some of its loans to businessmen. He said he had to do this because the government had taken away so much of the Bank's deposits. Some business firms, unable to get bank credit for carrying on their business, were compelled to close down. Many workers lost their jobs, especially in the manufacturing cities and towns of the Northeast. Biddle and the Whig friends of the Bank blamed Jackson for the trouble. The Jacksonians blamed Biddle. They said he had deliberately brought on the "Biddle panic" in order to make the administration end its anti-Bank policy.

If that was Biddle's aim, he failed. The government deposits were not restored to the Bank, and it ceased to exist in 1836. The Democrats claimed that Jackson had won a great victory for the common people.

After the passing of the second Bank of the United States, the state banks began to issue loans and banknotes more freely than they had for many years. Prices rose and business boomed. Suddenly, in 1837, a financial panic struck. Banks and businesses began to fail, and unemployment rapidly increased. This was much worse than the brief Biddle panic. It was the beginning of the worst depression the country had yet experienced.

The failure to recharter the Bank left the government with a problem: Some agency was needed to take care of the government's funds. The Democrats objected to the establishment of a new national bank, and the Whigs objected to the continued use of "pet banks." President Van Buren proposed to "divorce" the government from all banks and to let the government itself handle its money.

Finally, in 1840, Congress took Van Buren's advice and set up the Independent Treasury system. The Independent Treasury was a government agency which kept tax receipts and other income in vaults in Washington, D.C., and in other large cities. The Independent Treasury did no banking business; it made no loans and issued no notes. From the time the money was collected to the time it was disbursed, it remained out of circulation.

The next year, when the Whigs were in power under President Tyler, they abolished the Independent Treasury. In 1846, however, the Democrats succeeded in setting it up again. It continued to be the repository for government funds until the Federal Reserve System was established in 1913.

The Democrats opposed the protective tariff

In accordance with the compromise made in 1833, after South Carolina had attempted to nullify the tariff laws, the tariff rates were lowered year by year. By 1842, the general level of duties was to be back about where it had been in 1816. In 1842, however, the Whigs raised the tariff again.

Although they were not opposed to passing tariffs to obtain revenue for the federal government, the Democrats continued to oppose the use of tariffs to protect United States producers from foreign competition. Such protection, the Democrats argued, was undemocratic and unfair. It favored certain people, those whose products were protected, at the expense of others, those who had to pay increased prices for the protected goods.

In 1846, the Democrats in Congress passed a bill to lower the rates, and the Democratic President (James K. Polk) gladly signed it. Thereafter, the main effect of the tariff was to provide revenue, not to keep competing goods out of the country.

In the continual debates over the tariff, clashes of economic interest were involved. There was a contest between the manufacturers who demanded protective tariffs and most farmers and planters.

But there was also a question of principle, the question whether the government should aid certain groups or should treat all of them alike. From the Democratic point of view, at least, the reduction of the tariff represented a gain for the principle of democracy.

The Taney court opposed monopoly

While he was President, Jackson appointed seven new members to the Supreme Court (out of a total of nine). One of Jackson's appointees was Roger B. Taney, the former secretary of the treasury, who became chief justice upon the death of John Marshall. Though not so outstanding as Marshall had been, Taney also proved to be a great jurist.

There was no sharp break in constitutional interpretation between the Marshall court and the Taney court. There was, however, a change in emphasis. The Taney court was somewhat less nationalistic and more democratic than the Marshall court had been. The new judicial spirit was exemplified in the case of *Charles River Bridge* v. *Warren Bridge* (1837).

The facts of the case were these: Years earlier the Massachusetts legislature had given a company the right to build and operate a toll bridge across the Charles River. Later, the legislature authorized another company to build a free bridge. The first company objected on the grounds that the competition of the free bridge would deprive the company of its profits. This corporation brought suit to prevent the building of a new bridge.

The constitutional question was essentially the same as in the Dartmouth College case (1819). Could a state violate the terms of a charter it had granted to a private corporation? Would this be constitutional, considering the clause prohibiting each state from "impairing the obligation of contracts"? In the case of Dartmouth College, the Marshall court had said no. In the Charles River Bridge case, however, the Taney court said yes. Taney held that the new bridge would aid trans-

portation and commerce and thus would promote the general welfare. This, he said, was more important than the protection of property rights.

By permitting the bridge monopoly to be broken, this decision supported the Jacksonian principle that competition ought to be encouraged.

REVIEWING THE SECTION

1. Why did Jackson prevent renewal of the charter of the second Bank of the United States? What steps did he take to win the "bank war"? What was the primary function of the Independent Treasury?

2. Why did the Democrats favor a low tariff?

3. In what way did the case of *Charles River Bridge* v. *Warren Bridge* (1837) represent a victory for free enterprise?

REFORMERS TRIED TO IMPROVE SOCIETY AND MAN

Americans used the "principle of association" to combat all kinds of evils, from drunkenness to slavery. Societies were formed, money was raised, newspapers and pamphlets were published, petitions were drawn up and submitted to state legislatures or to Congress.

Some of the social reformers were Democrats, but a larger number were Whigs. (In the case of political reformers, those anxious to widen the suffrage, the reverse was true.) A few supporters were wealthy businessmen who contributed thousands of dollars to various causes. Most leaders and members of reform societies, however, were middle-class people—farmers, shopkeepers, professional men. Few were day laborers.

Some of the reformers came from the South, but the great majority were Northerners, and a remarkably large number were born or lived part of their lives in New England or upstate New York. While the reform agitation, the "freedom's ferment," swept over the Northeast and the Northwest, it scarcely touched the South.

Some reformers had no church connections and no religious convictions. Most, however, belonged

The Firemasters and Officers of the Volunteer Fire Companies of Charleston, by Christian Meyr, 1840

The People in a Democracy. Some nineteenth-century Americans reflected the brash spirit of the frontier; others took pride in their refined European heritage. The "firemasters" of Charleston, South Carolina, apparently preferred European-style dress uniforms, while Western trappers adapted comfortable Indian buckskins. (They are setting beaver traps.) The tradition of formal military exercises was carried out on "training day" in Salem, Massachusetts when all sorts of people gathered to watch parading militiamen and to enjoy the accompanying carnival. A dignified portrait of a mother and daughter typifies the elegance of the New England middle class. Two Midwest types are the backwoods politician and the rough men whose livelihoods depended on the Mississippi River.

The Stump Orator,
by George Caleb Bingham, c. 1850

Courtesy Mercantile Library Association, St. Louis. © 1959 by the University of Oklahoma Press

Mrs. Mayer and Daughter, by Ammi Phillips, c. 1835

Salem Common on Training Day (detail), by George Ropes, 1808

The Trappers, by Alfred Jacob Miller, 1837

The Wood Boat, by George Caleb Bingham, 1850

to one or another of the Protestant denominations. It was not that the churches, as a rule, officially favored reform. Many opposed it. Some reform-minded members, therefore, left their church and "came out" from under its influence; such people often were known as "come-outers."

There was one thing that all the reformers had in common. That was a belief in the perfectability of man, a belief that human beings and their lives on this earth could be made perfect or at least could be vastly improved.

Some faiths emphasized man's perfectability

In colonial times most religious groups, especially the Puritans, had taken a rather pessimistic view of man's potentialities both in this life and in the next. The Puritans believed that man was born in sin, and only God's "elect"—those He had foreordained to be saved—could escape eternal damnation. New religious movements in the early nineteenth century were more optimistic. These taught that salvation was open to all who would seek it. They implied that men could approach perfection not only in the next world but also in this one. Hence the new doctrines encouraged social reform.

Many of the Congregational churches remained conservative in both religious and social thought. They were, after all, the successors of the churches that had been founded by the Puritans. Many of the Presbyterian churches also remained conservative. They were based on Calvinistic doctrines similar to the Puritan beliefs. In the early nineteenth century, however, both of these churches began to divide into "Old Light" and "New Light" factions. The New Light people emphasized the possibilities of salvation.

Charles G. Finney, who preached in both Congregational and Presbyterian churches, held revival meetings in the states of New York and Ohio, from the 1820's on. In his sermons, Finney insisted that people must rely on good works as well as on faith in order to be saved. Finney's preaching

inspired a number of men and women to take up the cause of social reform.

Two new churches, the Unitarian and the Universalist, had been formed earlier by groups which had broken away from the Congregationalists. The Unitarians and the Universalists believed that salvation was open to all. A Boston Unitarian minister, Ralph Waldo Emerson, came to feel, however, that the Unitarian belief was too cold and lifeless. In 1832, he gave up the ministry and, as a writer and lecturer, began to develop his philosophy of transcendentalism.

This was an optimistic philosophy. Its essence was the idea of the "oversoul," which Emerson also called "truth" or "being." Every human soul was a part of this oversoul, a part of the reality which consisted only of the good and the true. By cultivating his intuition, a person could "transcend" the limitations of his earthly nature and identify himself more and more fully with the universe. Thus he could add to the sum total of the true and the good. So Emerson said.

Transcendentalism provided a rather mystical view of life, and yet it had practical consequences for its believers. It taught them to rely on themselves, to act with confidence, and to follow their hunches. "Nothing is at last sacred," Emerson wrote, "but the integrity of your own mind." Transcendentalism stimulated reform by teaching that human beings could improve themselves and their world.

States set up public school systems

Before the 1830's, a great many children in the United States learned to read, write, and do simple arithmetic. Most of them received their education in private schools or at home, from their parents or from hired tutors. In a few cities and large towns the children attended public schools. As yet, however, no state had a general system of public education, with full tax support, compulsory attendance, and a school in every community. In the 1830's, reformers—especially labor leaders—began to demand such a system. They reasoned that if all men were to be allowed to vote and hold office then all should at least be able to read and write.

Strong opposition to the public school movement arose. Many of the people who had no children objected to paying taxes for the education of other people's children. Members of religious groups who maintained parochial schools often considered it unfair to be required to support public schools for which they had no need.

Despite the opposition, rapid progress was made. Soon Massachusetts and Pennsylvania began to set up state-wide systems of elementary schools. Other states followed. By the 1850's, every state had such a system, at least on paper. In some parts of the country, especially in the West and the South, it was years before state-wide school systems were actually set up. As late as 1860, only one child in seven of elementary school age was actually going to school in the South, and only one in six in the rest of the country.

Under the leadership of educators such as Horace Mann, of Massachusetts, the quality of education was gradually improved. The school year was lengthened (from a few months to six months or more), and special training was provided for teachers. Previously, most of the teachers had been men, many of whom taught for only a few years after graduating from college and before going into the ministry, the law, or politics. (John Adams and Daniel Webster were two examples of the many prominent politicians who at one time had been schoolteachers.) Gradually, more and more women took up teaching, and it began to be looked upon as a career. In 1839, Massachusetts established the first state-supported "normal" school (teacher-training institution).

Public secondary schools became part of the American educational system later than public primary schools. Only a small proportion of young people, most of them boys, went on to get a secondary education. Though there were (by 1860) some tax-supported high schools, especially in Massachusetts and New York, there were twenty times as many private academies in the country as a whole.

In higher education, also, the principle of public support and control was slow to be adopted. By the time of the Civil War, a total of fourteen state universities were in operation. There were several times as many private colleges, most of them church related. Many of the denominational colleges were larger and better equipped and staffed than the state universities of that time.

Reformers attacked various social evils

Some reformers thought that poverty, crime, and other social evils were largely the fault of society itself. Such reformers hoped to improve mankind by improving society. They planned what they considered to be model communities, which they expected would set an example for other communities to imitate. In these model communities, private ownership of land, homes, or the means of production generally was prohibited, and people were expected to labor for the common good. Robert Owen, a textile manufacturer from Scotland, went to Indiana and founded the community of New Harmony, on the Wabash River. Followers of Charles Fourier, a French theorist who influenced many Americans although he never visited the United States, set up near Boston the community of Brook Farm. There, Nathaniel Hawthorne and other New England intellectuals spent considerable time. Somewhat similar experiments in social planning were tried in various parts of the country. None of these experiments succeeded.

Most reformers, instead of starting afresh and trying to create new communities, directed their efforts toward correcting specific wrongs in society as it already existed. Dorothea Dix, a Boston schoolteacher, devoted her life to improving conditions in jails and prisons and founding separate institutions for the mentally ill, who were often thrown in with convicts.

The American Society for the Promotion of Temperance, founded in 1826, agitated for "local

The Drunkard's Progress, by N. Currier, 1846

The spirit of reform which characterized the years 1815-1850 motivated the temperance movement. Temperance groups sought to prove that drinking was immoral, and they fought for legislation to prohibit the sale of alcoholic beverages. Other organizations attempted to remedy specific social, economic, and political evils. Most groups felt that uplifting the individual was the key to improving society.

option" laws, which would authorize local governments to prohibit liquor sales. Temperance crusaders persuaded Maine to adopt state-wide prohibition in 1851. Other reformers believed that tobacco, coffee, and improper foods were as bad as strong drink in preventing people from realizing their full potentialities.

Women, far more than men, faced handicaps in trying to develop their abilities and express themselves. By custom they were barred from professional careers other than school-teaching and were forbidden to appear as public speakers. By law they could not vote or hold office. Even in the reform societies they were discriminated against and kept in the background. Hence, in 1848, Lucretia Mott and Elizabeth Cady Stanton called a women's convention which met in Seneca Falls, New York. The delegates resolved that all men *and women* were created equal and endowed with certain inalienable rights.

The American Peace Society, founded in 1828, campaigned for the elimination of war. The society's founder, William Ladd of Maine, drew up a plan for a congress of nations and a court of nations to preserve world peace. Nothing came of the plan. The peace movement was weakened by disagreements among its members. Some thought they ought to support wars of self-defense; others thought they ought to oppose all wars. Most of the pacifists, especially in New England, denounced the Mexican War (1846-1848) as a war of aggression on the part of the United States. They believed, mistakenly, that Southern slaveholders had brought on the war in order to get from Mexico new territories for slavery. Generally the pacifists were also abolitionists. But when the Civil War came, they were willing to fight or at least to support others who fought, for they looked upon this as another war resulting from the aggressions of the "slave power."

REVIEWING THE SECTION

1. How did religious thought in the early nineteenth century contribute to reform? What were the attitudes of different religious groups toward reform?

2. Why did reformers promote state-supported public schools? Why did they meet strong opposition? What progress was made, by 1860, toward improving the quality of public education?

3. List the kinds of social reforms that many people sought in the early nineteenth century.

ABOLITIONISTS DEMANDED AN END TO SLAVERY

Reformers in Europe as well as in the United States campaigned against slavery. The Europeans achieved notable successes; Britain abolished slavery in the British West Indies (1833), and France abolished it in the French West Indies (1848). The American reformers could claim no such victory, but they did succeed in calling attention to slavery and raising serious questions about its continued existence.

The antislavery movement remained rather mild and weak in the United States until the 1830's. The largest antislavery organization was the American Colonization Society, which dated from 1816. This society undertook to transport free Negroes to West Africa, and it founded the colony of Liberia on the African coast to receive them. Supposedly, this kind of "colonization" would gradually decrease the number of slaves, since owners would be more ready to *manumit* them (free them from servitude) if sure that the Negroes, once freed, would be shipped out of the country. Prominent Southerners and Northerners, among them Henry Clay and Daniel Webster, supported the program. Year after year, however, the society managed to remove only a tiny fraction of the number of Negroes annually born in the United States.

During the 1820's, the most active crusader against slavery was Benjamin Lundy, a New Jersey Quaker. He organized societies in the states of the upper South to campaign for manumission. He also edited an antislavery newspaper, the *Genius of Universal Emancipation,* in Baltimore.

A young printer from Massachusetts, William Lloyd Garrison, worked on Lundy's paper. In 1831, Garrison started a paper of his own, *The Liberator,* in Boston. Garrison gave rise to a more determined, more extreme phase of the antislavery movement in the United States.

Antislavery societies multiplied

In 1833, Garrison helped organize the American Anti-Slavery Society, which sent out agents to set up local societies. By 1840, nearly two thousand societies were scattered throughout the North. They had a total membership of perhaps as many as 200,000.

Though Garrison was the best-known leader, there were others equally important. Theodore Dwight Weld, for one, probably made more converts than Garrison did. As a young man of twenty-two, Weld had joined a "holy band" of revivalists led by Charles G. Finney. After turning from revivalism to abolitionism, Weld compiled the most powerful of all nonfictional antislavery books,

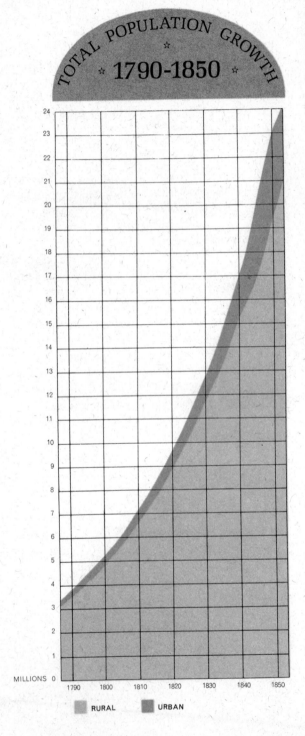

TOTAL POPULATION GROWTH
★
★ 1790-1850 ★

MILLIONS

RURAL URBAN

Slavery As It Is: Testimony of a Thousand Witnesses (1839), a collection of first-hand accounts. Included in the book were Southern newspaper advertisements for runaways, identifying them by scars and mutilations; these items gave proof of the brutality of slavery. Weld usually lectured to church groups, reaching numerous audiences from Ohio to New York.

Garrison, by contrast, refused to have anything to do with the churches, most of which he considered hostile to reform. Something of an anarchist, he also denounced government. He condemned the Constitution because it did not prohibit slavery, calling it "a covenant with death and an agreement with hell." A thoroughgoing pacifist, he advocated complete nonviolence and nonresistance. A believer in women's rights, he insisted that women be permitted to take an active part in the antislavery movement.

By his extreme attitudes and his harsh words, Garrison finally split the American Anti-Slavery Society in 1840. His opponents withdrew to form a separate organization, the American and Foreign Anti-Slavery Society. This division at the top did not slow down the movement. The local antislavery societies continued to grow and to carry on their activities.

Free Negroes played an important part in the antislavery movement. Even before the founding of the American Anti-Slavery Society, they held meetings and published newspapers and pamphlets to demand the abolition of slavery. Among the most influential of the Negro spokesmen were David Walker and Frederick Douglass. Walker, a Boston clothing dealer, wrote a powerful tract, Walker's Appeal (1829), in which he advised slaves to use force if necessary to gain their freedom—"kill or be killed." Douglass, after escaping from a Maryland plantation, became one of the most eloquent of all antislavery orators. When white men and women began to advocate abolition, most of the Negro abolitionists coöperated with them and joined the same societies. At one time, three fourths of the subscribers to The Liberator were Negroes.

The antislavery societies turned to political action

Most of the societies proclaimed "immediate emancipation" as their aim. The members did not really expect, however, to bring about emancipation in a day or a week. They realized that, at best, it would take many years. They explained that what they actually meant to achieve was emancipation "promptly commenced" but "gradually accomplished."

At first, they hoped to achieve their goal by "moral suasion." That is, they intended to appeal to the conscience of the slaveholder and convince him that slaveholding was a sin. They made little headway at this, though a few slaveholders were persuaded to turn loose their slaves and join the antislavery movement.

Later the societies, except for the strict Garrisonians, turned their attention to the government, federal and state. Nearly all the antislavery people agreed that the federal government had no power to deal with slavery within the states where it already existed. But they believed that the federal government had full constitutional power to abolish slavery in the District of Columbia, to prohibit it in the western territories, and to bring an end to the interstate slave trade. They demanded that the federal government do these things. In addition, they asked for the repeal of the Fugitive Slave Act of 1793, which provided for the return of fugitive slaves from one state to another.

In the case of *Prigg* v. *Pennsylvania* (1842), the Supreme Court held that it was the duty of federal officials to capture and return fugitives and that state authorities were not required to help. Immediately the antislavery societies began urging the Northern states to pass "personal liberty" laws, and several of the states did so. The personal liberty laws forbade state officials to assist in capturing or returning runaways.

Antislavery people often aided runaways directly. Along several routes from the slave states to the North and to British North America (Canada), friends of the slaves operated the "underground railroad," hiding the fugitives by day and moving them from one "station" to another by night.

In trying to influence the federal or state governments, the antislavery societies took part in politics as pressure groups. They flooded Congress with petitions, and they advised their members to vote for those political candidates who were the most favorable, or the least hostile, to the cause. Some of the leaders thought the antislavery people should also take part in politics as a political party. Hence they organized the Liberty party and campaigned for its candidates in the presidential elections of 1840 and 1844. The Liberty party men did not expect to elect a President of the United States, but they hoped to draw so many votes away from the Whig and Democratic parties that one or both of them would adopt antislavery aims in order to get antislavery support.

Antislavery societies influenced Northern opinions

In the beginning, the antislavery people, who were looked upon as troublemakers, faced a great deal of hostility in the North as well as in the South. Often speakers were pelted with stones or rotten eggs. Sometimes they were arrested and jailed. Occasionally, they risked serious injury and even death. In 1835, a Boston mob seized Garrison, put a rope around him, dragged him through the streets, and threatened to lynch him. In 1837, the enemies of Elijah Lovejoy, an antislavery editor of Alton, Illinois, shot and killed him.

As time passed, the antislavery campaigners received more and more sympathy from the Northern public, even from people who cared nothing about the slave. This change in Northern opinion resulted, in part, from the efforts of Southerners to stop the antislavery movement. In 1835, several Southern legislatures appealed to Northern legislatures to suppress the "incendiary" propaganda of the abolitionists. No Northern legislature complied. In 1836, however, Southerners induced the national House of Representatives to adopt a "gag rule" for tabling all antislavery petitions and thus ignoring them. John Quincy Adams, once a President, then a congressman, led the fight against the gag rule and finally secured its repeal in 1844. Such experiences as these convinced many Northerners that antislavery people were telling the truth when they said there was a great slave-power conspiracy which, if not checked, would deprive all Americans of the right of free speech.

Only a comparatively small number of Northerners were ever converted to abolitionism itself, but the great majority came to believe that slavery was, in some degree, a social evil and a moral wrong.

REVIEWING THE SECTION

1. How did Garrison and Weld contribute to the growth of the antislavery movement?

2. What methods did the antislavery societies use to accomplish their aim? What did many abolitionists mean by "immediate emancipation"?

3. Why did Northern opinion change toward abolitionists?

CHAPTER **9** CONCLUSION

A great many Americans were reformers of one kind or another during the period from 1815 to 1850. Not all these people wanted the same sort of changes, yet all were eager to make the nation more democratic in some respect. They wanted to provide greater equality of opportunity in political, economic, or social life. In all these areas they made important gains, though they did not achieve nearly so much as most of them would have liked.

As a result of the movements for *political reform,* a larger proportion of white men received the right to vote and hold office, and a larger number of offices were made elective. Free Negroes gained little, however, and even suffered setbacks; in Pennsylvania, for example, they lost their right to vote. Women obtained no political rights.

New techniques of mass politics were introduced, such as the nominating convention and the spoils system. Political parties became more active and more highly organized, and election campaigns more exciting. Not only did more men have a right to participate in politics but more of them acquired an interest in doing so.

As a result of the movements for *economic reform,* the federal government ceased to allow its own banking operations to be monopolized by a private corporation, the second Bank of the United States. The government was completely separated from all banks. Moreover, protective tariffs were almost eliminated, and states were permitted (as in the Charles River Bridge case) to end state-granted monopolies and encourage competition.

In some ways, these changes in economic policy were bad for business or, at least, for certain businesses. For example, many businessmen had relied on the Bank of the United States for banknotes which served as currency of wide acceptability and uniform value. Some manufacturers had depended on protective tariffs to keep prices up and assure profits. Certain political leaders—Whigs like Clay and Webster—contended that the tariffs, by encouraging American manufacturers, contributed to the prosperity of the nation as a whole. Nevertheless, the new banking and tariff policies meant greater opportunity for small enterprises to rise, through competition, to economic success. From the Jacksonian point of view, it seemed that these policies made for increased economic democracy, and to a considerable extent they actually did so.

As a result of the movements for *social reform,* a beginning was made toward the establishment of state-wide systems of elementary schools. Some improvements were brought about in the care of the criminal and the insane. In certain localities, drunkenness was discouraged by laws against the sale of strong drink. Except in the field of education, however, the drive for social reform fell far short of the intended aims. The antislavery crusade, for example, had not succeeded, by 1850, in imposing any specific limitation upon slavery, though the crusade had helped to create in the North a strong feeling of opposition to human bondage and to the pretensions of the "slave power."

Though failing to bring immediate results, some of the campaigns for social reform were, nevertheless, to have important consequences in the long run. Emancipation, for example, was eventually to come with the Civil War, and emancipation at that time would hardly have been conceivable without the long-continued labor of the abolitionists. Prohibition of the manufacture, sale, or transportation of intoxicating beverages was finally to be written into a constitutional amendment, the eighteenth, though this was to remain in effect for only a little more than a dozen years (1919-1933).

Reform agitation also had certain consequences that were not intended nor anticipated. The success of the campaigns against the national bank and the protective tariff antagonized the business interests, especially in the North, which the bank and the tariff had benefited. The abolition crusade produced among Northerners a suspicion against the South and among Southerners a fear of the North. Thus, the movement for greater democracy helped to create the sectionalism which was to lead to disunion and the Civil War.

Meanwhile, sectionalism was intensified also by the urge to expand the limits of the United States. The acquisition of new territories raised anew the question of the expansion of slavery. This question, more than any other, led directly to the division of the states.

FOCUSING ON SPECIFICS

1. What was the cause of the Dorr Rebellion?

2. Why did political parties become more organized as the states grew more democratic?

3. Why was the Anti-Masonic party organized? What contribution did it make to American politics?

4. What reason did members of the Democratic party give for distributing government jobs among party members?

5. What innovations were made by the Whigs in the method of conducting political campaigns?

6. What did the Whigs feel should be the proper relation between the government and the economy? What did the Democrats believe it should be?

7. How did Biddle retaliate against Jackson's refusal to renew the charter of the second Bank? What were the results?

8. What functions of the Bank of the United States were not performed by the Independent Treasury?

9. How did Charles G. Finney help to change attitudes toward reform?

10. What was Emerson's philosophy of "transcendentalism"? What significance did it have for the reform movement?

11. What were the objectives of the American Colonization Society?

12. What part did Negroes play in the antislavery movement?

13. What were the "personal liberty" laws?

14. What was the purpose of the "underground railroad"?

15. How did the Liberty party attempt to further the antislavery movement?

16. How did the "gag rule" influence Northern opinion?

REVIEWING MAIN THEMES

1. Between 1815 and 1850, in what ways were state constitutions made more democratic?

2. What did political parties contribute toward making politics more democratic?

3. What measures did the Jacksonians take to promote economic opportunity? Why did they feel these measures were democratic?

4. Name some of the social reforms advocated between 1815 and 1850. What steps did the reformers take to secure the enactment of their programs?

5. How did the antislavery movement change between 1830 and 1850? What results did the abolitionists achieve?

EVALUATING THE ISSUES

1. Reform agitation often has unintended effects. The antislavery crusade, for example, increased the sectionalism which eventually led to war. Discuss unintended effects arising from the following reforms: the failure to recharter the second Bank, the system of "rotation in office," the lowering of property qualifications for voting.

2. Why did the movement for the emancipation of women fail to gain strength before the Civil War?

CHAPTER **10** 1815-1850

The Advance to the Pacific

With the Louisiana Purchase (1803), the United States approximately doubled its territory. In 1819, East Florida was added, rounding out the nation on the southeast (West Florida had already been occupied). After that, some people in the United States were satisfied that their territory was large enough. Senator Thomas Hart Benton of Missouri, for one, said (in 1825) that he hoped the Rocky Mountains would remain the "everlasting boundary" of the republic. Others, however, insisted that the boundary ought to be pushed westward all the way to the Pacific Ocean. Still others thought the boundaries ought also to be pushed northward and southward, so that eventually the United States would cover the whole continent of North America.

There were a number of motives behind this expansionist feeling; some of these motives were economic. Fur traders hoped to get free access to the habitat of the beaver, without the competition of foreigners. Farmers desired fresh lands for farms, and planters for plantations. Merchants and ship-owners were interested in the great natural harbors of the Pacific coast, especially those in San Francisco Bay and Puget Sound, from which it seemed possible to develop a profitable Pacific trade.

Some Americans wanted to acquire new territories for strategic reasons. They believed that some foreign powers—Britain, France, Russia—might try to increase their territory or their influence in North America. If any of them should succeed in doing so, the national security of the United States might be endangered. By acquiring new territories, this nation could head off possible enemies.

Still other Americans wanted to acquire new territories for idealistic or psychological reasons. Expansionism was, in large part, an odd mixture of nationalism and humanitarianism. Many Americans believed they had a duty both to make additional room for their rapidly growing population and to extend the benefits of American democracy and civilization to neighboring peoples, by force if necessary.

This belief in expansionism came to be known as Manifest Destiny. The phrase, which first appeared in print in 1845, came from the pen of John L. O'Sullivan, the editor of a Democratic newspaper in New York City. It is "our manifest destiny," O'Sullivan wrote, "to overspread and to possess the whole of the continent which Providence has given us." Politicians soon picked up the phrase, and historians eventually adopted it to refer to the expansionist spirit.

In the 1840's, the enthusiasm for Manifest Destiny reached its height, and the doctrine was put rapidly into practice. The United States did not, of course, extend its boundaries to the equator and the North Pole, as some expansionists had urged. Nevertheless, in the short space of only three years, from 1845 to 1848, the following territories were acquired: Texas, the Oregon country (much larger than the present state of Oregon), California, and all the land between California and Texas. Several years later, in 1853, an additional strip of land along the Mexican border was purchased.

Meanwhile, boundary adjustments on the north and northeast had fixed permanently the entire boundary between the United States and British North America (Canada). Thus, by the 1850's, the conterminous territory of the United States (not including Alaska, Hawaii, or other possessions separated from the rest of the country by land or water) had reached the limits which still exist.

NEW U.S. BOUNDARIES WERE ESTABLISHED

When Napoleon sold Louisiana to the United States, the boundaries were not defined. The purchase treaty merely said that France was transferring the territory with the same boundaries it previously had had. But what were they?

It was commonly supposed that Louisiana consisted, roughly, of all the land between the Mississippi River and the Rocky Mountains and from the Gulf of Mexico to Canada, a British possession. President Jefferson argued that the purchase also included the part of West Florida that lay eastward from the Mississippi to the Perdido River. (The entire area of West Florida stretched along the Gulf of Mexico eastward from the Mississippi and contained parts of the present-day states of Louisiana, Mississippi, Alabama, and Florida.) In 1810 and again during the War of 1812, Americans seized pieces of West Florida, and the federal government extended its jurisdiction to include them. Spain, however, continued to claim all of West as well as East Florida and, in addition, disputed the southwestern boundary of the Louisiana Purchase.

On the north, the boundary between American and British possessions remained in doubt for many years after the Revolutionary War. As described in the peace treaty (1783), the line was, in some areas, difficult and even impossible to locate.

After the War of 1812, these boundary disputes with Spain and Britain still remained to be settled.

Andrew Jackson invaded the Floridas

The American desire for the remainder of Florida had been one of the causes of the War of 1812. This territory was important to Americans because of the richness of the land itself and because of its location, which made it possible for the Spaniards to interfere with trade on the Mississippi and other rivers flowing into the Gulf of Mexico. As one historian, Thomas A. Bailey, has written:

Like a giant pistol, with the peninsula serving as the butt and West Florida the barrel, it pointed directly at the mouth of the all-important Mississippi River.

The territory was important for still other reasons. Runaway Negro slaves frequently headed south across the border. More serious, Indian raiding parties often headed north across it. Americans feared the border would never be safe so long as Florida continued to be a Spanish possession.

In 1818, Andrew Jackson with a small army pursued a band of Indian raiders into Florida. He did not stop until he had seized the fort of St. Marks, the town of Pensacola, and every other important Spanish post except St. Augustine. He captured two British traders, tried them on charges of supplying and inciting the Indians, and had them put to death. He later said he was sorry he did not also hang the Spanish governor of the territory.

Already famous as the "hero of New Orleans," Jackson once again was hailed by most of his fellow Americans. "Among the people of the west," a Baltimore paper observed, "his popularity is unbounded—old and young speak of him with rapture,

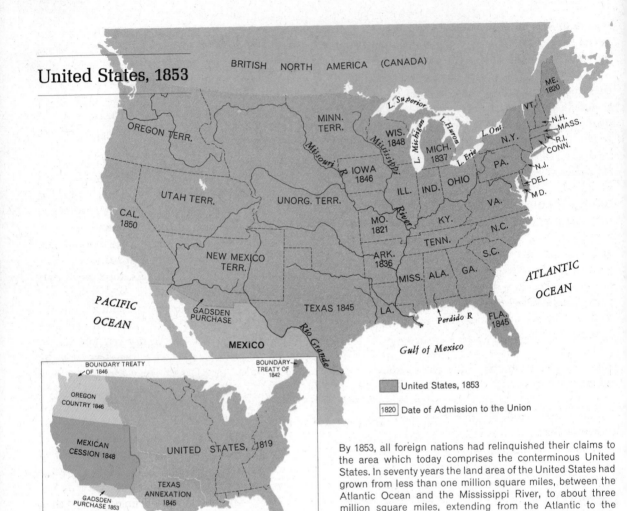

United States, 1853

BRITISH NORTH AMERICA (CANADA)

OREGON TERR.

MINN.
TERR.

WIS.
1848

MICH.
1837

ME.
1820

VT.

N.H.

MASS.

N.Y.

R.I.

CONN.

PA.

N.J.

DEL.

MD.

UTAH TERR.

UNORG. TERR.

IOWA
1846

ILL. IND. OHIO

VA.

CAL.
1850

MO.
1821

KY.

N.C.

NEW MEXICO
TERR.

ARK.
1836

TENN.

S.C.

GADSDEN
PURCHASE

TEXAS 1845

LA.

MISS. ALA. GA.

ATLANTIC
OCEAN

PACIFIC
OCEAN

MEXICO

Perdido R

FLA.
1845

Gulf of Mexico

■ United States, 1853

1820 Date of Admission to the Union

TERRITORIAL GROWTH OF THE UNITED STATES

BOUNDARY TREATY
OF 1846

BOUNDARY
TREATY OF
1842

OREGON
COUNTRY 1846

MEXICAN
CESSION 1848

UNITED STATES, 1819

TEXAS
ANNEXATION
1845

GADSDEN
PURCHASE 1853

By 1853, all foreign nations had relinquished their claims to the area which today comprises the conterminous United States. In seventy years the land area of the United States had grown from less than one million square miles, between the Atlantic Ocean and the Mississippi River, to about three million square miles, extending from the Atlantic to the Pacific Ocean.

and at his call, 50,000 of the most efficient warriors on this continent, would rise, armed, and ready for any enemy." Most of President Monroe's cabinet advisers felt, however, that Jackson had exceeded his orders and had unnecessarily complicated relations with Spain. All but one of the cabinet members thought he should be censured.

The Spanish government was outraged. It demanded that Jackson be punished and an indemnity be paid to Spain. At first, the British government also took offense. Before long, however, the British

adopted the view that the two victims of Jackson's hasty justice had deserved their fate. Britain refused to give even moral support to Spain, and Spain was far too weak to risk war without a powerful ally.

Spain agreed to a "transcontinental treaty"

At that time Monroe's secretary of state, John Quincy Adams, was negotiating with the Spanish minister to the United States, Luis de Onís, with

regard to the already existing disagreements between the two nations. Adams was the only one in
the cabinet who had opposed censuring Jackson.
Monroe sided with Adams, and Jackson was not
censured.

Adams used the Jackson affair to strengthen his
own hand in the bargaining with Onís. As secretary of state, he replied to the Spanish demands not
by apologizing but by accusing. He said the Spaniards themselves were to blame for all the trouble
in Florida. They were failing to live up to their
treaty obligations. In Pinckney's Treaty (1795)
they had promised to restrain the Indians and prevent raids across the border. After pointing this
out, Adams demanded that the Spanish government
punish the Spanish officials in Florida for their
negligence and pay the United States for the expenses of Jackson's expedition!

Adams went on to demand that Spain either
"place a force in Florida adequate at once to the
protection of her territory" or "cede to the United
States a province of which she retains nothing but
the nominal possession." He hinted that, if Spain
should refuse to do either of these things, the
United States could simply take Florida, as was
shown by the ease with which Jackson had marched
through the territory.

Finally, in 1819, Onís agreed to a treaty. By
its terms, Spain ceded all of Florida to the United
States. Spain also consented to a definite southwestern boundary for the Louisiana Purchase and
gave up her rather vague claim to the Oregon country. The United States abandoned its equally vague
claim to a part of Texas (which some Americans
claimed was part of the Louisiana Purchase). The
United States agreed, moreover, that Spain would
not have to pay damages to American citizens who
had suffered losses because of Spanish ship seizures
in earlier years. Instead, the United States promised to reimburse its own citizens for these losses
up to a total of $5 million.

The Adams-Onís Treaty of 1819 went into
effect in 1821. It is sometimes called the "Florida
purchase treaty." This is rather inexact, since no

money was paid directly to Spain. Besides, the
transaction included matters other than Florida. It
was a "transcontinental treaty" which drew a line
between Spanish and American possessions all the
way to the Pacific Ocean.

Clashes occurred on the northern border

The desire of Americans for Canada as well as
for Florida had contributed to bringing on the
War of 1812. Soon after the war, in 1817, the
Rush-Bagot Agreement between the United States
and Britain was signed in Washington. The two
nations agreed to partial and gradual disarmament
on the Great Lakes and Lake Champlain. The
agreement lessened, on both sides, the age-old fear
of invasion.

Another agreement, made in London in 1818,
defined the northwest boundary between the United
States and Canada. This boundary was fixed along
the forty-ninth parallel from the Lake of the
Woods to the crest of the Rocky Mountains. The
area beyond the Rockies—the Oregon country,
which both Britain and the United States still
claimed—was left "free and open" for settlement
by both British subjects and American citizens.
The new boundary gave a new northern limit to
the Louisiana Territory.

Eventually the boundary between the United
States and Canada was to be definitely set all the
way from the Atlantic to the Pacific, a distance of
some 3000 miles. This was to become the longest
"unguarded frontier" between two nations in the
entire world. The last fortifications along the border were not abandoned, however, for many years
—not until after 1871.

In the meantime there generally was peace
along the border. Americans and Canadians moved
freely back and forth across it. Many Americans
settled in Canada, and many Canadians settled in
the United States. Nevertheless, serious border conflicts occasionally broke out.

In 1837, a small minority of discontented Canadians in Upper Canada, led by William L.

Mackenzie, rose in rebellion against British rule. The rebel leader and some of his followers, aided by American sympathizers, took refuge on Navy Island on the Canadian side of the Niagara River. A United States steamboat, the *Caroline*, ferried supplies across the Niagara River from New York State to the rebels. Such nonneutral aid naturally angered both the Canadian loyalists and the British authorities. One night a band of Canadian soldiers attacked the *Caroline*, killed one of its American crewmen and wounded others, set fire to the boat, and let it drift down the river. The boat soon sank, but Americans afterwards circulated pictures which showed it going over Niagara Falls in flames, with screaming men aboard.

President Van Buren called upon all Americans to obey the neutrality laws (which forbade citizens to give military assistance to the enemies of nations with which the United States was at peace). Van Buren also sent an army to police the border and to keep American troublemakers at home. The British quickly put down the revolt, and quiet gradually returned to the border. But the *Caroline* affair continued to rankle in the memories of many anti-British Americans.

Trouble soon flared up again when Canadian and American lumbermen quarreled over land claims in the Aroostook Valley, the disputed area between Maine and New Brunswick. In 1839, militiamen from both Maine and New Brunswick were sent to the scene, and the United States government began to make war preparations. Before anyone was killed in the so-called Aroostook War, both sides agreed to a truce. Neither side abandoned its claims, however, and the danger of new and more serious quarrels persisted.

The northeastern boundary dispute was settled

By the beginning of 1842, it seemed that a third war with Britain might begin soon. To the existing ill feeling, another cause had been recently added. This was the *Creole* case (1841). On the *Creole*, an American slave ship sailing from Hampton Roads, Virginia, to New Orleans, the slaves had mutinied, taken charge of the ship, and brought it into a British port in the Bahamas. There the slaves were set free by the British authorities. Just as Northerners remembered the *Caroline*, so Southerners remembered the *Creole* as a grievance against Britain.

In Anglo-American relations, however, there were forces making for peace as well as for war. Britain was the best customer of the United States, buying much of the American wheat crop and most of the cotton crop, and the United States was the best customer of Britain. The United States had not yet fully recovered from the Panic of 1837, and any interruption of the trade with Britain would delay the return of prosperity.

Government leaders on both sides of the Atlantic were eager to improve relations between their two nations. The American secretary of state, Daniel Webster, admired the English, and they admired him. The British government sent Lord Ashburton (Alexander Baring), who had an American wife and was well disposed toward the United States, to negotiate with Webster.

Webster felt that the only way to settle the most serious dispute, the one concerning the northeastern boundary, was to compromise by dividing the disputed area. First, he had to get the consent of Maine and Massachusetts (Massachusetts still held land in its former territory of Maine). He did so by means of his "red-line map." This was supposed to be a copy of the map which the peacemakers had used at Paris in 1783. It was marked with a red line, and this line upheld the British claim. Secretly, Webster showed the map to commissioners representing Maine and Massachusetts. They decided they had better give up part of the disputed land rather than risk losing all of it.

Having made this "grand stroke," as he afterward called it, Webster entered into pleasant conversations with Lord Ashburton, and, in 1842, the two drew up a treaty. The most important provision split the disputed area and awarded the larger share (seven-twelfths) to the United States. The

Maine-New Brunswick boundary was fixed along its present-day line, and other provisions adjusted the boundary at the north of Vermont and New York and between Lake Superior and the Lake of the Woods. The British also conceded some 150 square miles of disputed territory at the head of the Connecticut River in New Hampshire. Nothing was said about the *Caroline* or the *Creole* in the treaty itself, but in an exchange of notes Lord Ashburton apologized for those incidents.

Democratic leaders, more anti-British than the Whigs, objected to what they said was an unnecessary sacrifice of United States territory. (Historians later discovered that Webster's red-line map had been wrong and that the true map, of which the British had a copy, really favored the American claim.) Using secret funds of the state department. Webster paid newspapers to publish propaganda favorable to the treaty. It was promptly ratified and proved quite popular.

On the whole, the Webster-Ashburton Treaty represented a fair bargain. Though the United States lost some land on the northeast, it gained land elsewhere as a result of the other boundary adjustments. The area gained at the north of Vermont and New York was strategically important. As a result of a surveying error, a United States fort had been built there, on what had been British soil until the treaty made it American. The area gained by the United States at the west of Lake Superior was economically important. It contained rich deposits of iron ore, discovered many years later. Even more important at the time, the treaty assured the maintenance of peace. For the moment, in 1842, Anglo-American relations were better than they had been for many years.

REVIEWING THE SECTION

1. Why was Florida of strategic importance to the United States? Why did Andrew Jackson raid Spanish posts in Florida?

2. How did John Quincy Adams get Spain to negotiate the Adams-Onís Treaty (1819)? What were the provisions of this treaty?

3. What was the *Caroline* affair? the Aroostook War? How did they affect British-American relations?

4. What were the provisions of the Webster-Ashburton Treaty (1842)? Why was the treaty of economic and strategic importance?

TEXAS WAS ANNEXED

When John Quincy Adams agreed to the treaty of 1819 with Spain, he was criticized for surrendering the American claim to Texas (a dubious claim, based upon the supposition that the Louisiana Purchase had included Texas). After becoming President he offered to buy the territory (1825) from Mexico, which had won its independence from Spain. Mexico refused to sell.

President Jackson tried again (in 1829), with no more success than Adams had had. Jackson's minister to Mexico, Anthony Butler, suggested using bribery to persuade the Mexican officials to sell. On the back of the minister's letter, Jackson wrote: "A. Butler. What a scamp." The Mexican government finally told Butler to leave the country.

For Mexico, the outlying district of Texas was hard to defend or to develop. Nevertheless, the Mexicans understandably wished to keep such a large and fertile piece of land. The United States finally managed to obtain Texas only after Texas had broken away from Mexico and set itself up as an independent republic.

Texans won their independence

In 1821, the Mexican government began to make large grants of Texas land to Americans, the first of whom were Moses Austin and his son Stephen. The grants were made on the condition that the grantees would bring in Roman Catholic families from the United States to settle on the land. The purpose was to develop farms which could be taxed and to acquire loyal Mexican citizens who would help defend the frontier. As things turned out, the Mexican government, so far as its own interests were concerned, was making a serious mistake.

By 1835, about 35,000 Americans were living in Texas, and they dominated that part of Mexico. Almost all these people were Protestants, a majority were Southerners, and many were slaveholders. Some were refugees from debt or jail. Throughout the United States, "Gone to Texas" became a popular phrase for explaining the whereabouts of absconders. The Texans who had come from the United States had difficulty in getting along with the native Mexicans.

The American settlers also found themselves in disagreement with the Mexican government. It passed laws to keep out additional slaves and immigrants from the United States and to revoke certain of the land grants that had already been made. A dictatorial president, Antonio Lopez de Santa Anna, who came to power in 1834, tried to centralize the government and extend his personal control throughout Mexico. The Americans in Texas began to fear that, under Santa Anna, the government might take away their lands, their slaves, and their political rights. These feelings caused the settlers to revolt.

In 1836, the Texans proclaimed their independence. A provisional government was established and Sam Houston was named commander of the army. They received supplies and enlistments from sympathizers in the United States. Santa Anna advanced with a large army to put down the revolt. At the Alamo mission in San Antonio thousands of Mexicans overwhelmed a garrison of about two hundred Texans, who fought to the last man. At Goliad the Mexicans defeated another small force and killed three hundred of the men after they had surrendered.

Then, at San Jacinto, the main Texas army met the much larger army of Santa Anna. With cries of "Remember the Alamo!" the Texans, led by Houston, smashed the Mexican army and captured Santa Anna himself. They forced him, practically at the point of a bayonet, to sign a treaty recognizing the independence of Texas. The Republic of Texas then began a career of nine years as a sovereign nation.

Annexation was delayed

The leaders of Texas had not intended for it to remain independent so long. Most of the Texans, being really Americans, wanted Texas to be a part of the United States. Besides, they feared the danger of attack from Mexico, and they looked upon membership in the Union as a necessary means of protection. The first president of the new republic, Sam Houston, promptly asked the United States government to recognize its independence. This, he thought, would be a step toward annexation.

President Jackson hesitated, however, to grant recognition. The antislavery people of the North opposed the idea of diplomatic relations with a new slaveholding nation. "Texas," the abolitionist Garrison wrote, "is the rendezvous of absconding villainy, desperate adventure, and lawless ruffianism—the ark of safety to swindlers, gamblers, robbers, and rogues of every size and degree." Finally, just before leaving the presidency in 1837, Jackson recognized Texas and opened diplomatic relations with it.

The Texas government then requested annexation. Jackson's successor, President Van Buren, was left to deal with the touchy subject. Annexation was popular in the South but unpopular in much of the North. The cautious Van Buren declined the offer made by Texas.

Thus rebuffed, the Texans turned away from the United States and looked abroad, to Britain and France. They did not seek annexation to either of these two countries but sought recognition, trade treaties, financial support, and protection against Mexico. Both the British and the French wished Texas to remain independent rather than combine with the United States. An independent Texas would provide opportunities for profitable trade without the interference of the United States tariff. So both the British and the French recognized Texas and made trade treaties with it.

THE PRESIDENTS OF THE UNITED STATES

JAMES MONROE
(1758-1831)
IN OFFICE: 1817-1825

JOHN QUINCY ADAMS
(1767-1848)
IN OFFICE: 1825-1829

Republican from Virginia. The period of Monroe's presidency, known as the "era of good feelings," was characterized by a lack of strong party rivalry. During his term of office, the northwest boundary between Canada and the United States was fixed (1818), Florida was purchased from Spain (1819), the Missouri Compromise was made (1820), and the Monroe Doctrine was promulgated (1823).

From Massachusetts. Adams was elected by the House of Representatives because the election of 1824 failed to give any one candidate a majority of electoral votes. Adams favored a program of extensive internal improvements, but Congress did not coöperate with him. The Tariff of Abominations (1828), passed during his term, hurt his chances for reëlection.

ANDREW JACKSON
(1767-1845)
IN OFFICE: 1829-1837

MARTIN VAN BUREN
(1782-1862)
IN OFFICE: 1837-1841

Democrat from Tennessee. Jackson's administration initiated the "spoils system," checked the program of federal internal improvements, and vetoed the recharter of the second Bank of the United States (1832). He asserted the authority of the federal government in the issue of nullification, and greatly expanded presidential power.

Democrat from New York. Van Buren's popularity declined as a result of the Panic of 1837 and a severe economic depression which began several months after his inauguration. His plan to replace the second Bank of the United States with an independent treasury system was put into effect in 1840. He was the presidential nominee of the Free Soil party in 1848.

The British also considered the possibility of a treaty guaranteeing the independence and the boundaries of Texas. By 1844, the Lone Star Republic seemed about to become a British satellite.

This possibility worried some prominent Americans. Unofficially, the Texans were informed that the United States at last would welcome them if they would again ask for annexation. They did so. Houston warned former President Jackson, however, that if Texas were to be "spurned" this time, "she would seek some other friend."

President Tyler hoped to have the glory of annexing Texas before he left office. He saw that a treaty of annexation was quickly drawn up. Before the Senate had acted on it, however, John C. Calhoun became secretary of state, and he did something which ruined whatever chance the treaty might have had to pass the Senate. Calhoun wrote a letter accusing the British government of conspiring to get rid of slavery in Texas. At great length he defended the institution of slavery as the best possible way of life, even for the slaves themselves. He said the institution would be endangered in the Southern states if it should be abolished in Texas, and it might be abolished in Texas if that nation should remain independent and fall under British influence. Therefore, he argued, annexation was necessary as a means of protecting slavery.

Calhoun's letter aroused strong feelings among many Northerners. They thought it proved that the abolitionists were right in saying annexation was really a proslavery plot. So much opposition was aroused that the treaty could not obtain the necessary two-thirds majority in the Senate. Thus, in 1844, annexation was frustrated again.

Texas was admitted to the Union

Expansion was the main issue in the presidential election of 1844. The Whig candidate again was Henry Clay. The Whig platform made no mention of Texas, and Clay declined to take a clear stand on the issue, hoping to get votes from both annexationists and their opponents.

The Democrats assumed that most of the voters wanted Texas in the Union. They turned down Van Buren, though he had expected the nomination. He had ruined his chances by issuing a statement that Texas should not be annexed without the consent of Mexico. Instead of Van Buren, the Democrats nominated an unexpected candidate, the first such "dark horse." This was James K. Polk, the former speaker of the House, a friend of Jackson's and a determined annexationist.

The Democratic platform called for "the re-occupation of Oregon and the re-annexation of Texas." By coupling Oregon with Texas, the Democrats hoped to appeal to Northerners as well as Southerners. Using the terms "re-occupation" and "re-annexation" they tried to give the impression that Oregon and Texas formerly had belonged to the United States. This, presumably, would strengthen the feeling in favor of acquiring both.

The Democratic campaign plan proved effective, for Polk defeated Clay. Yet Polk received only a small majority of the popular vote. Despite the narrowness of the victory, the Democrats claimed a mandate from the people in favor of expansion.

President-elect Polk, however, would not take office for four months, not until March 4, 1845. The Democrats, fearful of British intrigues in Texas, did not want to wait that long for its annexation. Though they did not have a two-thirds majority in the Senate (the number necessary to approve a treaty), they had a simple majority in both houses of Congress. Thus, though they still could not get an annexation treaty ratified, they could carry through both houses a joint resolution providing for annexation. This they finally did. On March 1, 1845, three days before he was to leave the White House, President Tyler signed the resolution, and it thus became law.

The Texans themselves still had to act. They had a choice between the United States offer of annexation and a British offer of guaranteed independence. In the summer of 1845, they elected delegates to a special convention to consider the matter, and the delegates voted almost unani-

THE PRESIDENTS OF THE UNITED STATES

WILLIAM HENRY HARRISON (1773-1841) IN OFFICE: 1841	**JOHN TYLER** (1790-1862) IN OFFICE: 1841-1845	**JAMES KNOX POLK** (1795-1849) IN OFFICE: 1845-1849

Whig from Ohio. Harrison's campaign, based on the popular appeal of parades, songs, and mass meetings, set a new pattern for presidential campaigns and won him the presidency. He called a special session of Congress to enact his party's program, but his death, one month after his inauguration, prevented him from carrying out his legislative plan.

From Virginia. Although originally a Democrat, Tyler was elected Vice President on the Whig ticket. Upon Harrison's death, Tyler succeeded to the presidency. His veto of the bills for a new national bank alienated him from the Whigs, and he again aligned himself with the Democrats. This alliance foreshadowed the gradual absorption of conservative Southern Whigs by the Democrats.

Democrat from Tennessee. Polk achieved all the major objectives of his campaign platform. Texas was admitted to the Union (1845); the Oregon boundary dispute with Britain was settled (1846); the territories of California and New Mexico were acquired as a result of the Mexican War (1846-1848); the tariff was lowered (1846); and the independent treasury system was reëstablished (1846).

mously to add the Lone Star to the Stars and Stripes. In December 1845, Texas was admitted as a slaveholding state.

REVIEWING THE SECTION

1. Why did Texas settlers proclaim their independence from Mexico?

2. Why was the annexation of Texas delayed for a number of years?

3. How did the Democrats succeed in getting Texas annexed to the United States in 1845?

THE OREGON COUNTRY WAS DIVIDED

The Oregon country was a vast territory extending from the Rocky Mountains westward to the Pacific Ocean, and from the forty-second parallel (the northern boundary of California) northward to the latitude of 54°40′ (the southern boundary of Russian America). Within that area now lie not only the state of Oregon, but also the states of Washington and Idaho, parts of Montana and Wyoming, and roughly half of the

Canadian province of British Columbia.

At one time, four nations had claimed the territory. Now only two, the United States and Britain, were left in contention. Spain gave up her claim, in the Adams-Onís treaty of 1819, and Russia gave up hers, in a treaty of 1824 with the United States and another of 1825 with Britain.

The United States based its claim largely on discovery and exploration. An American, Captain Robert Gray, had (1792) sailed his ship, the *Columbia*, into the river that afterward was known by that name. The explorers Lewis and Clark had gone overland and then down the river to its mouth. American fur traders and trappers from the United States had penetrated much of the country. But British explorers also had roamed through the Oregon country, and a huge British monopoly, the Hudson's Bay Company, had come to dominate most of the fur trade. Neither the United States nor Britain really possessed a clear title to all of the Oregon country.

The arrangement of 1818, providing for joint occupation by the Americans and the British, had been intended to run for only ten years. In 1827, since the two governments still could not agree on a division of the territory, joint occupation was renewed for an indefinite period. In 1842, Webster and Lord Ashburton discussed the Oregon question, but neither of the two then thought it very urgent. As yet, few Americans were greatly interested in the Oregon country. "I much doubt," Lord Ashburton remarked, "whether the Americans will for many years to come make any considerable lodgment on the Pacific."

Already, however, Americans were heading northwestward in increasing numbers, and excitement over the Oregon country was beginning to spread. Soon the question was to be urgent indeed.

An "Oregon fever" developed

By the 1830's, a few Americans were already in the Oregon country as traders and trappers or as missionaries to the Indians. A few others were beginning to arrive as settlers. They pioneered the way over the Oregon Trail, which started at Independence, Missouri, at the bend of the Missouri River, and led two thousand miles across the Great Plains and the Rocky Mountains to Astoria at the mouth of the Columbia River. The emigrants, with their covered wagons and cattle herds, took several months, usually from May to November, to make the long journey—if they succeeded in making it at all. Some died along the way from hunger, thirst, illness, or the bullets or arrows of hostile Indians.

By 1841, there were approximately five hundred Americans in the Oregon country. Year by year the numbers continued to grow. In 1845, a newspaper of Independence, Missouri, described how the busy streets of that town were filled with "long trains of wagons," each wagon drawn by "six or eight stout oxen," as travelers assembled to go west in caravans. There were "shouts of welcome" as "fellow voyagers" greeted one another. The editor cheered them on: "Whoo ha! Go it boys! We're in a perfect *Oregon fever.*" Some three thousand people made the overland crossing that year, more than doubling the number of Americans in Oregon, bringing the total to about five thousand.

A few were attracted to the Oregon country by the prospects of the fur trade or by the hope of saving the souls of Indians. Most, however, were drawn by news of the rich soil of the Willamette Valley, and they went as farmers. Some of the early arrivals became propagandists for the Oregon country. The missionary Dr. Marcus Whitman, for example, made a dramatic ride over the snow-filled mountains in the winter of 1842-1843 to visit Boston and persuade the Presbyterians to strengthen their Oregon mission. On his return, he guided a large wagon train over the Oregon Trail.

Many Americans became interested in the Oregon country for reasons other than furs, missions, or farms. People who had never thought of going west in a covered wagon were excited by reports of marvelous harbors on the Pacific coast. These harbors seemed important, both as ports for merchant ships and as bases for men-of-war.

In 1842, a naval lieutenant, Charles Wilkes, returned to Washington, D.C., from an exploring cruise and reported on his discoveries. The Columbia River itself, Wilkes said, would not provide suitable harbors, for its current was too swift and its mouth was obstructed by sand bars. But Puget Sound, farther north, contained many harbors which could accommodate the largest ships with ease. "I venture nothing in saying," Wilkes wrote enthusiastically, "there is no country in the world that possesses waters equal to these."

Democrats demanded all of Oregon

As the American population in the Oregon country increased, some expansionists felt certain that it would eventually become a part of the United States. Others thought the government should act, and promptly. One such expansionist introduced a bill in Congress (1841) for fortifying the Oregon Trail and for giving land grants to Americans settling in the territory. The British prime minister warned that, if this bill should pass, it would amount to a declaration of war. It did not pass.

Among Americans, joint occupation became more and more unpopular. Expansionists demanded that the United States proceed to occupy all of the Oregon country, by force if need be. A convention of expansionists, meeting in Cincinnati in 1843, resolved that the right of the United States to the whole territory was "unquestionable" and that it was the "imperative duty" of the federal government "forthwith to extend the laws of the United States over the said territory."

The Democratic party took up this demand and, in its platform of 1844, asserted that the American title was "clear and unquestionable" and that "no portion" of the Oregon country "ought to be ceded to England or any other power." In his inaugural address (1845), President Polk made this point emphatic:

Our title to the country of the Oregon is "clear and unquestionable," and already are our people preparing to perfect that title by occupying it with their wives and children.

In his first annual message to Congress, Polk asked for authority to end the joint-occupation agreement and to extend the protection of federal laws over the Americans in the Oregon country. When one congressman told the President that his policy might lead to war with Britain, Polk replied that "the only way to treat John Bull is to look him straight in the eye."

Most of the Whigs, in Congress and throughout the nation, did not think the American title was clear and unquestionable, nor did they think that all of the Oregon country up to 54°40', or any part of it, was worth fighting for. They made fun of the "Political Principles of President Polk," which they said were "P. P. P. P. Phifty-Phour Phorty or Phight." The Democrats quickly took up "fifty-four forty or fight" as their own slogan.

Whig businessmen of the Northeast, when interested in the Oregon country at all, were interested only in the harbor possibilities of Puget Sound. These lay far to the south of 54°40'. Democratic farmers and planters in the South were more interested in Texas than in the Oregon country, and the expansionist appetite of most of them was satisfied when Texas joined the Union.

During the winter of 1845-1846, Congress debated the Oregon question. Again, as in 1841-1842, a third war with Britain seemed likely unless some compromise could be reached.

Polk accepted a compromise

President Polk had spoken out for all of the Oregon country because his party had demanded it, and also because he wished to increase the diplomatic bargaining power of the United States. But Polk did not really think the United States had a good claim to all of it, nor did he want a war with Britain, especially since he was facing the prospect of a war with Mexico. While publicly asserting that the United States title was "clear and unquestionable," he privately offered to divide the territory along the forty-ninth parallel, that is, at about the middle.

In all previous discussions between United States and British diplomats, from 1818 on, the Americans had never seriously claimed anything north of 49°. The British had never insisted on anything south of the Columbia River. To the diplomats of the United States the line of 49° seemed essential because, if accepted, it would give the United States access to Puget Sound. There were, in 1845, no settlers from the United States north of that line; in fact, there were practically none north of the Columbia River. To British diplomats the river seemed indispensable because the Hudson's Bay Company used it in the fur trade. The company carried on little or no activity, however, south of the river. Thus, considered from the view of diplomacy instead of party politics, the real dispute concerned only a part of the Oregon country.

When Polk first renewed the idea of a division of the territory, the British minister in Washington, D.C., turned down the proposal without even referring it to his home government. When Congress, after a long debate, granted Polk the authorization he had asked for, he gave the British government an official notice that, in a year, the United States would consider the joint-occupation agreement terminated. At the same time, however, he expressed hope that this would lead to a friendly settlement.

A change in the British government and a change in the fur trade made such a settlement possible. In Britain the Whig party had come into power in 1845. The new British foreign secretary, Lord Aberdeen, believed that peace with the United States was worth more than the disputed portion of the Oregon country. He referred to the whole territory as a mere "pine swamp."

Already the fur trade was beginning to decline, partly because of changing styles in men's hats. For the "stovepipe" hat that men wore on dress occasions, silk was becoming more fashionable

than beaver, and so the demand for beaver pelts was falling off. As these became less saleable, as beaver itself became scarcer in the Columbia River region, and as the danger of trouble with the Americans increased, the Hudson's Bay Company began to withdraw to the north. In 1845, it moved its headquarters to Vancouver Island.

In 1846, Lord Aberdeen sent President Polk the draft of a treaty extending the boundary along the forty-ninth parallel from the Rockies to Puget Sound and then around the lower end of Vancouver Island, leaving the island to Britain. Polk, taking the advice of the Senate, accepted the treaty. Many in his own party denounced him for the "surrender" of land they said rightfully belonged to the United States. In Britain many people accused their own government of sacrificing British rights. Actually, both governments had finally arrived at what was probably the best possible solution to an old and troublesome problem.

REVIEWING THE SECTION

1. What caused the development of "Oregon fever"?

2. How did the Democrats and the Whigs differ in their views on the Oregon question?

3. Why did Polk and the British government accept a compromise on the Oregon question? How was the boundary line finally drawn?

CALIFORNIA AND NEW MEXICO WERE ACQUIRED

Through the agreement to divide the Oregon country, the danger of war with Britain was averted. By the time the agreement was reached, however, the United States already was at war with another nation—Mexico. The Mexican War (1846-1848) resulted from three subjects of dispute.

One of these disputes concerned Texas. The Mexican government refused to recognize Texan independence. True, after the Battle of San Jacinto, Santa Anna had signed a treaty granting independence, but the Mexican government maintained that the treaty was illegal, since Santa Anna had been forced to sign it. When Texas joined the Union, Mexico broke off diplomatic relations with the United States, expelled the United States minister from Mexico, and recalled the Mexican minister from Washington. Thus, in taking over Texas, the United States also took over the hostility which the Mexicans felt toward the Texans.

The United States also inherited a boundary dispute. Even if Texas were no longer a part of Mexico—which the Mexican government denied—Texas, according to the Mexican view, extended no farther to the southwest than the Nueces River. According to the Texan view, however, the state reached all the way to the Rio Grande and was practically twice as large as the Mexicans said it was. The United States government supported the Texans in their interpretation of the boundary with Mexico.

A second source of trouble between the two nations was a large debt owed by the Mexican government to United States citizens. Some of these Americans had provided loans or supplies to the Mexicans when the Mexicans were fighting for their independence from Spain (in 1821). The Americans had never been repaid. Other Americans, who owned property in Mexico, had lost their property and, in a number of cases, their lives as a result of revolutionary disorders following independence. All together, the Americans claimed that Mexico owed them about $5 million. The Mexican government had finally acknowledged a part of the debt—about $2 million of it—and had promised to pay it over a period of twenty years but, after a few installments, had stopped paying. The government of the United States felt that it had a just grievance against Mexico on account of the unpaid claims.

A third cause of difficulty with Mexico was the desire of United States expansionists for additional Mexican territory, especially California. War with Mexico might have been avoided if there had existed only the quarrels over the annexation and the boundary of Texas and over the money claims of United States citizens, though of course no one can be certain about this. War became inevitable, however, when President Polk tried to force the Mexican government to sell lands it did not want to give up.

Mexican lands lured Americans

To the west and northwest of Texas lay the Mexican provinces of New Mexico (much larger than the present state of New Mexico) and California, far from the nearest Mexican settlements and even farther from the Mexican capital. Both New Mexico and California were thinly settled and loosely held. Both of them, but especially California, had long attracted the interest of expansionist Americans.

The first Americans to visit California had arrived by sea. Even before 1800, New England shippers stopped along the coast to get sea otter pelts for the China trade. Later, Yankee whalers and, more important, buyers of cowhides and tallow visited California. Some remained to marry Mexican women and settle down as ranchers or merchants. Those who returned brought back reports of the fertile valleys, the pleasant climate, the easy life, and the magnificent San Francisco Bay. After his visit in 1841, Lieutenant Wilkes of the United States Navy said that the harbor there was "one of the finest, if not the very best harbor in the world." Many visitors, British as well as American, praised the beauties of California in articles and books. Most widely read was the first-hand account of the hide-and-tallow trade by Richard Henry Dana, Jr., *Two Years Before the Mast* (1840), which became a classic of American literature.

The first Americans to reach California overland were fur trappers and traders. One of these "mountain men," Jedediah S. Smith, arrived as early as 1826. Later, in 1841 and after, landseekers began to turn off from the Oregon Trail and head southwest for California with their covered wagons. The journey over the high Sierras was even more hazardous than the route to Oregon.

One wagon train, that of the Donner party from Illinois, was caught in the mountains by a blizzard in early autumn (1846), and most of the members of the party died, though some survived by turning to cannibalism. By 1845, there were seven hundred of the newcomers in California. They had settled not along the coast but in the Sacramento Valley, and they did not get along well with the native Californians as the earlier arrivals by sea had done.

The earliest American interest in New Mexico arose from the Santa Fe trade, beginning in 1821. Year after year the traders gathered at Independence, Missouri, for the summer trip eight hundred miles each way across the plains and back. The long wagon train carried manufactured goods to Santa Fe. It brought back gold, silver, furs, and mules. Except for a few traders who remained in Santa Fe for business reasons, this "commerce of the prairies" did not lead to American settlement in New Mexico. But it called to the attention of expansionists another direction in which the United States might expand.

The first Americans to settle in New Mexico in considerable numbers were the Mormons, who began to arrive in 1846. They settled far to the northwest of Santa Fe, in the vicinity of the Great Salt Lake (in what is now Utah).

The Mormons belonged to the Church of Jesus Christ of Latter-day Saints, which had been founded by Joseph Smith (1826) in New York State. The Mormons formed a closely knit economic as well as religious community, and from the beginning they had to face the hostility of jealous and suspicious neighbors. Seeking a place of refuge, Smith had led his followers to Ohio, to Missouri, and then to Illinois. More women than men were converted to Mormonism, and there were not enough men to go around. In Illinois, at the Mormon capital city of Nauvoo, Smith adopted a policy of "plural marriage," or polygamy, for Mormon men. He also began to exert influence in state politics through his control of Mormon votes. Soon afterward (1844) he was shot and killed by a member of a "gentile" (non-Mormon) mob.

Brigham Young then became the Mormon leader. He decided to get his people away from hostile Americans by starting a new community outside the United States. So he founded Deseret, as he called it, in the Salt Lake area of the Mexican territory. Thousands of Mormons crossed the plains and began to irrigate and cultivate the desert and also to sell supplies to non-Mormon emigrants going to the Oregon country or California. Even before the first Mormons arrived, however, the Mexican War had begun, and this war was to bring Deseret, along with the rest of New Mexico and California, into the Union.

Polk tried to get California

Americans interested in acquiring California assumed that the Mexican government ought to be glad to sell the province. The native Californians (Mexicans) felt little loyalty toward the Mexican government, and they frequently disobeyed and resisted the officials who were sent to rule them. It seemed that if Mexico should refuse to sell California, the Californians would eventually assert their complete independence, and then Mexico would lose the territory without getting anything for it. Nevertheless, Mexico refused to sell California.

President Jackson, and later President Tyler, tried to buy the San Francisco Bay area, without success. While Tyler was still trying to make the purchase, an American naval commander in the Pacific, Thomas ap Catesby Jones, heard a rumor that the United States and Mexico were at war, so he landed at Monterey, California, and ran up the American flag (1842). He later hauled it down and apologized. His precipitous action, suggesting the extreme eagerness of the United States to get California, made the Mexican government all the more unwilling to let it go.

President Polk was even more determined than President Tyler had been to acquire California, or at least a part of it. Polk justified his aim on the basis of Monroe's policy of 1823. (He did not use the term "Monroe Doctrine," which did not come into use until 1853.) Polk warned that if the United States failed to obtain California, the territory might fall under the control or even the ownership of Britain, and thus a European power would extend its influence, if not also its colonial possessions, in the American hemisphere.

Polk sent John Slidell to Mexico as the minister from the United States. Slidell took with him a price list for various pieces of Mexican territory. If Mexico would cede the territory between the Nueces River and the Rio Grande, and would thus agree to the Rio Grande as the Texas boundary, the United States would pay off its citizens who had claims against Mexico. For New Mexico, Slidell was to offer $5 million, and for California, $25 million more.

While thus attempting to open negotiations, Polk proceeded to back up his diplomacy with threats of military and naval force. He ordered an army under General Zachary Taylor into the disputed area between the Nueces River and the Rio Grande. Polk sent warships to the Gulf coast of Mexico. He sent other warships to the California coast to join the Pacific squadron, under Commodore Robert F. Stockton, whom he ordered to seize San Francisco in case of war. Polk instructed a secret agent, a New England merchant residing in Monterey, to encourage the Californians to separate from Mexico and join the United States. And he dispatched Captain John C. Frémont, an explorer, with a band of well-armed men, on a mysterious mission to northern California.

Polk would have been glad to achieve his aims by peaceful methods, but it began to appear that he could achieve them only by threatening and even using force. This he deduced from information furnished by a friend of Santa Anna, who had been exiled from Mexico and was living in Cuba. The friend told Polk that Santa Anna was planning to return to Mexico and recover control of the government. Once back in power, the friend said, Santa Anna would gladly sell Polk at least a

part of New Mexico and California. But no Mexican president would dare to sell the land unless it appeared to the Mexican people that he was forced to do so. Santa Anna's friend explained: "The U.S. would never be able to treat with Mexico without the presence of an imposing force by land and sea."

When Polk learned that the Mexican government had refused to deal with Slidell, he decided that the time had come to use a little force. He prepared a message calling upon Congress for a declaration of war. Before he had delivered the message, news came that a Mexican army had crossed the Rio Grande, attacked Taylor's army, and killed some of his men. Polk now revised his war message to say that Mexico had "invaded our territory and shed American blood upon the American soil." War already existed, he said, "by the act of Mexico herself." After receiving the message, Congress promptly declared war on Mexico (May 12, 1846).

A war was fought with Mexico

Polk did not expect a very long or hard war. He thought the Mexicans would soon see that they had no chance to win, and then they would be willing to make peace on his terms. Actually, at the start, the Mexican leaders were eager for war and confident of victory. Their regular army was four times as large (32,000 men) as the American army (8000), and they expected aid from Britain and France.

This aid did not materialize. With Americans volunteering by the thousands (especially in Tennessee, which now came to be known as the "volunteer" state) the army of the United States rapidly grew to many times its peacetime size (to more than 100,000). The United States had a fairly strong navy, and Mexico practically no navy at all. The United States had much greater industrial production. Even so, the Mexican War proved to be a considerably more difficult undertaking than Polk had anticipated.

The Mexican War, 1846-1848

July 7, 1846—January 10, 1847
The campaign in California. The American fleet (Commodore John D. Sloat) sailed from Mazatlán, Mexico, and took Monterey, California (July 7, 1846). Meanwhile troops (Colonel Stephen Kearny) from Fort Leavenworth, near Missouri, headed for California. They occupied Santa Fe (Aug.18), established a temporary government there, and moved on. They then occupied San Diego (Dec. 12). Hostilities ended in California when the combined forces of the army (Kearny and Captain John C. Frémont) and navy (Commodore Robert Stockton, who had replaced Sloat) took Los Angeles (Jan. 10).

September 24, 1846—March 1, 1847
The campaign in northern Mexico. After some early skirmishing, the campaign in northern Mexico got under way when the Americans (General Zachary Taylor) attacked and captured Monterrey (Sept. 24). From Monterrey, the American forces went to Saltillo and occupied it (Nov. 13). Meanwhile troops from San Antonio (General John Wool) had been sent to take Chihuahua. They won a battle at Monclava (Oct. 29), and then were ordered to take Parras. After occupying Parras (Dec. 5), they joined Taylor's troops at Saltillo (Dec. 21). The combined forces captured Buena Vista (Feb. 27). Other American troops (Colonel Alexander Doniphan) defeated the Mexicans at El Brazito (Dec. 25), El Paso (Dec. 27), and Sacramento (Feb. 28). Doniphan occupied Chihuahua (March 1).

March 9—September 14, 1847
Invasion of Mexico City. The deciding campaign of the war began with the landing of American troops (General Winfield Scott) at Veracruz (March 9) and the capitulation of that city (March 27). A number of battles took place as the American troops proceeded to Mexico City. The Mexicans were routed at Cerro Gordo (April 18) and at Contreras (Aug. 19-20). The Americans suffered heavy casualties at Churubusco (Aug. 20), but the Mexicans were forced to withdraw to Mexico City. The next American move was aimed at Chapultepec. After a heavy bombardment and an assault, the defenders were finally overcome (Sept. 14). The Americans entered Mexico City and occupied it. It took several days before the city was brought under control, but the shooting war was finally over. The Treaty of Guadalupe Hidalgo (Feb. 2, 1848) formally ended the war.

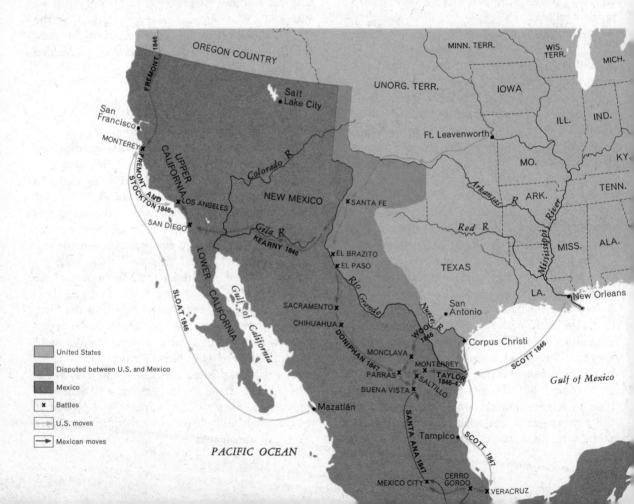

General Scott's Entrance into Mexico, 1847, by George Wilkins Kendall

The Capture of Mexico City by American troops on September 14, 1847, marked the end of fighting in the Mexican War. This painting shows the Mexican army (at right) surrendering near the Cathedral of Mexico. General Winfield Scott's men raised the United States flag over the Mexican National Palace, at the right.

Polk ordered General Taylor to cross the Rio Grande and invade Mexico from the northeast. After a hard battle, Taylor, whose soldiers called him "Old Rough and Ready," took the city of Monterrey (September 1846). Between Monterrey and Mexico City, the capital, there was rough, mountainous terrain. Taylor knew that he would have trouble in keeping up his supply lines if he were to try to move on southward. So he settled down with his army to occupy northeastern Mexico.

Meanwhile, Polk dispatched a small army under Colonel Stephen Kearny to New Mexico and California. Kearny marched to Santa Fe and occupied the town. Then, with part of his force, he proceeded on to California. In California a revolt was already under way. With the aid of Frémont and his men, American settlers had raised the Bear Flag as their emblem and had proclaimed independence from Mexico. Commodore Stockton had landed men from his ships, and these men were carrying on a separate campaign. The situation was confused when Kearny arrived, but he took command of all the American forces and, by the beginning of 1847, completed the conquest of California.

Thus, before the end of the first year of the war, the United States was in possession of California, New Mexico, and the northeastern part of Mexico itself. Yet the Mexican government refused to consider giving up. Even after Santa Anna returned from exile and resumed power, Mexico continued to resist.

Polk, therefore, decided to carry the war to the heart of Mexico. With the general in chief of the army, Winfield Scott, he worked out a plan for taking the capital. Scott commanded the operation. The navy landed his army at Veracruz, which he captured after a siege. Then he advanced inland toward Mexico City, 260 miles away. By skillful maneuvering, he forced the Mexicans to retreat. When, under Santa Anna, they made a stand at Cerro Gordo, Scott defeated them and drove them back. They did not face him in battle again until they were just outside the capital. He forced his way into the city, storming and capturing the fortress of Chapultepec on September 14, 1847. The fighting was over, but peace was yet to come.

The U.S. acquired territory from Mexico

From the very beginning many Americans had been opposing the war and demanding peace. The Whigs, though most of them in Congress had voted for the war declaration, denounced "Mr. Polk's war" as a war of aggression. They said that Polk himself had brought on hostilities by sending Taylor's army across the Nueces River into territory that really belonged to Mexico.

Antislavery people insisted (quite incorrectly) that Polk was trying to get land from Mexico in order to create new slave states. When Polk asked Congress for an appropriation with which to make peace, antislavery people and other opponents of the war supported the Wilmot Proviso, an amendment to Polk's bill introduced by David Wilmot of Pennsylvania. This amendment provided that slavery must be excluded from any territory acquired from Mexico. The Wilmot Proviso passed the House of Representatives but was voted down in the Senate.

Some of the Whigs, including Daniel Webster, went even further than opposing slavery in new territory. They opposed the acquisition of the territory itself. A number of other Americans began to propose that, when peace was finally made, the United States should take not only California and New Mexico but *all of Mexico*.

As people went to greater and greater extremes —for permitting slavery or prohibiting it, for taking all of Mexico or none of it—Polk became more and more embarrassed. He himself wished to acquire California (including Lower California), New Mexico, and the Rio Grande boundary for Texas. He feared that Congress might never agree on anything if the bickering continued and got worse. So, by the time Scott's army was approaching Mexico City, he wanted to make a quick peace. Accompanying Scott's army was a state department clerk named Nicholas P. Trist. He was instructed to make a treaty as Polk's personal representative. When, after the fall of Mexico City, Trist seemed unable to do what Polk wanted done, Polk ordered him to come home. But Trist stayed on and negotiated a peace treaty, which was finally signed in the Mexico City suburb of Guadalupe Hidalgo on February 2, 1848.

According to the Treaty of Guadalupe Hidalgo, Mexico would cede California and New Mexico and would recognize the Rio Grande as the Texas boundary. The United States would pay $15 million to Mexico and would take responsibility for paying the claims which United States citizens held against the Mexican government.

When Polk received a draft of the treaty, he decided to accept it even though it did not include quite all he wanted. The Senate approved the treaty, and the House and the Senate appropriated the necessary money, without the Wilmot Proviso.

Congress continued to wrangle, however, over the question of slavery in the new territories. The controversy extended to the territory of Oregon. Though Oregon was so far north that no one expected slavery ever to take root there, Southern extremists insisted that slavery be permitted in Oregon. They wanted to establish a principle which would later apply also to the Mexican cession. Oregon was not finally organized as a free territory until August 1848. For the time being, California and New Mexico remained without regular territorial governments.

California could not continue long without a government. Gold had been discovered there in January 1848, at the very time when the Treaty of Guadalupe Hidalgo was being drawn up. Soon the gold rush was on—a hundred thousand "forty-niners" swarmed into California in 1849. The rapidly increasing numbers of people in California needed a government of their own.

The lands ceded in the Treaty of Guadalupe Hidalgo were not the last to be obtained from Mexico. In 1853, Santa Anna, again president of Mexico, needed money. Some railroad promoters in the United States desired a strip of land suitable for the construction of a railroad to California. By the Gadsden Purchase in 1853 (the treaty was not approved until 1854), the United States paid Santa Anna $10 million for an area that now forms the southern parts of Arizona and New Mexico. This completed the conterminous territorial expansion of the United States.

REVIEWING THE SECTION

1. Why did Americans become interested in California and New Mexico?

2. Explain how Polk's determination to acquire California led to a declaration of war against Mexico.

3. What was the American strategy which led to Mexico's capitulation?

4. How did Americans differ in their ideas of what the peace terms should be? What were the terms of the Treaty of Guadalupe Hidalgo?

CHAPTER **10** CONCLUSION

At the end of the War of 1812, the United States consisted of the land that had been obtained at the end of the Revolutionary War plus the land that had been acquired in the Louisiana Purchase. On the north, south, and west, however, the boundary over long stretches was uncertain.

Before the Civil War, the United States obtained a clear title to West Florida, portions of which it already claimed, and also to East Florida. In addition, the following territories were added: Texas (all the way to the Rio Grande), Oregon as far north as the forty-ninth parallel, California, New Mexico, and the strip known as the Gadsden Purchase. Meanwhile, the boundary on the north, all the way from the Atlantic to the Pacific, was definitely fixed. Thus, by 1854, the United States had become a continental country, extending from ocean to ocean, with essentially the same conterminous area that it now possesses.

Those Americans who advocated this expansion—and some opposed various phases of it—justified it on the basis of Manifest Destiny, the Monroe Doctrine, and specific economic and strategic needs. Certainly, the territorial acquisitions did provide room for future population growth. They also forestalled the possible enlargement of European influence on this continent, and they presented bases for defense as well as ports for commerce.

To realize the importance of the territorial expansion, one has only to speculate upon the course of United States history if the expansion had not occurred. Suppose that Spain had kept Florida, Britain had kept the whole of the Oregon country, and Mexico had kept all her territories. No one can say what, in that case, the course of United States history would have been like, but obviously it would have been vastly different from what it actually has been.

Some of the consequences of expansion were not foreseen by those who advocated it. One of these consequences was the Civil War. This war, of course, had several causes, but it could hardly have occurred without the acquisition of western territories over which the free states and the slave states began to dispute. Even before the Mexican War had ended, the argument over slavery in the territories already was threatening to divide the nation. By renewing and intensifying the slavery issue, the Mexican War led to the Civil War.

The Mexican War was a forerunner of the Civil War in another way, also. The one war was a kind of unplanned rehearsal for the other. Ulysses S. Grant, Robert E. Lee, and most of the other Civil War generals, on both the Union and the Confederate side, had gained battle experience in Mexico.

FOCUSING ON SPECIFICS

1. What were the motives behind the expansionist feeling in the early nineteenth century?

2. Explain how the philosophy of "manifest destiny" combined nationalism and humanitarianism.

3. How did Webster succeed in arranging a compromise on the question of the boundary between Maine and New Brunswick?

4. Why did Britain and France wish Texas to remain an independent republic?

5. What was the basis of the American claim for the Oregon country? What was the basis of the British claim?

6. How did Marcus Whitman and Charles Wilkes stimulate interest in the Oregon country?

7. How did a change in the style of men's hats contribute to an amicable settlement of the Oregon question?

8. What main subjects of dispute between the United States and Mexico led to the Mexican War?

9. Why did the Mormons found the settlement of Deseret?

10. How did Mexico's actions in 1845 provide the United States with an excuse for declaring war on Mexico?

11. Why did the Mexican leaders believe they could win a war with the United States? What military advantages did the United States have over Mexico?

12. How did Colonel Stephen W. Kearny contribute to the American victory in the Mexican War?

13. What was the purpose of the introduction of the Wilmot Proviso in Congress?

14. Why was the strip of land known as the Gadsden Purchase obtained from Mexico?

15. How did the acquisition of territories from Mexico help to bring on the Civil War?

REVIEWING MAIN THEMES

1. What boundary disputes did the United States have with Spain and Britain between 1817 and 1842? How were these disputes resolved?

2. Explain how the annexation of Texas was affected by domestic differences and international power struggles.

3. Describe the steps by which the Oregon country became a part of the United States.

4. Describe the steps by which California and New Mexico became a part of the United States.

5. List the territories acquired by the United States between 1819 and 1853. What were the consequences of this territorial expansion?

EVALUATING THE ISSUES

1. How was the diplomacy of the United States between 1815 and 1850 influenced by the weaknesses and strengths of its neighbors? Was American diplomacy successful during these years?

2. Why did the feeling of a "manifest destiny" develop in the 1840's rather than in the 1830's?

3. Compare the expansion of the United States into lands claimed by other nations with that of a modern developing nation, as for example India or Indonesia, from the standpoint of (1) motives for expanding, (2) methods used, (3) rationale for the expansion.

EXAMINING THE TIMES

1. During the period from 1815 to 1850, vast changes took place in the growing nation. Summarize briefly the changes that took place in economic development, political democracy, and territorial growth.

2. What events or developments during this period tended to strengthen national unity? What events tended to weaken national unity?

Planned Communities

Washington, D.C., was not the only planned community in the United States. As the nation expanded, communities designed to fill particular needs were added to the landscape.

Some of the western states built new capitals. Many of them, like Jefferson City, Missouri, were built in the wilderness. The most prominent feature in all the capitals was the impressive, domed capitol which reflected the traditional American optimism about the future. It frequently took time until the rest of the town matched the grandeur of the capitol. The other impressive structure in Jefferson City was the huge, stone hotel (also shown in this view, c. 1855), which was built, hopefully, to accommodate the many visitors to the capital.

Another kind of planned community was the university town such as the one Thomas Jefferson designed (1819) at Charlottesville for the University of Virginia (view 1856). The school buildings were elaborate, particularly the main building which was modeled after the Pantheon in Rome. The state-supported university, such as this one, was uniquely American; it reflected the commitment to education.

Possibly the most interesting of the planned communities were the utopian and religious settlements. Economy, Pennsylvania, was established (1825) by a group of Germans. It boasted a museum and a grotto. The vine-covered assembly hall was the center of life in this utopian community, much as the meeting house had been in New England.

While most of the utopian communities floundered, some religious communities were conspicuous successes. Probably the most famous of all was Salt Lake City, where the Mormons converted a desert into a garden and built a neat, orderly city.

Assembly Hall, Economy, Pennsylvania

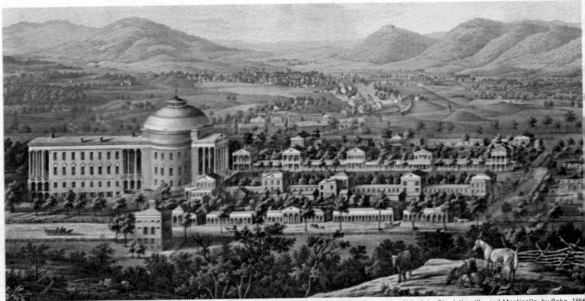

View of the University of Virginia, Charlottesville, and Monticello, by Bohn, 1856

Jefferson City (Missouri River), c. 1855

View of Great Salt Lake City, 1867

Speculative Communities

Possibly even more interesting than the planned communities of the period were those based on land speculation. These, too, reflected the traditional American optimism about the future.

Speculative communities included, among others, industrial towns, mining towns, and transportation towns. Real estate speculators purchased huge tracts of land at low prices, divided the land into lots, advertised for settlers to come to these "thriving cities," and hoped for huge profits. Some of these speculative communities were successful, others declined, and some just disappeared.

Galena, Illinois, on the Fever River (view 1857) was one such speculative community. It grew rapidly and prospered by shipping the lead ore mined in the vicinity. For awhile, Galena was the commercial center of the region, but when less expensive lead mines were developed further west, the people of Galena began to leave the town.

Speculative communities were also established at points where passengers and freight were transferred from one means of transportation to another. St. Louis, Missouri, became a prosperous town because of its strategic location on the Mississippi River. It was the jumping-off place for people and freight going west. By roads, rivers, and canals, they came to St. Louis and from there, went west. All river towns had one feature in common—a "front street," a broad avenue lined with piers and warehouses along the river front which was the commercial center of the town. Front Street in St. Louis (1840) was typical.

As the westward movement increased in momentum, outfitting wagon trains became one of the biggest industries in the west. Independence, Missouri, prospered as a result of this trade. A traveler, wandering through the central part of Independence (c. 1855) could find brick buildings, a court house, and a few places of public worship; he could even find several newspapers to read while waiting to start his journey west.

Speculative communities were established where canals met, such as this one (c. 1830) at the junction of the Erie and Northern canals. Like the river towns, the canal towns were built to accommodate passengers and freight; hotels and warehouses were a common sight. As canals became less important, however, the canal town stopped growing or disappeared.

Galena, on Fever River in Illinois, by Henry Lewis, 1857

View of Front Street, St. Louis, by J. C. Wild, 1840

Independence-Courthouse, Missouri, c. 1855

Junction of the Erie and Northern Canals, by J. Hill, c. 1830-1832

A View of Fort Snelling, by E. K. Thomas, c. 1838

The Frontier

When people began moving west in great numbers after the War of 1812, the war department authorized the building of many new forts in the wilderness to protect the incoming settlers.

Regardless of location, the fort, probably the most important structure on the frontier, fulfilled certain functions. It provided the settlers who built their homes around it with protection from hostile Indians. In addition, it often became the trading post for an entire region and the center of social life for the community which grew up around it. In some cases, friendly Indians set up their tepees near the fort and traded there, too.

The forts were usually built from the most plentiful material in the area. An exterior view of Fort Snelling, Minnesota

(c. 1838), showed a massive stone structure that dominated the entire area; Fort Laramie, Wyoming, in contrast, was built of wood. On a normal day, a fort such as Laramie (pictured 1837) was the scene of much activity. There soldiers went about their duties while settlers and Indians came to the fort to trade.

Although the majority of the Indians in the West lived in villages far away from the settlers and the forts, a few of them settled near the Indian agencies established by the federal government. One such community, among the Pawnees in Nebraska, was called Bellvue (picture 1833). The agency was run by a man named Dougherty, who spoke more than a dozen Indian dialects and who worked to help the Indian through a difficult period.

Fort Laramie on the North Platte River in Wyoming, by Alfred Jacob Miller, 1837

Bellvue, Mr. Dougherty's Agency on the Missouri, in Nebraska, by Carl Bodmer

"Lyndhurst," Tarrytown, New York, 1838, architect, Alexander Jackson Davis

Country Homes
and
Resort Towns

American Country Life, May Morning, by Currier & Ives, 1855

While communities were being built in the newer areas of the nation, changes were taking place along the eastern coast. Some Americans were becoming wealthy. Others were already wealthy. Some Americans had more leisure time than ever before. These people were looking for ways to spend their money and for new places to spend their leisure time.

Many wealthy easterners, eager to get away from the noise and "corruption" of the big cities, purchased large estates in the country and built elaborate homes where they could spend the summer months.

The country homes of the period generally were adaptations of the homes of the aristocrats of Europe, usually built in the Romantic style. "Lyndhurst," in Tarrytown, N.Y., (1838) was once described as a baronial castle. The elaborate, ornate home seen in the painting "American Country Life, May Morning," (1855) resembled the summer villas found in Italy often called Tuscan villas.

Resort towns, where the wealthy went for a few weeks during the year, became very popular during this period. One of the best known of the eastern resort towns was Saratoga Springs, New York. The simple, classic lines of the buildings (picture in 1828) provided an elegant background for the elegant ladies and gentlemen who relaxed there.

These classic lines could also be found in buildings all over the country. In the South, this style of architecture, adapted from ancient Greece, became especially popular and was used for many of the plantation houses of the ante-bellum period, as well as for private clubs such as the Oakland House and Racecourse (view 1840).

Saratoga Springs, by J. Milbert

akland House and Racecourse, Louisville, 1840, by Robert Brammer

Between 1850 and 1877, the American people quarreled among themselves, broke apart to form a separate North and South, fought a costly and bloody four-year Civil War, and then gradually brought about peace and national unity again. This—the division and reunion of the country—is the main theme of United States history during that period.

There was more to it than merely division and reunion, however. By 1877, the United States was different from what it had been in 1850. Not only did the nation have more people, bigger cities, and new kinds of machines. It also had a new class of people, the millions of Negroes who were no longer slaves, though not yet treated as free and equal. Above all, the United States had a much stronger and more active national government, which claimed more directly the loyalty of all the people. By 1877, all were citizens primarily of the United States as a whole and only secondarily of the particular state in which they happened to reside. Formerly it had been the other way around. As late as 1850, the United States could still be described as the Federal Union, a union of states which retained a sense of separateness. By 1877, it was well on the way to becoming the American nation, a much more uniform and consolidated nation.

Division and Reunion

During this same period, there was also a trend toward national consolidation in other parts of the world. Small states combined to form bigger ones; loose aggregations of people were brought together under more highly centralized governments; large and well-established nations remained large by defeating the efforts of discontented elements to break away.

In mid-century Europe, several fairly large and fairly old nations already existed: Britain, France, Russia, and Spain. The first three continued to grow stronger, but Spain, once great, was now in a decline. Russia soon underwent two experiences similar to those the United States was undergoing—emancipation and rebellion. In 1861, the tsar proclaimed freedom for the millions of Russian serfs. The next year he put down an uprising on the part of his Polish subjects, who had hoped to create a nation of their own.

At the middle of the century, though it was common to speak of "Italy" and "Germany," these were as yet only geographical expressions, not designations of united countries with central governments. Italy then consisted of several independent states, and Germany consisted of dozens of kingdoms, principalities, and city republics. Parts of both Italy and Germany were included in what was left of the old Holy Roman Empire, ruled by the Austrian Hapsburg family. This Hapsburg Empire contained not only Italians and Germans but also Austrians, Hungarians, and many other nationalities.

In the revolutionary movements of 1848, the revolutionary leaders of Hungary, Italy, and Germany attempted to set up new nations with representative governments. Americans generally cheered on these movements and made heroes of the leaders. Although the Hapsburg government, with the aid of Russian troops, crushed the Hungarian revolt, the Germans and the Italians later achieved their national independence.

Prussia and Austria were the largest and strongest of the German states. Prussia took the lead in German unification. In 1864, she invited Austria to join her in a war to acquire the German-speaking provinces of Schleswig and Holstein from Denmark. In 1866, Prussia picked a quarrel with Austria and defeated her in a six weeks' war. Then Prussia set up the North German Federation, bringing together the states of northern Germany. Finally, in 1871, after her victory in the Franco-Prussian War, Prussia broadened the confederation to include the south German states (but not Austria) and converted it into the German Empire.

Meanwhile the Italian leaders took advantage of Prussia's wars so as to further the work of Italian liberation and unification. By 1861, the Italians had recovered all of the country except for Venetia, with its capital of Venice, and the Papal States, including Rome. On March 17 of that year, less than two weeks after Abraham Lincoln's inauguration as President of the United States, the Italians established the Kingdom of Italy. In 1866, the new kingdom joined Prussia in the war against Austria and compelled Austria to cede Venetia. In 1870, facing defeat at the hands of Prussia, France withdrew the French troops which had been guarding the Papal States, and Italy promptly incorporated these. The kingdom now included all of Italy.

unit IV
1850-1877

The Hungarians also took advantage of Austria's plight. To get their support for the war against Prussia, the Austrian government promised concessions to them. The next year, 1867, the Austrian Empire was reorganized as the Austro-Hungarian Empire, with a separate parliament and cabinet for the Hungarians.

Thus, at about the time of the American Civil War, or soon after it, two new nations and a reorganized empire appeared in Europe.

In this same period a new nation emerged in Asia. Japan had been a hermit for more than two hundred years, living to herself and refusing even to trade with foreigners, except for the Dutch, who were allowed to send one ship a year. For an even longer time the nation had been ruled by great landlord families. The leader of one of these families served as shogun, or military governor, acting in the name of the emperor, who actually had no power.

Americans played an important role in opening Japan to the world. In 1853 and 1854, Matthew C. Perry, with a naval squadron, paid official visits to Japan and so impressed the Japanese that they agreed to a treaty permitting Americans to trade at certain ports. In 1860, the United States received the first delegation of diplomats ever sent abroad by Japan. After the United States established diplomatic relations with Japan, European nations followed suit.

The opening of Japan led to disturbances there and finally to a reorganization of the government. Some of the feudal lords objected to giving up the old policy of isolation, refused to obey the shogun, and from time to time attacked and murdered foreigners. In 1864, a United States warship joined with French, British, and Dutch warships to shell and destroy the fortifications of one feudal family who had been interfering with foreign shipping. Finally, in 1867, most of the influential Japanese agreed to the formation of a modern, European type of parliamentary government, with the emperor at the head of it. The new government was far more centralized and efficient than the old one. It maintained order throughout the country, which began rapidly to develop the railroads, shipping, industries, army and navy, and other features of the most advanced nations of the world.

During these years, China managed to preserve its national existence despite a terrible civil war, the Tai-ping Rebellion, which lasted fifteen years. The Chinese rebels, the Tai-pings, were influenced to some extent by ideas of nationalism which they had received from British traders, and by notions of Christianity given to them by American missionaries. But the British and the Americans in China, as well as their respective governments at home, supported the established government of the Manchu dynasty. The rebellion began in South China in 1850, spread over the Yangtze Valley, and kept the country torn and distracted until 1865.

Not only in Europe and Asia but also in parts of North America outside the United States, the trend toward centralization could be seen. By an act of the British Parliament in 1867, the formerly separate provinces of British North America were federated to form the Dominion of Canada, which remained a part

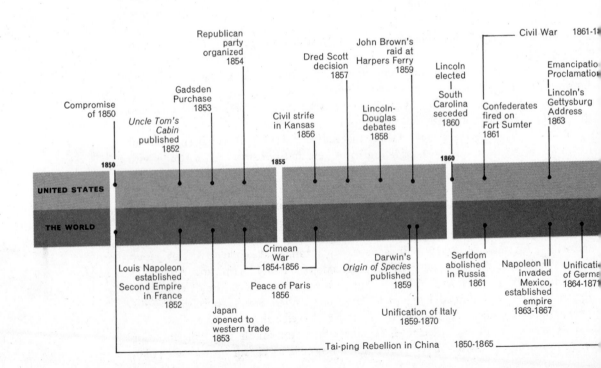

of the British Empire.

Thus the mid-nineteenth century was a time of widespread striving, in many places successful, to create larger or at least more highly unified nations. All this was a reflection of the spirit of nationalism. Nineteenth-century *nationalism* may be defined as a mystic feeling which people have that they belong together as a separate nation, with their own independent government. Usually these people have a common language, religion, and historical tradition. Nationalism does not necessarily make for bigger countries. For example, if Polish nationalism had realized its aim in 1863, there would have been two independent nations, Poland and Russia, where previously there had been only one. However, in the mid-nineteenth century nationalism did result in making countries bigger.

Large national units became feasible because of improvements in transportation and communication which enabled a government to keep in touch with people scattered over a wide area. But such improvements did not automatically bring about national unification. Wars were usually necessary.

The Civil War was the American war of national unification. The Union victory was in accord with the trend of the times. It did for the United States what contemporary struggles and victories did for such nations as Germany, Italy, and Japan. However, the Civil War did more than that. It gave a boost not only to strong, centralized government but also to democratic government—government of the people, by the people, for the people.

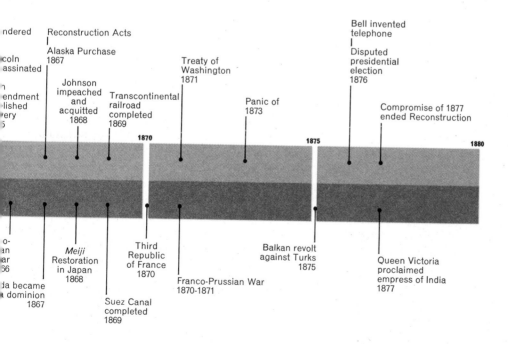

ndered

Reconstruction Acts

Bell invented
telephone

coln
assinated

Alaska Purchase
1867

Disputed
presidential
election
1876

Treaty of
Washington
1871

endment
lished
very
5

Johnson
impeached
and
acquitted
1868

Transcontinental
railroad
completed
1869

Panic of
1873

Compromise of 1877
ended Reconstruction

1870

1875

1880

o-
an
ar
66

Meiji
Restoration
in Japan
1868

Third
Republic
of France
1870

Balkan revolt
against Turks
1875

Queen Victoria
proclaimed
empress of India
1877

da became
dominion
1867

Suez Canal
completed
1869

Franco-Prussian War
1870-1871

CHAPTER **11** 1850-1861

North and South: Two Ways of Life

As the year 1850 opened, Americans had reason to be proud of their past and confident of their future. Their nation, now reaching all the way to the Pacific, was greater than ever. It was still growing in wealth and numbers. It was still progressing in industry, commerce, and facilities for travel and transport.

At the same time, Americans had grounds for serious concern. There was a possibility that, in the near future, the United States might cease to exist as a single nation. It might divide into two nations, one with slaves, the other without.

Already the North and the South were beginning to seem almost like separate nations. Travelers noted that the typical Northerner and the typical Southerner had different characteristics. A Connecticut Yankee, Frederick Law Olmsted, who traveled in the South in 1853, explained that slavery was the main reason for the distinctive traits of the Southern planter. Olmsted said that slavery, by giving the planter "uncontrolled authority," made him a proud, impulsive, careless, and easy-

going person, in contrast to the "calculating, indefatigable New Englander" or the "go-ahead Western man."

Indeed, the North and the South were beginning to seem like hostile as well as separate nations. For years, wealthy Southerners had summered at Northern resorts, such as Newport, Rhode Island, or Saratoga Springs, New York. Then, during the 1850's, Southern visitors felt that they were getting an increasingly rude reception. "We are treated worse in the North than if we were foreign enemies," complained the editor of a Virginia newspaper, the *Richmond Whig.* "Let us with one accord stay home and spend among our own people," he advised.

The growing antagonism was no mere accident. It was "an irrepressible conflict between opposing and enduring forces," as the New York political leader William H. Seward declared in 1858. It arose because the two sections of the nation had come to have such different ways of life, such different interests and ideals.

POPULATION GROWTH BROUGHT CHANGES

Throughout the nineteenth century, the population of Britain and western Europe grew very fast, but that of the United States grew even faster. Beginning in 1790, a federal census was taken every ten years, and each new one showed the population to be about a third larger. In 1850, the figure was approximately 23 million; in 1860, more than 31 million. The census showed that there were about eight times as many people in the United States in 1860 as there had been in 1790.

Most of the population growth in the United States resulted from the excess of births over deaths. But, a considerable portion of the growth, especially after 1850, resulted from immigration.

Only a few immigrants had arrived during the period from the end of the Revolutionary War (1783) to the end of the War of 1812. After that, the number that came increased slowly and irregularly. Then, in the 1840's, a mass influx began. Many of these newcomers were Roman Catholics. By 1860, nearly four million immigrants were living in the United States. One in eight of the total population had been born abroad.

The United States had always been a predominantly Protestant nation. Some of the native Protestants disliked and feared the Roman Catholic immigrants. Fearful Protestants joined organizations which sought to limit immigration and to deprive the immigrants of political rights. Thus religious conflict was intensified as a result of the population trends.

More important, sectional conflict also was intensified. The population changes affected the North and the South differently, making them less and less alike.

The North grew faster than the South

Not all parts of the nation were growing at the same rate. The Northeast gained less than the Northwest (which at this time included the states created out of the Northwest Territory—Ohio, Indiana, Illinois, Michigan, and Wisconsin—plus the state of Iowa and the Minnesota Territory). The Northwest gained less than the far west. For example, the population of California quadrupled, jumping from 100,000 to 400,000 in the 1850's. The South gained even less than the Northeast.

The United States was still predominantly rural. In 1850, five times as many people were scattered over the countryside as were concentrated in towns and cities. For decades, however, the United States had been becoming more and more urban. The population of the cities was growing much faster than that of the farms.

The Northeast continued to be the most highly urbanized area. New York, which together with Brooklyn had a population of more than a million by 1860, continued to gain as the nation's largest city and leading port. Some of the cities farther west grew even faster in proportion to their size. During the 1850's, St. Louis doubled in population, reaching 161,000, and Chicago tripled, reaching about 110,000.

The South had the second busiest port, New Orleans. Yet, on the whole, the South contained fewer cities, towns, and villages than the North. It was less densely settled. In 1860, the slave states had an average of about thirteen persons for each square mile; the free states, about twenty.

Immigration added to diversity

The immigrants who came to the United States hoped to make a better living in this country than they had been able to make at home. They learned about the United States from accounts, often exaggerated, which shipping companies and land dealers published in order to promote business. They also learned from "America letters" written by friends or relatives already in this country. "Now we get beef and pudding, tea and rum pretty regularly," an English immigrant wrote home; "to us who have been long half-starved in England, it appears like a continual feast."

IMMIGRATION TO THE UNITED STATES, 1820-1870

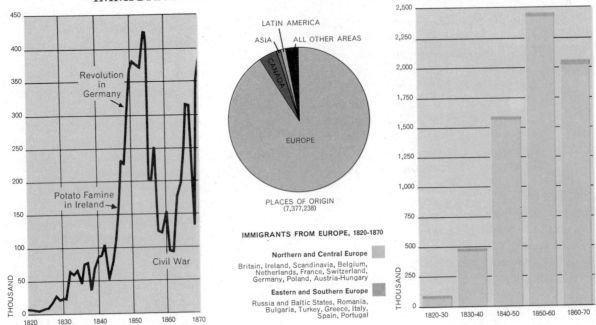

No longer did Europeans cross the ocean as indentured servants, with a master paying their way, as so many had done in colonial times, for the system of indentured servitude had gradually disappeared after the Revolution. Most could now pay their own way because transatlantic fares had been reduced several times by the shipping companies. Ships usually carried bulky exports, such as lumber, wheat, and cotton, from the United States to Europe and brought back compact imports, such as fine tools and machinery. On the return voyage, therefore, there was empty space, and shippers were glad to fill it with human cargo at almost any price.

The largest of the immigrant groups to come to the United States in the 1840's was the Irish. Many of these people had left their overcrowded homeland because of the terrible famines of 1845 and 1846, when much of the potato crop rotted at harvest time. Even after the worst of the famines, people continued to leave Ireland rather than pay the rent increases that landlords continually imposed. Most of the Irish who came to the United States settled in New York City or in other cities in the Northeast. Few went into the interior to look for farms, since few of them had money enough to buy land or, for that matter, even a railroad ticket.

Germans made up the second largest group of foreign-born in the United States. A few former leaders of the German revolutionary movement of 1848—an unsuccessful movement to set up a federal and representative government for a united Germany—were among this group. Most of the Germans who came to the United States were peasants or farmers, though not so desperately poor as the Irish. Many brought money enough to buy farms, and while some remained by choice in eastern cities, others spread out to become a very large element of the population not only in New York and Pennsylvania but also in Ohio, Illinois, Wisconsin, and Missouri.

Other groups came to the United States in considerable numbers, too, especially Englishmen, Frenchmen, Swedes, and Norwegians.

Comparatively few of the immigrants settled in the South. Most of them arrived at Northern ports, especially New York, and remained there. Some immigrants landed at Southern ports, especially New Orleans, but did not wish to remain in the South. Most of them disliked slavery on principle or wished to avoid the competition of slave labor, so they went up the Mississippi River to look for homes in the Northwest or the far west. As a result, the South remained primarily a section with a fairly homogeneous white population, while the population of the North became more and more diversified.

Opposition to immigrants arose

Many native-born Americans were alarmed by the influx of immigrants. Some of them believed that the impoverished newcomers were threatening American society with an increase in pauperism and crime. Others were alarmed because some immigrants were given fraudulent citizenship papers almost as soon as they had landed, and they were led to the polls to vote for corrupt big-city politicians. And some Americans were afraid they would lose their jobs to immigrants who were willing to accept lower pay. "Our public improvements, railroads, and canals are thronged with foreigners," a newspaper writer complained. "They fill our large cities, reduce the wages of labor, and increase the hardships of the old settler."

The prejudice against immigrants, most of whom were Roman Catholics (about half of the Germans and nearly all of the Irish), was greatly intensified because the nation had been predominantly Protestant up to that time. Many anti-Catholic writers insisted that these people were engaged in a gigantic plot to put the Pope in control of the United States. They were being deliberately sent to this country, it was said, to prepare the way by extending the influence of the Roman Catholic Church through their votes.

Strict laws were demanded by many of the native-born Americans to discourage immigration and to limit the political activity of the foreign-born people already here. One of the proposed laws would have stopped the immigration of Roman Catholics. Another would have required aliens to reside in this nation for twenty-one years before they could be naturalized. Still another would have barred all the foreign-born from public office, even after they had become citizens. None of these restrictive laws was passed.

In 1850, various antiforeigner groups combined to form a national society, the secret Order of the Star Spangled Banner. In 1854, they converted this into a political organization which they named the Native American party, but which was usually called the Know-Nothing party because the members were instructed to say, "I know nothing," whenever an outsider asked about the party's secrets.

Some Southerners supported the Know-Nothing movement even though there were comparatively few immigrants in the South. The Southerners wished to cut down on immigration because they could see that it was doing little for their section while it was contributing a great deal to the growth of the North and hence to its economic and political strength.

The Know-Nothings never had the support of a majority of the American people. A number of native-born citizens spoke out in defense of the immigrants. One said:

Laboring like slaves for us, they have built our cities and railroads; piercing the western wilds, they have caused them to blossom into gardens; taking part in our commerce and maufactures, they have helped to carry the triumphs of our arts to the remotest corners of the globe.

Another insisted that the "real American" was the man who, no matter where he had come from, gave "his mind and heart to the grand constituent ideas of the Republic."

1. In what respects was the population growth of the United States from 1830 to 1860 uneven?

2. Why was there such a large influx of immigrants to the United States in the 1840's? How was the population in the sections affected by this immigration?

3. Why did many of the native-born Americans want to discourage immigration to the United States?

ECONOMIC PROGRESS CONSOLIDATED THE NORTH

Before 1850, there had been not one North but two—the Northeast and the Northwest. The Northwest had at least as many economic ties with the South as it did with the Northeast. The Northwest and the South carried on a great deal of trade by way of the Mississippi River and its tributaries.

During the 1850's, however, economic developments brought the Northeast and the Northwest closer and closer together. Railroads, reaching from the Atlantic coast to the Mississippi Valley, made possible a growing east-west trade. The continued rise of industry in the Northeast and agriculture in the Northwest provided an abundance of goods for this trade. Thus an economic basis was laid for a single, united North.

Until 1857, both the North and the South were unusually prosperous. Vast quantities of gold, coming from the mines of California, were being turned into coins, and this abundance of money encouraged people to spend freely, thus stimulating business. The construction of railroads, on a larger scale than ever before, created thousands of new jobs. War in Europe (the Crimean War, 1854-1856) caused an abnormally large demand for the output of American farms, plantations, and factories. Ocean shipping as well as agriculture and industry consequently thrived.

The boom suddenly ended with the Panic of 1857, which marked the beginning of the third great depression of the nineteenth century (the

two previous ones having begun in 1819 and 1837). The North, with far more industry than the South, was hit much harder by the depression. As a result, the economic progress of the North was temporarily slowed.

Railroads tied Northeast and Northwest together

On a spring day in 1852, a train pulled into Chicago with passengers from as far away as New York. These people were the first to make so long a trip by rail. By 1860, Chicago had become a rail center, with fifteen lines radiating from it and with more than a hundred trains going and coming every day.

Traveling at a speed of twenty to thirty miles an hour, the trains gave much faster service than stagecoaches or river boats. From New York to Chicago, the stagecoach had taken three weeks and the passenger boat (by way of the Hudson River, the Erie Canal, and the Great Lakes) more than two. The steam train required only one week.

In areas beyond the reach of railroads, stagecoaches continued to run. Congress encouraged fast freight by paying a stage line, the Overland Mail Company, for carrying letters and packages. The company's coaches, drawn by six-horse teams which were changed frequently at relay stations, took 25 days to traverse the 2700 miles of a roundabout route from Missouri to California.

For nearly two years, in 1860 and 1861, the Pony Express carried messages much faster. The daring relay riders covered the gap between two telegraph lines, one being constructed eastward from California and the other westward from Missouri. When the lines were joined, telegrams could be sent from New York across the continent to San Francisco.

River steamers became bigger, gaudier, and busier than ever, but their business did not grow so fast as that of the railroads. Steamboatmen feared the growing railroad competition. In 1855, when a steamboat collided with the new Rock Island railroad bridge across the Mississippi, men representing the steamboat companies tried to persuade an Illinois court to order the bridge removed as a nuisance to river traffic. As an attorney for the railroad, Abraham Lincoln helped to defeat the steamboat interests in the Rock Island bridge case.

New patterns of inland commerce were being superimposed upon old ones. The new patterns of east-west trade, brought about by the railroads, became more and more important in comparison with the old patterns of north-south trade along the Mississippi and its tributaries. Increasingly, the farmers of the upper Mississippi Valley looked to New York and other Atlantic seaboard cities, rather than New Orleans, as a market for their crops. A Southern economist complained:

The great cities of the North have severally penetrated the interior with artificial lines until they have taken from the open and untaxed current of the Mississippi the commerce produced on its borders.

Communications with Europe were improved

From the Atlantic seaports, especially New York, surplus products of the Northwest (and some of the cotton of the South) were exported to Europe. Improvements in overseas communications encouraged this commerce during the 1850's.

When a transatlantic cable was laid in 1858, telegrams could be sent from New York across the ocean to London. Soon after the first messages were exchanged, however, the cable went dead. (It was relaid in 1866, after the Civil War, and continued to work from that time on.)

During the 1850's, ocean shipping was speeded up. By paying a mail subsidy, the national government enabled the Collins Line, an American company operating passenger steamers, to compete temporarily with the famed British Cunard Line. A Collins Line steamship, the *Baltic,* in August 1852, set a record by going from Liverpool to New York in less than ten days.

Americans were most successful, however, with sailing vessels, especially the marvelous clipper ships, in the freight business. The clipper was remarkably swift because of its slender, graceful hull and its abundance of square sails. When the winds were right, it could move almost as fast as the fastest steamer of the time. The clipper was designed originally for sailing from Atlantic ports around South America to bring trade to California. It was used also for the India trade—for carrying ice cut from New England ponds to cool the drinks of wealthy nabobs—and also for other trade in which speed was especially important. So successful was the United States with the clippers and with other wooden sailing ships that, for a short time, the United States merchant marine was the largest and busiest in the world, even surpassing the British.

Farm production increased

As people moved west, they extended westward, too, the cultivation of wheat and corn. By 1850, Ohio and Indiana had surpassed New York and Pennsylvania in the production of these crops, but by 1860, Illinois led all states, and Iowa and Missouri were close behind. On the black soil of the prairies, wheat and corn grew remarkably well. Total production increased, as well as production per acre and per man.

In areas where the soil was less fertile, farmers found it hard to compete. Many whose farms lay close to city markets turned to the growing of fruits and vegetables. Some farmers began to take better care of the land and to restore it with fertilizers. Interest in agricultural education grew. States and counties began to hold agricultural fairs, and several states provided for agricultural colleges. (The first state agricultural college was established in 1857 in Michigan.) More and more farmers demanded federal aid to agricultural colleges through the granting of public lands to the states. Meanwhile, the improvements in farming methods—learned through farmers' societies, newspapers, fairs, or colleges—added to the total output of Northern farms.

On many small farms, farmers continued to use hoes, spades, rakes, scythes, and flails, which they powered with their own muscles. On an increasing number of farms, however, especially on the larger ones of the Northwest, there could be heard the clatter of horse-drawn machinery. Reapers in the fields had become a common sight; in 1860, a man with a spyglass counted, from one spot, 146 reapers moving at the same time through wheat fields in Illinois. Mowing machines, hay rakes, corn planters, and other horse-drawn implements were coming into use. These enabled farmers to plant, cultivate, and harvest larger yields than they had been able to harvest previously. A man with a mowing machine, for instance, could cut an acre of hay three times as fast as a man with a scythe.

The horse was just beginning to be the most important draft animal of the Northern farm. Before 1850, the ox was generally preferred to the horse, because the ox was thought to have a stronger and steadier pull. Then, plowing and hauling contests at fairs demonstrated the horse's superiority. By 1860, horses were as numerous as oxen in New England. They soon became more numerous than oxen throughout the North.

Manufactures rapidly increased

Great as was the increase in farm production, the increase in the production of manufactured goods was even more remarkable. In 1850, the total value of manufactures was more than a billion dollars; in 1860, nearly two billion. That year, for the first time in the history of the United States, the output of the factories, mills, shops, and mines was worth more than the output of all the farms and plantations in the nation.

The Northeast still produced the largest share of manufactures. Three states—New York, Massachusetts, and Pennsylvania—together accounted for more than half of the total goods produced in the nation. But industrial centers were rising in the Northwest. Cyrus H. McCormick's decision (1847) to locate his reaper works in Chicago was a major

factor, for example, in that city's development as the center for the manufacture of farm implements. The Northwest was acquiring a common interest with the Northeast in the promotion and protection (through tariffs) of manufactures. As for the South, it gained some new industries, especially cotton mills, but as late as 1860, it produced only a small percentage of the nation's manufactures.

Numerous inventors, in addition to McCormick, designed machines or developed processes that helped to increase American productivity. Patents multiplied; more than four times as many were issued in 1860 as in 1850. A New England hardware merchant, Charles Goodyear, discovered (in 1839) a method of mixing rubber with sulphur so as to vulcanize the rubber and keep it from becoming gummy when hot, and brittle when cold. By the time he died in 1860, Goodyear had taken out sixty patents and had laid the foundation for a rubber industry already turning out hundreds of different products. In 1850, Elias Howe began to manufacture the sewing machine he had invented; the next year, Isaac Singer patented a much improved model. Soon the Howe-Singer machine was producing quantities of cheap, ready-to-wear clothing. Later, during the Civil War, it produced hundreds of thousands of uniforms.

Various machines helped speed production and reduce costs. One of them shaped railroad spikes at the rate of fifty per minute, so that a plant with only seven employees could produce five tons a day. Another took brass wire and formed it into pins so fast that a single factory had a daily output of 300,000. Machine tools of various kinds turned out parts for the famous Colt revolver. Samuel Colt carried further the principles of mass production (through the use of interchangeable parts) which Eli Whitney earlier had introduced, and eventually made his gun factory in Hartford, Connecticut, the largest in the world.

An American of the 1850's boasted that the United States offered

the best and cheapest farm implements, the best car-

TEN LARGEST CITIES IN THE UNITED STATES

	1840	1850	1860
1	New York, N.Y. 312,710	New York, N.Y. 515,547	New York, N.Y. 805,658 (including Brooklyn) 1,072,319
2	Baltimore, Md. 102,313	Baltimore, Md. 169,054	Philadelphia, Pa. 565,529
3	New Orleans, La. 102,193	Boston, Mass. 136,881	Baltimore, Md. 212,418
4	Philadelphia, Pa. 93,665	Philadelphia, Pa. 121,376	Boston, Mass. 177,840
5	Boston, Mass. 93,383	New Orleans, La. 116,375	New Orleans, La. 168,675
6	Cincinnati, Ohio 46,338	Cincinnati, Ohio 115,435	Cincinnati, Ohio 161,044
7	Albany, N.Y. 33,721	St. Louis, Mo. 77,860	St. Louis, Mo. 160,773
8	Charleston, S.C. 29,261	Albany, N.Y. 50,763	Chicago, Ill. 109,260
9	Washington, D.C. 23,364	Pittsburgh, Pa. 46,601	Newark, N.J. 71,941
10	Pittsburgh, Pa. 21,115	Louisville, Ky. 43,194	Louisville, Ky. 68,033

Note: City population, exclusive of metropolitan areas

In 1840, the largest cities in the nation were in the Northeast and the South. But in the next two decades, as the Northeast became increasingly industrialized, cities there grew faster than their rivals in the South. The most spectacular population gains were scored by the new cities in the Northwest.

penters' tools, the best locks, fire-engines, nails, screws, and axes; the best firearms, the cheapest clocks, the fastest steamers and sailing vessels, the cheapest railroads, the lightest wagons, and many of the most useful labor-saving devices in every department of industry.

Few workers became rich

"Every man worships the dollar," an Englishman wrote, after visiting the Northern states. Almost everyone seemed to be busily engaged in a scramble for wealth. Most of the people met with some degree of success. The great majority of Northerners were farmers who owned their farms. A number of these farmers became well-to-do, not so much from selling crops as from selling land that had risen in value. But the wealthiest people got their money from commerce and manufactures. Most of them lived in cities and industrial towns, where the poorest people lived, too.

Few wage earners made fortunes. They labored long hours—eleven or more for most of them. New England mill hands worked as many as fourteen or fifteen hours per day. Unskilled workers received about a dollar a day, and skilled workers seldom were paid more than two dollars. Thus, few laborers could earn more than $300 to $600 a year, even if lucky enough to have steady jobs. At any time, jobs were liable to disappear, temporarily or permanently, because of slack business in a particular industry, because of a general depression, or because of the introduction of labor-saving machinery. Poverty became a serious problem, particularly in manufacturing towns and cities.

Life was especially difficult for the Irish immigrants and the Negroes. The Irish huddled together in dark and dirty tenements and accepted whatever work they could get, usually the hardest and lowest paid. Many Irishmen swung pickaxes in construction gangs that laid railroad tracks and

Corn Husking, by Eastman Johnson, 1860

The Northern farmer. In the North, where farms were generally small and labor was scarce, the job of raising and preparing crops for market was shared by the entire family. In the Northwest, where the soil was new and fertile, the production of crops such as corn and wheat, which could easily be shipped long distances, became increasingly important.

In the Northeast, where the soil was less fertile, many farmers turned to truck and dairy farming to meet the growing needs of urban areas. Since these farms were close to the cities, the farmer had no transportation problem; he and his family simply loaded his cart with the perishable goods he had raised, such as fruits and vegetables, for the short trip to nearby markets.

New developments in methods and equipment such as the grain drill, invented in 1851, increased the general prosperity of Northern farmers. Such improvements helped them to produce more per man and per acre.

A force-feed grain drill

Preparing for Market, by N. Currier, 1856
Yale University Art Gallery,
Mabel Brady Garvan Collection

paved city streets. Discouraging though conditions were, the newcomers from Ireland could at least look forward to a better life for their children.

The Negroes in Northern towns and cities had less to look forward to. A few, a very few, made a comfortable living as merchants, bankers, lawyers, and the like. Other Negroes managed to get along fairly well as barbers and as servants in hotels or private houses. Most could get no work, however, except for the meanest of odd jobs. "Learn trades or starve!" the abolitionist leader and former slave Frederick Douglass advised his fellow Negroes. Those who did learn trades, such as masonry and carpentry, often could get no chance to practice them because of prejudice.

As an English traveler observed, the Negroes in the North formed "a race apart, a strange people in a strange land." They were excluded from the white man's neighborhoods, his streetcars, his schools. Primarily with the aid of white friends, Negroes did make some progress, especially in the field of education. In 1855, Charles Sumner secured the admission of Negroes to the Boston public schools, with the argument that separate schools were necessarily unequal.

New labor unions were organized, but these enrolled only skilled craftsmen. The unions did nothing for the great mass of unskilled laborers, whether Negro or white, native or foreign-born. Union members more and more frequently resorted to strikes. According to the common law, strikes were conspiracies and were illegal. In 1842, however, a Massachusetts court and, afterward, other state courts, held that strikes, if peaceably conducted, were permissible in certain cases.

Unemployed workers, most of whom had no union to represent them, took part in riots and mob demonstrations. The Panic of 1857 strengthened the fervor of the demonstrators. "We want work!" "Work or bread!" mobs shouted in New York, Chicago, and other cities. City governments and private charities set up soup kitchens to feed the many jobless. Speakers on street corners and in city parks harangued the idle crowds and urged the workers to rise and take the government into their own hands.

REVIEWING THE SECTION

1. What improvements were made in transportation and communication during the 1850's? How did these improvements affect trade between the sections?

2. What improvements were made in overseas communications during the 1850's?

3. Why did agricultural output increase substantially during the 1850's?

4. What improvements took place in manufacturing during the 1850's?

5. Give examples to show that the growing wealth of the Northern states was not shared by all segments of the population.

THE SOUTH RELIED ON COTTON AND SLAVERY

Life in the slave states was changing less rapidly than in the free states. People were less inclined to adopt new ideas, new ways of doing things. Railroads were built in the South, but less extensively than in the North. Some industries developed, such as the Tredegar iron works in Virginia and the Gregg cotton mills in South Carolina, but all of them together produced less than one tenth of the manufactures of the country as a whole. Southerners depended to a great extent on agricultural production, especially of cotton, which in turn depended on the labor of Negro slaves.

Cotton was by far the most important of the many Southern crops. It was the largest export of the United States and the greatest source of wealth for the South. It became far more than an extremely valuable crop. It became a symbol of the Southern way of life.

Cotton Is King was the title which David Christy of Cincinnati, Ohio, gave to a book he published in 1855. "Cotton *is* king," Southerners repeated over and over. A famous New Orleans newspaperman, James D. B. De Bow, explained: "To the slave-holding states, it is the great source of their

Cotton pressing, 1856

The planter and the slave. Although only a small percentage of the white population in the South owned large plantations, the lives of these planters set the standard for the Southern way of life. The grand plantation along the Mississippi River illustrates the ideal of most Southern whites. However, not all planters lived in such magnificent style. The more numerous small planters (those owning from 10 to 49 slaves) patterned their lives after those of the large planters, though of necessity on a more modest scale. Since Negro slaves did most of the work, the slaveowner and his family were able to enjoy a gracious and leisurely life.

A small plantation in Texas, by William Bollaert, c. 1850

power and their wealth, and the main security for their peculiar institution." By "peculiar institution," De Bow meant Negro slavery, which Southerners considered "peculiar" in the sense of "distinctive," not "odd." He went on:

Let us teach our children to hold the cotton plant in one hand and a sword in the other, ever ready to defend it as the source of commercial power abroad, and through that, of independence at home.

Southerners believed that King Cotton ruled the world. Certainly, it ruled their imaginations.

Planters dominated life in the South

Slavery was spread over the South unevenly, because of geographic conditions. The climate ranged from the subtropical to the subarctic, even within the one state of North Carolina. Slaves were most numerous in the lowlands, which were best suited for the larger plantations, and they were less numerous in the hilly or mountainous regions. Within the state of Mississippi, for instance, slaves were concentrated in the delta area of the Mississippi River and were scarce in the hill country of the northeast.

Crops varied from place to place. Cotton was grown in a "cotton belt" that stretched in a great arc from North Carolina southward and westward to Texas and Arkansas. Tobacco was grown in a belt that extended northward from North Carolina to Virginia and Maryland and westward to Kentucky. Rice was produced along the coast of South Carolina, and sugar in the lowlands of Louisiana.

Some novels and movies have given us a romanticized picture of the Old South—pillared mansions, vast fields of cane or cotton, grinning servants, singing field hands, and hospitable gentlemen and ladies. This romanticized South contains only kindhearted masters and carefree slaves, except perhaps

A plantation on the Mississippi, by Currier & Ives, 1868

for an occasional "poor white" who appears briefly on the edges of the scene.

In the South of historical fact, most of the people were neither slaves nor slave owners, nor were they poor whites. All except a very few of the Negroes were slaves, but only one in four of the white people was a slaveholder or a member of a slaveholding family. Of the nonslaveholders, only a tiny proportion could properly be classified as poor whites, that is, as shiftless and sickly people who barely managed to keep alive on wornout plantation lands or sandy, barren soils. Some other nonslaveholders were mountaineers living in rough and unproductive country; these highlanders were poor but vigorous, and fiercely independent.

The great majority of white Southerners were neither rich nor poor. They were farmers who owned land but no slaves. Some hired a slave or two for extra help in busy seasons. Among the minority who did own slaves, fewer than 2000 in the entire South owned more than 100 slaves each. Half of all slaveholders had fewer than 10 each. Planters who owned vast fields and imposing mansions were comparatively rare.

Though the planters were a minority of the people, they (especially the cotton planters) controlled most of the wealth of the South. They dominated its politics. They set the tone for its manners and its thought. So there is an element of truth in the myth which romanticizes plantation life.

Plantations were dependent on slave labor

On the plantation, the slaves did most of the work. Some labored as mechanics or artisans, a larger number as household servants, and the majority as field hands.

On a small plantation, with only a few slaves, they might work in the fields alongside the planter and his sons. On a large plantation, with dozens or even hundreds of slaves, it was necessary for them to be well organized. The owners of large plantations usually hired an overseer, generally a white man, who divided the field workers into gangs. One of the slaves was placed in charge of each gang. This slave, the "driver," carried a long whip which he used, if necessary, to keep his gang on the move.

The owner had a large investment in his slaves. It was in his interest to see to it that they were not worked too hard, were reasonably well fed and cared for, and were kept away from conditions dangerous to health or life. Slaves were seldom used for digging ditches in malarial swamps, for example, or for catching cotton bales at the bottom of chutes which brought the cotton from river bluffs to boat landings. Irish immigrants, when available, were used for such dangerous work or for work under unhealthful conditions. If a slave died, the owner lost property worth as much as $1000 or more. If a hired man died, the employer lost nothing.

Not always did the owner's economic interest assure good treatment for his slaves. The owner himself was not always guided by considerations of profit and loss. If kind, he would treat his slaves well. If cruel, he would find plenty of opportunity to vent his cruelty.

The overseer's interest in the slave differed from that of the owner. It was to the overseer's advantage to get as much work as possible out of the slaves, for the larger the crop, the larger his pay.

The master had almost absolute power over his own slaves. True, he could not legally kill them—except in self-defense or, accidentally, in the course of punishment. If he were forced to justify a death, however, the courts would take his word for it; they would not listen to the testimony of slaves. This ownership and tyrannical authority of one person over another was the basic evil of slavery.

The women were encouraged to have as many children as possible, since each new child added to the supply of slaves. But a slave could not claim his wife or children as his own because the laws did not recognize slave marriages. In spite of difficulties, the slaves tried to maintain their family life. The master might try to prevent the separation of mates or of parents and children, yet slave families often were broken up through sales, especially in the settlement of estates after the master's death.

Slaves had few ways of asserting themselves. They could resort to such methods as slowing down on the job, breaking or losing tools, or hiding out at busy times. They could run away, but unless a slave lived near the border of a free state, he had little chance of making good his escape. When recaptured, he would be punished with the lash and sometimes the branding iron. Yet some ran off again and again. In newspaper advertisements, owners sometimes described fugitives as having not only physical but also psychological scars, such as a stutter or a nervous twitch.

Now and then an exasperated slave would way-lay and kill his master. Seldom did a group of slaves attempt to revolt. On a night in 1831, however, the slave preacher Nat Turner and sixty or seventy followers, carrying guns and axes, killed fifty-five white Virginians. Even loved and trusted servants suddenly turned against their masters. Whole families, including defenseless women and children, were attacked and killed. A shudder ran through the entire South and afterward, planters and their families always wondered who among their slaves could really be depended upon.

The demand for slaves increased

The newer states of the South—especially Alabama, Mississippi, Louisiana, and Texas—were growing much faster than the older ones such as Maryland, Virginia, the Carolinas, and Kentucky. Planters continued to move southward and westward. They took with them their slaves, but these were not enough to meet the increasing demand. On the fresh and fertile lands of the newer states, there was a constant shortage of slaves. In the older states, where the soil had been relatively exhausted from long-time cultivation, the use of slave labor was no longer very profitable and there was a constant surplus of slaves.

In response to the conditions of demand and supply, an interstate slave trade had developed, and, in the 1850's, this trade thrived as never before. Slaves were taken to market by various routes. Some, chained together, were marched overland. Others were shipped from Chesapeake ports to ports on the Gulf of Mexico, such as New Orleans. Still others went by boat down the Mississippi (hence the expression "sold down the river").

At auctions, the slaves were put up for sale to the highest bidder. Many prospective buyers gave the slaves in the market the same kind of inspection they would have given an animal, requiring them to walk back and forth as they were scrutinized for physical defects. The buyers were cautious, for the dealer often tried to cheat them by such tricks as blacking gray hair to make a slave look younger.

Most planters looked down upon the slave trader, both because of his sharp practices and because of the inhumane business itself. Yet the trader could rise to respectability and popularity by making a fortune and investing it in a plantation of his own. For instance, Nathan Bedford Forrest, once a dealer in slaves, became a respected plantation owner and, later, a Confederate hero as a cavalry commander during the Civil War. Though the planters seldom recognized or admitted it, the slave trader performed a service that was indispensable to the growth of slavery. Someone had to buy and sell slaves if the planters in the newer parts of the South were to obtain enough slave labor to supply the demand.

A few Southerners began to think that, even at best, the domestic slave trade would not provide an adequate supply. They demanded the reopening of the foreign slave trade, which had been closed by federal law since 1808. Despite the law, a number of slaves were smuggled into the country every year. How large the number was, no one can say, but it was not large enough to have a noticeable effect on the supply or the price of slaves.

Many Southerners (and many Northerners) believed that slavery would need additional lands as well as additional slaves if it were to prosper or even survive. The assumption was that, with soil exhaustion, slavery would eventually die out in the newer states, as it seemed to be doing in the older states.

Southerners defended slavery

At one time, leading Southerners had questioned and criticized the enslavement of their fellow man. "Indeed I tremble for my country when I reflect that God is just, that his justice cannot sleep forever," Thomas Jefferson had written. As late as the 1830's, most Southerners disliked slavery. They put up with it as something they had inherited and could not easily get rid of. By the 1850's, however, they no longer apologized for it as a necessary evil. They now boasted of it as "a good—a positive good."

Propaganda had helped to convince the people, even those who owned no slaves, that slavery was a good thing. According to the proslavery argument, it was good for Negroes because they were by nature so primitive and childlike that they could not take care of themselves. Thanks to the master, they were better off than Northern free laborers, who had to worry about unemployment and old age. The people who favored slavery insisted that Negro slavery was good for Southern whites, whether they owned slaves or not, because it made the South prosperous, exempted it from strikes and other labor troubles, and enabled the two races to live there in peace. Indeed, the "peculiar institution" of the South was good for everyone, everywhere, and it was in accord with the teachings of the Bible. So its defenders argued.

One proslavery enthusiast said that, since slavery was such an ideal arrangement, it ought not to be used only on Southern Negroes. It ought also to be tried on other workers, white as well as black, Northern as well as Southern.

Among nonslaveholders in the South, censorship

silenced those whom propaganda failed to convince. The people seldom read or even received antislavery propaganda, for officials usually removed from the mails books, pamphlets, or periodicals that criticized slavery. People were jailed when caught with such "incendiary" literature in their possession.

A North Carolina farmer, Hinton R. Helper, wrote a book to prove that slavery was harmful to nonslaveholders. Helper said it caused the South to lag behind the North in economic progress. He denied that cotton was king. "Hay is king," he maintained, pointing out that the Northern hay crop was worth more than the Southern cotton crop. He called his book *The Impending Crisis of the South,* and (in 1857, after he had moved to the North) he got it published in New York. In the South, few had a chance to buy or read his book. In the North, it become a best seller.

Propaganda and censorship, by themselves, did not fully account for the nonslaveholder's support of slavery. In many cases, propaganda only confirmed the nonslaveholder in feelings he already had. Censorship merely kept him from reading things like Helper's book, which might have caused him to question whether he was really better off because of slavery.

His basic feelings were these: Under slavery, he, or at least his sons, had a chance to rise in the world, become slave owners themselves, and enjoy the delights of plantation life. Under emancipation, there would be millions of free Negroes, and he could not imagine himself and the rest of the whites living safely or happily beside them. (In the North, prejudice was as strong or stronger but Negroes were vastly fewer, and there was the expectation that, once emancipated, the former slaves would remain in the South.)

There would have been fewer proslavery men among the nonslaveholders if it had been feasible, as the American Colonization Society proposed, to send all of the Negroes, once they were freed, to western Africa. Many of the nonslaveholders would have been willing to let slavery disappear if they could have been sure that, at the same time, the Negroes also would disappear.

REVIEWING THE SECTION

1. Show how the ante-bellum South was substantially different from the South depicted in romantic novels and movies.

2. What kinds of work did slaves perform on Southern plantations? What rights and privileges, enjoyed by free laborers, were denied the slaves?

3. Why did the demand for slaves decrease in the older states of the South and increase in the newer states?

4. Why did most Southerners eventually sanction slavery?

THE NORTH AND SOUTH DIFFERED IN OUTLOOK

Slavery and cotton in the South, free labor and industry in the North—these were the basic differences which eventually caused the two sections to differ also in economic interests, constitutional views, and social ideals.

Various groups in the North wanted the national government to give them economic aid. Manufacturers, for example, desired high tariffs to protect them from foreign competition. Northerners generally felt that their prosperity depended upon governmental assistance.

Most Southerners, however, opposed such economic policies. Cotton growers disliked a tariff on manufactures because they thought (as had those South Carolinians who once attempted nullification) that it would raise the price of what they bought and lower the price of what they sold. They feared that governmental assistance to manufacturing, railroad building, shipping, or farming would promote the development of the North at the expense of the South.

As in earlier decades, so also in the 1850's, Americans debated in constitutional as well as economic terms. Northerners who favored a particular policy discovered, upon looking into the Constitution, that the national government had the power to take the desired action. Southerners who opposed the policy, however, could find no such power in the Constitution.

Though the North was far from being a perfect democracy, Northerners generally believed in democratic principles. Most Southerners, on the other hand, increasingly praised the ideals of aristocracy rather than democracy.

The sections had conflicting economic interests

Northern manufacturers desired high tariffs because these would raise the price of competing goods that came into the United States from foreign nations. Thus the manufacturers would be able to sell larger quantities of their own products and get higher prices than they otherwise could.

Tariff advocates maintained that without such protection some of the mill owners might have to go out of business. Then workers would lose their jobs. After the Panic of 1857, a number of mills did close, and the production of others was cut back. The panic made tariff protection seem more necessary than ever to manufacturers and their employees.

Northern shipowners wanted the government to aid them with mail contracts or other subsidies and with laws to keep foreign ships out of the coastal trade between American ports. Northern farmers wanted the government to aid them by providing free homesteads, supporting agricultural education, and helping to finance the construction of railroads which would facilitate the marketing of crops.

Some people in the North opposed one or more of these forms of government aid, and some people in the South favored them. The sugar planters of Louisiana, for example, advocated tariff protection, at least for their own product, since they wished to discourage the importation of Cuban sugar. Nevertheless, by 1860, a majority of Northerners had come to favor one or more such measures, and a majority of Southerners had come to oppose all of them.

Southerners argued that the North already had grown rich by exploiting them. A man named T. P. Kettell wrote a book, *Southern Wealth and Northern Profits* (1860), in an attempt to prove that Southerners produced more than their share of the nation's wealth but the North took away a large part of it. Another man complained:

Instead of keeping our money in circulation at home, by patronizing our own mechanics, manufacturers, and laborers, we send it all away to the North, and there it remains; it never falls into our hands again.

Supposedly, through control of shipping, banking, and manufacturing, the North managed to get forty cents out of every dollar that Southern cotton brought.

Year after year, delegates from Southern states met in commercial conventions to discuss means of making the South economically independent. These conventions accomplished little or nothing, largely because the delegates disagreed as to precisely what should be done.

Though the planters opposed government aid to Northern business, they demanded government support for their own labor system. Since they thought slavery had to expand in order to thrive, they wanted the government to guarantee its expansion. They wanted the government to make new territories available for the "peculiar institution" and to encourage and protect it within the territories.

The sections interpreted the Constitution differently

According to Northern tariff advocates, the Constitution gave Congress the power to pass tariff laws. True, the Constitution said nothing, in so many words, about tariffs for the protection and encouragement of manufactures, but it did say that Congress could levy taxes and could regulate commerce with foreign nations. The tariff could be viewed either as a tax or as a measure for the regulation of commerce. Therefore, though not included in the specified powers, it would come within the "implied powers" of Congress. However Southern opponents of the protective tariff insisted that Congress had no rightful powers except those which the Constitution specifically granted.

According to antislavery people in the North, Congress had the implied power to abolish the interstate slave trade, since Congress had the specified power to regulate interstate commerce. But Congress possessed no power to abolish slavery in the Southern states; both critics and defenders agreed that slavery in those states was a "domestic" institution which only the states themselves could abolish. According to critics of slavery, Congress had the constitutional right to abolish it in the District of Columbia, since this area was under federal jurisdiction. According to defenders of slavery, however, Congress could not properly do so. They said Maryland had ceded the area for the national capital with the understanding that slavery would continue to exist there.

Could Congress prohibit slavery in the territories? This became the most heatedly discussed constitutional question of the 1850's. The Constitution itself said:

The Congress shall have Power to dispose of and make all needful Rules and Regulations respecting the Territory or other Property belonging to the United States; and nothing in this Constitution shall be so construed as to Prejudice any Claims of the United States, or of any particular State. (*Article IV, sec. 3, para. 2*)

According to most Northerners, Congress could, indeed, legislate against slavery in the territories, since Congress could "make all needful Rules and Regulations" regarding them. Congress had, in fact, prohibited slavery in the Northwest Territory by repassing the Northwest Ordinance of 1787 (which was originally passed by the Confederation Congress before the adoption of the Constitution).

According to most Southerners, Congress could

by no means legislate against slavery in the territories, since nothing in the Constitution was to be "so construed as to Prejudice any Claims . . . of any particular State." Each state had as much claim upon the territories as any other state. The people of any state should be able to move to any territory and take along their property, including slave property, with full assurance that it would be safe.

Southerners continued to discuss and interpret state rights according to their particular needs and desires. Though they no longer mentioned the right of nullification, they still insisted upon the right of secession. Some Northerners also believed in state rights, such as the right to resist federal laws that were designed for the recapture of fugitive slaves. Very few Northerners, however, thought that any state had a right to secede.

Actually, the state rights doctrine which evolved in the South had more to do with state *powers* than with state *rights,* though its exponents did not admit this. It was not merely a defensive doctrine, intended to assure self-government within the states and to protect slavery against interference from the outside. It was essentially an aggressive doctrine. It asserted the power of the states to extend slavery beyond their own borders and into the territories. Southerners maintained that in making territorial rules and regulations, Congress had no choice but to accept and approve the state laws in regard to slavery. Thus, so far as the people of the territories were concerned, the state rights doctrine of the South did not affirm, instead it denied, the right of self-government. It denied the right of those people to exclude slavery, even if the great majority of them should wish to do so.

The sections had divergent social ideals

In the North, democracy was a prevailing ideal, though not in all respects an accomplished fact. People continued to believe in the words of the Declaration of Independence, "all men are created equal" and are born with "certain unalienable Rights." Of course, people did not always practice

ABOLITION OF SLAVERY, 1800-1865

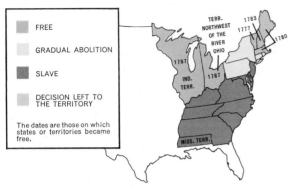

FREE	
GRADUAL ABOLITION	
SLAVE	
DECISION LEFT TO THE TERRITORY	

The dates are those on which states or territories became free.

1800. By 1800, slavery had been prohibited in the Northwest and Indiana territories, and almost half of the states had abolished slavery or had adopted gradual emancipation laws.

1820. With the exception of Missouri, the Missouri Compromise of 1820 prohibited slavery north of the parallel of 36°30' in the Louisiana Purchase territory.

1850. In 1848, slavery was prohibited in Oregon Territory; the Compromise of 1850 admitted California as a free state and allowed popular sovereignty in New Mexico and Utah.

1854. The Kansas-Nebraska Act in effect nullified part of the Missouri Compromise and brought popular sovereignty to the territories of Nebraska and Kansas.

1863. The status of slavery changed again in 1862, when Congress forbade slavery in all organized territories. In 1863, the Emancipation Proclamation prohibited slavery in those parts of the Confederacy still in rebellion.

1865. The abolition of slavery was completed on December 18, 1865, when the Thirteenth Amendment went into effect. Prior to this, Louisiana and Virginia had freed the slaves in areas not covered by the Emancipation Proclamation of 1863.

the ideal of equality. The rich and strong looked down upon the poor and weak. White people, rich or poor, generally looked down upon Negroes and treated them as inferiors. Nevertheless, Northerners became more and more convinced that Negroes, as well as white men, possessed the basic rights of life, liberty, and the pursuit of happiness, and should be allowed to exercise them. People were inclined to feel guilty about the gap between the ideal and the reality in Northern life.

In the South, many people were losing sight of democracy as an ideal. They had been taught to question the Revolutionary propositions regarding equality and liberty. Political leaders, such as John C. Calhoun, had ridiculed those propositions. He said they were as dangerous as they were ridiculous. They gave rise to fanatical movements like abolitionism, he explained, and unless these were checked, they might lead at last to civil war.

More and more, the slaveholders and even many nonslaveholders adopted aristocratic ideals. They came to believe that an upper class of gentlemen should run social and political affairs and, in fact, this is what the planters did. Romantic novels, particularly those of Sir Walter Scott, were read and enjoyed by the would-be aristocrats of the South,

who longed to be like the knights and ladies of old. The knights fought duels, and so did Southern gentlemen, who were touchy on points of personal honor. The knights were brave, mannerly, and kind to ladies—so were Southern gentlemen.

Even a Yankee like F. L. Olmsted could admire the "high-toned gentleman" of the South. "The honesty and unstudied dignity of character, the generosity and the real nobleness of habitual impulses, and the well-bred manly courtesy which distinguish him," Olmsted noted, "are sadly rare at the North." Still, Olmsted preferred the relatively democratic society of the North to the relatively aristocratic society of the South. He thought that Northerners, as a whole, were "better, more gentlemanly even," than Southerners, including all classes. This, of course, was only one man's opinion, and a Northerner's at that.

REVIEWING THE SECTION

1. How did the economic interests of the North conflict with those of the South?
2. Over which powers of Congress did Northerners and Southerners disagree?
3. How did the social ideals of the South differ from those of the North?

CHAPTER **11** CONCLUSION

By the 1850's, the differences between the North and the South had become numerous and deep.

The North was rapidly growing in population, adopting new mechanical inventions, and swelling the output of its factories, even more than that of its farms. Not everyone benefited alike from the increase in wealth. Poverty existed, especially in the cities, where it was particularly severe during depressions. On the whole, the people approved of government action to encourage business and agriculture, and they believed in, though they did not always practice, the ideals of social and political democracy. Despite the

faults and failures of the North, the people were optimistic and self-confident. They expected the wealth and power of the nation, particularly in their section, to keep on growing. They thought the future belonged to them, as in fact it did.

The South was growing and changing less rapidly. Though the people produced a variety of crops, and though most of the people owned no slaves, the section as a whole became more and more preoccupied with cotton and with slavery. Aristocracy began to replace democracy as the social and political ideal. Thoughtful Southerners knew that the North was surpassing their section in wealth as well as numbers. They knew that they themselves were out of step with the majority of Americans (and with practically all Europeans) on the question of slavery. As a proslavery minority, they looked to the Constitution for arguments with which to check the antislavery majority's will. Inwardly, they grew concerned about the situation of the South, though outwardly they boasted of Southern greatness. They feared the future and, so far as possible, clung to the past.

Yet, though the differences were many and deep, the similarities between the North and the South were even more numerous and fundamental. After all, both the Northerners and the Southerners were Americans, with a common heritage of European and especially English customs and beliefs. They shared the traditions of American patriotism, the flag, the gallery of heroes. First among the heroes, both North and South, was George Washington—the "father" of the whole country, not just one section of it.

Moreover, while Northerners and Southerners had conflicting interests, they also had interests in common. They benefited from trade with each other. They had ties of family and friendship, some Northerners having been born in the South and some Southerners in the North. They had ties of belief and membership affiliations which caused them to think of themselves not only as Northerners or Southerners, but also as Protestants or Roman Catholics, Whigs or Democrats.

Nevertheless, in recounting this period of United States history, it is necessary to emphasize the sectional differences rather than the similarities, the points of dispute rather than the areas of agreement. Eventually, the differences and disagreements prevailed. Only by paying close attention to these can it be understood how the United States came to be divided in two, and how Americans happened to go to war against other Americans.

FOCUSING ON SPECIFICS

1. In what areas of the country did most Irish immigrants settle? most German immigrants? Why?

2. Why did few immigrants settle in the South?

3. What advances were made in agricultural education during the 1850's?

4. How did the following men contribute to the growth of American industry: Howe and Singer, McCormick, Goodyear, Colt?

5. What problems were faced by the Northern Negro during the 1850's? the Irish immigrant?

6. Why did Southerners say that "Cotton is King"?

7. In what ways did geographical conditions affect the distribution of slaves?

8. What long-lasting effect did the Nat Turner revolt (1831) have on the South?

9. What arguments did advocates of slavery use to justify their position?

10. How did the South control the spread of antislavery propaganda?

11. Why did many nonslaveholders support slavery?

12. Why were most Southern cotton growers opposed to a tariff on manufactures?

13. What kinds of government aid did Southern planters favor?

REVIEWING MAIN THEMES

1. What changes took place in the nature and distribution of the population during the 1840's and 1850's?

2. What changes took place in the United States economy during the 1850's which brought the Northeast and Northwest closer together?

3. How did the economy of the South differ from that of the North?

4. How did the different ways of life in the North and South contribute to different ways of thinking?

5. What interests did the North and South have in common?

EVALUATING THE ISSUES

1. How do you account for the fact that the growth of cities between 1830 and 1860 was far slower in the South than in the North?

2. Many Southerners claimed that the Southern slaves were treated better and enjoyed a happier life than did the average Northern industrial worker. Do you think that this was true? Explain.

CHAPTER **12** 1850-1861

The Division of the Nation

It was April 12, 1861. In the early morning darkness a cannon boomed, sending a signal shell high into the air. Against the dark sky, this shell with its sputtering fuse made a thin red track, something like that of a Fourth of July rocket. As the track curved downward, the shell suddenly exploded with a dazzling light and a thunderous noise. The glare, reflecting on the water of Charleston harbor, revealed the outlines of a high-walled, five-sided fort. This was Fort Sumter, garrisoned by troops of the United States. Into it, big guns soon were pouring shot and shell from several directions.

Even before the firing on Fort Sumter, the nation had begun to divide into the United States of America and the Confederate States of America. With the Confederates opening fire, the two were now at war.

Separation and war came because of growing differences, real and imaginary, between the North and the South. The institution of slavery had disappeared in one of the sections, but not in the other, and industry was developing within each section at very different rates. Out of these divergences grew the "irrepressible conflict."

Conflict does not necessarily mean *war,* nor does it necessarily lead to bloodshed. Within a democracy there always are clashes of opposing interests and opposing views. These are the things with which politics is primarily concerned. Normally, politicians manage to smooth over the disputes. When conflicts go deep enough, however, politicians may act in such a way as to intensify rather than relieve the conflicts.

It was possible for politicians to deal fairly well with sectional disagreements so long as there existed two political parties organized on a national basis. It would become difficult if not impossible, however, once the national parties had disappeared and sectional parties had taken their place.

Long before the Civil War, George Washington had realized this. "In contemplating the causes which may disturb our Union," he said in his Farewell Address (published September 19, 1796), it occurs as a matter of serious concern that any ground should have been furnished for characterizing parties by *Geographical* discriminations, *Northern* and *Southern*, *Atlantic* and *Western;* whence designing men may endeavour to excite a belief that there is a real difference of local interests and views. One of the expedients of a party to acquire influence, within particular districts, is to misrepresent the opinions and aims of other districts.

In George Washington's time it seemed that if the nation should ever divide, it would probably divide into an East and a West. The Appalachian Mountains made a natural dividing line, and the Mississippi Valley formed a natural unit. Apparently, there was a danger that an Eastern party and a Western party might arise. By 1850, when the nation actually began to divide into the North and the South, the line of division cut across the natural barrier of the Appalachian Mountains and the natural unity of the Mississippi River valley. The danger now was that Northern and Southern parties might emerge.

For a while, the two national parties, the Whig and the Democratic, continued to exist. Within each party, Northerners and Southerners worked together. Between the two parties, as Whigs and Democrats, Northerners opposed Northerners and Southerners opposed Southerners. Thus partisan differences offset sectional differences, and the two parties served as bonds of national unity.

After the election of 1852, however, the national Whig party began to disintegrate. By election time in 1856, a new party—the Republican party—had been formed, and this one was sectional, with members only in the North. In 1860, the national Democratic party split into Northern and Southern Democratic parties. More and more, just as George Washington once warned they would do, politicians in each section were exaggerating rather than minimizing the conflicts with the other section. The danger he had foreseen—the organizing of parties on a *sectional* rather than a *national* basis—finally became a reality.

The consequences were to be seen in Charleston harbor on that April morning in 1861.

A COMPROMISE PREVENTED SECESSION IN 1850

About ten years before the firing on Fort Sumter, several of the Southern states had been ready to secede and, if need be, go to war, but Congress had managed to agree on the Compromise of 1850. At that time, the United States was facing a dangerous sectional crisis.

Several issues concerning slavery were rapidly approaching a climax. There were questions regarding what to do about slavery and the slave trade in the District of Columbia, about fugitive slaves escaping into the free states and, most important, about the extension of slavery into the Western territories. There was no question, however, whether or not Congress would take steps to abolish slavery within the Southern states, since nearly all Northerners agreed with Southerners that Congress had no constitutional power to do so.

Many Northerners wanted to keep slavery out of the territories because they considered the institution evil in itself. Some disliked Negroes, whether slave or free, and hoped to preserve the territories for the exclusive settlement of white men. Some were mainly concerned with preventing the creation of new slave states whose senators and representatives would vote with those of the South to defeat tariffs and other policies of benefit to Northern businessmen and farmers.

On the other hand, most Southerners feared that the interests of the South would suffer unless new slave states were created. Up to 1850, there had been a continuing balance between free and slave states, the same number of each. This meant that, even though it was outnumbered in the House of Representatives, the South had an equal vote in the Senate and could check unwanted measures there. If, in the future, none but free states should be formed from the territories, the South would lose all hope of political equality in the nation.

Long-standing issues divided North and South

To antislavery people in the North, it seemed shameful that slavery and the slave trade continued in the city of Washington. Here, close to the Capitol itself, were slave auctions and slave pens—sights the opponents of slavery considered shocking anywhere in the "land of the free." Members of antislavery societies continually petitioned Congress to rid the District of Columbia of both slavery and the slave trade.

This agitation offended and frightened Southerners. So did the Northern opposition to the federal Fugitive Slave Act (of 1793). The Supreme Court had ruled (in the case of *Prigg* v. *Pennsylvania,* 1842) that state officials need not help to enforce this act. After that, several of the Northern states adopted "personal liberty" laws. These laws forbade state officials to assist in the capture of runaway slaves. Thus, in the North, state laws partly nullified a federal act, but Southerners denounced that kind of nullification.

The issue of slavery in the territories, so far as the Louisiana Purchase territory was concerned, had been settled by the Missouri Compromise (1820). This prohibited slavery north of a certain line (36° 30′), except in Missouri itself, and permitted it south of the line. The line applied only to the Louisiana Purchase territory, however, and not to the newer territories of Oregon, California, and New Mexico.

Some people thought Congress ought to extend the line all the way to the Pacific Ocean. Others believed that the settlers in each territory ought to decide for themselves whether or not to allow slavery. This idea of letting the settlers decide came to be known as "popular sovereignty." The extremists of the North opposed it and demanded "free soil" instead. That is, they insisted that Congress must exclude slavery from *all* the territories. They upheld the principle of the Wilmot Proviso. This proviso, which had been introduced but not passed during the Mexican War (1846-1848), would have prohibited slavery in all the lands acquired from Mexico. Southerners violently opposed it. They maintained that Congress must permit and protect slavery in all the territories, even in Oregon. Not that they expected slavery actually to take root so far north, but they wanted to set a precedent for allowing it farther south, in California and New Mexico.

In regard to New Mexico, there was also another issue. There was a boundary dispute with Texas. The Texans claimed all the land westward to the Rio Grande which included a very large part of what New Mexico settlers thought was New Mexico. Northerners backed the New Mexicans, and Southerners the Texans. If Texas should make good its claim, the area of slavery would be enlarged, since Texas was a slave state.

Some Southerners threatened secession

Zachary Taylor, elected in 1848, was the first professional military man to become President (George Washington and Andrew Jackson were military heroes, too, but neither of them made a profession of army life). Though honest and courageous, he lacked experience in government.

The Whigs had run Taylor for the presidency without a specific platform. Few people knew what he stood for. Southern Whigs assumed that he would support proslavery policies, for he owned a Louisiana plantation with a hundred slaves. In fact, however, he had served with the army on the frontier for so long that he no longer felt any particular attachment to the South. As President, he often listened to the advice of free-soil Northerners, especially Senator William H. Seward of New York.

It seemed to President Taylor that California ought to become a state immediately, without going through the stages of territorial government. California needed strong agencies of law enforcement to maintain order in the wild mining camps, and had a population large enough to qualify for statehood. Taylor sent a messenger to tell some of the leading Californians that they should frame

THE COMPROMISE OF 1850

ISSUES	COMPROMISE
Antislavery Northerners wanted to have slavery abolished in the District of Columbia.	The slave trade, but not slavery itself, was abolished in the District of Columbia.
Several Northern states had virtually nullified the Fugitive Slave Law of 1793 by forbidding state officials to assist in the capture of runaway slaves. Southerners objected to this evasion of the law.	A stricter fugitive slave law was passed.
Problems arose over the extension of slavery into territories acquired from Mexico, land not covered by the terms of the Missouri Compromise. Until 1850, there were an equal number of slave and free states. Southerners feared that the admission of California as a free state would mean the loss of political power in the Senate.	California was admitted as a free state. In New Mexico and Utah territories, the question of slavery was to be decided by the inhabitants.
Conflict arose over a large area of land claimed by both Texans and the New Mexico settlers. Northerners supported the New Mexicans, who were against slavery. Southerners backed the claims of Texas, a slave state.	Texas gave up its claim to the disputed land; in return, the federal government assumed the debts that Texas had acquired while an independent republic.

The Compromise of 1850 temporarily provided a solution to the slavery controversy. Most Northerners and Southerners were willing to accept it as an alternative to disunion. Acceptance, however, was conditional; the terms of the agreement had to be fulfilled in good faith by both sections. With the passage of the Kansas-Nebraska Act in 1854, the slavery question was reopened and the sections again began to quarrel.

a state constitution and apply for admission to the Union. They did so, framing a constitution which prohibited slavery. Then, at the end of 1849, Taylor recommended that Congress admit California as a free state.

Through the early months of 1850, Southerners threatened that their own states would secede if California came into the Union. The legislature of Mississippi called a convention of Southern states to meet in Nashville, Tennessee, in June. At this convention, some Southern leaders expected to make plans for the slave states to secede as a group. The Mississippi legislature, when naming its own delegate to the convention, also appropriated money for "necessary measures for protecting the state." Obviously, some of the Southerners were thinking of the possibility of war.

Congress finally agreed to a compromise

While secession and war were threatening, Congress was discussing a plan for compromise. The aging senator from Kentucky, Henry Clay, had presented a bill which dealt not only with California but also with other matters in dispute. The main provisions of Clay's "omnibus bill" were:

(1) California would be admitted as a free state. This, of course, would be a concession to the North.

(2) In the rest of the area acquired from Mexico (that is, in New Mexico and Utah), territorial governments would be organized without any restriction on slavery. Presumably, these territories could adopt or reject slavery, according to the principle of popular sovereignty. This would

be a concession to the South, for it would mean leaving the way open for the possible creation of new slave states, which would counterbalance California and, later on, Oregon.

(3) Texas would give up her claim to a part of New Mexico, and, in return, the federal government would take over and pay the debts that Texas owed. (For the most part, this money was owed to people, including Northerners, who had lent money to Texas when she was an independent republic.) This arrangement would mean yielding something to the North and something to the South.

(4) The slave trade, but not slavery itself, would be abolished in the District of Columbia. This would concede something to the North but only a part of what many Northerners demanded.

(5) A new fugitive slave act, more drastic and more effective than the old one, would be passed. This would be a concession to the South.

Clay, a Kentucky slaveholder, spoke eloquently in favor of his bill. John C. Calhoun, a South Carolina slaveholder, now dying, condemned it in a speech which he wrote but was too weak to deliver; another man read it for him. Calhoun argued that the South was not being given sufficient guarantees for its interests, especially slavery. He had in mind a constitutional amendment providing for two Presidents, one from the North and the other from the South, each of them having a veto. Daniel Webster, a Massachusetts man, defended Clay's compromise and pleaded for calm on both sides. The New Yorker William H. Seward opposed the bill on the ground that in opening territories to slavery it violated the "higher law," the law of God, which required devotion to the cause of freedom.

Clay's bill, however, had no chance so long as Taylor remained in the presidency, regardless of the arguments for or against it. Taylor insisted that California should be admitted at once and without regard to the settlement of other issues. If the bill had passed, he would have vetoed it.

On the Fourth of July, Taylor attended patriotic ceremonies at the Washington Monument. The sun was hot. To cool off, he drank quantities of iced milk and ate quantities of fresh cherries. Soon he was sick, and it was thought he had indigestion. More likely, he had that dreaded epidemic disease, the cholera. In a few days he was dead.

Millard Fillmore, formerly Vice President, was now President. He was a New York Whig, as was Seward, but the two were neither personal nor political friends. Fillmore soon proved himself to be far more ready to accept a compromise than either Seward or Taylor had been. The new President appointed Webster to the office of secretary of state and other procompromise men to lesser offices. Fillmore and his appointees encouraged the passage of the compromise. It finally passed, but only after Clay's omnibus bill had been broken up into five separate bills. Fillmore promptly signed each of them.

The fugitive-slave issue remained unsettled

Southerners felt that in the Compromise of 1850 the North had got the better of the bargain and, indeed, it had. Some people in the South still talked about secession. They looked forward to the Nashville convention, which was postponed until November 1850. When it finally met, only about a third of the delegates arrived. They called for a new convention to represent the entire South. Most Southerners, though, preferred to wait and see how well the compromise worked. Their feelings were summed up in the Georgia Platform, a series of resolutions in which the Georgia legislature declared that the state would go along with the compromise—but only if the North lived up to all the terms, especially those regarding the return of fugitive slaves.

Northerners generally approved the Compromise of 1850, except for the new Fugitive Slave Law. Most of them felt that this law was unfair. According to its provisions, a man pursuing Negroes needed only to swear that they were his slaves. The Negroes themselves could not testify, nor could they have a trial by jury. Thus free Ne-

THE DIVISION OF THE NATION

groes would have no legal protection against a kidnaper who schemed to force them into slavery. Federal marshals were required to enforce the law, and citizens were forbidden to give any help to fugitives. Northerners protested that the law would make all the people "slave catchers."

Antislavery Northerners made themselves slave rescuers instead. In Boston (1851) a United States marshal arrested a fugitive slave from Virginia who had taken the symbolic name of Shadrach (in the Bible, Shadrach is thrown into a "fiery furnace," but he escapes injury). Boston abolitionists, Negroes and whites, managed to seize Shadrach from the authorities and spirit him off to a safe place. Here and there throughout the North opponents of the Fugitive Slave Law snatched other fleeing Negroes from the hands of federal officials. Each of these slave rescues, which got much attention in the newspapers, stirred up additional resentment of one kind in the North and of another kind in the South.

During the winter of 1851-1852, when the excitement over fugitive slaves was at its height, a remarkable story of "life among the lowly" appeared, chapter by chapter, in an antislavery periodical published in Washington, D.C. In 1852, the story was published as a book. Within a year the book had sold more than a million copies throughout the world. Soon the story was made into a play. This piece of fiction, one of the most influential ever written, was *Uncle Tom's Cabin.*

Its author, Harriet Beecher Stowe, came from a famous Puritan family of New England. Her father, her seven brothers, and her husband were preachers, and she herself was deeply religious. While living in Cincinnati, she made occasional visits across the Ohio River to Kentucky, where she made some first-hand observations of slavery. In her story, she aimed to show that slavery brutalized people who were connected with it, no matter what their sectional background. Therefore, she made some of her most appealing characters Southern ladies and gentlemen. The most hateful villain was a Yankee from Vermont, Simon Legree.

Nevertheless, Southerners were infuriated by the publication of *Uncle Tom's Cabin.* And Northerners were increasingly outraged as they read this dramatic account of oppressed and hunted Negroes.

REVIEWING THE SECTION

1. What were the main points of controversy between the North and South preceding the Compromise of 1850?

2. Why was the Nashville convention called?

3. What did the Compromise of 1850 concede to the North? to the South?

4. How were North-South relations affected by the new Fugitive Slave Law? by the publication of *Uncle Tom's Cabin?*

THE SECTIONAL QUARREL WAS REVIVED

The Compromise of 1850 proved to be no final settlement of the sectional issues, though the election of 1852 indicated that most of the people, throughout the country as a whole, preferred to accept it as final. In that election, a large majority of the voters chose the presidential candidate who was most emphatically in favor of abiding by all the provisions of the compromise. Apparently, most of the people wished to enjoy the years of prosperity with as little political disturbance as possible.

Nevertheless, in 1854, the spirit of sectionalism was suddenly aroused again. The man who did the most to stir up new trouble—though he did it quite unintentionally—was Stephen A. Douglas, a Democratic senator from Illinois. His main purpose was merely to prepare for the building of a railroad to the Pacific coast. He introduced a bill to organize and provide government for the territory through which he intended the railroad to run. To get Southern support, he agreed to include in that bill a provision which would open the territory to slaves, even though Congress years earlier had prohibited slavery in that area. The passage of this bill—the Kansas-Nebraska Act—provoked a violent and lasting political reaction in the North.

The slavery issue destroyed the Whig party

For the election of 1852, the Democrats adopted a platform wholeheartedly endorsing the entire Compromise of 1850, including the Fugitive Slave Law. They could not agree on which of their party leaders to nominate, so they chose a handsome and charming, but rather weak, man from New Hampshire, Franklin Pierce. He was what antislavery Northerners called a "doughface," that is, a Northern man with Southern principles. He made it clear that he would stand by his party's platform.

The Whigs were more divided than the Democrats. In their platform, the Whigs tried to evade the big issue by presenting only an ambiguous statement about the compromise. As their candidate, they selected, not the man already in office, Millard Fillmore—who everyone knew favored the compromise—but the Mexican War hero Winfield Scott, whose views on the subject were vague.

Though a Virginian, Scott had the support of antislavery Whigs. They counted upon him to attract votes because of his military record. But he did not attract enough of them. On election day many Southern Whigs, suspicious of Scott, either stayed home or went out and voted for the Democratic candidate. Pierce won.

Already, because of the slavery issue, the Whig party was beginning to fall apart. It was dividing into proslavery and antislavery factions, which in New England were known as Cotton Whigs and Conscience Whigs. Its old leaders, Clay and Webster, died in 1852, and no men of comparable stature were available to take their place. Scott's defeat came as a serious blow to the already disintegrating Whig party. It never recovered its old position as one of the two major parties.

Douglas planned a transcontinental railroad

Friends called Stephen A. Douglas the Little Giant. He was a great orator and an important figure, though only five feet tall. He had been born in Vermont and had moved as a young man to Illinois, where he taught school, practiced law, and rose to leadership in the Democratic party. With good reason, he expected someday to be President. Douglas was ambitious, both for his country and for himself. He wanted the nation to remain united and hoped to see it grow ever bigger and stronger.

As chairman of the Senate Committee on the Territories, Douglas was in a position to promote national unity and growth. He had actually guided through Congress the five bills that made up the Compromise of 1850. He also brought about a grant of federal lands to finance the construction of the Illinois Central Railroad. This line was to run southward through Illinois, one branch starting from Chicago and another from Galena. At the southern terminus, it was expected to connect with other lines which ultimately would reach all the way to the Gulf of Mexico. Thus the Illinois Central would help tie together the North and the South.

Douglas hoped to see another railroad extended to the Pacific coast, to tie the far west to the rest of the country. Such a line would require even more government aid than had been given to the Illinois Central. Douglas owned real estate in and around Chicago, and he thought Chicago ought to be made the eastern terminus of the transcontinental railroad. Other people in Illinois and the Northwest agreed with him.

But Chicago had rivals: St. Louis, Memphis, and New Orleans. Southerners insisted upon a southern route, preferably one having New Orleans as its starting point. They had the support of Secretary of War Jefferson Davis. A railroad along the route that Davis and other Southerners favored would run through Texas and New Mexico—areas which already had state or territorial government.

Douglas' northern route would have to pass through unorganized territory west of Iowa and Missouri. That area would need local agencies of law and order before a railroad could safely be constructed through it. In 1854, therefore, Douglas turned to the task of providing the necessary terri-

THE QUESTION OF SLAVERY: THREE VIEWS

JEFFERSON DAVIS

*Senator from Mississippi and
future President of the Confederacy*

The slave trade ... so far as the African was concerned, was a blessing .... It is a fact which history fully establishes, that through the portal of slavery alone, has the descendant of the graceless son of Noah ever entered the temple of civilization. Thus· has been. made manifest the inscrutable wisdom of the decree which made him a servant of servants. . . . [Antislavery Northerners] see that the slaves in their present condition in the South are comfortable and happy ... they see our penitentiaries never filled, and our poor houses usually empty. Let them turn to the other hand, and they see the same race in a state of freedom at the North; but instead of the comfort and kindness they receive at the South, instead of being happy and useful, they are, with few exceptions, miserable, de-graded, filling the penitentiaries and poor-houses, objects of scorn, ex-cluded, in some places, from the schools, and deprived of many other privileges and benefits which attach to the white men among whom they live. And yet they insist that elsewhere an institution which has proved beneficial to this race shall be abolished.

STEPHEN A. DOUGLAS

Senator from Illinois

There is but one possible way in which slavery can be abolished, and that is by leaving a State ... per-fectly free to form and regulate its institutions in its own way. That was the principle upon which this Re-public was founded, and it is under the operation of that principle that we have been able to preserve the Union thus far. Under its opera-tions, slavery disappeared from ... six of the twelve original slavehold-ing States; and this gradual system of emancipation went on quietly, peacefully and steadily, so long as we in the free States minded our own business .... But the moment the Abolition Societies were organ-ized throughout the North, preach-ing a violent crusade against slavery in the Southern States, this combi-nation necessarily caused a coun-ter-combination in the South, and a sectional line was drawn which was a barrier to any further emancipa-tion.

CHARLES SUMNER

Senator from Massachusetts

The slave is held simply *for the use of his master,* to whose behests, his life, liberty, and happiness, are de-voted, and by whom he may be ... shipped as cargo, stored as goods, ... knocked off at public auction, and even staked at the gaming table ... all according to law.... He may be marked like a hog, branded like a mule ... and con-stantly beaten like a brute; all ac-cording to law. And should life itself be taken, what is the remedy? The Law of Slavery ... pronounces the incompetency of the whole African race—whether bond or free—to tes-tify ... against a white man ....
If the offense of Slavery were less extended; ... if its victims were counted by tens and hundreds in-stead of millions, ... [all] would rise against it .... But what is wrong when done to one man cannot be right when done to many. ... And yet this is denied by the barbarous logic of Slavery, which ... claims immunity because its usurpation has assumed a front of audacity that cannot be safely attacked.

torial organization. He maneuvered to get and hold as much Southern support as possible, both for his railroad plans and for his presidential ambitions.

The Kansas-Nebraska Act antagonized Northerners

At first, Douglas introduced a bill to set up, at the west of Iowa and Missouri, a single new territory to be known as Nebraska. This bill displeased Southerners, however, for they would not be able to take their slaves into the new territory, since all of it would lie within that part of the Louisiana Purchase which the Missouri Compromise (1820) had closed to slavery.

To get Southern support, Douglas repeatedly amended his proposal. In its final form, it was known as the Kansas-Nebraska Act, and it contained the following provisions: There would be not one but two new territories—Kansas and Nebraska. The people of each, through their territorial legislatures, would decide whether or not to permit slavery, according to the principle of popular sovereignty. The prohibition of slavery in this part of the Louisiana Purchase territory—as provided by the Missouri Compromise—would be revoked, so that the people could choose slavery if they wished to do so.

Douglas assumed that Kansas would ultimately become a slave state and Nebraska a free state. He thought this balancing of the two ought to satisfy both the South and the North. He managed to get enough Southern as well as Northern Democratic backing to secure passage of the act, in the spring of 1854, but he provoked a much greater outcry than he had expected on the part of many Northerners. They looked upon the Missouri Compromise, which had stood for thirty-four years, as something like a sacred understanding. Now it was being undone, and soil long safely free was put in jeopardy. More and more Northerners began to believe those abolitionists who charged that there was a slave-power conspiracy to spread slavery, first over the free territories and then over the free states.

Cuba policy further angered Northerners

Soon the suspicious Northerners saw signs which, to them, indicated that the slave-power conspiracy also controlled foreign affairs and was plotting to acquire Cuba as additional land for slavery. There was, in this suspicion, a certain amount of truth, though not the whole truth.

Many Americans of the time believed in a strong and active foreign policy. In particular, a group of Democrats, members of the "Young America" movement and supporters of Douglas for the presidency, demanded that the United States take a larger part in world affairs. With respect to the Americas, Democrats in the Young America movement called for the acquisition of nearby lands, particularly Canada and Cuba. With respect to the Pacific area and Asia, they sought the annexation of Hawaii and the promotion of commerce. With respect to Europe, they favored assistance to the cause of republics, even to the extent of encouraging revolutions for overthrowing monarchies. These ideas attracted many Whigs as well as Democrats, and many Pierce men as well as Douglas men. Some Whigs and Democrats could not agree, however, on all the details. For example, the Northern Whigs, but not the Southern Democrats, were much more interested in obtaining Canada and Hawaii, which did not have slavery, than in obtaining Cuba, which did.

The Pierce administration pursued the interests of Southern Democrats. William L. Marcy, the secretary of state, suggested to the United States ministers in Madrid, Paris, and London that they get together and advise him what to do about Cuba. The three met at the seaside resort of Ostend, Belgium, and drew up a statement in which they said: (1) the United States should try to purchase Cuba; (2) if Spain refused to sell, and if she proved unable to keep order on the island, the United States should "wrest" it away from her.

In the fall of 1854, newspapers published this statement, the so-called Ostend Manifesto. It seemed to confirm the fears of many Northerners that the

Democratic party was devoting itself to the protection and promotion of slavery.

REVIEWING THE SECTION

1. Why did the Whig party fail to retain its position as a major political party?

2. What were the main problems encountered by Stephen A. Douglas in his plans for a transcontinental railroad?

3. Why was the Kansas-Nebraska Act offensive to many Northerners?

4. Why did the Ostend Manifesto disturb many Northerners?

FREE-SOILERS FORMED A NEW PARTY IN THE NORTH

As the Whig party disintegrated, the question arose: Who would take the place of the Whigs? For a time the Know-Nothings, with their anti-foreigner and anti-Catholic program, hoped to do so. The Know-Nothing or Native American party grew rapidly, but soon it began to divide into "North American" and "South American" factions. The party eventually fell apart because of disagreements over the slavery issue, just as the Whig party had done.

In the South, the former Whigs had little choice except, sooner or later, to combine with their old partisan foes, the Democrats. In the North, the former Whigs had a different alternative. Sooner or later, most of them joined a new party. They became Republicans.

The modern Republican party arose because so many Northerners thought the Democrats were proslavery and pro-South. The new party was organized as a result of the immediate reaction to the Kansas-Nebraska Act. It stood for Northern interests and, in particular, for free soil.

Though not the first free-soil party, this was the only one to succeed. Each of its predecessors had been a minor party, a "third" party. By 1856, the Republicans had become a major party, number two in the nation. By 1860, it was to be number one.

Earlier parties had advocated free soil

As early as 1840, a group of politically inclined abolitionists set up the Liberty party. They ran James G. Birney, reformed slaveholder from Kentucky, as their presidential candidate in 1840 and again in 1844. Birney obtained comparatively few votes, yet in 1844, he drew enough votes away from the Whig candidate Henry Clay to help elect the Democrat James K. Polk.

Strictly speaking, though the Liberty men were abolitionists, theirs was not an abolitionist party. That is, their platform did not call upon the federal government to abolish slavery in the South (since they believed, as most people did, that the federal government had no constitutional power to do so). Their platform did call upon the federal government to prohibit the slave trade and to prohibit slavery itself in the District of Columbia and in the territories. Thus the Liberty party was essentially a free-soil party.

In 1848, the free-soil movement suddenly grew much larger as a result of a quarrel among the Democrats. Some Northern Democrats thought President Polk too much a Southerner. They particularly resented his veto, in 1846, of a rivers-and-harbors appropriation bill which would have provided money for much-needed transportation improvements in the Northwest. The disgruntled Democrats combined with antislavery Whigs and men of the Liberty party to form the Free Soil Democratic party, and in 1848 they nominated former President Martin Van Buren. He drew enough votes away from the regular Democratic candidate Lewis Cass to help elect the regular Whig Zachary Taylor.

In 1852, there was a Free Soil party in the running (not to be confused with the Free Soil Democratic party), with John P. Hale of New Hampshire as its nominee. Many of the straying Democrats now went back to the regular fold. Hale received far less support than Van Buren had received in 1848.

The loyal, consistent free-soilers at last found a

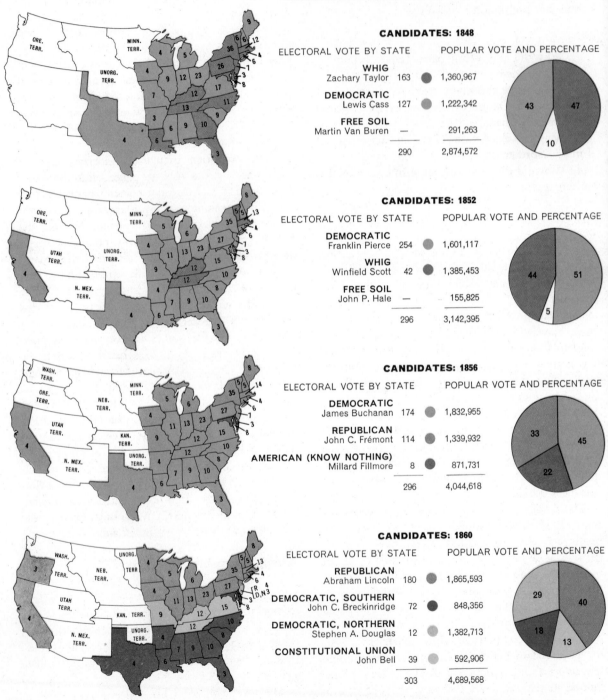

PRESIDENTIAL ELECTIONS: 1848-1860

CANDIDATES: 1848

ELECTORAL VOTE BY STATE

POPULAR VOTE AND PERCENTAGE

WHIG
Zachary Taylor 163 — 1,360,967

DEMOCRATIC
Lewis Cass 127 — 1,222,342

FREE SOIL
Martin Van Buren — 291,263

290 — 2,874,572

Pie chart: 47, 43, 10

CANDIDATES: 1852

ELECTORAL VOTE BY STATE

POPULAR VOTE AND PERCENTAGE

DEMOCRATIC
Franklin Pierce 254 — 1,601,117

WHIG
Winfield Scott 42 — 1,385,453

FREE SOIL
John P. Hale — 155,825

296 — 3,142,395

Pie chart: 51, 44, 5

CANDIDATES: 1856

ELECTORAL VOTE BY STATE

POPULAR VOTE AND PERCENTAGE

DEMOCRATIC
James Buchanan 174 — 1,832,955

REPUBLICAN
John C. Frémont 114 — 1,339,932

AMERICAN (KNOW NOTHING)
Millard Fillmore 8 — 871,731

296 — 4,044,618

Pie chart: 45, 33, 22

CANDIDATES: 1860

ELECTORAL VOTE BY STATE

POPULAR VOTE AND PERCENTAGE

REPUBLICAN
Abraham Lincoln 180 — 1,865,593

DEMOCRATIC, SOUTHERN
John C. Breckinridge 72 — 848,356

DEMOCRATIC, NORTHERN
Stephen A. Douglas 12 — 1,382,713

CONSTITUTIONAL UNION
John Bell 39 — 592,906

303 — 4,689,568

Pie chart: 40, 29, 18, 13

party in which they could be on the winning side when the Republican organization appeared in 1854.

"Anti-Nebraska" men organized the Republican party

Throughout the Northwest in the spring of 1854, abolitionists, free-soilers, antislavery Whigs, and anti-administration Democrats got together to hold meetings of protest against the passage of the Kansas-Nebraska Act. For a time, these people were known simply as "anti-Nebraska" men. Here and there they set up local organizations for co-operating against the party of Douglas and Pierce. Soon the anti-Nebraska men began to call themselves Republicans. In taking this name, the new Republicans wished to emphasize that they, like the Jeffersonians, who also had been called Republicans, represented the interests of the common man.

At first, the anti-Nebraska or Republican movement was most active in the Northwest and was mostly devoted to a single aim, that of keeping slavery out of the territories. Before long, however, the movement spread to the Northeast, and it took on additional aims: to raise the tariff, provide homesteads, and obtain federal money for railroads and other transportation improvements.

In the fall of 1854, the hastily organized Republicans amazed the country with their victories in state and local elections. Many of these victories were due to the coöperation of the Know-Nothings. The Republicans won control of several Northern states. Even more surprising, they came close to winning control of the United States House of Representatives. They could now look forward hopefully to still greater successes in 1856, a presidential election year.

Men fought over "bleeding Kansas"

By means of his Kansas-Nebraska Act, with its provision for popular sovereignty, Douglas had hoped to remove from Congress the question of slavery in the territories. He intended to let the settlers themselves quietly decide the question. For the time being, few people migrated to Nebraska, and that territory presented no problem. But large numbers moved to Kansas, and news of bloodshed soon came from there. Talk of "bleeding Kansas" prevailed in Congress and spread throughout the country. Things were not working out the way Douglas had expected.

Many of the people who went to Kansas were simply looking for a new home in a new territory, and much of the violence arose from the usual frontier lawlessness. Others went, however, with the deliberate purpose of making Kansas free—or slave. And at least part of the fighting was concerned with that issue.

The New England Emigrant Aid Company sent both men and guns to keep the soil of Kansas free. Armed bands of "border ruffians" rode over from neighboring Missouri to fight and vote for slavery. From the outset, the antislavery settlers outnumbered the proslavery people. Nevertheless, with the aid of the Missourians, the proslavery people got control of the territorial legislature and passed laws (1855) making slavery legal. This legislature had the backing of the Pierce administration. The free-soil majority set up a separate government, forbidding slavery, but this government had no official recognition.

In 1856, a small-scale civil war broke out in Kansas. With a proslavery federal marshal in the lead, a posse of about eight hundred men marched on Lawrence, arrested the free-soil leaders, and looted and burned the town. An antislavery fanatic with the fiery eyes and the long beard of an Old Testament prophet—John Brown—thought he was God's agent to avenge the sack of Lawrence. Brown calculated that five free-soilers had been killed. With a small band of followers, including a few of his sons, he went out one night and, at a settlement along Pottawatomie Creek, murdered a total of five supposedly proslavery men. This "Pottawatomie massacre" touched off further killings on both sides.

In Washington, D.C., at the height of the Kansas excitement, a Republican senator from Massachusetts delivered a very long and elaborate speech on what he called "the crime against Kansas." This senator, Charles Sumner—an imposing, eloquent, and learned man—had in mind, not the Pottawatomie massacre, but the efforts to force slavery upon the territory. In his bitter speech against the South and slavery, Sumner ridiculed one of his colleagues, Andrew P. Butler, a proud senator from South Carolina. A few days later, Sumner sat writing letters at his desk in the Senate chamber. A man came up to him and, attacking him with a cane, beat him about the head until Sumner collapsed. This assailant was Preston Brooks, a representative from South Carolina and Butler's nephew. (Sumner only gradually recovered from the caning; he did not return to the Senate until 1859.)

Afterward, Southerners applauded Brooks as a hero. They often gave him canes, with inscriptions such as: "Use knockdown arguments." Northerners, however, referred to him as "bully Brooks," said he was typical of the so-called Southern chivalry, and looked upon Sumner as a martyr to the cause of both liberty and decency. The very different reactions to the incident showed how far apart the North and the South were drifting.

In this atmosphere of sectional bitterness, the election of 1856 was held. The Democrats endorsed popular sovereignty and again nominated a doughface, James Buchanan of Pennsylvania. The Republicans chose John C. Frémont, a former senator from California, who was little known as a politician but famous as an explorer of the far west. They campaigned with the slogan: "Free Soil, Free Labor, Free Men, and Frémont." Another party, consisting of former Whigs and Know-Nothings, nominated ex-President Fillmore as its candidate.

Buchanan won the election, but Frémont and Fillmore together polled more popular votes than he did. The Republicans also gained additional state and local offices and congressional seats. The election was, as one of the Republicans said, a "victorious defeat" for them.

The Dred Scott decision intensified bitterness

In his inaugural address, on March 4, 1857, President Buchanan intimated that the Supreme Court was about to decide, once and for all, the question of slavery in the territories. Two days later, the Court gave its decision in the case of Dred Scott, but the decision did not put an end to the controversy. It only made it worse.

As the slave of an army surgeon, Dred Scott had lived at Fort Snelling in what is now the state of Minnesota—part of the Louisiana Purchase territory—at a time when slavery was illegal there because of the Missouri Compromise. Years later, after Scott's return to the slave state of Missouri, some abolitionists persuaded him to sue for his freedom. They said that, because he had lived in a free territory, he ought to be free. To bring the case before the Supreme Court, they arranged for a New Yorker to buy him. Thus Scott, in Missouri, would be suing his owner in New York. (The Constitution gives the Supreme Court authority to review cases in which a citizen of one state has sued a citizen of another.)

In giving the Dred Scott decision, Chief Justice Roger B. Taney, a former slave owner from Maryland, began by saying the Supreme Court did not really have jurisdiction over the case. Taney explained that, by Missouri law, no Negro could be a citizen of that state. He contended, further, that no Negro could ever become a citizen of the United States. He might have left the matter at that.

Instead, Taney went on to say that *if* the Supreme Court had had jurisdiction, he would have had to deny freedom to Dred Scott. A slave was property, Taney argued, and the Fifth Amendment forbade Congress to deprive any person of his property without "due process of law" (that is, without some kind of justifiable court proceedings). In adopting the Missouri Compromise, Congress had undertaken to deprive persons of their slave property in the territories. Therefore, according to Taney's reasoning, the antislavery provision of the Missouri Compromise (which the Kansas-Nebraska Act already had repealed) had been unconstitutional from the beginning.

The Dred Scott decision could be viewed as a severe blow to the Republican cause. In effect, the Supreme Court had declared unconstitutional the party's main principle—free soil. Certainly, the Republicans were angry at Taney and the other justices (a total of seven out of nine) who upheld the decision. Yet the party was helped more than it was hurt by the decision. Here seemed to be one more piece of evidence to prove that a great slave-power conspiracy was at work. Alarmed Northerners thought it more urgent than ever to back the new party that stood for free soil, so the Republicans gained additional support.

REVIEWING THE SECTION

1. How did the free-soil parties influence national politics between 1840 and 1854?

2. Why was the Republican party organized? What additional aims did it acquire as it spread to the Northeast?

3. What events arising from the issue of popular sovereignty in Kansas increased animosity between North and South?

4. How did the Dred Scott decision deepen the conflict between North and South? How did it contribute to the growth of the Republican party?

REPUBLICANS ELECTED A PRESIDENT

In addition to the Dred Scott decision, two other events of the year 1857 also helped the Republican party. First, Congress again lowered the tariff, which was already quite low. (Congress had reduced it before, in 1846.) Second, the Panic of 1857 began. Supporters of the protective tariff now said that prosperity had been destroyed by the destruction of the tariff. They looked to the Republican party as the only means of regaining influence and raising the tariff rates.

As the Republican party thus gained still further support, it began to change somewhat in its essential character. For the most part, the party originally had represented the farmers of the Northwest. Now it began more and more to represent the industrialists of the Northeast as well. It became essentially an alliance of those two groups. Increasingly, it emphasized the economic aims of farmers and businessmen, though it continued to oppose the extension of slavery into the territories.

During the next three years—1858, 1859, 1860—the Republicans steadily gained strength throughout the North. In their advance toward control of the national government, they were assisted by a split in the Democratic party.

Democrats argued among themselves

Like President Pierce before him, President Buchanan favored the proslavery element in Kansas. He tried to persuade Congress to admit Kansas as a slave state, regardless of the real feelings of a majority of the people in the territory. The Buchanan policy meant something quite different from the kind of popular sovereignty that Democratic Senator Douglas had advocated. Douglas had intended to give the settlers a real choice.

Douglas found himself in a dilemma. If he coöperated with the Buchanan administration, he would have to violate his own principles. Besides, he would lose the support of many Democrats in the Northwest, where the Buchanan policy was unpopular. If he refused to coöperate with the Buchanan administration, he would lose its support and also the support of most Southerners. Either way, he would jeopardize his chances for the presidency.

Douglas came out for his own principles, vigorously opposing Buchanan's efforts to make Kansas a slave state. He and Buchanan broke off all ties of political friendship. The Democratic party was now divided between the followers of the senator and the followers of the President.

Buchanan determined to prevent Douglas' re-

THE PRESIDENTS OF THE UNITED STATES

ZACHARY TAYLOR
(1784-1850)
IN OFFICE: 1849-1850

MILLARD FILLMORE
(1800-1874)
IN OFFICE: 1850-1853

Whig from Louisiana. General Taylor, a hero of the Mexican War, was the first professional soldier to be elected President. His opposition to the extension of slavery into the territories acquired as a result of the Mexican War helped to precipitate the crisis of 1850.

Whig from New York. Fillmore, who became President when Taylor died, signed the bills that made up the Compromise of 1850. His enforcement of the Fugitive Slave Law cost him support in the North. He ran unsuccessfully on the American (Know-Nothing) party ticket in 1856.

FRANKLIN PIERCE
(1804-1869)
IN OFFICE: 1853-1857

JAMES BUCHANAN
(1791-1868)
IN OFFICE: 1857-1861

ABRAHAM LINCOLN
(1809-1865)
IN OFFICE: 1861-1865

Democrat from New Hampshire. Pierce extended the southern border of the United States (Gadsden Purchase, 1853). After signing the Kansas-Nebraska Act (1854), he supported the proslavery faction in Kansas. This lost him the support of Northern Democrats, and he was not renominated.

Democrat from Pennsylvania. Although he believed that slavery was morally wrong, Buchanan supported the Supreme Court decision in the Dred Scott case. In 1860, as the Southern states began to secede, he denied their right to do so, but refused to use force to keep them in the Union.

Republican from Illinois. Lincoln was the first modern Republican President. The news of his election prompted the secession of seven Southern states before his inauguration (March 1861). Lincoln's policies as President were based on a belief in the supremacy of the Union.

election to the Senate in 1858. When Douglas began his campaign in Illinois, therefore, he faced opposition on two sides. On one side were the regular Democrats, the "Buchaneers," who did not put up a candidate against him but did everything else they could to bring about his defeat. On the other side were the Republicans, who were running an old friend and rival of his, an extremely able campaigner, Abraham Lincoln.

Lincoln became a national political figure

From the backwoods poverty of Kentucky and Indiana, Lincoln had risen to become one of the most respected lawyers of Illinois. He was also one of the best-known politicians—the leading Whig and then the leading Republican of the state. As a politician, however, he had not done nearly so well as Douglas. He had served a few terms in the state legislature and one term in the national Congress. That was all. He longed to be United States senator.

In Douglas, Lincoln saw a threat to his own ambitions. In popular sovereignty he saw a threat to the Republican program for free soil. Some prominent Republicans of the Northeast, such as Horace Greeley, the influential editor of the *New York Tribune,* were so pleased with Douglas for his resistance to Buchanan that they talked of adopting Douglas as a Republican candidate. Lincoln and his friends undertook to head off the Republicans-for-Douglas movement.

In those days the legislature in each state chose the United States senators. The supporters of Lincoln wished to make sure that the Republicans, if they should get control of the Illinois legislature, would choose him and not Douglas. So these friends induced the party to nominate Lincoln and pledge its support to him. This meant that a vote for a Republican in the state election was a vote for Lincoln in the senatorial contest.

When he accepted the Republican nomination, Lincoln made his famous "house divided" speech. "I believe this government cannot endure, permanently, half *slave* and half *free,*" he said.

Either the *opponents* of slavery will arrest the further spread of it, and place it where the public mind shall rest in the belief that it is in course of ultimate extinction; or its *advocates* will push it forward, till it shall become alike lawful in *all* the States, old as well as *new—North* as well as *South.*

Besides making a great many separate campaign speeches, Lincoln and Douglas appeared together in seven formal debates, one in each of the seven congressional districts of Illinois. Tremendous crowds came to these remarkable verbal duels between the tall, gangling, folksy Lincoln with his clear, high-pitched voice and the tiny, neat, dignified Douglas with his vibrant, booming tones.

In the debates, Lincoln stayed on the attack most of the time. He condemned Douglas as morally insensitive for saying, with regard to popular sovereignty, that he did not care whether slavery was "voted up or voted down." He maintained that the Douglas policy would encourage slavery to spread. He even accused Douglas of deliberately conspiring with Taney, Pierce, and Buchanan to fasten slavery upon the whole country.

Lincoln took advantage of the dilemma in which circumstances already had put Douglas. Again and again he asked Douglas whether the people of a territory could lawfully keep slavery out, since the Supreme Court had held that slavery could not lawfully be excluded. If Douglas answered "yes," he would offend Southern Democrats, who approved the Dred Scott decision. If he answered "no," he would offend those Northern Democrats who believed in popular sovereignty. So he avoided a clear-cut, yes-or-no reply. He said that, even though a territorial legislature could not pass laws *against* slavery, it could simply decline to pass laws *for* it, and then no slaveowner would bring slaves in. "Slavery cannot exist a day, or an hour, anywhere," he explained, "unless it is supported by local police regulations." This reply—called the Freeport Doctrine because it was stated during the debate in Freeport, Illinois—did not satisfy many

Southerners. By harping on the question, Lincoln helped to widen the rift within the Democratic party.

Throughout the country, the Illinois election received much more publicity than the other state elections. Newspapers gave a great deal of space to the Lincoln-Douglas debates. The Republicans swept most of the Northern elections, but they did not quite manage to get control in Illinois. So Lincoln lost—and yet he won. Soon Republicans began to talk of him as a possible President. He had not beaten Douglas in the senatorial contest, but he had prepared the way for beating him in the next presidential race.

John Brown's raid alarmed the South

John Brown, the grim fanatic of the Kansas killings, still thought that God had commissioned him to free the slaves.

Brown worked out a plan. First, he would capture the mountain town of Harpers Ferry, Virginia, and obtain guns and ammunition from the federal arsenal there. With Harpers Ferry as a base, he would raid plantations to set the slaves free. Then he would organize a Negro republic with its own army of freedmen. From further raiding, this republic would grow until, finally, it would be big and strong enough to force the South to give up the remaining slaves.

On an October night in 1859, Brown and eighteen followers descended on the town and got into the arsenal. From then on, nothing went as he had planned it. Local militia companies trapped him and his men inside an arsenal building. A detachment of United States marines arrived. In a continuous exchange of fire, Brown was wounded and eight of his followers were killed. Finally, the marines broke in and took Brown prisoner, along with the rest of the survivors. Several weeks later, he and six others were hanged for treason against the state of Virginia.

On the day of Brown's execution, the well-known writer Henry David Thoreau told a church meeting in Concord, Massachusetts: "He is not Old Brown any longer; he is an angel of light." Other prominent Northerners, including Thoreau's friend Ralph Waldo Emerson, also looked upon Brown as a martyr to a holy cause. Republican leaders such as Lincoln and Seward disagreed. They thought Brown a well-meaning but misguided man, and they disapproved of his Harpers Ferry raid. The views of Brown's admirers were more newsworthy, however, and those views gained the larger share of attention in the papers.

Southerners were terrified, remembering Nat Turner and his slave insurrection of 1831. They looked upon Brown as a devil, not an angel. They got the impression that most Northerners, at least most Republicans, sympathized with Brown. Southerners thought that if the Republicans should take over in Washington, they would set loose upon the South still more fanatics like him. Mississippi and other Southern states, preparing for self-defense, started to enlarge their militia forces and to accumulate military supplies. Many Southern students in Northern colleges were called home.

The fear which beset Southerners was real, even if it was irrational. It helps to explain why they reacted so violently when the Republicans won the presidential election in 1860.

Lincoln won the presidency

When the Democrats met, in Charleston, they could not agree on a plank with regard to slavery in the territories. The followers of Douglas still contended that the settlers themselves should decide, and his opponents still insisted that slavery could not, constitutionally, be excluded. When a majority of the delegates approved the "Douglas platform," which vaguely endorsed popular sovereignty and proposed that all questions regarding slavery in the territories be left up to the Supreme Court, most of the Southerners walked out of the convention, and it broke up. Later, the Northern and Southern Democrats had separate meetings and formed separate parties. The Northerners chose

Douglas, the Southerners John C. Breckinridge, a Kentuckian.

When the Republicans held their nominating convention, in Chicago, their hopes ran high because of the Democratic split. Still, most of them thought the party should take no chances. They wanted a sure winner.

Seward, rather than Lincoln, was the most prominent of the party's leaders, and Seward was the preconvention favorite. But some of the delegates had doubts about him. They feared he would repel former Know-Nothings because, years earlier, as governor of New York, he had given state aid to Roman Catholic schools. They also feared he would frighten off conservative former Whigs because, with his phrases such as "higher law" and "irrepressible conflict," he had gained a reputation as a fanatical antislavery and anti-Southern man. Many delegates thought that Lincoln, despite his "house divided" speech, would be a safer candidate, one who would lose fewer votes. On the first two ballots, Seward led but could not get a majority. On the third ballot, Lincoln was nominated.

Still another party was in the field, in addition to the parties of Douglas, Breckinridge, and Lincoln. The Constitutional Union party, consisting of remnants of the Whig and Know-Nothing parties, presented a platform that did little more than pledge loyalty to "the Constitution, the Union, and the laws." This party ran as its candidate a Tennessee Whig by the name of John Bell.

On election day, Lincoln received only about 40 in 100 of the popular votes throughout the country as a whole—and none at all in ten of the Southern states. Yet he won the electoral votes of every free state except for three of the seven from New Jersey, so he had more than a majority of all the electoral votes. Even if all the popular votes cast for Douglas, Breckinridge, and Bell had been concentrated on one of the three instead of being scattered among them, Lincoln still would have had a slight majority of the electoral votes.

Not only was the Republican victory close; it was also incomplete. Though the Republicans had elected a President, they had failed to gain a majority in either the Senate or in the House of Representatives.

REVIEWING THE SECTION

1. Why did Douglas break with Buchanan?

2. How did Lincoln's views on popular sovereignty differ from those of Douglas? How did the Lincoln-Douglas debates affect Lincoln's political future?

3. How did Northerners respond to John Brown's raid on Harpers Ferry? How did Southerners respond?

4. What factors enabled Lincoln to win the Republican presidential nomination in 1860? Why did the Democratic party split?

ELEVEN STATES LEFT THE UNION

During the campaign, Southerners had threatened that their states would secede if the "black Republican" candidate should be elected. Republicans had dismissed all the secession talk as bluff. Soon after the election, however, the secessionists began to carry out their threats, without waiting to see what Lincoln could do or would do after he was inaugurated as President on March 4, 1861.

South Carolina, the home of Calhoun and his doctrines, appropriately led off the secession march. On December 20, 1860, a special convention in Charleston declared South Carolina an independent state. The secessionists did not expect South Carolina to remain independent and alone. Other slave states held conventions to consider secession. The states also sent commissioners to one another to make plans for coöperation in seceding and in setting up a new confederacy.

Meanwhile, in the rest of the nation, people discussed what to do about the disunion threat. Some said that secessionists should be hanged as traitors. Others said they should be allowed to leave if they wanted to. Still others said they should be encouraged, by means of a new compromise, to stay in the Union.

Compromise efforts failed in 1860-1861

President Buchanan favored compromise. A state had no right to secede, he told Congress, but the national government had no right to force a state to remain in the Union.

In the Senate, John J. Crittenden introduced a compromise plan. Crittenden, like Henry Clay, the Great Compromiser, came from Kentucky. Kentuckians felt that they were in the middle, between the North and the South. They had relatives, friends, and business connections on both sides. If war should come, it would make Kentucky a battleground and disrupt the ties of family, friendship, and business. (In fact, the war later did divide the family of Crittenden himself. One of his sons became a Union general, and another a Confederate general.) So the Kentuckians were especially anxious for a peaceful settlement.

The Crittenden plan embodied a series of constitutional amendments. The two most important of these would have (1) guaranteed slavery forever in the states where it already existed, and (2) prohibited slavery above a certain line—36° 30'—and permitted it below that line in all present or future territories.

Republican leaders in the Senate and the House asked President-elect Lincoln for his advice. He had no objection to the first of the two Crittenden proposals. Congress adopted this one and sent it out to the states for ratification. If the war had not intervened, three fourths of them probably would have ratified. Then the Thirteenth Amendment would have guaranteed slavery instead of abolishing it!

But Lincoln objected to the proposal permitting slavery south of a certain line in all the territories which the United States held already or might acquire in the future. Such an arrangement, he feared, would settle nothing. It would only lead slave owners to agitate continually for new territories south of the line—in Cuba, Mexico, or Central America. "Let there be no compromise on the question of *extending* slavery," he advised. "Have

none of it. Stand firm. The tug has to come, & better now than any time hereafter." The Republicans stood firm, and this part of the Crittenden plan failed to pass.

Even if the proposal had passed, it would not have satisfied the extreme secessionists, the "fire-eaters." Possibly, though, it would have strengthened the Southern Unionists and even enabled them to prevent the secession of any more states. After the plan's defeat, six states—Mississippi, Florida, Alabama, Georgia, Louisiana, and Texas—followed South Carolina's example and withdrew from the Union.

The Confederacy was born

On February 4, 1861, exactly one month before Lincoln's inauguration, delegates from the seceded states met in Montgomery, Alabama, to form a government for the Confederate States of America.

The Montgomery convention, serving as a temporary Congress, passed laws for the new nation. It appointed a provisional president and vice president, Jefferson Davis and Alexander H. Stephens. And it drew up a constitution for a permanent government. Months later, after this constitution had been ratified, senators and representatives were elected to a senate and house, Davis to the presidency, and Stephens to the vice presidency.

In most of its provisions, the Confederate constitution was simply a copy of the Constitution of the United States. There were a number of changes, some of them interesting, few of them very important. For instance, the sovereignty of the separate states was now recognized, but not their right to secede from the Confederacy. The president and the vice president were given six-year terms and were limited to one term apiece. Cabinet members were allowed to sit in congress and defend their policies there.

The most striking differences between the Constitution of the Confederate States and the Constitution of the United States were those concerning slavery. In the Confederate constitution, congress

MEN IN HISTORY

DAVIS AND LINCOLN

Comparing Jefferson Davis with Abraham Lincoln just before the Civil War, an informed and unbiased observer might have favored Davis as the man more likely to succeed. Always self-confident, the handsome Davis held a position of wealth and prestige among Southern aristocrats. He had been given a fine classical education, and he had an excellent record of military and civilian service to his country.

Lincoln could scarcely have been expected to win a higher place in history than Davis. Ungainly in appearance and reticent in manner, Lincoln readily admitted that he "had no folks to speak of." His formal education totaled about one year; his experience in government was limited; and he had only negligible acquaintance with military matters.

At the time that Davis, a cadet, was enjoying a reputation as a gay young blade at West Point, Lincoln was grabbing every opportunity to read. He read and reread the works of Shakespeare and the Bible while he did farm chores and worked as a hired man in frontier Indiana and Illinois. In contrast to Lincoln, Davis rebelled at doing manual labor and once said that to work with his hands in the field would imply an equality with the laborers.

Lincoln studied law and opened an office in Springfield, Illinois, where he established himself as a quick-witted and clever lawyer. He served eight years in the Illinois legislature, became well known in Illinois political circles, and was elected to a term in the House of Representatives.

After graduating from West Point, Davis served with distinction in the army. As secretary of war under President Pierce, he brought about some notable reforms in the war department. He served portions of three terms in Congress, one as a representative, two as a senator. In each case he resigned before the term was completed—the first time to serve in the Mexican War; the second, to run for governor of Mississippi; and the third, to serve Mississippi when it seceded from the Union.

As president of the Confederacy, Davis was aloof, unyielding, and dedicated to the Southern cause. He had no time for nonsense and did not take the time to

create good will among his cabinet and other officials. He made no effort to keep in touch with the people he represented.

Davis would have preferred serving the Confederacy as a field commander instead of president, for he believed himself to be a military genius. Even as Sherman approached Atlanta, Davis said, "If I could take one wing and Lee the other, we would still wrest a victory from these people." Gravely concerned with every facet of the war, he became lost in a mass of detail and worked far into the war-torn nights, personally initialing requisitions for shoes, blankets, and socks.

Even after Richmond had fallen, Davis refused to recognize that the South was defeated, and he pleaded for the people of the South to rally to the cause again. He never acknowledged that the cause was lost.

Lincoln was extraordinarily able to lead his people in consecration to the cause for which the nation had gone to war. He gave point and meaning to the bloodshed when he resolved that "these dead shall not have died in vain—that this nation, under God, shall have a new birth of freedom—and that government of the people, by the people, and for the people shall not perish from the earth."

Lincoln made generous plans for rebuilding a defeated South. In his second inaugural address, March 4, 1865, he pointed the way when he said: "With malice toward none; with charity for all; with firmness in the right, as God gives us to see the right, let us strive on to finish the work we are in; to bind up the nation's wounds. . . . "

In his writings Lincoln left the American people a great heritage of thought and some of the most poetic prose in the English language. His published works, ranging from formal and official communications to personal correspondence, total more than the complete works of Shakespeare or the Bible.

Giving full allowance for Davis' admirable qualities and for the difficulties which he encountered as president of the Confederacy, Lincoln's place in history has been established as that of the incomparably greater leader and man.

was required to protect slavery throughout the Confederate territories. The Confederate congress was forbidden to abolish slavery anywhere. The states were not explicitly forbidden to abolish it, but they were required to recognize the right of a slave owner to travel and sojourn with his slaves; so, in fact, the states could not eliminate slavery from their own soil, even if they should wish to. Stephens, the vice president, spoke truly when he said that slavery was the "corner-stone" of the Confederate government.

Fort Sumter was fired upon

As they seceded, the Confederate states took over forts, mints, custom houses, post offices, and other pieces of federal property. By the time Lincoln was inaugurated on March 4, 1861, the United States flag still flew at only four forts on soil the Confederacy claimed. The people North and South focused their attention on one of the four—Fort Sumter, in Charleston harbor. Here, Major Robert Anderson remained at his post with only about seventy soldiers and only enough food to last for six weeks or so. Before this time was up, Anderson would have to abandon the fort—unless he got supplies.

In his inaugural address, Lincoln made it clear that he intended to "hold, occupy, and possess" all the places belonging to the federal government. He vowed to preserve the Union and enforce the laws. Yet he insisted that if bloodshed were to come, the Confederates would have to start it. He would not. "In your hands, my dissatisfied fellow countrymen, and not in mine," he said, "is the momentous issue of civil war."

Jefferson Davis and all the top Confederates were determined to obtain Sumter and the other three forts—by diplomacy if possible, by force if necessary. Davis sent three commissioners to Washington to negotiate for a peaceful transfer at a fair price. Lincoln refused to have anything to do with these men. (If he had dealt with them, he would have given the impression that he recognized the Confederacy as an independent nation.) Meanwhile, Davis pushed military preparations as fast as he could. He put General Pierre Gustave Toutant Beauregard in charge of the Confederate forces at Charleston. All around the harbor, Beauregard built up fortifications and batteries with big guns which pointed at Sumter as their target.

Finally, when Anderson's supplies had almost run out, Lincoln decided on a relief expedition. He sent a messenger to Charleston to announce that ships were on the way. The messenger repeated Lincoln's own words: an attempt would be made to "supply Fort Sumter with provisions only," and "if such an attempt be not resisted, no effort to throw in men, arms, or ammunition" would be made for the time being.

Without waiting for the expedition to arrive, Davis instructed Beauregard to demand Anderson's surrender and, if Anderson should refuse the demand, to open fire. Anderson did refuse it. Beauregard delayed as long as he could, for Anderson was an old friend and had been his professor at West Point. At last, April 12, 1861, Beauregard ordered the firing to begin. Two days later, the fort a smoking ruin, Anderson surrendered.

Despite the heavy shelling, no one on either side had been killed. One of Anderson's men was fatally wounded by a gun explosion, however, when a salute was fired to honor the Stars and Stripes as the flag was taken down.

North and South: The die was cast

The firing on the flag had an electric effect throughout the North. Previously, the section had been badly divided in its feelings about the secession crisis. Democrats had been criticizing Republicans, and Republicans had been bickering among themselves. Some of the Democrats preferred Davis to Lincoln. The news from Sumter changed all this. "Every man must be for the United States or against it," declared the Democratic leader Douglas after a visit with Lincoln; "there can be no neutrals in this war—only patriots and traitors." When Lincoln called for 75,000 volunteers to put down the insurrection, men rushed to enlist, without regard to politics.

Lincoln's call for troops—on top of his effort to hold Sumter—had a similar unifying effect upon the South. Now the people of the seven seceded states, many of whom never had really favored secession, became enthusiastically loyal to the Confederate cause. Soon four more states—Virginia, Tennessee, Arkansas, North Carolina—seceded and joined the Confederacy.

The Confederates had hoped to get all the slave states, including those of the border. Delaware had few Confederate sympathizers, but Maryland, Kentucky, and Missouri had many. A Maryland mob attacked Massachusetts soldiers passing through Baltimore on their way to defend Washington. Only by a stern policy of military arrests did Lincoln manage to prevent Maryland from seceding. Kentuckians wanted to remain neutral, but the state finally sided with the Union. Missourians fought a civil war of their own before Missouri

could be safely counted on the Union side.

Thus, as the Civil War got under way, the Confederacy numbered eleven states. (The Confederates claimed two more, Kentucky and Missouri, and the Confederate flag contained thirteen stars, but the Confederates did not really control either Missouri or Kentucky.) The Union had twenty-three. Fifty counties broke off from Virginia and combined in a new state, West Virginia. This, when admitted to the Union in 1863, made a total of twenty-four.

REVIEWING THE SECTION

1. What was the Republican response to the Crittenden plan? How did the failure of the Crittenden plan spur secession of the Southern states?

2. In what ways did the Confederate constitution differ from the United States Constitution?

3. What events led to the Confederate bombardment of Fort Sumter?

4. How did the bombardment of Fort Sumter affect opinions in the North and South?

CHAPTER **12** CONCLUSION

"You think slavery is *right* and ought to be extended; while we think it is *wrong* and ought to be restricted," Lincoln wrote to his old acquaintance Alexander H. Stephens during the secession winter of 1860-61. "That, I suppose, is the rub."

Certainly, that was the immediate "rub" which disrupted political parties and finally tore the nation apart. To most Northerners and Southerners, however, slavery was not only a moral issue, not only a question of right and wrong. It also had become a symbol of all the differences—economic, social, political—which set off the South from the North.

As early as 1850, these differences had threatened to break up the Union, but Congress managed to put together a sectional compromise. Compromise was possible at that time because there still existed two *national* parties, the Whig and the Democratic. With-

in each of the two parties, politicians coöperated to bring about a sectional adjustment. Afterward, however, antislavery Northerners refused to abide by one of the provisions of the Compromise of 1850, the new Fugitive Slave Law. Nevertheless, as the election of 1852 indicated, the majority of people throughout the country were willing to accept the compromise as final.

In 1854, the sectional controversy was renewed when Stephen A. Douglas secured the passage of his Kansas-Nebraska Act. This reopened to slavery a part of the federal territory which, twenty-four years earlier, the Missouri Compromise had closed to slavery. Opposition to the Kansas-Nebraska Act led to the formation of the Republican party, which consisted not only of former Liberty party members, but also of former Whigs and Democrats who opposed slavery extension. In the North, the Republican party soon replaced the Whig party, which had begun to disintegrate after the election of 1852.

The Republican party grew rapidly. One reason for this was the widespread Northern belief in the existence of a slave-power conspiracy to extend slavery throughout the country. Suspicious Northerners saw evidences of such a conspiracy in the passage of the Kansas-Nebraska Act itself, in the publication of the Ostend Manifesto, in the Kansas policies of Presidents Pierce and Buchanan, and in the Dred Scott decision of the Supreme Court. Another reason for the Republican party's rapid growth was the lowering of the tariff in 1857 and the coming of a business depression in that same year. Many Northerners joined the new party in the hope that, once in power, it would restore prosperity and promote economic development by means of protective tariffs, homestead laws, and subsidies for railroads and other internal improvements.

While the Republican party gained, the Democratic party suffered from an inner quarrel. Senator Douglas, insisting on true popular sovereignty for the territories, came out against the Kansas policy of President Buchanan, who had the support of Southern Democrats. In 1860, the Democratic party split into two parties, one Northern, the other Southern. No longer was there any truly national party to help hold the nation together.

Soon after Lincoln's election, seven states of the lower South seceded from the Union and formed a confederacy. Many Southerners favored secession because, ever since John Brown's raid (1859), they had feared that the Republicans, once in control of the presidency, would encourage further attacks on slavery, even within the Southern states. Meanwhile, Congress tried to arrange a new compromise to head off secession and preserve the Union. This time Congress failed, largely because there no longer existed two major parties having national support. Most of the Republicans, including Lincoln himself, refused to consider a division of the territories into slave and free areas. Most of the Southern Democrats, however, would not have been satisfied by such a division. Both sides were to blame for the failure of the compromise efforts.

Four additional slave states seceded after Lincoln's attempt to supply Fort Sumter, the Confederate bombardment of the fort, and Lincoln's call for troops. Thus the lines between the Union and the Confederacy were drawn, and the "irrepressible conflict" had led to the Civil War.

FOCUSING ON SPECIFICS

1. Why did several Northern states pass "personal liberty" laws?

2. How did Taylor's death make easier the passage of the Compromise of 1850?

3. Why was President Pierce called a "doughface" by antislavery Northerners?

4. Why did Stephen A. Douglas introduce the Kansas-Nebraska bill?

5. What were the major provisions of the Kansas-Nebraska Act?

6. What convinced Northerners of the existence of a slave-power conspiracy?

7. What were the goals of the "Young America" Democrats?

8. What was the aim of the Liberty party? the free-soil parties? Why cannot these parties be considered "abolitionist" parties?

9. What events caused Kansas to become known as "bleeding Kansas"?

10. How did the North and South react to the caning of Senator Charles Sumner?

11. What arguments did Chief Justice Taney use to nullify the Missouri Compromise in the Dred Scott decision?

12. Why did Douglas' Freeport Doctrine offend many Southern Democrats?

13. How did John Brown propose to free the slaves?

14. What were the positions of the four major parties of 1860 regarding the issue of slavery in the territories?

15. What were the provisions of the Crittenden plan? What was Lincoln's main objection to it?

REVIEWING MAIN THEMES

1. What changes took place within the major political parties after 1850 which made it increasingly difficult to settle sectional differences?

2. How did the Compromise of 1850 help alleviate sectional animosities?

3. What major issues and events contributed to a

revival of sectional antagonisms between 1854 and 1861?

4. What circumstances contributed to Lincoln's rise to the presidency?

5. What events occurring in 1860 and 1861 precipitated the Civil War?

EVALUATING THE ISSUES

1. In 1858, William H. Seward noted that the systems of slave and free labor were coming into ever increasing contact because of the growth of population, the settlement of new lands, and the extension of a transportation network which increased commerce and travel between the sections. He believed that, as a result of these developments, friction between the two systems was unavoidable. "It is an irrepressible conflict," he said, "between opposing and enduring forces, and it means that the United States must and will sooner or later become either entirely a slave-holding nation or entirely a free-labor nation." Do you agree with his analysis of the reasons for the increased hostility between the sections? Do you agree that the friction was inevitable or that a permanent compromise would have been possible? Give reasons for your answers.

2. Why did the Republican party, in contrast to the Liberty and free-soil parties, become a major party? How do you account for its rapid growth?

3. Do you believe that Southern grievances in 1860 and 1861 justified secession? If not, under what circumstances would Southerners have been justified in seceding from the Union?

War Between the Sections

Abraham Lincoln had little military experience. Once, as a young man, he served briefly in the Black Hawk War (1832), to drive the Sauk and Fox Indians out of Illinois and what is now Wisconsin. It was not much of a war, and Lincoln, a captain of Illinois militia, played no great part in it. Afterwards, he joked that he had seen no "live, fighting Indians" but had fought in "a good many bloody struggles with the mosquitoes."

Jefferson Davis, by contrast, was a professional soldier. After graduating from West Point, he officered troops on the frontier, distinguished himself by his heroism in the Mexican War (1846–1848), and gained a reputation as one of the greatest of all war department heads.

Thus it would seem that Davis, as president of the Confederate states, should have been a more successful war leader than Lincoln, as President of the United States. Certainly, Davis was an able, high-minded, and devoted man, yet Lincoln proved to be a much more effective war President. Indeed, Lincoln was one of the most valuable assets that the Union possessed. "If the Union and the Confederacy had exchanged presidents with one another," a present-day historian, David M. Potter, suggests, "the Confederacy might have won its independence."

The Union also had other advantages for the waging of war. Its population outnumbered the free population of the Confederacy by more than three to one. Its mills and factories produced ten times as much as those of the Confederacy.

Why, considering the disparity in resources, did the Southerners dare to risk a war with the North? The secession leaders believed the South possessed advantages which would offset the North's preponderance in men and materials. First, as these leaders saw it, the South would have better soldiers. Her people supposedly were more experienced at handling guns and horses, and they would fight harder and longer, since they would be fighting for the high ideal of independence, for the protection of their homes. Second, the South would have geographical advantages. Her armies would have the benefit of rivers, swamps, and mountains which would serve as natural lines of defense. Third, the South would get help from abroad. Britain and France would need Southern cotton in order to keep their mills going, so both nations surely would step in to prevent the North from interfering with the cotton supply. Fourth, the South would not have to conquer the North but would only have to stave off her own defeat. Eventually, the Northern people would divide and quarrel and grow weary of the war. Then they would quit and let the Confederacy alone. So it seemed to the hopeful Confederate leaders in 1861.

THE UNION MOBILIZED ITS RESOURCES

When the war began in 1861, the North was quite unprepared to fight. The United States Army numbered fewer than seventeen thousand officers and men, and these were widely scattered, most of them guarding the western frontier against the danger of Indian attacks. Theoretically, the militia of the various states totaled a million or two, but in fact only a few thousand militiamen, at most, were trained, organized, and ready for combat. The United States Navy consisted of only ninety vessels of all kinds, most of them either out of commission or stationed in foreign waters, far from home.

The Union needed to build up its armed forces and provide adequate supplies of guns, ammunition, uniforms, horses, wagons, and equipment of all kinds. The overwhelming wealth and population of the North could not, of course, bring about victory by themselves. They had to be converted into the means of military power and directed toward the enemy's defeat.

While providing for military needs, Congress also encouraged business and agriculture with measures which the Whigs and Republicans had advocated before the war but which the Democrats, especially those from the South, had defeated again and again. These measures included national banks, high tariffs, and land grants for railroads, for homesteads, and for agricultural education. The govern-

ment's war orders and its economic legislation brought about complete recovery from the depression that had followed the Panic of 1857. During 1862, 1863, and 1864, the North hummed with prosperity.

The draft brought out volunteers

The early enthusiasm, which caused a rush to join the army, did not last long. Soon it became necessary to attract more men than were volunteering. A soldier's pay ($11 a month until 1864 and then $16) was far below the wages a man could earn in civilian life. To make the service more attractive, city and state governments and the federal government paid bounties to men when they enlisted. The federal bounty alone rose from $100 in 1861 to $300 (plus an additional $100 for a reënlisting veteran) in 1864. By then, a recruit could obtain as much as $1000, altogether, in places where the state and local bounties were especially generous. Such money-making opportunities led to a practice known as bounty jumping. A bounty jumper would enlist in one locality and collect his bounties, then would desert and reënlist in another locality, and then in another.

The cash payments, generous though they were, failed to bring out as many men as the armed forces required. Therefore, in 1863, Congress passed the Conscription Act. This was something new. Though some of the states had resorted to conscription in previous wars, the federal government had never done so.

According to the Conscription Act, each state was given a quota of troops to raise. If a state filled its quota with volunteers, there would be no conscription in that state. If the state failed to raise its full quota, the balance would be made up by means of the federal draft. To be conscripted was to be disgraced, and the act was intended to shame men into serving as volunteers, rather than to force them into serving as conscripts. Of all the men who served in the Union armies, only six in a hundred were actually drafted.

If a man were caught in the draft, he still did not necessarily have to go to war. By the terms of the Conscription Act he could either send a substitute or buy exemption. Some men who could afford it hired substitutes. At first, the price of a substitute was $300 or less, since the price of exemption was $300, and naturally no drafted man would pay more for a substitute than he would have to pay for exemption. When the privilege of buying exemption was eliminated in 1864, the price of substitutes rose to heights which only the very rich could afford. A regular business developed in which "substitute brokers" provided men, usually immigrants who had just arrived, to take the place of wealthy conscripts.

Many people thought it unfair that the rich, but not the poor, could escape the draft. Many also thought it unfair that certain localities paid much higher bounties than others, thus drawing off volunteers and leaving the poorer localities with unfilled quotas, so that the draft would sometimes hit hardest where able-bodied men were fewest. Criticism of the Conscription Act—and opposition to the war itself—in some places led people to resist the draft. The worst troubles occurred in New York City. There, when names were first drawn for the draft in July of 1863, a riot broke out and nearly five hundred persons were killed.

Despite its serious faults, the system of conscription and volunteering finally succeeded in raising numbers huge enough to be more than adequate. According to the best estimate, approximately 1,500,000 men served at one time or another in the Union armies.

Means were found to pay for waging war

The Union had to find means to pay for the huge numbers of men and vast quantities of materials that were required. Over the four years of fighting, the government found the means chiefly by borrowing, that is, by selling bonds. Some money was raised by taxation, and a lesser amount by issuing paper money.

The government issued a great variety of war bonds. To increase sales, it appointed the banking firm of Jay Cooke and Company as the exclusive selling agent. Cooke, "the financier of the Civil War," carried on a high-pressure selling campaign by means of newspaper advertisements and door-to-door salesmen. Though he urged workingmen to put their savings into bonds, he was much more successful with bankers and other wealthy men, who had plenty of money to invest.

The government wished to create a still larger market for war bonds. This was one reason for the establishment of the National Banking System, by acts of 1863 and 1864. The government guaranteed the banknotes of banks which joined the system, but the banks were required to buy and deposit with the treasury department one dollar in bonds for every dollar in banknotes. Thus the national banks were encouraged to buy bonds and at the same time to provide a new currency, the national banknotes.

The war taxes were more numerous and more onerous than the federal government had ever before imposed. They were applied to almost everything that conceivably could be taxed. For the first time, a federal income tax was levied. It remained in effect from 1861 to 1872.

The paper money, consisting of the "greenbacks," reached a total of nearly $450 million. These were made legal tender. That is, they had to be accepted for all payments (except the payment of customs duties and of interest on government bonds). The government would not give gold in exchange for greenbacks, however, so paper dollars did not have the same value as gold dollars. The value of greenbacks fell whenever discouraging news came from the battlefronts. At its lowest, in 1864, a dollar in greenbacks was worth only about forty cents in gold.

Congress aided businessmen and farmers

Congress repeatedly raised the tariff during the war. In 1864, "countervailing duties" were added, so as to offset the excise taxes which manufacturers in the United States had to pay, but foreign manufacturers did not. The tariff now was much higher than it ever had been. Most manufacturers in the United States had little to fear from foreign competition.

Meanwhile, in 1862, Congress adopted the Pacific Railroad Act. This gave generous loans and land grants for the construction of a transcontinental railroad. While helping businessmen, Congress also took steps to aid farmers. In 1862, it passed both the Homestead Act and the Morrill Land Grant Act. The Homestead Act made it possible for any citizen (or any alien who had declared his intention to become a citizen) to register a claim to 160 acres of the public land. After building on the tract and living on it for five years, the citizen could acquire outright ownership for a small fee. The Morrill Act provided for grants of land to the states; the proceeds from the sale of the land were to be used for education in agriculture, engineering, and military science. This act contributed to the development of the "land-grant" colleges and universities.

Businessmen gained the most from the wartime boom. Not all business prospered—not the building trades, for example, nor the construction of horse-car street railway lines—but war industries of all kinds thrived. New industries grew up, among them the ready-made clothing industry. Before the war, clothes had been made at home or, by special order, at a tailor's shop, and they had been made by hand. Then, with the war, came the government's orders for tens of thousands of uniforms. Factories were set up and the use of cutting and sewing machines was introduced to speed up the filling of orders. After the Civil War, many of these factories turned to the manufacture of civilian clothes.

A class of the newly rich came into existence, particularly in the large cities. Some of these people made their fortunes by honest effort together with considerable luck, and some by profiteering. People often referred to the newly rich as the "shoddy aristocracy." *Shoddy* was a kind of reclaimed wool or cotton, and at least a few manufacturers foisted uniforms of this material upon the government. Some of the shoddy uniforms, it was said, disintegrated the first time they were worn in the rain.

Wartime society had its ugly features, but these were only a part of the picture. Most of the civilians throughout the North willingly labored and sacrificed to advance the war effort. Women sewed for soldiers at meetings of the ladies' aid societies. Women and men alike contributed time and materials to "sanitary fairs," held to raise money for the United States Sanitary Commission. This commission, a predecessor of the American Red Cross, assisted the military authorities in providing hospital and medical care for soldiers.

REVIEWING THE SECTION

1. What measures did the North take to obtain men for its armies throughout the war?

2. How did the North finance the war?

3. What legislation was passed by the Republican-controlled Congress to aid business and agriculture? How did wartime prosperity in the North affect different segments of society?

FREEDOM FOR THE SLAVES BECAME A WAR AIM

Before the Civil War, almost no one thought that Congress or the President had the constitutional power to interfere with slavery in the Southern states. At the outset of the war, the North's sole objective was to reunite the nation and restore the national authority over all of it. The House of Representatives made this quite clear in a resolution it passed on July 22, 1861, the day after a disastrous Union defeat at the first Battle of Bull Run. This resolution said the war was being waged not for "interfering with the rights or established institutions" of the Southern states but solely "to defend and maintain the *supremacy* of the Constitution, and to preserve the Union."

Soon people began to disagree about the wisdom

and justice of leaving the institution of slavery alone. Some thought that slave owners had forfeited all constitutional rights by rebelling against the government. They believed that slavery not only had caused the rebellion but also kept it going, for without slaves to till the fields at home and to drive the teams and dig entrenchments at the front, the Confederacy would lack the manpower to continue its resistance. The way for the North to win the war and bring lasting peace, it seemed, was to liberate the slaves, enroll them as soldiers, and send them to fight against their former masters.

Eventually, the Republican party, the Lincoln administration, and a majority of the Northern people committed themselves to a second war aim, the abolition of slavery. From that time, the war was fought for freedom as well as for reunion.

Lincoln proclaimed emancipation as a war measure

The slavery issue divided the Republican party into two factions. One of them, the Radical Republicans, called for a "vigorous prosecution of the war," using all means at hand, including emancipation; the other faction, the Conservative Republicans, held back. So did the opposition party, the Democrats.

Before the end of 1861, the Radical Republicans had begun to pass laws indicating that the war effort was going to be directed against slavery as well as secession. The first Confiscation Act (1861) authorized the taking and freeing of slaves whom the enemy was using for military purposes. The second Confiscation Act (1862) provided for the seizure of slaves belonging to disloyal owners, whether the slaves were being used for military purposes or not.

The enforcement of these laws was up to President Lincoln. Since he had doubts about the constitutionality of the confiscation acts, he did nothing, at first, to carry them out. Furthermore, when one of his generals, John C. Frémont, issued an order (1861) declaring that all the slaves of rebels in

Missouri were "freemen," Lincoln revoked the order. When another general, David Hunter, declared the slaves free in Georgia, Florida, and South Carolina (1862), Lincoln again overruled the action. Radical Republicans denounced him.

In 1862, replying to criticism from Radical Republicans, Lincoln said: "My paramount object in this struggle *is* to save the Union, and is *not* either to save or destroy slavery." He added: "I intend no modification of my oft-expressed *personal wish* that all men everywhere could be free."

Lincoln looked upon slavery as a horrible wrong, but he hesitated to act against it because he doubted his constitutional power to act. Moreover, he wished to avoid antagonizing the people of the border slave states, especially Kentucky, for those states might switch over to the Confederate side; then it would be harder than ever, if not impossible, to save the Union—his "paramount object." He was also concerned about the tremendous social and economic problems that would result from an attempt suddenly to transform the relationships of Negroes and whites in the slave states.

While the Radical Republicans' demand for emancipation was growing, Lincoln was working on an emancipation plan which would satisfy his own doubts. According to his plan, the states themselves would free the slaves. They would do it gradually, and they would provide compensation for slave owners. The federal government would assist by making loans to the states. The Negroes, as they were freed, would be resettled in Africa, or South America, or the West Indies, if they were willing to go. Lincoln hoped to start the process immediately in the loyal slave states and continue it after the war in the seceded states. He got nowhere, however, for the political leaders of the loyal slave states refused to try the plan.

Lincoln, therefore, decided to approach the problem in a different way. He issued his Emancipation Proclamation, first in a preliminary form (September 22, 1862), and then in a final form (January 1, 1863). The Emancipation Proclamation did not apply to all the slaves—not to those in the loyal slave states nor to those in the parts of the Confederacy which the Union armies already had occupied. It applied only to the slaves in the areas that were still in rebellion. Critics, both at home and abroad, ridiculed the proclamation by saying it applied only in places where Lincoln could not enforce it, and not in places where he could. But Lincoln saw it as a war measure, a step he could constitutionally take only because of his authority as commander in chief of the army and the navy. He could justify such a war measure, to himself, only if he applied it exclusively to those areas where the war was still going on.

Actually, the Emancipation Proclamation brought freedom to relatively few slaves, perhaps to as many as 200,000 (out of a total of more than 3,500,000) by the end of the war. Many of the freed slaves were among the more than 150,000 Negroes who served in the various Union armies. Since the proclamation was a war measure, even Lincoln himself was unsure whether it would confer permanent freedom on anyone. Nevertheless, it was extremely important as a symbol. It indicated that, henceforth, the war definitely was being fought for freedom as well as for reunion.

Lincoln kept himself in power

For the North to win the war and achieve its aims, including the emancipation of the slaves, it was important for Lincoln and the Republican party to remain in power. In order to be reëlected Lincoln had to be a skillful politician as well as a far-seeing statesman.

His first task was to hold his party together and maintain his leadership of it. This was difficult because of the differences between the two factions within his own party. He was careful to include in his cabinet outstanding Radical Republicans, such as Salmon P. Chase, the secretary of the treasury, and outstanding Conservative Republicans, such as William H. Seward, the secretary of state. In all appointments, high and low, he saw that party workers were rewarded and thus kept dependable.

In 1864, the Republicans renominated Lincoln, but some of them soon afterward began trying to remove him as the party's candidate. They were convinced that Lincoln could not possibly win, and he himself had serious doubts about his chances. At that time, the Union armies were winning no victories, and the war seemed more and more hopeless. "Many are the hearts that are weary tonight, wishing for the war to cease," ran the words of a song then popular.

At the moment, the prospects looked good for the Democrats, but the Democrats also were divided. The War Democrats opposed the Lincoln administration but supported the war effort. The Peace Democrats—or Copperheads, as the Republicans called them—opposed both Lincoln and the war. The leading War Democrat was George B. McClellan, one-time general in chief of the Union armies. The most conspicuous Peace Democrat was Clement L. Vallandigham, a former Ohio congressman. Vallandigham had been arrested in 1863 for making antiwar speeches, and Lincoln had banished him to the Confederacy, whence Vallandigham made his way to what is now Ontario, and then back to the United States.

At the Democratic convention, McClellan got the nomination, but Vallandigham drafted the platform. The platform condemned the war as a failure and called for an immediate conference with Confederate leaders to make peace—without the abolition of slavery. The contradiction between the platform and the candidate, who advocated fighting on to victory, greatly handicapped the Democrats. Their greatest handicap, however, was the news of glorious Union successes in battle, especially General William Tecumseh Sherman's capture of Atlanta (September 2, 1864).

Lincoln was triumphantly reëlected. More than ever, he was now master of his party.

The Thirteenth Amendment abolished slavery

The Thirteenth Amendment rather than the Emancipation Proclamation assured the end of slavery. Lincoln played an important part in bringing about the amendment and, for this, even more than for the proclamation, he deserves his reputation as the Great Emancipator.

In 1864, the Radical Republicans had insisted upon a demand for an antislavery amendment as the key plank of their platform. Lincoln approved. When the voters reëlected him and increased the Republican majority in Congress, he was convinced that Congress ought immediately to start the amending process. The Senate had passed the Thirteenth Amendment (in April 1864), but the House of Representatives had yet to take action on the measure.

Unfortunately for Lincoln's hopes, the old Congress, meeting for its last session in the winter of 1864-1865, contained too few Republicans to furnish the necessary two-thirds vote. The newly elected House, with its overwhelming Republican majority, would not meet until December 1865. A number of the Democrats in the old Congress would have to be brought to the support of the amendment, which practically all of them consistently had opposed.

Lincoln promptly set to work to win over some of the Democrats. In his annual message to Congress, he urged them to consider the people's voice. In conferences with individual representatives, he brought all his powers of persuasion to bear. Finally, on January 31, 1865, enough Democrats voted with the Republicans to carry the proposal by more than two thirds.

Lincoln rejoiced as the amendment went out to the states for ratification. He rejoiced again and again as his own state of Illinois began and other states followed one by one in acting favorably upon it. Lincoln, however, did not live to rejoice in its final adoption in December 1865.

REVIEWING THE SECTION

1. Why was Lincoln at first reluctant to free the slaves in rebel states? Why did he issue the Emancipation Proclamation?

2. How did Lincoln's political skill help him win renomination? What events helped him get reëlected?

3. What obstacles did the Thirteenth Amendment face in Congress? How did Lincoln surmount these obstacles?

THE CONFEDERACY MOBILIZED ITS RESOURCES

The South not only had fewer men and smaller material resources than the North; she also faced serious handicaps in trying to make effective use of the resources she did possess. One handicap was the very idea of state rights upon which the Confederacy had been based. Most of the secessionists disliked any centralization of governmental power; that was one of the reasons why they had led their states to secede. Yet a strong, centralized government was necessary for the most efficient development, organization, and application of the South's resources. The Confederate government was further handicapped because it was new.

As the war dragged on, the difficulties increased. Southern transportation, which was poor to begin with, was made still worse by the advance of Union forces on land and sea. River and coastal waterways were occupied or blockaded, and rail centers, such as Chattanooga and Atlanta, were taken. Southern banking facilities had always been inadequate, and the Confederacy lost its banking center when New Orleans was captured only a year after the beginning of hostilities. The South had been dependent upon the outside world for goods of many kinds; these became increasingly more scarce as the Union tightened its blockade of Southern ports. Meanwhile, in filling her armies, the South had to take a higher proportion of her manpower than the North did. The South's capacity to produce, already small by comparison, was made even smaller by the disproportionate reduction of her labor supply.

The armies needed more and more men

The Confederacy resorted to conscription in 1862, a year before the Union did so. At first, all

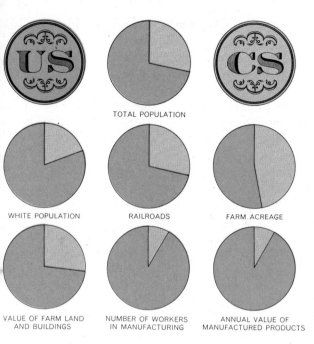

TOTAL POPULATION

WHITE POPULATION   RAILROADS   FARM ACREAGE

VALUE OF FARM LAND   NUMBER OF WORKERS   ANNUAL VALUE OF
AND BUILDINGS   IN MANUFACTURING   MANUFACTURED PRODUCTS

RESOURCES OF THE UNION
AND THE CONFEDERACY: 1860

When the Civil War began, the Union had far greater resources than did the Confederacy. It had more white men* to serve in its armies and an industrial system capable of supporting both a large military and civilian population. The Confederacy, in contrast, was forced to purchase most of its war materials in Europe. However, the North had to convert its factories to wartime production and it took time until economic advantages became an important factor in the defeat of the Confederacy.

*At first Negroes were excluded from both armies; however, more than 150,000 Negroes eventually served in the Union army.

able-bodied white men between the ages of 18 and 35 were subject to the draft (as compared with the ages of 20 to 45 in the North). Later, the age limits were extended in both directions, so that finally men from 17 to 50 years of age were called up. Boys younger than 17 and men older than 50 served in state "home guards." So desperate did the South become that, as General Ulysses S. Grant remarked, she had to rob both the cradle and the grave. The South raised a total of about one million troops. In other words, the South enlisted about two thirds as many men as the North, though the white population of the South was much less than half as large as that of the North.

The draft had some very unpopular features in the Confederacy as well as in the Union. The Confederate law did not provide for the purchase of exemption but did allow the sending of substitutes. The demand for substitutes grew so fast that the price soon rose from $1000 to $10,000 (in Confederate money). A Virginian put an advertisement in the paper offering a 230-acre farm for a

substitute. Even more unpopular than the provisions for substitution were those for exemption, especially the so-called twenty-Negro law, which exempted one white man for every twenty Negroes on a plantation. This provision was included because it was feared that white families would not be safe if left without able-bodied men to protect them from the slaves. But it caused men who owned small farms to feel that they were being compelled to fight for the benefit of men who owned large plantations, men who could escape the draft. It was frequently said that the war was "a rich man's war and a poor man's fight."

Near the very end of the war, the Confederacy needed additional troops so desperately that its congress passed a law for the enlisting and arming of slaves. The leading advocate of this measure was the Confederacy's greatest general, Robert E. Lee. He thought a "well-digested plan of gradual and general emancipation" should be worked out, for he considered it "neither just nor wise" to use Negroes as soldiers and still try to keep them as slaves.

The Confederate Congress never agreed to emancipation, and the war ended before any Negroes actually served in the Confederate ranks.

The South suffered from scarcities

The Confederacy was less successful in financing the war than the Union was. It relied much more than the Union on paper money and much less on borrowing and taxation. The Confederate government as well as the Confederate states, cities, banks, and other corporations issued notes which passed as money. The amount of currency of all kinds circulating in the South increased ten or eleven times in the three years from 1861 to 1864. Prices rose sharply, eventually reaching an average more than a hundred times as high as in 1861. This price rise was due to the swelling of the money supply, the shrinking in the quantity of goods available, and the growing fear that the Confederacy would lose the war.

Southerners suffered from the worst inflation that any Americans had experienced since the War for Independence. They had to pay fabulous prices for scarce items. For example, a cup of coffee cost $5.00 in a Richmond restaurant in 1864. Most people used coffee substitutes. A favorite kind of "Confederate coffee" was made from peas and corn which were scorched and then ground together.

Substitutes were found for a great many everyday necessities, but no substitute could be found for some of the most essential items, such as salt. Before the blockade became effective, the South imported most of her salt from Europe or the West Indies. When the usual sources of supply were cut off, the price of salt shot up, and people began to look frantically for new sources. Along the coasts they boiled seawater. Salt springs were discovered and salt wells or mines were dug in various places. Enough salt eventually was produced to take care of most requirements, though occasionally meat spoiled or cattle died for want of it.

Because of transportation difficulties, salt, grain, meat, and other goods seemed scarcer than they were. Often there was an abundance in certain localities but a shortage in others.

In some ways the Confederacy made excellent use of the inadequate railroads it had at the start of the war. For example, the Confederates were the first in history to send reinforcements by rail to an army in the midst of a battle (the first Battle of Bull Run, July 21, 1861). In other ways the Confederacy did less well with its railroads. The Confederate government finally took control of the railroads in 1863, but it could not get enough skilled mechanics or enough materials and equipment to keep the lines in good repair. As tracks and trains wore out, the Confederacy became less and less able to exploit its advantages in waging a defensive war.

The government tried to encourage manufacturing but seldom used very drastic methods. It relied mostly on indirect means. By manipulating the draft, for example, the government took men from nonessential industries and spared them for essential ones. By controlling the railroads, it allowed raw materials to go to some factories and not to others. It succeeded in stimulating war industries a great deal, but not enough.

To get scarce supplies, the government "impressed" them from farmers or merchants. That is, the government set its own price, then seized the goods it needed and paid for them at the set price. Farmers and merchants often hid their products, hoping to sell them later for much more than the government was paying. The government and many of the people complained about these "speculators." The more the goods were held back by such men, the more the prices rose. Thus, in some of its efforts to deal with inflation, the government only made matters worse.

The Southern people felt the impact of the war much more than the Northern people. The fighting came much closer to home in the South. Families lost a higher proportion of their menfolk, and often they lost everything, even the roof over their heads. Southerners were too poor and their economic system was too badly organized to provide the same degree of soldier care and comfort that Northerners provided.

Political disputes undermined the war effort

Political parties did not have time to develop in the Confederacy. Only one presidential election was held, on November 6, 1861, and Jefferson Davis and Alexander H. Stephens ran unopposed. These two had earlier been appointed *provisional* president and vice president; now both were elected to regular six-year terms. Though there were no organized parties, political opposition to the Davis administration soon arose. This opposition centered around the vice president and the governors of two states, Georgia and North Carolina.

Stephens, a former Whig, and Davis, always a Democrat, differed in their backgrounds. All of his life, except for congressional terms served in Washington, Stephens had lived in Georgia, one of the original thirteen states. He felt a deep sense of state pride. Davis, born in Kentucky and educated in New York, had made his home in the comparatively new state of Mississippi and had spent many years at frontier army posts as well as in Washington. He had no reason for such strong loyalty to a particular state.

Not only the earlier experiences but also the positions of the two men in the Confederate government were quite different. As president, Davis held great responsibilities; as vice president, Stephens held none. Stephens could afford to indulge in fantasies about the high ideal of state rights. Davis had to face up to the hard, practical realities of carrying on the war—a war for national independence, a war that required the use of national powers.

State rights as opposed to national powers—this issue already had broken up the United States, and now it threatened to break up the Confederate States, too.

Stephens seldom appeared in the Confederate capital, which had been moved from Montgomery to Richmond in May 1861. He spent most of his time at his Georgia plantation home. There, in private meetings with other discontented leaders, he criticized almost everything that Davis did or tried to do. Stephens finally hoped to make peace without independence but with a guarantee of state rights within the Union.

The governors of Georgia and North Carolina refused to coöperate fully with the Davis government. Like Stephens, these men denounced the draft as unconstitutional, and they enabled many of their own citizens to evade it by appointing them to state offices. At times, the Georgia governor forbade Georgia soldiers to serve outside the state. The North Carolina governor objected to "foreigners"—men from other states of the Confederacy—recruiting in North Carolina or serving as officers of North Carolina troops. He hoarded supplies for his state. While Lee's men in Virginia were going ragged, warehouses in North Carolina were full of surplus uniforms.

As the Confederacy lost more and more ground, Davis' critics in the newspapers and in the congress put the blame increasingly upon him. He became the most unpopular man in the entire South. After the war the federal authorities imprisoned him for more than two years, thus making him seem a martyr. Only then did he become a Southern hero again.

REVIEWING THE SECTION

1. Why was the Confederate government faced with a continuing shortage of soldiers? What measures were used by the Confederacy to obtain men for its armies?

2. Why did the Confederate states suffer greater hardships from the war than did the Union states?

3. What caused the political discord within the Confederacy? How did this discord undermine the war effort?

EUROPE KEPT OUT OF THE WAR

For both the Union and the Confederacy, Britain was much the most important of the European nations; both directed their major diplomatic efforts at her. The Confederate aim was positive: to induce Britain to recognize and help establish the independence of the Confederacy. The Union aim was negative: to prevent her from doing so. Britain never went far enough to please the South, yet she went too far to suit the North.

At the beginning, Southerners felt certain that cotton—or rather the lack of it—would help them to achieve their purpose with Britain and with France as well. Hence, in 1861, they destroyed a large part of the crop and kept the rest from being shipped abroad. They thought that the British and the French would soon feel the pinch, and the mill owners either would have to close their mills or the governments would have to recognize the Confederacy, prevent the establishment of a blockade and, perhaps, even stop the war so that cotton could be obtained.

It was true that the British, who led the world in cotton manufacturers, and also the French had been buying most of their cotton from the American South. It was also true that the British ruling classes and the French emperor hoped to see the Confederates win. Some British leaders calculated that if the United States were permanently divided, it would cease to be so dangerous as a competitor in world politics and world trade.

Cotton diplomacy failed to win European support

Nevertheless, the Southerners failed to get the kind of foreign help they had counted on. There were a number of reasons for this.

First, the cotton shortage was slow to hit Britain. In 1861, British warehouses were bulging with cotton. The dealers were happy enough about the threat of scarcity, for they could get a high price for the stocks they had on hand. When the shortage finally became serious, in 1863, it hurt most the mill workers and their families. These people sympathized with the Union cause, however, especially after it had also become an antislavery cause. When they were thrown out of work, they were supported by British and Yankee charity, and they remained Union sympathizers.

Second, the British expected the shortage to be temporary, for they looked to other nations, particularly India and Brazil, for new sources of cotton. Soon, shipments from India did begin to increase considerably.

Third, Northern wheat proved to be as important as Southern cotton to the British people. During the war, wheat exports took the place that cotton exports formerly had held in Anglo-American trade relations.

Fourth, in the beginning the British leaders thought the Confederates were going to win without British aid. Later, at the time the cotton shortage was beginning to be felt, the British could see that the war was going against the Confederacy. To enable the Confederacy to win, Britain now would have to provide a great deal of assistance. She would also have to risk a dangerous and costly war with the United States, and Confederate independence scarcely seemed worth the probable cost.

Fifth, the European powers themselves were divided. They were jealous and fearful of one another. None of them wanted to go ahead alone, get deeply committed in North America, and thus expose itself to possible attack in Europe. The French dared not go ahead without the British, and the British hesitated to go ahead without the Russians. The Russians, who had recently lost the Crimean War to the British and the French, were opposed to European intervention in the American Civil War. They wished the United States to remain a strong and undivided country, for they hoped this nation would serve, at some time in the future, as a valuable ally against Britain and France.

The Confederacy's status was challenged

Not long after the firing on Fort Sumter, Queen Victoria proclaimed Britain's neutrality and, later, France and a few other nations also proclaimed theirs. Seemingly, this ought to have been quite satisfactory to President Lincoln and to the Northern

MEN
IN
HISTORY

GRANT AND LEE

General Ulysses S. Grant, commander in chief of the Union armies, sometimes has been regarded merely as a "lucky" general who won the Civil War because of an overwhelming advantage in numbers and resources. At the same time, General Robert E. Lee, commander of the Army of Northern Virginia, often has been considered one of the greatest of all American generals. Historians have found little to detract from the luster of Lee, but there has been an increasing appreciation of the generalship of Grant.

Grant was the son of an Ohio tanner. He always loathed the stench of the tanyard, but because of financial reverses, was forced at one time to engage in the business he despised. A graduate of the United States Military Academy at West Point, Grant served creditably in the Mexican War (1846-1848) but resigned from the army in 1854.

When the Civil War came, Grant was commissioned a colonel in the Twenty-First Illinois Volunteer Infantry. He was elevated to the rank of major general of volunteers after the capture of Fort Donelson, where he won the nickname "Unconditional Surrender Grant."

Grant's personal appearance was not one of great magnetism. An observer said he could pass for a slouchy, dumpy, little subaltern who was fond of smoking. But he had an unusual way with men, and in a crisis they looked to him. He early won Lincoln's confidence. Explaining why he liked Grant, Lincoln said, "He doesn't worry and bother me. He isn't shrieking for reinforcements all of the time. He takes what troops we can give him . . . and does the best with what he has got."

Grant became widely recognized for his skill at handling men and for his ability to remain relaxed under pressure. The art of war was "simple enough," he thought. "Find out where the enemy is. Get at him as soon as you can. Strike at him as hard as you can and as often as you can, and keep moving on."

Robert E. Lee belonged to a proud Virginia family. His marriage to the great-granddaughter of Martha Washington profoundly influenced his life, for he felt obliged to uphold the family reputation.

Lee, like Grant, was a graduate of West Point and served with distinction under

General Winfield Scott in the Mexican War. His brilliant military career included three years as superintendent of the United States Military Academy at West Point.

The Union was very dear to Lee. As he saw the states seceding, he said, "I wish to live under no other government, and there is no sacrifice I am not ready to make for the preservation of the Union save that of honor." When war was imminent, Lincoln offered Lee the field command of the United States Army, but Lee declined. He could never forget that he was first of all a Virginian. "Though opposed to secession and deprecating war," he explained, "I could take no part in the invasion of the Southern states."

Jefferson Davis did not grant Lee power to initiate or carry out broad military plans. Lee predicted that the war would be long and bloody and warned that Britain would not come to the support of the Confederacy.

Lee had a unique ability as a tactician. He seized the initiative against the Union army and made use of his uncanny ability to foresee what his adversary might do. One Union soldier observed that everywhere the Union army went, it found rebels already there.

Lee's qualities of leadership enabled him to maintain a fighting force during the last winter when his army was bootless, ragged, and half starved, and under siege by Grant's well-fed and well-clothed army. The men under Lee's command had great personal affection for him. One private observed that Lee had a gentle and soothing magnetism "that drew everyone to him and made them love, respect and honor him." Lee's love for God was one of his most remarkable features. Throughout the war, he believed that he should seek out and execute the divine will.

Grant finally won the war with a strategy that he and Lincoln had agreed on. Lincoln gave him sufficient authority, and Grant brought together the necessary force and relentlessly applied it against the South. While other Union commanders slashed through the western half of the Confederacy, Grant kept Lee pinned down in the eastern theater and forced him to fight the kind of war that Lee himself had said he could not win.

people, but actually it was not. Lincoln, Secretary of State Seward, and many other Northerners violently objected.

In their neutrality proclamations, Britain and the other nations acknowledged that a state of war existed in the United States, and they indicated that they would treat both sides alike. This meant that Confederate ships would be given the same rights as Union ships to navigate the seas. It also meant that the Confederacy was recognized as a *belligerent,* that is, as an entity capable of waging war, though not as an independent nation in all respects.

The queen issued her proclamation of neutrality in response to a proclamation of blockade that Lincoln had just issued. She took it for granted that the United States was actually carrying on a war and that the Confederacy was the enemy. After all, a nation scarcely could be expected to impose a blockade in peacetime or to apply the blockade against its own rather than an enemy's ports.

Nevertheless, President Lincoln and Secretary Seward at first insisted that there was no war in the usual sense. They maintained that there was, on the one hand, only an insurrection, or rebellion, and on the other hand only a kind of police effort to put it down. Lincoln and Seward further asserted that the rebels were not entitled to the rights of foreign enemies under international law but deserved to be treated as traitors or pirates and executed when captured and convicted.

Lincoln never carried out such a policy. Early in the war, the Confederates took a large number of prisoners and threatened to retaliate, man for man, if any Confederates were shot or hanged after being captured. The Union proceeded to treat its prisoners as if they were foreign enemies. Lincoln ceased to insist that there was only a rebellion. Indeed, he justified some of his measures, such as the Emancipation Proclamation, on the basis of his war powers, and he could hardly have done so without first implying that there was a war going on.

Finally, the official attitude in the North recognized that there was both a rebellion and a war. It was officially called the War of the Rebellion. In the official view, the Confederates could be looked upon as foreign enemies who were entitled to the benefits of international law. They could also be looked upon as domestic rebels who might be treated in some respects—in the confiscation of their property, for example—as if they were traitors.

Even so, Lincoln, Seward, and other Northerners continued to complain because some foreign governments, particularly the British, had acted on the assumption that there really was a war. This continued to be a Yankee grievance to 1865 and long after that. At the same time, Davis and the Southerners were dissatisfied because the British and other European governments did not go further and actually recognize Confederate independence.

The Union had trouble with Britain

After the queen's proclamation of neutrality, trouble between the United States and Britain flared up on three other occasions during the Civil War—in 1861, 1862, and 1863.

The first was the *Trent* affair, which occurred in 1861. The *Trent,* a British merchant ship, was bound for Britain with two Confederate commissioners, John Y. Mason and John Slidell, aboard. The captain of a United States warship stopped the *Trent,* took off Mason and Slidell, and sent them as prisoners to Boston. Northerners rejoiced. They seemed to think that if Mason and Slidell had not been captured and had arrived at their respective destinations in Britain and France, those nations would have received them as regular diplomats, thus recognizing Confederate independence.

Soon the British government protested against the capture as "an affront to the British flag and a violation of international law." The prime minister, Lord Palmerston, exclaimed to his cabinet colleagues: "You may stand for this but damned if I will!" Palmerston demanded that the United States release the two Confederates and apologize to Britain. To back up his demands, he began to make war preparations and sent eight thousand troops to Canada.

Finally, the United States government yielded. Though Seward did not apologize, he disavowed the capture and let Mason and Slidell go. He pretended that the capture was similar to the old British practice of impressment and that, in protesting it, Britain had at last adopted the principles for which Americans had contended in the War of 1812.

In 1862, the British government came close to stepping in and trying to make peace. Lord Palmerston and his cabinet considered "an arrangement upon the basis of a separation" between the North and the South. One cabinet member, William E. Gladstone, said in a speech:

Jefferson Davis and other leaders of the South have made an army; they are making, it appears, a navy; and they have made what is more than either—they have made a nation.

In the Battle of Antietam (September 17, 1862), however, General George B. McClellan's Union army turned back General Robert E. Lee's Confederate army and ended the first Confederate attempt to invade the North. When this news arrived in Britain, Palmerston and his colleagues felt less confident that Davis had created a nation that would endure. Never again did the British cabinet seriously discuss intervention.

In 1863, a crisis arose over the question of British shipyards building Confederate warships. The British shipbuilders, rather than Davis and other Confederate leaders, had been making a navy for the South. British authorities allowed several British-built cruisers to be sold to the Confederates, though this was contrary both to British law and to Britain's obligations as a neutral. The United States minister in Britain, Charles Francis Adams, protested repeatedly but in vain. Besides new cruisers, some rams also were under construction. These were specially designed vessels with long, pointed iron prows for ramming and sinking the wooden ships of the Union blockading squadrons. "It would be superfluous in me to point out to your lordship that this is war," Minister Adams wrote to the foreign secretary, in demanding that he prevent the departure of the rams.

The cabinet finally did prevent their departure, as well as the departure of any more cruisers. British leaders had come to think it unwise to set an example by allowing British-built ships to be used against a nation with which Britain was at peace. These men feared that, in the future, the United States might follow that very example and provide Britain's enemies with ships.

REVIEWING THE SECTION

1. Why did the South fail to receive European recognition and support for the war?

2. What problems arose over the question of whether the Confederates were belligerents or rebels? How did the North resolve this question?

3. What wartime incidents led to friction between the North and Britain? How were they resolved?

THE UNION ARMIES CONQUERED THE CONFEDERACY

In comparison with previous wars, the Civil War seems very modern because of the many new devices that were used. Among these were the railroad, telegraph, armored ship, observation balloon, repeating rifle, and a primitive form of the machine gun. The Civil War seems modern also because it involved so fully the energies and resources of the opposing sides. Most wars of the eighteenth century had been fought by small professional armies and for limited objectives; this one was fought by huge citizen armies and for all-out victory. It approached total war.

Neither the Union nor the Confederacy made the fullest and best conceivable use of the new devices, though the Union with its superior resources was able to do somewhat better than the Confederacy. Both armies relied primarily on the Springfield rifle and a brass cannon known as the "Napoleon." The rifle was a single-shot muzzleloader. Before firing it, the infantryman had to pour in powder, tamp the powder down, then ram in a musket ball. The cannon also was a one-shot, muzzleloading gun. Despite their slowness in firing, these weapons had range and accuracy far greater than the guns used in earlier wars. Yet the generals on both sides hesitated to give up old-fashioned ideas of tactics. Generals continued to spread out their troops in long lines and send them over open country to make frontal attacks on entrenched positions. As a result, the dead and wounded piled up in numbers never before seen.

Lincoln and Davis determined the overall strategy

Lincoln and Davis, according to the terms of their respective constitutions, were commanders in chief of their armies and navies. They were responsible for seeing that war plans were made and carried out. In doing this, Lincoln, for all his military inexperience, succeeded better than Davis.

At first, Lincoln relied for advice on his general in chief, Winfield Scott. A veteran of the War of 1812, a hero of the Mexican War, Scott had been a great soldier but now was old, fat, gouty, and infirm. He proposed that the Union forces merely blockade the Southern ports, move down the Mississippi River to its mouth, and sit tight. Thus, having cut the Confederacy in two, the Union forces would encircle the main part and deprive it of all outside supplies. Newspapers called this the Anaconda Plan, because it resembled the action of the giant snake that wraps itself around its prey.

Lincoln approved of Scott's plan as far as it went, but he wished to make it more active and, like the anaconda, to continue to squeeze. "I state my general idea of this war to be," he wrote after much thought,

that we have the greater numbers, and the enemy has the greater facility of concentrating forces upon points of collision; that we must fail, unless we can find some way of making *our* advantage an overmatch for *his*; and that this can only be done by menacing him with superior forces at *different* points, at the *same* time.

He was convinced that in order to win the Union must never sit still but must fight on.

Lincoln had worked out his overall strategy. His next task was to find a general in chief who could successfully take charge of all the Union armies and carry out the plan. He dismissed Scott and tried George B. McClellan and then Henry W. Halleck, but neither of them measured up. At last, he found Ulysses S. Grant, the one Union general in the field who was consistently winning. In March 1864, he made Grant general in chief, and during the final year of the war Grant provided the kind of military leadership that Lincoln had been seeking.

Just as Lincoln tried to make the most of Northern wealth and numbers, so Davis had to adapt his plans to the limited Southern resources. Southern critics accused Davis of favoring a "dispersed defensive" strategy—a strategy which they thought unwise. They said he scattered the troops and kept them on the defensive when, instead, he should concentrate his forces, take the offensive, and constantly threaten the North. By this kind of "offensive defensive," they argued, he could save the Confederacy. Davis replied that the Confederacy lacked the means for keeping up such aggressive, concentrated activity. "Without military stores, without the workshops to create them, without the power to import them," he explained, "necessity not choice has compelled us to occupy strong positions and everywhere to confront the enemy without reserves." Despite all the handicaps, Davis did, in fact, make use of the "offensive defensive" on several occasions. For example, he authorized Lee to invade Pennsylvania in the campaign that culminated in the Battle of Gettysburg.

Davis never worked out with Lee a command system comparable to the one that Lincoln formulated with Grant. Lee, a brilliant soldier with an outstanding record, served under Davis most of the time only as commander of the Army of Northern Virginia and had no authority over the rest of the Confederate armies. Davis preferred to act as his own general in chief. Not until 1865 did he appoint Lee to that position; then, it was too late for Lee to accomplish anything with his new authority.

The Union blockade was tightened

At the beginning of the war, the Union navy consisted of less than a hundred vessels of all kinds. It grew to number nearly seven hundred by the end of the war. The navy's main task was to close off the commerce of the South, and as time passed, it did the job more and more effectively. At each of the major Southern seaports a blockading squadron was stationed. Once this was done, no regular ocean-going ship could get in or out, so the South was cut off from her normal overseas trade.

Many small boats and a number of craft specially built with low silhouette and light draft sneaked through the blockading squadrons. This was most often accomplished at night. Some boats managed to escape detection by landing at lonely spots along the coast. These blockade-runners carried away cotton and brought back both military supplies and expensive luxuries to the South. Most of the goods were transshipped at West Indian ports, the busiest of which was Nassau, in the Bahamas. At first, the great majority of the blockade-runners got through. Each year, more and more were captured; in 1865 only half were getting through. Never did blockade-running make up for the regular trade which the South had lost.

Union naval and military forces closed gaps in the blockade by occupying Southern coasts and seaports. During the first year of the war, these forces recovered most of the coastal area and off-shore islands of the Carolinas. Then they took New Orleans (1862), Mobile and Savannah (1864), and Wilmington (1865). Despite a number of desperate and costly assaults, they never managed to retake Fort Sumter so that they could get at Charleston from the sea, but Charleston was sealed off from the land side before the final surrender.

The Confederates made one dramatic attempt to break the blockade. They salvaged a warship, the *Merrimac,* which the Union navy had scuttled

at Norfolk, and covered her with armor plate. On March 8, 1862, the clumsy *Merrimac* steamed into Hampton Roads, destroyed two of the wooden blockading vessels, and scattered the rest. That very night a brand-new and quite different ironclad vessel arrived—the Union's *Monitor.* It was designed by John Ericsson, with a turret on a low, flat deck, like a tin can on a shingle. The next day the *Monitor* engaged the *Merrimac* in the first duel ever fought between armored warships. The duel ended in a draw, but the *Merrimac* never again threatened the blockade.

With its British-built cruisers, the Confederacy attempted a kind of counterblockade. These cruisers preyed upon Northern merchant vessels and interfered with Northern shipping. The *Alabama,* the most famous of these cruisers, sank, burned, or captured 69 ships on the Atlantic in two years. The Union warship *Kearsarge* finally caught up with her on June 19, 1864, off Cherbourg, France, and sent her to the bottom. Though the *Alabama* and the other raiders did serious damage to Northern shipping, they had no significant effect upon the outcome of the war.

Lee held his own in the east

Impatient to begin a land offensive, Lincoln ordered an inexperienced army to attack the Confederates in July 1861, at Manassas, Virginia, a railroad junction about thirty miles from Washington. In the war's first big battle, the Battle of Bull Run (July 21, 1861)—Southerners called it Manassas—the Confederates drove the Federals back in a rout.

From 1861 to 1863, the Union forces fighting on the Virginia front met frustration again and again in their effort to capture Richmond, the capital of the Confederacy. General Lee, who took command of the Army of Northern Virginia in 1862, successfully resisted a whole series of Union generals who followed one another as commanders of the Army of the Potomac.

George B. McClellan did an excellent job of

training and equipping this army, but he hesitated to lead it into battle. Under Lincoln's prodding, McClellan finally started to advance. He went down the Potomac by boat, landed on the peninsula between the York and the James, and began his Peninsular Campaign (March–July 1862) to try to take Richmond by the "back door." Thomas J. Jackson, who had earned the nickname "Stonewall" at Manassas, was dispatched by Lee northward to threaten Washington. To head off Jackson, Lincoln sent a force that McClellan had been counting on for additional support. Suddenly Jackson rejoined Lee, and the combined Confederate forces drove McClellan back from Richmond. Lincoln, concluding that McClellan was too timid, finally called off the campaign.

The boastful John Pope replaced McClellan and held command long enough to be outmaneuvered and badly beaten by Lee and Jackson at the second Battle of Bull Run, or Manassas (August 29–30, 1862). Then McClellan got another chance. At the Battle of Antietam, or Sharpsburg (September 17, 1862), he managed to turn Lee back from Maryland but could not prevent his returning to Virginia.

Next appeared Ambrose E. Burnside, who feared he was unfit for high command. He proved it at Fredericksburg (December 13, 1862), when he sent wave after wave of bluecoats to fall before Lee's impregnable position on the heights above the town. Joseph Hooker, though known as "Fighting Joe," fought no better when his turn came. Dividing his army, Hooker tried to outflank Lee at Chancellorsville (May 1–4, 1863), but Jackson outflanked him in a surprise counterattack and threw the Federals into confused retreat. That was the last brilliant exploit by Jackson. That evening he received a fatal wound when one of his own men mistook him for a Federal and shot him.

When Lee again carried the war to the North, George Gordon Meade took over the Union troops in midcampaign. The two armies happened to come together at Gettysburg, Pennsylvania, and a three-day battle ensued (July 1–3, 1863). This time the Federals held the high, protected ground, and the Confederates wasted themselves with repeated assaults, culminating in the desperate effort known as "Pickett's charge." On July 4, Lee ordered the remnant of his army to withdraw. Once more he was able to get his men safely back below the Potomac, to fight again and yet again.

Grant won in the west

The Battle of Gettysburg is generally thought to mark the "high tide of the Confederacy" and the turning point of the Civil War. Undoubtedly, it did climax the fighting on the eastern front, but, long before that battle, Union forces had begun to win important victories on the western front, in the Mississippi Valley.

As the year 1862 opened, there were two Union armies in Kentucky: the Army of the Tennessee under Grant and the Army of the Ohio under Don Carlos Buell. Opposing them were widely scattered Confederate forces under Albert Sidney Johnston, whom many Southerners thought was potentially a greater general than Lee. The two strongest points in the Confederates' long defensive line were Fort Henry on the Tennessee River and Fort Donelson on the Cumberland, in Tennessee. With the coöperation of a river flotilla, Grant took both of these forts (February 6 and 16, 1862). Thus he compelled the Confederates to pull far back to the south and attempt to make a new and much shorter defensive line. The Confederates abandoned half of Tennessee.

Then Grant moved south, with Buell following to give him support. Suddenly Johnston fell upon Grant in the hope of destroying his army before Buell could join it. Thus began the bloody Battle of Shiloh (April 6–7, 1862) in southwestern Tennessee. On the first day of the battle Grant was driven back, but Johnston was killed; he was replaced by P. G. T. Beauregard. On the second day Buell arrived with fresh troops, and Grant recovered the ground he had lost. Beauregard withdrew. For the North, this was a narrow victory; for the

South, it was a serious defeat since the two Union armies had been able to combine deep inside the Confederacy.

In an attempt to split the Confederacy, other Union forces, naval and military, were opening up the Mississippi River southward from Cairo, Illinois, and northward from New Orleans. By June 1862, they controlled most of the river except for a section of it around Vicksburg, Mississippi. This Confederate stronghold, high on a bluff, was assigned to Grant as his objective. Several times he tried and failed to get at the town by way of the rough, broken terrain to its north. In the spring of 1863, he began a new approach. He by-passed Vicksburg by marching his army down the other side of the river, through Louisiana. Then he recrossed the river and closed in upon Vicksburg from the rear. After a siege of about six weeks, Vicksburg capitulated on the same day that Lee withdrew from Gettysburg (July 4, 1863). "The signs look better," Lincoln afterward said. "The Father of Waters again goes unvexed to the sea."

While Grant was busy with the Vicksburg campaign, Buell had been trying to get to Chattanooga, a strategic river port and railroad center in southeastern Tennessee. Braxton Bragg, at the head of the Confederate Army of Tennessee, took the initiative and invaded Kentucky at about the same time that Lee first invaded Maryland. Buell went after Bragg, met him at Perryville, Kentucky (October 8, 1862), and sent him back into Tennessee, but Buell followed so slowly that Lincoln put William S. Rosecrans in his place. Rosecrans fought Bragg at Murfreesboro, or Stone's River (December 31, 1862–January 2, 1863), and compelled him to retreat again. Eventually Rosecrans entered Chattanooga (September 9, 1863).

Soon Rosecrans pushed on to the south, across the Georgia line. Bragg lay in wait, with reinforcements which had come by rail from Lee's army. Suddenly he pounced upon the Federals. In the Battle of Chickamauga (September 19–20, 1863) he drove them back into Chattanooga, and besieged them there.

Now Grant came and took charge. He replaced Rosecrans with George H. Thomas, who, by standing firm in the recent battle, had gained the nickname of the "Rock of Chickamauga." Grant and Thomas broke the siege, opened supply lines, and reinforced the army. Finally they sallied out to begin the Battle of Chattanooga (November 23–25, 1863). The battle ended with Union soldiers going beyond their orders and rushing up the slope of Missionary Ridge to take the Confederate positions at the top. Bragg tried to rally his men, but they panicked and ran.

The Union victory at Chattanooga ranks in importance with the decisive Union victories at Gettysburg and Vicksburg. The Union forces already had split the Confederacy once, along the Mississippi. They had gained control of most of Louisiana and Arkansas as well as Tennessee, and they were in a position to cut through Georgia and to split the Confederacy again.

Grant finally defeated Lee

After taking command of all the Union armies (March 9, 1864), Grant chose to make his headquarters in the field rather than in Washington. He accompanied the Army of the Potomac, though Meade remained technically in charge of it. Grant planned two major campaigns for 1864. One was intended to bring Lee to a showdown in Virginia, and the other to wear down the Confederate army in Georgia.

In Virginia, Grant headed into a rough, wooded area known as the Wilderness. Twice Lee struck savagely. Each time, Grant pushed on, instead of retiring and recouping as the Union generals formerly had done. The third time he met Lee, at Cold Harbor, only a few miles from Richmond (June 3, 1864), Grant himself did the attacking, throwing his men against strong Confederate entrenchments. This month-long Wilderness campaign resulted in heavy casualties. Although Grant lost five men for every three that Lee lost, the campaign brought no decision.

The Civil War, 1861-1865

Union strategy was threefold: (1) a blockade of the coast to starve the South; (2) an eastern campaign to capture Richmond, capital of the Confederacy; and (3) a western campaign to clear the Mississippi and Tennessee river valleys and split the Confederacy into several sections. In addition to defense, the Confederate strategy called for invasion of Maryland and central Pennsylvania in order to cut the Northeast off from the Northwest and force the Union to seek peace. All major battles of the Civil War were directed toward these strategic aims.

THE CAMPAIGN IN THE EAST

July 21, 1861

Battle of Bull Run. Confederate victory. Union troops (General Irvin McDowell) marching toward Richmond were defeated by the Confederates (Generals Joseph E. Johnston and Pierre G. T. Beauregard).

May 4-July 2, 1862

Peninsular campaign. Confederate victories. Union troops (General George McClellan) sailed down the Potomac from Washington and occupied Yorktown, Virginia (May 4). They were prevented from engaging the main part of the Confederate forces (Johnston) at Williamsburg (May 5) by a stubborn rear-guard action. During an attack on part of McClellan's army at Fair Oaks (May 31), Johnston was wounded and replaced by General Robert E. Lee (June 1). Lee and McClellan engaged in the Seven Days' Battles (June 26-July 2). Union forces lost most of the encounters but finally held at Malvern Hill (June 1). Lee withdrew toward Richmond (July 2), but the Union troops had failed in their attempt to reach Richmond.

August 29-30, 1862

Second Bull Run. Confederate victory. After the failure of the Peninsular campaign, Union troops (General John Pope) tried again to reach Richmond but were defeated by the Confederates (Lee).

September 17, 1862

Antietam. Drawn battle. McClellan caught Lee as he invaded Maryland but failed to break his lines. Because Lee retreated to Virginia, McClellan could claim a technical victory.

December 13, 1862

Fredericksburg. Confederate victory. In an attempt to take Richmond by way of Fredericksburg, Union troops (General Ambrose Burnside) suffered heavy losses at the hands of the Confederates (Lee).

May 2-4, 1863

Chancellorsville. Confederate victory. In another attempt to take Richmond, Union troops (General Joseph Hooker) failed to break Confederate lines at Chancellorsville. Hooker was forced to retreat.

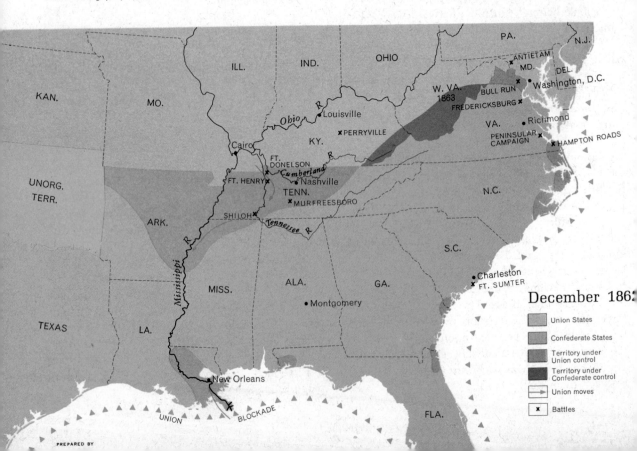

July 1-3, 1863

Gettysburg. Union victory. Lee, carrying the war to the North, was forced into battle at Gettysburg, Pennsylvania. After three days of bitter fighting, Lee retreated to Virginia.

THE CAMPAIGN IN THE WEST

February 6, 1862-January 3, 1863

Operations in Kentucky and Tennessee. Union victories. Combined Union forces (General Ulysses S. Grant and Commodore A. H. Foote) captured Fort Henry (Feb. 6) and Fort Donelson (Feb. 16). Grant marched to Shiloh (April 6-7). The Confederates (General Albert S. Johnston) caught Grant off guard. After a day of confused fighting, Northern reinforcements arrived (Generals Don Carlos Buell and Lew Wallace) and the Union gained the upper hand. In the fall, the Confederates (General Braxton Bragg) tried to advance on Louisville but were stopped by Buell at Perryville (Oct. 8). They were forced to withdraw from central Tennessee after a costly defeat at Murfreesboro (Dec. 31-Jan. 3) by Union troops (General William Rosecrans).

July 4, 1863

Vicksburg. Union victory. After many assaults on Vicksburg, Mississippi, Grant finally captured the city. The entire Mississippi River was in Union hands and the Confederacy was split.

September 19-20, 1863

Chickamauga. Confederate victory. Moving east, Union troops (Rosecrans) maneuvered the Confederates (Bragg) out of Chattanooga (Sept. 9) without a battle. Reinforcements were rushed to Bragg, and the Union line was broken at Chickamauga. The Union army retired to Chattanooga and Bragg besieged the city.

November 23-25, 1863

Chattanooga. Union victory. Grant, now in charge of the western campaign, took the offensive and routed Bragg's army. Union troops were now ready to divide the South by marching across Georgia.

THE SWEEP TO VICTORY

May 7-September 2, 1864

Invasion of Georgia. Union victory. Union troops (General William T. Sherman) set out from Chattanooga and began the invasion of Georgia. Confederate forces (General Joseph E. Johnston) fought a skillful series of defensive actions at Resaca (May 13-16), New Hope Church (May 25-28), and Kennesaw Mountain (June 27). Johnston was replaced by General John B. Hood, who twice attacked Sherman but was forced into Atlanta. He evacuated Atlanta (Sept. 1) and Sherman occupied it (Sept. 2).

November 14-December 22, 1864

The march to the sea. Union victory. Sherman left Atlanta and began the march across Georgia, destroying factories, warehouses, bridges, railroads, public buildings, and crops. He was virtually unopposed and occupied Savannah (Dec. 22).

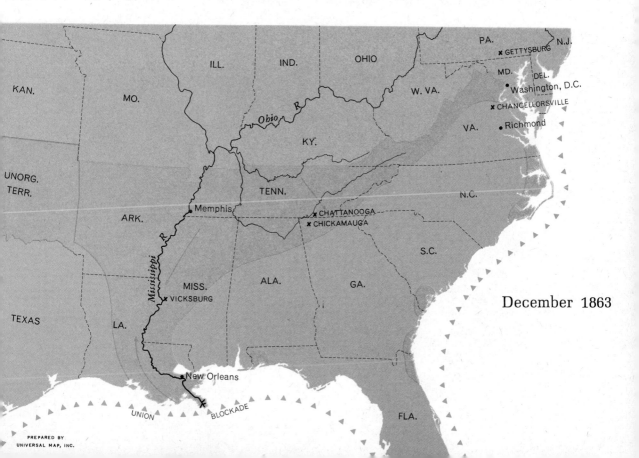

December 1863

December 15-16, 1864

Nashville. Union victory. While Sherman marched through Georgia, Confederate General Hood went after Union troops (General George H. Thomas) in Tennessee. Hood was repulsed at Franklin (Nov. 30) by General John Schofield, who then joined Thomas at Nashville. Hood's army was virtually destroyed there.

January 16-March 21, 1865

Invasion of the Carolinas. Sherman left Savannah and began a march which was even more destructive than the one through Georgia. The fall of Columbia (Feb. 17) led to the evacuation of Charleston (Feb .18). Sherman moved into North Carolina, fought Joseph E. Johnston (again in command) at Bentonville (March 19-20). Union troops occupied Goldsboro (March 21). (Johnston formally surrendered to Sherman on April 18.)

May 5, 1864-April 2, 1865

The drive to Richmond. Union victory. With the Battle of the Wilderness (May 5-6) Grant began to hammer away at Lee's army. Despite heavy losses, Grant moved south. He failed to flank Lee at Spotsylvania (May 8-12). A frontal assault at Cold Harbor (June 3) failed, but Lee's army suffered heavy

punishment. Grant then decided to take Richmond from the rear. He moved his army to Petersburg but failed to take it (June 15-18). He then initiated a siege which lasted nine months. Lee failed to break the siege at Fort Steadman (March 25) and at Five Forks (April 1). Lee evacuated Petersburg and Richmond (April 2).

April 9, 1865

The surrender at Appomattox Courthouse. After evacuating Petersburg and Richmond, Lee headed for Lynchburg, where he hoped to move by train to North Carolina and join forces with Johnston. Grant, however, won the race and blocked his path. Lee asked for terms and he met Grant at Appomattox (April 9).

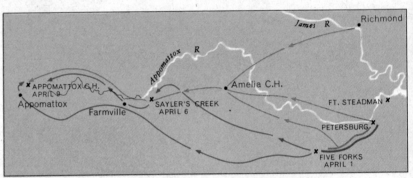

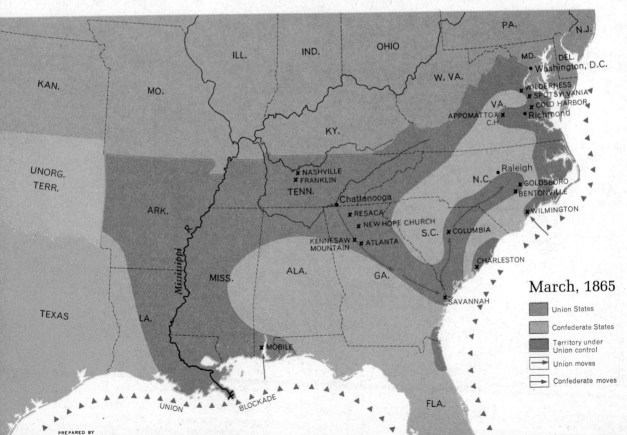

March, 1865

Union States
Confederate States
Territory under Union control
Union moves
Confederate moves

Brigadier General Francis Barlow's Charge at Cold Harbor, June 3, 1864, by Alfred R. Waud

Grant decided not to keep on slogging toward Richmond, though he earlier had said that he would "fight it out on this line" if it took all summer. Instead, he slipped away to the south and across the James River in the direction of Petersburg, a rail center below Richmond. He tried to storm his way into Petersburg (June 15–18, 1864) but failed and settled down to a siege, which he had hoped to avoid. During the next eight months, he stretched his siege lines farther and farther around Richmond and Petersburg.

Meanwhile, William T. Sherman commanded the Union army in Georgia and Joseph E. Johnston the opposing Confederate army. Heading for Atlanta (May and June 1864) Sherman repeatedly threatened to outflank Johnston, and to avoid open battle, Johnston kept falling back to new entrenchments. When the two armies reached the outskirts of Atlanta, Davis (July 17, 1864) directed Johnston to turn his command over to John B. Hood. Hood promptly made two attacks and suffered two defeats (July 20 and 22, 1864), then withdrew into Atlanta. Surrounding the city with his troops, Sherman forced Hood out and occupied Atlanta himself (September 2, 1864).

Several weeks later, Sherman sent George H. Thomas to hold Nashville and then sent John M. Schofield to reinforce Thomas. Hood started north into Tennessee, expecting to draw Sherman after him. At Franklin, Tennessee (November 30, 1864), Hood caught up with Schofield and ordered a series of suicidal attacks on the Union fortifications. Although Hood gained the field, he failed to prevent Schofield from joining Thomas. Pressing on to Nashville, Hood awaited an attack from Thomas. When it came, in the Battle of Nashville (December 15–16, 1864), Thomas gave Hood the worst beating of the war.

Instead of going after Hood, Sherman himself had headed in the other direction, toward Savannah and the sea. Marching through Georgia, Sherman and his men met little resistance as they laid waste a strip of country sixty miles wide. His goal was to bring the war home to the Southern people and destroy both their resources and their will to win. After taking Savannah (December 21, 1864), he turned northward and continued his march through the Carolinas.

By April 1865, Lee had concluded that he could no longer hold Richmond and Petersburg. He withdrew his army (April 2, 1865) and moved west. After a week's pursuit, Grant overtook him. On April 9, 1865, at Appomattox Courthouse, Lee surrendered.

REVIEWING THE SECTION

1. What was Lincoln's general plan of strategy? What was Davis' plan?

2. Why was the Union successful in establishing a blockade of the South? What attempts were made by the Confederates to weaken the Union blockade?

3. What were the Union and Confederate forces in the eastern theater trying to accomplish?

4. What was the strategic goal of the Union forces in the fighting on the western front? What was the military significance of Sherman's march to the sea?

CHAPTER **13** CONCLUSION

In the Civil War the North had the advantage of wealth and numbers, but the South hoped to win by means of her own determination and military skill plus foreign aid. The South came fairly close to doing so. The North was slow to bring the full weight of her population, resources, and industries to bear against the South. Serious difficulties developed between the North and Britain. Northerners quarreled among themselves, especially on the question of abolishing slavery, and many began to demand an end to the war. Meanwhile, the South seemed to be making more effective use of her limited military means.

Eventually, however, the tide began to turn. The war-making power of the Union grew, while that of the Confederacy declined. After considering intervention, Britain and France decided to leave the fighting to the Americans themselves. Lincoln proved more successful than Davis in uniting his people behind him and in directing the armed forces in order to bring forth their greatest efforts. At last, Lee had no choice but to surrender, and the Confederacy soon collapsed.

This was a costly war. Judged by the loss of life, it was much the costliest in which Americans ever have taken part. The North and South together suffered approximately 600,000 deaths, and the North alone approximately 360,000. In World War II, by comparison, the United States lost about 400,000 men, yet the population of the United States in the 1940's was nearly seven times as large as the population of the Union in the 1860's. In the Civil War, in addition to those who died from disease or battle wounds, there were many others who were wounded but survived, some of them badly maimed or horribly disfigured. The total casualties, Union and Confederate, were more than a million.

What did this costly war accomplish? It preserved and strengthened the nation, and it brought an end to slavery. It also vindicated the principle and practice of democracy.

At the beginning of the war, Lincoln had said that the issue of secession involved the fate not only of the United States but also the rest of the world. "It presents to the whole family of man the question whether a constitutional republic or a democracy—a government of the people, by the same people—can or cannot maintain its territorial integrity against its own domestic foes," he declared. "It presents the question whether discontented individuals...can... break up their Government and thus practically put an end to free government upon the earth. It forces us to ask: 'Is there, in all republics, this inherent and fatal weakness? Must a government, of necessity, be too *strong* for the liberties of its own people, or too *weak* to maintain its own existence?'"

The outcome of the Civil War demonstrated that the United States government *could* maintain itself without destroying civil liberties or human rights.

FOCUSING ON SPECIFICS

1. Why was the Conscription Act objectionable to many people in the North?

2. How did the Homestead Act aid farmers?

3. What was the purpose of the confiscation acts? Why did Lincoln refuse to enforce them?

4. Why did Lincoln believe the Emancipation Proclamation was constitutional?

5. In what respects were the Democrats handicapped in the election of 1864?

6. What was the offensive-defensive strategy advocated by many Southerners?

7. What was the purpose of the Union blockade?

8. Why were the battles of Vicksburg and Chattanooga crucial victories for the North?

REVIEWING MAIN THEMES

1. What advantages did the North have over the South in waging war? Why, in spite of their disadvantages, did many Southern leaders think the Confederacy could win the war?

2. What measures did the Union take to direct its resources toward winning the war?

3. What influenced the issuance of the Emancipation Proclamation and the passage of the Thirteenth Amendment?

4. How was the South handicapped in its efforts to wage war?

5. Why were diplomatic relations strained between the Union and Britain during the war?

6. How did the Union's leadership and strategy contribute to its success in achieving military victory?

EVALUATING THE ISSUES

1. The historian, David M. Potter, is quoted in this chapter as contending that if Lincoln had been president of the Confederacy and Davis President of the Union, the South might have won the war. Give reasons why you agree or disagree.

2. In 1864, Lincoln said, "I claim not to have controlled events but confess plainly that events have controlled me." Do you think his judgment of himself could be applied to his emancipation policies? Explain your answer.

3. Was Sherman's march through Georgia an unjustifiable series of atrocities or was it a legitimate method for waging war? Can any limits be set on means of waging war?

CHAPTER **14** 1865-1877

The Restoration of the Union

The Civil War had determined that no state could secede from the Union and that no man could own another as his slave. The war itself had not decided, however, what should be the future relations of the states to the federal government or of the Negroes to the whites. There remained the question of the conditions on which the states of the former Confederacy should be readmitted to the Union and the related question of the position which the former slaves were to occupy in Southern life. In other words, there remained questions in regard to reconstructing the Union and reconstructing the Southern states.

The South needed to be reconstructed physically as well as politically and socially. The war had left widespread desolation, especially along the route of Sherman's march through Georgia. There and elsewhere, the results of war and defeat were appalling: railroad tracks and bridges torn up, houses and barns burned or looted, fields left to grow up in weeds.

To rebuild would take money, but there was little coin to be had, and Confederate currency was worthless. So were the war bonds in which Southerners had invested their life savings. Property once valued at billions of dollars—the slaves—no longer could be counted as property at all. To rebuild also would take a great deal of labor, but the traditional labor system was gone. A large proportion of the white men who would have been in the prime of life were dead or disabled, and the Confederate veterans who returned home without disabling wounds were at first dispirited by defeat and discouraged by the immensity of the task before them.

The Negroes faced problems equally serious. Thousands wandered about, homeless and hungry, in need of immediate relief. What the Negroes most desired was land of their own to work. Next to a farm, they were most eager for an education. They also wanted dignity, respect, and the rights of citizens. Some began to hope for the right to vote.

The economic reconstruction of the South was delayed because of disputes over political and social reconstruction. The majority of white Southerners thought their states ought to be readmitted to the Union promptly, with as little change as possible in society and government. The majority of Northerners thought the states should not be admitted until certain more or less drastic changes had been made. Some Northerners even believed that political power ought to be taken from the former slave owners and given to the former slaves.

Some Northern Republicans were concerned that if the Southern states were readmitted to the Union after making only minor changes, the former Confederates would be able to keep the upper hand at home. Perhaps they also could join with Northern Democrats and get control of Congress and the presidency. A quick and easy reconstruction, therefore, would be to the advantage of the men responsible for secession, and also to the advantage of the Democratic party, North and South.

Such a quick and easy peace did not appeal to most Republicans, Northern businessmen, or Southern Negroes. Republicans, who had been able to win two presidential elections only because of the North-South division of their opponents, might never be able to win another one. Businessmen might lose the government aid (in the form of national banks, protective tariffs, and railroad subsidies) which they had gained during the war. And the former slaves, their fate left to their former masters, might find themselves little better off than before emancipation.

THERE WERE DIFFERENT PLANS OF RECONSTRUCTION

At the end of a war with a foreign nation, the President takes the lead in arranging peace terms, for the Constitution provides that he "shall have Power, by and with the Advice and Consent of the Senate, to make Treaties" (*Art. II, sec. 2, para. 2*). At the end of the Civil War, however, there was to be no treaty of peace, since the Union government refused to recognize or deal with the Confederate government. Yet a settlement had to be arranged somehow. The President and the Congress

presumably should have worked together as peacemakers, each exercising the appropriate constitutional powers, executive and legislative. Instead, the proper role of the President and Congress became, itself, one of the matters in dispute.

This dispute arose because both President Abraham Lincoln and his successor, Andrew Johnson, differed with the majority of the Republican representatives and senators on reconstruction policy. Both Lincoln and Johnson favored the prompt restoration of the Southern states, on relatively mild terms. The Republicans in Congress disagreed among themselves on reconstruction planning. Some of them, for example, advocated Negro suffrage from the beginning, while others at first opposed it. Most of them agreed, however, that Lincoln's and Johnson's proposals were too mild.

At first the President, Lincoln and then Johnson, took the initiative in planning for peace but both men ran into difficulties with Congress. Eventually, Congress got the upper hand and began to lay down policies of its own.

Lincoln favored an easy peace

In December 1863, President Lincoln had proposed a plan for restoring to the Union those states in the areas of the South already under Union control. At that time he promised that he would pardon all Confederates (except the leaders and certain others) who would give up and take an oath of future loyalty to the United States and its laws, including the Emancipation Proclamation. He also announced that whenever ten per cent of the voters in a state had taken the oath, they could reëstablish government in that state. He expressed the hope that the reorganized states would "recognize and declare" the permanent freedom of, and provide education for, those Negroes who already had been freed.

Under the "ten per cent plan," new constitutions and governments were formed in Arkansas, Tennessee, and Louisiana during 1864. To the first "free state" governor of Louisiana, Lincoln wrote to ask whether, when voting qualifications were decided upon, "some of the colored people might not be let in—as, for instance, the very intelligent, and especially those who have fought gallantly in our ranks." But Louisiana gave no Negroes the vote at that time.

In Congress, most of Lincoln's fellow Republicans disapproved of his plan. They feared that, under it, the reconstructed states might continue to permit slavery for most Negroes, since the plan did not appear to require complete and permanent abolition (and the Thirteenth Amendment had not yet been passed). Republicans also feared that former secessionists, by taking Lincoln's loyalty oath, could recover control of the new states. The majority in Congress, therefore, refused to recognize the states that were formed according to Lincoln's plan.

The Republicans supported, instead, a reconstruction plan sponsored by the Radical Republicans Benjamin F. Wade and Henry Winter Davis, in 1864. The Wade-Davis bill provided that a majority of a state's voters, not just ten per cent, must take an oath of *past* rather than future loyalty. That is, they had to swear that they had never willingly borne arms against the United States. The new states would be required to free all slaves, though not to give them the vote. When Congress passed the bill, the first congressional reconstruction plan, Lincoln pocket-vetoed it. Its sponsors then bitterly denounced him in a public letter, the "Wade-Davis manifesto."

Thus, by the time of Lee's surrender, Lincoln already was at odds with Congress. In the last public address of his life (April 11, 1865) he appealed to Congress to accept his "ten per cent" government in Louisiana, though he did not insist that the same plan necessarily be followed in dealing with all the other states. He and the Radical Republicans, however, now were further apart than ever, despite the passage of the Thirteenth Amendment, which removed the differences between them on the subject of slavery.

No one knows how well Lincoln would have succeeded as a reconstruction President. He died on the morning of April 15, 1865, the victim of a madman's bullet. The assassin, John Wilkes Booth, was the mastermind of a plot aimed also at Vice President Johnson and Secretary of State Seward. Booth's accomplices fortunately were bunglers; Johnson was unharmed and Seward, though badly injured, managed to survive.

Shocked and horrified, Northerners were inclined to believe the false rumor that desperate leaders of the dying Confederacy were behind the plot. This belief intensified hostile feelings toward the South and increased the demands for a punitive peace. The Radical Republicans now gained more popular support and they looked forward to taking charge of reconstruction under the presidency of Johnson, whom they considered a Radical like themselves.

Johnson began his plan for reconstruction

Though a Southerner and a former slave owner, Andrew Johnson had never been a secessionist or a friend of the planter class. He was born (1808) into a poor family in North Carolina and, when a young man, moved to Tennessee. He had no formal education, but he studied and educated himself while he worked as a tailor. As a Democratic congressman before the war, he advocated a homestead law, which most Southern politicians opposed. When Tennessee seceded, Johnson, a senator, refused to go with his state; he remained in Congress as a loyal Unionist, the only senator from a seceding state who did so. In 1862, he was appointed governor of conquered Tennessee. In 1864, he was nominated for the vice presidency in order to make the Republican party seem a true "Union party," with a Southern Democrat as well as a Northern Republican on its national ticket.

Though Johnson at first agreed with the Radicals on the "crime" of secession, he disagreed with them on a number of important matters. He opposed economic policies favorable to Northern business, policies such as the tariff, which many of

PRESIDENTIAL ELECTIONS: 1864-1876

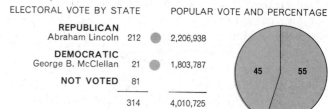

CANDIDATES: 1864

ELECTORAL VOTE BY STATE		POPULAR VOTE AND PERCENTAGE
REPUBLICAN Abraham Lincoln	212	2,206,938
DEMOCRATIC George B. McClellan	21	1,803,787
NOT VOTED	81	
	314	4,010,725

CANDIDATES: 1868

ELECTORAL VOTE BY STATE		POPULAR VOTE AND PERCENTAGE
REPUBLICAN Ulysses S. Grant	214	3,013,421
DEMOCRATIC Horatio Seymour	80	2,706,829
NOT VOTED	23	
	317	5,720,250

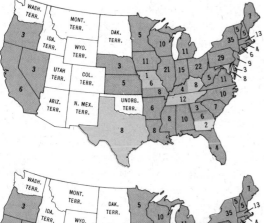

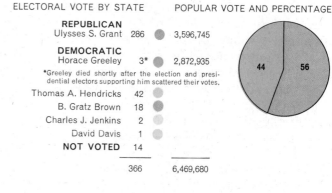

CANDIDATES: 1872

ELECTORAL VOTE BY STATE		POPULAR VOTE AND PERCENTAGE
REPUBLICAN Ulysses S. Grant	286	3,596,745
DEMOCRATIC Horace Greeley	3*	2,872,935

*Greeley died shortly after the election and presidential electors supporting him scattered their votes.

Thomas A. Hendricks	42
B. Gratz Brown	18
Charles J. Jenkins	2
David Davis	1
NOT VOTED	14
	366

6,469,680

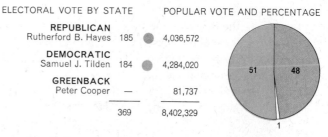

CANDIDATES: 1876

ELECTORAL VOTE BY STATE		POPULAR VOTE AND PERCENTAGE
REPUBLICAN Rutherford B. Hayes	185	4,036,572
DEMOCRATIC Samuel J. Tilden	184	4,284,020
GREENBACK Peter Cooper	—	81,737
	369	8,402,329

the Radical Republicans advocated. He sympathized much less than most of them did with the newly freed slaves. While the Radical Republicans emphasized national power, he viewed himself as a strict constitutionalist whose duty it was to protect the states in the exercise of their proper rights. It soon became apparent that he had more in common with his fellow Democrats than with the Radical Republicans.

In Johnson's view, the Southern states never had really left the Union. True, their leaders had pretended to bring about secession and, temporarily, had resisted the national authority. These secessionists must now be replaced by men who were from the same states and who were loyal to the Union. The new leaders must come not from the aristocracy of planters but from Johnson's own class, the middle and lower class of white farmers. Thus white men's democracies would arise in the South.

In the spring of 1865, while Congress was not in session to oppose him, Johnson launched his state-making program. He required the reorganized states to do three things: annul their ordinances of secession, abolish slavery (by passing laws of their own and by ratifying the Thirteenth Amendment), and repudiate their war debts. He proclaimed amnesty for all former rebels except the top leaders and the largest landowners, and he offered to pardon those people individually if they would apply to him in person.

During the summer of 1865, the Southern states proceeded to adopt new constitutions and to elect state officers and national representatives and senators. Secession was annulled, slavery abolished, and war debts repudiated, but the old leadership was not overthrown. Most of the men elected were former Confederate leaders. Johnson had to pardon them so that they could take part in politics, and pardon them he did, by the hundreds.

The kind of political revolution Johnson had hoped for in the South had not occurred. Nevertheless, he approved what had been done, and he concluded that reconstruction, or "restoration" as he preferred to call it, was now over. He was confident that when Congress met in December 1865, it would have no choice but to recognize the Southern states and admit their congressmen.

When Congress met, however, the Republican majority refused to seat any of the representatives or senators from the South. The two houses then set up the Joint Committee on Reconstruction to consider what must be done before the Southerners would be admitted.

The South tried to solve its postwar problems

A prompt restoration of the Southern states, in accordance with Johnson's plan, would seem to be justified if most white Southerners accepted the consequences of the war, gave loyal obedience to federal authority, and treated the Negroes as truly free people. Otherwise, a delayed program with stricter requirements would seem to be called for.

Johnson received quite different reports from two men he had sent to investigate conditions and attitudes in the South in the summer of 1865. "I am satisfied," General U. S. Grant told him, "that the mass of thinking men of the South accept the present situation of affairs in good faith." Carl Schurz, a leader in the Republican party, found that there was "among the Southern people an *utter absence of national feeling*" and that the Negro, "though no longer considered the property of the individual master," was "considered the slave of society."

Events in the South during 1865 and 1866 seemed to most Northerners to confirm the Schurz report. The majority of Southern whites, however, felt that they were doing the best that could be done, under the circumstances, to solve the postwar problems of the South.

The immediate problem was to make a living, and this was difficult for farmers and planters who had depended on slave labor. Some thought the Negro would work only as a slave, never as an employee. Others began to experiment with hiring Negroes, often their own former slaves. Many employers insisted upon labor contracts which generally required the Negroes, if they were to be paid, to remain on the plantation until the harvest.

Another urgent problem, as white Southerners saw it, was to preserve order. They feared that Negroes, without the bonds of slavery to confine them, would become vagrants and criminals. There were frequent rumors that the Negroes were plotting an uprising against the whites.

After the war, soldiers of the United States Army, many of them Negroes, continued to be stationed in the South. White Southerners resented the presence of the army and especially of the Negro troops. Southerners protested that the army, instead of maintaining peace and order, would encourage the former slaves to make trouble.

The Negroes also had urgent problems. Thousands were homeless and hungry. Some took freedom to mean exemption from labor and from all responsibility. The great majority, however, were willing to work for a fair wage, though they would have preferred to work on land of their own.

Some assistance came from freedmen's aid societies, which Northern churches and charitable groups had organized during the war. These societies provided food, medical care, schools, and teachers. An army agency, the Bureau of Freedmen, Refugees, and Abandoned Lands (created in March 1865), also provided some assistance. The Freedmen's Bureau undertook to resettle Negroes on abandoned or confiscated lands, but not much land was available, for as President Johnson pardoned the former Confederates, these men were able to reclaim their confiscated property. Besides providing education, transportation, and relief of various kinds, the bureau supervised the making of labor contracts, so as to safeguard the Negroes' interests. The army stood ready to back up the agents of the bureau, by force if necessary.

The Negroes depended on such outside help in getting a new start in life. Most white Southerners, on the other hand, wanted to be left alone, to deal as they saw fit with the problems of the South.

After the Southern states had been reorganized on Johnson's plan, they passed laws, known as "black codes," to define the legal position of the former slaves. According to some of these codes, Negroes were to be compelled to work for a white employer, and if they quit before the expiration of their contracted term of labor, they were subject to arrest. Those not employed could be arrested for vagrancy and could be assigned to the highest bidder to work out their fines. According to the Mississippi code, Negroes could not own land to farm independently. These laws appeared to many Northerners as efforts to reëstablish slavery in disguise. "We tell the white men of Mississippi," the *Chicago Tribune* said

that the men of the North will convert the state of Mississippi into a frog pond before they will allow any such laws to disgrace one foot of soil over which the flag of freedom waves.

Negroes, Southern white unionists, and Northerners residing in the South said that they risked their lives whenever they tried to assert their rights, especially if they supported the Republican party. From time to time, Negroes and their white sympathizers were beaten or murdered.

Johnson opposed Republican measures

Events in the South during 1865 and 1866—especially the election of former Confederates to office, the passage of the black codes, and the mistreatment of Negroes and white Republicans—convinced the Republicans in Congress that they should require further changes in the Southern states before allowing them to be represented in either the Senate or the House.

At first, the Republicans disagreed among themselves as to how drastic the changes ought to be. The Radical Republican leader in the Senate, Charles Sumner of Massachusetts, insisted upon Negro suffrage. The Radical Republican leader in the House, Thaddeus Stevens of Pennsylvania, demanded that plantations be confiscated and divided among the Negroes. These Radical Republicans argued that no states, only territories, existed in the South, because (as Sumner said) the states had committed suicide by seceding, or because (as Stevens said) they had been reduced to "conquered provinces" through defeat in war. Therefore, Congress could do as it pleased with the South, without regard to state rights. Most of the Republicans, however, refused to go along with Sumner and Stevens. The more moderate senators and representatives wished only to make sure that Southern Negroes were protected in their rights to life, liberty, and the pursuit of happiness.

To give Negroes protection, the Republicans passed a bill (February 1866) to enlarge the powers and prolong the life of the Freedmen's Bureau. Johnson vetoed the measure. Then (March 1866) Congress passed a bill to make Negroes citizens of the United States and to assure them the same civil rights as white persons. Johnson vetoed the civil rights bill also, but the Republicans repassed it over his veto, and they later repassed an amended version of the Freedmen's Bureau bill.

In June 1866, Congress approved and sent out to the states for ratification a constitutional amendment, the fourteenth. This reinforced the Civil Rights Act by putting guarantees of Negro citizenship and civil rights into the Constitution itself. The amendment gave the Southern states a choice of letting Negroes vote or losing congressional representatives in a number proportional to Negro population. It also disqualified most of the former Confederate leaders from holding either state or federal office.

This was the second reconstruction plan to be passed by Congress, and it went considerably beyond the first, the Wade-Davis bill. No representatives or senators were to be accepted from a Southern state until the state had ratified the Fourteenth Amendment. Johnson advised the states not to ratify it, and for the time being none of them did so except Tennessee, which Congress then (1866) readmitted to the Union.

As a result of his obstructionist stand, Johnson lost the sympathy of Republicans, even those who at first had thought the Radical Republicans too extreme. Moderate Republicans had sponsored the civil rights and Freedmen's Bureau bills, and when he vetoed these, the moderates had little choice but to join the Radical Republicans in opposing him. More and more Johnson was forced to rely on the support of Democrats, Northern and Southern.

In the congressional elections of 1866, Northern voters had an opportunity to choose between Johnson's position and the Republican policies. The voters overwhelmingly endorsed the Republicans, who consequently increased their majority in Congress. Henceforth they could easily override the President's veto.

REVIEWING THE SECTION

1. How did Lincoln's "ten per cent plan" for reconstruction differ from the Wade-Davis plan? Why did Radical Republicans believe a harsher peace was necessary?

2. What steps did Johnson take during the spring and summer of 1865 to reconstruct the Southern states? How did Congress initially respond to Johnson's actions?

3. What was the status of the Southern Negro under the state governments reconstructed by Johnson? Why did many Northerners want a harsher policy toward the South?

4. Between December 1865 and the elections of 1866, what steps did Congress take to reconstruct the South?

REPUBLICANS GOVERNED THE SOUTHERN STATES

After the war, the governments of the Southern states went through a bewildering series of changes. These states were reconstructed twice, the first time at the direction of President Johnson, the second time at the direction of Congress.

As the war ended, the governments that had belonged to the Confederacy collapsed, and the United States Army took responsibility for maintaining law and order. Within a few months, new governments were formed under the Johnson plan, with the former Confederates recovering power and denying political rights to Negroes. These governments lasted for about two years (1865-1867), but during that time they had no representatives or senators in Congress.

Then (1867) Congress put into effect a plan that is known as Radical Reconstruction. Now came a period of military rule, lasting about a year in some states and about three years in others. After that, new state governments were launched, with Negroes taking part and with most of the leading Confederates temporarily excluded. In the beginning, practically all of these governments were controlled by Republicans, Negro and white.

From the outset, the Republicans in the South faced violent opposition from the majority of white Southerners, some of whom organized terrorist groups, such as the Ku Klux Klan, to help in trying to overthrow the Republican governments.

The Radicals took charge of reconstruction

In a series of Reconstruction acts in 1867, the Radical Republicans presented the third congressional program for the defeated South. According to these acts, the South was to be divided into five districts, each under the command of any army officer, with troops to enforce his authority. Military rule was to continue until a new state constitution and government, satisfactory to Congress, had been formed. No one was to participate in constitution-making except those adult males, black or white, who could take an "ironclad oath" that they never willingly had supported the Confederacy. The states, thus reorganized again, had to ratify the Fourteenth Amendment and give voting and office-holding rights to Negroes.

Six states (Arkansas, North Carolina, South Carolina, Louisiana, Alabama, and Florida) complied with these requirements by the summer of 1868. Congress accepted the newly elected senators and representatives, and the military authorities allowed the newly elected state officials to take charge of the state governments.

The four other states (Mississippi, Virginia, Texas, and Georgia) failed to satisfy Congress in 1868. Congress imposed a fourth plan of reconstruction upon them. This included all the previous requirements and an additional one—ratification of the Fifteenth Amendment, which forbade the states to deny any person the vote on account of "race, color, or previous condition of servitude." Not until 1870 were these states readmitted to the Union and relieved of direct military rule.

Meanwhile, President Johnson had done his best to frustrate the congressional program by means of his appointments of civil and military officials and his orders to the ruling generals in the South. This was the primary reason why, in 1868, the Radical Republicans tried to remove him from office. They could do so, constitutionally, only by the process of impeachment, and only on the grounds of "high crimes and misdemeanors." When Johnson dismissed the secretary of war, Edwin M. Stanton, the Radicals charged him with violating an act of Congress, the Tenure of Office Act (passed March 1867), which was intended to prevent him from removing certain high officials from office without the consent of the Senate.

Johnson was impeached and tried. No crimes were proven against him except that of disagreeing with Congress, opposing its measures, and speaking disrespectfully of Radicals. These were not really crimes at all. Nevertheless, the Radicals demanded that all Republicans in the Senate vote for conviction out of loyalty to the party. If all the Republicans had done so—or all but six—he would have been convicted and removed. At the trial, seven Republicans and all the Democrats, held him not guilty of impeachable offenses. He was saved by the margin of a single vote.

Republicans controlled the South

Through the Reconstruction acts, the Republicans in Congress intended to put Republicans in control of the Southern states. Since there had been no Republican party in the South before the war,

RECONSTRUCTION: TWO VIEWS

ANDREW JOHNSON
Seventeenth President
1865-1869

THADDEUS STEVENS
Representative from Pa.
1849-1853, 1859-1868

To me the process of restoration seems perfectly plain and simple. It consists merely in a faithful application of the Constitution and laws. . . .

It is clear . . . that the States lately in rebellion are still members of the National Union. . . . If we admit now that . . . [the ordinances of secession] were valid . . . we sweep from under our feet the whole ground upon which we justified the war. . . .

. . . I would be unfaithful to my duty if I did not recommend the repeal of the acts of Congress which place ten of the Southern States under . . . military masters. . . .

. . . The punitive justice of this age, and especially of this country, does not consist in stripping whole States of their liberties and reducing all their people, without distinction, to the condition of slavery. *(1867)*

Nearly six years ago a bloody war arose between different sections of the United States. Eleven States . . . formed an entirely new . . . government. . . . On the result of the war depended the fate . . . of the contending parties. . . .

The Federal arms triumphed. The confederate armies and government surrendered unconditionally. The law of nations then fixed their condition. They were subject to the controlling power of the conquerors. . . .

To reconstruct the nation . . . to guaranty republican governments to old States are all legislative acts. . . .

. . . Unless the rebel States, before admission, should be made republican in spirit, and placed under the guardianship of loyal men, all our blood and treasure will have been spent in vain. *(1867)*

the party had to be organized as a new combination of political elements. It came to consist of Negroes and two groups of white men, the so-called scalawags and carpetbaggers.

Negroes constituted the largest block of Republican voters in most of the states under Radical Reconstruction. Negroes did not receive offices in proportion to the number of votes they provided. Negroes served as state and local officials, legislators, and even as United States representatives and senators, but they never held a majority of offices except in the South Carolina legislature. Though some attained state offices as high as lieutenant governor, none was ever elected governor. Many of the Negro officeholders, having been slaves, had received no schooling and had not learned to read and write. Others, most of whom were free persons before the war, and some of whom had been born and raised in the North, were well educated. Several were eloquent speakers and effective leaders.

The *scalawags* were native white Southerners who, temporarily at least, joined the Republican party. Some of them were hill-country farmers who never had owned slaves, who long had disliked the planter aristocracy, and who had given the Confederacy little or no support during the war. Others were wealthy or once wealthy planters and businessmen who had opposed secession but had "gone with their states" and had served in the Confederate army. Having once been Whigs, they did not feel quite at home in the Democratic party, and they were willing to once more join with the former Whigs (now Republicans) of the North. Moreover, they believed they could advance their own interests by coöperating with the Negro and, if possible, by controlling his vote.

The Southern white Republicans did not, of course, call themselves scalawags. They were called that by their political opponents, the Democrats, who viewed them as scoundrels. The Democrats

RECONSTRUCTION: TWO REACTIONS

HENRY C. DIBBLE
*Louisiana Judge
and Politician*

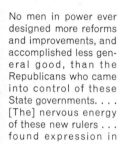

No men in power ever designed more reforms and improvements, and accomplished less general good, than the Republicans who came into control of these State governments. . . . [The] nervous energy of these new rulers . . . found expression in elaborate schemes for . . . a new era for the South. . . . [But] a political party at war with the greater portion of the intelligence and wealth in the States, could not successfully execute plans for . . . public improvement. . . .

. . . [It] is unjust . . . to lose sight of the condition of public affairs throughout the country. It was an era of corruption. . . . The Republican ring at Washington, and the Democratic ring in New York, stole more than all the carpet-baggers, scalawags, and colored politicians in all the ten reconstructed States. *(1877)*

FREDERICK DOUGLASS
*Negro Journalist
and Abolitionist*

[To-day], in most of the Southern States, the fourteenth and fifteenth amendments are virtually nullified. . . . [The] newly enfranchised . . . [are] in a condition but little above that in which they were found before the rebellion. . . . Our reconstruction measures were radically defective. . . . [In] the eager desire to have the Union restored, there was more care for sublime superstructure of the republic than for the solid foundation upon which it could alone be upheld. . . .

. . . When the serfs of Russia were emancipated, they were given three acres of ground upon which they could . . . make a living. . . . [Our slaves] were sent away empty-handed, without money, without friends, and without a foot of land . . . . Old and young, sick and well, were turned loose to the open sky, naked to their enemies. *(1880)*

---

held the same view of the *carpetbaggers*—Northerners who, as Republicans, took part in Southern politics after the war. The Democrats termed them carpetbaggers in order to give the impression that they were mere fortune-seekers who had gone south with all their possessions in a carpetbag (at that time a common kind of traveling bag, covered with carpeting material).

Actually, the carpetbaggers included a variety of men from the North, well-off and poor, honest and dishonest. Nearly all were veterans of the Union army. Most of them had taken up residence in the South during the war or within a year or two after its close. Some had arrived as Freedmen's Bureau agents or as tax collectors or other federal officials. Others had come as planters, businessmen, or professional men who thought they saw in the postwar South a new frontier of economic opportunity. Though not numerous enough to be important as voters, the carpetbaggers were clever

and courageous enough to be extremely influential as leaders, once the Reconstruction acts had given them an opportunity to participate in Southern politics. More willing than the scalawags to mingle socially with Negroes, the carpetbaggers were more successful in winning their confidence and support.

Under Radical Reconstruction, the South seemed to be turned upside down politically, with the recent slave imposing laws upon his former master. White Democrats complained of "Negro rule." Yet, in fact, Negroes alone never ran the Southern states. For a time, they helped to govern, but they did so in coöperation with white men, some from the North, a much larger number from the South.

State governments undertook new activities

The Republican state governments did not go to such great extremes as might have been expected. For example, they refrained, except in a few cases, from legalizing interracial marriages or requiring integrated schools (in New Orleans, some of the schools were racially integrated for a brief period). Nevertheless, the new governments were quite different from the ones which preceded them. The earlier ones had not taken upon themselves costly projects and, therefore, had not spent large sums, levied heavy taxes, or gone deeply into debt. The new ones undertook to do things that their predecessors had not done at all or had done only on a small scale.

One of these things was to provide education for masses of children, Negro as well as white. Before the war, every Southern state had adopted some kind of public educational system, at least on paper, but none except North Carolina had actually seen to the establishment of public schools throughout the state. In trying to educate hundreds of thousands who had never been educated before, the Republican governments faced an expensive task. They had to build many schoolhouses and hire many teachers, most of whom had to be attracted from the North at salaries higher than those at home.

Another function assumed by the new state governments was the improvement and expansion of transportation. The Republicans—and, for that matter, many of the Democrats—believed that the South could recover its prosperity only if trade were encouraged by the construction of additional railroad lines. They believed, further, that the states must give financial aid to railroad companies if construction were to be carried on as fast and as far as was necessary. Some of the governments under Johnsonian reconstruction had helped to finance railroad construction, but the Republican governments did much more. The usual procedure was this: the states issued bonds and gave them to the railroad companies in exchange for company bonds; the companies then sold the state bonds (which were easier to sell than company bonds) to investors in the North.

The states borrowed money (by issuing bonds) not only for aiding railroads but also for other purposes, such as the building of schools and the rebuilding of streets, roads, bridges, levees, and courthouses. Consequently, the state debts increased, some of them to a level several times as high as the prewar debts. Taxes also went up, both to pay interest on the debts and to meet increased running expenses.

Unfortunately, not all the money raised by taxing and borrowing was used for public improvement or the general welfare. Some portion of the money (no one can say how much) was simply wasted or was diverted for private gain. Negroes, scalawags, and carpetbaggers were not the only ones involved. Negroes were no more corrupt than white men, Republicans no more corrupt than Democrats, Northerners no more corrupt than Southerners. During the postwar years, there appears to have been a letdown in public morality, and corruption was widespread throughout the nation.

The Klan opposed Republican control of the South

In opposing the Republicans and their policies, the Democratic party in the South was handicapped by the political limitations which Radical Reconstruction had placed upon many of the most prominent Democrats. Few or none of them could vote for, or serve as, delegates to the state constitutional conventions of 1867. Once the conventions had completed their work, however, the right to vote depended upon the provisions of the new constitutions themselves. In only three of the states —Alabama, Arkansas, and Louisiana—did the constitutions disfranchise men because of their Confederate record. In all the other states, the former Confederate leaders were allowed to vote, but in none of the states could they hold office, since the Fourteenth Amendment excluded them from either state or federal officeholding. President Johnson, despite his pardoning power, could not remove this disability; only Congress could do so. The amendment kept from office about 100,000 to 150,000 white men in comparison with about 650,000 whom it did not affect.

The former Confederate leaders still could exert a great deal of influence, both through the Democratic party and through secret societies such as the Ku Klux Klan. The Klan's founder and first Grand Wizard was the Tennessean Nathan Bedford Forrest, a former slave trader, planter, and Confederate cavalry commander. Wearing white hoods and robes, Klansmen went on night rides to terrorize Negroes and their scalawag or carpetbagger associates. The avowed aim of the night riders was to preserve order, protect white womanhood, and offset the activities of the Union Leagues. The Union Leagues, too, were secret societies, but Republican ones, which enrolled Negroes and trained them in politics.

To check Klan terrorism, Congress in 1870 and 1871 passed three Enforcement (or Ku Klux) acts, which outlawed the Klan and authorized the use of the United States Army against it. In 1871, federal soldiers went to the assistance of Republican officials in the South on at least two hundred separate occasions. Martial law was declared in nine South Carolina counties. There and elsewhere, Klansmen were arrested, and some were convicted and imprisoned. After that, the Klan itself went to pieces, but "Ku Kluxism" (the use of terror for political ends) continued.

REVIEWING THE SECTION

1. What were the chief provisions of the third and fourth congressional programs for reconstruction? Why did the Radicals impeach President Johnson?

2. What role did carpetbaggers and scalawags play in Southern politics during Radical Reconstruction? What role did Negroes play?

3. What new tasks were undertaken by the Republican state governments in the South during Radical Reconstruction?

4. Why was the Democratic party handicapped in its efforts to oppose Republican control of the South? What methods did the Ku Klux Klan use to strike at Republican control? How did the Republicans combat the Klan?

TROUBLES MULTIPLIED UNDER GRANT

Since it brought into being a new group of Republican voters in the South, Radical Reconstruction was a help to the Republican party in national politics. The party could attract voters, in both the North and the South, by identifying itself with the ideals of union and freedom. Most of the Union veterans were Republicans, and many of them joined the Grand Army of the Republic (the G.A.R.), a veterans' organization which supported the party. In 1868, the party appealed to war memories and patriotic feelings—and won the presidential election—by running the popular hero Ulysses S. Grant.

Grant, one of only three professional soldiers who have ever been elected President, up to that time had shown little interest in politics and had had no experience in government. During his eight years in office (1869-1877), Grant encountered problems for which his military experience had not prepared him.

Scandals marred Grant's administration

In the presidency, Grant showed the effects of his military background. He kept as official or unofficial advisers a number of old army cronies, and out of personal loyalty he supported them even after some of them had proved themselves dishonest or incompetent. Knowing little of politics, he deferred to certain party bosses, took their advice in the distribution of the spoils of office, and relied upon them and their subordinates to manage legislation in Congress. When he had decided upon a policy, he expected it to be carried out, just as he formerly had expected his army orders to be followed.

Though Grant himself was honest, he failed to keep his administration free from political scandal. The first affair to be exposed was that of the Crédit Mobilier, a construction company controlled by a group of Union Pacific Railroad stockholders. They had arranged to have the railroad pay this company huge sums for constructing the railroad line. Some of this money, part of which came from the federal government, was diverted into their own pockets. To head off an investigation, the Crédit Mobilier managers bribed a number of congressmen with company stock. Though all this had happened before Grant's presidency, the truth came to light during his first term, and it seemed to smirch his administration because his Vice President, Schuyler Colfax, had been one of those congressmen who accepted bribes.

One scandal followed another during Grant's second term, and these affairs touched him more closely. In the case of the "Whiskey Ring," his private secretary and certain treasury officials coöperated with a group of distillers to make false reports of sales and thus cheat the government out of taxes. Grant defended his private secretary and removed the head of the treasury department, who had discovered the fraud. In the Belknap case, the secretary of war was shown to have taken a bribe from an Indian trader, and Grant again sided with the wrongdoer, who resigned to escape impeachment. Other cases, in the navy and treasury departments, involved officials who defrauded the government of money, which they used to enrich themselves and finance Republican political machines.

Before the end of his presidency, Grant openly confessed his political incompetence and apologized for the "mistakes" of his administration.

Liberal Republicans organized a separate party

Even before the end of Grant's first term, a number of prominent Republicans had become disgusted with what they called "Grantism." By this they meant the corruption, the spoils system, and other policies. They also meant Radical Reconstruction, which the administration was attempting to enforce, but which seemed to them to be producing more evil than good.

In 1872, these anti-Grant men decided not to support the President for reëlection. Calling themselves Liberal Republicans, they organized a sepa-

rate party and nominated the eccentric reformer and editor of the New York Tribune, Horace Greeley. They needed the votes of Democrats as well as Republicans to elect him, but Greeley had a long record as an antislavery man and Republican extremist. Without much enthusiasm, the Democratic party gave him its nomination, too, but on election day an unusually large number of Democrats stayed home. Grant beat him decisively.

An economic depression added to the discontent

At the time of Grant's second inauguration (1873), the nation seemed to be highly prosperous. Before the end of the year, however, the famous investment banking firm of Jay Cooke and Company collapsed, and other banks began to close their doors in order to forestall runs by depositors. The Panic of 1873 was on. It was followed by the longest and deepest depression Americans had yet known, one that lasted for approximately six years and brought a drastic drop in agricultural prices, tens of thousands of business failures, and unemployment affecting as many as a half million people at a time.

Farmers suffered because their production and marketing costs remained high while the prices of their crops fell. The plight of the farmers impelled them, for the first time, to organize on a large scale.

Before the panic, an organization known as the Patrons of Husbandry, or the National Grange, had been formed to bring together farmers, along with their wives and children, for social and educational meetings. After the panic, the Grange attracted many more members, eventually a total of almost a million, and they took steps to improve their economic condition. The Grangers set up coöperatives for the purchase as well as the manufacture of farm machinery and other goods.

The Grangers also went into politics. They supported candidates, either Democratic or Republican, who were favorable to the idea of state regulation of railroads. In Illinois, Wisconsin, Iowa, and Minnesota, the farmers and their friends secured the passage of "Granger laws" regulating freight rates. The Supreme Court upheld these laws in the case of *Munn* v. *Illinois* (1877).

Hard times provoked farmers to organize but discouraged laborers from doing the same. Jobs were so scarce that workers hesitated to antagonize their employers and risk being fired. The total number of union members fell from 300,000 in 1872 to 50,000 in 1878. Nevertheless, labor troubles became serious toward the end of the depression. A railroad strike in 1877 led to bloody and destructive rioting in Pittsburgh, Chicago, and St. Louis. Federal troops were called out to put down the violence.

Besides arousing farm and labor discontent, the depression caused many voters to turn from the Republican to the Democratic party, and in 1874, the Democrats won a majority in the House of Representatives. The depression also intensified a public debate, which had been going on ever since the war, with regard to the national currency.

Paper money became a controversial issue

There were two kinds of paper money in circulation after the war. One consisted of the greenbacks printed during the war (to the amount of $450 million). The other consisted of various forms of currency, including the national banknotes issued by private banks belonging to the National Banking System and guaranteed by the United States Treasury. There was a big difference between the greenbacks and the other paper currency: the greenbacks could not be exchanged for gold. As a result, they fluctuated in value.

Some bankers and businessmen, especially in New England, thought the government should get rid of the greenbacks and rely only on what these people called "sound money," that is, coin or paper money which could be exchanged for coin. Other businessmen and most farmers, especially in the West and South, thought the government should not only keep the greenbacks in circulation but also print more of them and use them to pay off

the war bonds as these fell due. The greenback advocates desired inflation, that is, an increase in the money supply and a rise in the price level. They believed that rising prices would encourage business, provide jobs, and make it easier for farmers to pay their debts.

In the midst of the controversy (in 1870), the Supreme Court by the margin of a single vote declared the original greenback laws unconstitutional. The Court held that Congress had no power to issue paper money and make it legal tender. This decision unsettled business and disturbed President Grant. There happened to be two vacancies in the Court, and Grant filled them by appointing men who believed the greenbacks constitutional. The Court, by a five-to-four decision, then reversed itself on the question.

In 1875, Grant signed the Specie Resumption Act. This provided that more banknotes would be issued, that greenbacks would be kept in circulation, and that greenbacks as well as the banknotes would be exchangeable for gold after 1879. The Specie Resumption Act was a compromise, and it did not satisfy all those who favored inflation. Some of them formed a new party, the Greenback party, which nominated a presidential candidate in 1876.

REVIEWING THE SECTION

1. How was Grant's administration directly touched by scandal?

2. Why did the Liberal Republicans organize a separate party in 1872?

3. How were farmers and laborers affected by the depression which followed the Panic of 1873? What steps did farmers take to improve their economic condition?

4. What were the chief issues in the controversy over greenbacks?

UNITED STATES DIPLOMACY MADE SOME GAINS

Neither the Johnson nor the Grant administration was very successful in dealing with domestic affairs. In foreign affairs, however, both administrations accomplished a great deal. This was largely the work of two of the ablest secretaries of state the nation has ever had—William H. Seward, who served through Johnson's as well as Lincoln's presidency, and Hamilton Fish, who served almost from the beginning of Grant's administration.

Seward believed in an active foreign policy and desired, above all, to acquire additional territory for the United States. He long had been an expansionist and once had said the United States flag ought someday to wave over all of North America. He also believed in an active and acquisitive policy for reasons of expediency; by diplomatic triumphs he hoped to draw public attention away from the quarrel between Johnson and the Republicans and to make the Johnson administration more popular than it was.

Hamilton Fish proved to be much the best of all Grant's appointees. Fish, a wealthy New York lawyer, had served as a member of the House of Representatives, governor, and a United States senator, but he was not a party leader comparable to Seward, nor was he so daring and aggressive in his views of diplomacy. What the nation needed, however, was a calming and stabilizing influence in its foreign affairs, and this he could provide. He took office with a determination to reëstablish good relations with Britain, the power whose friendship he considered the most valuable to the United States.

Seward pursued an active and acquisitive policy

As the Civil War came to an end, the most urgent task Seward faced was that of persuading the French to get out of Mexico. Napoleon III, the French emperor, had put Maximilian, a brother of the Austrian emperor, upon a golden throne as emperor of Mexico. Napoleon III was keeping Maximilian on that throne by using French troops against the Mexican people and army. This effort by a European power to dominate a Latin-American nation and change it from a republic into a monarchy was the most flagrant violation of the Monroe Doctrine that had occurred up to that time.

In dealing with France, Seward had to be cautious so long as the United States was preoccupied with winning the Civil War. As Union victory neared reality, he began to protest more and more sternly, and then to demand the withdrawal of the French troops. Finally, Napoleon III agreed to remove them, and, in 1867, the last of them departed from Mexico. Maximilian stayed on and was shot by a Mexican firing squad. The Mexican republic was restored, and the Monroe Doctrine vindicated.

Seward took more interest in the Pacific area and the Far East than had any secretary of state before him. He coöperated with European powers in naval demonstrations against Japan, whose rebellious feudal lords were resisting the efforts of foreigners, including Americans, to develop trade with that nation. He negotiated the Burlingame Treaty (1868) which gave Americans additional rights of travel and residence in China, and which permitted Chinese laborers to come and live in the United States.

His greatest achievement, however, was the acquisition of Alaska and, with it, the Aleutian Islands.

By 1867, Alaska was all that remained of Russian America. The tsar of Russia, Alexander II, knew there was gold in Alaska, and yet he wished to sell the territory. He feared that if he did not dispose of it, sooner or later either the British would seize it, or the Americans would settle in it and take it over as they once had done with Texas.

On a March evening in 1867, Seward was playing whist in his Washington home when the Russian minister called upon him to say the tsar was willing to sell. The minister suggested that a treaty be drawn up the next day, but Seward pushed away the card table and said: "Why wait till tomorrow, Mr. Stoeckl? Let us make the treaty tonight!" They completed and signed it at four o'clock in the morning.

The Senate promptly approved the treaty, but opposition to it arose in the House of Representatives, which had to appropriate $7.2 million to pay for the purchase. Opponents referred to Alaska as "Seward's Folly" or "Seward's Icebox" and argued that it was too far away and God-forsaken to be worth the price—though this amounted to less than two cents an acre. After more than a year, in July 1868, the appropriation bill finally was passed.

Hamilton Fish improved relations with Britain

Relations between Britain and the United States were bad at the end of the Civil War. Northerners still blamed the British government for having allowed the *Alabama* and other cruisers to be built in British shipyards and sold to the Confederacy. These Americans demanded payment of the *Alabama* claims, that is, the claims for losses the various cruisers had caused to Union shipping. Charles Sumner, chairman of the Senate Foreign Relations Committee, argued that the claims should also include the whole cost of the war for its last two years—since, he said, British policy had prolonged the war by that much. These "indirect damages" he estimated at approximately $2 billion. He and others expected Britain to make payment by ceding Canada to the United States.

Such talk worried the Canadians. They had a number of grievances against their neighbors to the south. There were disputes over the northwest water boundary, fishing rights, and Fenian activities. The Fenian Brotherhood, an organization of Irish Americans, hoped to conquer Canada and thus compel Britain to grant independence to Ireland. Between 1866 and 1871 the Fenians made several raids across the border into Canada. The troubles with the United States helped bring Canadians together in a federation of the provinces known as the Dominion of Canada (1867).

To deal with the disputes, Secretary Fish arranged for a joint high commission of one Canadian, two Britishers, and three Americans to meet in Washington in 1871. They agreed to a treaty which arranged for the settlement, in one way or another, of all the difficulties except the Canadian claim to damages for Fenian raids.

An international tribunal of arbitrators (Swiss, Italian, and Brazilian as well as American and British) met in Geneva to decide on the *Alabama* claims. They awarded $15.5 million to the United States. The German emperor arbitrated the boundary question, and he decided in favor of the Americans, upholding their claim to the San Juan Islands in Puget Sound. Special Anglo-American commissions granted a total of about $7.5 million to Britain as compensation for losses suffered by British subjects during the war, and as payment for American rights to fish in Canadian waters. Thus, on balance, the United States received about $8 million.

The Treaty of Washington of 1871 marked a turning point in the history of Anglo-American relations. Long traditional rivals, the United States and Britain now began to draw together and gradually to become permanent friends.

REVIEWING THE SECTION

1. What diplomatic gains did Seward achieve in Mexico? in the Far East? in Alaska?

2. How did Hamilton Fish improve relations between the United States and Britain? What was the significance of the Treaty of Washington?

RECONSTRUCTION CAME TO AN END

Ten years after the passage of the Reconstruction acts, the national leaders of the Republican party stopped trying to enforce the reconstruction program. Even before that time, however, the program had been frustrated in most of the Southern states.

The Southern Republicans strove against increasing handicaps after 1872. They were weakened by the party split, and some of them, as Liberal Republicans, turned to coöperating with the Democrats. All but about five hundred of the Democrats were now relieved from the officeholding ban provided in the Fourteenth Amendment, for Congress lifted the ban in the Amnesty Act of 1872. In both the North and the South, the Democrats gained in

MAJOR EVENTS IN UNITED STATES FOREIGN AFFAIRS: 1853-1877

1853-1865 (From the Gadsden Purchase to the end of the Civil War)

STATEMENTS OF POLICY

1861 *Proclamation of blockade* of the Confederacy by the Union led to a neutrality proclamation by Britain. Violating its position as a neutral nation, Britain built the *Alabama* and other warships for the South.

1863 *Emancipation Proclamation* committed the North to the abolition of slavery as a war aim and gained in Europe favorable public opinion for the Union.

BOUNDARY SETTLEMENTS AND ACQUISITIONS

1854 *Ostend Manifesto* recommended that the U.S. purchase Cuba or seize the island if Spain should refuse to sell. The administration was accused of trying to add a new slave state, so efforts to acquire Cuba were dropped.

Treaty for annexation of Hawaii (uncompleted) provided for Hawaii's entrance into the Union as a state.

ECONOMIC POLICY AND COMMERCIAL TREATIES

1854 *Treaty of Kanagawa*, Japan's first treaty with a Western nation, ended more than 200 years of seclusion. Although the treaty gave the U.S. only limited trade privileges, it included a most-favored-nation clause.

Marcy-Elgin Treaty with Britain. The treaty provided for reciprocal fishing rights and duty-free trade in certain products between the U.S. and the British North American provinces (Canada).

1858 *Treaty of Tientsin* with China extended trade privileges gained by the U.S. in 1844. Through the most-favored-nation principle, the U.S. received from China concessions already made to Britain and France.

Harris' treaty, Japan's first full commercial treaty with a Western nation, gave extraterritorial rights to U.S. citizens living in Japan.

Commodore Matthew C. Perry and a group of naval officers arrived in Japan in 1854 to negotiate a treaty of friendship and trade. The Japanese, at first suspicious of the foreigners, soon relaxed their restrictions and arranged sightseeing trips for them. The treaty, signed at Kanagawa, opened new markets for the U.S. in the Far East.

Procession of Foreigners in Yokohama, by Ichikawa Hoin Ga, c. 1855

1865-1877 (From the end of the Civil War to the end of Reconstruction)

STATEMENTS OF POLICY

1867 *Monroe Doctrine* had been challenged in 1863 when France replaced the republican government of Mexico with a monarchy. Though the doctrine was not invoked by name, it influenced Napoleon III to withdraw all French troops from Mexico. The doctrine gained new respect both in the U.S. and in Europe.

BOUNDARY SETTLEMENTS AND ACQUISITIONS

1867 *Purchase treaty* with Russia. U.S. bought Russian America (Alaska) for $7.2 million, less than 2 cents per acre.

Annexation of Midway Islands by U.S. occupation.

Purchase treaty signed with Denmark for Danish West Indies (Virgin Islands) was not voted on by Senate.

1869 *Treaty for annexation* of the Dominican Republic by the U.S. was signed but failed to pass in the Senate.

ECONOMIC POLICY AND COMMERCIAL TREATIES

1867 *Transit treaty* gave the U.S. the right to an interoceanic canal route through Nicaragua.

1868 *Burlingame Treaty* opened the U.S. to unrestricted Chinese immigration and gave U.S. citizens additional rights of travel and residence in China.

1875 *Reciprocity treaty* with Hawaii provided for duty-free importation of Hawaiian sugar and pledged Hawaii not to give any of its territory to another nation.

ARBITRATION TREATIES

1871 *Treaty of Washington* provided for settlement of long-standing disputes, including the "Alabama" claims, between the U.S. and Britain by international arbitration commissions. The treaty ended an era of ill will in U.S. relations with Britain and British North America.

popularity with the coming of the Panic of 1873 and with the revelations of corruption in the national government and in the reconstructed states. After the Democrats won control of the House of Representatives in 1874, the Southern Republicans could no longer count on getting favorable legislation from Congress. Nor could they always depend on President Grant, who grew weary of their requests for army support.

Without the army to back them, the Southern Republicans could not hold out against the violent methods which the Southern Democrats used to regain power. When the last of the troops were removed, in 1877, reconstruction came to an end.

Republicans lost control of the South

Within a few years after the Southern states had been readmitted to the Union—that is, within a few years after 1868 or 1870—the Democrats recovered control in most of them. In Virginia, they were already in power when the state was readmitted in 1870. Where the Negroes were relatively few, the task was comparatively simple for the Democrats. They had only to win over the vote of white men, including the scalawags. Most of the scalawags, losing all hope of controlling their Negro and carpetbagger allies, eventually deserted to the Democrats.

By 1875, the Democrats held all but four of the former Confederate states: Mississippi, South Carolina, Louisiana, and Florida. In Mississippi and South Carolina, where Negroes constituted a very large part of the population, the Democrats sought to win elections by keeping them away from the polls. The Democrats carried Mississippi in 1875, by organizing mounted rifle companies which drilled and demonstrated openly and threatened all Republicans, colored or white. Governor Adelbert Ames, a carpetbagger from Maine, dared not call out his Negro militia for fear of starting a race war.

In South Carolina, in 1876, the Democrats copied the "Mississippi plan." Armed men, wear-

ing red shirts as their uniforms, rode into Republican meetings and broke them up. After the election, the Red Shirts claimed victory for their leader, the former Confederate cavalry commander Wade Hampton, as governor of the state. The Republicans insisted that Governor D. H. Chamberlain, a carpetbagger from Massachusetts, had been reëlected. Chamberlain continued to occupy the statehouse in Columbia, and federal soldiers were stationed in and around the statehouse to protect him from the Red Shirts. If the troops should be removed, he would have to give up.

Somewhat similar situations existed at the same time in Louisiana and Florida. In these states, Republicans held on, but only with army support. The political future of Louisiana and Florida, as well as South Carolina, depended on the outcome of the presidential election of 1876.

The presidential election was disputed

In 1876, both the Republican and the Democratic national conventions chose "reform" candidates, so as to appeal to voters who were tired of corruption and misgovernment. The Republicans nominated Rutherford B. Hayes of Ohio, a veteran of the Union army and a critic of the spoils system. The Democrats nominated Samuel J. Tilden of New York, a conservative lawyer who had prosecuted and helped to break up the Tweed Ring, a corrupt political machine in New York City.

On the morning after election day, the *New York Tribune* came out with the headline: "Tilden Elected." But Hayes and the Republican leaders refused to concede defeat. Republicans soon began to insist that the Democrats wrongly claimed one of the electoral votes from Oregon and all the electoral votes from South Carolina, Louisiana, and Florida.

In Oregon, the situation was this: One of the Democratic electors was a state official and hence ineligible. He was replaced by the elector with the next highest number of votes, a Republican. One of the Oregon electoral votes was thus transferred from Tilden to Hayes, yet Tilden still held a sizable lead in the electoral college. Hayes needed *all* the other disputed votes in order to be elected.

In South Carolina, Louisiana, and Florida, the situation was more complicated. Here the reconstructed governments had set up special "returning boards" to go over the election returns and throw out improper or fraudulent ballots. These boards threw out enough Democratic votes to carry the three states for the Hayes electors.

The Twelfth Amendment to the Constitution provides that if no presidential candidate gets a majority in the electoral college, the House of Representatives shall choose "from the persons having the highest numbers not exceeding three on the list of those voted for as President." The House had done so in 1824 when it elected John Quincy Adams, but the problem was quite different in 1876. This was not a case where none of the candidates had a majority. One of them did. The question was, which one? The answer depended on which of the two sets of returns from South Carolina, Louisiana, and Florida were counted—the Democratic returns, or the Republican.

The dispute raged on into the winter of 1876-1877, with the people in doubt as to who their next President was to be. Finally, Congress set up a special electoral commission, of fifteen members, chosen from the House, the Senate, and the Supreme Court. Eight of the fifteen were Republicans and seven, Democrats. By a vote of eight to seven, the commission ruled in favor of the Republican returns from the South.

Even so, the Democrats in Congress could have prevented the final approval of Hayes ("Old Eight to Seven," some called him) as President. As always, the official count of the electoral vote had to be made in the House of Representatives, and the Democrats were in the majority there. Some Democrats, Northern and Southern, talked of resisting and, if necessary, even waging a new civil war. Eventually, the Southern Democrats yielded and allowed Hayes to be counted in as President.

Republican leaders, acting in Hayes' behalf, had persuaded the Southern Democrats by promising that Hayes would remove the last of the federal troops from the South, appoint a Southern Democrat to his cabinet, and give lesser government jobs to other Southerners. In addition, the Republicans in Congress would approve federal expenditures for railroad construction and river and harbor improvements in the South.

These promises were made informally and unofficially, in an understanding among politicians, yet the agreement was just as important as earlier sectional compromises (such as the Compromise of 1850) made by acts of Congress. Historians call this agreement the Compromise of 1877.

Democratic power was restored in the South

Soon after his inauguration, President Hayes ordered the last of the federal troops out of the South. Immediately, the Republican governments in South Carolina, Louisiana, and Florida collapsed. Hayes hoped to reëstablish Republican rule in the South by reorganizing the party so as to base it on well-to-do and conservative Southerners, especially former Whigs, instead of Negroes and carpetbaggers. But the Democrats, having gained control of all the Southern states, prevented opposition from arising for a long time. They set up a one-party system and thus created the Solid South.

Democrats looked upon their own return to power as the restoration of "white supremacy" and the redemption of the South from "Negro rule." They did not, however, immediately put an end to quite all Negro voting and officeholding. The complete disfranchisement of Negroes by state laws was not to come for twenty years or more (not until the 1890's and early 1900's).

After 1877, the Negroes had little political freedom and little economic independence. Very few of them had managed to acquire farms of their own. Most Negroes had become sharecroppers, as had many poor whites also. Sharecroppers lived and worked on land which the owner, perhaps a former planter, had subdivided into a number of

THE PRESIDENTS OF THE UNITED STATES

ANDREW JOHNSON
(1808-1875)
IN OFFICE: 1865-1869

ULYSSES SIMPSON GRANT
(1822-1885)
IN OFFICE: 1869-1877

RUTHERFORD BIRCHARD HAYES
(1822-1893)
IN OFFICE: 1877-1881

From Tennessee. Johnson was the only Southern senator to remain loyal to the Union during the Civil War. Although a Democrat, he was elected Vice President on the Union-Republican ticket in 1864 and became President upon Lincoln's assassination. His conflicts with Congress over Reconstruction led to an attempt to remove him from office; that attempt failed by only one vote (1868). During his term of office, Alaska was purchased from Russia (1867).

Republican from Illinois. Grant, a hero of the Civil War, had no political experience prior to his terms as President. During his administration, the Fifteenth Amendment, guaranteeing Negro suffrage, was added to the Constitution (1870); the Treaty of Washington was signed with Britain (1871); and civil service reform was begun. The reputation of his administration was severely damaged by the disclosure of corruption in the cabinet.

Republican from Ohio. The dispute over the election of 1876 was settled by a special commission appointed by Congress. Hayes was declared the President in return for the Republican promise to withdraw federal troops from the South and to provide money for Southern internal improvements. Hayes was an advocate of government reform; he was opposed to political patronage and established the merit system in several departments.

farms. The owner commonly furnished supplies and equipment as well as land. The tenants paid him not with cash but with a share of their crop. At the end of a season, their crop might not bring enough to pay all they owned him. They went deeper and deeper into debt and were forbidden to leave the land until their debts were paid. So far as Negro labor was concerned, the sharecropping system developed in the postwar years as a kind of substitute for slavery.

REVIEWING THE SECTION

1. How did the Democrats regain control of most of the Southern states after the readmission of these states to the Union? Why did Republican control of Louisiana, Florida, and South Carolina depend upon the outcome of the election of 1876?

2. How was the dispute over the outcome of the election of 1876 resolved?

3. What was the status of the Negro in Southern society after 1877?

When Lee surrendered to Grant, on April 9, 1865, Northerners celebrated this as the day of victory. Peace had yet to be made, however, and it remained to be seen whether the war aims of reunion and emancipation would be fully achieved. This was the basic question to be decided in the course of reconstruction.

President Lincoln favored a quick and easy peace, with a nucleus of white Southern unionists (at least ten per cent of the voting population in a state) taking the lead in reorganizing state governments. He was assassinated before any of the states had been readmitted to the Union under his "ten per cent plan." President Johnson also favored a prompt restoration of the Southern states, and he, too, intended to rely on white unionists. When new states had been formed under his supervision, however, these were found to be in the control of former Confederates whom Johnson had pardoned.

Republicans in Congress believed that Congress, not the President, should make reconstruction policy. Despite the Thirteenth Amendment, they feared that the former slaves would not be truly free if their fate were left to their recent masters. The Republicans also feared that if they accepted Johnson's plan, Southern and Northern Democrats would combine to get control of Congress and the presidency. Therefore, they refused to seat the representatives and senators who had been elected in the South. They also imposed further conditions on the Southern states—notably the Fourteenth Amendment, the Reconstruction acts, and the Fifteenth Amendment.

Under the congressional program of Radical Reconstruction, Negro and white Republicans temporarily governed the Southern states. The Republican governments accomplished a number of reforms but suffered from the taint of graft and corruption. The Democrats, often with the aid of the Ku Klux Klan and other terrorist groups, recaptured control of one state after another.

Meanwhile, President Grant had to deal with national problems of finance and diplomacy as well as with the sectional problem of reconstruction. His administration was marred by numerous scandals but achieved successes in foreign affairs under Secretary Fish (as the Johnson administration had done under Secretary Seward). At first, Grant tried to enforce Radical Reconstruction but, as time passed, he became less and less enthusiastic about it. During his administration, the Democrats made great gains, winning majorities in the congressional elections of 1874 and in the presidential election of 1876.

Disputing this presidential election, the Republicans finally obtained the victory for their candidate, Hayes. In return, Hayes made concessions to the Democrats. Most important, he removed all the federal troops from the South, and the last of the Republican regimes in the South then collapsed. Reconstruction was over.

Thus, twelve years after Lee's surrender, the issues of peacemaking were settled in the Compromise of 1877. As a result of that compromise, the Republicans retained the presidency, but the Democrats took over all the Southern states. Government policies favorable to Northern business—such as the protective tariff and the national banking system—remained intact. Southern Negroes were left somewhere between slavery and freedom.

The Compromise of 1877 has been called a combination of "Reunion and Reaction." It appeased recalcitrant Southerners and made them loyal to the Union again, but it did so at the expense of much of the idealism which the earlier antislavery movement and then the war itself had generated.

FOCUSING ON SPECIFICS

1. What constitutional justification did the President have for claiming the right to arrange peace terms with the Confederacy without the consent of Congress?

2. Following the war, what assistance did Negroes receive from various Northern groups?

3. How did the "black codes" control Negro labor?

4. How was the second congressional program

for reconstruction stronger than the first? What reasons did Johnson give for opposing the second plan?

5. What were the provisions of the third congressional program for reconstruction? How did the Southern states react to the conditions imposed by Congress under this plan?

6. Why did Liberal Republicans refuse to support Grant's bid for a second term?

7. What policies were promoted by the Grangers?

8. Why did Secretary of State Seward favor an active foreign policy?

9. Why did Southern Republicans lose more and more political influence after 1872?

10. Why did many people oppose the acquisition of Alaska?

11. How did the "Mississippi plan" help to reëstablish white supremacy?

12. How did the sharecropping system operate?

REVIEWING MAIN THEMES

1. In what ways was the dispute between the President and Congress over reconstruction policy affected by economic considerations? by interest in the welfare of the Negro? by different interpretations of the Constitution? by political considerations?

2. What conditions during 1865 and 1866 prevented a quick and easy reconstruction?

3. What were the differences between the first, second, third, and fourth congressional programs for reconstruction? How did these programs differ from Johnson's plan?

4. What problems plagued the administration of President Grant?

5. What was the status of the Southern Negro during the period of Johnson's reconstructed state governments? during the period of Republican government? after the Democrats came to power?

6. What significant diplomatic achievements were made during the Johnson and Grant administrations?

EVALUATING THE ISSUES

1. To what extent was the impeachment of Johnson a threat to the basic structure of our national government?

2. Do you feel that Radical Republican policies were *radical* in the sense of being extreme measures taken to meet postwar problems? Were their measures justified by existing conditions? Explain your answers.

3. Many critics of Radical Reconstruction have criticized the Republicans for giving Southern Negroes the vote so soon after they were emancipated. These critics claim that the Negroes were still too irresponsible and uneducated to be trusted with political power. Do you agree with this view? What standards, if any, should be set in a democracy for deciding who may vote? Explain your answers.

4. How effective was the work of the Freedmen's Bureau in helping to solve the problems of millions of emancipated people?

EXAMINING THE TIMES

1. What economic changes after 1850 gave the North a military advantage over the South?

2. What social, economic, and political features of the South in 1850 set it apart from the rest of the nation? To what extent had these features changed by 1877?

3. What major events between 1850 and 1860 led to increasing hostility between the North and South? What events led to hostility after the war?

4. Between 1850 and 1877, what changes took place in the lives of Southern Negroes? In what respects did conditions improve for them? In what respects did conditions become worse?

The City at Mid-Century

Between 1850 and 1877, the United States was becoming more and more industrialized. Immigrants and unemployed farm workers were pouring into the cities in search of jobs and the cities needed to house them.

At first, old buildings were converted into residences for workers. They deteriorated rapidly and became slums. To provide inexpensive housing for workers, a new type of building was created—the tenement. A tenement (which has come to mean slum) was originally a single unit in a multiple dwelling. Usually each tenement, or apartment, was approximately 18 x 20 feet, and consisted of 2 rooms. One room was used as a kitchen, parlor, pantry, and dining room; the other was the bedroom for the entire family. A tenement building, like the one pictured in 1865, was crowded; it often contained as many as 24 apartments on each floor, and consisted of 5 floors.

For those with more money, apartments called "French flats" were available. The apartment house, adapted from the French, consisted of a building "several stories high . . . with all the rooms required for a family grouped together on one-level . . . and these approached through one hall-door from the public staircase." The Pontalba buildings on Jackson Square in New Orleans (pictured in 1852), are often called the first apartment buildings in the United States. But, they are modifications of row houses with shops on the ground floor.

As changes were taking place in the residential areas, changes were also taking place in the business areas. Business was expanding and needed more floor space. Technological improvements made possible taller buildings, thus providing the needed space. One such improvement was the development in 1852 of the first practical elevator with safety devices. And, William L. Jenney made use of a skeleton framework of iron and steel which eliminated the need for massive walls to provide support for buildings. In constructing (c. 1883-1884) the Home Insurance Building in Chicago, Jenney used a wrought-iron frame up to the sixth floor and Bessemer steel beams above that level.

With the expansion of industry and the growth of population, cities became more crowded and ugly. City planners, therefore, began to think in terms of allotting space for parks, such as Central Park (pictured in 1863). To eliminate traffic noises, the designers crisscrossed the park with sunken roadways. Although small public promenades had long existed in some cities the creation of Central Park was a milestone in the history of the United States landscape.

New Orleans (Louisiana) from St. Patrick's Church, 1852, Lithograph by Smith Bros. & Company

View of Central Park in New York City, by John Bachman, 1863

The Chicago Building of the Home Insurance Company of New York, c. 1883-1884, Lithograph by L. Prang & Company

The Tenement Houses of New York, from sketches by Albert Berghaus, 1865

Merrimack Mills and Boardinghouses, Dutton Street, Lowell, Massachusetts, 1849

Industrial Towns

The early industrialists in the United States seemed to have felt a responsibility to their employees and to have taken pride in the appearance of their town. Mill towns such as Lowell, Massachusetts, usually consisted of four- or-five story mills (grouped together along the river bank), blocks of large and dignified boarding houses (like those pictured in 1849) for single workers (often New England farm girls), and rows of private dwellings for the married workers. Often, high on a hill above the town, were the elaborate homes of the mill owners. The buildings of the town were, according to one writer, "distinguished by gracious detail and pleasant proportions." After the 1850's, the New England farm girls were replaced by immigrants and many of the mill owners lost interest in the towns; the housing deteriorated. By the 1880's, only the mills (like those of the Appleton Company) seemed the same.

The company town such as Pullman, Illinois (now Chicago's far south side), founded by George M. Pullman, manufacturer of the railway "palace car," was another kind of planned industrial town. Pullman got the idea from the industrial cities of the Ruhr area (Germany), not the New England mill towns.

Pittsburgh and Allegheny (Pennsylvania), 1849

The Appleton Company, Lowell, Massachusetts, 1880

Pullman, the first town in the United States completely planned by an architect, was noted for its porticoed square, its landscaped parks, its library, its brick and stone buildings, and its uniformity. However, low wages and high rents led to a series of strikes and violence which gave Pullman and other company towns a bad name.

Not all industrial towns were planned; some grew quite haphazardly. Pittsburgh was originally a transportation town; one of the most important of the early routes to the West from the central Atlantic coast led from Philadelphia to Pittsburgh and then down the Ohio River. The building of the National Road made Pittsburgh less important as a transportation and supply center. However, the discovery of coal, iron, and oil nearby guaranteed the continued existence—and growth—of the city of Pittsburgh.

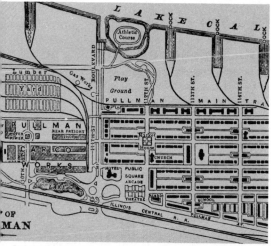

Plan of Pullman, Illinois, 1885

The Mining Frontier

Some of the most interesting of the booming industrial towns were the mining towns.

Pottsville (pictured c.1850), where anthracite coal was mined, is sometimes called the first American boom town. Lumber for its houses was nailed into frames at Philadelphia and transported by canal in prefabricated parts to Pottsville. Clapboard or rough wooden logs then were stretched between the frame timbers and a wooden town was created. The town became so wealthy, cast-iron fronts were added to many buildings.

The often short-lived, wild mining towns were found most often in the West. The rapid growth of these boom towns was made possible by the development of the "balloon frame," in 1833, which consisted of thin plates and studs, running the height of the building and held together by nails. Anyone with a hammer and nails (and a little help) could quickly put up a building.

When gold or some other valuable mineral was discovered, as it was in Last Chance Gulch (pictured in 1865), prospectors moved in, putting up tent cities near the ore diggings. Wooden

View of Pottsville, Pennsylvania, c. 1850

shelters and clapboard buildings were soon erected and, in order to give the appearance of height and stability to the town, false fronts were added. Mark Twain described such a mining town, Virginia City, Nevada, in his book *Roughing It.* "The sidewalks swarmed with people.... The streets themselves were just as crowded.... Joy sat on every countenance, and there was a glad, almost fierce intensity in every eye, that told of the money-getting schemes that were seething in every brain.... There were ... banks, hotels, theaters, 'hurdy gurdy' houses, wide-open gambling palaces, powwows, civic processions, streetfights, murders, inquests, riots, a whiskey mill every fifteen steps ... a dozen breweries, and half a dozen jails ... in full operation."

Not all of the towns on the mining frontier were thrown together. In San Francisco (pictured in 1852), houses like those in the East were shipped in completely made and ready to set in place. In their public buildings, the San Franciscans frequently followed the tradition of an earlier period—the classic lines of the public buildings in the national capital.

"When Helena (Montana) Was Last Chance Gulch," 1865

The City of San Francisco, California, 1852, Lithograph by F. Michelin

The Cattle Frontier

One of the most interesting, though short-lived, industries of the post-Civil War period, was the range-cattle industry. It began with a demand for beef in the East and a surplus of cattle in the West.

The enterprising Westerner built himself a home and a corral similar to the Colorado Cimarron Corral (pictured c.1898) for his livestock. For the cowboys, who were his hired hands, the rancher built a crude bunkhouse like the OW Bunkhouse on Hat Creek, Wyoming (pictured c.1885).

The rancher and his cowboys rounded up the cattle, fattened them on the open range, and then drove them to a railroad town such as Dodge City, Kansas, for shipment to the East.

The life of the cowboy was hard, lonely, and dangerous. On the ranch he lived in a bunkhouse which was usually constructed of logs and covered with dirt. When he went on the "long drive" he often spent several months "nursing" cows, sometimes fighting Indians and bandits, riding a horse most of each day and part of each night in hot, cold, wet, or dry weather, and he had no other company except the other cowboys.

Once the cattle were delivered, the cowboy was given his pay and time off before he had to return to the ranch and begin the process all over again. After several months on the trail, the cowboy usually went off on a spree. Since the cowboy was essentially a wanderer, his social life was often limited to the time he had at the end of the drive (and the winter months when there was little to do on the ranch) and centered in the hospitable saloons of the cow towns. In Dodge City (pictured in 1878), Front Street consisted of a general store, three dance halls, and six saloons, all of which catered to the needs of the cowboy. Many businessmen prospered as a result and, like the prosperous businessmen of the mining towns, added false fronts to their establishments.

Many of the cow towns had little or no law and order and, like Tascosa, Texas (pictured c.1908), became known as wild towns. In time, the cow towns were divided into two sections—the people of the town lived in one section, the cowboys played in the other. In Tascosa, the section containing the adobe dance halls, saloons, and gambling-houses was known as Hog Town.

Although the range-cattle industry did not last very long, it did live long enough to provide the basis for many of the romantic stories of the old West.

OW Bunkhouse on Hat Creek, Wyoming, 1885

Hitching Rack in Tascosa, Texas, 1908, photograph by Erwin E. Smith

Colorado Cimarron Corral, c. 1898, photograph by William H. Jackson

Front Street, Dodge City, Kansas, 1878

Ever since primitive times, man has been a tool-using animal, but he improved his tools only gradually until the beginning of the Modern period. Then he began to invent new and better tools more rapidly, and to devise new and better machines (it is often hard to make a clear distinction between a "tool" and a "machine," but a machine may be looked upon as a complicated tool, one having movable parts). The development of technology—that is, of the art of using tools and machines—speeded up remarkably in the eighteenth century and still more in the nineteenth. Today, it is going ahead faster than ever. Thus there has been a continuing and accelerating "industrial revolution" throughout Modern history.

Problems of an Industrial Nation

When historians refer to *the* Industrial Revolution, however, they have in mind a particular set of technological and economic changes that commenced in England in the early eighteenth century, spread to some other parts of the world in the eighteenth and nineteenth centuries, and had the most important consequences in the latter part of the nineteenth century. From the 1870's to about 1900, not only Britain but also the United States, Germany, France, Italy, and Japan became important industrial nations, and many other nations were industrialized at least to some extent. Americans, Germans, and people of other nationalities as well as Britons contributed various inventions to the development of industry.

Accompanying the so-called Industrial Revolution was an agricultural revolution. In both industry and agriculture, scientific knowledge was increasingly applied to methods of production, machines became more numerous and more complex, and to a greater and greater extent they were powered by steam engines instead of men, animals, windmills, or water wheels. *Steam* power was characteristic of the nineteenth-century Industrial Revolution at its height; other kinds of power—*electricity, petroleum,* and *atomic energy*—have characterized the continuing industrial revolution of the twentieth century.

The Industrial Revolution and the accompanying agricultural revolution had far-reaching consequences, which were especially noticeable during the 1870's, 1880's, and 1890's. These consequences varied in detail from country to country, but they were felt to a greater or lesser extent in all the countries undergoing technological change. The most obvious and most direct result was a tremendous *increase in the production of material goods.* By 1900, for example, the textile machines of Britain were turning out billions of yards of cotton cloth a year—many times as much as the people of that country could have made if all of them, men, women, and children, had been set to work with old-fashioned spinning wheels and hand looms.

The technological advances made possible a remarkable *population growth.* Britain, for example, had about three times as many people in 1900 as in 1815. The main reason for the increase, in Britain as in other countries, was not that families had more children but that more babies survived and people in general lived longer. The death rate declined both because more food became available and because progress was made in sanitation and in the cure of disease. Medical science made its greatest single advance when, near the middle of the nineteenth century, a French professor of chemistry, Louis Pasteur, proved that many diseases were caused by bacteria.

At the same time, more and more people were crowding together in cities. That is to say, there was a great increase in *urbanization.* As late as 1850, there were only two cities of over a million in Europe, London with 2.4 million and Paris with 1.2 million, and there were none in the United States. By 1900, London had more than 6.5 million inhabitants and Paris more than 2.6 million, and there were three other cities in Europe with more than a million apiece—Berlin, Leningrad, and Moscow. There were two in the United States, New York with nearly 3.5 million and Chicago with about 1.7 million. The new technology made large cities necessary, and it also made them possible. Large masses of labor were needed to operate the machines; the machines and hence the workers, together with shopkeepers to serve them, were concentrated in places where power and raw materials were readily available. Technology made large cities possible by producing steam locomotives and steamships which could bring food from a distance to feed the workingmen and shopkeepers.

The technological and economic changes gave rise to a new kind of *industrial conflict.* The owners of the industries—and the owners came to consist largely of corporations—were naturally interested in obtaining the greatest possible profit. The workers, just as naturally, wanted to get the highest possible wages. To increase profits, the employers insisted upon long working hours and low pay. To raise wages and improve working conditions, the employees formed unions, resorted to strikes and boycotts, and demanded that laws be passed to regulate industry. The workers acquired two social philosophies that encouraged and justified them in their struggle against the employers.

One of these philosophies was "scientific socialism," or *communism.* Its chief founder was Karl Marx, a German who came from a well-to-do family and received a good university education. With his friend Friedrich Engels, he issued the *Communist Manifesto* (1848), calling upon the workers of the world to unite and throw off their chains. Marx also wrote a long and learned work, *Das Kapital* ("Capital"), the first volume of which appeared in 1867, to elaborate upon his economic theory and his philosophy of history. According to his economic theory, all wealth was created by and belonged to labor, and the workers were being exploited when they failed to receive the whole value of what they produced—when

unit V
1877-1900

part of it went to the employer-capitalists in the form of profits. According to his philosophy of history, the class struggle was the main theme of all history, and this struggle was bound to eventuate in victory for the working class, the *proletariat*. Marx's philosophy, with its prediction of a future working-class heaven on earth, served almost as a religion for many of his followers.

Another revolutionary doctrine was *anarchism,* as put forth by the Frenchman Pierre Joseph Proudhon. In his book *What Is Property?* (1840), Proudhon said, "Property is theft," yet government existed to protect it. Government, he concluded, was the worst of evils, and men would never be truly free and happy until it was abolished. Proudhon and some of his followers were opposed to the use of force; indeed, that was why they hated government, which depended on force. But other followers made use of violence. Between 1881 and 1901, anarchists assassinated a tsar of Russia, a president of France, an empress of Austria, and a President of the United States (William McKinley).

In Europe, the working class gained the support of many people who were not Communists or anarchists but who sympathized with the poor and supported legislation for improving conditions of life and work. The capitalists had the support of many people who were not themselves capitalists but who feared communism and anarchism. In the United States, similarly, politics involved reformers and antireformers and was by no means simply a contest between workers and capitalists. Though this contest was an important theme, there were also other conflicts, such as the conflict between farmers and businessmen and the one be-

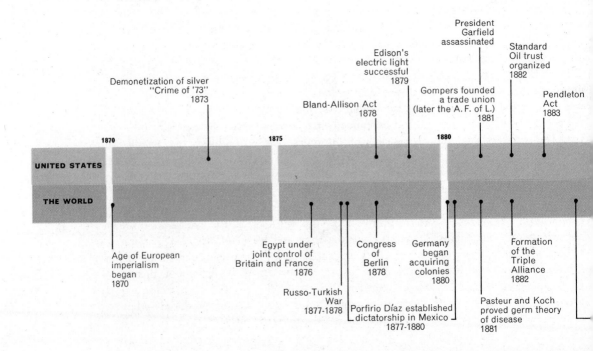

tween Negroes and whites. Communism and anarchism made far less headway in the United States than in Europe. Most American workers disliked to think of themselves as permanent members of a working class. They hoped that they or their children could, individually, improve their economic and social standing.

Another consequence of the Industrial Revolution was *imperialism,* a new movement for the acquisition of colonies. In earlier times, colonies had been desired mainly for purposes of trade. In the late nineteenth century, the industrialized nations began to seek colonies not only as markets for surplus goods but also as sources of raw materials and as places for the investment of excess funds. The new industrial system produced more goods than could be profitably sold in Europe, demanded more raw materials than could be obtained there, and yielded more profits than could be advantageously reinvested there. Hence European businessmen looked for economic opportunities in the "backward countries" of Africa, Asia, and Latin America. These businessmen called upon their own governments to extend control over such countries in order to protect the economic interests that the businessmen acquired there. The governments themselves were eager to get additional territory for military or naval bases, and many of the people, even many of the working class, supported national expansion for reasons of patriotism. Between the 1870's and 1900, Great Britain enlarged her empire by one third, and France and Germany built up their empires from practically nothing to extensive overseas possessions. The United States joined the scramble for colonies and, by 1900, had acquired a far-flung empire of its own.

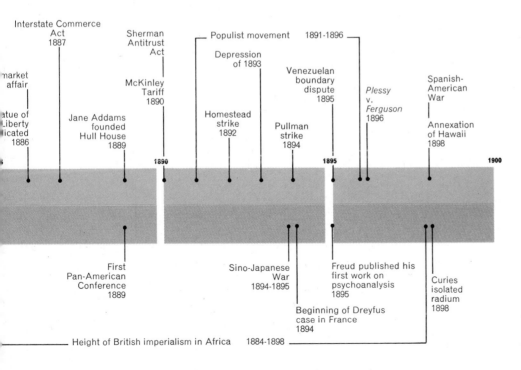

CHAPTER **15** 1865-1900

The Rise of Industry

The most remarkable development in United States history during the period 1865-1900 was the tremendous increase in the output of mills and factories. Factories had existed in this country since the 1790's, and industrial production had advanced fairly steadily up to the time of the Civil War. After the war, however, production increased much more rapidly than ever before. By 1900, the United States had become the greatest manufacturing nation in the world.

The Civil War stimulated the growth of certain industries, such as meat-packing, flour-milling, and the manufacturing of shoes and cloth. But the war was not responsible for the development of the oil and steel industries, and it temporarily set back some occupations, such as railroad and building construction. In short, the remarkable postwar industrial growth was not due primarily to the war itself.

The rapid industrial development resulted from a number of factors. One of these was the technological skill and inventiveness of Americans. A rough measure of inventiveness is given by the United States Patent Office records. In all the years before 1860, only 36,000 patents had been granted. Then, in the thirty years from 1860 to 1890, approximately 440,000 were issued.

A second factor was business leadership. There happened to be, in the United States, an unusually large number of "captains of industry" with outstanding ability to organize and direct extensive and complicated business operations. A few of these men, among them Andrew Carnegie, came from abroad. Most of them, like John D. Rockefeller, were native-born Americans.

A third factor was a large and growing labor force. A majority of workers in the unskilled and low-paying industrial jobs were immigrants. Without them, there would not have been nearly enough cheap labor for such a rapid development of heavy industries like the steel industry.

In addition, the physical resources of the country contributed to its industrial growth. Vast stores of natural resources—oil, coal, iron ore, and other minerals, as well as timber and fertile soils—were available within the United States. Few of the raw materials needed for industry had to be imported.

Government policies also favored industrial development. Much of the land originally owned by the federal government was rich in natural resources, and vast tracts of these valuable lands were given away to businessmen and corporations. High tariffs protected manufacturers from foreign competition; government loans and land grants encouraged the building of railroads; and the national banking system provided a uniform and dependable currency (the national banknotes). At the same time, neither the federal government nor the state governments interfered with business activities by seriously attempting to regulate them.

Finally, the United States constituted the kind of mass market that mass production requires. The population more than doubled between 1860 and 1900, growing from less than 32 million to more than 75 million. These people, as consumers, bought the manufactured goods or paid for the use of the facilities (such as the railroad lines) which the rising industries turned out. Trade flowed freely from one part of the country to another, with practically no restrictions by the various states. The construction of new railroads, creating a nation-wide rail network, made it possible to move finished products as well as raw materials rapidly from seller to buyer.

All these factors—technological skill, business leadership, labor supply, natural resources, governmental policies, mass market—contributed to the rapid progress of the United States in industrial productivity. Not that the people in the United States had an advantage over Europeans in all respects. In basic technological knowledge, for example, Americans borrowed from abroad far more than they originated at home. The kind of industrial transformation going on in this country was also going on in Britain—the most advanced industrial nation in the world—and in Germany, France, and Japan. The United States attained the lead in industrial production because of its *combination* of advantages.

TRANSPORT AND COMMUNICATION IMPROVED

Rapid transportation and communication made possible the rise of large-scale industry. Big business in the late nineteenth century depended upon the extension and improvement of railroad service and the development of the typewriter and the telephone. As a means of transportation, the railroads continued to be supplemented by waterways such as the Great Lakes, the Mississippi and other rivers, and the Erie Canal. To a lesser extent, the railroads were supplemented by highways, but highway maintenance and construction lagged until a movement for good roads was begun.

By 1860, the railroads themselves had already become the biggest of all businesses. During the Civil War railroads prospered, but their roadbeds, locomotives, and cars were allowed to deteriorate, especially in the South. After the war the railroads began to rebuild old lines, construct new ones, add to their equipment, and adopt many new devices.

A network of railroads covered the country

The most dramatic railroad construction was in the West. The first of the transcontinental lines, begun during the Civil War, was completed in 1869. One company, the Union Pacific, laid tracks westward from Omaha, and another, the Central Pacific, eastward from Sacramento. The work was difficult because of the tremendous distances and the deserts and mountains to be crossed. Men with picks and shovels and horse-drawn scrapers prepared the roadbed; other crews laid the rails by hand, while armed guards watched out for hostile Indians. Immigrants were hired to do most of the heavy labor on the railroads.

Later other rail lines were extended to the west coast—the Southern Pacific, the Northern Pacific, the Great Northern, and the Atchison, Topeka, and Santa Fe. All except the Great Northern were built with government aid. The federal government followed a generous policy toward these and other railroads; it provided millions of dollars in loans and millions of acres in land grants. The grants consisted of alternate one-mile-square sections on both sides of the right-of-way. (The government retained every other section, and thus the granted and ungranted lands formed a checkerboard pattern.) The government benefited from its generous policy because the value of the land it kept was increased by the construction of the railroads, and because the railroads receiving the grants were required to carry mail, troops, and military supplies for less than the regular rates. State governments also encouraged railroad construction by buying railroad stocks and bonds and by giving additional grants of land. Farmers and businessmen were eager to get rail transportation, but without generous public help, most of the railroads in thinly settled areas would not have been built until much later.

The Great Northern, connecting Lake Superior with Puget Sound, was built by James J. Hill, one of the greatest of the railroad builders. Hill aimed to promote trade with the Far East and settlement on the Great Plains as well as to make money for himself. With no federal loans or lands, he financed the construction as he went along. As each stretch of track was opened for business, he gave free transportation to people taking up farms along the route, and he sold them tools and machinery on easy credit. As farms developed, he made enough from the shipment of crops to pay for building his railroad farther to the west.

In the East the most important railroads were the New York Central, the Pennsylvania, the Erie, and the Baltimore & Ohio. By 1874, each of these had incorporated a number of relatively short lines and from them had created a large system reaching from New York City, or its vicinity, to Chicago. The New York Central was developed by Cornelius Vanderbilt. Once a ferryboat captain and thereafter known as "Commodore," Vanderbilt had made a fortune from the shipping business and from speculating on the stock market. He sometimes defied both the law and public opinion. Yet he had the imagination and the ability to project and to carry out his great plan for connecting New York and Chicago by a "water-level route" up the Hudson and Mohawk valleys and then west along the shore of Lake Erie.

In the South the first task of the railroads after the Civil War was to repair the war damage. Then new lines were constructed; by 1890, the South

had six times as much trackage as in 1865. Finally, through consolidations, large systems were created —the Southern Railway, from Washington to New Orleans; the Atlantic Coast Line, from Richmond, Virginia, to Jacksonville, Florida; and the Illinois Central, from Chicago by way of Cairo, Illinois, to New Orleans and Savannah, Georgia. Most of these railroads were constructed with money from private investors, many of whom were British.

Railroad service was improved

So many railroads were built that, especially in times of depression after the panics of 1873 and 1893, there was not enough freight and passenger traffic to go around. Some investors temporarily received little or no return on their investment.

To get business, competing lines often cut their rates drastically. Then they would try to end the "rate wars" by agreements to stop the competition, put all their earnings into a common "pool," and divide them up. Where no competing line existed, a railroad usually charged "all that the traffic would bear." Thus a railroad would charge more for a short haul between two points served by only the one line than for a long haul between two points served also by a competing line. Though rates were different in different places, and though they fluctuated from one time to another, the average charge for a ton of freight fell from two cents a mile in 1860 to three quarters of a cent a mile in 1900.

The railroads were able to carry freight and passengers more and more economically and rapidly because of technological improvements. Steel rails replaced iron ones, and a uniform gauge (4 feet, 8½ inches) was adopted, so that cars could be interchanged between one line and any other. Faster and more powerful coal-burning steam locomotives were introduced. High speeds were relatively safe because of the air brake, which George Westinghouse invented in 1868, and the block-signal system (with lights along the tracks to warn of a train in the "block," or section of the

Major Railroads in Operation, 1890

Principal railroads

Other important railroads

PREPARED BY
UNIVERSAL MAP, INC.

track, ahead), which was brought over from Britain in 1874. Nevertheless, a number of terrible train wrecks occurred and accidents at road-crossings were common.

As railroad service became faster and more frequent, railroads had difficulty in making out their schedules because of confusing variations in local time. Each locality followed its own "sun time," with noon corresponding to the zenith of the sun. The railroads began to base their schedules on "railroad time," but this added to the confusion, for it differed from sun time, and it varied from one railroad to another, even in the same area.

Finally, in 1883, the railroad owners of the United States and Canada agreed upon an arrangement for the standardization of time. They divided the continent into standard time zones running north and south. Within each zone all railroad clocks were set alike; between each zone and the

one to the east or west of it there was a time difference of one hour. Soon local communities and the states adopted standard time. Later, the zones in the United States and Canada were revised and twenty-four time zones were designated for the world. Eventually, almost all nations adopted standard time.

Other forms of transportation were improved

As the railroad network spread, transportation by inland waterways continued but, on the whole, became relatively less important than it had been. An exception was the Great Lakes, on which traffic steadily increased. Year after year the federal government spent millions to improve lake channels and harbors. In 1881, it took over the Soo Canal (St. Marys Ship Canal) which the state of Michigan had built with federal aid (1855) near the town of Sault Ste. Marie to connect Lake Superior and Lake Huron. In 1894, a new set of locks was completed. During the months from April to November, when the canal was open, it was one of the busiest waterways in the entire world.

For many years transportation by highways declined, except for local hauling to and from the nearest rail depot. Highways fell into disrepair until, by the 1890's, they were commonly worse than they had been a hundred years earlier. Finally a "good roads" movement began, stimulated to a large extent by a new invention, the bicycle.

The bicycle of the 1880's, an English invention, had a large hard-rubber-tired wire wheel in front and a tiny one behind. The rider, sitting high over the front wheel, ran the risk of "taking a header" whenever he hit a stone in the road. By 1890, this high-wheeler was being replaced by the "safety bicycle" with low wheels of equal size, pneumatic tires, and a chain-and-sprocket drive. Almost anyone could ride the safety bicycle, and during the 1890's, millions of Americans did so.

The bicycle led to the improvement of roads. A national organization of cyclists, the League of American Wheelmen, kept up a constant propaganda and lobbying activity. By 1900, more than half of the states had responded by passing laws for better highway construction and maintenance.

By bringing about road improvements, the bicycle helped to prepare for the coming of the automobile, which was beginning to appear in experimental forms. The bicycle also helped to prepare the way in other respects. Its components— wire wheels, pneumatic tires, tubular steel, chain-and-sprocket drive—were used in the construction of the first automobiles. Most of the early automobile builders, such as Henry Ford, had once been bicycle repairmen.

Messages were delivered faster

As railroads were extended, so was the postal service. Before the Civil War, a person had to pick up his own mail at the local post office. In 1863,

Congress authorized free delivery of mail, and by 1871, mail was being delivered in fifty-one cities. Gradually, mailmen appeared in smaller and smaller towns, and after 1896, with the beginning of rural free delivery, carriers even made the rounds of farm homes. Meanwhile, the cost of postage was reduced.

Two inventions that further helped to facilitate communication were the typewriter and the telephone. The first practical writing machine was developed by Christopher L. Sholes and his associates in Milwaukee between 1867 and 1872. In 1874, they arranged for the well-known gunmakers E. Remington & Sons to manufacture a number of typewriters.

The typewriter evenutally made its way into practically every business office. It created new and respectable jobs for women, and it changed the office atmosphere, as ladylike typists took the place of cigar-smoking and tobacco-chewing penmen and clerks. Without the record keeping and rapid correspondence which the typewriter made possible, neither business nor government could have grown to such a scale as they ulitmately did.

Nor could business and government have grown as they did without the convenience of the telephone. This was chiefly the work of Alexander Graham Bell, a Scottish-born teacher of the deaf in Boston. Bell got his idea for the telephone by experimenting with a dead man's ear. He patented his invention in 1876 and exhibited it that year at the first world's fair in the United States, the Centennial Exposition in Philadelphia.

Within a few years telephone exchanges were in operation in nearly all cities in the United States with more than 10,000 population. By 1889, it was possible to call long distance from Boston to Washington, D.C., or to Buffalo, New York, and by 1892, all the way to Chicago. Before the end of the century, telephone wires had been extended to most small towns and even to a few farms.

REVIEWING THE SECTION

1. How was the transportation network im-

proved between 1865 and 1900? How was the construction of transportation facilities financed?

2. How was railroad service improved after the Civil War?

3. Between 1865 and 1900, what improvements were made in travel by water? by land?

4. In what ways was communication improved between 1865 and 1900?

NEW INDUSTRIES GREW UP

After the Civil War, a number of old and familiar industries were so transformed that they seemed almost like new ones. They now were carried on in larger plants, with a greater division of labor and with more complicated machinery. And they were more highly concentrated in one part of the country than another. Outstanding examples are meat-packing and flour-milling.

Chicago became the great meat-packing center. It was well located in relation to the cattle-growing areas of the Great Plains and the hog-raising areas of the Middle West, and it had railroad connections which made it easy to bring in livestock. The refrigerator car, cooled by artificial ice, made it feasible to ship fresh meat to more distant markets than before. Large-scale slaughtering by increasingly efficient methods made it possible to undersell most local slaughterhouses. In the Chicago slaughterhouses an animal carcass was moved along on an overhead conveyor past a line of workers, each of whom cut off a part. This "disassembly line" provided the inspiration for the assembly line which was later to be used in the manufacture of automobiles and other products.

Minneapolis became the flour-milling center. It was near the largest wheat-growing area, which, by that time, was in the upper Mississippi Valley. The Minneapolis millers introduced, from Hungary, iron rollers which turned out a finer and whiter flour than did old-fashioned millstones. Neither small local mills nor local slaughterhouses disappeared all at once, but a larger and larger proportion of the nation's flour, like its meat,

came from the big processors.

While old industries were being transformed, some entirely new ones grew up. Three of the most important were those concerned with oil, steel, and electric power.

The oil industry became big business

The people in western Pennsylvania, and in other areas as well, had known of the existence of petroleum or "rock oil" for years. They had noticed an oily film on the surface of the springs and streams and had wondered what could be done with it. A few enterprising men bottled it and sold it as medicine. After analyzing a sample, a Yale professor reported (1855) that, when refined, it could be used for illumination and lubrication. In 1859, Edwin L. Drake put down, near Titusville, Pennsylvania, the first oil well, and though observers scoffed at the well as "Drake's folly," it soon was yielding five hundred barrels of oil a month.

An oil boom followed in western Pennsylvania and later in the adjoining areas of Ohio and West Virginia. This was much like a gold rush, with fortune seekers flocking to the petroleum country. Year after year production increased. In the 1870's, the annual output came to twenty million barrels, and petroleum and petroleum products took fourth place among the nation's exports.

From the beginning, the oilmen faced difficulties in transporting the petroleum to the refineries. Boats or rafts carried it in barrels down Oil Creek and the Allegheny River, or wagons hauled it over hilly and muddy roads. But it was being pumped out of the ground faster than it could be taken away. Eventually, railroads were extended to the oil fields, and the oil was carried at first in huge wooden casks set on flat cars and later in modern-type iron tank cars. Refineries, meanwhile, had sprung up throughout the oil region, especially in Pittsburgh and Cleveland.

In the early days it did not take much money to go into the oil business. A number of men who became known as "coal oil Johnnies," starting with little capital, got rich almost overnight. As production increased, however, it became harder to make a profit. Producers and refiners competed madly, and prices fluctuated wildly, sometimes falling below the costs of production. Finally a business organizer brought order out of the chaos.

That man was John D. Rockefeller. Born on a modest New York farm, Rockefeller went to Cleveland and, as a youth of nineteen, became a partner in a company which made huge profits by selling produce to the government during the Civil War. At the end of the war he went into the oil-refining business in Cleveland. He proceeded to buy out other refineries. In 1870, he formed the Standard Oil Company of Ohio.

The Standard Oil Company continued to reduce the number of competitors by driving them out of business. It made arrangements with railroads for secret rebates on the charges for the oil it shipped. It engaged in price wars, and when these succeeded in forcing competitors to close down or sell out, it raised its prices again. It hired a large staff of salesmen who used high-pressure selling techniques. By the 1880's Rockefeller's company so dominated the oil industry that it could fix prices.

Even with price fixing, however, prices were low enough to encourage the widespread use of petroleum products. Kerosene took the place of whale oil, camphor, and other fuels for lanterns and lamps. Petroleum oil and grease took the place of animal fats for lubricating wagons, locomotives and cars, and industrial machines. Without petroleum, the new age of machinery could never have progressed as it did.

New processing methods stimulated the steel industry

Nor could the new age of machinery have progressed without steel. In earlier times the production of steel required the laborious processing of iron, and steel was so expensive that it was used only for such things as swords, knives, and high-grade tools. After the Civil War the production

increased and the price fell so much that steel could also be used in tremendous quantities for rails, locomotives, and other heavy machines.

This resulted from the introduction of new steel-making methods which had been invented in Europe. One of these was known as the Bessemer process, in which air was blown through molten pig iron to burn out the carbon and other impurities and thus convert it into steel. In another method, the "open-hearth" process, the pig iron was heated by gas or oil flames passing over it. The impurities floated to the top and were drawn off.

Iron ore for the new steel furnaces came primarily from the mines of the Lake Superior region. In the 1840's, rich iron deposits had been discovered in the upper peninsula of Michigan. Later, other deposits began to be exploited farther west, in Wisconsin and Minnesota. By the 1890's, the Mesabi Range in Minnesota was becoming the greatest ore-producing region in the world. Meanwhile, other deposits were found in the vicinity of Birmingham, Alabama.

The ironworks of the prewar period had been rather small and had been scattered throughout the country, near local sources of ore as well as wood, which was needed to produce the charcoal used in the earlier smelting process. The new steel mills were vastly larger and were concentrated in various places, sometimes at a considerable distance from the iron ore and the coal, which now was used instead of charcoal. The Pittsburgh area was the greatest steel center, but other centers arose along Lake Erie and Lake Michigan. All of these places had easy access to iron ore brought by lake steamers through the Soo Canal and to coal brought by railroad cars from the coal fields of Pennsylvania, West Virginia, and the Middle West.

The greatest organizer of the steel industry was Andrew Carnegie. Beginning as a poor immigrant boy from Scotland, Carnegie worked his way up from the position of bobbin boy in a Pennsylvania cotton mill to that of a partner in the management of the Pennsylvania Railroad. In 1873, he opened his first steel mill, near Pittsburgh. Like

Rockefeller in the oil business, Carnegie obtained railroad rebates, carried on price wars, and bought out competitors. He also set out to control all stages of steel manufacture. His company leased a part of the Mesabi Range, bought railroads and coal mines, and operated its own ore boats on the Great Lakes. Soon the Carnegie companies dominated the steel industry.

The electric-power industry developed

Batteries which produced electric current by chemical action had been in use since about 1800. Though the current was rather weak, such batteries had sufficient power to operate the telegraph and the telephone. Meanwhile, a number of European scientists showed the theoretical possibility of creating a much more powerful current by mechanical means, that is, by generators or dynamos. In the late 1800's, the theory began to be put into practice by a number of inventors.

One of them was Thomas Alva Edison, who was born in the small town of Milan, Ohio. Edison lost his hearing when he was still a young man. He did not mind his deafness, for it allowed him to concentrate all the more on the things that interested him, and these included all kinds of mechanical and electrical problems. He learned to get along with very little sleep—a few cat naps during the day or night. "Genius," he once said, "is one per cent inspiration and ninety-nine per cent perspiration." In 1876, he set up a laboratory at Menlo Park, New Jersey, which soon became famous.

Here Edison originated and worked out improvements upon many existing devices, such as the telegraph, the incandescent light, the electric motor, and the generator. He hit upon his most original production, the phonograph (1877), while trying to find a way to record telegraph messages. He devised a method for sending a number of messages at once over the same telegraph wire. After two years of experimenting with different materials for a filament—searching for something that would glow brightly without burning out

when a current passed through it—he succeeded (1879) in making the first practical electric light for indoor use. Then (1882), in New York City, he opened a steam-operated electric-power plant, which distributed current to 400 of his newly invented lamps in 59 neighboring buildings.

Edison's kind of power plant, however, was not widely used. It produced only direct current, and this could be distributed no farther than a mile or two. Alternating current, on the other hand, could be sent long distances. In 1886, George Westinghouse bought the French patents for an alternating-current generator and began to promote its use.

While many steam-powered or water-powered plants were built on Edison's plan, a still larger number were built on the one designed by Westinghouse, and these eventually became the standard. The Westinghouse Company won the contract for lighting the Columbian World Exposition of 1893 in Chicago and made the fairgrounds a fairyland at night by flooding the all-white buildings with the light from 5000 arc lamps and 100,000 incandescent bulbs. That same year the Westinghouse Company got the contract for building dynamos at Niagara Falls in the world's greatest hydroelectric development up to that time.

By the end of the century, electricity was lighting many homes and factories and was beginning to power the wheels of industry.

REVIEWING THE SECTION

1. Describe the development of the petroleum industry in the nineteenth century.

2. What new methods of steel production stimulated the steel industry?

3. What contributions did Thomas Edison and George Westinghouse make to the development of the electric-power industry?

BUSINESS GREW BIGGER AND BIGGER

While the total output of industry in the United States was increasing, the number of individual plants was decreasing. Thus, by 1890, there were about two thirds as many iron and steel mills as there had been in 1880, fewer than one half as many factories making farm implements, and only one fourth as many manufacturing leather goods. The big establishments were producing a larger and larger share of the total output. By 1900, a small fraction of the total number of plants—about one fiftieth of them—accounted for almost half of all the manufactured goods.

As plants grew fewer and on the average larger, so did the business firms that operated them. Before the Civil War, the typical firm had been the individual proprietorship or the partnership, though a number of corporations already existed. After the war, corporations became larger and more numerous, and some were combined in one way or another so as to create even larger organizations. These amounted to monopolies or near monopolies in various fields.

For the owners of a company, bigness had certain advantages. It enabled the company to lower its costs through mass purchasing and mass production. At the same time, if bigness meant the weakening or elimination of competitors, as it often did, it enabled the company to maintain or even to raise prices. With low manufacturing costs and high selling prices, the organization large enough to dominate a particular industry enjoyed greater profits than a small firm competing fiercely with a number of other small firms.

For the public as a whole, big business was not necessarily so advantageous. To the extent that low costs led to low prices, as happened when enough competition remained, the consumer benefited. This happened less often than it should have, according to the contemporary critics of big business.

Trusts were organized

There were several ways of forming larger and larger business units. One was the *merger,* two or more corporations combining to form a single corporation. Another was the *pool,* an agreement by which several companies coöperated and acted pretty much like one organization, dividing the market and putting their profits into a common fund. Usually the pooling agreements did not last long, for they were hard to enforce.

A third form of combination was the *trust.* In a trust, the stockholders (that is, the owners) of two or more companies gave their shares of stock to a group of trustees to hold for them. In return for the stock, the owners received "trust certificates" which entitled them to their usual dividends. The trustees, however, exercised the voting rights of the stock. Controlling several companies in this way, the trustees could operate them like a single company.

A fourth kind of organization was the *holding company,* a corporation that owned the stock of other corporations. Obviously, it could control the others if it owned more than half of the stock in each. Often it could do so even if it owned less than half, for the rest of the shares might be divided among numerous, widely scattered stockholders, who could not easily coöperate against the holding company.

A fifth means of combining was the *interlocking directorate.* This came into being whenever the same group of men held office as directors in two or more companies. The companies might be separately owned and legally independent; nevertheless, the directors could operate them as if the companies were combined.

No matter which of these forms of consolidation was used—whether the trust or some other form— the general public referred to any large and monopolistic or semimonopolistic business organization as a trust.

This term came into use when, in 1879, Rockefeller created the Standard Oil Trust to bring together refining companies in a number of states. The new organization owned or controlled nearly ninety per cent of the refining business in the entire country. By the 1890's, trusts of one kind or another dominated many industries in addition to oil refining. The Carnegie Steel Company (reor-

BUSINESS ACTIVITY 1850-1898

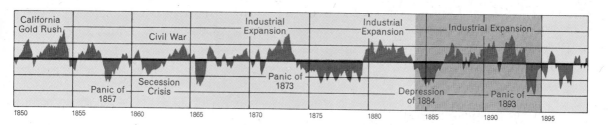

Panics and depressions often result from overspeculation in a period of great economic activity. Between 1877 and 1898, business activity fluctuated with frequency. It was a time of extensive railroad construction, with rail mileage far exceeding the needs of the western population of that day. The development of many other important industries, as well, stimulated economic growth. Overproduction in heavy industry was responsible for much economic instability. Overspeculation and overinvestment in plants and equipment led to recurring panics and depressions. In spite of the economic instability, industrialization proceeded rapidly, due in part to new inventions and technological improvements, such as the Bessemer process of steel manufacture. By 1890, the United States led the world in volume of industrial production, surpassing even Britain.

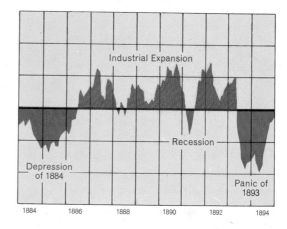

ganized in 1892) produced about one fourth of the nation's steel. Other companies or combinations practically monopolized meat-packing, sugar-refining, tobacco-processing, and the manufacture of products such as salt, whiskey, matches, wire, nails, and bicycles.

Financiers took control of business

Business leaders like Rockefeller and Carnegie, who had worked their way to the top in their industries, gained wealth and power through skill in organizing them. Such men are known as "industrial capitalists." In the 1890's, a different group of men began to get control of many businesses. These men were investment bankers who provided the money needed to expand business operations and to make large companies still larger. Such bankers are known as "finance capitalists." The greatest of the finance capitalists was J.

Pierpont Morgan. Morgan was not a self-made man like Rockefeller or Carnegie. Morgan was raised with all the advantages of wealth; he had traveled widely and had been educated at the University of Göttingen in Germany. From the 1870's, when he set up his banking firm on Wall Street, Morgan led in the financing of corporations for more than thirty years.

Morgan and other investment bankers dealt in corporation stocks and bonds. When a corporation needed money for expansion, it issued new securities and asked the investment bankers to sell them. The reputation of the bankers depended on the continuing value of the securities they sold, so they often required that their representatives be put on the corporation's board of directors. The bankers' representatives could then see to it that the corporation made a profit and paid dividends to stockholders. Thus the bankers came to control corporations through interlocking directorates.

Morgan achieved his biggest feat of consolidation when, in 1901, he created the United States Steel Corporation. He bought the Carnegie Steel Company and merged it with ten other steel companies. The face value of the new stock he issued amounted to more than $1 billion, so United States Steel became known as the first "billion-dollar corporation." Actually, the combined value of all the merged companies came to less than $700 million. The difference, more than $300 million, represented *watered stock,* stock issued in excess of the real worth of the corporation. For his services in bringing about the merger, Morgan charged a fee of $75 million.

By the end of the century, the age of *industrial capitalism,* with the industrialists controlling their own businesses, was coming to an end. The age of *finance capitalism,* or banker control, had begun.

Big business was defended and criticized

In 1892, a survey indicated that slightly more than four thousand millionaires lived in the United States. Except for a few who had inherited fortunes, these men had made their money since the Civil War, and the great majority had made it in business.

Most of the men who got rich were understandably satisfied with the economic system which had made it possible for them to do so. They had earned their money by being shrewd, industrious, and thrifty. They believed that God rewarded such virtues, and if most people were less well off, this was simply because most people were unintelligent, lazy, and wasteful.

Many of the wealthy believed in the philosophy of Social Darwinism. According to the English scientist Charles Darwin, living things—plants and animals—had evolved through a process of natural selection. In nature, there was a constant struggle for existence, and only the "fittest" survived. According to the Social Darwinists, the same was true in the business world.

Some of the wealthy men believed that their money had been given them by God to use in helping other people who were less able and less fortunate. In his book *The Gospel of Wealth* (1901) Carnegie said the man of wealth was really the mere trustee and agent for his poorer brethren, bringing to their service his superior wisdom, experience, and ability to administer, doing for them better than they would or could do for themselves.

Carnegie gave away many millions of dollars, principally to establish public libraries. Rockefeller and others also devoted part of their fortunes to philanthropy.

Most of the people in the United States admired and envied the very rich but resented the practices of big business. *Trust* became a word with bad connotations. Books denouncing the economic system were widely read.

Henry George's *Progress and Poverty* (1879) was reprinted again and again, and became one of the ten best-selling books ever published in the United States. George, an economist and reformer, noticed that poverty was common despite the progress of the times. He thought that monopolies, especially monopolies of land, were to blame for the unequal distribution of wealth. He proposed to eliminate both monopoly and poverty by means of the "single tax." This was to be a tax on the increase in land values resulting not from the owner's improvements but from society's development. It was to be high enough to take away entirely the unearned increment of land value. Supposedly, it would make possible the repeal of all other taxes. Many of George's readers joined single-tax societies and, in 1886, his followers almost succeeded in electing him mayor of New York.

Another popular book was Edward Bellamy's *Looking Backward* (1888). In this novel a young man goes to sleep in 1887 and wakes up in the year 2000. He finds no one poor and everyone happy. The reason, he discovers, is that all trusts have at last given way to one big trust, which the people themselves own and operate. Soon after

Bellamy's book had appeared, more than a hundred "Nationalist Clubs" were advocating the Bellamy brand of socialism.

REVIEWING THE SECTION

1. What new methods of business combination made it possible for many industries to be dominated by monopolies or semimonopolies?

2. How did financiers, such as J. P. Morgan, gain control of many business enterprises?

3. What were the major principles of Social Darwinism? How did Henry George and Edward Bellamy propose to eliminate poverty?

LABOR BOTH GAINED AND LOST

The rise of industry made more goods available and it created additional jobs. Thus, in the long run, it benefited the people both as consumers and as wage earners. For the time being, however, it brought hardships as well as opportunities to a great many industrial workers, who, by 1890, were almost as numerous as farmers and farm laborers.

During the period from 1865 to 1900, the wages of unskilled, nonfarm workers averaged no more than a dollar and a half a day. Over the years the cost of living fell somewhat, so the "real wages" or purchasing power of those men who were steadily employed rose proportionately, even though money wages remained about the same. Millions were unemployed from time to time, however, especially during the long depressions beginning in 1873 and 1893. The working day ranged from ten to twelve hours, and there were six days in the working week. Conditions of labor were often disagreeable and dangerous. There were, as yet, practically no laws to require safe conditions or to provide compensation in case of injury or death on the job.

In earlier times, when most industrial workers were skilled artisans, they had enjoyed a good deal of independence. Their employer needed them as much as they needed him, for skilled labor was scarce, and since the employer usually ran his business by himself, they could bargain with him on nearly equal terms. In the new industrial era, however, all but a few of the workers in mines and mills were unskilled, and the employer, usually a big and impersonal corporation, could fire any one of them at will and hire another man in his place. So most workers no longer had a feeling of importance and independence.

If the workers were going to raise wages, shorten hours, improve working conditions, and restore their sense of pride and importance, they would have to bargain collectively with their employers. They would have to organize and act together.

This would be very hard for them. It would require a strong sense of common interest, but most people in the United States were individualistic. They did not like to think of themselves and their children as permanently belonging to a working class. They hoped to rise above the rest. They shared the dream of personal success that formed the plot of dozens of widely read Horatio Alger novels, with titles such as *Luck and Pluck* and *From Rags to Riches,* which told of poor boys who became wealthy businessmen. Had not the dream come true for men like Rockefeller and Carnegie?

Moreover, most native-born workers found it hard to coöperate with immigrants, who were arriving in larger numbers than ever before. The newcomers included not only the familiar British, Germans, and Scandinavians but also groups hitherto strange to the United States, such as Slavs, Italians, and Polish and Russian Jews. The various groups, with their differences in language and tradition, were often suspicious and hostile toward one another. Yet, by 1900, the immigrants made up a majority of the unskilled industrial workers.

Among skilled craftsmen, who were mostly native-born Americans, a strong federation of unions was formed in the 1880's. Among the industrial workers, however, efforts at organization were less successful; no more than one tenth of them were enrolled in unions before 1900. The unions usually lost when they attempted to oppose the big corporations.

Immigration increased and changed

From 1860 to 1890, the total population of the United States increased by about 31 million. During that time, more than 10 million foreigners entered the country. Plainly, immigration accounted for a very large part of the population increase. By 1900, in New England and the Middle Atlantic states, more than half of the people were either foreigners by birth or the children of foreigners.

During the 1880's, nearly twice as many immigrants arrived as had come during the previous decade, and during the 1890's, the numbers increased again. While immigration was growing as never before, its character was changing. Before the 1880's, almost all the immigrants had come from the British Isles or other parts of northwestern Europe. Then more and more began to come from eastern and southern Europe, and by the late 1890's, three of every five immigrants to the United States were coming from this area.

The new immigrants—mainly Italians, Czechs, Slavs, Hungarians, and Polish and Russian Jews—were essentially like the earlier ones, who, for the most part, were English, Scottish, Irish, German, Norwegian, Swedish, and French; they had left their homes, friends, and familiar ways of life because they had heard that America was a land of opportunity. Arriving in New York harbor, they were greeted by the Statue of Liberty, a gift from the people of France (1886). Inscribed on its base were these words (by Emma Lazarus):

Give me your tired, your poor,
Your huddled masses yearning to breathe free....

Once they had landed, however, the newcomers generally got an indifferent or hostile reception from native-born Americans. This was due in part to *nativism,* the feeling on the part of the native-born that they were somehow superior to the foreign-born. Before the Civil War, the same feeling had been shown toward earlier arrivals, such as the Irish.

Hostility toward immigrants was due also to the fear, on the part of native-born workers, that the foreigners would compete for jobs and thus keep wages down. In fact, the peasants from eastern and southern Europe often were willing to accept pay which seemed rather good to them because they were accustomed to a low standard of living, but which was unacceptable to native-born Americans.

Workingmen generally supported demands that the federal government act to cut down immigration. Companies employing large numbers of workers opposed such demands. Although it imposed a few restrictions, the government did little to halt immigration to the United States until after the end of the nineteenth century. The Chinese Exclusion Act (1882) stopped the few Chinese who wanted to come to the United States. Another act of Congress (1885) prohibited employers from bringing in immigrants and holding them to labor contracts made before the immigrants arrived. Still other laws forbade the entry of undesirable individuals such as paupers, lunatics, convicts, and those with certain kinds of diseases.

Skilled workers formed the most successful union

After the collapse of the National Labor Union in the 1870's—which had never been very strong or truly "national"—two other organizations tried to bring workers together on a large scale. One of these, the Noble Order of the Knights of Labor, reached its peak of strength and membership in 1886, then began to decline and finally disappeared. The other, the American Federation of Labor, was reorganized that same year and grew steadily from then on. The two were quite different.

The Knights hoped to create one big union that would include practically all kinds of workers, skilled and unskilled, male and female, white and Negro, native-born and foreign-born. The order aimed to improve not only the economic condition but also the social standing of its members. It wished to give them a sense of the "nobility" of

IMMIGRATION TO THE UNITED STATES, 1870-1920

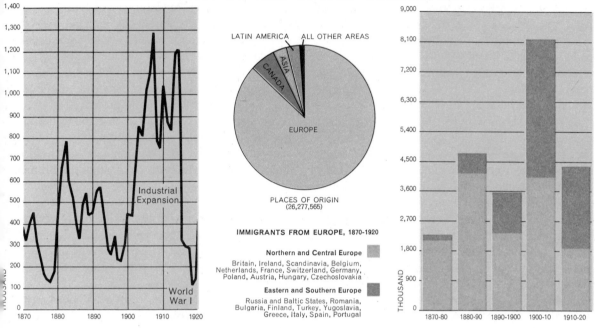

PLACES OF ORIGIN
(26,277,565)

IMMIGRANTS FROM EUROPE, 1870-1920

Northern and Central Europe
Britain, Ireland, Scandinavia, Belgium,
Netherlands, France, Switzerland, Germany,
Poland, Austria, Hungary, Czechoslovakia

Eastern and Southern Europe
Russia and Baltic States, Romania,
Bulgaria, Finland, Turkey, Yugoslavia,
Greece, Italy, Spain, Portugal

labor. It encouraged worker education, founded coöperative factories and stores, and advocated the arbitration of disputes between employers and employees. At first it was secret, to protect its members from employers who automatically fired union men.

The Knights' greatest leader was Terence V. Powderly, a Pennsylvania machinist who had lost his job and had been *blacklisted,* barred from future employment in industry, because of union activities. As "Grand Master Workman" of the Knights, however, Powderly ended the rule of secrecy and saw the organization grow to 700,000 members. Although he disliked strikes and violence, he could not keep his men from participating in them, and indeed the order grew largely because local leaders sponsored a series of successful railroad strikes.

Then, in 1886, occurred the Haymarket Riot. On May Day, workers throughout the country had gone on strike to dramatize their demand for an eight-hour day. On May 3, Chicago police killed several strikers near the McCormick Harvester Works. That evening a crowd met in Chicago's Haymarket Square to protest the brutality of the police. When mounted policemen tried to break up the meeting, someone threw a bomb. Seven policemen and four others were killed and more than a hundred were wounded.

Afterwards eight German immigrants were tried and convicted for their part in the riot. Four were hanged and one committed suicide. (Governor John P. Altgeld pardoned the other three in June 1893.) No evidence had been brought forth to connect any of the eight with the actual making or throwing of the bomb. All of them, however, were anarchists who had opposed all government.

Certainly the Knights of Labor had had nothing to do with the bombing. Yet, because they had taken a leading part in the May Day demonstrations, the Knights came to be generally viewed as dangerous radicals. This was one reason for the decline of the organization. A more important reason, however, was the Knights' continuing failure to attract many skilled workers.

The American Federation of Labor, on the other hand, was interested only in skilled craftsmen, such as carpenters, plumbers, and bricklayers. The A. F. of L. made no effort to organize miners, steelworkers, or other unskilled laborers. It was not one big union but rather a large federation of separate unions organized along craft lines.

For nearly forty years (1886-1924) the president of the A. F. of L. was Samuel Gompers, a cigar-maker. His Dutch-Jewish parents had brought him as a boy from London to New York. Under his shrewd leadership, the A. F. of L. concentrated on what he called "pure and simple" unionism, that is, the winning of higher wages bit by bit through direct bargaining with employers. Gompers favored strikes and boycotts to back up the workers' demands, but he managed to keep the A. F. of L. from taking part in any serious acts of violence. By 1900, about half a million men belonged to the member unions.

Industrial workers fought losing battles

On several occasions industrial workers took part in strikes which became bloody when the employers used force against the strikers. Two of the worst cases were the Homestead strike of 1892 and the Pullman strike of 1894.

At the Homestead plant of the Carnegie Steel Company, while Carnegie himself was out of the country, his manager Henry Clay Frick decided to cut pay rates. The union, a branch of the American Association of Iron and Steel Workers, refused to accept the wage cut. So Frick closed the plant and hired three hundred Pinkerton detectives to guard it. The strikers attacked the "Pinkertons," captured and disarmed them, and drove them out of town. Then Frick called upon the Pennsylvania governor for troops, and for five months the state militia guarded the plant. Public opinion supported the strikers until a young anarchist shot and wounded Frick. Finally, the men had no choice but to accept the pay cut and go back to work.

George M. Pullman, inventor of the sleeping car, had set up the "model town" of Pullman, near Chicago, for his employees. During the Panic of 1893, the Pullman Company laid off a third of the men and reduced the wages of the rest but did not lower the rent on the company-owned houses nor the prices at the company-owned stores. The men who still had jobs left them in protest.

The American Railway Union came to the support of the Pullman strikers and saved them from starvation. Eugene V. Debs, founder and head of this union, once had been an official of the Brotherhood of Locomotive Firemen. He thought all railroad workers ought to belong to a single organization, so he had left the exclusive brotherhood to form his own broad and inclusive union. Its members now refused to handle Pullman cars on trains. Not only was railroad traffic tied up between Chicago and New York, but many cars were looted and burned as tramps and angry workers without jobs took advantage of the railroads' trouble.

At the request of the railroad companies, the federal government sent troops to Chicago to protect the United States mails, preserve order, and break the strike. The governor of Illinois, John P. Altgeld, sympathized with the strikers and objected to such outside interference. Frightened property owners already looked upon Altgeld as a dangerous radical because he had pardoned three of the Haymarket anarchists who had been sent to prison. Now the worried property owners thought they had proof of the governor's radicalism.

The railroad companies also obtained a federal *injunction,* a court order, prohibiting Debs from doing anything to support the strike. When he defied the order, he was sentenced to six months in jail. The strike soon collapsed.

In the conflicts at both Homestead and Pullman, there were two major causes for the strikers' failure. The employers could afford to hold out much longer than the strikers, and the employers had the assistance of either the state or the federal government.

A few workers turned to Marxian socialism

None of the important unions of the time had revolutionary ideas. None of them sought to overthrow the government or radically to change the economic system. They sought only to gain for workingmen a larger share of the benefits of capitalism. They looked upon anarchist activity as a hindrance rather than a help to their cause.

A few labor leaders, however, concluded that there could be no real hope for the mass of workers until *capitalism,* the private ownership of the means of production and distribution, was replaced by *socialism,* public ownership. These men adopted the revolutionary views of Karl Marx, a German who, along with Friedrich Engels, had written the *Communist Manifesto* (1848) and *Das Kapital* (1867). Marx said that all history had been essentially a struggle between social classes. He predicted that the working class eventually would win and put an end to the struggle. The workers would become more and more numerous and more and more impoverished until, in desperation, they would rise up, take over both business and government, and create a peaceful, happy, classless society.

The most important convert in the United States to Marxian socialism was the union leader Debs, who read Marx's writings while in jail. Later Debs founded and for many years led the American Socialist party. In 1912, he received about a million votes as a candidate for President of the United States. He and most of his followers believed that socialism could be introduced gradually and peacefully in this country.

REVIEWING THE SECTION

1. How did the pattern of immigration to the United States change after 1880? Why did many Americans demand restrictions on immigration?

2. What were the aims of the Knights of Labor? of the American Federation of Labor? Why did the Knights of Labor decline as a force in the labor movement?

3. What conditions led to the Homestead and Pullman strikes? Why did the strikers fail to achieve their goals?

4. How did the views of the majority of union leaders differ from those of the Marxian socialists?

MORE AND MORE PEOPLE LIVED IN CITIES

Cities were growing faster than ever. Between 1880 and 1900, for example, New York grew from about two million to almost three and a half million, and Chicago from about a half million to more than a million and a half. By 1900, one third of the people in the United States lived in communities of eight thousand or more; a century earlier, only one thirtieth of the people had lived in communities of that size.

The cities drew population from the surrounding countryside and from Europe. Americans continued to leave the farms and small towns in such numbers that, as in earlier years, some rural counties actually lost population. Immigrants, most of whom remained in the cities after arriving, came very largely from peasant villages abroad.

The city had many attractions. Here were most of the rising industries which provided many job opportunities. Here were new comforts and conveniences, such as the telephone and the electric light, which had not yet reached the farms or even the small towns. Here, too, were activity and excitement—an appealing contrast to the isolation and dullness of rural life.

Although the city was alluring, it proved a difficult and disagreeable place in which to live for the great majority of those who flocked there. They found traffic congestion, noise, filth, poverty, disease, crime, and misgovernment. As the cities grew, so did their problems—physical, social, and political.

The cities faced physical problems

The cities made some progress in dealing with their problems of transportation, street lighting, sewage disposal, and water supply. They did not make enough progress, however, to take adequate care of the fast-growing population.

Urban transportation depended primarily on horse-drawn wagons, carriages, and carts. Horses were indispensable to the life and growth of the nineteenth-century city. Their importance was apparent whenever an epidemic spread among them, as it occasionally did. With deliveries held up, most businesses were almost paralyzed.

Horses and wagons made for neither cleanliness nor quiet. Horse droppings littered the streets and attracted flies, and iron horseshoes and wagon tires clattered on brick or cobblestone pavements. Newer paving materials, such as wooden blocks or asphalt, deadened the noise somewhat.

Smoother and quieter were the horse-drawn cars that ran on street railways. As the cities expanded, they generally built up fastest along the railways as these were extended farther and farther from the center of the city. Thus many of the cities developed in a kind of star-shaped pattern.

Horsecars began to be replaced by electric cars in 1888, when the first electric street railway went into operation in Richmond, Virginia. By 1895, more than eight hundred cities had electric lines. Some of those in New York were elevated railways, over which steam trains had run before the invention of the electric locomotive. In 1898, Boston opened the first subway.

Since the early nineteenth century, streets had been lighted by dim gas lamps. In the 1880's, these were supplemented with brilliant arc lights, which made the streets somewhat safer at night. The coming of electric lights and telephones brought some problems, however, for the streets became cluttered with poles and wires.

Sewer systems were developed slowly. Cesspools and even privies remained common in the city as well as in the country. Sewer gas made indoor toilets obnoxious until the flush toilet was perfected in the 1870's.

Water-supply systems, sometimes built and operated by privately owned companies, were ap-

pearing in even the smaller cities. Few of the waterworks filtered or purified the water, however, and pollution was a constant danger. Epidemics of typhoid were fairly frequent.

The cities faced social problems

More serious than the physical problems of the city, and much more difficult to deal with, were the social problems. The worst of these arose from poverty. In the large cities the life of the wealthy few contrasted glaringly with the life of the impoverished many.

The very rich lived in imposing mansions, such as those which lined Fifth Avenue in New York. They were waited upon by numerous servants, and rode about in fancy carriages. With money and time on their hands, some of these people turned to extravagant amusements.

Only a few blocks from Fifth Avenue were long rows of shanties in which poor Irish families lived and kept their goats. Elsewhere stood huge tenement houses honeycombed with rooms, many of them sunless and airless, into which whole families were jammed. More than half of the people in New York City lived in such tenements.

People who were brought up in the slums were tempted to take up crime as an escape from the misery of their existence. Street gangs turned to robbery and murder. This was one reason why the homicide rate of the United States, already twice as high as that of Britain or Germany, went still higher while the rates of Britain and Germany were falling.

In the cities there was a middle class of shopkeepers, businessmen, professional men, and skilled artisans. Some of these people, their consciences aroused, contributed to the support of charitable societies. The societies' agents took the view that poverty was due primarily to moral defects and only partly to misfortune. They tried to find and help the "deserving" poor.

More good was done by middle-class social workers, of whom one of the greatest pioneers was Jane Addams. After visiting London, Miss Addams borrowed the English idea of the "settlement house" and, in 1889, established Hull House in a slum district of Chicago. By 1900, there were more than fifty similar institutions in large cities in the United States. The settlement houses were equipped with club rooms, playgrounds, and libraries. They not only provided recreation and education for slum children but also gave experience to a growing profession of social workers.

Another social-service agency was the Salvation Army, which began its work in the United States in 1879, a year after it was founded in London. At first the uniformed men and women with their tambourines and brass bands concentrated upon religious revivals. Soon the army also turned its attention to the physical welfare of "slumdom."

The cities faced political problems

The typical large city had a weak, inefficient, and corrupt government. Authority was divided among many officeholders—the mayor, councilmen, local judges, and other officials. Their authority was limited, however, by the state legislature, which could interfere in municipal affairs. Thus no one man or group had clear-cut responsibility.

This confusion of authority made possible the rise of the political "boss" and "machine." The boss was the real ruler of the city, though he did not necessarily hold any official position. The machine was the party organization through which he controlled a majority of those who were in office. As a kind of "invisible government," he and his organization provided the centralized power which was lacking in the regular government.

The boss made money for himself and financed his machine through corruption. He awarded contracts for the construction of streets, sewers, public buildings, and other projects at prices far above the real cost. The surplus he divided between himself and his friends. He also sold franchises for the operation of railways, waterworks, electric-power systems, and other utilities.

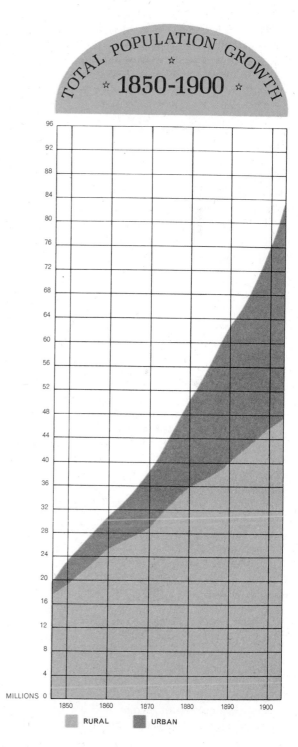

TOTAL POPULATION GROWTH
☆ 1850-1900 ☆

RURAL   URBAN

The boss had the support of wealthy and prominent citizens who profited from their deals with him. He also got the votes of the needy, many of whom were immigrants. They looked to him for help, and he furnished occasional relief, such as a turkey at Thanksgiving or a gift package at Christmas. He often stepped in to save them from punishment for petty crimes. Most important, he rewarded them with political jobs, with opportunities to rise in the party organization. In most cases the boss himself was of immigrant stock and had come up from poverty.

Thus "boss rule" had its democratic aspects. It flourished because it took care of needs which no other institution of the time adequately met. Yet, at best, the machine was a wasteful and vicious perversion of democracy. As the friendly British critic James Bryce declared, after analyzing the United States in the 1880's, the "one conspicuous failure" of government in the United States was to be found in the great cities.

REVIEWING THE SECTION

1. What physical problems confronted the cities in the late nineteenth century? How were these problems solved?

2. What social problems developed in the cities? How did reformers try to solve these problems?

3. What political conditions led to "boss rule" in city government?

CHAPTER **15** CONCLUSION

By 1900, the United States led all nations in industrial production. It managed to do so because of a combination of advantages—technological skill, organizing ability, natural resources, marketing possibilities, labor supply, and governmental assistance.

While the nation was advancing to the position of world leadership, internal transportation and communication were being improved. Railroads were extended until a rail network covered the whole country. Although highways were long neglected, a "good roads" movement was begun, largely as a consequence of the popularity of the bicycle. The post office began to carry the mails faster, farther, and more cheaply than ever before. The typewriter facilitated correspondence and record-keeping, and the telephone supplemented the telegraph as a means of rapid communication.

Old industries grew larger, more highly mechanized, and more heavily concentrated in certain geographical areas. New industries developed and made possible a new kind of machine age. The oil industry, exploiting newly discovered petroleum deposits, provided not only fuel for lamps but also lubricants for the wheels of transport and industry. The steel industry, based upon new processes for refining iron ore, reduced the price of steel, making it available for widespread industrial use. The electric-power industry, arising from the inventions of Thomas A. Edison and others, furnished superior light for homes, factories, and streets, and more efficient power for streetcars and industrial machinery.

As industrial plants increased in size, so did the firms that owned and operated them. "Captains of industry," such as John D. Rockefeller in oil and Andrew Carnegie in steel, set up various kinds of business combinations, which were popularly known as trusts. Eventually investment bankers such as J. Pierpont Morgan, who created the first "billion-dollar corporation," began to get control of big business and thus to replace industrial capitalism with finance capitalism. To the men who made fortunes from it, big business seemed a good thing—a result of the "survival of the fittest." These men justified their wealth as a God-given reward for their superior ability and virtue. The public generally envied and admired rich men but disapproved of trusts. Books denouncing the monopolistic methods of business were popular.

The rise of industry created not only a new class of wealthy industrialists but also a new and vastly larger class of poorly paid industrial workers. The majority of these came from eastern and southern Europe as participants in the "new immigration." It was hard for native-born workers to coöperate with the foreign-born, and for immigrants of different nationalities to coöperate with one another, yet coöperation was necessary if workers, as a whole, were to better their lot. Since business was well organized, labor, too, would have to organize in order to bargain effectively for higher wages and shorter hours. The Knights of Labor tried to form one big union, including workers of practically all kinds, but it failed to attract skilled workers, and after the Haymarket Riot the Knights rapidly lost membership. The American Federation of Labor brought together unions of skilled workers only, and for them the growing and thriving federation proved a source of strength. A few unions of industrial workers engaged in bitter and bloody conflicts with corporations, as in the Homestead strike and the Pullman strike, but the industrial workers eventually lost these strikes and most other important ones. A very small minority of labor leaders, discouraged by the failure of their bargaining efforts, became socialists and proposed to eliminate the private ownership of industry.

Urbanization went along with industrialization. A larger and larger part of the population of the United States lived in cities. The cities attracted farmers from the surrounding countryside and peasants from the European countryside. As the cities grew, their physical, social, and political problems became worse. The cities made some progress in improving their public facilities, less progress in alleviating human poverty and misery, and still less in reforming corrupt and inefficient government.

FOCUSING ON SPECIFICS

1. In what ways did the policies of the federal government aid industrial development between 1865 and 1900?

2. What factors influenced the establishment of rates for railroad service?

3. What methods did the Standard Oil Company use to reduce the number of its competitors?

4. How did the typical form of business organization change after the Civil War?

5. Explain the following forms of business consolidation: mergers, pools, trusts, holding companies, interlocking directorates.

6. Why were bankers, such as J. P. Morgan, on the board of directors of many corporations?

7. What did Andrew Carnegie believe was the role of men of wealth in society?

8. Why did industrial workers of the late nineteenth century feel it was necessary to bargain collectively with their employers?

9. Why did many immigrants support political bosses?

REVIEWING MAIN THEMES

1. What factors accounted for the rapid industrial development in the United States after the Civil War?

2. In what ways did transportation and communication improve after 1865? How did improved transportation and communication make possible the rise of large-scale industries?

3. In the late nineteenth century, why did American industry become concentrated in corporations which grew increasingly larger in size, but fewer in number?

4. How did industrial workers attempt to improve their lot? What successes did they achieve?

5. What problems arose as cities became larger? In the late nineteenth century, what attempts were made to solve the problems of the cities?

EVALUATING THE ISSUES

1. Henry George's single tax theory was based on his observation that land values increased because of social accident. For example, land was more valuable per acre in the city than in rural areas only because of the concentration of people living in the city, and not necessarily because the owner of city real estate had done any work to make the land more valuable. Thus rent on land ought to be paid to the state as a tax, George argued. Do you believe his ideas had validity? Explain your answer.

2. How did the growth of large corporations cause increased discord between owners and workers?

3. Considering the widespread dissatisfaction among many workers regarding their wages and working conditions, why did only a small number of workers become Marxian socialists?

4. Describe advantages to the public which derived from the increased consolidation of business enterprise.

CHAPTER **16** 1865-1900

The Revolution in Agriculture

While industry in the United States was being transformed, agriculture was undergoing a transformation almost as remarkable. The population was growing everywhere in the nation, but in the rural areas it was increasing less rapidly than in the cities. More and more land was brought under cultivation, and the number of farms multiplied. By 1900, there were more than twice as many acres being tilled and more than twice as many farms in operation as there had been in 1860. The output of these farms was increasing even faster than was the number of farms. By 1900, for example, the wheat crop was about three times as large as it had been forty years earlier.

The agricultural revolution in the United States consisted of four great changes, all taking place at the same time. First, the previously unpopulated areas of the West were settled, and most of the land that could be farmed was broken by the plow. Second, the South reorganized its agricultural system and largely recovered from the economic setback that had been caused by the Civil War. Third,

scientific methods and machines were used more and more extensively in farming throughout the country. Fourth, agriculture increasingly became a business enterprise in which the farmer produced materials for sale rather than for his own use; and, with improvements in transportation, the market in which he sold his products was widened to include the whole world.

None of these developments was entirely new. The settlement of the last frontier was a continuation of the westward movement which had begun with the founding of Jamestown in 1607. The New South of the period after reconstruction grew out of the ante-bellum South. Long before the Civil War, machines and scientific methods had begun to be employed on farms in the United States. Ever since colonial times, *commercial farming,* production for sale, gradually had been replacing *subsistence farming,* production for home consumption. In the 1870's, 1880's, and 1890's, however, these trends amounted to a revolution in agriculture because they now went so much faster and further than ever before.

To the extent that the various changes contributed to the tremendous increase in farm output, they benefited the nation and the world. Yet they brought serious problems for many farmers in the United States. As good, cheap land in the West grew scarce, there were fewer opportunities for men to acquire new farms of their own. In the South, with the reorganization of agriculture, most of the Negroes and many of the whites were left as poverty-stricken tenants, living and working on someone else's land. When farmers anywhere tried to buy the new machinery, they found it so expensive that often they had to go into debt to pay for it. Now that they concentrated on raising crops and livestock to sell for cash, they had to sell at a price that was set by world conditions of demand and supply, and to the farmers this price often was ruinously low.

Thus, in an age of agricultural progress, many farmers had difficulty in making a living, especially during the depressions of the 1870's and the 1890's. Farm people suffered not only from economic hardships but also from social and psychological disadvantages. With the growth of modern cities, farm life seemed more and more lonely, less and less attractive. City ways were becoming the accepted standard, and many city people began to look down upon their country cousins as "hicks," "rubes," and "hayseeds." A century earlier, things had been quite different. At that time, most people in the United States had agreed with Thomas Jefferson when he praised the tillers of the soil as "God's chosen people" and held up the ideal of a "republic of free and independent farmers."

THE LAST FRONTIER WAS OPENED TO SETTLEMENT

As late as 1860, most of the western half of the United States was still unsettled (that is, most of it had a population of less than two persons per square mile). A horseman riding west from Omaha —across plains, mountains, and deserts—would find hostile Indians and plenty of buffalo, but he would find only a few settlers until he reached Oregon or California.

By 1900, this "last frontier" had been settled, but within it there were (and still are) large areas containing fewer than two persons per square mile. A traveler again making the westward trip, this time by railroad, would encounter few Indians, unless he visited the reservations to which they had been confined. He would probably see no buffalo at all, for the herds had been practically wiped out. Along most of the way, however, he could observe such signs of civilization as ranches, farms, towns, and cities, though he would notice that the West, as a whole, remained quite thinly populated in comparison with the East.

In 1860, the only states that had been established in all the western territory were Texas, California, and Oregon. By 1890, most of the rest of the territory had been divided into states—Kansas (1861), Nevada (1864), Nebraska (1867), Colorado (1876), Washington, Montana, and North and South Dakota (1889), Idaho and Wyoming (1890), and Utah (1896). The remaining territory later became the states of Oklahoma (1907) and New Mexico and Arizona (1912).

On the last frontier, the earliest settlers were mostly miners who came in search of gold or silver. The arrival of these prospectors and other men led to conflict with the Indians, and a series of wars were fought before the West was made safe for the settlers.

The rush for gold and silver brought settlers

When the California Gold Rush began in 1849, a few of the gold hunters "struck it rich" when they found gold nuggets in stream beds or near the surface of the ground. Before long, however, mines were being dug to reach gold ore, and mills were being built to refine it. All this was too expensive for most of the miners. Some of them stayed on as laborers in the mines or mills, or as farmers raising grain or fruit. Others left California to look for gold or silver elsewhere in the West.

A number of mining booms followed the one in California. The second one occurred in what is now Colorado, in 1858. Some of the wagons then heading west bore the words "Pikes Peak or Bust," and some of them later returning east had those words crossed out and the following painted in: "Busted, by Gosh." In the 1870's, rich silver mines were opened near Leadville, and in the 1890's productive gold mines began operation in the vicinity of Cripple Creek. Meanwhile, in Utah territory in 1859, the fabulous Comstock Lode was discovered. In one year it was to produce more than $15 million worth of gold and silver. During the 1860's, other discoveries drew prospectors to the territories of Idaho, Montana, New Mexico, and Arizona. In 1876, a boom developed in the Black Hills area in the southern part of the Dakota Territory.

Life in a mining camp was crude and often violent. The miners slept in tents or shacks and spent their leisure time in the saloons, gambling-houses, and dance halls that lined the one, long, winding street in town. Women were few, and virtuous women still fewer. Crimes were frequent. Miners sometimes "jumped," or took over, the claim that another had "staked out," and then a fight often would follow. Gangs of outlaws preyed upon the stagecoaches that carried gold and silver from the mines to the nearest railroad stations. Wells, Fargo & Company, however, used steel-lined, heavily guarded coaches in the Black Hills. From there, one coach safely hauled away $350,000 worth of gold on a single trip (July 1877).

Local government was slow to develop in some parts of the mining country. Hence the citizens sometimes formed vigilance committees to deal with claim-jumpers, horse thieves, stagecoach robbers, and other "bad men." The vigilantes, seeking to establish law and order, captured, tried and hanged suspects. Even after a sheriff had been appointed, the vigilantes sometimes continued to ride in posses, taking the law into their own hands. Often it was hard to tell who represented the side of law and order—the vigilantes or the sheriff.

In the newer mining districts, as in California,

the prospectors' hopes of making a fortune were soon dimmed. Gold and silver production, if it continued at all, became a big business. In some places, it eventually declined and disappeared. In the territories of Montana and Arizona, copper proved to be much more abundant than silver or gold, and it laid the basis for a profitable and long-continuing copper industry. The gold and silver rushes, whether or not they led to long-range mining, usually resulted in the introduction of local agriculture. The mining towns provided a market at high prices for hay, fruit, and vegetables. In various parts of the West, as in California, some of the disappointed miners remained as farmers.

The danger from hostile Indians was removed

At one time (about 1840), it was the plan of the federal government to set aside as a permanent home for Indians the land west of the "great bend" of the Missouri River. However, men soon began to cross the area on their way to the Oregon country, California, and the other mining areas. The government then made new treaties with the Indian tribes, forcing them to give up additional territory. The government also set up army posts, such as Fort Kearny (in what is now Nebraska) and Fort Laramie (in what is now Wyoming) to protect the trails and settlements. More and more discontented, the Indians awaited their chance to recover their old hunting grounds.

With the coming of the Civil War, most of the regular troops were withdrawn from the frontier posts for service against the Confederacy. Some of the Indians then went on the warpath, menacing settlers as far east as Minnesota. The settlers took a fearful revenge. In Minnesota, for example, thirty-eight Sioux were hanged (1862) for the murder of five settlers. In Colorado Territory, militiamen fell upon a peaceful camp of Arapaho and Cheyenne along Sand Creek and slaughtered about a hundred men, women, and children.

After the Civil War, the federal government adopted a new Indian policy, intended to end the

Indian Warfare, by Frederic Remington, 1908

American Indians, during their great wars of resistance, displayed fantastic skill on horses, which had first been introduced in the New World by Europeans. While riding at full gallop, and under enemy fire, an Indian could retrieve the body of a fallen comrade. Not all Indians were hostile; some served as scouts for the army or for pioneers, guiding them across Western badlands. Although the cavalry had the double duty of protecting pioneers from hostile Indians and protecting peaceful Indians from encroaching pioneers, the soldiers usually sided with the pioneers.

A Reconnaisance, by Frederic Remington, 1891

Cavalry Charge on the Southern Plains, by Frederic Remington, 1907

Indian troubles and bring permanent peace to the frontier. No longer would treaties be made with the various tribes as if they were more or less independent nations, nor would the tribes be allowed to roam over vast areas. Instead, the Indians would be treated as "wards of the nation." They were to be confined on reservations and supported by the government.

The Indians were understandably reluctant to give up their old freedom. For years, units of the United States Army, transferred from the South to the West, were kept busy with efforts to enforce the new policy. The most important military campaigns were directed against the Sioux, the Nez Percés, and the Apaches.

The gold rush in the Black Hills brought thousands of men into the reservation which had been set aside for the Sioux. These Indians, alarmed, fled to the west, under the leadership of Sitting Bull and Crazy Horse. An army was sent out to round them up. Moving ahead of the main army, the Civil War cavalry hero George A. Custer, with more than two hundred cavalrymen, intended to surprise the Sioux. Instead, the Sioux surprised him. Custer and all his men were killed in the Battle of the Little Big Horn in Montana Territory (1876). The rest of the army, however, later defeated the Sioux and brought them back to the reservation in the Dakota Territory, while Sitting Bull escaped to Canada.

After several years, Sitting Bull was persuaded to return to the reservation. When the Sioux took part in new religious rites which featured a "ghost dance," the reservation authorities mistook their frenzied activities for a war dance. They ordered the arrest of Sitting Bull, and when he seemed to resist, he was shot and killed. Once more, the frightened Indians left the reservation. After pursuing and surrounding them, the United States troops massacred the Indians in the Battle of Wounded Knee (1890).

Meanwhile, the Nez Percés, a small and comparatively civilized Indian tribe, abandoned their reservation in the Idaho Territory and set out for Canada (1877). Under their remarkable leader, Chief Joseph, they eluded the army during a zigzag chase which covered more than a thousand miles before they were headed off. "I am tired of fighting," Chief Joseph said when he decided to surrender. "My heart is sick and sad. From where the sun now stands I will fight no more forever."

In the Southwest, the fierce Apaches resisted the army until 1886, when their most determined chief, Geronimo, finally surrendered. After that, the Indians were subdued and the West became safe from their attacks.

Most of the Indians continued to live on reservations, but the reservation policy was now modified. The Dawes Act (1887) allotted individual tracts of reservation land to Indians. On receiving his allotment, an Indian became a citizen, but he did not gain outright ownership of the land until he had worked it for twenty-five years. By gradually replacing tribal ownership with individual ownership, the Dawes Act was intended to break down the tribal organization of Indian society and turn the Indians into settled, landowning farmers. The law, however, was not a complete success. Most of the Indians held on to their old customs as best they could in their new circumstances.

REVIEWING THE SECTION

1. How did the mining booms set the stage for the introduction of agricultural communities in the West?

2. After the Civil War, how did the policy of the federal government change in regard to the Indians?

RANCHERS AND FARMERS SETTLED THE PLAINS

The Great Plains extend from approximately the hundredth meridian on the east to the Rocky Mountains on the west, and from the Rio Grande to the delta of the Mackenzie River in Canada. The region is high and dry, ranging in altitude from 2000 to more than 7000 feet and averaging less than twenty inches of rainfall a year.

When first explored, the Great Plains were covered with short, tough grass, and there were almost no trees. The few trees were to be found along the creeks and rivers, many of which were dry beds, except following a heavy rainfall. At that time, vast herds of buffalo roamed the plains.

As late as 1870, the buffalo numbered more than five million, although Indian and other hunters had begun to kill them off. The Indians hunted the buffalo primarily for meat and hides. Unlike the Indians, others hunted the animal with high-powered rifles for sport, and left the carcasses to rot. By 1885, only about a thousand of the buffalo remained alive. The extermination of the buffalo deprived the Indians of a major source of food and much needed hides and helped to make possible the defeat of the Indians and their confinement on reservations.

Even after the removal of the Indian menace, the Great Plains presented unusual difficulties for settlers. On earlier frontiers, in the eastern half of the United States, the pioneers generally had found plenty of wood and water. On the nearly treeless and semiarid plains, they had to adapt themselves to an unfamiliar environment in order to survive.

One use to which the plains were put was the large-scale raising of cattle, at first on the open range—the vast expanse of land that had not yet been taken up by private owners—and later on individual ranches. Another was the growing of wheat and other crops on farms (all of which, in the West, were known as ranches, regardless of what they produced).

Cattle were raised on the open range

At one time, the Great Plains served as a gigantic cow pasture. The short grass provided feed throughout the year, even during the winter, when it dried and turned into a kind of natural, uncut hay. As the Indians were brought under control, as the buffalo were killed off, as the railroads were pushed westward, great herds of cattle began to move over the plains, grazing on the open range.

The range-cattle industry began in Texas, where it developed from techniques that had been practiced in Mexico for centuries. At the end of the Civil War, Texas had an abundance of longhorn cattle, descended from stock originally developed by the Spaniards. The problem was to get the cows to distant markets. In 1866, in the first of the "long drives," thousands of the longhorns were driven to Sedalia, Missouri, at that time the nearest railhead. In later years, as the railroads were built farther west, the herds were directed to other "cow towns," among them Abilene and Dodge City, Kansas, and Cheyenne, Wyoming. From these places, the cattle were shipped to meat-packing centers, such as Kansas City and Chicago. Texas cattle were also driven north to establish new herds on the northern plains, and the longhorns were crossed with other breeds to produce better beef.

Since the cattle grazed widely on public land, they had to be branded so that each owner could identify his property. Twice a year, in spring and fall, the cattlemen in a particular area held a roundup at which the different herds were sorted out and the newborn calves were marked with one brand or another. The mavericks, or stray calves, were divided among the various owners in proportion to the total number of cattle each possessed.

In the days of the open range, a cattleman needed very little land of his own. He usually acquired at least a small ranch as his headquarters, and he had to have access to streams or water holes in the vicinity of his ranch and along the route to the point of shipment. The pasturage was free. Hence, with a small investment, cattlemen could make a large profit. Not only individuals but also corporations went into the cattle business.

The cowboys were the hired hands of the cattlemen or the cattle companies. The largest number were Southerners, including many veterans of the Confederate army. The next largest number were Negroes. There were also some Northerners, as well as Mexicans and other foreigners. On their cow ponies (mostly mustangs, wild horses which, like the longhorns, had descended from stock de-

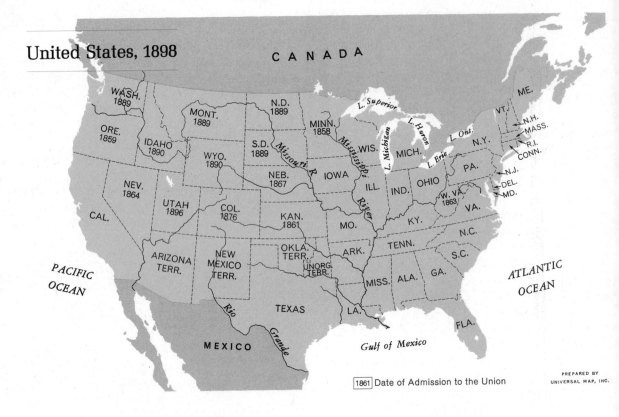

United States, 1898

CANADA

WASH.
1889

MONT.
1889

N.D.
1889

ORE.
1859

IDAHO
1890

S.D.
1889

MINN.
1858

ME.

L. Superior

L. Huron

VT.

N.H.

MASS.

WYO.
1890

NEB.
1867

IOWA

WIS.

MICH.

L. Michigan

L. Ont.

L. Erie

N.Y.

PA.

R.I.

CONN.

NEV.
1864

UTAH
1896

COL.
1876

ILL.

IND.

OHIO

W. VA.
1863

N.J.

DEL.

MD.

CAL.

KAN.
1861

MO.

KY.

VA.

ARIZONA
TERR.

NEW
MEXICO
TERR.

OKLA.
TERR.

UNORG.
TERR.

ARK.

TENN.

N.C.

S.C.

PACIFIC
OCEAN

MISS.

ALA.

GA.

ATLANTIC
OCEAN

Rio

TEXAS

LA.

FLA.

Grande

MEXICO

Gulf of Mexico

1861 Date of Admission to the Union

PREPARED BY
UNIVERSAL MAP, INC.

veloped by the Spaniards), these cowhands performed the chores of the roundup and the long drive. The cowhands' work was tedious, sometimes dangerous, and generally low-paid. In the saloons and gambling houses of the cow town at the end of the trail, they often spent their meager earnings in one wild, drunken spree. In the real, everyday life of the cowboys, there was little glamour.

The open range lasted only about twenty years, from the 1860's to the 1880's. During this time, the cattlemen and cowboys had to contend against various enemies besides the Indians. "Rustlers," or cattle thieves, made off with many cattle, altered the brands, and sold them. Farmers, or "nesters," settled on much of the land and fenced in their farms, thus obstructing the trails and the access to water. Sheepherders brought in large flocks of sheep which cropped the grass so short as to kill it. At times, cattlemen and cowboys engaged in

gunfights, not only with rustlers, but also with nesters and sheepherders.

The range-cattle industry began to disappear because, with increasing settlement, the open range itself was largely disappearing. Meanwhile, the range was being more and more heavily stocked with cattle. These could be supported only so long as the weather remained comparatively mild. The winter of 1885-1886 was unusually cold on the plains; it was followed by a hot, dry summer, and then (1886-1887) another bad winter, with terrible blizzards. Thousands and thousands of cattle starved or froze to death, and many cattlemen saw their business ruined.

After that, the range-cattle industry was abandoned. Cattle continued to be raised on the plains, and soon their numbers were larger than ever. Now, however, they were raised on privately owned ranches, where grazing lands were fenced and where shelter and supplementary feed was available in the winter.

New farms were created despite hardships

While some people were raising cattle on the plains, a much larger number were moving in to take up family-size farms. These settlers included many Union veterans of the Civil War and also many newly arrived immigrants, especially from the Scandinavian countries. Such land seekers, rather than gold hunters or cattle raisers, accounted for most of the remarkable population growth of the plains area. The population of the best farming portion—Kansas, Nebraska, and the Dakota Territory—increased from about half a million in 1870 to a million and a half in 1880 and three million in 1890.

Some of the newcomers obtained land directly from the federal government. Under the Preëmption Act of 1841 (in effect until 1891), a settler could buy 160 acres of government land for as little as $1.25 an acre. Under the Homestead Act of 1862, a citizen of the United States or an alien who was over 21 years of age and who had declared his intention of becoming a citizen could acquire 160 acres by paying a few dollars in fees and living on and improving the land for five years. Under a law of 1870, a Union veteran or his widow could count his years of army service; thus, if he had served four years, he or his widow could get a homestead by occupying it for only a year. Under the Timber Culture Act of 1873, a person could secure an additional 160 acres by agreeing to plant trees on part of that land.

In 1889, three million acres of land in Indian Territory (present-day Oklahoma), which had been set aside for Indians, were opened to homesteaders. On opening day, fifty thousand people, who had been waiting on the border, raced into the territory on foot or horseback, on bicycles, in wagons or trains to stake out their claims. The sooner a person arrived, the better his chances of getting good land hence the name "Sooners," by which Oklahomans were afterwards to be known. Within a few hours, all the available land was taken up.

Throughout the West as a whole, however, individual homesteaders obtained far less of the public domain than did railroad, mining, timber, and land companies. The railroads received tremendous government grants; some of the other companies acquired much of their land by fraud, by hiring men to take up homesteads for example, and then turning the land over to the company. More numerous than the homesteaders were the settlers who bought their farms from the government or from a railroad or land company. To hasten the sale of their land and also to increase their permanent traffic by encouraging settlement, the railroads often gave cheap and even free transportation to land seekers.

Once a man began farming on the plains, he ran into difficulties because of the lack of timber for housing, fuel, and fencing. A sod house might shelter him and his family for a time; they would dig out a space in the ground, erect low walls of mud bricks around it, and save their scarce and costly wood for the roof and for door and window frames. For fuel, the people commonly burned cow or buffalo "chips" (dried dung), sunflower stalks, corncobs, or twisted tufts of dry grass. For fencing, they experimented with the Osage orange and other hedges but found nothing really satisfactory until the invention of barbed wire, which became available for use in 1874.

To deal with the water scarcity, deep wells were drilled and highly efficient windmills to operate pumps were erected on derricks. In some of the river valleys, dams and ditches were constructed for irrigating the fields. Where irrigation was out of the question, farmers resorted to dry farming. This was a method of tillage which conserved the small amount of moisture in the soil by leaving a thin top layer of pulverized earth which slowed down evaporation. Crops which were especially adapted to endure droughts were grown.

Farmers everywhere had had to contend with

the forces of nature, but these created problems that were especially troublesome to the farmers on the plains. There the farmers faced terrible droughts, cloudbursts and floods, hailstorms, tornadoes, and blizzards. Grasshoppers, often called locusts, swarmed every seven or eight years, arriving in a cloud which darkened the sky, and making a noise like a hailstorm. Once they had landed on a growing field, they left nothing but bare stalks.

Settlers were attracted to the plains in especially large numbers during the early 1880s, when there was a succession of unusually moist summers. These, however, were followed by a series of extremely dry years, beginning in 1886. For a time, the westward movement was reversed, as some of the settlers abandoned the plains and turned back toward the east. No longer was there another West further on to which people could go; practically all of the virgin land that was well suited for farming had been taken up.

REVIEWING THE SECTION

1. How did the cattle-raising industry change after the 1880's? Why?

2. What were the initial difficulties experienced by the settlers on the plains? How were the difficulties overcome?

THE NEW SOUTH BECAME DEPENDENT ON COTTON

After the Reconstruction period, some Southerners hoped for a "New South" modeled on the North, with the same pattern of farms and factories, cities and trade. In 1886, the leading advocate of the New South, Henry W. Grady, editor of the Atlanta *Constitution,* proposed the creation of

a hundred farms for every plantation, fifty homes for every palace, and a diversified industry that meets the complex need of this complex age.

To some extent, the South succeeded in expanding its industrial production, as Grady and others

wished it to do. In the 1880's and 1890's, its railroad mileage grew half again as fast, and its pig-iron output twice as fast, as that of the country as a whole. Its production of timber and coal and other minerals also increased remarkably. Its tobacco industry became more and more mechanized and more and more productive. New cotton mills sprang up, the capital invested in them rising sevenfold in twenty years.

Yet, on the whole, the industries of the South grew less rapidly than those of the rest of the country. In 1900, the South actually possessed a somewhat smaller proportion of the nation's factories than in 1860. Thus, despite the New South movement, the region continued to be overwhelmingly agricultural and rural, much more so than the Northeast or the Middle West.

The number of Southern farms increased, as Grady hoped they would, and their average size fell to about half of what it had been before the Civil War. Agricultural production recovered, at first rather slowly and then quite rapidly, from the war's effects. Not until 1878 did the cotton crop equal that of 1860. By 1894, however, it was nearly twice as big as before the war, as were most of the other staple crops.

Still, the statistics regarding farms and farm output were misleading. The great majority of the Southern farmers did not own the land they worked, nor did they share very largely in the benefits of its productivity. The increase in farm production was achieved at considerable cost to the farmers and, indeed, to the Southern people as a whole.

A farm-tenancy system led to a one-crop economy

Where a single plantation had stood in the Old South, a number of separate farms appeared after the Civil War. This division of plantations into farms helped to account for the increase in number and decrease in size of agricultural units. The *ownership* of the land, however, was not so widely distributed. Most of the land remained in the possession of the original planters or was acquired by others to add to already large holdings. The majority of the farms—about seven out of ten by 1900—were occupied by tenants.

Some of these tenants were renters who paid a fixed amount of cash or cotton for the use of the land. Others were sharecroppers who gave a part of their crop (one fourth to one third or more of it) for the rent and also, in many cases, for the use of farm animals and equipment. Usually, the sharecroppers had no savings and owned practically nothing—no land, no livestock, no tools. Most of the Negroes could not afford to rent land, so they became sharecroppers.

The farmer, whether a renter or a sharecropper, usually bought his food and other supplies from a country store, which generally belonged to the landlord himself. The farmer bought on credit, hoping to pay his bill at the end of the growing season, when his crop was sold. The planter-storekeeper, to insure that the bill would be paid, took a lien on the crop. This lien was a legal form which gave him the rights to enough of the harvest to cover the debt.

Often, especially in times of poor harvests or low prices, the farmer found that the proceeds from his crop were not enough to pay what he owed. He then had to go deeper into debt. So long as the debt remained, he was compelled to go on working for the same landlord and trading at the same store. Thus he became the victim of a kind of *peonage*, or debt-slavery.

This system was obviously bad for the tenant himself. For his groceries and other supplies, he had to pay whatever was demanded, and this was often twice as much as cash customers paid. The typical Southern tenant of that time had little or no education, did not understand figures, and could easily be cheated by a storekeeper.

On the other hand, the system did not necessarily benefit the landlords. Some of them made a good living, but others went into debt themselves, despite the high prices they charged at the store. The yield of the land in the South was not nearly so large as it ought to have been. The tenants had

little incentive to work hard, increase output, or improve or even maintain the farms.

For these and other reasons, the system was also harmful to the South as a whole. It caused Southerners to depend very largely on one-crop agriculture, with cotton most often that crop. The landlord, who was in a position to dictate what the tenants grew, insisted that they plant cotton, since it was a staple, cash crop—one that could always be sold at some price and could be stored for long periods, if necessary. He ordinarily forbade the tenants to raise hogs, corn, vegetables, or other foods for their own use, since this would take land and labor away from cotton and trade away from his store. Hence, in large areas of the South, cotton and nothing but cotton was planted year after year.

This kind of one-crop agriculture had serious consequences for the region. Many of the people, living on an insufficient and monotonous diet of "meat, meal, and molasses," suffered from diseases such as hookworm and pellagra. Much of the soil, already poor, was further worn out by the poor farming methods—the repeated cotton plantings without crop rotation or the regular use of fertilizers. Whenever the price of the one staple dropped, those who depended directly or indirectly on cotton had nothing else to turn to for income, and they became still more impoverished.

The one-party system handicapped Southern farmers

In the South after the Reconstruction period, the farmers in general and the Negroes in particular suffered from social and political as well as economic disadvantages. The so-called Solid South came into being with the development of a one-party system in each of the Southern states. The single party—known as the Democratic or the Conservative party—was dominated by the men with large landholdings and by the men who controlled big business. Hence it was difficult for the farmers to improve their economic condition through political action.

After the Reconstruction period had ended, the

Southern Negroes were abandoned by their former Republican friends in the North. No longer could the Negroes look to the federal government to guarantee the civil and political rights that had been promised in the Fourteenth and Fifteenth amendments. Furthermore, the Supreme Court greatly weakened these amendments in a series of decisions concerning them.

Congress had provided in the Civil Rights Act of 1875 that all persons, regardless of race, were entitled to the "free and equal enjoyment" of public facilities such as hotels, railroads, steamboats and theaters and other places of amusement. In the Civil Rights Cases of 1883, however, the Supreme Court decided that the Fourteenth Amendment (with its phrases concerning "life, liberty, and property" and the "equal protection of the laws") applied only to the state governments and not to the people of the states. Thus, according to the Court, public officials could not discriminate against Negroes, but private individuals and corporations could do so.

In the case of *Plessy* v. *Ferguson* (1896), the Supreme Court went further and permitted the states themselves to discriminate. The Court now upheld a Louisiana law requiring the separation of white and Negro passengers on railroad trains. According to this decision, laws providing for "separate but equal" facilities for the two races were constitutional.

In the case of *Williams* v. *Mississippi* (1898), the Supreme Court approved of Mississippi's new voting requirements—a poll tax, a literacy test, and long residence in a particular precinct—which kept all but a few of the state's Negroes from casting their ballots.

All the Southern states proceeded to pass laws to enforce the segregation of the races and to prevent Negroes from voting. The enactment of these laws did not become widespread, however, until about 1900. Up to the 1880's, many Negroes used the same public facilities, with the exception of schools, as the whites; many Negroes continued to vote; and a few even held offices.

The outstanding Negro leader of the time was Booker T. Washington, a former slave who became (1881) the head of the Tuskegee Institute of Alabama, an agricultural and industrial school for Negroes. Washington advised his people to concentrate on economic opportunities rather than social or political rights. He believed that, in the long run, Negroes would best obtain their rights not by agitation and demands for equality but by careful training, hard work, and self-improvement. "The opportunity to earn a dollar in a factory just now," he told a mixed white and Negro audience at the Atlanta Exposition (1895), "is worth infinitely more than the opportunity to spend a dollar in an opera house."

Those Negroes who continued to vote were allowed to do so, for the most part, only so long as they cast their ballots for Democratic candidates. The landowners generally controlled the vote of their Negro tenants. Thus the Democratic leaders —commonly known as the Bourbons—added to their own political power. (They were called Bourbons because, like the Bourbon kings of France, who supposedly had learned nothing from the French Revolution, they were said to have learned nothing from the Civil War.)

The white farmers, like the Negroes, had many grievances against the landlords. It would have been to the advantage of white farmers to join forces with Negroes and resist the Bourbons in politics, but this was hard for white farmers to do. Poor whites held strong prejudices against Negroes, even stronger prejudices than wealthy whites held. The poor as well as the wealthy were in the habit of supporting the Democratic party. To form an effective new party, the white farmers would have to overcome their prejudices and change their political habits.

If the whites, landlords and tenants, should begin to oppose one another—if, in other words, the Solid South should be disrupted and a two-party system reëstablished—the Negroes might come to hold the balance of power between the two parties. The Negroes would then be able to exert considerable influence in politics. The Bourbons constantly warned against the danger of what they called "Negro domination."

REVIEWING THE SECTION

1. How did the farm-tenancy system lead to a one-crop economy? What were the consequences of one-crop agriculture for the South?

2. How did the one-party system in the South handicap Negroes and white tenant farmers? Why were Southern Bourbons able to maintain their political dominance?

SCIENCE AND MACHINERY AIDED PRODUCTION

After the Civil War, agricultural production in the United States increased faster than either the amount of land brought under cultivation or the number of men working on farms. In some places, production increased even when the number of people engaged in agriculture declined.

There were two main reasons for the overall rise in productivity, both per acre and per man. One was the introduction of farm machinery on a larger and larger scale, and the other was the development and spread of agricultural science.

The use of labor-saving machines was still encouraged, as it had been in earlier years, by the high cost of agricultural labor (except in the South). The use of scientific methods, on the other hand, formerly had been discouraged by those same high labor costs, which made it extremely expensive to undertake careful, intensive tillage. Such tillage had been discouraged also by the abundance of cheap and even free land, which made it more profitable to deplete the soil than to preserve or to restore it. Scientific agriculture had been discouraged, moreover, by the lack of dependable scientific knowledge. After the Civil War, as good, fresh land became scarcer and as exact knowledge grew and was made readily available, scientific as well as mechanical methods began to be applied on American farms as never before, despite the continuing high cost of labor.

New and more efficient machines were introduced

Even before the Civil War, a number of improvements had been made in farm equipment, and many farm machines had been put to limited use. After the war, devices for planting, cultivating, and harvesting were further improved, sometimes dramatically, and they came into much wider use.

The steel plow (1833) was far more efficient than the earlier wooden, iron-plated, or solid cast-iron plow, but it had a tendency to break. It was made more durable (1868) when an outer surface of finely tempered steel was combined with an inner core of soft iron. It was further improved, during the next thirty years, by the development and perfection of the sulky or riding plow, with two or three wheels. The way was now prepared for the gang plow, with which a single operator could make several furrows at once.

Exhibitions, especially at state and county fairs, helped in the development and sale of improved plows and other implements. In plowing contests, rival manufacturers competed with one another, and both they and the farmers learned the advantages and disadvantages of various new designs. Other improved devices coming into use were often exhibited at state and county fairs.

The most dramatic progress was made in the improvement of the reaper. Originally, the reaper had required a crew of six to ten men, who could cut and bind from ten to twelve acres of grain in a day. One of the men drove the horses, and another raked the cut grain from a platform behind the cutting blades. The others followed along to pick up the grain and tie it in bundles. Later, the reaper was improved by the addition of a conveyor belt which brought the grain to a kind of table, where men could bind it while riding on the machine. Still later, experiments were made with devices for binding the grain automatically, and finally, in 1878, a successful "twine binder" was patented. With the new binder, one man could do as much as several men had done with the old-fashioned reaper.

Horses generally pulled and powered the binders and other farm machines. Even the mechanical thresher was at first powered by horses walking on a treadmill. In the 1870's, steam-powered threshing machines, which had first appeared thirty years earlier, came into general use. After 1900, gasoline engines began to replace steam engines, and the reaper and thresher were eventually combined in a single machine called the combine, which performed the entire harvesting operation from cutting the grain to bagging the kernels.

Farm machines were introduced more rapidly in some parts of the country than in others. Their use spread the fastest in the plains states (especially in Kansas, Nebraska, and the Dakotas) and in such states as Ohio, Indiana, Michigan, Illinois, Wisconsin, Minnesota, and Iowa. There the farms were reasonably large and level, farm wages were relatively high, and the wheat and other grains were naturally more suited to mechanical cultivation and harvesting—except for corn, which, though planted and cultivated by machines, continued to be picked by hand. Machines were adopted most slowly in the South, where the farms were generally small, the incomes of the tenants low, and the cotton and tobacco crops not well suited to mechanical processes. The cotton bolls matured at different times, and each time they had to be picked with tender care. Tobacco had to be transplanted, and its leaves also had to be carefully handled. No successful mechanical picker for either cotton or tobacco was to be developed until long after 1900.

Farmers benefited from new ideas in agriculture

Both the federal government and the state governments promoted agricultural research and education. The Department of Agriculture, founded in 1862, became a full-fledged department in 1889, when its head finally was made an official member of the President's cabinet. According to the law, the department was supposed

to acquire and diffuse among the people of the United States useful information on subjects connected with agriculture in the most general and comprehensive sense, and to procure, propagate, and distribute among the people new and valuable seeds and plants.

As Congress appropriated more and more money for it, the department developed into the nation's most important institution for agricultural research. It also coördinated the work of other institutions and brought together the results of their work.

Agricultural studies were further stimulated by the Morrill Act (1862), which gave public lands to the states for the purpose of assisting colleges that were primarily intended to teach "such branches of learning as are related to agriculture and the mechanic arts." According to the law, the states had to sell the land given to them, and invest the proceeds, using only the interest for educational purposes. Most of them realized comparatively little from the sales, and for a time many of the land-grant institutions struggled for existence. As state appropriations increased, the training in agricultural sciences improved. Few graduates of the "agricultural and mechanical" colleges went into farming itself; most of them looked for careers in teaching or research. Many practicing farmers, however, attended the "short courses" which the colleges offered in order to spread elementary, practical information.

Agricultural experimentation was also encouraged by the Hatch Act (1887), which gave federal support to an agricultural experiment station in each state and territory. These stations, some of them located on the campuses of land-grant colleges, were devoted to testing theories and discovering facts. In the beginning, they concentrated on immediate, practical problems. Later, they were authorized to carry on long-term projects of original research, "with a view to the discovery of principles and the solution of the more difficult and fundamental problems of agriculture."

With the aid of the new research institutions, many improvements were made in breeds of cattle, hogs, and other livestock. The dairy industry was

"Bonanza farming" was the term used in the 1880's to describe large-scale farms on the Great Plains, where the use of mechanized equipment resulted in a "mine of wealth" to the farmer. The machines often were ganged together and covered wide areas as they moved across the field.

developed, particularly in Wisconsin. That state had faced an agricultural crisis because of the movement of wheat-growing to more productive fields farther west. An agriculture professor at the University of Wisconsin, Stephen M. Babcock, invented the "Babcock tester," which measured exactly the butterfat content of milk. By using this tester, farmers could tell which of their cows produced the richest milk and were most valuable for breeding good stock. Short courses at the university offered training in dairying and cheese-making. Largely through applied science, dairy farming was substituted for wheat farming in the state, and its farm crisis was overcome. By 1890, Wisconsin was on the way to becoming the leader in the production of milk and milk products.

Animal diseases were successfully attacked. In the 1880's, for example, researchers in the Depart-

ment of Agriculture discovered that the Texas fever, which had been plaguing the southwestern cattle herds, was carried by ticks. A dip was devised "to kill the ticks without killing the cattle," and the fever was brought under control.

Plants were improved. In a number of instances, new varieties were imported from abroad, and those that did well were given publicity by the Department of Agriculture and the agricultural colleges. Mennonite farmers from Russia brought to Kansas a hard, red, winter wheat which eventually converted Kansas into the foremost wheat-producing state. A large part of California's agriculture was based on crops not native to the area—plums, raisin grapes, navel oranges. Sugar beets, previously grown in Germany, were tried in various states in response to Department of Agriculture propaganda and, in the 1890's, the beets became an important crop in Michigan, Colorado, California, and Utah.

To deal with insect pests, insecticides were developed—an arsenic mixture for certain kinds of insects and an emulsion of kerosene and soap for others. A kind of moth that threatened the orange groves of California was eliminated by a natural enemy, a special kind of beetle, which was brought in from Australia for that purpose.

Methods of cultivation, especially the use of fertilizer, were made more effective in consequence of scientific discoveries regarding soils and plant life. The essential plant foods—nitrogen, potash, and phosphates—were combined in an artificial fertilizer for the first time in the 1870's. The rapidly increasing use of this combination contributed enormously to the fast-rising productivity of farms in the United States.

REVIEWING THE SECTION

1. After the Civil War, what improvements were made in farm machinery? Why were farm machines used less extensively in the South than in the West?

2. In what ways did the federal and state governments promote agricultural research and education? What improvements in agriculture resulted from scientific discoveries made during the latter part of the nineteenth century?

FARMERS LOST SOME OF THEIR INDEPENDENCE

At one time, the farmer (except for the Negro farmer) had been relatively independent in raising and marketing his crops. As Ida Tarbell wrote:

He had hauled his produce to town where in the open market he traded it in and returned home with the fruits of his labor in calico, sugar, seeds, new implements. It was an intimate, personal process which gave him a sense of adequacy and control.

By the 1890's, all this had changed. The farmer now sold his crops for money, and he sold them in markets that he never actually saw—the markets of the world. There, his grain and meat competed with those from Canada, Australia, and Argentina; his cotton, with that from Egypt, India, and Brazil. The railroad and the steamship carried his produce everywhere, and the telephone, the telegraph, and the transatlantic cable kept sellers and buyers informed of the conditions of demand and supply and the resulting prices. No longer did the farmer deal directly with the buyers, as he once had done. He now had to depend on warehouses, called elevators, to store and load his grain, on railroads to haul it away, and on other intermediaries to handle it and distribute it among the final buyers.

The farmer also had to depend upon people who were some distance from him for the things he bought, and he had to depend upon moneylenders when he needed loans with which to buy them. With the aid of tariffs and trusts, the manufacturers of farm machinery, fertilizers, and other supplies were able to keep their prices high. The farmer, lacking such protection and organization, had no control over the prices of the products he sold, and these prices often fell. Hence the farmer's income decreased while his expenses increased, and he went deeper and deeper into debt.

The farmer—North, South, East, and West—concluded that he was not getting his fair share of the tremendous increase in the wealth of the nation. He resented the riches of the prospering businessmen and the predominance of the growing cities, where the people enjoyed social and intellectual advantages that he and his children were denied.

The farmer's plight was due primarily to complex world-wide economic changes which he but dimly understood. Yet, with considerable justice, he blamed railroad men, speculators, moneylenders, and all the middlemen who stood between him and the ultimate consumer. Certainly, such men often did prosper at the farmer's expense.

Farmers had no control over prices

To the farmer, it seemed that most merchants

MEN
IN
HISTORY

CHIEF JOSEPH AND GERONIMO

From the conflicts between white settlers and Indians in the West, two famous Indian leaders have emerged, Chief Joseph of the Nez Percés and Geronimo of the Apaches.

The Nez Percé tribe occupied the high, grassy hills and canyon-scarred plateau where the present-day states of Washington, Oregon, and Idaho come together. French fur trappers called them nez percé (pierced nose) because some members of the tribe wore pieces of shell in their noses.

Provoked by incidents with settlers and by attempts to reduce the size of their reservation, the Nez Percés grew restive. Under the leadership of Chief Joseph, the members of the tribe sought to flee to Montana, where there were grazing grounds near the Canadian border, and where they thought they would be allowed to live in peace. En route, when repeatedly attacked by the United States Army, the Indians managed to achieve a series of brilliant victories.

The army frequently found itself outwitted because it attempted to fight the Nez Percés with conventional tactics. In rough mountain terrain, troopers used artillery, gatling guns (machine guns of an early type), and other heavy equipment which reduced the soldiers' mobility. Chief Joseph's people, with never more than one hundred braves, sought to avoid their more numerous and more powerful enemy, and when battle did occur, broke contact as quickly as possible.

The Nez Percés conducted this guerrilla warfare in a most civilized manner. They paid settlers for supplies, obtained weapons from the enemy as "booty of war," and refused to victimize women and children. Chief Joseph, who was known to be a humanitarian, was given credit for this conduct, though it was tribal policy.

When Chief Joseph, over the strong opposition of other members of his council, arranged the surrender of his undefeated people, he added to his prestige among the settlers and confirmed their belief that he was the supreme leader of the Nez Percés.

The Apaches were a diversified tribal group who had been pushed by the Comanches out of Texas and into the Sierra Madre Mountains of Mexico and the deserts of Arizona.

The discovery of gold in California made it necessary to build roads through Apache territory, and demands were made for the tribe's conquest and confinement to a reservation. Although all the Indians of the Southwest were subdued in a bloody four-year war which ended in 1875, a group of Apaches, under the leadership of Geronimo, revolted.

When he fled the reservation because of corrupt activities by government officials, Geronimo was a strong-willed brave leading thirty-five men, eight young boys, and a hundred and one women and children.

Though having no supplies, except what they could seize from the enemy, Geronimo and his band maintained themselves for eighteen months. Arrayed against them was a government force of more than six thousand men, yet Geronimo's "army" rode triumphantly over an area of eight hundred square miles. During the time that he was inflicting over 200 casualties on his pursuers, Geronimo lost only ten members of his party, and some of those losses were sustained when he sent a party on a peace mission.

Many people took credit for the capture of Geronimo, but in reality, he was never captured by anyone. He was tricked into surrendering. Army officers made him a number of promises, but the pledges were broken, and he and his followers were imprisoned.

Geronimo was a bitter brave, who had seen his entire family killed by settlers and who had been brought up to raid and plunder these enemies. In contrast, Chief Joseph was a humanitarian, a man of peace, who had fought beside his people only because it was the will of the majority to do battle.

Yet, while the two Indian leaders were very different, both men represented the proud Indian, to whom reservation status was humiliating. To the United States government both men stood as dangerous examples—examples that seemed to urge all Indians to leave the reservations and return to their former ways of life as free and independent men. But if the Indians had done so, the settlement of the whole frontier would have been jeopardized, and that was something nineteenth-century America refused to allow.

and manufacturers were guilty of profiteering—especially the manufacturers of farm machinery. American-made reapers often cost more in the United States than in foreign countries. Sales agencies received a high commission on every machine they sold.

To the manufacturer, however, the prices seemed reasonable enough. Cyrus Hall McCormick, whose Chicago factory was the largest farm-implement producer, pointed out that the sales agencies performed essential services, among which was the assembling of machines from parts shipped from the factory. McCormick also explained that nearly two thirds of his reapers were sold on credit, and he had to hire men to investigate credit ratings and to collect time payments.

Whether the price of farm machines was excessive or not, it was high in relation to the prices that farmers were receiving for their product. For most of the time between 1873 and 1893, the prices of cotton, wheat, and corn had been falling. Before 1873, the price of cotton had averaged more than 15 cents a pound, but after the Panic of 1893, it was less than 6 cents. Yet it was costing Georgia farmers, on the average, 7 cents a pound to produce it. During the same period, the price of wheat dropped from more than a dollar to less than 65 cents a bushel and corn from 43 to 29 cents. At times, corn was even lower; in 1889, it was bringing only ten cents a bushel in Kansas. At that price, the corn was not worth the expense of picking it and hauling it to the railroads, and many farmers were burning it for fuel.

Such were the prices quoted on the leading exchanges, such as the Chicago Board of Trade and the New York Cotton Exchange, where dealers bought and sold agricultural commodities—farm products—in large quantities for immediate or future delivery. These dealers commonly speculated, that is, bought or sold commodities in the hope of making a profit from a rise or a fall in the price. If a speculator *sold* (at the current price) for *future* delivery, a commodity which he had not as yet purchased, he would profit if the price should fall,

for he could then make delivery at the already agreed-upon price, but he himself would have to pay only the new, lower figure. Thus a price decline, which necessarily meant losses to many farmers, brought gains to those speculators who had gambled on such a decline. To the farmers, such profiting from the misfortunes of others seemed downright wicked, especially since the farmers suspected the speculators of deliberately manipulating the market so as to cause the price to fall.

In any case, the price quoted on the exchanges was not the amount that the farmer actually received. From the market price, several charges were deducted—the fee for storing and loading the crop, the freight, the insurance, and the commissions of merchants and brokers (the middlemen) who had taken part in a string of transactions through which the crop had finally reached the market.

These charges, especially those of the grain elevators and the railroads, seemed exorbitant to the farmer. He often complained that it took one bushel of wheat or corn to pay the freight on another. Freight rates in the South and the West, where there was little or no competition among railroads, were from two to three times higher than those between Chicago and New York, where there were competing lines. Rates generally were higher for those who shipped small quantities than for those who shipped large quantities; hence the rate was higher for the individual farmer than for the great manufacturing corporation.

Originally, the farmer had considered the railroad as his best friend and had done all he could to encourage rail construction. From the 1870's on, he believed the railroad was his worst enemy.

The farmers' burden of debt grew

In the plains area and in some of the older states of the Middle West, as in the South, most farmers possessed little or no savings of their own, so they had to borrow money in order to farm. They needed both long-term loans, which were repayable in several years, and short-term loans, which were repayable in several months. The long-term loans were used to pay for land and equipment. Even the homesteaders, though needing practically no cash to get their land, had to have money for fences, buildings, and windmills and other machinery. Short-term loans were used to buy seed, livestock, and other supplies, and to pay for operating expenses during the growing season.

To obtain a long-term loan, a farmer could not depend on the banks. State banks hesitated to make loans on real estate, and national banks were forbidden by law to do so. Hence the farmer usually borrowed from an individual moneylender or from an investment company. Investment companies sold bonds, which were secured by farm mortgages, in order to raise the money to lend, and the bonds were bought mostly by Easterners. By 1889, people living in just one New England state, New Hampshire, had invested a total of $25 million in mortgages on property in the West. The borrowing farmer was charged a high interest rate and other fees. If he could not raise the money to pay off the loan when it fell due, he ran the risk of having the mortgage foreclosed—which meant that his farm would be sold to pay the debt.

Nor could the farmer depend on the banks for short-term loans, since the banks would not accept as security the crops or livestock he had not yet raised. In much the same way that the Southern farmer got credit from a country storekeeper, the Western farmer usually obtained it from a local merchant. The interest he paid for such credit was exorbitant, often running as high as fifteen or twenty per cent, and the price of the goods he bought also was excessive.

The farmer's debt—the interest and the principal—represented a fixed cost for him, a cost that remained the same and had to be met regardless of the amount of crops he sold or the price he got for them. He also had another fixed cost, the taxes on the land he owned; and this expense, too, bore no relation to his ability to pay. In those days, there were no state income taxes, and with the exception of the years 1863-1872 and 1894-1895, there were

no federal income taxes. State and local governments obtained almost all of their revenue from the taxation of real estate.

With interest, taxes, and other costs remaining high and the price of farm produce falling, the farmer found it harder and harder to make ends meet. By the 1890's, nearly one third of all the farms in the nation were mortgaged. The proportion of mortgaged farms was even higher in certain areas—nearly one half of the farms in Wisconsin and Michigan, slightly more than one half of those in Iowa, and much more than one half of those in Minnesota, Kansas, Nebraska, and North and South Dakota.

With the disappearance of cheap or free farm lands in the West, it became more and more difficult for a man to acquire land of his own. With the growing burden of debt, many farm owners found it difficult or impossible to hold on to land they already possessed. Not only in the South but also in other parts of the nation, farm tenancy increased. In 1880, about one fourth of all the farms in the nation were operated by tenants; by 1890, more than one third.

To debtor farmers, it seemed that there was too little money in circulation. They thought that if more money were issued, the prices of farm products would rise. (This was probably true; for, as a rule, the more money there is in circulation, the higher prices in general will be.) The farmers believed that if agricultural prices rose high enough —and if other prices did not rise too high—they might be able to pay off their debts. Hence most of them were *inflationists,* or advocates of increasing the money supply.

REVIEWING THE SECTION

1. Why did the farmer believe that manufacturers, commodity dealers, and railroads were guilty of profiteering at his expense?

2. Why did the farmers' burden of debt grow larger in the late nineteenth century? What action did the farmers think the government should take to enable them to pay off their debts?

In the latter part of the nineteenth century, the last frontier in the West was settled. Prospectors led the way, flocking to one mining area after another, to look for gold and silver. The arrival of miners and settlers resulted in trouble with the Indians, but the army finally subdued them, and they were confined on reservations. The removal of the Indian danger and the slaughter of the buffalo, upon which many of the tribes had depended for their existence, made possible the agricultural development of the Great Plains. For about twenty years, herds of cattle were allowed to graze on the open range and were rounded up and driven long distances to places from which they were shipped east to slaughterhouses. Eventually, the range-cattle industry gave way to the ranch-cattle industry. Meanwhile, farmers moved on to the plains, taking up homesteads or buying land from the government or from railroad or land companies.

While the West was being settled, the South was developing a new agricultural system which replaced the old plantation system that had been destroyed by the emancipation of the slaves. The plantations now were divided into farms, but most of the land continued to be owned by comparatively wealthy planters. It was worked by sharecroppers and other tenants, Negro and white. They were compelled by circumstances to concentrate on the production of certain crops and, above all, on cotton. Cotton production eventually rose far above the ante-bellum level, but most of the farmers, and especially the Negroes, benefited little. They suffered from social and political as well as economic handicaps.

Because of improved scientific methods and mechanization, farm production increased more rapidly than did the amount of land farmed or the number of men engaged in agriculture. The most important of the mechanical improvements were those made in the reaper, which evolved into the binder, and in the threshing machine, which came to be steam powered. Scientific farming was encouraged by the Department of Agriculture, the land-grant colleges, and the federally supported experiment stations, all of which carried on research and helped to bring new-found knowledge to farmers.

Farming became not only more of a science but also more of a business. Like businessmen, farmers were engaged in producing for sale rather than merely for their own use. They were selling in a nation-wide and even a world-wide market. Unlike the men who operated big businesses, however, the farmers lacked the benefit of tariffs, to protect them from foreign competition, and of trusts, to keep their output down and their selling prices up. The prices of agricultural commodities fell, but the costs of farm production remained high, and farmers were forced to go more and more into debt in order to continue farming.

These broad developments—the settlement of the West, the changes in the South, the spread of mechanized and scientific agriculture, and the widening of the farmer's market—constituted an agricultural revolution. To the extent that they made available an increasing abundance of farm products, these trends benefited the nation and the world. Many of the farmers, however, had little share in the benefits. Indeed, the increase in production was the basic cause of the decline in agricultural prices, and that decline was, in turn, the basic cause of the farmers' distress.

Farmers in different parts of the nation—for example, the sharecroppers in the South and the homesteaders on the plains—had special problems of their own. Farmers in all parts of the nation, however, also had common problems and common grievances. Everywhere, they complained about the unfair charges of railroads and other middlemen, the high costs of equipment and supplies, the burdensome interest rates and property taxes, and the ruinously low prices for farm products.

Many of the farmers agreed on what they believed would remedy the inequities. As they saw it, the railroads and other handlers of the crop on its way to market should be strictly regulated. Tariffs should be lowered and monopolies broken up. Cheaper loans should be provided, and at least a part of the tax burden should be shifted—by means of an income tax—to those who could best afford to bear it. More money should be issued, so that agricultural prices would rise.

All these things, however, would necessitate strong

action on the part of the government, especially the federal government. To get the government to act, the farmers would have to gain political power, and to do that, they would have to organize and work together. This was hard for them to do. They were individualists, accustomed to working alone. They had different political traditions; in the North, most of the farmers were Republicans, and in the South, most of them were Democrats. There were also racial and other differences among them.

Nevertheless, the farmers eventually were to succeed in forming political combinations through which they could bring pressure to bear in state and national politics.

FOCUSING ON SPECIFICS

1. How did the Dawes Act (1887) modify government policy in regard to the Indians?

2. How did federal legislation enable homesteaders to obtain land from the federal government?

3. Why did many Southern farmers become victims of debt slavery?

4. How did the decisions of the Supreme Court in the Civil Rights Cases of 1883 allow Southern individuals to discriminate against Negroes? How did the Court's decision in *Plessy* v. *Ferguson* (1896) permit the states to discriminate against Negroes.

5. How did the Supreme Court make it possible for Southern states to bar Negroes from voting?

6. Why did Booker T. Washington advise Negroes to concentrate on improving their economic opportunities before taking action to gain social or political rights?

7. Explain why white farmers did not unite with Negro farmers to resist domination by the Bourbons.

8. Before the 1890's, the farmers were relatively independent in raising and marketing their crops. How and why did this change?

9. Why did farmers, unlike manufacturers, have little control over the prices of their products?

10. How did commodity dealers often make a profit from the decline in the price of agricultural products?

11. Why did agricultural prices decline in the late nineteenth century?

REVIEWING MAIN THEMES

1. Between 1865 and 1900, what major changes took place in agriculture?

2. What difficulties did ranchers and farmers have in settling the Great Plains?

3. What important economic developments took place in the South after the Civil War?

4. After the Civil War, why did farmers lose much of their former independence and their position in society?

EVALUATING THE ISSUES

1. Farmers maintained that the railroads were unfair in setting higher rates for short hauls than for long hauls and in charging higher rates in the West and South than in the East. What arguments did railroad owners use to justify the unequal rates? In your opinion, who had the stronger case, the railroad owners or the farmers?

2. In 1903, W. E. B. Du Bois, a critic of Booker T. Washington, wrote that Washington was "striving nobly to make Negro artisans business men and property-owners; but it is utterly impossible, under modern competitive methods, for workingmen and property-owners to defend their rights and exist without the right of suffrage." Do you agree with Du Bois?

3. A critic of the Supreme Court decision of 1954 that segregated schools were unconstitutional stated: "If the Supreme Court can alter the Constitution by its decisions, then five men—a majority of the Court—can make the Court a constitution maker instead of a constitution defender.... The Court should have upheld the Constitution its members are sworn to uphold. It should have upheld the doctrine of separate but equal facilities which had been sustained by the Supreme Court in 8 different cases since 1896." Was the Court a "constitution maker" or a "constitution defender" in its decisions on the Civil Rights Cases of 1883 and *Plessy* v. *Ferguson*? In view of your answer, do you believe that the Court should have upheld the doctrine of separate but equal facilities?

4. How did the industrialization of the United States contribute to the agricultural revolution?

5. In the recurring wars between the United States government and the plains Indians, in what way was the government at fault? the Indians?

The Politics of Discontent

"The two major parties in this period were like two bottles," said James Bryce, a British historian who knew the United States well. "Each bore a label denoting the kind of liquor it contained, but each was empty." Although this was an exaggeration, the similarities between the two parties were certainly more important than the differences, and neither party offered a definite, consistent program of legislation.

The Republican party was still, as it had been since 1860, basically an alliance between two groups: the industrialists of the Northeast and the more prosperous farmers of the Middle West. It had the support of the Union veterans' organization, the Grand Army of the Republic, sometimes appropriately called the "Grand Army of the Republican Party." Republicans were fond of referring to their party as the party of Union and freedom, the party that had won the Civil War and emancipated the slaves. To keep wartime memories alive, it continued to nominate former Union army officers for the presidency. After

Ulysses S. Grant and Rutherford B. Hayes came James A. Garfield, Benjamin Harrison, and William McKinley—all of them Union veterans (and all of them born in Ohio). The only time the Republicans nominated a nonveteran, James G. Blaine, they lost the election (1884). To appeal to Union patriotism, the Republicans also made a practice of "waving the bloody shirt," that is, reminding the Northern people that their former enemies had been Democrats.

The Democratic party was more heterogeneous than the Republican. It could count upon the Solid South after 1877, when Reconstruction was ended and the control of the Southern states was left to the local Democrats. The party also depended upon the political machines of New York, Boston, and other Northeastern cities, where most of the immigrant and native-born workers were attracted to it. Moreover, it had the support of many merchants and bankers in the North. It claimed, as it had before the Civil War, to stand for the principle of state rights. Its one successful presidential candidate, Grover Cleveland (elected in 1884 and again in 1892), had no record of war service; as the sole support of an aged and widowed mother, he had been exempted from the wartime draft.

On the whole, the Republican party contained a larger number of well-to-do persons, and the Democratic party a larger number of poor, yet both parties included people of all economic levels and all economic interests. Both tried to appeal to as many voters as possible in order to win elections. As in earlier times, the winning party rewarded its active supporters with government jobs, and most politicians were more interested in these than in principles.

In national politics, the parties were fairly evenly matched. Of the six presidential elections during the period, the Republicans won four (1880, 1888, 1896, 1900) but actually gained a majority of the popular vote in only two (1896 and 1900). The Republicans managed to control the presidency and both houses of Congress for only six years (1889-1891 and 1897-1901), and the Democrats succeeded in doing so for only two years (1893-1895). The rest of the time, one party controlled one or both of the houses of Congress, and the other party controlled the presidency.

Congress, especially the Senate, was jealous of its powers and suspicious of any President, no matter which party he belonged to, who might try to usurp those powers. Often called the "Millionaires' Club," the Senate contained many rich and powerful members who headed state political machines and who really represented large business corporations rather than the people. The leading senators, as one of them remarked, would have taken it as a "personal affront" if the President had asked them to pass a bill they did not like. This senator said that if they visited the White House, it would be "to give, not to receive advice."

Under the circumstances, it was hard to enact extensive national reforms. Yet, while the major parties hesitated to take a definite stand on any important issue, more and more of the people began to think that something should be done about what they considered to be serious evils, such as the spoils system, the tariff and the trusts, the high rates charged by railroads, and the scarcity of money. These people, especially the farmers, grew more and more discontented with the federal government's slowness to act. Many of them finally tried to express their discontent in national politics by bringing pressure to bear upon the major parties and by setting up a separate, third party.

CIVIL SERVICE REFORMS WERE BEGUN

Under the spoils system, government jobs rarely went to the men who were best fitted to perform the duties; they usually went to the men who had done the most for the party and its leaders. Party bosses, among them a number of United States senators, held their political machines together and kept themselves in power by seeing that their faithful followers were appointed to government offices. The bosses then collected a portion of the salaries of these officeholders as campaign contributions. The machines also received money from wealthy individuals or corporations in payment for political favors, such as the passage of a desired law. Thus the spoils system led to governmental inefficiency, irresponsibility, and corruption.

Reformers demanded that the spoils system be replaced by a merit system, under which the offices would go to the best-qualified applicants, regardless of their political views or party services. These reformers were mostly journalists and scholars of fairly high social standing, aristocratic-minded men who had little sympathy for the mass of workers and farmers. The outstanding leader was George William Curtis, who edited *Harper's Weekly,* a widely read journal of news, political comment, and ladies' fashions. Practical politicians, such as the New York State boss, Senator Roscoe Conkling ridiculed Curtis and the rest of the civil service reformers. Conkling dubbed them "snivel service" reformers, and he said they forgot that "parties are not built up by deportment, or by ladies' magazines, or gush!"

As early as 1871, Congress had passed a law that seemed to promise the beginning of reform. This law provided for a commission to draw up rules for a merit system, and President Grant named Curtis as the chairman of the commission. Nothing came of the effort, however, for Congress soon refused to appropriate money for continuing the commission's work. It was to take the assassination of a President to bring Congress (1883) to pass the first effective civil service reform act.

Hayes attacked the spoils system

There was nothing striking or colorful about Rutherford B. Hayes, but he had the virtues of honesty and determination. When he took office as President (1877), he intended to lead Congress and the country, and he hoped to bring a measure of purity into political life. In his inaugural address he declared that "he serves his party best who serves his country best," and that "party leaders should have no more influence in appointments than other equally respectable citizens."

But Hayes ran into difficulties. Throughout the four years of his term, the Democrats controlled the House of Representatives, and during the last two years they also controlled the Senate. Many of the Republicans in Congress turned against him; at one time only three members of the Senate gave him their support. Republicans as well as Democrats questioned his right to the presidency, charging that he had won the disputed election of 1876 by means of fraud. Senator Conkling sneeringly called him "Rutherfraud B. Hayes." Despite his opponents, Hayes made at least a little progress toward improving the civil service by executive action.

The President antagonized the Republican bosses by his independence in making appointments. He named a civil service reformer, Carl Schurz, as secretary of the interior, and Schurz proceeded to set up a merit system in his own department. A former Confederate, the Tennessee Democrat David M. Key, was made postmaster general, the cabinet official who had most to do with dispensing patronage. Many less important jobs also went to Southerners. By this patronage policy, Hayes aimed, unsuccessfully, to build up a new Republican party in the South.

Hayes again shocked Republican politicians when he issued his remarkable "Order Number 1." This forbade federal officeholders to "take part in the management of political organizations, caucuses, conventions, or election campaigns." If the order had been strictly obeyed, which it was not, it would have destroyed the entire spoils system.

Hayes began his most important attack on the spoilsmen when he appointed a commission to investigate the New York custom house. This was much the largest and busiest of all the custom houses. So many jobs existed there, and so much money was received in customs duties, that opportunities for patronage and graft abounded. It was said that whoever controlled the custom house controlled the state of New York. The chief officer, the collector of the port of New York, Chester A. Arthur, was a henchman of Senator Conkling. The other officials and most of the employees also were Conkling men. The investigating commission found that at least one fifth of the employees were unnecessary, and that the place was riddled with "ignorance, inefficiency, and corruption."

After seeing the commission's report, Hayes boldly dismissed Arthur as collector and another Conkling man as naval officer at the New York custom house. Conkling was irate. He persuaded the Senate to refuse to confirm the replacements whom Hayes chose for the officials he had removed. Hayes stood up to Conkling and kept on sending new appointments to the Senate until it finally approved his choices.

Though Hayes had won a battle against the spoilsmen, he had by no means ended the spoils system. Throughout his term, he repeatedly urged Congress to appropriate money for reviving the civil service commission that had had a brief existence under Grant. Each time, Congress failed to respond.

PRESIDENTIAL ELECTIONS: 1880-1892

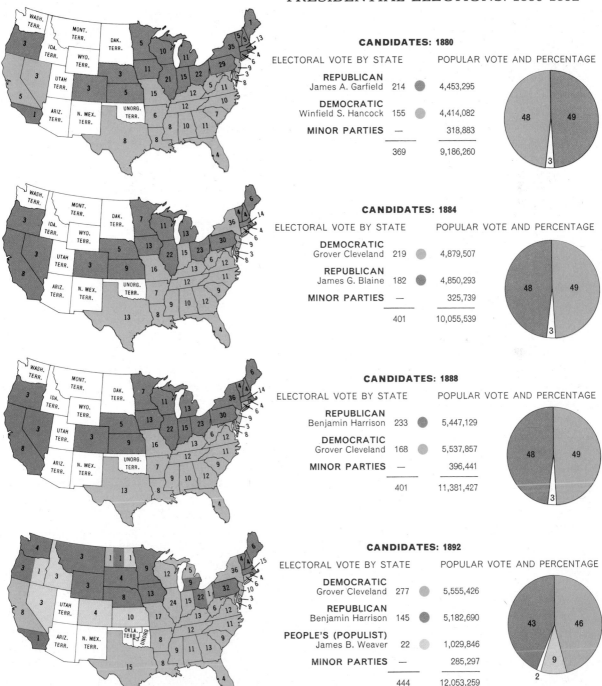

CANDIDATES: 1880

ELECTORAL VOTE BY STATE		POPULAR VOTE AND PERCENTAGE
REPUBLICAN James A. Garfield	214	4,453,295
DEMOCRATIC Winfield S. Hancock	155	4,414,082
MINOR PARTIES	—	318,883
	369	9,186,260

48 49 3

CANDIDATES: 1884

ELECTORAL VOTE BY STATE		POPULAR VOTE AND PERCENTAGE
DEMOCRATIC Grover Cleveland	219	4,879,507
REPUBLICAN James G. Blaine	182	4,850,293
MINOR PARTIES	—	325,739
	401	10,055,539

48 49 3

CANDIDATES: 1888

ELECTORAL VOTE BY STATE		POPULAR VOTE AND PERCENTAGE
REPUBLICAN Benjamin Harrison	233	5,447,129
DEMOCRATIC Grover Cleveland	168	5,537,857
MINOR PARTIES	—	396,441
	401	11,381,427

48 49 3

CANDIDATES: 1892

ELECTORAL VOTE BY STATE		POPULAR VOTE AND PERCENTAGE
DEMOCRATIC Grover Cleveland	277	5,555,426
REPUBLICAN Benjamin Harrison	145	5,182,690
PEOPLE'S (POPULIST) James B. Weaver	22	1,029,846
MINOR PARTIES	—	285,297
	444	12,053,259

43 46 9 2

A patronage quarrel led to Garfield's assassination

Before the end of the Hayes administration, the Republican party had divided into factions. One group, the "Stalwarts," followed Senator Conkling, and another, the "Half-Breeds," followed Senator James G. Blaine of Maine. The Stalwarts, who included most of the state bosses, stood frankly for machine politics and the spoils system. The Half-Breeds pretended to favor reform but actually differed very little from the Stalwarts, so far as political principles went. The two factions had arisen primarily because of a personal quarrel between the leaders, Conkling and Blaine, who were competing for the control of the party. A third group of Republicans, the Independents, tried to keep the party from breaking up, as it seemed about to do.

The factional fight came to a head when the Republicans met to pick a presidential candidate in 1880. Hayes declined to run for reëlection. The Stalwarts hoped to nominate Ulysses S. Grant for a third term. Most of the Half-Breeds supported Blaine. Grant led for thirty-five ballots but failed to get the majority necessary for nomination. Finally, the convention turned to a dark-horse candidate, a compromise candidate who had not been considered a contender, James A. Garfield. Although an Independent, Garfield was closer to the Half-Breeds than to the Stalwarts. To balance the ticket and appease the Conkling men, the convention chose as the vice-presidential candidate that close friend of Conkling's, Chester A. Arthur, whom Hayes recently had removed as collector of the port of New York.

This time, the Democrats also nominated a former Union general, Winfield Scott Hancock, who had gained fame at the Battle of Gettysburg. During the campaign, neither the Republicans nor the Democrats took a clear stand on any public issue; instead, both sides dealt in personalities. The Republicans accused Hancock of cowardice during the Civil War, though in fact his record was so excellent that he had been called "Hancock the Superb." The Democrats insisted that, as a congressman, Garfield had accepted a bribe from the Crédit Mobilier, the company that had constructed the Union Pacific Railroad, but this charge was never proved. On election day, Garfield got fewer than 40,000 more popular votes than Hancock and less than a majority of the total number of votes cast (some of which went to third-party candidates), yet he won the election.

Up to this time, Garfield's life had been a success story; he had been born in a log cabin and he now lived in the White House. He was handsome, athletic, genial, and well educated, a former college professor and president (at Hiram College in Ohio). It was said that he could write Greek with one hand and, at the same time, Latin with the other. But he was eager to be well liked, and as a consequence he often seemed indecisive, timid, and changeable. As President, he was soon overwhelmed by the demands that job seekers made upon him. "My God!" he once exclaimed. "What is there in this place that a man should ever want to get into it?"

Yielding to Blaine's influence, Garfield awarded most of the patronage to the Half-Breeds. He gave Blaine himself the top cabinet position, that of secretary of state. Garfield showed his independence, however, by naming a civil service reformer, Thomas L. James, as postmaster general, and he backed James when James began to expose some misdoings in the Post Office Department. Garfield appointed one of Conkling's bitter foes as collector of the port of New York.

Conkling, furious, demanded that the Senate refuse to confirm this appointment. When the Senate nevertheless approved it, he dramatically announced his resignation from that body. His fellow senator from New York, Thomas C. Platt, also resigned (and thereafter was known as "Me Too" Platt). Conkling and Platt expected the New York legislature to reëlect them as United States senators and thus rebuke the President. The legislature, however, finally chose two other men. Many of Conkling's followers were bitterly disappointed when they failed to get the jobs they had sought. One of these men, the mentally unbalanced Charles J. Guiteau, held a grudge because Garfield had refused to appoint him as consul in Paris. On July 2, 1881, when the President was about to leave on a vacation trip, Guiteau stepped out of the crowd in the Washington, D.C., railroad station and fired two pistol shots at him. As Garfield fell, the assassin shouted: "I am a Stalwart and Arthur is President now!"

The merit system was begun under Arthur

In fact, Chester A. Arthur did not become President till September 19, 1881, when Garfield, after lingering for eighty days with a bullet in his back, finally died. At this news, reformers were dismayed. They expected the worst from Arthur, who had the reputation of being a spoilsman and an irresponsible playboy. The challenge of the presidency, however, brought out his best qualities, and the responsibilities of the job sobered him. When old cronies slapped him on the back and called him "Chet," he gave them a stony stare, and they soon learned to address him properly as "Mr. President." He did not turn the patronage over to Conkling, as many had thought he would do. Instead, he took up the cause of reform.

The country was in a reformist mood because of the shock of Garfield's assassination. Shortly before he was shot, Garfield had written in his diary: "Some civil service reform will come by necessity after the wearisome years of wasted Presidents have paved the way for it." These words proved to be prophetic.

The demand for reform was intensified by the exposure of scandals in the Post Office Department. Arthur followed the lead of his predecessor, Garfield, in encouraging Postmaster General James' investigation. This revealed the so-called star-route frauds. On certain western mail routes, which were designated by stars, private contractors carried the mail in stages or on horseback. The investigation showed that contracts had been awarded to Re-publican politicians who were receiving excessive pay for their services. Arthur denounced these spoilsmen, and their contracts were terminated.

In his first message to Congress, Arthur recommended the passage of legislation to reform the civil service. Both Republicans and Democrats now were eager to demonstrate their opposition to the spoils system. A Democratic senator from Ohio, George H. Pendleton, introduced a reform measure, which was passed by an overwhelming bipartisan majority in both houses of Congress early in 1883.

The Pendleton Act authorized the President to appoint a three-man bipartisan civil service commission. The commissioners were to arrange "open competitive examinations for testing the fitness of applicants for the public service now classified or to be classified." The law itself classified—that is, put under the competitive, merit system—only a comparatively small number of lower offices. But the law provided that the President, on his own initiative, could add to the "classified list" and thus include other positions. The law also prohibited the enforced collection of campaign contributions from federal officeholders and protected from dismissal men who refused to make such party payments.

Arthur faithfully put the law into effect, appointing known civil service reformers to the new commission. At first, the commission had jurisdiction over only about one eighth of the federal offices (roughly 14,000 out of a total of 110,000). Until 1900, the Presidents who succeeded Arthur were alternately Democratic and Republican. Each one extended the classified list to include some offices held by his own appointees and thus protected them from removal by his successor. (These officeholders did not have to take examinations, but when they died or resigned, their replacements had to do so.) In this way, for political reasons, the scope of the merit system was steadily enlarged. By 1900, it covered two fifths of all the federal offices.

Politics still played a part in federal appointments, even the appointments to places on the classified list. Usually the commission certified more than one candidate for a particular job. The appointing officer could almost always find, among those who were certified, at least one man of the officer's own party. Nevertheless, the new procedure meant that a growing number of officeholders had at least some qualification, other than political, for their positions. It also meant that the worst abuses of the spoils system were noticeably reduced.

Another consequence of civil service reform was less fortunate. As politicians lost some of their old-fashioned patronage, they had to look for new sources of political support. More and more frequently they turned to wealthy businessmen who gave contributions in return for anticipated favors.

REVIEWING THE SECTION

1. How did Hayes attempt to reform the spoils system? What successes did he achieve?

2. What divided the Republican party into two factions? How did a quarrel over patronage lead to Garfield's assassination?

3. Why was Arthur able to achieve passage of legislation which reformed the civil service? How was the merit system steadily expanded after the passage of the act?

EFFORTS TO LOWER THE TARIFF FAILED

Tariff reform was as badly needed as civil service reform, and it was even more difficult to bring about. During the Civil War, the general level of tariff rates had been raised to unprecedented heights, and then extra duties (countervailing duties) had been added to compensate for the wartime excise taxes that domestic manufacturers had to pay. After the war, most of these excise taxes were abolished, but the countervailing duties remained in effect. Although the regular rates on some items were lowered from time to time, those on other items were raised. An overall reduction seemed nearly impossible. Protectionists claimed that if rates were reduced cheap foreign goods

would flood the country, resulting in ruin for firms in the United States and unemployment for their workers. The protected industries supported one another, maintained powerful lobbies in Washington, D.C., and made friends among both Republicans and Democrats in Congress.

As consumers, however, many people in the United States complained that high duties led to exorbitant prices for manufactured goods and excessive profits for manufacturing corporations. According to the critics, the tariff not only added directly to prices and profits, but also, as the "mother of trusts," encouraged the growth of monopolies by preventing competition from abroad. Import and export merchants, too, objected to the tariff, on the grounds that it interfered with foreign trade. Most economists agreed that the existing rates were much too high for the good of the country.

Nevertheless, no serious effort was made to deal with the tariff till more than twenty years after the end of the Civil War. Even then, though some new laws were passed, no significant reform was accomplished.

Cleveland tried to lower the tariff

In 1884, the Democrats won a presidential election for the first time since 1856. The new President, Grover Cleveland, eventually called attention to the tariff and made it a leading political question. During the election campaign, however, neither the Democrats nor the Republicans had had much to say about the tariff or any other significant subject. Each party simply tried to show that the other party's candidate was unfit for office. Even more than in 1880, mudslinging took the place of a serious discussion of issues.

The Republican candidate, James G. Blaine, was his party's most popular leader. He had a magnetic personality and a flair for oratory. Five times he had been a contender for the presidential nomination, but only this time did he obtain it. People loved him but many did not trust him because he

The Political Poor Relation—an Unwelcome Guest, **Puck**, April 4, 1888

The Discontented Farmer in this cartoon asks, "Here, gents, where do I fit in?" Seated at the banquet table are the nation's prominent "monopolists." Their meal of "trust roast" and "monopoly pudding" was prepared in the "congressional kitchen."

had been accused of using his influence in Congress to get a land grant for an Arkansas railroad in which he had a financial interest. In 1884, this charge was revived, the Democrats having managed to get hold of some Blaine correspondence, the "Mulligan letters," which seemed to implicate him in the unethical deal.

Cleveland, on the other hand, had gained a reputation for honesty in public service as mayor of Buffalo and governor of New York. His nomination caused a number of reform-minded Republicans, the "Mugwumps," to change sides and support the Democratic ticket. Then, in the midst of the campaign, the newspapers published a scandalous story that Cleveland, a bachelor, once had fathered an illegitimate child.

This put the Mugwumps in a dilemma, for Blaine had led an impeccable private life and was highly regarded as a model husband and father. But one of the Mugwumps found a way out of the dilemma. He told his fellow Republicans that:

We should elect Mr. Cleveland to the public office he is so eminently qualified to fill and remand Mr. Blaine to the private life he is so eminently fitted to adorn.

This the voters did, though by a narrow margin.

Among the Presidents from Lincoln to Theodore Roosevelt, Cleveland stands out as the ablest. Short and heavy-set, unimaginative, brusque, he charmed no one, but he had the courage to say no and the stubbornness to stand by his convictions.

His concept of reform was limited; it amounted to little more than a belief in efficient and frugal government. Even if he had taken office with a thoroughgoing reform program, he would have run into trouble in trying to carry it out, for the Republicans had a majority in the Senate. He and Congress often disagreed.

Already known as a "veto governor," Cleveland set new records as a vetoing President. He vetoed, among other measures, more than two hundred bills for pensioning Civil War veterans. The existing pension laws were broad and generous; they applied to every Union veteran with an honorable discharge and a disability resulting from his war service. A man who failed to qualify under the general laws, however, could ask his congressman to arrange for a special pension. Congress passed special pension bills in batches, often with no investigation or discussion. These were the measures that Cleveland rejected in such large numbers, though he signed many more than he vetoed. At the urging of the Grand Army of the Republic, Congress passed a "pauper" pension bill to give a stipend to every disabled veteran (with an honorable discharge) or veteran's widow who needed money, regardless of how or when the veteran had been disabled. Cleveland vetoed this too.

Such a law was enacted later on, however, during Harrison's administration, in 1890. As a consequence, the appropriations for pensions nearly doubled, rising to more than $150 million a year. Pensions eventually cost the government far more than the war itself.

During Cleveland's first term, the federal government annually was taking in about $100 million more than it was spending. This resulted in a treasury surplus, which Cleveland thought encouraged the extravagance of Congress. The surplus was due mainly to the tariff, the largest source of federal income at that time. In 1887, Cleveland began to call for tariff reduction as a means of lessening government waste. Referring to the surplus, he said: "It is a *condition* which confronts us, not a theory."

The Democratic majority in the House of Representatives followed Cleveland's lead and approved a low-tariff bill (1888). The Republican majority in the Senate, however, adopted a different measure, one that made some revisions but maintained a generally high level of duties. Neither house would accept the other's bill, so the tariff question remained unsettled; it became the main issue in the presidential election of 1888.

Harrison was elected and the tariff was raised

In 1888, the Democrats renominated Cleveland and made tariff reduction the key plank of their platform. The Republicans nominated Benjamin Harrison, the grandson of an earlier President (William Henry Harrison), and publicized him as a candidate whose political record was perfectly clean, though admittedly quite undistinguished. Harrison and his party took a protariff stand. Corporations desiring tariff protection contributed heavily to the Republican campaign fund, and the Republicans spent more money than any party had spent in any previous campaign. Even so, Harrison failed to get a majority or even a plurality of the popular votes, though he carried enough of the large Northern states to gain a sizeable majority in the electoral college.

President Harrison had far from complete control over his own administration. He was not really his party's leader, and though he was an eloquent speaker, he was too cold a person to deal effectively with people. "Harrison can make a speech to ten thousand men and every man of them will go away his friend," an associate remarked. "Let him meet the same ten thousand in private, and every one will go away his enemy." Harrison was as honest as Hayes or Cleveland, but he had considerably less personal force than either.

Without a strong President to restrain it, Congress proceeded to hand out money more freely than ever. It made large appropriations for pensions, river and harbor improvements, government buildings, coast defenses, and other purposes. Newspapers began to call it the "billion-dollar Congress."

Meanwhile, with the Republicans now controlling both houses, Congress put together a tariff bill with higher duties on manufactured goods than the government ever before had levied. To encourage the founding of new industries, the bill even gave protection to industries that did not then exist in the United States. The measure was intended to cut down the treasury surplus while protecting manufacturers. It was expected to reduce the surplus in two ways. First, its prohibitive rates would keep out certain foreign products entirely and thus would decrease customs receipts. Second, the bill eliminated the tariff on imported sugar and compensated sugar producers in the United States by giving them a bounty of two cents a pound; the bounty would take money out of the treasury. This measure became a law, the McKinley Tariff Act, in 1890.

After Cleveland's return to the presidency (1893) for his second term, he tried again to bring about a downward revision of the tariff. He was hopeful, since the Democrats now had a majority in both houses of Congress. A Democrat introduced a tariff-reduction bill in the House of Representatives, but in the Senate some of the Democrats joined with Republicans to add 633 amendments to it. The resulting Wilson-Gorman Tariff Act, which Congress adopted in 1894, ended the sugar bounty and restored the sugar duties. On the whole, the new law established rates lower than those of the McKinley Tariff, yet not nearly so low as Cleveland desired. He refused to sign the Wilson-Gorman bill but allowed it to become a law without his signature.

After the Republicans had returned to power, they raised the level of duties again by passing the Dingley Tariff Act (1897). This imposed such a steep duty on steel rails that British manufacturers could no longer sell them in the United States. But American manufacturers could get a higher price than ever in the United States while also exporting rails to Britain and making a profit on them even at the comparatively low British price.

As a whole, the new rates were so high that imports and hence customs receipts fell off sharply.

REVIEWING THE SECTION

1. What efforts to achieve economy in government did Cleveland make during his first administration? Why did he have difficulty in achieving tariff reform?

2. How did the political situation affect the tariff level between 1883 and 1898?

THE GOVERNMENT TRIED TO REGULATE BUSINESS

The federal government stepped in to regulate railroads and other corporations only after a number of the states had tried to do so and had failed. In the 1870's, in response to pressure from a farmers' organization, the Patrons of Husbandry (the National Grange), several states in the Middle West had passed laws setting up commissions to supervise railroads and grain elevators and prevent them from charging exorbitant or discriminatory rates. By the 1880's, a total of fifteen states and territories had enacted antimonopoly laws. These regulatory efforts, however, came into conflict with certain provisions of the federal Constitution as interpreted by the Supreme Court.

The Constitution gives Congress the power to regulate commerce among the states (*Article I, sec. 8*). In an 1877 ruling, the Supreme Court upheld the so-called Granger laws and conceded the right of a state to control a railroad's charges. In 1886, however, the Court said the state's regulations must apply only to traffic within the state; the state must not interfere with interstate commerce. Since this commerce made up about three fourths of the railroads' business, the state commissions were left with little authority.

The Constitution requires that each state give "full faith and credit" to the public acts of every other state (*Article IV, sec 1*). The Supreme Court long had interpreted this to mean that a corporation chartered in one state could operate freely in any other. Thus a monopolistic company chartered in Delaware, New Jersey, or West Virginia—all of which allowed incorporation with few restrictions—could also carry on business in states with antimonopoly laws.

The Fourteenth Amendment forbids every state to "deprive any person of life, liberty, or property, without due process of law." From 1886 on, the Supreme Court maintained that these words applied to corporations ("artificial persons") as well as to individuals, and that the amendment prohibited a state from depriving companies of their property (that is, their profits) through laws interfering with their business.

Therefore, if railroads were to be regulated and monopolies were to be prevented, the task was up to the federal government. When Congress finally took action on these matters, however, the Supreme Court frustrated the federal laws as it had already done with the state laws.

Congress passed the Interstate Commerce Act

To provide for federal regulation of the railroads, Congress passed the Interstate Commerce Act in 1887. This stated that all railroad rates must be "reasonable and just." It forbade railroads to discriminate in favor of certain shippers by means of *rebates* (secret discounts), *drawbacks* (payments to one customer out of receipts from other customers), or the *long and short haul* (charging more for short distances, over which there was no competing line, than for long distances over which there was cutthroat competition). The act also outlawed *pooling* agreements (to apportion traffic or earnings and thus avoid competition) and other common abuses.

The act provided for the appointment by the President of the Interstate Commerce Commission, consisting of five members, but failed to provide the commissioners with enough authority to accomplish much. They were empowered to investigate the management of railroads, to require from them annual reports of operations and finance, and to hear complaints from shippers. But they were not allowed to fix rates or enforce any rulings. If the commissioners felt that the law was being violated, they could only sue the offending railroad. The federal courts would then decide what action, if any, was to be taken. Since its language was so vague, it was hard for either the commissioners or the judges to know whether the law was actually being broken. What, after all, were "reasonable and just" rates? The commissioners soon found that they could get little help from the courts. Suits dragged on endlessly and, when cases finally reached the Supreme Court, the decisions almost always favored the railroads.

Some observers suspected, with good reason, that the Interstate Commerce Act had been designed more to quiet the public than to make possible real regulation. A senator described the law as "a delusion and a sham, an empty menace to great interests, made to answer the clamor of the ignorant and unreasoning." Not till nearly twenty years after its passage was the act amended so as to make the Interstate Commerce Commission an effective agency. Since then, the law has been further strengthened. Despite its weaknesses, the original act of 1887 was important because it marked the beginning of federal regulation of business.

Congress passed the Sherman Antitrust Act

In 1890, Senator John Sherman of Ohio declared:

Congress alone can deal with [the trusts], and if we are unwilling or unable there will soon be a trust for every production and a master to fix the price of every necessity of life.

Throughout the country, more and more people were demanding that Congress do something to prevent this. Others questioned whether even Congress had the constitutional power to do so, since there is nothing in the Constitution about monopolies. Advocates of federal action, however, pointed to the power given Congress by the Constitution to regulate interstate commerce and argued that, since business combinations often restricted competition and impeded the free flow of commerce, Congress had a right to deal with them.

Accordingly, in 1890, Congress passed the Sherman Antitrust Act. This law made illegal "every Contract, combination in the form of trust or otherwise, or conspiracy, in restraint of trade or commerce among the several States, or with foreign nations." In addition the law defined as a misdemeanor any "attempt to monopolize, or combine or conspire with any other person or persons to monopolize, any part of the trade or commerce among the several states or with foreign nations." It set only relatively light punishment for violators: a fine, not to exceed $5000, or imprisonment, not to exceed one year, or both. The law also provided that any person suffering a loss as the victim of an illegal combination might sue to recover "threefold the damages by him sustained."

Some of the congressmen who helped to pass this measure had no serious intention of getting rid of monopoly. They only hoped (as had some of those who helped to pass the Interstate Commerce Act) to appease the public discontent, appeal to the voters, and thus get themselves re-elected to Congress. One senator explained:

The conduct of the Senate...has not been in the line of honest preparation of a bill to prohibit and punish trusts. It has been in the line of getting some bill with that [antitrust] title that we might go to the country with.

The Sherman Antitrust Act was as difficult to enforce as the Interstate Commerce Act. To break up a trust, the federal government had to prove that the company or combination of companies was actually breaking the law. Again, the government had to sue the company, and the final decision was left to the Supreme Court. The President and his attorney general were responsible for starting the action, and they would do so only if they personally were concerned about monopolies. Before 1901,

the Department of Justice brought in only eighteen antitrust suits, and it lost most of these cases.

In the case of *United States* v. *E. C. Knight Co.* (1895), the government charged that the Knight company controlled ninety-eight per cent of the country's sugar-refining business. The Supreme Court conceded this, but concluded that the company's activities were perfectly legal, nevertheless. Sugar refining, the chief justice reasoned, was *manufacturing* and not commerce (even though the raw material came from widely scattered sources and the finished product was sold throughout the country). Therefore, according to the Supreme Court, the Sherman Antitrust Act had no bearing on the case. This decision made the law practically unenforceable against industrial monopolies.

REVIEWING THE SECTION

1. What were the provisions of the Interstate Commerce Act? Why was it difficult to enforce?

2. What were the provisions of the Sherman Antitrust Act? Why was it difficult to enforce?

THE POPULISTS BECAME ACTIVE IN POLITICS

In addition to calling for tariff reduction, railroad regulation, and antitrust action, the discontented farmers of the country demanded a number of other national reforms. By the 1880's, businessmen already were well organized and extremely influential in politics, but the farmers needed to form combinations of their own to give effect to their demands. Although they still had a national organization, the National Grange, it was no longer the large, crusading body it had been in the 1870's, when it induced several states in the Middle West to undertake the regulation of grain elevators and railroads. The Grange had lost most of its members and had become essentially a fraternal and recreational society, whose leaders represented the more contented and conservative farmers. Advocates of reform began to develop new, politically active organizations.

In their efforts to influence national legislation, the farmers had a choice of two approaches: to throw their support to either of the two major parties—whichever would promise the greater help —or to create a new party. It took a vast amount of money and political skill, however, to create a new party, and the history of recent third parties offered little encouragement. One or more of them —the Greenback, Labor, Prohibition, and other parties—had put up candidates in every national election from 1876 to 1888, but none had made much headway (though, in the congressional elections of 1878, the Greenbackers polled a million votes and elected fifteen congressmen).

The discontented farmers, especially those in the West and the South, tried both approaches, at first bringing pressure to bear upon the major parties and later setting up a new political organization. This, the People's party, the most important of all the third parties of the period, provided excitement in the election of 1892.

The Farmers' Alliances went into politics

Two large farm groups were organized during the 1880's. One was the National Farmers' Alliance of the Northwest, usually known as the Northern Alliance. It had its largest membership in the wheat-growing states of Kansas, Nebraska, Minnesota, and North and South Dakota, where the farmers' problems were particularly severe because of prolonged drought. The other was the Farmers' Alliance and Industrial Union of the South, or Southern Alliance, with members throughout the Southern states. Affiliated with it was a separate organization for Negro farmers, the National Colored Farmers' Alliance.

Located in the Great Plains and the South, the Alliances differed from the Grange, which, in the days of its greatest influence, had been strongest in the Middle West, especially in Illinois, Indiana, and Wisconsin. Yet in their activities the Alliances at first were very similar to the old Grange. They carried on social and educational programs, set up coöperatives for buying and selling, and tried to secure the enactment of state laws to protect agricultural interests.

By 1890, however, the Alliance men had come to believe they ought to play a more direct and active role in politics. The McKinley Tariff, which Congress had passed that year, antagonized the farmers and increased their discontent. They concluded that, if they were to get assistance from government, state or federal, they could no longer rely on voting for Republicans or Democrats who promised to help them. Instead, they would have to nominate and elect candidates of their own.

In the Western states, the farmers now began to support Alliance tickets in competition with the Republican and Democratic tickets. In the Southern states, however, the white farmers hesitated to form a separate party and thus disrupt the one-party system of the Solid South. The Democratic party in the South stood for "white supremacy." If a new party should compete with it, one or both of the two might be tempted to seek Negro support. And if the Negroes were thus encouraged to vote, they would probably hold the balance of power between the two parties. Fearing such a consequence, the Southern white farmers chose to remain, for the time being, within the Democratic organization. They tried to get members of the Alliance nominated on the Democratic ticket.

Alliance members were encouraged by the state and congressional elections of 1890. The Northern Alliance elected a number of state legislators in Kansas, South Dakota, and Minnesota, and a majority of them in Nebraska. It also elected two representatives from Nebraska, a senator from South Dakota, and five representatives and a senator from Kansas. The Southern Alliance appeared to have done even better. Its candidates, running on the Democratic ticket, became governors of four states and gained control of the legislatures in eight. Forty-four were sent to the House of Representatives and three to the Senate. Many of these, however, later went back on their promises to support the farmers' cause.

The People's party was launched

Their successes in 1890 encouraged some of the Northern and Southern Alliance leaders to get together during the next two years and organize a new nation-wide party for the election of 1892. They proceeded to do so in a fanatical, crusading spirit such as the country had not seen since the heyday of the abolitionists.

At meetings in Cincinnati and St. Louis in 1891, Alliance leaders made plans for a national organization and drew up a statement of grievances. This read in part:

The fruits of the toil of millions are boldly stolen to build up colossal fortunes...while their possessors despise the republic and endanger liberty.

As a result, there had arisen "two great classes—paupers and millionaires." The Alliance men saw themselves as preparing for a struggle of the people against the plutocrats, so they named the new organization the People's party. From the Latin word for people, *populi,* came the related terms Populist and Populism.

The Populist leaders, most of them professional men rather than farmers, were a colorful lot. For example, Ignatius Donnelly of Minnesota was a brilliant though unstable man who wrote books to prove that the mythical island of Atlantis had really existed and had sunk in the Atlantic Ocean, that Francis Bacon had written Shakespeare's plays, and that the oppressed poor would someday join a "brotherhood of destruction" and bring civilization to an end. Thomas E. Watson of Georgia at one time favored political coöperation with Negroes, but he later turned violently against Negroes as well as Roman Catholics and Jews. Jerry Simpson of Kansas, after making fun of an opposing candidate who wore silk socks, gained the title "Sockless Jerry, the Socrates of the prairies." Mrs. Mary E. Lease, a fiery woman orator of Kansas, once advised the farmers to "raise less corn and more hell." Unfortunately for the movement, few of the leaders had much skill as practical politicians.

The Populists hoped to broaden their organization so as to make it a truly popular, farmer-labor party. The large and growing American Federation of Labor, however, refused to combine with it. Only the Knights of Labor were willing to coöperate, and by this time the organization was almost extinct. Not even the farmers showed much interest except in the West and parts of the South, and in the South most of them continued to operate within the Democratic party. This was the case, for example, with the outstanding South Carolina leader Benjamin Tillman, another colorful figure, who was known as "Pitchfork Ben" because he once threatened to tickle President Cleveland's ribs with a pitchfork. Only a minority of the Southerners dared, like Tom Watson, to break away from the Democrats, much less to cultivate the support of Negroes.

Despite their handicaps, the Populists showed tremendous enthusiasm, in 1892, as they gathered for their first national nominating convention in Omaha, Nebraska, near the heart of the discontented West. They adopted a platform demanding a long series of radical reforms. Among these were the following:

(1) A drastic inflation of the currency, either through the issuance of new paper money or through the production of additional silver coins.

(2) Government ownership and operation of the railroads and telegraph and telephone systems.

(3) The so-called sub-treasury plan. According to this plan, farmers could store their surplus crops in government warehouses and, with the crops as security, could borrow money from the government in the form of special treasury notes. The primary purpose was to enable the farmers, when prices were low, to hold their products off the market and wait for prices to rise.

(4) A federal income tax, to be "graduated" in such a way as to take a much higher proportion of large than of small incomes.

(5) The establishment of postal savings banks.

(6) A shorter working day for workers in industrial factories.

(7) The initiative and referendum. The *initiative* would enable the people, by petition, to introduce bills for the consideration of Congress or the state legislatures. The *referendum* would permit the people to vote on, and to defeat if they wished, bills that already had been passed.

(8) Election of United States senators by direct vote of the people instead of election by the state legislatures.

(9) A single term for the President and the Vice President.

After approving these planks, the Populist convention nominated James B. Weaver of Iowa as their presidential candidate. Weaver, a former Union general, had run on the Greenback ticket in 1880. He was less picturesque but more dependable than most of the Populist leaders. For his running mate, the convention chose a former Confederate general, James G. Field, from Virginia. With such a platform and such a ticket, the Populists hoped to make a good showing in 1892.

The Populists left their mark

In 1892, the Republicans nominated Benjamin Harrison for a second term, despite his lack of popular appeal. They still advocated the high protective tariff, even though the McKinley Tariff had turned voters away from the party and caused it to lose control of the House of Representatives in 1890. The Democrats campaigned for tariff reduction, with former President Cleveland again their candidate. When the returns were in, Cleveland had a decisive majority in the electoral college (277 to 145), but he received less than a majority of the popular votes. He did, however, receive more of the popular votes than Harrison (about 5.5 million to fewer than 5.2 million).

More than one million popular votes went to Weaver, the Populist candidate. He also gained a total of twenty-two electoral votes—from Kansas, Colorado, Idaho, Nevada, North Dakota, and Oregon. For the first time since the Civil War, a third party received votes in the electoral college. The Populists that year also elected a total of ten representatives, five senators, three governors, and approximately fifteen hundred state legislators.

From these returns, the Populists took heart, and they became even more optimistic of political success when, after the Panic of 1893, the worst business depression yet known began. As unemployment in the cities grew and incomes on the farms fell, the number of discontented Americans increased, and so did the popular appeal of the Populist party. As a result, in the state and congressional elections of 1894, nearly half again as many voters cast their ballots for the party's candidates as in 1892. To the more optimistic of the Populist leaders, it seemed that history was about to repeat itself. The Republicans had gone from their first national election in 1856 to national victory in 1860; could not the Populists do the same thing between 1892 and 1896?

The Populist party, however, soon suffered the same fate as has befallen a number of other third parties; one of the major parties stole its thunder. The most popular plank in the Populist platform of 1892 had been the demand for the additional coinage of silver. In 1896, the Democrats made this the main plank of their own platform, and the Populists then felt that they had little choice but to support the Democratic candidate. After that, the Populist party rapidly disintegrated.

Nevertheless, the Populists left their mark on United States history. Some of the measures they advocated were later enacted into law. An income tax, for example, was included in the Wilson-Gorman Tariff Act of 1894. The next year, the Supreme Court declared the income tax unconstitutional, but later (1913) the Sixteenth Amendment gave constitutional authority for such a tax. The Seventeenth Amendment (also 1913) provided for the direct, popular election of United States senators. In time, many states adopted the initiative or the referendum or both. Postal savings banks (now discontinued) were established, and the working day has been drastically shortened. Something similar to the Populists' sub-treasury plan has been in operation since the 1930's; farmers now get government loans on crops in storage.

The results of the Populists' efforts are indicative of the important influence a third party may exert without getting control of the government. Not that the Populists were wholly responsible for any of the measures eventually passed, but their demand for these measures helped to arouse public interest and induce one or both of the major parties to champion them and secure their ultimate adoption.

The Populist movement, however, also had unfortunate consequences. In the South, it helped to bring about the passage of laws and state constitutional amendments to debar Negroes from politics. Since the end of the Reconstruction period, most of the Southern Negroes had ceased to vote, for the dominant whites generally discouraged them from going to the polls. When a few of the Populists began to seek Negro support, other Populists objected, and thus the new party was divided and weakened. Sometimes the Democrats managed to bring Negroes out to vote for the Democratic instead of the Populist ticket. Each party usually blamed the Negroes whenever its candidates were defeated, and both sides came to believe that the Negroes ought to be completely disfranchised. These feelings gave added stimulus to a drive, already under way in the South, to take away the Negroes' right to vote.

The disfranchisement drive had begun in response to a bill that Representative Henry Cabot Lodge of Massachusetts introduced in Congress, in 1890, to provide federal control of elections in order to enforce the Fifteenth Amendment and guarantee the right to vote. Although it failed to pass, the Lodge bill alarmed many Southerners. In 1890, the Mississippi constitution was amended in such a way that Negroes legally could be kept from the polls. By 1910, laws or constitutional amendments having the same purpose had been adopted in all the former Confederate states and

in Oklahoma. The Supreme Court upheld measures of this kind in the case of *Williams* v. *Mississippi* (1898). According to this decision, the measures did not violate the Fifteenth Amendment since (as judged by their language, at any rate) they did not disfranchise Negroes because of "race, color, or previous condition of servitude." Instead, the new measures imposed poll taxes, literacy tests, or other requirements which could be used to disqualify Negroes. The literacy tests did not prevent a white man from voting, no matter how illiterate he might be, since they contained a "grandfather clause" excusing from the test any man whose grandfather had been able to vote. Southern Negroes could not be excused because most of their grandfathers had been slaves.

REVIEWING THE SECTION

1. Why were the farmers' alliances organized? By what means did the various alliances attempt to achieve their objectives?

2. What were the objectives of the Populist party?

3. Why did the Populist party rapidly disintegrate after 1896? What laws which had been supported by the Populists in 1892 were later enacted? What factors led to the disfranchisement of Southern Negroes?

GOLD WON THE "BATTLE OF THE STANDARDS"

During the 1890's, the American people divided into gold and silver advocates as they fought the "battle of the standards" to determine what the nation's monetary system was to be. Both sides carried on the struggle with almost the fanaticism and zeal of participants in a war of religion. Both believed that the salvation of the country, if not the salvation of their very souls, depended on the outcome.

The gold men advocated *monometallism,* a single gold standard, and the "silverites" insisted upon *bimetallism,* a combined gold-and-silver standard. The gold standard meant essentially that the

1619
The first group of African Negroes arrived in America at Jamestown. They probably were considered indentured servants.

1664
The Maryland legislature passed a law enslaving Negro servants. During the seventeenth century, Negro slavery was established to serve the developing plantation economy, and harsh slave codes were enacted to prevent slave uprisings. At first slaves could gain freedom through Christian baptism, but this practice was abandoned. There also were free Negroes in both the North and South, but their legal rights were usually curtailed.

1776
The Declaration of Independence proclaimed that "all men are created equal." Many colonists considered slaves as people and believed slavery to be contrary to "natural" law. Those who considered slaves as property felt that the Declaration did not apply to slaves.

1787
The Northwest Ordinance forbade slavery in the Northwest Territory.

1789
The Constitution, although it did not specifically use the word slavery, recognized the institution in three provisions: congressional apportionment (*Art. 1, sec. 2, para. 3*); the importation of slaves (*Art. 1, sec. 9, para. 1*); and fugitive slaves (*Art. 4, sec. 2, para. 3*).

1808
Congress banned the foreign importation of slaves.

THE
CHANGING STATUS
OF THE
AMERICAN NEGRO
1619-1896

Civil War Infantrymen

1863
The Emancipation Proclamation, which freed slaves only in the rebellious states, legally was an emergency measure of the Civil War. It has since become a symbol of Negro freedom in the United States.

1865
The Thirteenth Amendment freed all slaves in the United States.

1866
Black codes in the defeated Southern states sharply limited the rights of freed slaves. These harsh measures encouraged Congress to pass Reconstruction laws to give the freedmen legal and political equality. During Reconstruction, Negro legislators were elected in the South.

1868
The Fourteenth Amendment granted citizenship to all persons born or naturalized in the United States, thus including American Negroes. Another provision, to become important to Negroes in the twentieth century, gave all citizens equal protection of the laws.

1870
The Fifteenth Amendment prohibited voting restrictions based on "race, color, or previous condition of servitude."

1875
A Civil Rights Act passed by Congress granted all citizens "the full and equal enjoyment" of accommodations, public transportation, and theaters, regardless of race. In this way, Congress hoped to combat the "Jim Crow" laws passed in the 1870's to establish and enforce segregation.

1820
The Missouri Compromise further limited slavery in the territories. The necessity for this compromise highlighted the economic tension that slavery had helped produce and the developing abolitionist movement.

1857
In the Dred Scott decision the United States Supreme Court said that slaves were property and that the Constitution did not allow Negroes to become citizens.

1883
The United States Supreme Court declared the Civil Rights Act of 1875 an unconstitutional invasion of private rights.

1896
In the case of *Plessy* v. *Ferguson* the Supreme Court gave legal recognition to segregated transportation facilities on a separate but equal basis. This ruling was applied to educational facilities as well, and it became an encouragement to further define and enforce segregation.

monetary unit, the dollar, should be defined as a certain amount of gold, and that the government should exchange gold, on demand, for other forms of money. The bimetallic standard meant that the dollar should be defined both as a certain amount of gold and as a certain amount of silver, and that the government should exchange either gold or silver for other forms of money.

The United States had been on a bimetallic standard since 1792. For many years, the dollar had been defined as a fixed quantity of gold (approximately one twentieth of an ounce) and also as sixteen times that quantity of silver. In other words, the "mint ratio" between silver and gold was sixteen to one. If a person took sixteen ounces of silver to the mint, he could get one ounce of gold in exchange.

By 1873, however, nobody was taking any silver to the mint, for the price of silver had risen, and a person could sell sixteen ounces of silver on the market (to be used for jewelry and other purposes) for somewhat more than an ounce of gold. While the mint ratio was sixteen to one, the "market ratio" was less than sixteen to one. Since no silver was being brought to the government to be coined, Congress passed a law in 1873 to discontinue the coinage of silver.

Already, however, the price of silver had begun to drop. It did so because the supply was increasing and the demand decreasing; new silver mines were producing larger amounts than ever, and a number of foreign nations were abandoning silver as the basis of their monetary systems. Soon the price had fallen so low that the market ratio was more than sixteen to one; that is, it took more than sixteen ounces of silver to buy an ounce of gold on the market. And the price of silver continued to fall.

The owners of silver mines now urged that the government start buying and coining silver again, at the old mint ratio of sixteen to one. If the government should buy, at that ratio, all the silver they could produce, the mineowners would no longer have to worry about the market price.

If the silver producers alone had been interested in it, the silver question would never have been the engrossing issue that it became. But the clamor for "free silver" (the unlimited purchase and coinage at the old ratio) soon aroused the discontented farmers as well.

The cry for "free silver" grew louder and louder

Farmers suffering from debts and depressed prices for their products wanted the government to put more money into circulation because they felt, quite correctly, that an increase in the money supply would lead to a price rise and would make it easier for them to pay their debts. On the other hand, people with fixed incomes, such as the income from interest on loans, opposed such monetary inflation, since they stood to lose from rising prices. Many others also opposed it on the grounds that a currency tied closely to gold was the only dependable one, for stable business conditions.

At first, the debtor farmers favored the issuance of additional paper money (greenbacks), but from their point of view the coinage of large amounts of silver money would do just as well, and they soon joined the mineowners in supporting the silver cause. To the silver advocates, it began to seem that Congress had done a deliberate wrong in passing the act of 1873 to discontinue silver coinage. They referred to the act as the "Crime of '73," and they agitated for a new law to undo the evil they thought had been done. They gained a partial success in 1878, when Congress passed the Bland-Allison Act, but this provided for the purchase and coinage of only a limited amount of silver ($2 to $4 million worth a month, to be paid for at a price equivalent to sixteen to one). Twelve years later, in 1890, they achieved a much greater victory when Congress adopted the Sherman Silver Purchase Act, which required the government to buy an amount of silver approximately equal to the output of all the mines in the United States (4.5 million ounces a month, also at the sixteen-to-one ratio).

These gains for the silver forces were lost, however, soon after Grover Cleveland took over the presidency for the second time, in 1893. Cleveland now faced a problem very different from the one he had encountered during his first term. By 1893, the treasury surplus had practically disappeared, and gold was flowing out of the government vaults at an alarming rate. Cleveland felt that he must maintain a large enough "gold reserve" to redeem all the paper and silver money that might be presented in exchange for gold. Otherwise, the government might have to go off the gold standard, and to Cleveland, that seemed a disastrous prospect. He asked Congress to repeal the Sherman Silver Purchase Act, which he blamed for much of the gold drain. After a bitter debate, Congress finally repealed the act (1893).

Meanwhile, the onset of the business depression in 1893 had intensified the popular cry for currency inflation. Jacob S. Coxey of Massillon, Ohio, proposed that Congress issue $500 million in new paper money and use this to hire the unemployed on road-building projects. He also proposed that the federal government lend paper money to cities for the construction of streets, schools, and other buildings, thus providing additional work relief. To present his plans to Congress, Coxey led five hundred men in a march on Washington, D.C. There, he and several of his followers were arrested for disobeying a "keep off the grass" rule, and "Coxey's Army" soon dispersed.

Cleveland believed (like all the nineteenth-century Presidents) that the government had no responsibility for dealing with a depression and trying to promote recovery. He considered it his duty to protect the gold standard and maintain the government's credit, but that was all. The majority in Congress agreed with him. To the silver advocates, however, it seemed that the government ought to do something to bring prosperity and, furthermore, that the government could bring it very easily—by merely restoring silver to its old place in the monetary system.

Silver propaganda, much of it put out by mine-owners, swelled in volume during the depression. The most widely read and most influential of all the pieces of propaganda was a little book written by William H. Harvey, entitled *Coin's Financial School* (1894). In its pages "Professor Coin," who supposedly ran an economics school in Chicago, presented some of his lectures and discussions. He claimed that all the ills of the nation could be cured if only the government would go back to the free-silver policy. He wrote:

It means work for the thousands who now tramp the streets...food and clothes for the thousands of hungry and ill-clad women and children...the restoration of confidence in the business world...the reopening of closed factories...hope instead of despair ...life instead of death.

Bryan led the silverites and lost to McKinley

The election of 1896 proved to be the most exciting since 1860. So great was the popular interest in the money question that neither of the major parties could ignore the issue, though it threatened to split both of them.

When the Republicans met for their convention in St. Louis, the silverites among them threatened to bolt the party unless its platform contained a plank supporting the free-silver policy. The gold advocates held the upper hand, however, and they secured the adoption of a plank that read:

We are unalterably opposed to every measure calculated to debase our currency or impair the credit of our country. We are, therefore, opposed to the free coinage of silver, except by international agreement with the leading commercial nations of the world, which we pledge ourselves to promote, and until such agreement can be obtained the existing gold standard must be preserved.

Since the chances for an international agreement on bimetallism were slight, this statement amounted to a repudiation of silver. Thirty-four silverite

THE PRESIDENTS OF THE UNITED STATES

JAMES ABRAM GARFIELD
(1831-1881)
IN OFFICE: 1881

CHESTER ALAN ARTHUR
(1830-1886)
IN OFFICE: 1881-1885

Republican from Ohio. Garfield, who had served in both the House and Senate, was a moderate Republican who wished to promote government reforms. He was fatally shot by a disappointed office seeker shortly after his inauguration. His death did much to convince people of the necessity of making a positive effort toward major civil service reform.

Republican from New York. Although a supporter of the spoils system before becoming President, Arthur reversed his position after Garfield's assassination. During his administration, Congress passed the first civil service act, the Pendleton Act (1883), which set up a merit system for the employment of federal workers.

GROVER CLEVELAND
(1837-1908)
IN OFFICE: 1885-1889, 1893-1897

BENJAMIN HARRISON
(1833-1901)
IN OFFICE: 1889-1893

Democrat from New York. Cleveland was the first Democrat to be elected President after the Civil War and the only President to serve nonconsecutive terms in office. During his first term, the Interstate Commerce Act was passed (1887). During his second term, the nation was faced with a severe economic depression (1893-1897), which Cleveland was unable to combat successfully.

Republican from Indiana. Exercising little personal leadership, Harrison allowed the party leaders to control the administration and its policies. Pensions to war veterans were increased, the tariff was raised (1890), and the Sherman Silver Purchase Act was passed (1890). The Sherman Antitrust Act was also passed (1890), but not enforced. Six new states were added to the Union.

Republicans, under the leadership of Senator Henry M. Teller from the silver-mining state of Colorado, walked out of the convention hall in protest.

The convention proceeded to nominate William McKinley, governor of Ohio and former congressman from that state, as the Republican candidate for the presidency. McKinley had no reputation as a gold man; he had coöperated with the silverites in favoring the Bland-Allison Act and the Sherman Silver Purchase Act. The Republicans nominated him because he was a dependable, regular party man, one whom they could count on to support the party's policies, and also because he was a personal friend of Marcus Alonzo Hanna, an Ohio industrialist and political boss who wielded considerable power in the Republican party. Hanna was determined to make his friend President and, even before the convention met, had secured enough of the delegates' votes to give the nomination to McKinley.

When the Democrats assembled at Chicago a few weeks later, the majority of them thought they saw a good chance for victory in the election by coming out unequivocally for silver. By doing so, they would alienate President Cleveland and other "gold bugs" in the party, but they could gain the support of the disaffected Republicans and of silverites in general. Accordingly, the majority approved the following plank:

We demand the free and unlimited coinage of both silver and gold at the present legal ratio of sixteen to one without waiting for the aid or consent of any other nation.

In the debate on the platform, one man stood out by virtue of his remarkable eloquence. This man was thirty-six-year-old William Jennings Bryan, a former congressman from Nebraska. Bryan had written and spoken a great deal on the money question, and he was ready with a well-rehearsed speech to denounce the gold bugs and the Cleveland administration. A witness described him: "Serene and self-possessed, with a smile upon his lips, he faced the roaring multitude with a splendid consciousness of power." He proceeded to make an emotional appeal, not a reasoned analysis of theories and facts. He drew applause again and again, and then a thunderous ovation when he concluded with the words: "You shall not press down upon the brow of labor this crown of thorns, you shall not crucify mankind upon a cross of gold." Before that speech, Bryan had not been considered a serious contender. Now, on the fifth ballot, he obtained the Democratic nomination.

Bryan, the "Boy Orator of the Platte," carried on a campaign such as the country had never seen before. He traveled eighteen thousand miles and spoke to hundreds of audiences, totaling about five million people. Previous candidates had made campaign tours to a few selected points; Bryan was the first to stump the whole country and tell the voters frankly that he wanted to be President.

McKinley did not attempt to match Bryan's oratory. On the advice of his campaign manager, Hanna, he conducted a "front-porch" campaign. That is, he stayed at home, in Canton, Ohio, and greeted delegations of visitors with noncommittal remarks. Other Republican campaigners were busy, however, praising him as the "advance agent of prosperity" and denouncing his opponent as a dangerous radical. Corporations made even heavier contributions than in 1888, to pay for what Hanna called a "campaign of education." As election day approached, some employers told their workers that there would be no jobs for them, and some moneylenders told debtor farmers that their mortgages would not be renewed, if Bryan should win.

This campaign was much more than a personal contest between Bryan and McKinley. The nation itself was deeply divided, more so than in any election for many years. A majority of the people in the South and the West were aligned against the Northeast; most farmers and laborers were opposed to the business interests.

In the late summer, it seemed that Bryan's chances were good. By November, however, the price of wheat had risen considerably, because of a poor harvest abroad, and an abundant harvest in the United States. Many traditionally Republican farmers of the Middle West and Far West consequently were less willing to vote Democratic. On election day, McKinley scored a decisive victory over Bryan.

The gold standard was officially adopted

By the time McKinley was inaugurated, in 1897, prosperity was already returning, and the recovery continued during the rest of his term. The prosperous times, together with McKinley's cheerful and gracious ways, made him a well-liked President, though he was not a strong-willed or decisive one. The improvement in economic conditions also seemed to demonstrate the wisdom of Republican policies.

Once in office, McKinley delayed taking action on the money question, so as to avoid antagonizing the silverites in his own party. The first thing he did was to call for a revision of the tariff (and Congress responded with the extremely high rates of the Dingley Tariff Act). Then he appointed a commission to go abroad and look into the possibility of "international bimetallism" by agreement with foreign powers. To nobody's surprise, Britain refused to consider such an agreement.

Finally, though not till three years after McKinley had taken office, Congress disposed of the monetary problem by passing the Gold Standard Act (1900). For many years, ever since 1873, gold had been the actual basis for the currency, and this act now made it the legal basis. Silver coins continued to circulate and even to be coined, but the dollar ceased to be defined in terms of silver; hereafter, it had only a gold backing.

The official adoption of the gold standard provoked no such outcry as might have been expected from the people who formerly had been fanatical about silver. With the return of prosperity, agricultural prices were fairly high, and farm discontent was declining. The nation's money supply no longer seemed so inadequate as it once had seemed,

for the quantity of money in circulation had increased considerably, even though there had been no large new issues of paper or silver currency.

The increase in the money supply had come about through a rise in the world's production of gold. From 1873 to 1890, the amount of new gold mined each year had remained about the same. Then production began to grow faster and faster and, by 1898, the total output was nearly two and a half times as large as it had been in 1890. This rise in productivity was due partly to the discovery of rich gold deposits in Alaska, Canada, Australia, and South Africa. It was due also to the introduction of a new method of gold refining—the cyanide process—which made it possible to extract much more of the metal from a given amount of ore and to use even low-grade ores.

Bryan and the silverites (and, earlier, the Greenbackers) had been right in saying the country needed more money, though they were wrong in thinking free silver would cure all the troubles of the time. The country eventually got more money, experiencing a gold inflation instead of a paper or silver inflation. This inflation of the currency was, indeed, one reason for the prosperity that came in McKinley's time. Another reason for the prosperity, so far as the farmers were concerned, was a growing overseas demand for their crops. By 1900, the farmers had entered upon a period of comparatively high incomes, a period that was to last for nearly twenty years. Hence the money question lost its charm for them.

REVIEWING THE SECTION

1. By 1890, what legislative gains had been made by the advocates of a silver currency? Why did Cleveland oppose the Sherman Silver Purchase Act?

2. In the election of 1896, how did the Democratic and Republican campaigns differ? Why was McKinley able to win the election?

3. How did legislation passed during McKinley's administration reflect Republican principles? Why did the demand for silver currency decline?

The industrial and agricultural developments of the late nineteenth century resulted in a remarkable abundance of material goods. In consequence, the United States as a nation became far richer than ever before. The wealth was distributed quite unevenly among the people, however, and many of the farmers and factory workers came to feel that they were receiving far less than their fair share. These discontented people, especially the farmers of the West and the South, looked to the federal government to do something for them. They wanted the government to take away the special privileges, such as tariff protection, which it granted to manufacturing corporations. They also wanted the government to regulate the railroads, prevent monopolies, and lessen the burden of debt by inflating the currency. Other reformers, primarily professional men in the cities of the Northeast, wished to end the spoils system, eliminate machine politics, and make the government more responsive to the people.

By 1900, only a little had been accomplished by way of reform. A merit system existed, but it was expanding rather slowly, and it embraced only a minority of the whole number of federal employees. The tariff had been lowered somewhat, but only for a time; after 1897, it stood at the highest level in history. A law had been passed for the regulation of railroads, but the Interstate Commerce Commission, established by that law, was given little power, and when it tried to exercise such authority as it had, it was usually overruled by the Supreme Court. Another law had the ostensible aim of breaking up monopolies, but again it was interpreted by the Supreme Court in such a way that it proved almost completely ineffective. Only one of the basic reforms advocated by the Populists, the income tax, was enacted before the end of the century, and this too ran afoul of the Supreme Court, which declared it unconstitutional. The hope for currency inflation through the "free and unlimited" coinage of silver was dashed when Bryan lost to McKinley in the election of 1896.

There were a number of basic reasons for the failure of reformers to accomplish more than they did. One was the nature of the federal government, with its division of powers among the legislative, executive, and judicial branches. If a President (such as Cleveland) favored a particular reform (such as tariff revision), he was likely to be checked by one of the two houses of Congress, especially since one or both houses were often controlled by the party opposed to the President. If the President and the Congress were in agreement, the resulting legislation might be voided by the Supreme Court, as happened with the income tax, or rendered practically unenforceable, as happened with the Interstate Commerce Act and the Sherman Antitrust Act.

Another handicap was the division among the reformers themselves. Those who advocated the purification of the civil service, mostly aristocratic and well-to-do men, had little sympathy for the farmers or the factory workers. The farmers and factory workers, in turn, had little in common with one another, as was indicated by the frustration of Populist leaders when they tried to form a combined farmer-labor party.

A third difficulty lay in the party system. Both of the major parties were dominated by bosses, many of them senators, who were in league with business interests that were opposed to change. Most of the politicians were concerned primarily with keeping themselves in power, and the safest way to do this was to evade troublesome issues; hence these were evaded as long as possible. Practical politicians took notice of popular discontent only when large numbers of the discontented threw their votes to selected candidates of the opposing major party or to the candidates of a third party. When a third party managed to make noteworthy gains, the politicians of one or both of the major parties seized upon its program and its following.

This happened to the Populists after 1892. The Democrats, under the leadership of Bryan, took over the most appealing of the Populist demands, the demand for free silver, and made it the all-absorbing issue in 1896. Although Bryan was denounced as a wild-eyed radical, the proposal of inflation through silver coinage was not really radical at all, no more so than the inflation through gold coinage which already was actually occurring. The preoccupation with silver was yet another reason for the failure to enact needed reforms, for the other Populist proposals were, taken together, not only more thoroughgoing but also more practical and important than the supposed panacea of free silver.

FOCUSING ON SPECIFICS

1. How did a Supreme Court decision in 1886 limit state regulation of railroads?

2. After 1886, how did the Supreme Court interpret the due process clause of the Fourteenth Amendment so as to prevent regulation of monopolies?

3. What action were members of the Interstate Commerce Commission empowered to take against railroads which violated their rulings? Why did this action prove ineffective?

4. How did the Supreme Court decision in the case of United States v. E. C. Knight Co. (1895) weaken the power of the Sherman Antitrust Act?

5. Why were members of the Southern Alliance reluctant to form a third party?

6. What political successes had been achieved by the farmers' alliances by 1890?

7. What were the achievements of the Populists in the election of 1892?

8. How did the Supreme Court decision in the case of Williams v. Mississippi (1898) allow the Southern states to disfranchise Negroes?

9. Why did the United States abandon the coinage of silver in 1873? How did the changing price of silver lead to demands for a return to bimetallism?

10. Why did Coxey's Army march on Washington? Why did Cleveland oppose the demands made by Coxey's Army?

REVIEWING MAIN THEMES

1. Between 1877 and 1900, what issues divided the Democratic and Republican parties? Which groups supported the Democrats? Which groups supported the Republicans?

2. Why was there a great demand for civil service reform? Why were advocates of civil service reform able to achieve some success?

3. Why did many people demand a lower tariff after the Civil War? Why was it difficult for advocates of a lower tariff to achieve their aim between 1877 and 1900?

4. Why was there pressure for the federal government to regulate railroads and other corporations? Why was the legislation regulating these corporations difficult to enforce?

5. What reforms were advocated by farm groups in the 1880's and 1890's?

6. Why did many people demand the free coinage of silver after 1873? Why were these demands opposed? What were the achievements of the advocates of silver currency?

7. Why did reformers find it difficult to gain reform legislation between 1877 and 1900?

EVALUATING THE ISSUES

1. What are the advantages and disadvantages of gold-standard currency?

2. Why has it always been difficult for third parties in the United States to become major parties?

The Beginnings of Imperialism

"Take up the white man's burden," wrote the English poet Rudyard Kipling in 1899, addressing himself to the American people. The year before that the United States had defeated Spain in a short but decisive war. Americans now had to decide whether or not to annex the Philippine Islands, which belonged to Spain. The powers of Europe—Britain, France, Germany, and Russia— were already acquiring new colonies in Africa and Asia. In his poem, Kipling implied that the white men of Europe and America had a duty to govern and uplift the darker-skinned peoples of the world.

Although many Americans opposed it, the United States kept the Philippines, got possession of Hawaii, Samoa, Guam, Wake Island, and Puerto Rico, and obtained control of Cuba during or immediately after the Spanish-American War. Thus the United States joined the great powers of Europe in the scramble for distant territories and suddenly came to be considered as a great power itself.

Territorial expansion was already an old theme in the history of the United States. Before the Civil War, the United States had enlarged its boundaries repeatedly until, by 1853, they embraced the whole area of the present adjoining forty-eight states. The spirit of expansion—of Manifest Destiny—remained strong in the 1850's, and additional territories might soon have been acquired if the nation had not been divided by the sectional controversy and the Civil War. After the war, Alaska (1867) and the Midway Islands (1867) were obtained, but further expansion had to wait because the American people were preoccupied with the reconstruction of the South, the settlement of the West, and the development of the industrial system.

The American expansionism of the 1890's—the new Manifest Destiny—differed in important ways from the expansionism of earlier times. That of the early nineteenth century had been concerned primarily with obtaining new territories which were (1) contiguous to the already existing territory of the United States, (2) sparsely populated and suitable for settlement by migrating Americans, and (3) expected to be organized sooner or later as states. The new expansionism, on the other hand, was concerned with the acquisition of territories which were (1) separated from the United States by water, by thousands of miles of it in some cases, (2) already densely populated or otherwise unsuitable for settlement by Americans, and (3) expected to remain indefinitely, if not forever, in a territorial or colonial condition.

The acquisition of overseas territories, or the exertion of influence or control over them, is often called *imperialism.* In the case of the United States, as well as that of the European powers, the imperialism of the late nineteenth century was an outgrowth of both nationalism and industrialism. Colonies were desired as means of increasing a nation's strength; they could serve as the bases and coaling stations upon which the steam-powered navies of that time depended. Colonies were also desired as means of increasing a nation's prosperity and wealth. With the mechanization of agriculture and industry, it was widely believed that more goods would be produced than could be sold in the home country, that more profits would be made than could be reinvested in it, and that more raw materials would be needed than could be obtained in it. Colonies were expected to serve as places for disposing of surplus products, investing excess funds (in railroads and other enterprises), and procuring scarce raw materials.

Thus, in the late nineteenth century, the foreign policy of the United States, like the domestic politics, reflected economic developments. So, too, did the intellectual life of the people.

CULTURAL TRENDS REFLECTED THE TIMES

The growing productivity of factory and farm meant a gradual increase in leisure time for a large number of Americans, even for many of the workers. These people could spend a little more time in self-improvement or recreation. Some advances were made in education, particularly at the university level, where increased emphasis was given to practical subjects. The best novelists of the period undertook to write realistic fiction. Popular entertainment began to be a big business. And newspapers and magazines, gained a greater circulation than ever.

In the realm of thought, as in the world of business, stress was more and more placed on the practical, the productive, the scientific. Even religion showed the influence and prestige of the scientific attitude. When a New England woman, Mary Baker Eddy, founded a new faith, she named it Christian Science. Mrs. Eddy gave an authoritative statement of her views in her book *Science and Health With Key to the Scriptures* (1875). God is both infinite and good, she explained, and asked, "What can there be besides infinity?" She answered: "Nothing! Therefore the Science of good calls evil *nothing.*" Mrs. Eddy taught that "matter and evil (including all inharmony, sin, disease, death) are *unreal.*" Healing through prayer is an important part of Christian Science. This faith rapidly gained believers among people of the rising business class, especially in the cities.

Universities began to stress the practical

A key date in the shift to a practical and scientific emphasis in universities was 1869. In that year Charles W. Eliot, a scientist, became president of Harvard University, the nation's oldest institution of higher learning. Eliot raised entrance requirements, enlarged the faculty, introduced new courses, and strengthened professional schools, such as those of law and medicine. He also put the elective system into practice. Under this system, required courses were reduced to a handful, and students were given wide freedom in choosing subjects. A few other institutions, among them the College of William and Mary and the University of Michigan, had previously allowed upperclassmen some choice of courses. But Harvard's system had a greater influence on other colleges.

The Johns Hopkins University, founded in Baltimore, Maryland, in 1876, set the pattern for advanced study in the United States. Unlike other universities, Johns Hopkins primarily offered graduate work. Its president, Daniel Coit Gilman, who was influenced by what he had seen in German universities, stressed training in research through the use of laboratories and small seminars.

The new scientific and practical trends made most rapid headway in several new private universities, which were financed by millionaires of the industrial age. Two of the most notable were Stanford University, founded in 1885 by railroad builder Leland Stanford, and the new University of Chicago, created in 1891 and endowed by John D. Rockefeller.

State universities, too, responded to the new educational trends. In the beginning, these institutions had received inadequate support from state legislatures. The Morrill Act (1862) gave the states some help, by grants of public lands, in improving their finances. Legislatures generally insisted that modern languages, modern history, and mechanical and agricultural sciences should be included in the curriculum. Unlike the private colleges, most of the state universities admitted women on an equal basis with men.

Writers turned to realism

During the 1870's and 1880's, three important writers—William Dean Howells, Henry James, and Mark Twain—produced some of their best work. Although they differed from one another in subject and style, all three were interested in some form of realism and were revolting against *romanticism,* against a fanciful and sentimental approach to literature. All tried to write fiction that would be true to human experience, that would portray men and women as they really behaved.

William Dean Howells, who served as editor of *The Atlantic Monthly* in the 1870's and as contributing editor of *Harper's Monthly* in the 1880's, was the leader of the realist school. A prolific writer, Howells recorded in his novels some of the problems of life in industrial America. His most widely read novel, *The Rise of Silas Lapham*

(1885), dealt with the problem of a self-made businessman in a changing society.

Unlike Howells, Henry James found the United States, with its materialistic atmosphere, uncongenial as a place in which to write. He left New England for old England and eventually became a British subject. His was a psychological realism that often dealt with the impact of sophisticated Europe on innocent Americans. One of his finest novels, *The Portrait of a Lady* (1881), explored the moral dilemma of a naïve American girl caught in a decadent European society with which she could not cope.

Mark Twain, whose real name was Samuel L. Clemens, was more successful than any other writer in capturing the tone, the values, and the attitudes of contemporary American society. His book *The Gilded Age* (1873), written in collaboration with Charles Dudley Warner, ridiculed the materialism and the get-rich-quick spirit of the times. Twain based *The Adventures of Tom Sawyer* (1876) on his own boyhood in Hannibal, Missouri, and followed it with a sequel, *The Adventures of Huckleberry Finn* (1884). In this, his greatest novel, he exposed—through the sharp-witted but uneducated Huck Finn and his Negro friend Jim—the brutality, greed, and hypocrisy he found in the American society he knew.

The United States produced few important poets in the late nineteenth century, but Emily Dickinson was one of the most distinguished ever to appear in this country. Spending her life in seclusion in the college town of Amherst, Massachusetts, Miss Dickinson wrote hundreds of gem-like bits of verse in which she expressed a vivid concern with humanity and nature. She remained virtually unknown until long after her death because she permitted only two of her poems to be published while she was alive.

Popular culture thrived

Most Americans ignored the works of the serious novelists and poets. The reading public, which grew larger as literacy and leisure spread, preferred stories of romance and melodramatic adventure. One of the best-selling novels of the period, General Lew Wallace's *Ben Hur* (1880), carried a religious message as well as an adventure theme. Poets such as James Whitcomb Riley wrote sentimental verse about childhood and country life.

Literature for children found a growing market. One of the earliest and most successful books for children was Louisa May Alcott's *Little Women* (1868). For boys, a number of books about roguish youths were available, such as George W. Peck's *Peck's Bad Boy* (1883) and the success stories of Horatio Alger, who wrote 135 books on essentially the same rags-to-riches theme between 1867 and 1899. Boys also delighted in "dime novels," crudely written adventure tales which were published in cheap paper bindings.

Public libraries, as well as the writers of dime novels, catered to the popular appetite for reading. After the Civil War, hundreds of communities began to support lending libraries with tax funds. Beginning in 1881, Andrew Carnegie did more than any other person to spur the public library movement. He paid for the building of libraries on the condition that towns supply the land and the tax funds for maintenance. Carnegie helped to establish more than 2500 public libraries.

The adult education movement also spread popular knowledge. In the late nineteenth century, the Chautauqua assembly gained the greatest attention. This assembly began in 1874, at Lake Chautauqua, New York, with a summer program for the training of Sunday school teachers. Within a few years, other places had Chautauqua assemblies of their own or had the benefit of programs sent out from the Chautauqua headquarters. Audiences throughout the country heard bands, singers, and speakers, including scholars such as William James and social workers such as Jane Addams.

For entertainment, however, Americans turned mostly to other sources. One of these was the traveling circus, the most famous of which was Phineas T. Barnum's "greatest show on earth."

Vaudeville became increasingly popular after 1885, when Benjamin F. Keith's theater in Boston introduced continuous performances at low prices. Spectator sports drew a larger and larger attendance. The first league of professional baseball teams was formed in 1876, and post-season championship games began in 1883. College football developed rapidly after 1869 when the first intercollegiate game was played between Princeton and Rutgers. Basketball was invented by Dr. James Naismith of Springfield, Massachusetts, in 1891. Boxing became more or less respectable in the 1880's, after the introduction (from England) of the Marquis of Queensberry rules, which required padded gloves, limited the rounds to three minutes each, and outlawed certain rough practices.

The most interesting and enduring American music of the period came from the people—from gang laborers on the railroads, from cowboys on the plains, from farmers in the Ozark Mountains, and especially from Negroes in the South. The spirituals, blues, and jazz of the Negroes enriched America's folk music. By 1900, Negro ragtime and jazz—which became the basis of much American popular music—were being played by white as well as Negro musicians in Mississippi River cities from New Orleans to St. Louis.

Newspapers reached a wide public

With the introduction of the Linotype machine (1886), printers no longer had to set type by hand, and newspapers therefore could be printed much more quickly and cheaply. This improvement in technology, together with increased literacy, enabled newspapers to reach a much larger reading public in the late nineteenth century.

The journalist who pioneered in making the newspaper an organ of mass culture was Joseph Pulitzer, an immigrant from Hungary. In 1878, Pulitzer bought the bankrupt *St. Louis Dispatch* and, five years later, after making the *Dispatch* a going concern, he also bought the *New York World*. Under Pulitzer, the *World* crusaded for

Portrait of the William Astor Family, by Lucius Rossi, 1875

Grand Street, New York, at night, 1889

AND HE ASKS FOR MORE!

The Gilded Age is an appropriate term for the late 19th century, when life among the upper classes in the cities was glamorous and extravagant, but highly artificial. While a number of wealthy leaders contributed greatly to American culture, others contrived new ways to squander their money.

The elaborate decor of the Astor home was typical of the taste of the very rich. To the rapidly growing middle class of Americans, too, the exotic, the overdecorated, the ornate became symbols of comfort and prestige.

In the Columbian World Exposition of 1893, Americans pointed with pride to what had been accomplished in the New World. Streets had been lighted in New York City since the 1880's, facilitating travel about the city at night. New inventions, such as the telephone and the Welsbach gas burner, had brought additional conveniences to city dwellers. With the invention of labor-saving devices many people had time for fun. New theaters, libraries, tennis courts, and golf links helped meet the increased demand for recreational activities and facilities.

Leaders of transportation and industry gained wealth and power as corporations grew and trusts and monopolies were formed. Meanwhile, low-paid workers suffered and blamed big business for the steadily rising cost of living.

A poster advertising the Columbian World Exposition, 1893

reforms and also gave its readers sensational accounts of murders and other crimes, superior news
coverage, and special features such as the first comic
strip in color, "The Yellow Kid." The *World* became the first modern mass-circulation newspaper
in the United States.

Pulitzer's success attracted imitators, one of
whom was William Randolph Hearst, a wealthy
young man from San Francisco. After buying the
New York Journal in 1895, Hearst outdid Pulitzer
in sensationalism while attempting to draw readers
away from the *World*. Since both papers used yellow ink in their comics, their sensational, lurid,
and sometimes cutthroat methods came to be
known as "yellow journalism." As practiced by
Pulitzer and Hearst, yellow journalism had some
redeeming qualities. Pulitzer retained a basic decency that made his paper generally public-spirited.
Hearst, in the nationwide network of papers he
developed, denounced religious prejudice and appealed for social justice.

Many other newspapers throughout the country
followed the pattern set by Pulitzer and Hearst.
Most of them tried to report the news honestly and
accurately, though often sensationally. They broadened their coverage of foreign news and, through
their influence on public opinion, sometimes affected the course of United States diplomacy.

REVIEWING THE SECTION

1. What changes took place in higher education
after the Civil War?

2. Between 1865 and 1900, what types of literature developed in the United States?

3. What changes occurred in journalism?

FOREIGN POLICY BECAME MORE ACTIVE

"Whether they will or not, Americans must
now begin to look outward," Alfred Thayer Mahan
declared in 1890. Mahan, an officer of the United
States Navy, was the most influential American
advocate of overseas expansion. He wrote a number of books and articles on the influence of sea

power in history. Mahan believed that a great nation, to insure its safety and prosperity, must control ocean routes throughout the world. He therefore advocated that the United States build up its
navy and merchant marine and take possession of
islands in the Caribbean and in the Pacific for use
as naval bases and coaling stations. He also urged
the construction of a canal across the Isthmus of
Panama.

Already, many Americans were beginning to
"look outward," beginning to take a serious interest in foreign affairs. One reason for this was the
rapid growth of American exports (from $392
million in 1870 to $857 million in 1890 and
$1394 million in 1900). Another reason was the
imperialism of the European powers which were
dividing Africa into separate colonies and were
threatening to do the same with China. This made
it seem to men such as Mahan that the United
States, for its own trade and its own defense, must
join the rush to acquire overseas territories.

In the minds of some American leaders, there
was still another reason for adopting an imperial-
istic policy. The American people, many of them
bitterly discontented, were quarreling among themselves. The nation was badly divided by the Populist movement, the free-silver agitation, and the
labor disputes. An active, dramatic foreign policy,
some of the leaders thought, would divert the people from their domestic problems and would reunite the nation in a surge of patriotism.

Hawaii and Samoa were annexed

The acquisition of California and, later, of
Alaska had helped turn the attention of Americans
to the Pacific, but long before that, United States
ships had been trading with the Far East. The first
of these entered Canton, China, shortly after the
American Revolution. Trade with China grew
steadily, and in 1830, the first American missionaries entered that country. American whalers soon
began to roam the Pacific in search of whales,
which were becoming scarce in the Atlantic. Com-

modore Matthew C. Perry opened the door to commerce with Japan in 1854. Traders, fishermen, and naval officers put in at various Pacific islands to look for economic or strategic possibilities.

From the American point of view, the most important Pacific islands were those of the Hawaiian group. In 1820, some New England missionaries arrived there to save souls; they and their descendants remained to grow pineapples and sugar cane. In time, the Americans living in Hawaii managed to exercise considerable influence over the native rulers. Most of the ships in Hawaiian ports were American, and most Hawaiian trade was with the United States. American businessmen and statesmen were determined that the islands should fall to no other power. A treaty of annexation was drafted as early as 1854, but Southerners opposed the acquisition of free territory, and the treaty was never ratified.

Hawaii continued, however, to be drawn closer and closer to the United States. In 1875, the islands were practically converted into a United States *protectorate,* a nation whose independence was protected and whose foreign policy was controlled by the United States. By the terms of a commercial reciprocity treaty, Hawaiian sugar was allowed to enter the United States duty free, and the Hawaiian government was bound to make no economic or territorial concessions to other powers. In 1887, another treaty renewed the existing relationship and gave the United States the exclusive right to use Pearl Harbor, near Honolulu on the island of Oahu, as a naval base.

Trouble began in 1891, when Queen Liliuokalani came to the Hawaiian throne. "Queen Lil" intended to reign as an absolute monarch and put an end to American influence. Two years later, the American residents in Hawaii carried out a revolution with the help of the United States minister to Hawaii, who ordered United States Marines to be landed from a warship at Honolulu, ostensibly to protect American life and property. The Americans deposed the queen, set up a provisional government, and requested annexation.

A treaty of annexation was drawn up, but before the United States Senate had approved it, the Republican administration of Benjamin Harrison ended, and Grover Cleveland returned to the presidency for his second term (1893). Cleveland thought it was improper for the marines to have taken part in the revolution. He withdrew the treaty from the Senate and tried to arrange for the restoration of Queen Lil to her throne. When she threatened to cut off the heads of the revolutionists, however, Cleveland decided to let the matter drop. He recognized Hawaii as an independent republic but refused to consider annexation.

Annexation had to wait until after the Republicans were back in power with William McKinley as President. The war with Spain (1898), which involved fighting in a more distant set of Pacific islands, the Philippines, drew attention to the strategic importance of Hawaii. Even so, the McKinley administration doubted whether the necessary two thirds majority for an annexation treaty could be obtained in the Senate. Hence Hawaii was annexed, in 1898, by a joint resolution (as Texas had been in 1845), which required the approval of both houses of Congress but only a simple majority in each.

The interest of the United States in the Samoan Islands led to conflict with European powers. American land companies looked to the Samoan Islands as a place for real-estate development, and American steamship companies regarded them as a stopping point on the ocean route to Australia. The United States government was most attracted by the harbor of Pago Pago (pronounced and sometimes spelled *Pangopango*) on the island of Tutuila, one of the three principal islands in the Samoan group. The almost land-locked Pago Pago harbor, one of the finest natural harbors in the South Pacific, was an ideal spot for a naval base. In 1872, a Samoan king and a United States naval officer made a treaty giving the United States the use of the harbor. British and German firms, however, also were interested in Samoa, especially on account of its valuable coconut crop, and the Brit-

MAJOR EVENTS IN UNITED STATES FOREIGN AFFAIRS: 1877-1899

1877-1899 (From the end of the Reconstruction period to the end of the Spanish-American War)

STATEMENTS OF POLICY

1882   *Immigration. Chinese Exclusion Act,* which suspended Chinese immigration for 10 years, reversed U.S. policy established by the Burlingame Treaty of 1868. Later laws extended to 1943 the exclusion of Chinese immigrants.

1895-1896   *Monroe Doctrine* was restated by U.S. during boundary dispute between British Guiana and Venezuela. Britain at first refused to recognize that the doctrine was valid in international law, but finally agreed to submit the boundary dispute to arbitration.

WARS AND PEACE TREATIES

1898   *Spanish-American War,* fought in Spanish possessions of Cuba, the Philippines, and Puerto Rico, was ended with the *Treaty of Paris.* The U.S. aided Cuban revolt for independence from Spain.

TERRITORIAL SETTLEMENTS AND ACQUISITIONS

1889   *Three-power protectorate over Samoa* established by the U.S., Germany, and Britain.

1898   *Annexation of Hawaii.* By joint resolution of Congress, the Hawaiian islands became an American possession, the first important overseas acquisition of U.S. Earlier attempts at annexation (1854, 1893, and 1897) had not been successful.

1898   *Treaty of Paris.* Spain gave up sovereignty over Cuba and ceded Guam, Puerto Rico, and the Philippine Islands to U.S. in exchange for $20 million.

1899   *American Samoa* (Tutuila) acquired by the U.S. Treaty signed with Germany and Britain ended the three-power protectorate established in 1889.

Wake Island formally occupied by U.S. after being claimed during the Spanish-American War.

When the U.S. acquired the Philippines from Spain, many Filipinos were reluctant to accept U.S. rule and supported a native government set up by the insurrectional leader Emilio Aguinaldo. In the cartoon, Uncle Sam is saying to Aguinaldo, "Come inside, you rascal; I'm tired of chasing you around in the wet." The other colonies which have been taken over from Spain are secure within the U.S. tent.

From the **Utica Saturday Globe,** 1899

ECONOMIC POLICY AND COMMERCIAL TREATIES

1884   *Frelinghuysen-Zavala Treaty* with Nicaragua (uncompleted), in violation of the Clayton-Bulwer Treaty of 1850 with Britain, gave the U.S exclusive right to build an isthmian canal across Nicaragua.

1887   *Reciprocity treaty* of 1875 with Hawaii was extended. The treaty gave the U.S. the exclusive right to establish a fortified naval base at Pearl Harbor.

1888   *Bayard-Chamberlain Treaty* with Britain (uncompleted) attempted to settle the long-standing dispute over U.S. fishing privileges in Canadian waters. Although the treaty was rejected by the Senate, the two nations worked out a temporary arrangement pending a final settlement.

DIPLOMACY OF WAR PREVENTION

1889   *Pan-Americanism.* The first modern Pan-American conference resulted in the formation of the International Bureau of American Republics (Pan-American Union) for the exchange of scientific, economic, and cultural information. The conference set a precedent for future inter-American conferences and coöperation on common problems.

1899   *First International Peace Conference* at The Hague in the Netherlands, attended by representatives of 26 nations, including U.S., met to discuss disarmament and war prevention. Although disarmament was not achieved, the delegates set up the Permanent Court of Arbitration.

ARBITRATION TREATIES

1892-1893   *Bering Sea Sealing Dispute.* An Anglo-American arbitration treaty referred the controversy between the U.S. and Britain over sealing rights in the Bering Sea to an international tribunal for settlement. The decision denied the U.S. claim to exclusive rights to a closed sea.

ish and German governments were aware of its naval potentialities.

A three-way rivalry for the control of the Samoan Islands developed among Germany, Britain, and the United States. In 1889, some German and United States warships, gathered along with British vessels in Apia harbor, almost came to blows. Suddenly, a hurricane struck, scattering or sinking most of the ships and ending the threat of a battle. That same year, the three powers agreed to a tripartite protectorate over the islands. But this resulted in renewed disputes. Finally, in 1899, Germany and the United States divided the islands between them, the United States retaining Tutuila (American Samoa) with its valuable harbor at Pago Pago. Britain surrendered its claims in return for rights in West Africa and elsewhere in the Pacific.

Blaine revived Pan-Americanism

The essence of Pan-Americanism is the idea that the United States and the Latin-American nations have important interests in common and ought to coöperate closely to further those interests. In the United States, Pan-Americanism is considered a corollary of the Monroe Doctrine. The first Pan-American conference had been called by the South American revolutionary leader Simon Bolívar to meet in Panama in 1825. The United States had been invited to send delegates to the Panama congress, but one of the two delegates died on the way, and the other arrived after the meeting had adjourned. The United States played a leading role, however, at the next Pan-American conference, which met in Washington, D.C., in 1889. The man who did the most to revive Pan-Americanism was James G. Blaine, secretary of state under President Garfield (1881) and under President Harrison (1889-1892).

Blaine was distressed because Britain had captured the bulk of the Latin-American trade, and he hoped to improve relations with the Latin-American nations so that they would buy more manufactured goods from the United States. During the Garfield administration, he planned a conference to discuss matters of mutual concern—the settlement of disputes and the improvement of communications and commerce—with the United States taking the part of the "elder sister." The conference was delayed, however, until Blaine had returned as secretary of state under Harrison.

In 1889, delegates from seventeen Latin-American nations arrived in Washington, D.C. First, they were taken by special train on a 6000-mile tour of the industrial centers of this country. When the exhausted delegates returned to Washington, they accomplished three important things. One was an agreement for the mutual reduction of tariffs on each other's goods. A second achievement was the formation of the International Bureau of American Republics (later called the Pan-American Union) to distribute information, encourage better understanding, and promote the peaceful settlement of disputes. The governing body of the Pan-American Union consisted of the Latin-American diplomatic representatives in Washington and the United States secretary of state, who was the presiding officer. A third result was the establishment of a precedent for further Pan-American, or Inter-American, conferences. These have been held every five or six years since 1889, and there have also been many special conferences.

Cleveland strengthened the Monroe Doctrine

The Monroe Doctrine, as originally announced in 1823, stated the opposition of the United States to any effort on the part of a European power to extend its possessions or influence in the Americas. Since 1823, the doctrine had been invoked a number of times, most notably in the case of the French intervention in Mexico (1861-1867). In 1895-1896, the doctrine was restated in its broadest and most forceful terms yet. The occasion was a boundary dispute between Britain and Venezuela.

The boundary between British Guiana and Venezuela had never been definitely settled, and the quarrel over it was intensified when gold was discovered in the disputed area. By 1895, President Cleveland had begun to fear that Britain might use its superior power to impose its own interpretation of the boundary upon weak Venezuela. With Cleveland's approval, Secretary of State Richard T. Olney accused Britain of violating the Monroe Doctrine. He warned:

Today the United States is practically sovereign on this continent, and its fiat is law upon the subjects to which it confines its interposition.

The British government, in its reply to Olney's note, refused to recognize the Monroe Doctrine as international law and asserted that, in any case, the doctrine had no bearing on the boundary question. This made Cleveland "mad clear through," as he said. He proposed to Congress that the United States take charge of the matter, send a commission to locate the true boundary, and be prepared to maintain this line by force. "In making these recommendations," he said, "I am fully alive to the responsibility incurred and keenly realize all the consequences that may follow." This was a diplomatic reference to the possibility of war.

Cleveland's message to Congress aroused a good deal of fighting spirit in Britain and in the United States, and war preparations were begun on both sides of the Atlantic. Soon, however, cooler heads and more sober thoughts prevailed. A friendly petition, signed by 354 members of the House of Commons, was sent to Washington. The English people did not want to go to war for a remote stretch of tropical jungle, rich in gold though it might be. Besides, the British government was having troubles with the Dutch in South Africa (troubles that were to culminate in the Boer War) and had no wish to add to its difficulties. Britain backed down, agreeing to submit the Venezuela boundary to arbitration, as Cleveland and Olney had demanded. In the final settlement (1899), the arbitrators awarded to Britain substantially the territory she had claimed in the first place.

By his stand on the Venezuela boundary, Cleveland successfully "twisted the lion's tail" and enforced the Monroe Doctrine against the greatest naval power in the world. The prestige of the doctrine was enhanced. At the same time, strangely enough, Anglo-American relations were vastly improved. The threatened clash, like a thunderstorm, had cleared the air. Henceforth, war between the two great English-speaking nations seemed unthinkable.

REVIEWING THE SECTION

1. How did Hawaii and Samoa become territories of the United States?
2. Why did Secretary of State Blaine promote Pan-Americanism?
3. Why did the Cleveland administration accuse Britain of violating the Monroe Doctrine?

A WAR WAS FOUGHT WITH SPAIN

The Spanish-American War began with an effort by the United States to free Cuba from Spanish misrule. Fighting took place not only in Cuba but also in other Spanish colonies—in Puerto Rico and, more extensively, in the Philippine Islands. The war ended with the United States dominating Cuba and acquiring outright possession of Puerto Rico, the Philippines, and Guam.

Ever since the time of Thomas Jefferson, Americans had been interested in Cuba, which lies only ninety miles from Florida. Before the Civil War, the United States government had tried again and again to purchase the island, and American *filibusters,* persons engaging in unauthorized military expeditions to aid or incite a revolution, had made several attempts to liberate Cuba from Spain. The Cubans themselves grew more and more discontented with Spanish rule; they revolted and fought, unsuccessfully, a ten-year war for independence from 1868 to 1878. At that time, Americans generally sympathized with the Cuban rebels, and some Americans thought the United States government ought to step in and help the rebels. But

President Grant's secretary of state, Hamilton Fish, opposed intervention and managed to prevent it.

When the Cubans revolted a second time, in 1895, a much more insistent demand for intervention arose in the United States. Americans now had a greater interest in Cuba than ever. Some of them had invested large sums of money in Cuban mines, tobacco plantations, and sugar fields and mills. Certain political leaders, particularly the ones who had read the works of Mahan, were deeply impressed with the strategic importance of Cuba; they expected a canal eventually to be built somewhere in Central America, and the island stood near the Atlantic approach to such a canal. Since 1865, the older people in the United States had largely forgotten the horrors of war, and a new generation had grown up that never knew them. A war to liberate Cuba could now seem like a glorious adventure, and with sensational newspapers playing up stories of Spanish atrocities against the Cubans, such a war could also seem like a holy crusade.

Americans remembered the *Maine*

The Cuban revolt of 1895 came about largely because of economic conditions on the island. These had grown worse with the coming of the world-wide depression in 1893, and still worse with the passage of the Wilson-Gorman tariff (1894), which put a high duty on Cuban sugar and thus cut down the sales to the United States. As unemployment and poverty spread throughout Cuba, the rebels further aggravated conditions by devastating the island. Operating at night, bands of guerrillas burned sugar mills and laid waste sugar plantations, deliberately destroying American as well as Spanish property in the hope of provoking the United States to intervene, stop the rebellion, and bring about Cuban independence.

To suppress the insurrection, the Spanish government sent General Valeriano Weyler to Cuba with large reinforcements of troops. Weyler found it impossible to put down the revolt by regular military methods, since the rebels avoided open battle. They used guerrilla tactics, burning and destroying property at night and becoming peaceful citizens in the daytime. So, in the areas of greatest destruction, Weyler rounded up men, women, and children indiscriminately and put them in camps where he could watch them. Thousands of these people died of starvation and disease.

The American people were aroused by news of Weyler's activities and by stories of other Spanish atrocities. The *New York World* and the *New York Journal,* then at the height of their rivalry, made the most of their opportunity to sell papers by printing sensational news. These and other papers throughout the country gave much space to the doings of "Butcher" Weyler and to other cases of real or alleged Spanish cruelty, but they seldom mentioned the destruction and suffering which the Cuban rebels themselves were causing. Representatives of the insurrectionists were busy in New York and other cities in the United States arousing sympathy and securing money and arms for the revolutionary effort.

The excitement in the United States reached a climax with the reporting of two events within the same week in February 1898. First, the Hearst papers published a private letter written by the Spanish minister in Washington, Dupuy de Lôme, to a personal friend in Havana. The letter had been stolen from the Cuban post office. In the letter, de Lôme described President McKinley as a "would-be politician" who was "weak and a bidder for the admiration of the crowd." Hence, said de Lôme, the United States would probably get involved in war with Spain, since McKinley wanted to keep "on good terms with the jingoes of his party" and could not or would not resist their demand for war. When this letter was published, de Lôme immediately resigned, but his resignation did not satisfy the American people, who considered his words an insult to the President and to the nation.

Six days later, on February 15, 1898, the American battleship *Maine* blew up while anchored in Havana harbor, and some 260 members of the crew were killed. Americans generally jumped to

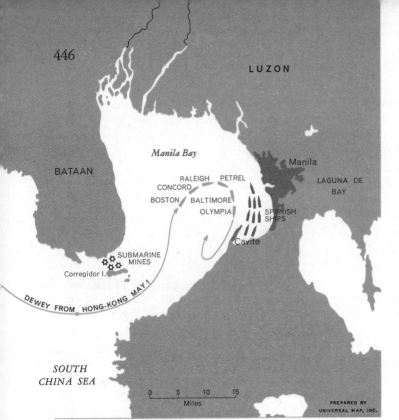

The Spanish-American War, 1898

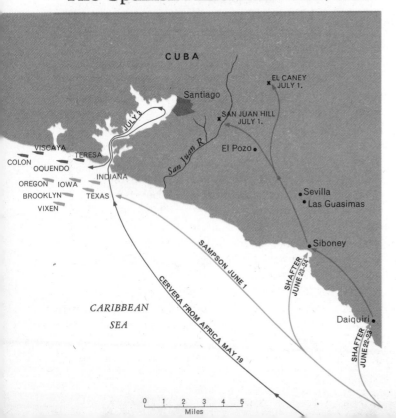

MANILA CAMPAIGN

May 1

Battle of Manila Bay. United States victory. The United States Asiatic Squadron (Commodore George Dewey) sailed from Hong Kong to the Philippines, where six U.S. combat ships battled a Spanish squadron at Manila Bay. The Spanish were completely overpowered after only seven hours of fighting, and all ten Spanish ships were either captured or destroyed. No American sailors were killed, but the Spanish lost 381 men.

August 13

Fall of Manila. Additional American troops arrived at Manila Bay in July and formed an invasion force. Some of these troops had stopped at Wake Island in the central Pacific Ocean and claimed it for the United States (July 4). While Dewey blockaded Manila harbor, the American troops (General Wesley Merritt) and Filipino guerrillas (General Emilio Aguinaldo) occupied Manila.

CUBA CAMPAIGN

May 29

Blockade of Santiago. The main purpose of the United States fleet in the Atlantic was to find and destroy the Spanish fleet (Admiral Pascual Cervera) that had crossed the ocean from Africa. A United States squadron (Commodore Winfield S. Schley) discovered the Spanish ships in the narrow harbor of Santiago, which Schley blockaded. Additional ships arrived June 1, and Rear Admiral William T. Sampson took command.

July 1

Battles of El Caney and San Juan Hill. United States victories. Having landed at Daiquiri and Siboney (June 22), United States troops (General William Shafter) marched toward Santiago. At El Caney, about 7000 Americans broke through heavy fortifications and defeated 600 Spanish defenders. Meanwhile another contingent stormed and seized San Juan Hill. Now in command of the heights to the north and east of Santiago, the United States Army began an artillery barrage of the city.

July 3

Destruction of the Spanish fleet. In a dramatic attempt to escape from Santiago harbor, Admiral Cervera tried to run the United States blockade. The battle along the coast, which lasted about four hours, resulted in total destruction of the Spanish fleet, and Spain's virtual defeat. Spanish troops in Santiago surrendered July 17.

July 25

Invasion of Puerto Rico. United States victory. A force of 3500 American troops (General Nelson Miles) sailed from Cuba to Puerto Rico (July 25). They met little resistance during their occupation of the island; in fact they were cheerfully greeted by the Puerto Ricans.

Battle of Manila, 1898

The Rough Riders Charging up the San Juan Hill, by William J. Glackens, 1898

Wounded Rough Riders near Siboney, by Howard Chandler Christy, 1898

the conclusion that the Spanish authorities had deliberately destroyed the ship. Actually, the Cubans had more reason than the Spaniards for doing so, since the Cubans and not the Spaniards were eager to bring the United States into the war. The cause of the explosion has never been determined; it may have been accidental.

Nevertheless, the yellow journals attributed the disaster to Spanish agents and demanded United States intervention in Cuba. "THE WHOLE COUNTRY THRILLS WITH WAR FEVER," a headline in the *New York Journal* declared. Soon Americans were repeating the slogan: "Remember the *Maine!*"

The United States government, which already had sent repeated protests to the Spanish government, now insisted that home rule be granted to the Cubans and that peace be restored on the island. Step by step, Spain moved toward accepting all of the American demands. Finally, on April 9, she ordered a suspension of hostilities in Cuba.

Two days later, President McKinley sent Congress a war message which he had drafted previously and to which he now added only a brief mention of the latest Spanish concessions. He asked Congress to authorize the use of the armed forces to compel the Spanish to withdraw completely from Cuba. Congress passed the desired resolution on April 20 after adding the Teller Amendment, which pledged that the United States would "leave the government and control of the Island to its people," after freeing and pacifying Cuba.

American arms quickly triumphed

The war that followed was short. It lasted only 115 days and cost fewer than 3000 American lives; of these, more died from disease than from battle wounds. Despite considerable mismanagement on the part of the army, the fighting resulted in an overwhelming victory for the United States.

Thanks partly to Theodore Roosevelt, the young and aggressive assistant secretary of the navy, the navy was a ready and efficient fighting force. As early as February 28, 1898, Roosevelt had secretly ordered Commodore George Dewey to gather the Pacific fleet at Hong Kong and be prepared to head for the Philippines in the event of war with Spain. Following orders, Dewey steamed to Manila Bay after the war declaration. There, on May 1, he fought and won the first battle of the war, systematically destroying a Spanish fleet without the loss of a single American life. He had no troops with which to take the city of Manila, however, so he waited for reinforcements. Late in July, a United States army arrived, and on August 13 the city surrendered.

Meanwhile, the people living on the Atlantic coast of the United States were worried about the possibility of a Spanish attack after learning that another Spanish fleet, under the command of Admiral Pascual Cervera, had left its base near Spain and was crossing the Atlantic. The navy department reasoned, correctly, that Cervera was heading for some port in Cuba or Puerto Rico. A fleet under Admiral William T. Sampson was sent out to intercept him, but Cervera eluded Sampson and slipped into Santiago harbor (May 19). Sampson then proceeded to blockade the harbor, thereby bottling up Cervera's fleet.

The United States Army was much less ready for war than the navy had been. Consisting of only 28,000 officers and men, the regular army was led by senior officers who had seen service in the Civil War and were too old and physically unfit to lead troops into battle, particularly in the tropics. At its head was General Nelson A. Miles, a sixty-year-old veteran. Commanding the troops sent to Cuba was General William R. Shafter, who was sixty-three years old and weighed three hundred pounds.

To supplement the regular army, Congress authorized the calling of 125,000 volunteers. Roosevelt resigned his navy department position and helped to organize a volunteer cavalry regiment known as the Rough Riders, a colorful assortment of cowboys and college students. They were led by Colonel Leonard Wood and Roosevelt.

In May, the combined army began to assemble at Tampa, Florida, amid scenes of congestion and confusion which grew worse as more and more volunteer units arrived. Many of these lacked essential equipment and found no campsites ready to receive them. They were supplied with heavy woolen uniforms, wholly unsuitable for the hot Cuban sun, and with unpalatable and sometimes spoiled canned meat, which they called "embalmed beef."

Despite the difficulties, a part of the army managed to sail on June 14, and soon about 17,000 troops landed on the southern coast of Cuba. The plan was for them to march to Santiago and approach the city from the land side. Spanish troops defending the city occupied positions on San Juan Hill. Here occurred the most important fighting of the Cuban campaign. On July 1, with the aid of the Rough Riders, the American regulars succeeded in capturing the last of the Spanish positions. Although Roosevelt had a relatively minor part in the battle, he was hailed in American newspapers as the hero of San Juan Hill.

Cervera, with his fleet in Santiago harbor, now had no choice except to surrender or to try and escape. On July 3, the Spanish left the harbor and tried to run the American blockade. All of Cervera's ships were sunk or were forced aground, while Sampson lost none of his ships and only one of his sailors. Two weeks later, on July 17, the Spanish army in Santiago surrendered.

On July 26, General Miles landed a force on Puerto Rico. His men moved rapidly across the island, receiving an enthusiastic welcome from the Puerto Ricans and very little opposition from the Spaniards. Only three Americans were killed in the entire Puerto Rican campaign.

The United States acquired new overseas territories

On August 12, 1898, Spain agreed to an armistice. Commissioners representing the United States and Spain met in Paris in October to make peace terms. The men on both sides readily agreed that Cuba should be given independence and that two

Spanish Islands, Puerto Rico and Guam, should be ceded to the United States. The most difficult question the peacemakers faced was what to do with the Philippines.

Before the war, few Americans had been aware of the existence of these islands. As one historian (Samuel Flagg Bemis) has written, "The average American citizen could not have told you whether Filipinos were Far Eastern aborigines or a species of tropical nuts." There was, however, a small group of influential men, including Roosevelt and Mahan, who knew about the Philippines and wished to get them for the United States. These men were interested in Manila Bay as a naval base, and they also valued the Philippines for economic reasons. Presumably, the islands would provide opportunities for trade and investment and would also serve as stepping stones to the commerce of China. In the course of the war, many United States businessmen became aware of the economic possibilities of the islands.

When the war ended, President McKinley had not made up his mind what to do with the Philippines. Finally, he decided that the United States ought to keep them, and he so instructed the American peace commissioners in Paris. The Spaniards proved unwilling, however, to give up the islands. They agreed to do so only after the United States promised to pay $20 million to Spain.

The Treaty of Paris (signed on December 10, 1898) was approved by the Senate (February 6, 1899) only after a spirited debate, and by the margin of a single vote. Thus the war, which had begun as a crusade to free one of the Spanish colonies from Spain, ended with the transfer of other Spanish colonies to the United States.

REVIEWING THE SECTION

1. Why did the United States declare war on Spain?

2. How did the United States gain control of the Philippines, Cuba, and Puerto Rico?

3. Why did imperialists want the United States to retain control of the Philippines?

ISSUES OF IMPERIALISM AROSE

The armed forces of the United States had scored quick and decisive victories on land and sea, and the American diplomats had got what they wanted at the peace conference in Paris. Nevertheless, a famous Yale professor, William Graham Sumner, afterwards wrote an article with the title "The Conquest of the United States by Spain." Professor Sumner contended that Spain had really won the war, for her colonial policies were being adopted and continued by the United States. Thus, he said, Spanish ideas and practices were victorious.

There was an element of truth in what Professor Sumner wrote. In the Philippines and in Cuba, the United States found itself in a position somewhat similar to the one that Spain had occupied before the war. The Filipinos, like the Cubans, had been fighting for independence from Spanish rule, and soon they were rebelling against American authority. The United States put down the revolt in the Philippines (1899-1901) with Spanish coöperation and, to some extent, with Spanish methods. The United States also maintained occupation troops in Cuba (1898-1902) and imposed certain restrictions on the new Cuban government. In both Cuba and the Philippines, however, the United States did much more than Spain had ever done to promote the welfare of the people and to prepare them for eventual self-government.

In the United States, meanwhile, a lively debate went on between imperialists, who favored keeping the Philippines, and anti-imperialists, who opposed the idea. This debate had begun in 1898, as soon as the question of peacemaking arose. The discussion continued through the election of 1900. Anti-imperialists hoped that this election would serve as a great referendum in which the voters would show their disapproval of overseas expansion by choosing the anti-imperialist candidate William Jennings Bryan, instead of the imperialist candidate, William McKinley. Bryan still stood for free silver, and some anti-imperialist voters probably disliked his monetary views even more

than they liked his opinions on foreign policy. Although McKinley again defeated Bryan in 1900, a vote for McKinley was not necessarily a vote for keeping the Philippines—it might have been a vote for the gold standard, or for maintaining prosperity. Hence the election provided no clear referendum on imperialism.

U. S. influence prevailed in Cuba and the Philippines

Under General Leonard Wood as military governor (1899-1902), the United States occupation forces restored order to Cuba and gave the people an efficient government such as they had never known. Improvements were made in education, transportation, and particularly in public health. During a yellow-fever epidemic, Dr. Walter Reed, an army surgeon, proved by dangerous experiments that mosquitoes carried the disease. By 1901, Havana was entirely free from yellow fever.

In the Teller Amendment to the war resolution (1898), Congress had promised that the United States would return control of the island to the Cubans. After the war, however, the fear arose that Cuba, having been freed from Spain, might come under the influence of Germany or some other power which then could use the island as a base for threatening the United States. Hence Congress adopted an amendment, introduced by Senator Orville Platt of Connecticut, to the army appropriation bill of 1901. The Platt Amendment provided (1) that Cuba should make no treaties which might impair its independence and should allow no foreign power to control any part of the island, (2) that Cuba should contract no public debt too large to be paid from the island's own revenues, (3) that the United States should have the right to intervene in order to preserve Cuban independence or to maintain law and order, and (4) that the United States should be permitted to lease certain parts of the island and use them as naval bases. These provisions had to be written into the Cuban constitution and into a treaty with the United States before the United States troops were

Imperialism is the theme of this British cartoon of 1898. The United States dines on Cuba, "Porto" Rico, and the Philippines while other nations carve up China. England remarks, "We can't grudge him a light lunch while we are feasting."

removed from Cuba. In effect, Cuba had become a protectorate of the United States. After being withdrawn in 1902, troops were sent back on several occasions to put down unrest and restore order.

In taking over the Philippines, the United States became involved in a war that dragged on longer than the war in Cuba. Many of the Filipinos had no more desire to be ruled by the United States than to be ruled by Spain. They supported a native government set up by insurrectionary leader Emilio Aguinaldo. On February 4, 1899, fighting broke out between Aguinaldo's forces and United States

troops. Both sides resorted to savage methods of warfare and treated their prisoners cruelly. After trapping Aguinaldo, in March 1901, the Americans won over most of his followers by offering them pardons and food.

Already, the United States had inaugurated a colonial policy which was designed to improve the welfare of the Filipinos and prepare them for eventual self-rule. In 1900, President McKinley sent a commission, headed by William Howard Taft, to the Philippines to see to the formation of a civil government. Taft served as the first American governor of the Philippines (1901-1904). In 1902, Congress authorized the establishment of a legislature with a lower house to be elected by Filipino voters and an upper house to consist of the commission and three appointed Filipinos.

Meanwhile, the American authorities in the Philippines encouraged the development of schools, the construction of roads, railroads, and telegraph lines, and the improvement of sanitation. Illiteracy declined, infant mortality was greatly reduced, and smallpox and cholera were virtually wiped out. Under United States control, the Philippines soon enjoyed more prosperity than ever before.

Imperialists and anti-imperialists debated

In the Senate and throughout the country, from 1898 to 1900, the debate on imperialism was focused mainly on the specific question: should the United States keep the Philippines? Most of the Republicans, including Senators Henry Cabot Lodge of Massachusetts and Albert J. Beveridge of Indiana, favored doing so. Lodge and Beveridge led the struggle for approving the peace treaty with Spain. The advocates of annexation used a variety of arguments. They appealed to national pride by asserting that it would be dishonorable to "haul down the flag" in the Philippines. They appealed to economic interests by maintaining that American industry and labor would benefit from Philippine trade and raw materials. And they appealed to the missionary spirit of the country by declaring that Americans had a duty to take care of the Filipinos and teach them democracy and Christianity (though a majority of the Filipinos were already Christians, having long since been converted by the Spaniards).

Some Republicans and most of the Democrats took the anti-imperialist side. The anti-imperialists contended that it would be undemocratic as well as unconstitutional to hold alien peoples in subjection as mere colonists. Yet it would be impossible, the anti-imperialists argued, to provide democracy of the American type for peoples who were so different from Americans in race, religion, language, and customs. To impose undemocratic government on colonies would weaken democracy at home, they said. Moreover, the control and protection of overseas possessions would require an increase in the army and the navy and, along with this, an increase in taxation. The anti-imperialists insisted that imperialism would also involve the United States in entanglements and possibly in wars with European powers or with Japan. The Philippine insurrection, with all its cost in money and in blood, was proof enough of the evils of forcing American rule upon unwilling people, they said.

Opponents of Philippine annexation—leaders in both parties, prominent educators and authors, and other well-known public figures—formed the Anti-Imperialist League. Its membership included two former Presidents of the United States, Benjamin Harrison and Grover Cleveland, and a number of college and university presidents, among them Charles W. Eliot of Harvard and David Starr Jordon of Stanford. Also joining the league were such famous people as William James, Carl Schurz, Jane Addams, Mark Twain, Andrew Carnegie, and Samuel Gompers.

The former Democratic presidential candidate William Jennings Bryan was another leading opponent of imperialism. He was, however, largely responsible for the Senate's approval of the peace treaty, with its provision for the transfer of the Philippines to the United States. The Senate at that time contained enough Democrats (more than a third of the total membership) to defeat the treaty. Bryan advised the Democratic senators to vote for it. His aim, he later said, was to have the United States take the Philippines from Spain and then set them free. He and the Democrats hoped to win the election of 1900 by demanding independence for the Philippines.

McKinley was reëlected as an advocate of imperialism

As the election of 1900 approached, President McKinley was extremely popular, partly because of the prevailing prosperity and partly because of his successful conduct of the war with Spain. He easily won renomination when the Republicans held their convention in Philadelphia. Mark Hanna, the wealthy Ohio industrialist who guided Mc-Kinley's political strategy, indicated the administration's approach to the campaign. "We'll stand pat," Hanna said. The party platform endorsed prosperity, the gold standard, and expansion.

Since Vice President Garret A. Hobart had died during the preceeding year, the Republican convention had to choose a new man for second place on the ticket. This gave Tom Platt, the political boss of New York State, a chance to get rid of the state's young governor, Theodore Roosevelt, the hero of San Juan Hill. Roosevelt was vigorously attacking corruption, promoting social legislation, and refusing to coöperate with Platt. Why not, Platt wondered, make him Vice President and get him out of the way?

McKinley went along with Platt's idea, since Roosevelt, as a war hero, would bring additional glamour to the Republican ticket. But Roosevelt saw through Platt's scheme and threatened to return to private life rather than be retired to the powerless position of Vice President. Nevertheless, he accepted the nomination when it was offered to him. Mark Hanna, who distrusted Roosevelt, told McKinley: "Your *duty* to the country is to *live* for four years from next March."

The Democrats, meeting in Kansas City, nominated William Jennings Bryan as their presidential candidate for the second time. At his insistence, the Democratic platform both demanded free silver and condemned Republican imperialism.

As in 1896, McKinley stayed home and conducted a "front porch" campaign. Republicans speaking in his behalf made the most of the nation's prosperity, repeating the party slogans: "The Full Dinner Pail" and "Let Well Enough Alone." Bryan again stumped the country, insisting this time that imperialism was the "paramount" issue. McKinley won by a larger margin than in 1896, now receiving 7.2 million votes or 51 per cent of the votes cast. Some Republicans claimed that the returns meant a mandate for imperialism. It was not that. If the people had voted for one thing more than another, they simply had voted for continued prosperity.

Six months after his second inauguration, Mc-Kinley went to Buffalo, New York, to give an address at the Pan-American Exposition. On the afternoon of September 6, 1901, the day after his speech, he stood at the head of a reception line shaking hands with visitors. He stretched out his hand to greet a short, slender young man who had a handkerchief wrapped around his right hand. Two shots rang out, and McKinley slumped. A young anarchist, Leon Czolgosz, had concealed a pistol beneath the handkerchief. Several days later, on September 14, McKinley died and Roosevelt became President.

REVIEWING THE SECTION

1. How did the Platt Amendment make Cuba a protectorate of the United States?

2. What were the arguments for and against control of the Philippines?

3. In the election of 1900, how did the campaigns of the Republicans and Democrats differ?

CHAPTER 18 CONCLUSION

In the late nineteenth century, cultural trends and foreign affairs, like domestic politics, reflected the economic developments of the period. The most important of these developments were the rapid mech-

anization of industry and agriculture and the resulting increase in the production of material things.

As a result of the introduction of more and more labor-saving machines, a larger and larger number of people began to have time to spend in pursuits other than making a living. They could spend considerable time on education and recreation. Education, particularly in the colleges, showed the intensely practical spirit of industrialism by increasingly stressing practical subjects. The best writers responded to the conditions of industrializing United States by trying to describe life as it really was under those conditions. The production of entertainment became organized and commercialized, like the production of almost everything else, and a mass market appeared for the sale of amusement, a market that was exploited by the publishers of cheap novels, the impresarios of circuses and vaudeville shows, and the promoters of professional sports. Newspapers, with the aid of further mechanization, especially through the Linotype machine, produced larger and larger editions and reached a wider and wider public. These trends were to go much further during the twentieth century, but all of them began before the end of the nineteenth.

The economic developments affected foreign policy by making it more active, more expansionist. In the light of the vast and growing productivity of factory and farm, it seemed to many Americans that the United States would soon be producing, if indeed it was not already doing so by the 1890's, greater quantities of goods than could be consumed at home. It seemed, moreover, that the factories would need more raw materials than could be obtained, and would yield greater returns than could be profitably invested, in the United States. This was one of the primary reasons why some influential Americans began to look abroad for territories to be controlled or annexed. As a result Hawaii and Samoa came under United States control.

Meanwhile, American statesmen asserted in stronger and stronger terms the dominance of the United States in the Western Hemisphere. Secretary of State James G. Blaine made this country the leader of coöperation among all the American nations when he called the first of the modern Pan-American, or Inter-American, conferences (1889), which resulted in the establishment of the Pan-American Union. President Grover Cleveland and his secretary of state, Richard T. Olney, gave new vigor to the Monroe Doctrine by applying it to the Venezuela boundary controversy (1895-1896) and threatening to enforce it, even at the risk of war, against Britain.

In doing so, the Cleveland administration heightened the nationalistic and jingoistic spirit of the American people, a spirit that later, with further stimulation, helped to bring on the Spanish-American War (1898) and the wave of imperialism that followed. Yet Cleveland himself was an anti-imperialist, and so long as he remained in the presidency he managed to resist the popular demand for war with Spain. After William McKinley took office, this demand increased in response to the yellow journalism employed by the newspapers' treatment of Spanish policy in Cuba, the de Lôme letter, and the *Maine* explosion. Yielding to popular clamor, McKinley asked Congress to authorize the use of armed force against Spain, even though the Spanish government already was yielding to practically all of his demands with regard to Cuba. The United States forces, fighting not only in Cuba but also in the Philippines and (with little opposition) in Puerto Rico, quickly defeated the enemy forces in the ensuing war. In the Treaty of Paris (1898), Spain gave up its sovereignty over Cuba and, in exchange for $20 million, ceded Guam, Puerto Rico, and the Philippine Islands to the United States.

The United States could not easily annex Cuba because of the anti-annexation pledge that Congress had given in the Teller Amendment to the war resolution (1898). American troops occupied Cuba for four years after the war, however, and they were not withdrawn until the newly established Cuban government had agreed to the Platt Amendment to the army appropriations bill of 1901. The Platt Amendment (which was to remain in effect until Congress repealed it in 1934) made Cuba a United States protectorate. United States troops also remained in the Philippines, where they had to fight to put down an insurrection (1899-1901). The Filipinos then were given a share in their own government, but the United States retained control of it through the appointment of the governor and other officials. The political future of the Philippine Islands was left uncertain. (They finally received their independence in 1946).

During the immediate postwar years, Americans in and out of Congress debated the question of imperialism, especially with reference to the Philippines. Imperialists insisted that the United States should keep the islands; anti-imperialists demanded that they be set free. The anti-imperialists looked to the election of 1900, hoping that William Jennings Bryan would win and, as President, would see that the Philippines got their independence. But Bryan again lost to McKinley. The McKinley victory did not necessarily mean that the majority of the voters had endorsed imperialism, since many of them preferred McKinley not because he stood for imperialism but because he advocated the gold standard and, even more important, because they expected him to maintain the existing prosperity. Nevertheless, the McKinley victory indicated that the majority of the people did not feel strongly enough about imperialism to vote for Bryan on that question alone, without regard to the other issues. Thus the United States was launched, at least temporarily, upon a career of overseas expansion.

FOCUSING ON SPECIFICS

1. How did Johns Hopkins University set a pattern for advanced study in the United States?

2. How did the Chautauqua assembly further adult education in the United States?

3. In what ways was American music enriched during the late nineteenth century?

4. How did Joseph Pulitzer influence the newspaper industry?

5. Why did Alfred Thayer Mahan believe that the United States should develop a large navy and expand overseas?

6. In what way did some American leaders believe that an active foreign policy could alleviate certain domestic problems?

7. Why did Cleveland oppose the annexation of Hawaii? How did the war with Spain facilitate Hawaiian annexation?

8. Why did many Americans believe that Cuba was of strategic importance to the United States?

9. Why did Cuba accept the Platt Amendment to its constitution?

10. How did the United States attempt to improve conditions in the Philippines after they became a colony?

11. Why was Theodore Roosevelt chosen as Republican candidate for Vice President?

REVIEWING MAIN THEMES

1. In the late nineteenth century, why did many Americans wish to acquire overseas colonies? How did American expansionism of the 1890's differ from that of the 1840's and 1850's.

2. Between 1865 and 1900, what cultural changes took place?

3. Why did the United States pursue an active foreign policy in Hawaii, Samoa, Venezuela, and Cuba? Why did it attempt to improve relations with Latin America?

4. How did the United States become involved in a war with Spain? How did the victory over Spain lead to the development of an American empire?

5. How did economic developments in the United States between 1865 and 1900 lead to the growth of mass culture? How did they affect the foreign policy of the United States?

EVALUATING THE ISSUES

1. If overseas colonies could increase the strength and prosperity of a nation by providing markets for its products and naval bases for its ships, should not the United States have made greater efforts to secure a larger overseas empire?

2. Why did the United States decide to make the Philippines a colony instead of granting them independence?

3. Why did the United States decide to go to war with Spain in spite of the fact that the Spanish had indicated their willingness to accede to American demands regarding Cuba?

EXAMINING THE TIMES

1. Between 1865 and 1900, what changes took place in American industry and agriculture?

2. What reforms were promoted by farmers during this period? How did industrial workers attempt to improve their economic position?

3. What changes took place in American foreign policy during this period?

Small's Opera House, Walla Walla, Washington Territory, 1887

Main Street, U.S.A.

Court House, Defiance, Ohio, 1883

During the last 25 years of the 19th century, often called the Gilded Age, the United States was becoming a highly industrialized nation, and more and more people were moving to the cities. Technology was rapidly altering the landscape. More than 60 per cent of the population, however, still lived in towns with less than 4000 inhabitants or in the country.

Small towns such as Elizabeth, New Jersey (pictured c. 1880), were frequently the social and economic centers for the surrounding countryside. Stores were strung along one street, often called Main Street. One day a week, usually on Saturday, people from miles around came into town to sell their produce, buy supplies, and gather in the general store on Main Street to visit and exchange news. These small towns were quiet—often the only excitement came when volunteer firemen raced off to fight fires. The towns were quaint and picturesque.

Technology, however, was beginning to change the small town. On Pawtucket Avenue (Main Street), Pawtucket, Rhode Island (pictured c. 1890), for example, tracks for horse-drawn streetcars had been laid, and the noise of the horses' hooves on the cobblestone street could be heard all through the business district. Telephone and telegraph wires had been haphazardly strung throughout the town—Pawtucket was "modernized."

Probably the most important building in the county seat, the political center of the countryside, was the courthouse, and it was designed to reflect that importance. Like the government buildings of an earlier period, the courthouse was usually a massive stone structure with elaborately carved decorations. The designers of the courthouse in Defiance, Ohio (pictured in 1883), added ornamental ironwork to the steep roof and an equally ornamental clock tower.

Since the small town did not wish to be considered culturally backward, much thought was given to the fine arts even in areas considered part of the wild "frontier." Small's Opera House (pictured in 1887) was not so elaborate as the Defiance courthouse, but it was quite an achievement for Walla Walla, Washington Territory. It, too, was a massive building with elaborately carved decorations.

The people in the small towns took great pride in the elaborateness of their buildings for they felt this reflected their sophisticated taste and the affluence of their towns.

Elizabeth, New Jersey, by E. Opper, c. 1880

Pawtucket Avenue, Pawtucket, Rhode Island, c. 1890

The
American
Home

Mark Twain and Charles D. Warner wrote a book describing the era in which they lived, an era, one writer has said, of flamboyance, crassness, and vulgarity; they called it *The Gilded Age* (1873). And nothing, said another writer, "exhibits better the excesses of the Gilded Age than its architecture." This style of architecture has since been called Neo-Gothic-Renaissance-Victorian-Americana.

The men who became enormously wealthy during the period wanted to live in great splendor. Those who were less than enormously wealthy wanted to live in splendor, too. So they built themselves elaborate homes and decorated them lavishly —and then decorated the decorations.

Since the main streets and business districts of towns and cities were becoming crowded and noisy, Americans began to build their homes in residential areas on the edges of the towns and cities. They laid out long, wide avenues like those in Portland, Oregon (pictured in 1888), usually with rows of trees on either side. Noisy cobblestone streets gave way to smooth asphalt where ladies and gentlemen paraded in their elegant clothes or rode in their elegant carriages and admired their elegant homes.

In the more modest houses of the period, such as the residence of A. T. Thayer in Denver, Colorado (pictured in

Portland, Oregon, lithograph by C. L. Smith, 1888

1880), the decorations were limited to carvings around the windows and the door, and to the ironwork of the fence and gate. In the more elaborate houses, such as the home of C. P. Dibble in Marshall, Michigan (pictured in 1877), the Victorians had greater scope for their imagination. The house was set in the midst of a formal garden; the inevitable decorations outlined the windows and doors; and a cupola was added—a final touch like the icing on a cake. This excessive

Residence of A. T. Thayer, Denver, Colorado, 1880

Residence of C. P. Dibble, Marshall, Michigan, 1877

ornamentation led people to call this type of house a ginger-bread house.

The homes of the wealthy, even those along unpaved streets such as Cascade Avenue in Colorado Springs, Colorado (pictured c. 1890), combined features from many ages and many countries; they were monuments to the imagination of the people of the time. The half-timbered style of the house (in the foreground) was extremely popular in 16th-century England.

In an attempt to find the unusual, the original, the picturesque, the Americans of the Gilded Age used dormers, towers, turrets, bays, mansard roofs and other features adapted from European styles; to these they added decorative touches of their own. Perhaps, as some historians have said, it was a vulgar, ostentatious age. But perhaps the showy taste of the period was simply an extension of the driving energy of the people.

Cascade Avenue, Colorado Springs, Colorado, c. 1890

The American Farm

View of Benjamin Reber's Farm, Berks County, Pennsylvania, 1872, by Charles Hofmann

Sod House from primitive to sophisticated, near Clear Creek, Custer County, Nebraska, 1887

From the colonial period on, American farmers had been moving west in search of the wealth and success that was always just beyond the next hill. Some found good land and settled down; others kept moving until there was no longer another hill to cross. After 1890, according to the Bureau of the Census, there was no longer any place to go; the frontier had ceased to exist in the United States.

In the East, most farms, like Benjamin Reber's in Berks County, Pennsylvania (pictured in 1872), were neat and prosperous. The fields, lush and green, were fenced off, and many of the buildings, although well worn, were sturdy. They were a permanent part of the United States landscape.

Even though much of the farm land in the East was rich, some farmers began to move west in search of new land. Some found it in what is now the Middle West. Here, too, the farms, like that of E. R. Jones of Dodgeville, Wisconsin (pictured in 1881), were prosperous. Neat fences divided the fields and the well-cared-for buildings were solidly built.

There were still some farmers who were eager to explore the land beyond the next hill; they moved on westward. But the lush, green lands of the Middle West soon gave way to the brown, almost barren land of the Great Plains. Neatly fenced fields and sturdy wooden farm buildings gave way to houses made of sod, often built into the ground for protection from the wind. The rude sod house in the foreground of the picture, taken near Clear Creek, Custer County, Nebraska (in 1887), the first home of the farmer and his family, soon was replaced by the larger sod house in the background.

Since there were still some hills to cross, some farmers moved on again, this time to the southwest. But there was less and less good land available. One of the last areas to be homesteaded was the Cherokee Outlet in Oklahoma Territory. Here, a farmer and his wife (pictured c. 1890), posed proudly in front of their home, a crude cabin made of wood. In spite of the fact that this shelter served as the office of the justice of the peace and as a law office, it had about it none of the permanence of the farm buildings in the East and the Middle West.

Residence of E. R. Jones, Dodgeville, Wisconsin, 1881, by Paul Seifert

Homesteader and wife in front of their log home in the Cherokee Outlet, Garfield County, Oklahoma Territory, c. 1890

Parade Ground with Officers' Quarters in background, Fort Ringgold, Texas, 1878

Forts and Indian Agencies

When the colonists settled in the New World, they occupied land that belonged to the Indians. When the Indians protested —forcefully—the army was called in, forts were built, and the Indians were pushed farther west. The process was repeated over and over again as Americans moved westward.

U. S. Government School for Indians, Pine Ridge, South Dakota, 1891. Photo by Grabill of Deadwood, S. D.

The heyday of the forts and Indian agencies came during the Gilded Age. Small forts were enlarged, others were re-activated, and new ones were built. The army now had to protect the settlers, the railroad workers who were building railroads from coast to coast, and the mails.

Like the forts of previous periods, the new ones, such as Fort Keogh, Montana (pictured in 1879), were self-contained units. There were barracks for the enlisted men; elaborate quarters, such as those at Fort Ringgold, Texas (pictured in 1878), for the officers; and other buildings such as stores, a hospital, a jail, and a parade ground (where the soldiers drilled in full view of the Indians).

By the time of the Gilded Age, some of the Indian fighting was over. Sitting Bull, the Sioux leader, was a fugitive in Canada by 1877. Chief Joseph of the Nez Percés surrendered that same year. Almost every American Indian was forced onto a reservation by 1885, and with the surrender of Geronimo and his renegade Apaches (some of whom are shown at Fort Bowie, Arizona) in 1886, serious fighting by the plains Indians ended.

In 1887, the government tried to end tribal life for the Indians by dividing the reservations into 160-acre family farms and by providing schools, like the one at Pine Ridge, South Dakota (pictured in 1891), to "civilize" them and teach them to be peaceful farmers. That was a slow process and many white men, eager to find new land, were impatient. Some of the Indians, such as those in the Cherokee Outlet, were forced off the reservation, others were cheated of their 160-acre farms, and some were shipped off to areas where the land was poor. As one traveler said facetiously, "people who eat their meals in four minutes and a half, and push railway lines across the prairie at the rate of two miles a day, cannot wait a hundred years to give the Indian time to bury his tomahawk, wash his face, and put on a pair of trousers."

Fort Keogh, Montana, 1879, by Hermann Stieffel

Geronimo's Apaches at Fort Bowie, Arizona, 1886

At the close of the nineteenth century, Europe was the center of world power. The nations there, together with the United States, had become the most highly industrialized in the world. These industrialized nations, with growing power, wealth, and technical knowledge, held great advantages over other states whose resources were not as yet developed. These highly industrialized nations exploited their advantages by seeking to establish control over many of the less developed countries of the world and by building modern colonial empires.

The Emergence of a World Power

Since the areas for colonial expansion were limited, the powers of the western world became rivals. This rivalry expressed itself in an imperialism of various forms. Expanding or imperialist powers tried to invest capital in foreign lands for profit, searched for foreign markets for goods from their prolific factories, and sought raw materials from abroad to keep their machines whirring. National pride, or aggressive nationalism, fused itself with technology and imperialism. These conditions intensified international rivalries and threatened the peace of the world.

Imperialism and nationalism demanded big armies and navies, either to protect trade and colonies or to enhance international prestige. Britain was the world's greatest imperial and naval power. Those who admired naval strength and overseas colonies, as did America's naval and historical theorist Admiral Alfred Thayer Mahan, used Britain as a model. Those who admired military efficiency looked to Germany as the model. In two short wars Germany had defeated Austria and France, two of Europe's leading powers, to emerge as the most powerful nation on the continent.

The powers of Europe poured millions of dollars into the building of huge navies and armies. They built up their armed forces on the basis of conscription, a compulsory draft of young men from the farms and factories, though the officers usually came from aristocratic families. Professional soldiers on general staffs prepared careful plans for war against possible enemy states. Men had always fought wars, but now they had worked out something new—organized, professional, peacetime planning for war. Planners even worked out hour-by-hour schedules for the mobilization of the huge conscript armies.

In the first dozen years of the twentieth century, a series of crises and limited wars, mainly in the Balkans, threatened to trigger the mobilization of these armies Full mobilization could lead to world-wide war because a system of alliances had divided Europe into two armed camps.

Europe had been divided by an alliance system before. Through most of the nineteenth century a vague system called the Concert of Europe attempted to restrain international rivalries. The new alliance system began to take shape in 1878 when Germany and Austria-Hungary formed the Dual Alliance. Four years later when Italy joined, this agreement became the Triple Alliance.

Fear of this combination, but mainly of Germany, drew France and Russia together in the 1890's. This same fear led Britain to overcome her traditional antipathy to France and Russia. In 1904, Britain signed an agreement with France called the *Entente Cordiale.* Three years later France succeeded in bringing Britain and Russia together to form the *Triple Entente.* Now two great rival alliances faced each other in Europe. Since the rivals had interests and colonies all over the world, any clash would affect the distribution of power all over the world.

The recurring crises placed everyone's nerves on edge. In 1913, the French ambassador in Vienna reported that "the feeling that the nations are moving toward a conflict, urged by an irresistible force, grows day by day." In June of the following year, as the international tension continued, a young Serbian terrorist killed Archduke Francis Ferdinand, heir to the thrones of Austria-Hungary, as the archduke was driven through the streets of Serajevo, the capital of the province of Bosnia. Austria decided to crush Serbia. Germany backed Austria and Russia supported Serbia. Fearing that a first blow from an enemy might catch them unprepared, generals began mobilizing armies according to the prearranged schedules. At the same time the alliance systems went into operation. After Austria declared war on Serbia late in July 1914, Germany declared war on Russia and France, hoping to defeat France before Russia could mobilize effectively, and then move east and smash Russia. Soon Britain joined France, and in the following year Italy took the side of the *Entente* powers. Ultimately, the United States, too, went to war against the Central powers.

So well planned was the mobilization of armies that in August 1914, the first month of World War I, fifteen million men put on uniforms. Before the war ended seventy million men, at one time or another, were engaged in the military discipline of making war. Thirty-one countries in six continents eventually entered the war. Nowhere did the people themselves have a chance to decide on war or peace. In the great imperial nations not even the parliaments had a chance to approve or disapprove the declarations of war. In the United States, at least, Congress, which represented the people, voted the declaration of war.

In almost every country, patriotism, regardless of the suffering and sacrifice required, became the highest good. People, almost unthinkingly, followed the lines laid out by their leaders. In almost all of the armies aristocratic or upper middle-class officers led conscripts from the working classes in battle. Military rank usually corresponded to social rank, especially in the imperial countries. At the same time, because of conscription, the armies were democratic, or represented the broad masses of belligerent populations.

World War I lasted four years and drained Europe of blood and money. Like the fighting, the devastation was massive. The cost of the war, according to intelligent estimates, was $350 billion. Ten million men, almost all of them young, died violently. About 13 million civilians died from diseases, starvation, or injuries brought by the war. Twenty million men were maimed or suffered mental wounds.

Germany and the Central powers went down in defeat, but all the European empires fell apart. From the pieces of the Austro-Hungarian empire emerged a number of new states; from the German empire a weak republic, and from the remnants of the empire of the tsars rose a Communist dictatorship. France suffered such severe wounds that recovery would take a great many years. Britain's cost was so high that she could hardly afford another such victory.

The war was revolutionary in the sense that it overturned the old order. Colonies and spheres of influence all over the world were redistributed. Colonial peoples, as in India, began demanding the right to govern themselves. Nineteenth-century imperialism was on the decline. Europe, too, declined as a center of world power. Two nations, Japan and the United States, emerged from the war stronger

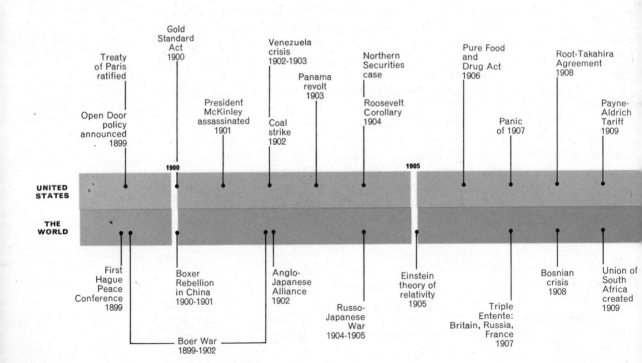

than they had entered it. Neither one was a European power.

In Paris in January 1919, twenty-seven of the victorious states, representing Europe, America, Africa, Asia, and Oceania held a peace conference. They wrote peace treaties that punished the losers and established the League of Nations, which was designed to bring order and justice out of the chaos unleashed by war. That league came into existence in January 1920, with headquarters in Geneva, Switzerland, on the shores of Lake Leman. But it was crippled from the start. Three of the world's great powers, Germany, the Soviet Union, and the United States were not members of the league.

Although the old alliances and imperial lusts were gone, the aggressive nationalisms were as strong as ever. The United States had not been active in the old system of power but it could not escape entanglement in the new one. It was now the greatest power in the world.

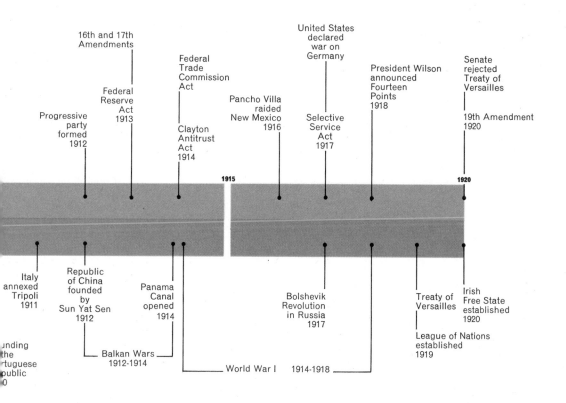

CHAPTER **19** 1900-1915

The Changing Society

As the United States entered a new century, its people could look back with some pride at what had been accomplished during the last one hundred years. In the nineteenth century Americans had conquered and settled a wilderness and had laid the foundations for the greatest agricultural and industrial empire in the world. They had created modern America with a powerful, dynamic, and productive economy. As a result, the people of the United States had acquired a reputation for being builders and doers. By the end of the century they had built a society rich in material goods.

This rich society also had problems. Many of these problems stemmed from the decades following the Civil War, a period often called the Gilded Age because beneath society's glittering surface of growing wealth lay unsightly political corruption, ruthless economic warfare between businessmen, and a general lack of concern for the welfare of others. The people of the United States had paid a high price for the feverish and uncontrolled building of an industrial society.

Industrialization brought continuing unemployment, exploitation of men, women, and children, and exploding cities where millions of Americans lived in squalor and misery. Some industrialists and economists accepted these conditions as inevitable. According to their arguments, life was a struggle in which the losers had to accept their fate, even if that fate were poverty or death.

As the United States entered the new century, some Americans became concerned about the exploitation of people which had accompanied much of the industrialization. They wished to eliminate the high costs in human suffering but, at the same time, to preserve and to spread the material benefits which industrialization had brought.

This kind of thinking led some men to question the theory of laissez faire, that government should not interfere in economic matters, which was widely accepted during the Gilded Age. The believers in laissez faire argued that the government must allow unrestrained economic competition except for aid to industries in the form of a tariff. Critics of this theory also attacked the idea that life was an inescapable blind struggle. They argued that the purpose of government was to protect the people and that it should take a direct part in their lives.

Americans were not completely preoccupied with material things. Many people devoted themselves to cultural matters, too—to art, literature, education, and science. American scientists, writers, artists, and teachers did as much in their own way to shape the nation as did the industrialists and politicians. Religious leaders also responded to the challenges which arose from the problems of an industrial United States.

Americans did not always understand or fully appreciate what the teacher, the preacher, the writer, or the artist offered. Yet they were becoming aware of the need for more education and for the benefits as well as the pleasure they received from art and the field of entertainment.

Americans at the beginning of the twentieth century differed from those at the beginning of the previous century. In 1800, only about six per cent of the population was urban. Instead of living on farms or in farm communities, as most of their fathers and grandfathers had done, the Americans of the twentieth century were becoming city dwellers. In 1900, about forty per cent of the people lived in cities or towns, and in 1920, over fifty per cent lived in urban communities.

Even the ethnic composition of the nation was changing. In the nineteenth century most people in the United States came from British or other northern or central European stock. Late in that century and early in the twentieth century a great wave of immigration from southern and eastern Europe brought a change—the population of the United States became less Anglo-Saxon and more broadly European in inheritance.

About ten per cent of all people in the United States were not of European extraction. The largest number in this group were Negroes whose ancestors had been brought from Africa as slaves. Negroes and members of other minority groups encountered special problems in the industrial age.

The population of the United States was increasing rapidly, both from immigration and from births. In 1900, there were about 76 million Americans. Ten years later there were almost 92 million people in the United States, an increase of twenty-one per cent. In size, wealth, and numbers of people the United States at the opening of the twentieth century was one of the truly great powers in the world.

THE GROWTH OF BIG BUSINESS CONTINUED

Soon after the new century opened, the pride with which the people of the United States viewed their nation's rapid economic growth gave way to an uneasy concern. And they became increasingly aware that in their land of plenty, where most of the people enjoyed a rising standard of living, there were many men, women, and children who suffered from hunger, cold, and disease. As American society became more and more industrialized, the evils seemed to spread. Some Americans came to believe that poverty and ignorance lay at the root of these evils.

Many of these people believed that the social, economic, and political difficulties stemmed from the steadily increasing concentration of the nation's economic power in fewer and fewer hands. This concentration of power, clearly evident in industry, banking, and transportation, brought about one of the most important changes in the nation's history. A group of super corporations rather than a large number of small, competitive producers dominated the economy.

Businessmen who favored the growth of super corporations did so chiefly because such combinations produced greater profits than did small businesses. Critics of the system argued that the corporations brought high prices as well as high profits. The majority of the people, therefore, did not benefit from the growth of industrial combinations. Indeed, the critics said, the corporations acted as monopolies and increased the gap between the rich and the poor. Businessmen argued that the super corporations made possible efficient production, lowered the prices of goods for most consumers and, in effect, raised the standard of living for all of the people in the United States.

Whether or not the super corporations were as much to blame for social evil as the critics charged, monopolies at that time did raise the prices of the goods and services they sold. Some Americans, therefore, demanded investigations of the great industrial empires. They wanted to halt the growth

470

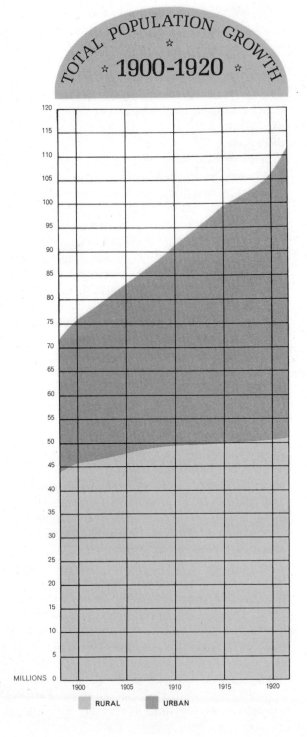

TOTAL POPULATION GROWTH
☆
☆ 1900-1920 ☆

MILLIONS

RURAL   URBAN

of monopolies, or at least bring the corporations under effective public control. They also wished to stop, or prevent, the monopolists from dominating the nation's political life.

Even though some people recognized that the American ideal of equal opportunity for all had functioned imperfectly, they now feared that it would be lost. They saw that industry was moving toward greater consolidation. They became pessimistic about the outlook for American society.

The super corporation dominated industry

Industrial consolidation was achieved by means of the corporation. This type of industrial organization, which grew out of the fierce competition of the Gilded Age, was the most important development in American industry in the late nineteenth century. By selling stock, the corporation could draw on the savings of thousands of people for its finances and had other advantages, including a more stable future. It replaced other forms of ownership, such as the partnership, as the chief means of bringing capital and labor together to produce goods. So great was corporate growth that, by 1899, sixty-six per cent of all manufactured goods in the United States was turned out by incorporated businesses. Ten years later the corporations' share of production had increased to seventy-nine per cent.

The corporation was not a new device, but it had not been widely used prior to the Civil War. In the years of corporate growth after the Civil War the men who owned the businesses had managed them. They had made the important decisions that affected the corporations.

The first years of the twentieth century saw the emergence of super corporations. Their ownership was spread among so many stockholders that the people responsible for the operation of the corporation had little, if any, contact with those who owned it. As the large corporation took shape and came to life, it produced a class of professional industrial managers. Although in theory responsible to the stockholders, this class became in fact an independent center of economic power.

Another result of corporate growth was the rise of investment bankers to the most powerful positions in industry and transportation. Most often these men gained power because they commanded the vast sums of money that could buy power rather than the special knowledge needed to operate a business.

With ownership dispersed among many stockholders, with investment bankers such as J. P. Morgan in control of its finance, and with a new professional class of managers running the business, the modern corporations had come of age.

State and federal laws aided corporate growth

Various laws, but primarily a body of state law, made possible the growth of super corporations and placed bankers and administrators in control of United States industry. New Jersey had taken the lead, in 1888, with laws that permitted industrial consolidations. Until 1913, it did a thriving business in chartering corporations. Then other states, too, became eager for the revenue from corporation fees and taxes.

Various state laws helped the bankers gain control of industries. Many of those laws gave to boards of directors of corporations control over property without imposing on such directors any clear obligations to the stockholders, the actual owners of the property. These loose laws, therefore, often allowed the fleecing of persons who made only small investments—men who usually knew little about the business they helped to finance.

After 1895, federal laws were enacted which permitted the growth of super corporations. Before that time, however, laws enacted by Congress and various state legislatures against conspiracies in restraint of trade had helped end the first movement toward industrial concentration, known as the trust movement, which took place between 1879 and 1890. The industrialists themselves had organized that movement. Since few of them were willing

to risk losses in federal and state courts, the movement had been stopped. But the situation changed in 1895 when the Supreme Court ruled that the federal antitrust law did not apply to combinations in the field of manufacturing.

Another factor that helped bankers gain control of industries in the early twentieth century was the increasing wealth of upper-class and middle-class Americans. This wealth often went into banks and insurance companies. It was this money that investment bankers used in their expansion into industrial and railroad enterprises.

The removal of a federal barrier to industrial combinations, the favorable state laws, the election of a President favorable to big business (William McKinley) in 1896, and the return of prosperity in 1897 cleared the way for the second movement toward consolidation of industry that brought banker control.

Many men were worried by the new movement in industrial consolidation and by the power of the bankers. This power was demonstrated in the fight between the House of Morgan and the Rockefeller interests over control of the western transcontinental railroads.

Bankers tightened their control of industry

By 1904, the two great financial empires in Wall Street were the House of Morgan and a group of brokers allied with the interests of John D. Rockefeller, who controlled the oil industry. Around each of these empires were clustered a number of smaller financial houses.

Before 1907, the Morgan and Rockefeller empires competed for control of railroads and insurance companies. After a costly battle for control of the western transcontinental railroads, the two empires decided to coöperate rather than compete with each other.

By 1900, Morgan, in coöperation with James J. Hill, had gained control of two northern transcontinental railroad systems, the Northern Pacific and the Great Northern. Edward H. Harriman, supported by Kuhn, Loeb & Company of the Rockefeller group, controlled two western lines to the south, the Union Pacific and the Southern Pacific. But neither empire owned a key line into Chicago.

Hill's lines used the Burlington Railroad's tracks to reach Chicago. In 1901, Hill persuaded the owners of the Burlington to sell out to him and Morgan. When Harriman asked for a one-third interest in the Burlington, Hill refused. Then Harriman and Jacob H. Schiff, the head of Kuhn, Loeb & Company, tried to gain control of the Northern Pacific on the open market. At that point Morgan and Hill entered the market, and in the battle that followed, the price of Northern Pacific common stock jumped from $100 to more than $1000 per share. So costly was the battle that both sides agreed to a truce. Both joined in forming a new corporation, or holding company—the Northern Securities Company—which controlled the Northern Pacific and Great Northern Railroads. Harriman and Schiff gained representation on the boards of directors of these lines and of the Burlington. Now the two great financial empires controlled the major railroads west of the Mississippi River plus a key line into Chicago.

Although the bankers' control of the railroads brought few benefits to most people, the bankers did make money for themselves and for their stockholders. To assure profits the railroads often charged exorbitant rates for poor service, and some of the new managers even deliberately bankrupted their railroad properties for immediate profit.

A few years after the battle over the Burlington line Morgan again demonstrated his great financial power. In order to prevent the complete demoralization of the stock market during the Panic of 1907, he brought together the resources of Wall Street bankers. After this new demonstration of power the Rockefeller group offered no further opposition to Morgan. In the next few years, therefore, the Morgan and Rockefeller groups joined together to form what was, in effect, one huge financial empire which stifled competition and would not permit industrial struggle.

REVIEWING THE SECTION

1. What were the developments in corporate growth during the Gilded Age?

2. How did state and federal laws aid the growth of large corporations?

3. How did the Morgan and Rockefeller financial interests stifle competition?

SOCIAL AND EDUCATIONAL IDEAS CHANGED

Material progress was one of the most striking features of the United States at the turn of the century. The very idea of progress became the center of philosophical and social discussions. Philosophers, social thinkers, and educators became less concerned with the theoretical problems of man and society and more concerned with the practical measures needed to bring the benefits of material progress to the majority of the American people. They believed that man and the state were not helpless, that they could root out poverty. Some of these men revolted against the ideas of laissez faire and Social Darwinism—the belief in the survival of the fittest in industry—but accepted Darwin's scientific findings, especially the idea of evolution.

Lawyers and judges no longer looked upon law as a body of unchanging truth. They regarded law as something which society created, and which it could, therefore, change. Men who were concerned about the problems of society questioned social and economic theories, such as the theory of the survival of the fittest and the theory of supply and demand. Teachers, too, became aware of the changes in ideas.

Educational opportunities were expanding for children in the United States. Every year the people built more schools, and every year the enrollment in those schools increased. It seemed that the people in the United States had embraced the idea of progress in education more closely than in any other area of endeavor. Whether in the grade schools or in the universities, educators at the turn of the century had begun to abandon the idea that children should go to school merely to acquire a body of information. In addition, they believed that children should be taught how to live in the industrial society of their time.

Some economic theories were attacked

Lester Frank Ward, usually considered the father of American sociology, disagreed with the theory of Social Darwinism. In his major work, *Dynamic Sociology* (1883), he argued that it was wrong to compare human society to the animal world. He did not believe that a blind struggle for existence rigidly governed man's behavior. Civilized society, he said, protected its citizens from the evils and uncertainties of raw nature. Ward believed that man could control his environment and achieve greater progress through education and government, which expressed and enforced the collective will of society, than through natural selection.

Professional economists, too, attacked the ideas of Social Darwinism, the theory of laissez faire, and various laws of classical economics. In the autumn of 1885, some of these economists met in Saratoga, New York, and organized the American Economic Association. In their statement of principles they asserted that the assistance of the state in economic matters was essential to human progress and that changing economic conditions had to be met by changing laws. Laissez faire, they said, was "unsafe in politics and unsound in morals." This was virtually a declaration of war against the classical school of economics.

One of the most original of the critics of the industrial society as it existed at the turn of the century was Thorstein B. Veblen, an economist who had grown up in the Middle West and taught in various universities. In his first two books, *The Theory of the Leisure Class* (1899) and *The Theory of Business Enterprise* (1904), he rejected the idea that millionaires were more fit than others.

He attacked the economic and social practices of the rich and the orthodox laws of the classical economists. His work taught economists to be suspicious of theories that described economic life as being governed by simple, unchanging laws.

Pragmatists taught that truth was relative

Philosophers, too, were affected by Darwin's theories, and by the problems of the industrial society. In the period after the Civil War those who believed that ideals were most important in the life of man were dominant in formal philosophic thought. They formed a school of philosophy called idealism. These idealists tried to reconcile Darwin's idea of change through evolution with the traditional Christian idea of an unchanging God.

In the late nineteenth century the one major American philosopher who defended idealism was Josiah Royce, a graduate of the University of California who taught at Harvard. Royce's beliefs were explained in his major work, *The Philosophy of Loyalty* (1908). He believed that the quality in men which raised them above the level of animals was loyalty, a principle that included the ideals of devotion, unselfishness, and sacrifice.

Much more influential than idealism at the turn of the century was pragmatism. Pragmatism taught that truth was relative and was governed by changing circumstances for each new generation and each society. Pragmatists said that truth was not absolute and unchanging; it was practical.

The founders of the pragmatic school were Charles S. Peirce, a brilliant but erratic man who lectured for a time at Harvard University, and William James, a psychologist and a teacher at Harvard. Peirce advanced a narrow pragmatism which James broadened. According to James' view, the truth or value of an idea could be measured by how it worked, or what it did. True ideas, he said, are those "that we can assimilate, validate, corroborate and verify. False ideas are those we can not." James' pragmatism was a philosophy of individualism because it required each man to establish truth, or practical values, for himself.

The greatest and most influential of the pragmatists was John Dewey, a philosopher from Vermont who spent most of his teaching career at the University of Chicago and Columbia University. His pragmatism differed from that of James and his thinking was more systematic and rigorous. Dewey concerned himself more with society as a whole than with the individual. He sought to apply pragmatic thinking to the immediate problems of society and to make it an instrument of social change.

Dewey wanted to use philosophy to help the individual adjust to social change and to aid in creating a society which would serve the highest human purposes. The pragmatists taught, in effect, that man could work out problems in his complex industrial society. In addition, Dewey believed that a new kind of education appropriate to the industrial environment was needed to make the good society.

Opportunities for education were expanded

Even before the age of industrialization, many Americans believed that in order to build a good, democratic society, all the people in that society must be educated. Men such as Horace Mann had embraced this idea and had laid the foundations for a public education system free of religious controls. After the Civil War, the United States needed men whose education went beyond the ability to read. The new industrial society required men who could keep books, read blueprints, use more than elementary mathematics, and who had enough education to become engineers, doctors, lawyers, and administrators in industry.

After 1870, educational statistics showed that progress was being made in bringing schools to the people, but such progress was slow. In 1870, 20 per cent of the population above ten years of age could not write. By 1910, that figure, despite the influx of a number of immigrants who were illiterate, had fallen to 7.7 per cent. From 1890 to 1900, the number of children enrolled in all schools, public and private, had increased by 19.2 per cent. But this progress was irregular. In the North the improvement was more substantial than the figures indicated, but in the South the situation was worse. Northern children received an average of almost seven years of education in public schools; but Southern children received an average of three years of schooling. Northern states spent a yearly average of about $21 for the education of each pupil; Southern states spent less than $10 for each child of school age.

As important as the laws and the increased school attendance was the quality of American education. The one-room red schoolhouse of legend and fact performed a service, but it was inadequate to meet the educational needs of an industrial society. It often was poorly equipped, and staffed with poorly trained teachers who were underpaid.

At the end of the nineteenth century the situation changed as education, too, felt the effects of the new ideas in science and philosophy. Public education was transformed by men such as Lester Frank Ward, William James, and John Dewey. Teachers began to show greater interest in the process of learning than in the information learned. They began to think of education as a part of life itself, not simply as a preparation for life. As Dewey had urged, subject matter was changed to suit the abilities of children, not the abilities of adults. The children became active participants in the learning process rather than passive observers. This kind of experience began in the kindergarten, a system of preschool training (in use in Germany) that spread rapidly in the United States in the early years of the twentieth century.

More important than the spread of the kindergarten was the expansion of the high school, which replaced the academy as the main institution of secondary education. In 1900, the United States had about 6000 public high schools with a total enrollment of 500,000 pupils. Fourteen years later, the number of public high schools had increased

The People in a Democracy. At the turn of the century, American artists could choose from a variety of subjects. John Singer Sargent painted wealthy socialites, like Mrs. Stokes. She posed in an informal tennis costume, thus giving an impression of fashionable leisure. Robert Henri chose many of his subjects, like this winsome Negro girl, from the people of New York City. A realistic painting of laborers by Thomas Anshutz shows steelworkers washing at an outdoor pump.

Mr. and Mrs. Isaac Newton Phelps Stokes, by John Singer Sargent, 1897

Steelworkers' Noontime, by Thomas P. Anshutz, c. 1890

Eva Green, by Robert Henri, 1907

to 11,500, with an enrollment of some 1.2 million students. Not only were more of America's children going to school, but they were also staying there longer. A substantial part of the lives of Americans was spent in acquiring an education.

Higher education acquired a new excellence

Colleges and universities, as well as grade schools and high schools, increased their enrollments, expanded their course offerings, and responded to new ideas at the beginning of the new century. Earlier, most college presidents had come from the ranks of ministers and preachers. They headed institutions that trained students in religion, philosophy, mathematics, Latin, and Greek.

Despite expanded course offerings, the courses in science were few and, usually, the only experiments students saw were those demonstrated by the professor. Many colleges offered no work in modern languages such as French and German. They also ignored modern history and other subjects which dealt with the social forces of the present and of the recent past. In effect, the American college had not changed much in more than two centuries. It had retained a course of instruction, taken from seventeenth-century England, that had little to do with current social and economic conditions. Change came with the demands of the industrial society for educated men who had technical knowledge useful in that society.

In 1900, with the formation of the Association of American Universities, the nation's colleges and universities began an intensive campaign to raise educational standards. Important improvements followed. State legislatures expanded their aid to universities, colleges, and junior colleges. Enrollments in state universities began to climb, and leading state universities, such as California, Michigan, Wisconsin, and Illinois, offered excellent opportunities for education. In the early twentieth century higher education in the United States was no longer inferior in quality to education in Europe. It had acquired an excellence of its own.

Benefits for Negroes came slowly

Some segments of society did not immediately benefit from the changes going on. The social and economic status of most Negroes was worse than that of the immigrants in the United States in the late nineteenth century. In a society dominated by other men, the Negroes found it almost impossible to carve out a respected place.

The Civil War and Reconstruction had not changed the determination of many people of the South to keep Negroes in an inferior status. Slavery in the South, where most of the Negroes lived, was replaced by a legal caste system in which the Negro was segregated in public schools, in restaurants, and in other establishments. Gradually, too, the Negro in the South was prevented from exercising the right to vote, which had been granted to him by the Fifteenth Amendment.

Even basic educational opportunities were not readily available to Negro children. As late as 1910, for example, in all the Southern states from Maryland to Texas there were only 141 Negro high schools, and these enrolled only slightly more than 8000 pupils. Yet there was some progress. From 1865 to 1900, illiteracy among the Negroes declined from 95 to 44.5 per cent and went down further in the next decade. And, after 1900, some Southern states recognized the need for public aid to Negro education.

In these years of increasing discrimination, Booker Taliaferro Washington emerged as the spokesman for Negroes in matters regarding race relations. Born a slave in Virginia, he managed to acquire an advanced education at Hampton Institute, a Negro vocational school in his native state. He earned his way by working as a janitor. Washington believed that Negroes could not gain social and political equality with other men in the United States in one quick leap. He urged his fellow Negroes to put aside, for a time at least, demands for social and political recognition and to concentrate on improving their economic status. In 1881, he founded the Tuskegee Institute in Alabama, where

Negroes could learn a useful vocation. Men all over the country praised Washington's doctrine, but later the more militant Negroes criticized what they called the Washington compromise.

Although Washington did much to train Negroes for jobs in industry, he disliked the city and encouraged Negroes to stay on the farm. Migration to the cities was urged, however, by William E. B. Du Bois, a Negro born in Massachusetts and the first one to earn a doctorate in history from Harvard University. After 1900, Negroes fled from many regions of the South for jobs in the industrial cities of the North.

In June 1905, Du Bois met with a small group of Negroes at Niagara Falls, Canada, where they adopted a program that called for full equality for the Negro. Few paid attention to the Niagara Movement, until August 1908, when a race riot erupted near Abraham Lincoln's Home in Springfield, Illinois. Northern humanitarians began to awake to the plight of the Negro.

As a result, in February 1909, educators, clergymen, editors, and others met with a group of Negroes in New York City to organize the National Association for the Advancement of Colored People. This group adopted the principles of the Niagara Movement and sought to end the segregation of Negroes. During its formative years, Du Bois was the only Negro official of the organization. He also edited the Association's magazine, *The Crisis.* In the early twentieth century, among Negro leaders the more militant views of men like Du Bois had greater influence than the more passive course of action recommended by Booker T. Washington.

REVIEWING THE SECTION

1. How did Lester Frank Ward, Thorstein B. Veblen, and the organizers of the American Economic Association attack the theories of laissez-faire economics and/or Social Darwinism?

2. What were the major tenets of the philosophy of pragmatism? In what way was William James' pragmatism a philosophy of individualism?

How did John Dewey make the philosophy of pragmatism an instrument of social change?

3. How were opportunities for public education expanded in the early twentieth century?

4. How did the universities change their curriculums in response to the new emphasis on social and scientific problems?

5. How did the Negroes' opportunities for improving their social status deteriorate during the period following Reconstruction? How did Booker T. Washington and W. E. B. Du Bois differ in their views on improving opportunities for Negroes?

SCIENCE AND TECHNOLOGY BROUGHT A BETTER LIFE

At the turn of the century, science and technology became increasingly important elements in the growing wealth and power of the United States. Each profited from the expansion and improvement of the universities, particularly from the new graduate and professional schools. Each also became important in the United States primarily because industry needed them. The support given to science and technology by men such as John D. Rockefeller and Andrew Carnegie brought scientists a respect they had not previously known. Many people in the United States came to realize that technical knowledge and scientific investigation were keys to a better life.

Scientific knowledge and investigation also brought uneasiness and discomfort, particularly to many religious groups. Darwin's theory of evolution, as made popular by Herbert Spencer and the Harvard philosopher and historian John Fiske, set off the harshest conflicts.

By 1900, Darwin's theory had the support of scientists as well as many religious leaders and philosophers. But millions of Americans did not accept Darwin's theories, and in many areas teachers were forbidden to teach about evolution.

Despite this conflict between science and religion, church membership in the United States continued to grow. New religious sects were established, and old ones responded to the challenge of the industrial society with new activities and programs.

Advances were made in science and technology

In the United States the industrial age following the Civil War was a time of greater technical achievement. Americans took pride in the work of men such as Alexander Graham Bell. The prolific inventor Thomas A. Edison became something of a national hero. Such technical achievements continued into the twentieth century. In December 1903, on the side of a hill at Kittyhawk, North Carolina, Orville Wright flew the motor-driven machine he and his brother Wilbur had invented. That flight lasted for twelve seconds and covered a distance of 120 feet. The Wrights became the first men to fly a motorized, heavier-than-air machine. Like Bell, Edison, and others, the Wright brothers contributed to the technology that made the United States the foremost industrial nation in the world.

The work of all these men had a number of characteristics in common. All contributed to triumphs of man over his environment. All contributed to a revolution in industry and in the lives of the people of the United States. The American way of life changed with the increasing use of the telephone and electricity, and, eventually, the airplane. When systematic investigation and experimentation met a practical need or required mechanical knowledge, Americans showed outstanding ability.

In the field of pure science, in which scholars may spend years patiently probing for new knowledge that might not have immediate practical application, Americans lagged behind Europeans. Toward the end of the nineteenth century, however, Americans began their own researches in the field of pure science.

In the field of *genetics,* the science of heredity, investigators modified Darwin's theory of evolution. They showed that changes in an animal species could come suddenly rather than slowly over a long period of time. American scientists made experiments in the field of physics which were more fully developed in the twentieth century. In 1879, at the age of twenty-seven, Albert A. Michelson announced his first results in the measurement of the speed of light, one of the basic problems in physics. At the beginning of the twentieth century, the scientists of the United States were making contributions in theoretical sciences in keeping with the wealth and resources of their nation. American science had become the equal of American technology.

The automobile replaced the bicycle

Until the early 1900's, one of the most important forms of transportation in the United States was the bicycle, but a machine developed in the 1890's, the automobile, soon began to replace it. Men had been intrigued by the idea of a "horseless" carriage for many years and throughout the nineteenth century had experimented with engines driven by steam or electric power. European inventors were ahead of American inventors; by the 1870's, French, German, and Austrian designers had begun to develop the gasoline engines which soon replaced all other types. France took the lead in the early automobile industry, and from the French come such terms as *garage, chassis,* and the word *automobile* itself.

In the United States, meanwhile, inventors were also busily designing automobiles. The most important of these were the Duryea brothers, Charles and J. Frank, Ransom Olds, and Henry Ford. The first vehicle operated by a gasoline motor in the United States was built by the Duryea brothers in 1893. Three years later Ford produced the first of the cars that would bear his name. When Ransom Olds built 1500 Oldsmobiles with curved dashboards in 1901, he became the first mass-producer of automobiles.

The production of automobiles gradually came to be centered at Detroit, Michigan, because that city had an established carriage industry that could construct automobile bodies, and it was close to supplies of iron ore and lumber. Although the automobile companies turned out over 4000 cars in 1900, the industry was not even listed separately in the census. Production did not immediately increase for a number of reasons. Only seven per cent of the roads in the United States, mainly those covered with gravel or some other surfacing, were suitable for automobile travel. In addition, the cost of manufacturing resulted in cars priced too high for a mass market. The manufacturer had to order parts for the cars from many sources before he could begin the job of assembling them. When the producers turned to mass production, using the technique of the constantly moving assembly line, the automobile industry became one of the giants of the American economy. By 1909, the output of automobiles had increased 3500 per cent. The automobile had begun to transform many aspects of life in the United States.

Henry Ford became the leading figure in the automobile industry—the "flivver king." Although he did not introduce mass production and the use of interchangeable parts, he took over these techniques and used them more effectively than did his competitors. The Model T Ford, first built in 1909, was cheap, simple, and sturdy. It came out of the factory the same way year after year. A buyer could have a Model T in any color he wanted, Ford once said, so long as it was black.

Religion faced new challenges

Although the people of the United States eagerly accepted the benefits of science and technology, many religious leaders were faced with the challenge of restating their faith in the light of this new-found knowledge and the problems created by an industrial society.

One of the most important religious and social movements of the last two decades of the nineteenth century was linked to the revolt against laissez faire. This was the social gospel movement, which taught that the saving of society was necessary to the saving of individual souls. The acute poverty in the cities, the loss of church membership among the working people, and the wide acceptance of science which had weakened old attitudes, caused religious leaders, particularly the young ministers, to rethink some of the concerns of the church. Leaders of the social gospel movement said that much of the poverty in the industrial cities arose from conditions for which the individual could not be blamed.

The most influential leader of the social gospel movement was Walter Rauschenbusch, who had absorbed the writings of the economist and social thinker Henry George and other reformers. In the 1880's and 1890's, he had served as pastor of a small German Baptist church in Hell's Kitchen, one of New York's worst slums. This experience led him to question the basis of a society that permitted the poverty and deep suffering he saw with his own eyes. Later, as preacher, teacher, and writer, he attacked American industrial life, particularly its emphasis on the making of money, as being antagonistic to Christianity.

Despite the influence of men like Rauschenbusch, the social gospel movement deeply affected only a small part of Protestantism. The majority of churchgoers were as yet but little touched by this movement.

The Roman Catholic Church, too, felt the challenges of science and the industrial society. Its hierarchy took a conservative stand in regard to the new scientific trends, and in the United States some Roman Catholic leaders opposed the social agitation of the 1880's and 1890's. But others, such as James Cardinal Gibbons and Archbishop John Ireland of St. Paul, Minnesota, believed that the workers and the poor—many of them Roman Catholic immigrants—suffered from social injustice and needed the help of the church. In 1891, in an *encyclical,* a public letter, called *Rerum Novarum,* Pope Leo XIII supported this view. He condemned the evils of the industrial system as "laying upon the shoulders of the working classes a yoke little better than slavery itself." In the twentieth century, many Roman Catholic, Jewish, and Protestant religious leaders worked actively to gain social and economic benefits for workers and the poor.

REVIEWING THE SECTION

1. What were some of the technological and scientific achievements made by Americans in the early twentieth century?

2. How did new production techniques make possible the development of the automobile industry?

3. How did the leaders of the social gospel movement challenge the philosophy of laissez faire? How did the Roman Catholic Church respond to the challenges of social injustice?

CULTURAL ACTIVITIES BECAME MORE IMPORTANT

Societies with increasing wealth and leisure have often supported art, music, literature, and other cultural or creative activities. To some extent this was true of the United States in the late nineteenth century, but the cultural accomplishments of this society were not notable when compared to those of advanced European nations. One reason for this, among many, is that the United States of this period was a land of varied cultural groups. Often there was little cultural exchange among these groups.

With their new wealth the families of the industrial barons created a distinctive and sumptuous way of life modeled after that of the wealthy aristocracy of Europe. They also supported many philanthropies—orphanages, hospitals, and colleges—and became the recognized patrons of the arts. The paintings and sculptures they collected were of European origin or were copied from European models. In addition to their intrinsic value, they were prized because they gave status to the owner or patron. The creative work done in the United States at that time often did not reflect what was vital in American society.

The most popular forms of entertainment were more closely related to the lives of those who enjoyed it than were the arts. Refined literature and the dramatic theater, for example, had only small audiences. But the penny newspapers, the dime novels, the circus, and vaudeville attracted large followings. By the beginning of the twentieth century, however, American art and literature came to grips with American life. They dealt with important themes or problems in American society.

Writers set a new literary trend

Toward the end of the nineteenth century an important group of writers turned from realism, or the effort to represent facts and people as they are, and established a new literary school called naturalism. This school took its philosophy from the leading French naturalist, Émile Zola. He said the writer must study human nature in the same way the biologist studied the animal world. The writer must describe life without applying moral judgments. Naturalists accepted the view of the Social Darwinists that life was an endless struggle against the blind forces of nature. They viewed society as harsh and impersonal.

Stephen Crane launched the American naturalist school in 1893, when he published, at his own expense, *Maggie: A Girl of the Streets,* a tragic story of a girl's struggle for existence in the slums of New York. Few read the book. Crane gained fame with his next novel, *The Red Badge of Courage* (1895). It described the ordeal of a young soldier during the Civil War. There was nothing romantic or noble about war in this novel. It depicted war as brutal and senseless.

Naturalism was treated in a direct, simple manner by two California writers, Frank Norris and Jack London. In his best-known works Norris concentrated on the theme of struggle and survival in industrial America. *The Octopus* (1901), dealt with a ruthless struggle between the Southern Pacific Railroad and wheat growers in California. It was followed by *The Pit,* published posthumously in 1903, which told of struggle and turmoil among speculators in Chicago's wheat market. Jack London wrote about struggle in nature in *The Call of the Wild* (1903), and struggle among men, in *The Sea Wolf* (1904). He was the most widely read of the naturalists, primarily because he wrote exciting, action-filled stories.

The greatest and most sophisticated of the naturalists was Theodore Dreiser. He, too, saw man as an animal, but with ability to reason, driven by his instincts to struggle for survival. Dreiser also viewed environment as impersonal. Social forces, he suggested, drove man to violence. His first novel, *Sister Carrie* (1900) with its bold emphasis on literary realism, marked a turning point in American literary history. Naturalism and realism were found in all of Dreiser's novels, including *Jennie Gerhardt* (1911) and *An American Tragedy* (1925). Although all American writers did not join the naturalist school, by 1914 most of the young authors were trying to project naturalism through their works.

Newspapers gained a mass audience

The modern newspaper recognized industrial America's interest in organized spectator sports. Its sports pages followed the baseball games of the National League, and then of the American League. After the playing of the first modern world series in 1903, baseball became both prosperous and popular. Other sports that attracted the attention of newspaper writers were college football and professional boxing. The Boston "strong boy," John L. Sullivan, and "Gentleman Jim" Corbett, heavyweight champions in the 1880's and 1890's, were highly publicized figures who attracted popularity to the sport. But humanitarians and moralists attacked boxing because of its brutality and its close ties to gamblers.

Like the newspapers, magazines reacted to the social and cultural forces in the industrial society. Magazines, too, profited from improvements in printing and other production techniques. They also catered to the thirst for knowledge and culture among the people, and zoomed ahead in circulation at a rate faster than that of the newspapers. In the 1880's and 1890's, a number of magazines, low in price but relatively high in quality, gained mass circulation. Among those were *Cosmopolitan, Collier's, National Geographic Magazine, Munsey's Magazine,* and the *Saturday Evening Post.* Most successful of all was the *Ladies' Home Journal,* founded in 1883, and edited during its period of growth by the brilliant Edward W. Bok. Some of the older literary journals, such as *The Century, North American Review,* and *Harper's,* lost circulation. Many Americans found excitement and adventure, as well as knowledge and discussion of the problems of the time in the new magazines.

American art broke with European traditions

Most Americans enjoyed the art they saw in monthly magazines and weekly journals, but in the United States there were artists capable of far greater contributions. They struggled for a recognition that usually came slowly.

After the Civil War most American painters studied in Europe and followed European traditions. A few American artists lived in Europe, or spent a good part of their lives there. Massachusetts-born James McNeill Whistler became a leading figure in London art society, never returning to the United States after he reached the age of 21. John Singer Sargent, who grew up in Italy, gained fame as a portrait painter of both American and European society. Mary Cassatt, daughter of a wealthy Philadelphia family, was better known for her impressionist technique in Paris than in the United States.

Three major American painters did not follow European traditions. Winslow Homer applied a rugged, powerful technique to American themes and scenes, especially the New England seacoast. Albert Ryder, who lived as a recluse in New York, painted mystical and imaginative scenes. Thomas

United States Painting. As the nineteenth century ended, American artists were in the midst of a revolt against discreet, pleasant subjects. Thomas Eakins, a forerunner in the revolt, realistically painted scenes previously considered unsuitable for art. He depicted a surgical operation in ''Gross Clinic.'' John Sloan found excitement and grace in familiar activities, such as women drying their hair atop a tenement roof. Realistic details, like clothes hanging in the breeze, typified the ''Ash Can School'' of painting.

A second trend veered away from realism and emphasized abstract shapes and color rather than actual details. When James McNeill Whistler tried to represent fireworks on canvas (''Nocturne in Black and Gold''), he was accused by a critic of ''flinging a pot of paint in the public's face.''

Careful organization of shapes and bold splashes of color distinguish the impressionistic painting ''Ponte della Paglia.'' In ''Nature Symbolized, No. 2,'' artist Arthur Dove abandoned actual shapes and used totally abstract forms to convey an inner feeling.

Gross Clinic, by Thomas Eakins, 1875

Sunday, Women Drying Their Hair, by John Sloan, 1912

Ponte della Paglia, by Maurice Prendergast, 1899

Nocturne in Black and Gold—The Falling Rocket,
by James McNeill Whistler, 1874

Nature Symbolized, No. 2, by Arthur G. Dove, 1914

Eakins of Pennsylvania was probably the most creative artist of the late nineteenth century. He rebelled against popular romantic painting, insisting on factual presentation of his various subjects, usually drawn from life around him. Eakins and his students led the early twentieth-century movement toward realism in American art. Realistic painting, like literary realism, dealt with individuals, not types, and depicted ordinary and even ugly things as subjects One group of realistic painters was dubbed the "Ash Can School," because their works concentrated on the details of city life. Robert Henri, John Sloan, and Maurice Prendergast were members of this school.

At the end of the nineteenth century almost every American town of any consequence had a sculptured monument of some kind. This indicated there was a market for sculptures, but it did not indicate popular appreciation for the art. Most of the statues were mediocre. The outstanding American sculptor of the period was Augustus Saint-Gaudens. The hooded figure sometimes called *Grief* (created as a memorial to Mrs. Henry Adams) is an example of the rare quality of beauty found in his sculptures.

Like painting and sculpture, American architecture was wedded to European models — the Greek Classic, the Gothic, and the Romanesque. One of the first architects to adapt this European tradition successfully to American conditions was Henry Hobson Richardson. He developed an American Romanesque style that was monumental, beautiful, and functional.

After a fire which destroyed a major part of the city of Chicago in 1871, a group of architects, influenced by Richardson, developed the skyscraper, an American form of architecture that combined function with beauty. The construction of these tall and often graceful buildings was made possible by the new methods of steel production and by the perfection of the electric elevator. The most original architect of the Chicago group and of the time was Louis H. Sullivan. His guiding principle was that "form follows function." The functional, steel-ribbed skyscraper brought a new appearance and almost a new way of life to great cities such as Chicago and New York.

REVIEWING THE SECTION

1. How did the novels of Stephen Crane, Frank Norris, Jack London, and Theodore Dreiser reflect the views of Social Darwinism?

2. How did newspapers and magazines reflect the tastes of the reading public?

3. How did American painting change in the early part of the twentieth century? How did changes in architecture at the end of the nineteenth century reflect the changes in American technology?

CHAPTER **19** CONCLUSION

Life in the United States in the last years of the nineteenth century and the beginning of the new century reflected the many changes in American society brought about by industrialization. These years also saw the growth of two economic trends that would become more significant in the twentieth century. The first of these trends was an increase in the export of manufactured goods such as steel and textiles. The second trend was the sending of increasingly larger amounts of American capital to foreign countries for investment. These exports brought about a change in the nation's foreign trade as well as changes in the domestic economy.

During most of the nineteenth century, Americans primarily had exported agricultural products and raw materials and had imported manufactured goods. As new industries developed, they met most of the American need for manufactured goods and, as a result, imports from abroad dropped. These new industries stimulated a demand for the import of raw materials, such as tin and rubber. The changed nature of America's foreign trade becomes apparent in the following statistics. In 1900, some sixty per cent of the nation's exports was made up of agricultural products, and thirty-five per cent was manufactured goods. Fourteen years later manufactured goods accounted for nearly forty-nine per cent of all exports.

Industrialization had several important effects on America's foreign trade. It reduced dependence on foreign manufactures, helped cut down the foreign debt, increased the demand for foreign raw materials, and stimulated investments of dollars abroad. More than at any time in the past the United States was participating as a major power in world economic affairs.

The demand for foreign raw materials showed how great was industry's need. Those who built America's industries at first had met the need from within, often wasting the nation's natural resources such as land, timber, and minerals. To gain control of these resources, and to obtain other favors, they bribed or bought politicians and, at times, dominated state and city governments. Even officers of the federal government sometimes jumped when the great industrialists commanded. Control of government by the businessmen meant that society could not easily stop their assaults on the nation's natural resources. In the new century thoughtful Americans expressed concern over the corruption in government, the need to place great wealth under some measure of control, and the necessity of saving the nation's resources before they were totally squandered. Newspapermen, magazine editors, and others alerted the people to these problems.

Despite serious problems, the most striking feature of American society in the first years of the twentieth century was its affluence. Even though wealth was not distributed evenly, and tended to be concentrated in fewer hands than before, most Americans enjoyed a rising standard of living. More had steady employment than ever before. Even farm income from 1900 to 1910 increased by more than one hundred per cent. In these years, despite the problems of industrialization, Americans had a richer and more varied cultural life than they had ever known, and enjoyed a stability

and prosperity that other peoples envied.

FOCUSING ON SPECIFICS

1. What were the principles of the theory of economics known as laissez faire?

2. What arguments were advanced by those who criticized the growth of large corporations? Why did many businessmen favor the growth of large corporations?

3. What developments led to the formation of the National Association for the Advancement of Colored People?

4. What advances in the field of pure science were made by Americans at the turn of the century?

5. Why did the social gospel movement reject the principles of laissez faire?

6. How did the ideas of Émile Zola influence American literature?

7. How did the industrialization of the United States affect foreign trade?

REVIEWING MAIN THEMES

1. In the late nineteenth century, what developments took place in the organization and control of United States industry? How did state and federal laws influence these developments?

2. How did new ideas in philosophy and economics lead to social reform movements and changes in education?

3. What new ideas among religious groups led to social reform movements?

4. What important scientific and cultural trends were evident between 1895 and 1910?

EVALUATING THE ISSUES

1. At the turn of the century, many clergymen tried to correct the injustices resulting from the new industrial era. Many other clergymen argued that it was not the function of the clergy to engage in social protest movements. With which position are you inclined to agree? Why?

2. Why has the philosophy of pragmatism been so widely accepted by Americans?

3. Social Darwinism was generally used in defense of laissez faire and the status quo. In what way might Social Darwinian arguments have been used to justify social reform movements?

The Response of the Progressives

Historians usually refer to the first sixteen years of the twentieth century as the Progressive era. In these years many Americans devoted themselves to a reform movement that sought to eliminate the worst economic, social, and political injustices from their society. Since these Americans believed in the idea of social progress, their program is known as the Progressive movement.

The Progressive movement did not come to life suddenly as the new century began; it had its roots in the American past. It also was affected by reform programs in Europe. Ever since 1870, some men had expressed alarm over the evils that had come with industrial life. These men had denounced the most glaring abuses and had demanded reforms. While many people read their protests, governments, whether state or federal, had not acted.

After 1900, those who became reformers were not content merely with intellectual protest. In large numbers they entered politics and achieved some practical results.

In many ways these concerns for the welfare of the people resembled the attitudes of the Populists of the 1890's. Progressives took over from the Populists many specific proposals for reform, such as the direct election of United States senators and a federal income tax. But there were important differences between the two movements.

Populism had emerged in the years of panic and depression among the rebellious farmers in the West and South. Progressivism grew during years of prosperity and drew its support primarily from the middle classes in the towns and cities. It had followers in both the Republican and Democratic parties. Among the men who were leaders in the Progressive movement were bankers, lawyers, editors, clergymen, prosperous farmers, and owners of small business concerns. The rank and file, to a large extent, was made up of clerks, sales people, and technicians who worked for the corporations or the businesses in the cities. These men, often called white-collar workers because they wore white shirts, in contrast to laborers who more often wore blue shirts, comprised a new and growing element among the middle-class people of the United States.

Although the Progressives were not united behind any one program of reform, they had a number of common objectives. Most Progressives believed that society should advance to a point where all Americans could enjoy social and economic justice. The reformers wanted to do away with privileges gained through the corruption of government. They wanted to make political life more democratic by bringing more people actively into the working machinery of government.

The Progressives did not always agree on the means for achieving their objectives. The social workers among them insisted on economic reforms that would protect human beings from exploitation. Other Progressives insisted that clearing the city governments of corruption and freeing state governments from control by big business was of the first importance.

Unlike socialists, communists, and others, Progressives accepted the capitalist system. Indeed, they looked with pride on the industrial strength of the United States. They wished to reform the industrial system, not destroy it. They hoped to use science and technology to eliminate poverty and other social ills. They thought they could achieve their objectives within the old agrarian pattern of American democracy.

The Progressives had a great deal of faith in laws as instruments of reform, and the Progressive movement inspired considerable reform legislation that won support from both Republicans and Democrats. Progressivism stimulated some of the best features of Theodore Roosevelt's Square Deal and of Woodrow Wilson's New Freedom. Some of the Progressive reforms were failures, but others brought lasting benefits to millions of Americans.

THE PROGRESSIVE MOVEMENT GAINED STRENGTH

One of the important factors that turned middle-class Americans into reformers was fear of the wealth and power that the great financiers had gathered into their hands. These reformers believed that such a concentration of economic power would limit the economic and political opportunities for many Americans.

Some middle-class Americans also looked with alarm on the discontent of the industrial workers. They disliked the growing strength of organized labor but, even more, they hated the increasing influence of socialism, which threatened to change the structure of their society. The Progressives, therefore, wanted to use the power of the government to guarantee equal economic opportunity for all. They wanted to make government more democratic than it had been during the Gilded Age so that it would respond to reform efforts. In turn, they hoped that reforms would help to divert the discontented lower classes from socialism by improving their living conditions. Moreover, they hoped by reforms to curb the power of big business.

At the end of the nineteenth century, it seemed unlikely that the reformers would be able to influence the federal government. William McKinley's election, in 1896, was a triumph for big business. New and larger corporations came into existence, and with prosperity few government leaders paid attention to the discontent of the workers. Progressive reforms, therefore, began in city and state governments but did not spread to the national government until after McKinley's death.

The muckrakers attacked corruption

McKinley and those working closely with him had shown little interest in reform, but there were other people who had. Some of these men worked for agencies in the federal and state governments. Neither these men nor the agencies for which they worked could eliminate the evils they saw around them, but they could make the ugly facts known. They hoped to arouse public indignation and thus bring about reforms.

The task of getting the facts and making them known to the public fell to a remarkable group

PRESIDENTIAL ELECTIONS: 1896-1904

CANDIDATES: 1896

ELECTORAL VOTE BY STATE		POPULAR VOTE AND PERCENTAGE
REPUBLICAN William McKinley	271	7,102,246
DEMOCRATIC William J. Bryan	176	6,492,559
MINOR PARTIES	—	315,398
	447	13,910,203

CANDIDATES: 1900

ELECTORAL VOTE BY STATE		POPULAR VOTE AND PERCENTAGE
REPUBLICAN William McKinley	292	7,218,491
DEMOCRATIC William J. Bryan	155	6,356,734
MINOR PARTIES	—	386,840
	447	13,962,065

CANDIDATES: 1904

ELECTORAL VOTE BY STATE		POPULAR VOTE AND PERCENTAGE
REPUBLICAN Theodore Roosevelt	336	7,628,461
DEMOCRATIC Alton B. Parker	140	5,084,223
MINOR PARTIES	—	809,251
	476	13,521,935

of journalists called muckrakers. They gained their name from Theodore Roosevelt; he compared them to the man in John Bunyan's *Pilgrim's Progress* (1678) who was so intent on raking muck that he could not see the better things above him. The muckrakers formed the literary voice of the Progressive movement. Although the muckrakers had begun their exposures of corruption in business and government earlier, they did not gain widespread attention until 1902.

McClure's Magazine began the muckraking trend with a series of articles on the Standard Oil Company by Ida M. Tarbell. Another series of articles by a gifted reporter, Lincoln Steffens, described corruption in city governments which Steffens attributed to a profitable alliance between businessmen and political bosses. A third muckraker, Ray Stannard Baker, wrote an article attack-

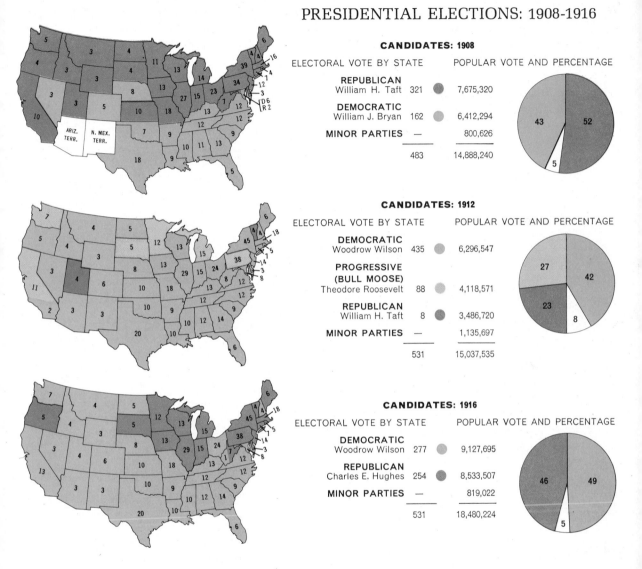

PRESIDENTIAL ELECTIONS: 1908-1916

CANDIDATES: 1908

ELECTORAL VOTE BY STATE	POPULAR VOTE AND PERCENTAGE
REPUBLICAN William H. Taft 321	7,675,320
DEMOCRATIC William J. Bryan 162	6,412,294
MINOR PARTIES —	800,626
483	14,888,240

52 · 43 · 5

CANDIDATES: 1912

ELECTORAL VOTE BY STATE	POPULAR VOTE AND PERCENTAGE
DEMOCRATIC Woodrow Wilson 435	6,296,547
PROGRESSIVE (BULL MOOSE) Theodore Roosevelt 88	4,118,571
REPUBLICAN William H. Taft 8	3,486,720
MINOR PARTIES —	1,135,697
531	15,037,535

42 · 27 · 23 · 8

CANDIDATES: 1916

ELECTORAL VOTE BY STATE	POPULAR VOTE AND PERCENTAGE
DEMOCRATIC Woodrow Wilson 277	9,127,695
REPUBLICAN Charles E. Hughes 254	8,533,507
MINOR PARTIES —	819,022
531	18,480,224

49 · 46 · 5

ing the malpractices of a union during a coal strike in Colorado.

Other magazines, such as *Collier's* and *Cosmopolitan,* began to publish articles of economic and social significance and many of the nation's best-known authors wrote muckraking articles for them. In 1906, at the height of the movement, these magazines were reaching about three million people. In addition, some of the articles were re-printed in newspapers and collected in books.

Three of the most sensational exposures appeared in 1906. In *The Bitter Cry of the Children,* John Spargo described in painful detail the exploitation of children working in factories. David G. Phillips published a book, based on his articles for *Cosmopolitan,* called *The Treason of the Senate.* Using exaggerated evidence he charged that the majority of the senators had sold out to the corporations, and hence had betrayed the people. Upton Sinclair's *The Jungle* described the deplorable working conditions and the filth in Chicago's meat-packing plants.

In 1909, muckraking began to die out, and three years later it had passed from the American scene. It lost its effectiveness because business had grown increasingly hostile to it, and the people had grown tired of sensational exposures. The muckrakers, however, had aroused the public conscience, stirred the politicians to action, and given a push to the entire Progressive movement.

Reform movements began in the cities

Before and during the time the muckrakers were making their exposures, some reformers were actively fighting corruption and trying to bring decency to city governments. They began to attack the special problems of the cities, especially machine politics, in the 1890's. In 1894, for example, reform forces overthrew New York's political machine, called Tammany Hall. One of the outstanding city reformers was Tom L. Johnson, a successful railway operator and steel manufacturer who had been converted to reform after reading Henry George's *Progress and Poverty.* From 1901 to 1909, Johnson served as mayor of Cleveland. He attacked tax inequities, entrenched public utilities, and graft. With his Progressive program, he earned for Cleveland the reputation of being the nation's best-governed city.

Another wealthy manufacturer, Samuel "Golden Rule" Jones, turned to reform because of his interest in the social gospel. By applying the Golden Rule in his relations with others, he brought Progressive government to Toledo while he was mayor (1897 to 1904). His conduct earned him his nickname. Reformers in other cities followed the examples set by the mayors of Cleveland and Toledo.

Progressives also created new forms of government to deal with the special problems of the cities. These were the commission and city-manager plans of government. Under the *commission plan* a group of administrators replaced the mayor and his council. This plan was first used in Galveston, Texas, in 1900, after a tidal wave had devastated that city. As a result of its effectiveness, the commission plan was adopted in other cities.

In 1913, after a flood had inundated Dayton, Ohio, the people adopted a modification of the commission plan, called the *city-manager plan.* The commissioners, elected on a nonpartisan basis, made laws and policies, but they appointed a manager to run the city's departments. Since the manager was usually an expert in city administration, this plan had the advantage of combining democratic government with expert administration. It therefore won wide adoption throughout the nation.

Progressives took up these devices for expert government because they wanted to break the grip of business corporations and machine politicians upon city governments. But this was not enough. Many of the political machines in the cities were allied to machines in state governments.

Progressives gained control of state governments

Since corrupt or reactionary state governments often blocked reforms for the cities, the Progressives attacked the state political machines. Under the leadership of Robert M. La Follette, the most famous Progressive in state politics, Wisconsin became a hotbed of reform. Although "Battling Bob" La Follette had championed reforms in the 1890's, he made no headway against Wisconsin's statewide Republican machine until he was elected governor in 1900. In his three terms La Follette helped gain passage of laws that regulated railroads and public utilities, developed a fair tax system, conserved the state's natural resources, and offered some protection to industrial workers.

Other states, too, produced successful reform programs. Two of the best-known of the Progressive governors were Hiram W. Johnson of California who broke the Southern Pacific Railroad's grip on the state, and Woodrow Wilson of New

Jersey, who helped change his state from the haven of large corporations to a state that strictly regulated them.

These Progressive governors, as well as reformers in the cities, frequently found that the legislatures or city councils refused to enact their reform programs. So Progressives tried to get around this obstacle with new political devices such as the referendum, initiative, and recall. The referendum permitted the voters to accept or reject a law passed by a city council or a legislature; the initiative allowed the people themselves to propose laws; and recall made it possible for voters to remove elected officials from office. By 1918, more than twenty states had adopted one or more of these devices.

In the nineteenth century, voting had been public, and voters had expressed their preferences orally. Often the political parties had supplied the ballots. Progressives helped gain widespread adoption of the Australian (secret) ballot which the state governments printed and supplied. Progressives saw this reform as a deterrent to corruption at the polls.

One of the most important reforms championed by Progressives was the direct primary election. Many people in the United States believed that political bosses dictated the nomination of candidates. *The direct primary* allowed the people to nominate the party candidates in special elections. By 1916, all but three states had adopted some form of direct primary.

Progressives also gained the passage of considerable economic and social legislation. To prevent or to break up great concentrations of economic power, many states set up commissions that strictly regulated corporations. State after state passed laws to protect women and children from hazardous or unhealthy working conditions, as well as laws requiring factory inspections and a minimum-wage standard.

Some women were active in the Progressive movement, but they were unable to exert political pressure on the federal government because they did not have the right to vote. Progressives believed women should have that right, and they supported woman suffrage. By 1914, eleven states, most of them in the West, had given women the right to vote. Advocates of woman suffrage considered this slow progress; so they turned to the federal government for action. Progressives sought the aid of the national government on other issues, too, for Progressivism had now become a powerful force in national politics.

REVIEWING THE SECTION

1. What social and economic problems did the muckrakers expose?

2. What problems in the cities did reformers try to solve? How did reformers combat these problems?

3. What reforms were initiated by Progressives in control of state governments?

THEODORE ROOSEVELT DRAMATIZED REFORM

The Progressive movement became a powerful force in the federal government after Theodore Roosevelt took over the White House. He was the first President to work for reform on a national scale.

When McKinley died, no one knew what Roosevelt's policies would be. Yet the forty-two-year-old Roosevelt was already one of the most famous men of his day. He had been born into one of New York's wealthy families, had received a good education, had traveled in Europe and, shortly after graduation from Harvard University, had served as an assemblyman (1882-1884) in New York's legislature. This marked the beginning of his career as a politician. As president (1895-1897) of the New York City Board of Police Commissioners, he fought crime and vice; then he became assistant secretary of the navy under McKinley and, in 1898, he was elected governor of his state.

Roosevelt led an active life, one that revealed one of his outstanding characteristics—an unquenchable energy. He wrote books on history, such as *The Naval War of 1812* (1882) and *The Winning of the West* (1889-1896). He also was a rancher in the Bad Lands of the Dakotas, where he personally chased bandits. And, as a colonel of cavalry, he led the "Rough Riders" up San Juan Hill in the Spanish-American War (1898).

Like many wealthy Progressives, Roosevelt disliked the greed of some businessmen and the vulgarity of many of the new millionaires; he felt compassion for the poor; and he feared that many of the discontented people in the United States would turn to socialism if the evils in society continued to be ignored. Yet Theodore Roosevelt was neither an idealist nor a do-gooder; he was a practical politician who could, when necessary, compromise with bosses and businessmen. Some Progressives did not consider him a reformer at all.

Roosevelt emerged as the Progressive movement's greatest national asset. With the actor's fine sense of timing and the politician's love of power, he kept himself at the center of the national stage. In this way he retained his own popularity and kept the purposes of Progressivism before the people. He dramatized reform on a grand scale.

Roosevelt gave labor a "Square Deal"

Roosevelt's willingness to make a dramatic break with the past was evident in one of his first acts as President, when he intervened in a labor dispute. In May 1902, some 140,000 miners in the anthracite coal fields of eastern Pennsylvania went on strike, causing the nation's greatest work stoppage up to that time. Led by John Mitchell, president of the United Mine Workers of America, the miners asked for improved working conditions, a pay increase of twenty per cent, a reduction in the working day from ten to eight hours, and recognition of the union. Few could deny that the miners were victims of numerous accidents, such as cave-ins and explosions, that they worked long hours underground, and that their wages were low.

The mine operators, many of them officials of the railroads which owned the mines, had refused even to consider the workers' pleas. George F. Baer, president of the Philadelphia and Reading Railroad Company and spokesman for the railroads which owned extensive mine properties, expressed his contempt for all workers in a letter he carelessly allowed to fall into the hands of the press. In response to an appeal to him to settle the miners' strike, Baer replied that the interests of workers would not be protected "by the labor agitators but by the Christian men to whom God in His infinite wisdom has given the control of the property interests of the country." Although the public was generally prejudiced against unions, this and similar statements won considerable sympathy for the miners.

As the strike dragged on, Roosevelt decided something should be done. In October he summoned the mine operators and union leaders to the White House. Mitchell agreed to arbitrate to end the strike, but the mine operators called the union leaders anarchists and criminals and said that the operators would never deal with them.

Infuriated by this attitude, the President became convinced that the mine operators were prolonging the strike. He also believed that the national welfare was being endangered. So he threatened to seize the mines and operate them with federal troops. Faced with this threat, as well as pressure from J. P. Morgan, whose financial empire included some of the mines, the operators grudgingly agreed to submit the dispute to arbitration.

The arbitrators worked out a settlement that corrected some of the worst abuses in the mines, gave the miners a working day of nine hours, and a wage increase of ten per cent. But the owners refused to recognize the union.

What was most significant about Roosevelt's action was not its drama, but its departure from precedent. In the past government either had done nothing in labor disputes or had intervened only on the side of business. For the first time, a President had used the power of government to seek an impartial settlement in a strike. By showing that he was not afraid to fight business, Roosevelt won considerable prestige. His action had been in keeping with what he called his Square Deal for business, labor, and the general public.

Roosevelt curbed big business

Before the coal strike, Roosevelt had been preparing for one of his most dramatic moves, an attack against the giant corporations. Basically, he believed that the corporations, or trusts, were not in themselves evil, but that some of them were monopolies that endangered the national welfare. He suggested that corporations should be regulated by the government rather than destroyed.

Roosevelt had not waited for Congress before making his first move against the trusts. In February 1902, he ordered the attorney general to file suit against the Northern Securities Company, asking that it be broken up because it violated the Sherman Antitrust Act of 1890.

Since the struggle that had led to the creation of the holding company had aroused public hostility and the case involved the nation's greatest financiers, Roosevelt's move was politically astute. Progressives were delighted, but Wall Street bankers were alarmed. J. P. Morgan thought this might be the start of an attack on his financial empire.

Early in March 1904, after the case had dragged on for two years, the Supreme Court, in a five to four decision, ruled that the Northern Securities Company had violated the law and must be dissolved.

This triumph came as the time for the presidential election approached. "Teddy, the Trust Buster," as the people called him, was such a popular President that Republican leaders did not dare drop him for a more conservative candidate. Roosevelt won his party's nomination by acclamation. The Democrats, meeting in St. Louis, turned from William Jennings Bryan and gave their nomination to Judge Alton B. Parker, a drab, conservative lawyer from New York.

The campaign was dull and the outcome never

BUSINESS ACTIVITY   1898-1920

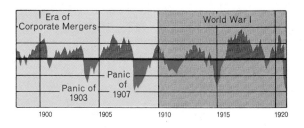

With the outbreak of a war, business prospects often become uncertain, and trade and industry are seriously disturbed. Yet war production frequently stimulates, or even creates, prosperity. In 1913, even before the onset of World War I, business activity in the United States seemed to be entering the first stages of a depression. The beginning of the war in Europe caused a further decline in prices and employment. But Europe's requirements for raw materials, war supplies, and food forced it to turn to United States industry and agriculture. Before the end of 1915, these European purchases transformed the recession into a period of prosperity. With United States entry into the war in 1917, demands upon its capacity for production were further increased. These demands touched off the greatest industrial effort in the nation's history. Reconversion to peacetime production resulted in only a temporary decrease in business activity. Industries which had been held back during the war quickly began great expansion. Consumers, eager to spend wartime savings, provided a large market for goods as they again became available. Prices soared until late 1920, when the postwar boom ended and a depression began.

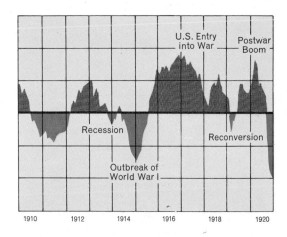

really in doubt. The people were impressed by "Teddy" himself, and by his record, and he easily won the election.

Now that Roosevelt had been elected President in his own right, he could carry out his own policies, particularly the Square Deal he had promised, so he began his second administration with new assaults on the trusts. While dramatic, Teddy's "trust busting" did not halt the growth of giant corporations, nor did it alienate them.

Yet Roosevelt's trust busting forced the corporate financiers to proceed carefully. For the first time the President effectively used the powers of government to curb big business. A precedent was set permitting the government, as well as the bankers, to exercise control over the economy.

New laws protected the people

In his second administration Roosevelt made his most notable attack against the railroads' abuses of the public. The Interstate Commerce Commission had proved ineffective in policing the railroads, primarily because the courts had restricted its authority. Finally, after some practices had become flagrant, the railroads themselves asked Congress for help. In February 1903, Congress passed the Elkins Act which prohibited railroads from giving rebates and shippers from accepting them.

Progressives wanted to give the Interstate Commerce Commission power to fix railroad rates. Roosevelt, therefore, prodded Congress, and in June 1906, it passed the Hepburn Act which proved to be the first truly effective law in regulating the railroads. This act broadened the powers of the Interstate Commerce Commission by giving it authority over express companies and pipe-line companies, as well as over the railroads. Most important, the new law gave the commission the power to fix maximum rates.

During the struggle over the Hepburn Act, Roosevelt had also used the power of the presidency to gain new laws to protect the people's health. When Upton Sinclair's novel, *The Jungle,*

was published, Roosevelt named a commission to investigate conditions in the meat-packing industry. The investigators confirmed Sinclair's findings. Faced with this evidence and an aroused public opinion, Congress passed (June 1906) the Pure Food and Drug Act and the Meat Inspection Act. The first law prohibited the manufacture or sale of adulterated or mislabeled foods and drugs in interstate commerce. The second law provided for the enforcement of sanitary regulations in meat-packing establishments and federal inspection of all companies preparing meat for interstate shipment.

Roosevelt crusaded for a conservation program

In no area of reform did Roosevelt work longer or harder for the interests of the nation and of the people than in the conservation of the natural resources of the nation. To gain support for his program, the President had to fight to change old, and in some cases, valued practices.

Since the establishment of the United States, the federal government had followed a simple policy toward the natural resources it controlled. It had distributed public lands, mineral deposits, and other riches as quickly and as cheaply as possible to men who would develop them.

During the Gilded Age some Americans began to express concern over this wholesale private exploitation, saying that if it continued, it would exhaust the nation's natural resources. Some conservation, or reclamation, laws were passed, but they proved to be inadequate. As a hunter, rancher, and lover of nature, Roosevelt was particularly interested in preserving the wilderness areas. His first conservation victory came in June 1902, when he signed the National Reclamation Act (the Newlands Act). It allowed the federal government to use the money it obtained from the sale of public lands in western and southwestern states to pay for the construction and maintenance of large irrigation projects in those states. Under this law the government built great dams, such as the Roosevelt

Dam in Arizona, and numerous irrigation works which made it possible to cultivate thousands of acres in Arizona, California, Colorado, and Utah.

It was not until his second term that Roosevelt put all the resources and power of his office into the conservation crusade. When he had taken office, about three fourths of the nation's forests had been cut, and most of the remainder was in private hands. Through use of existing laws, he tried to stop the exploitation. During his administrations, more than 125 million acres were added to the national forests, and millions of acres of phosphate and coal beds were set aside as national reserves. In addition, he created five national parks and established over fifty wildlife refuges.

Roosevelt considered conservation one of his most valuable contributions to the nation. Although he was unable to stop the looting of the national domain, he did save some of it. Equally important, he created a lasting national interest in conservation.

Roosevelt strengthened the federal government

Roosevelt believed it was the President's duty to be a leader and to exercise power. Unlike previous Presidents, he took the position that he could act unless the law or the Constitution specifically forbade him to do so. By applying his interpretation of presidential power he advanced the conservation program, despite heavy opposition. It was through the application of this interpretation of the powers of the President, too, that he expanded the powers of the government over the economy.

Critics have maintained that Roosevelt's policy toward trusts was frequently more talk than action; as an example, they have pointed to his action during the Panic of 1907. Businessmen laid the blame for the panic on Roosevelt's breaking up of the trusts. Roosevelt lashed back, accusing "certain malefactors of great wealth" of forcing the crisis so that he would ease his attack on the corporations.

Regardless of the charges and countercharges, Roosevelt wanted to keep the panic from spreading. He was convinced by some bankers that he could stop the panic by allowing U.S. Steel to take over control of one of its competitors; he allowed the company to do so, even though that action might be a violation of the Sherman Antitrust Act.

This episode led Progressives to question Roosevelt's dedication to reform. But the episode had a deeper significance. It showed the power of the bankers over the economy. It also showed that in some instances Roosevelt recognized the limitations of his power. He believed that the President had great power, but he also thought "that responsibility should go with power"; he was willing, therefore, to compromise to achieve his ends.

Many economists and other people, too, believed that the panic had been caused by the inability of banks to expand currency and credit, not by the breaking up of the trusts. So Congress passed an emergency law in May 1908, the Aldrich-Vreeland Act, which sought to make the currency elastic by authorizing national banks to issue circulating notes on a more liberal basis than in the past.

To millions of Americans Roosevelt embodied the Progressive spirit in spite of his action during the panic. He did this not only by bringing color and excitement to the White House, but also by strengthening the federal government and by making the presidency more powerful than it had been. Roosevelt increased the authority of the federal government not so much because he enjoyed having power, but because he believed that the government needed such power to meet the challenges of an industrial society. In this extension of federal power to advance the national welfare, Roosevelt can be considered the first of the truly modern Presidents.

REVIEWING THE SECTION

1. How did Roosevelt help settle the coal miners' strike? What was the significance of his action?

2. What was Roosevelt's attitude toward the trusts? What was the result of his efforts to control them?

3. How did the Hepburn Act and the Pure Food and Drug Act regulate certain United States industries?

4. What were Roosevelt's contributions to the conservation movement?

5. How did Roosevelt strengthen the federal government? What was his view of presidential power?

THE PROGRESSIVES REVOLTED

On the night of his election to the presidency in 1904, Roosevelt had announced that the three-and-a-half years of McKinley's unexpired term he had served constituted his own first term. "The wise custom which limits the President to two terms regards the substance and not the form," he said, "and under no circumstances will I be a candidate for or accept another nomination."

Within the next four years this decision proved to be both painful and embarrassing. It pained Roosevelt because he liked being President and really did not want to leave the White House. It embarrassed him because as his second term ended he was immensely popular with the people and was under pressure to forget his pledge of 1904 and seek a third term. Roosevelt, however, resisted the pressures and stood by his promise.

Since Roosevelt was the unchallenged leader of the Republican party, it was within his power to choose the party's candidate. At the Republican convention in Chicago, he used that power to gain the nomination for Secretary of War William Howard Taft. Roosevelt chose Taft for his successor because Taft had been a staunch supporter of the President's policies, and he seemed to be committed to continuing them.

The Democrats, meeting in Denver in July 1908, nominated William Jennings Bryan for the third time. The campaign was dull, though both candidates expressed support for Progressive poli-

cies. Bryan attacked the trusts and promised to reduce the high Republican tariff. Taft promised to continue the Square Deal program and to revise the tariff.

Taft won the election but not so easily as had Roosevelt four years earlier. Early in 1909, shortly after Taft was inaugurated, Roosevelt departed to hunt big game in Africa. Taft was on his own.

The Progressives quarreled with Taft

The new President had had a distinguished career in government service. He had served as a federal judge, as the first civil governor of the Philippine Islands, and as secretary of war. Although Taft by temperament was cautious and conservative, he believed as did Roosevelt that the President should be more concerned with public welfare than with the profits of corporations. Taft considered himself a Progressive.

Taft took office in troubled times. The old guard Republicans, who had been unable to defeat the Progressive measures they opposed because of Roosevelt's popularity, were discontented and the party stood in danger of splitting. Only bold and clever political leadership could avoid such a split. Taft could not offer such leadership.

One of the first issues to demonstrate Taft's political ineptness was that of the tariff. From the beginning of the Progressive era, many people had demanded a reduction of the high Dingley Tariff of 1897. By 1908, the pressure for action had become so great that the Republican platform came out for tariff revision, and Taft himself promised a reduction in rates.

In March 1909, shortly after his inauguration, Taft called Congress into special session to consider revision of the tariff. What emerged was the Payne-Aldrich bill, a bitter disappointment to Progressives and farmers. A small group of Midwestern senators, led by Wisconsin's La Follette, fought the bill.

Although the Republican Progressives failed to prevent passage of the bill, they succeeded in adding to the bill a tax on the net income of corporations. They also gained assurance that an amendment to the Constitution to permit a federal income tax would be submitted to the states.

Despite these few redeeming features and some meager reductions, the new tariff that reached the President's desk represented another victory for eastern manufacturers and old guard Republicans. Taft thought it contained a few worthwhile reductions, so in August he signed the bill into law.

The Progressives relentlessly attacked the Payne-Aldrich Tariff, so in September Taft decided to go to the people to defend his position. He showed poor political judgment in a number of instances, but he committed his worst blunder at Winona, Minnesota. In a hastily written speech he said, "On the whole...the Payne bill is the best bill that the Republican Party has ever passed." Progressives suspected that he had repudiated his campaign pledge and had aligned himself with old guard Republicans.

The Progressives soon came to believe that Taft was no more to be trusted on conservation than on the tariff. The controversy began when the secretary of the interior, Richard A. Ballinger, reopened some water-power sites in Montana and Wyoming to development by private companies and made available to a syndicate of bankers some valuable coal lands in Alaska.

Ballinger was accused by one of his subordinates, Louis Glavis, and by the chief of the forest service, Gifford Pinchot, of having betrayed the conservation policies of Roosevelt. Taft investigated the matter (1910) and decided that Ballinger had done nothing illegal. For making the controversy public, Glavis and, later, Pinchot were dismissed. To the increasingly hostile Progressives, Taft had once again aligned himself with the old guard Republicans.

The Republican party was split

Taft also encountered trouble in the revolt of Progressives against Joseph G. Cannon, the speaker of the House of Representatives. Cannon had been a member of the House for almost fifty-five years when Taft became President. Cannon was skilled at political maneuvering; he ruled the House with an iron hand. Progressives disliked him because he was a friend of the corporations, and a reactionary in politics. They felt frustrated because he used his position to block Progressive legislation.

Cannon was one of the most powerful men in government. As speaker of the House, he appointed the members of its committees and selected their chairmen. He increased his own power by appointing himself chairman of the Committee on Rules, which worked out the order of business in the House. He could, therefore, prevent any bill from leaving the rules committee to go to the House for debate. As speaker, he could recognize or refuse to recognize members who sought the floor and thereby control the issues brought before the House.

In 1909, shortly after Taft became President, Progressive Republicans in the House made plans to limit Cannon's power. Speaker Cannon appealed to the President for help, promising in return to support Taft's legislative program. Although Taft disliked Cannon, he thought he needed the support of the speaker; the President, therefore, endorsed Cannon. The revolt failed, and some of the insurgents suspected that Taft had betrayed them.

In 1910, the Progressive Republicans again attacked Cannon. This time Republican insurgents worked closely with Democrats to gain enough backing to outvote the regular, or conservative, Republicans. Cannon himself fought back savagely when Congressman George W. Norris of Nebraska finally, in March 1910, was able to introduce a resolution that would limit the power of the speaker of the House. It passed by a vote of 191 to 156; more than forty insurgent Republicans had voted with the Democrats.

Under the new rules, the House would elect the members of the rules committee, the speaker could not serve on the committee, and the committee would choose its own chairman. A year later, the speaker was also deprived of the authority to appoint members of other committees. In effect, the speaker no longer could rule the House as a dictator; he was merely the presiding officer.

Progressives did not capture control of the House. Cannon remained as speaker and conservative Republicans continued to control the committees. But the Republican party was split. Since the President had done nothing to help them, Progressives were convinced that he had sided with Cannon. Taft, however, had not favored Cannon.

The President was convinced that the Midwest insurgents wanted to destroy his political career. So he worked openly with conservatives in the Midwest to defeat the insurgents in the elections of 1910. This move turned out to be disastrous; in the primary elections west of the Mississippi River the Progressives defeated the regular Republicans.

In the November elections, the Republican party suffered a major defeat. The Democrats captured control of the House. Republicans retained their grip on the Senate, but because of the insurgents that grip was weak. These election results suggested that without the support of the Progressives, the Republican party was in danger. Many felt that Taft's blunders, as much as any single factor, had split the party.

Taft and Roosevelt became bitter enemies

Progressives were too harsh in their criticism of Taft. He favored many Progressive objectives, and continued many of Roosevelt's policies. For example, Taft's attorney general initiated ninety suits against corporations for violations of the Sherman Antitrust Act. In seven-and-a-half years the Roosevelt administration had started only about half that number. But Roosevelt had launched the movement against the trusts, and his cases were more important.

The Taft administration could also take some credit for an important advance in the regulation of railroads, though Progressives did most of the work. In June 1910, Congress passed the Mann-Elkins Act which enlarged the powers of the Interstate Commerce Commission and placed telephone, telegraph, cable, and wireless companies under its jurisdiction.

Two new amendments to the Constitution were proposed during Taft's term. The Sixteenth Amendment, which authorized a federal income tax, became part of the Constitution in February 1913. The Seventeenth Amendment, which provided for the election of senators directly by the people, went into effect in May 1913.

The Department of Labor was established before Taft left office. Congress created a postal-savings system which made many post offices safe, convenient banks, and a parcel-post service for the inexpensive and reliable delivery of packages. In 1912, Arizona and New Mexico, two territories controlled by the Progressives, were admitted to the Union.

Except for the antitrust suits, most of these measures passed primarily because Progressives pushed them. Regardless of Taft's accomplishments, Progressives turned against him.

While in Africa and Europe, Theodore Roosevelt heard rumors that his policies had been abandoned by the President. Roosevelt returned to the United States in the summer of 1910, during the peak of the controversy between Taft and the Progressives. At first he said nothing publicly about the dissension within his party, but privately he felt that Taft had let him down. He was particularly upset because the strong party which he had built had fallen apart under Taft. The President, in turn, was hurt by the coolness of his old friend.

In January 1911, prominent insurgent leaders formed the National Progressive Republican League. It sought to defeat Taft and gain the Republican nomination for Senator La Follette, who had become the nation's leading Progressive.

When La Follette, exhausted and worried, delivered a rambling speech in Philadelphia in Febru-

THE PRESIDENTS OF THE UNITED STATES

WILLIAM McKINLEY
(1843-1901)
IN OFFICE: 1897-1901

THEODORE ROOSEVELT
(1858-1919)
IN OFFICE: 1901-1909

Republican from Ohio. The nation acquired new territories during this period. Hawaii was annexed (1898); the Philippines, Guam, and Puerto Rico were acquired (1899) as a result of the Spanish-American War. McKinley's domestic policy reflected conservative interests: the tariff was raised (1897), and the Gold Standard Act was passed (1900). He was assassinated in 1901.

Republican from New York. To give Americans a "square deal," Roosevelt led the fight to conserve natural resources and sponsored the Pure Food and Drug Act (1906). To protect American interests, Roosevelt took an active role in world affairs. He was awarded the Nobel Peace Prize for his successful intervention in the Russo-Japanese War (1905).

WILLIAM HOWARD TAFT
(1857-1930)
IN OFFICE: 1909-1913

WOODROW WILSON
(1856-1924)
IN OFFICE: 1913-1921

Republican from Ohio. Taft's administration was active in the prosecution of trusts which violated the Sherman Antitrust Act. His support of the Payne-Aldrich Tariff (1909) lost him the support of Progressives. His foreign policy, often called dollar diplomacy, was aimed at controlling the affairs of foreign nations through the pressure of financial investment.

Democrat from New Jersey. Wilson's achievements in domestic affairs include the passage of the Underwood Tariff (1913), the creation of the Federal Reserve System (1913), and a new antitrust act (1914). At the end of World War I, Wilson helped to create the League of Nations, but was unable to bring the United States into the League.

ary 1912, many Progressive insurgents deserted him and turned to Roosevelt. The Rough Rider had changed his mind about a third term and was ready to fight for the Republican nomination. In February he announced his candidacy. "My hat is in the ring," he told the people. Roosevelt's announcement touched off a bitter primary campaign. Taft and Roosevelt had become opponents for their party's nomination for President.

The Democrats triumphed

Thirteen states held primary elections. In these Roosevelt won most of the delegates who would go to the Republican National Convention in Chicago in June. But the majority of the delegates were chosen by state conventions, which were usually controlled by conservative Republicans. Most of the delegates, therefore, went to Taft. In a dispute over the seating of delegates at the convention, Taft won almost all the seats because his supporters controlled the convention. Angered, Roosevelt's delegates refused to participate in the voting and stormed out of the hall. Taft was renominated on the first ballot.

Roosevelt addressed his followers, shouting that he would fight for the presidency as the candidate of a third party. The reformers then organized the Progressive party; their convention was held in Chicago, too, in August. Roosevelt was in fine spirits when he arrived, claiming he felt "as fit as a bull moose." That animal became the Progressive party's symbol.

The convention adopted a platform that included almost all of the reforms which Progressives had long desired, such as the initiative, referendum, and recall, and child labor laws. The adoption of that platform marked a high point in the Progressive movement. Roosevelt, of course, was given the Progressive nomination.

Sensing that victory was within their reach, the Democrats had held their convention in Baltimore late in June. There they too went through a battle that pitted a Progressive candidate against a more

conservative one. The opponents were Woodrow Wilson, the governor of New Jersey, and James Beauchamp ("Champ") Clark, speaker of the House, a politician from Missouri. Clark led in the early balloting, but Wilson gained enough votes to win the nomination on the forty-sixth ballot.

The platform Wilson's party adopted also called for reforms that Progressives always had wanted. But it did not go as far in its demands as did the "Bull Moose" platform.

Wilson and Roosevelt both campaigned as Progressives. This led Taft to remark, "I have no part to play but that of a conservative." Soon he practically dropped out of the running, and the struggle was narrowed to Wilson and Roosevelt.

Roosevelt campaigned for the "New Nationalism," a program that marked the culmination of his Progressive ideas. To distinguish his program from the New Nationalism, Wilson thought up the phrase "New Freedom." The New Freedom would, Wilson suggested, free the people from the fetters of big business.

When the ballots were counted in November 1912 and Wilson proclaimed the winner, it was clear that he had profited from the Republican split. He won slightly less than forty-two per cent of the total vote, but that was enough for victory. The Democrats also won control of both houses of Congress.

Although Wilson was a minority President, he did represent the majority will in the sense that the majority, as shown in his and Roosevelt's combined vote, wanted a Progressive government. With a united party behind him, as well as Progressive Republicans to help, Wilson had a good chance of providing such a government.

1. Why were the Progressives angered by Taft's support of the Payne-Aldrich Tariff? Why did the Progressives accuse Taft of being anti-conservationist?

2. How did Taft's support of Cannon contribute to the split in the Republican party? Why did in-

surgents limit the powers of the speaker of the House?

3. How was Progressivism furthered by the Taft administration? Why did Roosevelt turn against Taft?

4. Compare the campaigns of Wilson and Roosevelt. What factors enabled Wilson to win the election of 1912?

WOODROW WILSON EXPANDED REFORM

The tall, lean man wearing pince-nez glasses who had won the presidency seemed somewhat like a preacher and somewhat like a professor. Born in Virginia, the son of a Presbyterian minister, Wilson grew up in Georgia and the Carolinas of the Civil War and Reconstruction eras. He obtained a law degree from the University of Virginia, but when he practiced law in Atlanta, he was unsuccessful. So he turned to graduate studies in political science and history at Johns Hopkins University, wrote a book on congressional government in the Gilded Age, obtained a Ph.D. degree, and became a college professor.

In 1902, Wilson became president of Princeton University, where he began a number of educational reforms that brought him national prominence. Wilson had always been interested in politics, and his position and status now gave him a chance to speak out on political issues with some assurance that people would listen. At first his views were not unlike those of many conservative Southern Democrats. But gradually he sensed that the Progressive movement was the wave of the future.

Two situations that came to a climax in 1910 gave Wilson a chance to plunge into politics. Because of a disagreement at Princeton over the question of a new graduate school, he was willing to resign his post as president of the university. At this time, too, New Jersey's Democratic bosses were looking for a respected, educated, and cultured figurehead to run for governor. When Wilson was offered the nomination, he accepted; he

then went on to win the election. But as governor, Wilson was not a figurehead. He turned against the bosses and pushed a bold reform program through the state legislature. From that success he went on to capture the presidency.

The tariff was lowered

Woodrow Wilson's inaugural address was a stirring statement of the Progressive creed. "I summon all honest men, all patriotic, all forward-looking men, to my side," he announced. "God helping me, I will not fail them, if they will but counsel and sustain me!" Few men ever became President with a program more clearly defined and with the means for carrying it out more carefully planned than did Wilson. Basic in his plan was presidential leadership that would keep the Democrats in Congress under control. With such control Wilson could gain enactment of his program, the New Freedom, calling for equal opportunity for all Americans. Unlike Roosevelt, Wilson had the support of a party majority in Congress.

On the day he took office, Wilson called Congress into special session to deal with the first objective of the New Freedom—the lowering of the tariff. Like many Democrats, Wilson believed the high tariff gave special favors to big business which allowed the building of monopolies. When the special session met early in April, he dramatically broke a precedent that had been followed by Presidents for over a hundred years. Instead of sending his messages to Congress by messengers, to be read by someone else, Wilson himself strode into the hall of Congress to explain what he wanted. Like a lawyer, he pleaded his case for tariff reform.

The Underwood Tariff of 1913 passed easily in the House of Representatives. This bill called for the cutting of duties on European goods low enough to bring them into competition with United States manufactures. This alarmed industrialists whose lobbyists exerted pressure on the

Senate to raise the rates. The President stepped into the battle; he issued a public statement denouncing the lobbyists. He said that since "the people at large have no lobby," he would speak for them. Public pressure became so strong that the Senate approved the bill with essentially the low rates the administration desired.

To offset the expected loss of revenue from the new tariff, Representative Cordell Hull from Tennessee had drafted a special section for the bill. As permitted by the new Sixteenth Amendment, this section set up a graduated federal income tax. This measure marked the beginning of great change in the system of taxation in the United States. The nation was now committed to the principle of taxing according to ability to pay.

The Federal Reserve System stabilized the currency

Before the tariff issue had been settled, Wilson had turned to the second part of his program—the reform of the nation's money and banking system. The Panic of 1907 had shown how serious the defects of the system were, and almost everyone agreed that it had to be changed. But there was no agreement on the nature of the reform.

The Aldrich-Vreeland Act of 1908 was only a temporary measure, but it had provided for the National Monetary Commission to study the banking problem. After four years of investigation, the commission, headed by a conservative Republican financier from Rhode Island, Senator Nelson W. Aldrich, made its report. It recommended a system with a great central bank, as in England, which private bankers would own and control.

Shortly thereafter, in 1913, an investigating committee in the House of Representatives, under the leadership of a Louisiana Democrat, Arsène Pujo, published its report. It showed that a few great investment bankers on Wall Street, such as those in the Morgan and Rockefeller groups, controlled much of the nation's wealth. Wilson and other Progressives had denounced this control as a monopoly over money, or the "money trust."

In June 1913, Wilson made his second appearance before Congress. He asked for new banking laws that "must not permit the concentration anywhere in a few hands of the monetary resources of the country." He also said:

the control of the system of banking and of issue which our new laws are to set up, must be public, not private, must be vested in the Government itself.

Democrats differed among themselves over what the banking system should be. For a while the issue threatened to disrupt the Democratic party. Then the President and his advisers worked out a compromise bill that made its way through both houses of Congress. He signed that bill, the Federal Reserve Act, into law late in December 1913.

The Federal Reserve System was a significant achievement for the United States government. It combined centralization with decentralization and while it left money and banking mostly in private hands the government supervised the whole system in the interests of the people.

Corporations felt new restraints

The President next concentrated on the problem of giant corporations which had continued to increase their power through the use of such devices as the holding company and the interlocking directorate.

During his 1912 campaign, Wilson had promised to act against these business practices. Late in January 1914, he asked Congress for laws against holding companies and interlocking directorates, and for a federal commission to supervise big business.

In September, after months of debate and compromise, Congress passed and the President signed the Federal Trade Commission Act. This law established a bipartisan commission which could investigate industries suspected of violating antitrust laws and could issue "cease and desist" orders against

THE FEDERAL RESERVE SYSTEM

THE BOARD OF GOVERNORS

The Federal Reserve System is supervised by a Board of Governors, with members serving fourteen-year terms. They are appointed by the President with the approval of the Senate. The board formulates the nation's monetary policy.

FEDERAL RESERVE DISTRICTS

The nation is divided into twelve Federal Reserve Districts, each having one Federal Reserve Bank. Often called "bankers' banks," Federal Reserve Banks hold the reserves of all public commercial banks that are members of the system and also keep the depositories of the federal government. Reserve Banks issue the paper currency, Federal Reserve notes.

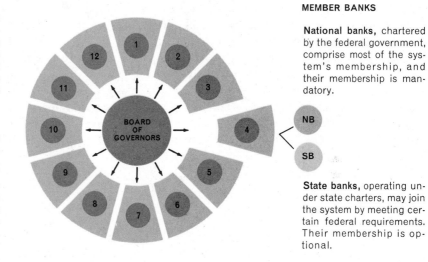

MEMBER BANKS

National banks, chartered by the federal government, comprise most of the system's membership, and their membership is mandatory.

State banks, operating under state charters, may join the system by meeting certain federal requirements. Their membership is optional.

FEDERAL RESERVE OPERATIONS

ECONOMIC CONDITIONS	FEDERAL RESERVE SYSTEM	MEMBER BANKS	RESULT
stable prices and wages with moderate business activity	provides a flexible supply of money and credit for the nation's financial operations	make loans to meet the demands of business and the public	business borrows money, as needed, to maintain a gradual rate of economic growth

ECONOMIC CONDITIONS	FEDERAL RESERVE SYSTEM	MEMBER BANKS	RESULT
business boom with danger of inflationary increase in prices	through various control methods, can limit the money and credit available ·to member banks for loans	have less money to lend and charge more interest on loans, thus discouraging borrowing	contraction of business activity because there is less money and credit in circulation

ECONOMIC CONDITIONS	FEDERAL RESERVE SYSTEM	MEMBER BANKS	RESULT
business recession hampering the growth of the economy	through various control methods, can make more money and credit available to member banks for loans	have more money to lend and charge less interest on loans, thus encouraging borrowing	business expansion because there is more credit available to finance new projects

those found guilty of using unfair methods of competition. If these orders failed to work, the commission could bring the accused corporation to court for trial. Since the commission could publish reports of its investigations, it was hoped that unfavorable publicity would be enough to stop harmful practices. In other words, the law was designed more to prevent and stop unfair methods of competition than to punish offenders.

The Clayton Antitrust Act, which became law in October 1914, was supposed to strengthen the Sherman Antitrust Act by making interlocking directorates among large corporations, and other practices that lessened competition, illegal. It made officers of corporations individually liable for violations of the antitrust laws.

With the passage of these two regulatory laws, the President thought he had completed his reform program. But he was wrong. The antitrust struggle did lose momentum, however.

The Federal Trade Commission and Clayton acts were passed just after war had broken out in Europe. It was also a time of depression and unemployment. Once again Americans were uneasy. Although the depression was caused by conditions in Europe and the outbreak of war, businessmen in the United States blamed the Underwood Tariff and other New Freedom laws for it. The President tried to placate the businessmen with mild applications of the new reform laws. When the United States was drawn into the war, industrial demands increased and the government suspended application of the antitrust laws.

Workers and farmers obtained new benefits

Before Wilson's time, organized labor had suffered greater penalties under the antitrust laws than had the corporations. The courts held that various activities such as strikes and boycotts by labor and farm unions restrained trade and were punishable under the Sherman Antitrust Act. Since organized labor could obtain no help from the Republicans, it turned to the Democrats. In

1912, Samuel Gompers and other leaders of the American Federation of Labor campaigned for Wilson. When he was elected President, they assumed they had a friend in the White House.

The first test of the attitude of the Wilson administration toward labor came with the Clayton Act. The act declared that labor unions and farm organizations were not conspiracies in restraint of trade; it allowed strikes and peaceful picketing and prohibited the use of injunctions in labor disputes except when necessary to prevent "irreparable injury to property, or to a property right." Actually, as the courts were to show later, this law did not make unions immune from prosecution under the antitrust laws.

In 1916, Congress passed an act that gave federal employees compensation during periods of disability, a model for other such legislation. Wilson himself worked for passage of the Keating-Owen Act of that year, the first federal child-labor law. It forbade the shipment in interstate commerce of goods manufactured by children. Even though the Supreme Court in the case of *Hammer* v. *Dagenhart* (1918) invalidated the law as an invasion of state rights, it marked a beginning of federal control over aspects of manufacturing and showed a concern for social justice that had hitherto been slight in Wilson's Progressivism.

The labor law that attracted greatest attention in 1916 was the Adamson Act. It came out of a dispute in which the brotherhoods of railroad men demanded an eight-hour day, which the railroad managers refused to grant. The railroad unions threatened a strike that would have paralyzed the nation's internal commerce. Wilson offered to mediate, but both sides turned his offer down. Finally, he decided that the workers' basic demand was just and asked Congress for a law that would prevent the strike. In September Congress passed the Adamson Act, which gave the railroad workers an eight-hour day at the rate previously paid for a ten-hour day. Businessmen were furious, but the law prevented the strike and established the principle of the eight-hour day.

Like the laborers, the farmers had received few benefits from the Republicans. They expected better treatment from Wilson and the Democrats. With the President's support, in July 1916, the Federal Farm Loan Act was passed, setting up special banks in each of the Federal Reserve districts. From these banks farmers could borrow money on a long-term basis at a low rate of interest. The farmers would use their land and improvements for security. The Federal Farm Loan Bank would watch over the whole system.

Farmers also benefited from two other laws passed during the Wilson administration. The first of these was the Smith-Lever Act of May 1914, which provided federal funds for rural education through the coöperation of the Department of Agriculture and the land-grant colleges. In February 1917, the second law, the Smith-Hughes Act, provided federal money to support vocational education in agriculture and the trades.

With the passage of these and other laws, Wilson and the Democrats could rightfully boast that they had carried out most of the Progressive measures they had promised in 1912. Yet Wilson had not fought for these measures out of any deep personal commitment to social reform. Political conditions had made Wilson's New Freedom more Progressive than he had at first intended it to be.

Wilson was reëlected

In its first phase the New Freedom had not been much concerned with social justice. It had been a limited program of reform that struck at economic evils which stood in the way of free competition. In 1914, Wilson thought he had achieved this objective, and he called a halt to further reform. At first he opposed the bill for land banks to help farmers, refused to fight for a child-labor bill, and would not support woman suffrage because he considered, these measures unconstitutional.

Progressive candidates were despondent; they lost everywhere in the congressional elections of 1914. The Republican party, united behind its candidates reduced the Democratic majority in the House of Representatives from seventy-three to twenty-five. Republicans also regained power in key eastern states, and looked strong enough to win the presidency in 1916.

Early in 1916, Theodore Roosevelt indicated he would rejoin the Republican party and take his Progressive following with him. If this happened, the Democrats faced almost certain defeat. To prevent this, Wilson decided to try to lure many of the Roosevelt Progressives into the Democratic party by showing that the party was committed to social and economic reform. The first sign of this change was his appointment of Louis D. Brandeis, a labor lawyer and well-known reformer, to the Supreme Court. Then followed the various reform laws. These laws passed Congress because most Democrats accepted Wilson's course as the best means of staying in power. One Georgia legislator said that the Democrats had to "support the Administration or be turned into the wilderness for forty years more." As a result, Wilson was able to go to the people in the fall with the most impressive record of Progressive laws enacted up to that time.

This record was not the only issue of the campaign. At the Democratic convention in St. Louis, where Wilson was renominated by acclamation, it became clear that foreign policy would also be an issue. Speakers pointed out that Wilson, despite provocations, had kept the United States at peace while the nations of Europe were fighting a great war. The Democrats adopted as a campaign slogan, "He kept us out of war."

Meeting in Chicago, the Republicans by-passed Roosevelt who had fought for the nomination, and chose as their candidate Charles Evans Hughes, an associate justice of the Supreme Court and former governor of New York. Hughes was acceptable to both factions of the party, the Progressive Republicans and the conservatives. The Progressive party, also convening in Chicago, offered its nomination to Roosevelt. He refused it because he did not want to split the Republican vote again, and he did want to see Wilson defeated. The Progressive party did not nominate another candidate. Many of the Bull Moosers, as well as Republican farmers in the Midwest who had voted for Roosevelt in 1912, now turned to the Democrats.

Wilson campaigned boldly on two issues, Progressivism and peace. Hughes proved an unexciting and evasive campaigner. On most domestic issues he took a conservative position and on matters of foreign policy he allowed himself to appear favorable to intervention in the war. Roosevelt's support did not help, for he had abandoned Progressivism by that time and was going around the country making speeches in favor of war.

Wilson was reëlected and the Democrats retained control over both houses of Congress by a narrow margin.

Progressivism, when fused with the peace issue, still seemed attractive enough to the voters to give victory to a minority Democratic party over a united Republican party. Wilson intended to continue on his course of Progressivism and peace, but the war in Europe diverted him.

REVIEWING THE SECTION

1. Why did Wilson work for tariff reform? How did the Sixteenth Amendment change the system of taxation in the United States?

2. How did the Democrats reform the nation's money and banking system?

3. What attempts were made during Wilson's first administration to control trusts?

4. What benefits were gained by workers and farmers during Wilson's administration?

5. How did Wilson's reform program change between 1913 and 1917? Why did it change? What factors enabled Wilson to win the election in 1916?

CHAPTER **20** CONCLUSION

The Progressive era had a unity that went beyond the program of any one political party. It began during the presidency of Theodore Roosevelt, though its roots were in the 1890's. Under Roosevelt the Progressives managed to gain passage of a number of reform laws, win the support of men in government and politics, and build up a public following. The Taft years were a time when some reforms were enacted but many were not. This was a time of Progressive impatience and later, of open struggle between Progressives and conservatives in the Republican party. Wilson and the Democrats profited from the fight in the Republican ranks, took over the leadership of the Progressive movement, and built upon Roosevelt's foundations. Even though the New Freedom started out as a reform program with limited objectives, it changed into one of sweeping achievement. It marked the climax of the Progressive movement, which gradually faded away after 1917.

In sixteen years the Progressive movement had made a deep impact on American life. It had changed the structure of local and state governments and the relationship between those governments and the people. Officials at all levels of government became increasingly concerned with popular feeling and more responsive to it than they had been only a decade earlier. Businessmen, too, became concerned with people as well as with profits and showed a new respect for the power of government. The President, as evidenced in the Roosevelt and Wilson administrations, gained and used new power. The President became an active leader of government, and the people accepted his enlarged role because the President, more than anyone else, was expected to look after their interests and welfare.

For years Progressives had urged enactment of many reforms. Before Wilson left the White House, most of them had become law. New laws regulated corporations, protected the people's health, and conserved natural resources. Constitutional amendments permitted a federal income tax, gave the people the right to elect their senators directly, and bestowed on women the right to vote. This last reform came late—not until August 1920, when the Nineteenth Amendment was ratified. But many women had been voting in state elections long before this. State after state had granted women the vote, and women were active in politics and the professions to an extent never before witnessed in American society. At the same time, direct primary elections were being held in all but three states. The initiative, referendum, and recall had become law in scores of states and cities.

Yet the results of many of these reforms were disappointing. Antitrust laws did not stop the trend toward the concentration of economic power. The initiative, referendum, and recall did not greatly change the practice of politics. The direct election of senators did not noticeably improve the quality of the Senate; it even may have helped in the election of some demagogues. Direct primaries did not eliminate political bosses and, by increasing the cost of campaigning, may have given an advantage to the rich candidate over the poor one. Even woman suffrage, which was supposed to elevate the moral tone of political life, failed to measure up to the expectations of Progressives. In brief, many of the Progressive reforms could not cope with the complexities of twentieth-century American society.

Even though the achievements of the Progressives did not fulfill their hopes, they had fought for political and corporate honesty, for social justice, and for high public morals. When they left the scene, evil men had not become saints, but the United States was more honest and more just in her politics and economics than at any time in the past. Most Americans had a better chance to enjoy a better life with the Progressive reforms in effect than without them.

FOCUSING ON SPECIFICS

1. How did Progressivism differ from Populism? How did Progressives differ from socialists?

2. What objectives united the Progressives?

3. Why did many middle-class Americans become reformers at the turn of the century?

4. How did *The Jungle* influence reform?

5. How did Tom L. Johnson and Samuel "Golden Rule" Jones contribute to the reform movement?

6. Describe the new forms of city government developed by the Progressives.

7. What reforms were championed by Robert M. La Follette of Wisconsin?

8. What were the functions of the initiative, the referendum, the recall, and the direct primary?

9. What steps to regulate big business were taken by Roosevelt?

10. How did the Pujo report influence the development of the Federal Reserve System?

11. What was the function of the Federal Trade Commission?

12. What provisions of the Clayton Antitrust Act were intended to curb trusts?

13. Why did the struggle against the trusts lose momentum during Wilson's first administration?

REVIEWING MAIN THEMES

1. What reforms were made during the Progressive era?

2. In what ways was the role of the federal government increased during the Progressive era?

3. Compare the roles of Roosevelt, Taft, and Wilson in promoting reforms.

4. Which political, economic, and social reforms had only limited success? Why?

EVALUATING THE ISSUES

1. Roosevelt believed that the President could do anything that the Constitution did not specifically prohibit. Could this attitude lead to the development of a dictatorship? In your answer consider the constitutional limitations on the President's power.

2. Roosevelt is remembered as having been one of the great Presidents. Taft, on the other hand, is remembered as having been weak and ineffectual. How much of Roosevelt's reputation is based on his public image rather than on his accomplishments as President?

3. Many Progressives believed that popular control of government would mean better government. Do you agree? Explain your answer.

4. By instituting the city-manager and commission forms of city government, Progressives hoped to make city politics "nonpartisan." Do you think that political decisions can be "nonpartisan"? Discuss.

CHAPTER 21 1900-1920

The Growing Involvement in World Affairs

After the Spanish-American War, the United States stepped up its participation in the international politics of Asia and soon became an important power in that part of the world. Secretary of State John M. Hay set for his successors the pattern for relations with the Far East, even though he was unable to convince the major powers of Europe to follow his lead. His policy, known as the Open Door policy, was based on the principles of commercial equality in China and the preservation of China's territorial integrity.

President Theodore Roosevelt frequently followed an aggressive foreign policy, called big stick diplomacy. This aggressiveness was apparent in his handling of the isthmian canal problem, the Venezuelan problem, and the Alaska boundary dispute with Canada. A conspicuous example of Roosevelt's aggressiveness involved the republics south of the Rio Grande and in the Caribbean. Disorders in that area led Roosevelt to formulate a corollary to the Monroe Doctrine, which had been designed to prevent European powers from intervening in the Western Hemisphere. The corollary justified intervention by the United States in the internal affairs of the Caribbean countries to maintain order and to keep out European governments.

In his diplomacy Roosevelt mixed aggressiveness and caution. This mixed approach can be seen in his handling of the Moroccan crisis and in his relations with Japan.

Roosevelt's successor, William Howard Taft, worked out a policy which has come to be known as dollar diplomacy. Taft did not content himself merely with the protection of United States property and investments abroad; he encouraged United States bankers and industrialists to invest money in foreign lands. He applied that policy unsuccessfully in China, but with some success in Latin America.

Taft scored a diplomatic victory when he arranged for a settlement of the northern fisheries problem, which, since the colonial period, had plagued relations between Britain, and eventually

Canada, and the United States. That triumph was offset, however, by the fight over tariff reciprocity which again strained the relations with Canada.

Taft left a number of vexing problems for his successor, Woodrow Wilson. The most conspicuous of these involved the tolls the United States charged for passage of ships through the Panama Canal and the distrust of the United States that prevailed in Central and South America and in Mexico.

None of these problems could be compared to those Wilson faced when war broke out in Europe in 1914. And after his country had fought in that war, Wilson's great dream of the United States becoming the moral leader of the world was shattered. The United States Senate, and then the people, rejected the Treaty of Versailles and the League of Nations.

During the period between 1900 and 1920, the United States was one of the great powers in the world. The other major powers recognized that status but the United States did not always live up to its world responsibilities. Yet it did use its influence and power to further its policies in the Far East, in the Caribbean area, and in Europe. Although the United States became disillusioned with world politics after World War I, the nation could not entirely avoid its responsibilities as a world power.

THE UNITED STATES ACQUIRED NEW INTERESTS

By 1900, the United States had acquired a colonial empire that stretched from the Caribbean Sea to distant places in the Pacific Ocean. That empire included Puerto Rico, Alaska, Hawaii, American Samoa, Guam, the Philippine Islands, and other islands in the Pacific. The United States government had to decide how to govern these new territories.

In addition, the acquisition of an empire in the Pacific involved the United States directly in the politics of the Far East. The government, therefore, had to formulate a policy for dealing with the nations of Asia and with the European nations with interests in that area. Two developments strongly influenced the nature of the American involvement. One was the continuing weakness of China; the other was the rise of Japan to the status of a great power.

In 1895, Japan had defeated China in a war for dominance over Korea. Before Japan could profit from her victory, Russia, Germany, and France intervened and forced Japan to give up territory she had taken from China. Within a few years, China's weakness led Britain, France, Russia, and Germany, as well as Japan, to demand more than privileges in trade and investment; they threatened to partition China.

At first this threatened breakup did not alarm the United States because trade with China had never been great. Some American businessmen, however, believed that China would be a market for vast trade in the future. If China were dismembered, each nation with a Chinese colony would probably discriminate against traders from the United States and other foreign nations. The United States would then be frozen out of the Chinese market.

The first tests faced by the United States as a world power in the twentieth century concerned her newly acquired empire.

The United States adopted a new policy on expansion

When the United States had acquired territory earlier in the nineteenth century, it had set up a territorial system of government in the new lands. The annexed territories were expected to become part of the Union, and the people in them were given all the constitutional rights and privileges enjoyed by other citizens of the United States. In dealing with most of the new island possessions, however, the government of the United States did not follow this old pattern. Instead, it established a system of government that resembled colonial administration in the old British Empire.

This new colonial system was based on the be-

MAJOR EVENTS IN UNITED STATES FOREIGN AFFAIRS: 1899-1920

1899-1920 (From the emergence of the United States as a world power to the end of World War I)

STATEMENTS OF POLICY

1899-1900 *Open Door policy.* The U.S. sought to insure for all nations free and open trade in areas of China under foreign influence and to preserve China's independence.

1901-1909 *Big stick diplomacy,* an aggressive foreign policy followed by Roosevelt in many U.S. negotiations, including an isthmian canal route, the Alaskan boundary dispute, and the European dispute over Morocco.

1904 *Roosevelt Corollary to the Monroe Doctrine* declared the right of the U.S. to intervene in Latin America to keep order and to prevent European intervention there, such as occurred in Venezuela in 1902. First applied in the Dominican Republic in 1905, the corollary justified U.S. control over several Caribbean republics.

1909-1913 *Dollar diplomacy.* President Taft encouraged private U.S. investment in foreign nations. It was unsuccessfully applied in China in an effort to further the Open Door policy. In the Caribbean, notably in Nicaragua (1911), the policy was applied to prevent possible European intervention in U.S. canal area.

1913-1915 *Official recognition of Huerta government* in Mexico withheld by Wilson. This refusal to extend recognition to a government actually in power broke a U.S. precedent set by President Washington.

1914 *Proclamation of neutrality* by Wilson at the outbreak of World War I. Germany's unrestricted submarine warfare led U.S. to declare war in 1917.

EXECUTIVE AGREEMENTS

1907-1908 *Gentlemen's Agreement.* Japan agreed to stop emigration of Japanese laborers to the U.S.

1908 *Root-Takahira Agreement.* Japan and U.S. agreed to support the status quo in the Pacific, and to support the Open Door policy in China.

WARS AND PEACE TREATIES

1905 *Treaty of Portsmouth,* mediated by Roosevelt, ended the Russo-Japanese War. It confirmed Japan as a major world power and its dominance in Korea and southern Manchuria.

1917 *U.S. entered World War I.* In 1918, hostilities ended.

1919-1921 *Treaty of Versailles,* signed with Germany, later rejected by Senate. By congressional resolution, the war was declared officially ended in 1921, and peace treaties were signed with Germany, Austria, and Hungary.

TERRITORIAL SETTLEMENTS AND ACQUISITIONS

1901-1915 *Protectorates.* With the Platt Amendment to the Cuban constitution (1901), Cuba became the first of 5 U.S. Caribbean protectorates. Others: Panama (1903); Dominican Republic (1905); Nicaragua (1914); and Haiti (1915).

1903 *Alaska-Canada boundary* settled in favor of U.S. by British-U.S. arbitration commission.

1916 *Virgin Islands* purchased from Denmark for $25 million.

1917 *Jones Act* made Puerto Rico a U.S. territory and gave U.S. citizenship to Puerto Ricans.

Supply centers, such as Dyea, Alaska, bustled with activity in the late 1890's as gold seekers prepared for the rigorous trip to the Canadian Klondike. The influx of prospectors from the U.S. aggravated the dispute over the boundary between Alaska and Canada.

Landing of Yukoners on Dyea Flats, Alaska, 1897

ECONOMIC POLICY AND COMMERCIAL TREATIES

1901-1914 *Isthmian Canal. Hay-Pauncefote Treaty* (1901) with Britain abrogated the Clayton-Bulwer Treaty of 1850 and cleared the way for U.S. control of an isthmian canal. Colombia rejected a treaty (1903) giving U.S. canal rights in its province of Panama. *Treaty with Panama* (1903), a new republic, guaranteed Panamanian independence and gave U.S. a lease in perpetuity on a 10-mile-wide canal strip. Panama Canal opened to traffic (1914) on equal terms to all nations. *Bryan-Chamorro Treaty* (1914) with Nicaragua gave U.S. rights to Nicaraguan route.

DIPLOMACY OF WAR PREVENTION

1906 *Algeciras Conference.* During Moroccan crisis, Roosevelt interfered diplomatically in European affairs.

1918 *Fourteen points for peace* presented to Congress by Wilson included a proposal for a league of nations.

1919-1920 *League of Nations.* By rejecting the Treaty of Versailles, the U.S. rejected membership in the League of Nations.

ARBITRATION TREATIES

1909 *North Atlantic fisheries settlement.* Britain and U.S. submitted the long-standing dispute to the Hague Court.

lief that people such as the Puerto Ricans, Filipinos, and Samoans were not yet ready for self-government. Since the Constitution guaranteed rights of self-government to all citizens of the United States, the administration of the new dependencies posed a serious constitutional question.

The Supreme Court provided an answer to this question in a number of controversial decisions in the so-called Insular Cases between 1901 and 1922. The Court said that the United States could acquire and rule subject peoples and that the Constitution did not apply in all places under United States control. In arriving at these decisions, the Court made a vague distinction between what it called incorporated and unincorporated territories. It held that people in the incorporated territories, such as Alaska and Hawaii, would enjoy the full rights guaranteed under the Constitution to citizens of the United States. But people in the unincorporated territories, or dependencies such as Puerto Rico, the Philippines, Guam, and American Samoa, were not entitled to all of the constitutional rights and privileges. Congress, therefore, could govern the colonies in almost any way it wished.

John Hay sent the Open Door notes

Until 1898, the British, who controlled about eighty per cent of China's foreign trade, had supported the idea and usually the practice of equal commercial opportunity in China for all nations. In 1899, Britain, Russia, Germany, and France seemed intent on carving China into spheres of commercial and political influence—an act that would have killed the policy of equal economic opportunity. At the same time, people in the United States were becoming more interested in China. American businessmen, in particular, believed the government should save China from partition.

In September and November 1899, Secretary of State John Hay sent notes to Britain, Germany, Russia, Japan, France, and Italy. These dispatches, known as the first Open Door notes, asked those nations to support equal commercial opportunity for all nations in China, even in areas they dominated such as the spheres of influence. All the replies were either qualified or evasive; in effect, the powers turned down Hay's request without openly rejecting it. Yet in March 1900, Hay announced that the powers had given him satisfactory assurances. On the surface it seemed that Hay had prevented the breakup of China with brilliant diplomacy.

Hay's Open Door policy was put to a test when a violent anti-Western uprising, the Boxer Rebellion, broke out in China. In June 1900, powerful bands of Chinese nationalists, known as Boxers, overran Peking, China's capital, and besieged the foreign legations in the city. In August an international army, which included some 2500 United States troops, rescued the trapped Europeans and Americans.

Secretary of State Hay feared that some of the powers would use the Boxer troubles as an excuse to take Chinese territory, or at least to exercise some control over it. In July 1900, at the height of the crisis, he had sent a note, called a circular, to the several powers asking them to preserve China's territorial integrity as well as freedom for trade. Thus the complete Open Door policy was made up of Hay's notes of 1899 and his circular of 1900. That policy included two principles. The first was equal commercial opportunity, and the second was respect for China's independence.

Hay's Open Door policy did not save China, for the great powers did not pay much attention to it. What saved China from dismemberment was the mutual jealousies of the powers. Nonetheless, Hay had made the position of the United States clear. Even though the United States would not back the Open Door policy with force, it did give the impression of being particularly concerned over China's fate.

Roosevelt mediated between Russia and Japan.

Hay's notes had little effect on Russia, which used the Boxer troubles to gain control of Manchuria. Russia's moves alarmed the Japanese, who also wished to take over Manchuria. Late in 1903, therefore, Japan tried to reach an understanding with Russia regarding the future of Manchuria and Korea. When Russia would not accept Japan's terms, Japan broke off negotiations and, in February 1904, attacked the Russian fleet at Port Arthur, Manchuria. Since all the land fighting in the Russo-Japanese War took place on Chinese soil, that conflict endangered the Open Door policy.

As soon as the war began, President Roosevelt reasserted the Open Door policy. He asked Japan and Russia to respect China's neutrality and independence. Although Roosevelt and the American people sympathized with the Japanese, the President decided that the nation's interests in Asia would be served best by a balance of power between Japan and Russia. So he tried to mediate a peace that would not drive Russia out of eastern Asia.

Such a mediation became possible because the Japanese wanted to negotiate peace. They were winning victory after victory, but the war was driving them to bankruptcy. In the spring of 1905, therefore, the Japanese asked Roosevelt to mediate. He quickly agreed, obtained Russian consent to peace negotiations, and offered facilities at Portsmouth, New Hampshire, for the peace conference. In addition, he helped arrange a compromise which led to the Treaty of Portsmouth that ended the war (September 5, 1905).

Almost everyone but the Japanese praised Roosevelt's peacemaking efforts. In the following year he even received the Nobel Peace Prize for his diplomacy. The Japanese people believed that the compromise arranged by Roosevelt had robbed their nation of the fruits of victory. They turned against the United States, and anti-American riots swept over Japan.

The Treaty of Portsmouth marked the first victory of an Asian nation over a major world power, aroused a new nationalism in parts of Asia, confirmed Japan as a world power and as the dominant power in Korea and southern Manchuria.

The Japanese resented United States policy

Developments within the United States increased tension with Japan. There was mounting pressure in the nation for the exclusion of Japanese immigrants and, in October 1906, the San Francisco school board segregated 93 Japanese children in a special school. The people of Japan took the segregation as an insult to their nation, so it seemed as if the crisis could trigger a war.

Roosevelt followed a policy of firmness toward the Japanese, combined with efforts to find a peaceful solution for the differences. He was fond of quoting an old West African proverb, "Speak softly and carry a big stick." While he negotiated with the Japanese, he held his big stick, the navy, in reserve.

Roosevelt persuaded the San Franciscans to end their segregation in return for a promise to stop the immigration of Japanese laborers. From the Japanese he obtained a promise that they would stop the flow of immigrants to the United States. This arrangement became known as the "gentlemen's agreement."

Yet talk of war persisted. So Roosevelt decided to send the United States battleship fleet, then the second largest in the world, on a world cruise to impress the Japanese with the futility of war. In 1908, the fleet visited Japan where it made a vivid impression, received a friendly welcome, and helped end the crisis.

The Root-Takahira Agreement, signed in Washington, D.C., in November 1908, by Secretary of State Elihu Root and Japanese ambassador Baron Kogoro Takahira, also helped ease the crisis. In that agreement both nations agreed to respect the Open Door policy in China and to support the existing state of affairs in Asia.

The Open Door policy was modified

William Howard Taft would not accept the existing state of affairs in Asia. He introduced a change in the concept of the Open Door policy which became known as "dollar diplomacy." It was based on the idea that money invested in China and Manchuria could help block Japan's efforts to close the door there and would help preserve China's independence. At the same time, businessmen of the United States could make a profit.

One of the first ventures in dollar diplomacy involved a loan agreement, made in 1909, between the Chinese government and a group of British, French, and German bankers. Despite the resistance of the European bankers, President Taft intervened, in 1910, to gain admittance to this *consortium,* or partnership, for United States bankers.

Under Woodrow Wilson, relations with Japan continued to deteriorate. In January 1915, while Europe was at war, Japan presented the Chinese government with twenty-one demands that would have made China almost a vassal of Japan. When the Chinese told the United States government about them, President Wilson protested. Japan gave up some of her harshest demands, but China was forced to accept most of the twenty-one demands.

After the United States had entered World War I (in April 1917) and had become an ally of Japan, the two nations tried to reach an agreement on China. In the Lansing-Ishii Agreement of November 1917, they reaffirmed their respect for the Open Door policy and China's independence. But the United States also said it recognized that Japan had a special position in China. Some people in the United States considered the contradictory agreement a betrayal of the Open Door policy. Actually, it merely recognized the existence of Japan's sphere of influence, and by doing so, helped ease Japanese-American tension during the war.

REVIEWING THE SECTION

1. How did United States control of the Philippines, Puerto Rico, and American Samoa differ from its control of territories acquired earlier in the nineteenth century? Why?

2. What was the Open Door policy? How did the United States apply this policy?

3. How did dollar diplomacy change the meaning of the Open Door policy? What changes in the Open Door policy were made by Wilson's administration?

THE U.S. DOMINATED THE CARIBBEAN AREA

At the end of the Spanish-American War, the United States found that, in addition to its involvement in the politics of Asia, it was in control of Cuba and was the dominant power in the Caribbean Sea. In order to maintain that dominance, the United States followed a policy of intervention which led to steadily deteriorating relations with the nations of Latin America.

Expansionists were eager to take over Cuba in order to control the approaches to a future canal across Central America. The United States did not annex Cuba, but neither did it grant the immediate independence that Cubans wanted. The terms imposed on Cuba by the United States became known as the Platt Amendment to the Cuban constitution (1901). This amendment gave Cuba self-government in internal matters but reserved to the United States the legal right to intervene in Cuban affairs when necessary. Cuba thus became the first United States protectorate in the Caribbean.

The desire of the United States for a canal across Central America prompted President Roosevelt to intervene in the affairs of Colombia, which, in turn, led to the creation of Panama, the second United States protectorate in the Caribbean.

The United States became increasingly sensitive to any form of European intervention in Latin America. When Britain, Germany, and Italy landed troops in Venezuela in order to collect money owed those countries, Roosevelt developed a *corollary,* or additional principle, to the Monroe Doctrine and became the "policeman" of the Caribbean area. President Taft applied a version of dollar diplomacy to Latin America. President Wilson, however, denounced dollar diplomacy in the Caribbean area and announced a new policy of friendship for Latin America. Wilson's actions did not fit his words. In the Caribbean area and Mexico his interventions were more extensive than those of Roosevelt or Taft.

The U.S. decided to build an isthmian canal

The idea of cutting a canal through Central America was an old one. In the 1880's and 1890's, French and American companies had tried to build canals across Nicaragua and the Isthmus of Panama but had failed. These failures had convinced the United States that the building of an interoceanic canal was beyond the resources of private companies. Such a canal would have to be constructed by the government. But the United States government wanted to have full control over any canal it built, and the terms of the Clayton-Bulwer Treaty of 1850 with Britain stood in the way of such control.

After extended negotiations, the British agreed to a new treaty, the Hay-Pauncefote Treaty (November 1901), which permitted the United States not only to build a canal, but also to fortify and operate it.

The United States now had to decide where to build the canal. After investigating two possible routes, one across Panama and the other across Nicaragua, the United States chose the Panama route. At the time Panama was a part of Colombia.

In January 1903, a treaty was completed with the Colombian representative in Washington granting the United States control for one hundred years or more of a strip of land six miles wide across Panama. For this grant the United States would pay $10 million in gold and an annual rent of $250 thousand. Colombia's government, however, rejected the treaty; it wanted more money.

The rejection infuriated President Roosevelt and alarmed the people of Panama. They had long been discontented with Colombian rule, and they wanted the canal to be built. So a group of them prepared to secede from Colombia.

Philippe Bunau-Varilla, an engineer for the French company which had earlier tried to build a canal across Panama, met with the conspirators in September 1903, and promised to support a revolution. In October he talked with Secretary Hay and President Roosevelt and deduced that the United States would, in effect, prevent Colombian troops from suppressing the revolt.

The revolution began on November 3; Panama declared her independence on November 4; and the United States recognized Panama's independence on November 6. On November 18, Secretary Hay signed a canal treaty with Bunau-Varilla, who had made himself Panama's first minister to the United States. The treaty guaranteed the independence of Panama, granted the United States control of a ten-mile wide canal strip in perpetuity, and provided for a payment of $10 million to Panama, plus $250 thousand annually after nine years. The Senate approved the treaty in February 1904.

Roosevelt's big stick diplomacy had made Panama the second United States protectorate in the Caribbean, and it had aroused resentment throughout Latin America against "Yankee imperialism."

Many people in the United States were upset by Roosevelt's ruthless action. Finally, in 1921, the United States government gave Colombia $25 million as payment for her loss of Panama.

Theodore Roosevelt became a Caribbean policeman

While Congress was considering rival canal routes, a dispute in Venezuela caused trouble for the United States. Venezuela's unscrupulous dictator, Cipriano Castro, had defaulted on some of the country's foreign debts. After futile negotiations, three of the creditor nations—Britain, Germany, and Italy—landed troops in Venezuela and blockaded its main ports (December 1902).

At first President Roosevelt saw nothing wrong in this. Later, as American public opinion became more hostile toward Germany, which used the greatest force, he changed his mind and put pressure on the creditor nations to arbitrate the dispute and get out of Venezuela. The powers did arbitrate and, in February 1903, they lifted the blockade.

This episode revealed a widespread distrust of Germany, the most belligerent of Venezuela's creditors, in the United States and a sensitivity to virtually any form of European intervention in Latin America. Its outcome also gave new dignity to the Monroe Doctrine. As a result of this experience, Roosevelt decided to formulate a corollary to the Monroe Doctrine.

The President expressed his theory officially in his annual message to Congress in December 1904. He said that

in the Western Hemisphere the adherence of the United States to the Monroe Doctrine may force the United States, however reluctantly, in flagrant cases of . . . wrongdoing or impotence, to the exercise of an international police power.

In other words, to prevent any excuse for European intervention the United States would act as a policeman and force the Latin-American countries to behave. He applied the corollary first in the Dominican Republic.

Like Venezuela, the Dominican Republic had borrowed heavily from foreign nations. Early in 1904, it was clear that the republic was bankrupt. It seemed likely that European creditors might intervene, as they had in Venezuela, to force some kind of debt settlement.

In January 1905, the United States took over the collection of Dominican customs, made payments on the republic's debts, and for years kept that nation's finances in order. The Dominican Republic, as a result, became the third United States protectorate in the Caribbean area. Most foreign debtors were satisfied with United States control because it assured them a reasonable return on the debts. But Dominicans and other Latin Americans disliked the intervention.

William Howard Taft intervened in Central America

President William H. Taft and Secretary of State Philander C. Knox went a step further than Roosevelt by applying to Latin America a version of dollar diplomacy.

Under Taft, the United States tried to keep order and prevent European intervention in the Latin-American nations, particularly in the Caribbean republics, by removing the excuse for intervention. Taft attempted to keep out new European investments and to force out European capital already there. With assurance of protection from the government, United States investments could then replace European investments. In theory, the Caribbean nations would gain stability, the United States would block intervention in the sensitive canal area, and United States investors would profit.

Taft's intervention in Nicaragua was the clearest example of dollar diplomacy in action. Like other Caribbean republics, Nicaragua had borrowed from European investors.

After a successful revolution in August 1910, Nicaragua turned to the United States for a loan to help stabilize its precarious finances. In June 1911, Secretary of State Knox worked out an agreement for a loan to Nicaragua. According to the terms of the agreement, an official of the United States would be placed in charge of the finances of the Nicaraguan government for the term of the loan. Before the plan was completed, Nicaragua defaulted on her European debt. Encouraged by Taft, bankers in the United States loaned money to Nicaragua, and a United States Army officer took charge of her finances.

When another revolution threatened the United States investments in July 1912, Taft sent more than 2500 troops into Nicaragua and crushed the revolt. Then he stationed a warship and a military guard there to discourage future uprisings.

Woodrow Wilson continued Taft's policy in Nicaragua. In August 1914, the United States and Nicaragua signed the Bryan-Chamorro Treaty. In return for $3 million to pay her debts, Nicaragua gave the United States the exclusive right to build and operate a canal and a naval base in Nicaragua. Thus, Nicaragua also became a protectorate.

Woodrow Wilson practiced missionary diplomacy

Woodrow Wilson's interventions in Latin America grew out of a zeal to do good. He and Secretary of State William Jennings Bryan wanted to save the peoples of Mexico and the Caribbean republics from internal anarchy and foreign dangers, and help them establish sound governments. This attitude, a kind of "missionary diplomacy," was behind Wilson's action in Nicaragua.

In the Dominican Republic, Wilson not only continued the financial protectorate Roosevelt had established, he expanded the scale of control. After an uprising in 1916, United States marines occupied the nation, and an American military governor ruled as though he were at the head of the state. It is true that the Wilson administration brought peace and stability to the Dominican Republic, but it was a peace based on naked force.

Haiti, too, was continually racked by violence and revolution. In July 1915, after two revolutions within a year, Haiti's president, Vilbrun Guillaume Sam, brutally killed about 167 political prisoners. This infuriated the people of Port-au-Prince, the capital. Sam fled to the French legation for safety, but a mob dragged him out and tore his body to pieces in the streets.

President Wilson then sent in marines to curb the violence and to occupy the country. Using guerrilla tactics, the Haitians fought the occupation, but to no avail. In September the United States forced a treaty on Haiti that gave Americans tighter control of that nation than they had in any other Caribbean republic. Although the Americans introduced many reforms, they failed to bring lasting stability and democracy to the republic.

Wilson had trouble with Mexico

Wilson's missionary diplomacy encountered its greatest difficulties in Mexico. The problem in Mexico began when Francisco I. Madero, a young reformer, led a revolution (1911) that overthrew a long-established dictatorship under Porfirio Díaz.

Madero planned to build a new, democratic society for Mexico. But his leading general, Victoriano Huerta, seized power, and apparently was involved in Madero's murder (February 1913).

When Wilson became President (March 1913), he refused to recognize Huerta's government. He said the United States would not recognize governments that came to power by force and that did not represent the will of the people.

A civil war began in Mexico when General Venustiano Carranza, a follower of Madero, opposed Huerta. President Wilson offered to mediate the Mexican civil war but Huerta turned down Wilson's offer.

Wilson then followed a policy of watchful waiting, hoping that Huerta would be forced to resign. Finally, Wilson used force.

In April 1914, some American sailors who had gone ashore from a warship off Tampico were arrested and then released. Although Huerta's subordinate apologized, Huerta would not offer the kind of apology the American admiral demanded. Wilson then ordered battleships to Tampico.

However, news reached Washington, D.C., of a German ship that was headed for Veracruz loaded with guns for Huerta. Wilson, therefore, ordered the navy to take Veracruz, instead of Tampico, to prevent the unloading of the guns. The Mexicans resisted. Before the city was occupied, 19 United States marines and 126 Mexicans had been killed.

War was prevented when Argentina, Brazil, and Chile helped mediate the quarrel in a conference at Niagara Falls, Canada, in the summer of 1914. A short time later Huerta fled Mexico, and Carranza's forces took Mexico City. In October 1915, Wilson formally recognized Carranza's government. This did not end the troubles with Mexico. An illiterate former bandit, Francisco "Pancho" Villa, hoped to become a national hero by fighting Yankees. In January 1916, he murdered a number of Americans in northern Mexico and, in March, he burned the town of Columbus, New Mexico, killing seventeen Americans.

Wilson sent troops commanded by Brigadier

MEN
IN
HISTORY

ROOSEVELT AND WILSON

Before the outbreak of World War I in Europe, President Woodrow Wilson declared: "The United States must be neutral in fact as in name during these days that are to try men's souls." Theodore Roosevelt supported this position when he stated, "nothing but urgent need would warrant breaking our neutrality and taking sides one way or another."

But, in 1915, the German torpedo which sank the *Lusitania,* and with it 128 Americans, put an end to any further agreement between the two leaders. Former President Roosevelt regarded the sinking as an act of piracy and a just cause for war. Once again the popular "Teddy" became the advocate of the "big stick." President Wilson reacted differently, stating that, "The example of America must be . . . of peace because peace is the healing and elevating influence of the world and strife is not." The President was the defender of efforts to maintain neutrality, a stand which Roosevelt attacked, calling the presidential advisers "mollycoddles, and flapdoodle pacifists."

Theodore Roosevelt was among those who believed in applying the theory of the survival of the fittest. He saw war and armed strength as a natural necessity and a means of social progress. Force, and the willingness to use force, was a measure of the fitness of a nation to survive. Roosevelt believed America should "play a great part in the world, and especially . . . perform those deeds of blood, of valor, which above everything else bring national renown." This view had brought him to advocate war with Mexico and Spain, the annexation of Hawaii and the Philippines, the building of an isthmian canal to facilitate movement of a big navy, and the right of the United States to intervene in the affairs of the republics of the Western Hemisphere.

Woodrow Wilson's philosophy embodied a confidence in man's virtue. Man, he believed, could solve all human problems if privilege and despotism were eliminated. He thought it important that small nations be free from control of larger, more powerful nations. Soon after his election he announced that the United States was abandoning the "big stick" policy and recasting the Monroe Doctrine.

This was a philosophy that gave expression to the principle of national self-determination, and had led Wilson to try to prevent the outbreak of the European war through a treaty to preserve the peace of the world.

The philosophies of the two men now clashed before a divided nation. Both men were gifted with great intellectual capacity, a high sense of personal dignity, and a good sense of humor, though Wilson's humor often failed him when talking to the people. In verbal exchanges, Roosevelt was quicker and more resourceful than Wilson, whom he considered a phrasemonger. Wilson was anxious to avoid open controversy with his vehement and impetuous critic, whom he disliked politically and personally.

Both men understood the need to dramatize their attitudes and policies. Roosevelt was the master of dramatic politics, combining pungent phrases and telling epithets with a Rough Rider uniform and an intensity of manner. Wilson's subordinates were hard pressed to explain some of his statements, such as "too proud to fight," and "the distinction of self control." Roosevelt's "the shots that count are the shots that stick," and "speak softly and carry a big stick," needed no explanation and were easily interpreted by the American people.

The differences between Roosevelt and Wilson, which came to a head over America's entrance into World War I, continued during the war and later centered around the idea of a league of nations. Wilson's basis for world peace was presented in his "Fourteen Points." These proposed, among other things, unrestricted world trade, freedom of the seas, "open covenants, openly arrived at," and the League of Nations. At the very moment when Wilson was attempting to put his dreams into reality, Roosevelt stated to the press, "Mr. Wilson has no authority whatever to speak for the American people. . . . His leadership has . . . been emphatically repudiated by them." Roosevelt thought the Allies ought simply to "dictate peace by the hammering guns."

Roosevelt's death early in 1919 ended the debate between the two men. For Wilson the struggle continued.

General John J. Pershing into Mexico to capture Villa. Pershing never did catch Villa, but his soldiers had several clashes with Mexican troops. The Carranza government threatened to declare war if the United States did not withdraw its troops. Finally, Wilson decided that a mounting crisis with Germany was more serious than the capture of Villa. So, in February 1917, he withdrew the last of Pershing's troops from Mexico.

REVIEWING THE SECTION

1. What role did Roosevelt play in obtaining United States control of the Isthmus of Panama?

2. What was the Roosevelt Corollary to the Monroe Doctrine?

3. How and why did Taft apply dollar diplomacy in Central America?

4. In what ways did Wilson intervene in the Caribbean area?

SOME DISPUTES WERE SETTLED PEACEFULLY

Many people in the United States at this time believed that since the nation had become a world power, it had an obligation to help maintain peace. The government reacted to public opinion by trying to settle disputes, even those that did not involve the United States, without resorting to force.

One of the most dramatic incidents concerned the North African nation, Morocco. Although the United States had no direct interest in that area, President Theodore Roosevelt acted, in 1906, to prevent war between France and Germany over control of Morocco.

Less dramatic but more important to the United States was the slow, steady development of friendship with Britain that took on the characteristics of an unwritten alliance. This did not mean that the United States and Britain managed to avoid disagreements. They had serious differences and they sometimes quarreled bitterly. But their differences were not deeply rooted, and it was usually possible to make peaceful adjustments.

Several of the most serious controversies with Britain grew out of Canada's relations with the United States. The first of these disputes concerned the boundary between Alaska and Canada. The long-standing dispute over privileges for the United States in the fishing grounds off the shores of Nova Scotia and Newfoundland also remained to be settled. And, an American tariff led to renewed difficulties with Canada.

In addition to the controversies with Canada, Anglo-American friendship was endangered by a United States law concerning the payment of tolls for the Panama Canal.

All these disputes were settled peacefully. Although Canadian-American relations deteriorated somewhat, relations between Britain and the United States steadily improved.

Roosevelt prevented a war over Morocco

Morocco had become a center of international controversy in which France and Germany were particularly concerned. For many years the French had been dominant in Morocco. In 1905, after gaining the support of Britain, France went ahead with plans to take over complete control of Morocco. Germany opposed the French plan; the Germans had built up some trade in the North African country and wanted Morocco for themselves. For a while it looked as if Germany's determination to force a settlement would touch off a war. At this point, President Roosevelt stepped in. He persuaded France and her ally Britain to meet with Germany and other powers to discuss the Moroccan question. The conference opened in January 1906, in Algeciras, a small Spanish seaport across the Strait of Gibralter from Morocco.

At the conference Germany found herself almost alone in her demands for a share in the control of Morocco. Britain stood firmly by France, and even the United States favored the French position. Roosevelt finally worked out a compromise which was accepted by Germany. It preserved the principle of international control in Morocco but gave the real power to France.

Critics in the United States attacked Roosevelt for participating in the diplomacy of the Moroccan crisis. They said he had violated the traditional United States policy of avoiding entanglements in European quarrels. Roosevelt justified his diplomatic intervention by saying that the crisis threatened world peace and that he had prevented war. Whether or not his actions had prevented war, Roosevelt had taken a significant step. He had used the power of the United States in a distant crisis on the theory that a threat to the peace of the world affected the United States. As a world power, the United States could not easily turn its back on international tensions. Significantly, the outcome of the Algeciras conference foreshadowed a shift in United States foreign policy toward sympathy with an Anglo-French alliance.

Two Canadian-American problems were solved

When gold was discovered in the region of Canada's Klondike River in 1896, thousands of men, most of them from the United States, rushed to the area. They usually landed at Skagway, crossed the Alaskan panhandle, and headed northward. Canada claimed a boundary between itself and Alaska that would have given Canada control of the access by sea to the gold fields. Her claim would also have made the panhandle much narrower than it was.

President Roosevelt called the Canadian claim "an outrage pure and simple." The British feared the dispute might injure their friendship with the United States; so, in January 1903, they worked out an agreement that placed the case in the hands of six judges. Three were chosen by Britain, and three by the United States. The decision, in October 1903, was almost entirely favorable to the United States, and the Canadians felt that they had been sacrificed to the cause of Anglo-American friendship.

A long-standing dispute between Britain and the United States still remained to be settled. The United States wanted broad privileges in the fishing grounds off the shores of Nova Scotia and Newfoundland. The Canadians wanted to restrict those fishing privileges, or obtain concessions for them, such as the repeal of a United States tariff against Canadian fish.

In January 1909, in keeping with the new spirit of friendship, Britain and the United States signed a general arbitration treaty, an agreement for peaceful settlement of differences, that submitted the fisheries dispute to the Permanent Court of Arbitration at The Hague. The decision, made in September 1910, was a compromise that allowed fishermen from the United States to continue their work in the disputed fishing grounds, subject, however, to local fishing regulations. Although these terms were modified later, the longest dispute in the history of United States foreign relations was settled.

Two United States laws caused new controversy

Canadian-American relations soon deteriorated, however. The Payne-Aldrich Tariff of 1909 struck at Canadian products with a special impact, and Canada threatened to retaliate. To prevent a tariff war, President Taft and Prime Minister Sir Wilfrid Laurier of Canada, in January 1911, concluded a commercial reciprocity agreement. This meant that each nation would give special consideration to the goods of the other. Reciprocity was to go into effect through laws passed by the United States Congress and the Canadian parliament, not by treaty, which would have involved Britain.

Under pressure from Taft, Congress passed a reciprocity law (1912). In urging its passage, the President and other supporters of reciprocity had given the impression that it would lead to the annexation of Canada. This attitude aroused Canadian nationalism to such an extent that the reciprocity bill in parliament went down to defeat. Even though the defeat embarrassed Taft, it did not touch off a tariff war with Canada or injure the Anglo-American friendship.

The second law that caused trouble with British

subjects was passed in August 1912. In that law Congress said that United States ships engaged in the coastwise trade from New York to California would not have to pay tolls when going through the Panama Canal. The British argued that this exemption violated the Hay-Pauncefote Treaty (1901) which said the canal would be open on equal terms to the ships of all nations. If United States ships did not pay tolls, the British pointed out, then foreign ships would be charged higher tolls to make up the loss.

President Wilson became convinced that the British were right. So he asked Congress to repeal the exemption on tolls, as a matter of friendship and national honor. Congress voted the repeal in June 1914. In August, the Panama Canal was officially opened on equal terms to all nations.

REVIEWING THE SECTION.

1. Why did Roosevelt help resolve the Moroccan crisis? Why was he accused of violating traditional United States policy?

2. How were the disputes between Canada and the United States over the Alaskan boundary and fishing privileges finally resolved?

3. Why did the Canadian parliament refuse to pass the commercial reciprocity bill? Why did Britain charge the United States with violating the Hay-Pauncefote Treaty?

THE UNITED STATES ENTERED WORLD WAR I

Despite a widespread concern for peace, the forces that made war were stronger in the summer of 1914 than those that kept peace. These warlike forces included an extreme feeling of *nationalism,* or an exaggerated patriotism that often led to hatred of other peoples; *imperialism,* a policy of extending the rule of one nation over another; *militarism,* an excessive reliance on arms and armies; and *international anarchy,* the lack of any true international means of controlling outbursts of violence among nations.

On June 28, 1914, in Sarajevo, Bosnia (a part of present-day Yugoslavia), a young Serbian nationalist assassinated Archduke Francis Ferdinand, heir to the throne of Austria-Hungary. Few Americans thought a student's revolver shots in a distant Balkan province could lead to a world war. But they did. Austria-Hungary, determined to stamp out Serbian nationalism, served an ultimatum on Serbia, which the Serbs rejected. Austria-Hungary then declared war and her ally, Germany, supported her. Other declarations of war followed, for Russia stood by Serbia, and France and Britain sided with Russia.

By August 12, Germany and Austria-Hungary were formally at war with France, Britain, and Russia. Germany and Austria-Hungary were later joined by Bulgaria and Turkey; the four became known as the Central powers. Japan and Italy later joined with France, Britain, and Russia and this group was called the Allied powers, or the Allies. An intricate system of alliances and mobilization schedules for huge armies had set off the series of war declarations.

Woodrow Wilson tried to maintain neutrality

President Wilson promptly issued declarations of neutrality and offered to mediate, but the warring nations refused the offer. Then he appealed to the people of the United States to be "impartial in thought as well as in action."

Most Americans were never impartial. Although the majority favored the Allies, because of ethnic, business, and cultural ties, some favored the Central powers. Many German-Americans were strongly attached to their fatherland; some Irish-Americans were anti-British, and some Jews and Poles were anti-Russian.

At first, most of the difficulties which the United States encountered over neutral rights, primarily those of trade and travel by sea, were with the British. The British navy was superior to that of Germany. Through her control of the seas, Britain could have access to the goods of most of the world while denying them to the Central powers. At first the British mainly stopped ships that were carrying *contraband,* or implements of war such as guns, destined for Germany and neighboring nations. Later, they tried to stop all trade with Germany, whether or not it involved contraband. They even blockaded Denmark, the Netherlands, and Sweden—neutral states bordering Germany which imported goods by sea.

By the summer of 1915, the British navy had strangled practically all United States trade with the Central powers and with the neutral states of Europe. The United States protested these violations of its neutral rights, but it never used force to protect them because the British did not go too far in their violations. The British were carefully trying to retain the friendship of the United States.

Germany used submarine warfare

United States relations with the Central powers were not damaged by controversy over neutral rights until Germany decided to try to break the Allied blockade through use of the submarine. Germany began her submarine warfare in February 1915, after proclaiming the seas around the British Isles a war zone. She announced that her submarines would destroy on sight enemy ships within the zone. President Wilson immediately protested this violation of international law.

On May 7, 1915, off the Irish coast, a German submarine torpedoed and sank the British passenger liner *Lusitania.* There were 128 Americans among the 1198 who went down with the ship. The President demanded that Germany pay for injuries and the loss of lives, and abandon the submarine campaign against passenger liners. Although the German government did not publicly surrender to Wilson's demands, it secretly ordered its submarine captains not to attack passenger liners.

During this period of controversy, Wilson began building up defenses and also tried to end the war through mediation. In January 1915, the President had sent his personal adviser, Colonel Edward M. House, to Berlin, Paris, and London

to offer mediation. The effort had failed.

In August 1916, while campaigning for reëlection, Wilson signed a bill for the building of a huge navy as part of his preparedness program. After winning the election, Wilson continued his preparedness program, and tried again to bring about a negotiated peace. He spoke about "a peace without victory." These efforts, too, were fruitless.

Even though they knew it would bring the United States into the war, the Germans decided to resume unrestricted submarine warfare. They gambled that the submarine could assure victory before the power of the United States could be brought into the war. The Germans informed Wilson of their decision on January 31, 1917. Three days later he broke off diplomatic relations with Germany.

The President still hoped to avoid war. Then the British gave Wilson a message sent by Alfred Zimmermann, the German foreign secretary, which they had intercepted. The Zimmermann note proposed that Mexico join an alliance with Germany if the United States went to war against Germany and that Japan be invited to join that alliance. Mexico's reward would be recovery of Arizona, New Mexico, and Texas. When the United States government published the note on March 1, intensified anti-German feeling swept over the country.

On the evening of April 2, 1917, after several American ships had been sunk by the Germans, Wilson told Congress that German submarines were waging war "against mankind" and "against all nations," and asked for a declaration of war, saying that "the world must be made safe for democracy." Congress declared war on April 6.

The American people mobilized

Intervention by the United States came at a crucial time for the Allies, at least so far as the sea warfare was concerned. German submarines were sinking ships twice as fast as the Allies could replace them. The United States Navy, therefore, joined the British in fighting the submarines and in

Europe, 1914

ICELAND

NORWAY

SWEDEN

NORTH SEA

DENMARK

BALTIC SEA

RUSSIAN EMPIRE

UNITED KINGDOM

NETH.

GERMAN EMPIRE

BELG.

LUX.

FRANCE

SWITZ.

AUSTRIA-HUNGARY

ROMANIA

BLACK SEA

ATLANTIC OCEAN

PORTUGAL

SPAIN

ITALY

MONTENEGRO

SERBIA

BULGARIA

ALB.

OTTOMAN EMPIRE (TURKEY)

GREECE

MEDITERRANEAN SEA

AFRICA

European Allied Powers

Central Powers

Neutral Nations

PRE UNIVERS

---

tightening the blockade against the Central powers. On land, also, the Allied cause became shaky. French armies were weary; some divisions had mutinied. The Russians, too, were exhausted and tired of the war.

To help the Allies, the United States had to mobilize for war. Instead of relying on volunteers, the government decided to use conscription. Despite opposition from those who preferred the American tradition of a volunteer army, Congress passed the Selective Service Act on May 18, 1917. This law required all men between the ages of 21 and 30 to register for military service. Later, the limits were extended to include men between 18 and 45 years of age.

Congress gave the President practically dictatorial powers, so that the national mobilization could be carried out quickly. President Wilson delegated many of these powers to six wartime agencies. One of the most important of these was the War Industries Board, directed by Bernard M.

Baruch, a New York banker. It was created to coördinate purchases, allocate raw materials, control production, and supervise labor relations.

Herbert C. Hoover, a mining engineer, became the director of the Food Administration. He worked to increase the production of food and to eliminate waste. The United States Shipping Board, through the Emergency Fleet Corporation, worked to provide desperately needed ships. The railroads, which had to carry goods, guns, and troops to the ships, were placed under the control of the government. The government also took over other means of transportation and communication, such as telephone and telegraph companies.

Labor went through a period of prosperity and change, but it did not profit as much from the wartime boom as the farmer and the manufacturer. The demand for labor was so great that thousands of women went into industry. Negroes in great numbers migrated north for jobs in the war industries. In 1918, the government set up the National War Labor Board to handle labor disputes.

To arouse patriotism Congress created the Committee on Public Information. The committee scattered propaganda everywhere designed to show that Germans were evil and that the Kaiser had started the war. In the name of patriotism, hatred and intolerance became widespread.

Two laws, designed to crush disloyalty and enforce conformity, were passed. The Espionage Act of June 1917 provided a fine and imprisonment for anyone who interfered with the draft or encouraged disloyalty. The Sedition Act of May 1918 provided punishment for anyone who said or wrote anything "disloyal, profane, or scurrilous" about the government and its activities. Few Americans protested these restrictions on civil liberties, even though more than fifteen hundred people were convicted of violating these laws.

The United States fought to victory

Since it took time to build, train, and equip an army, almost a year passed before an American fighting force reached the battlefront. The first troops from the United States arrived in France in June 1917, but they were token forces designed to boost the sagging morale of French and British soldiers. These first "doughboys," as the American soldiers were called, went to quiet sectors of the battlefront as replacements in French and British units.

In the fall of 1917, Allied military losses created a pressing need for fresh troops. In October 1917, German and Austro-Hungarian forces unleashed an attack at Caporetto, in present-day Yugoslavia, that almost crushed the Italian army. With help hastily provided by the French and British, the Italians averted disaster. On the eastern front Russian resistance was collapsing. Revolution swept over Russia, and in November, when the Bolsheviks, or Communists, took control of the government, they offered the Germans peace.

In an address to Congress on January 8, 1918, President Wilson proclaimed a program of fourteen points for peace. The first five points dealt with general principles such as freedom of the seas and reduction of armaments. The next eight points promised territorial adjustments such as German evacuation of Russia and Belgium, freedom for the people of Austria-Hungary, and an independent Poland. The fourteenth point, which was Wilson's key to future peace, offered an association of nations that would help keep world peace.

These fourteen points were widely publicized and generally accepted as the Allied peace program, but at first they did not make much of an impact on the Germans. In March 1918, the Germans forced the Bolsheviks to sign a harsh peace treaty, the Treaty of Brest-Litovsk, that gave Germany a great slice of eastern Europe and ended the war in the east.

The Russian collapse permitted the Germans to shift troops to the western front and to gain a numerical superiority there. In an effort to smash the Allies before many troops arrived from the United States, the Germans, in March, launched an offensive at the Somme River. In April, the Germans aimed a second great blow at Flanders. These attacks nearly broke the Allied armies. The Allies pleaded for reinforcements from the United States.

American troops had their first real taste of battle when some thirty thousand doughboys were thrown in the path of the Germans at Château-Thierry on the Marne River only fifty miles from Paris. They helped blunt the German attack. In June, American troops cleared Belleau Wood and forced the Germans back across the Marne. By July 1, General John J. Pershing, commander of the American Expeditionary Force, had an army of a million men.

Two weeks later, the Germans launched their third great offensive toward Paris. This time 85,000 United States soldiers fought to throw back the attack. The fresh American troops helped turn the tide of battle when shortly thereafter the Allied commander, Marshal Foch, began a counteroffensive that kept the Germans in steady retreat.

World War I

Central Powers

Allied Powers

Neutral Nations

Area controlled by Central Powers

x Battles

SWEDEN

NORWAY

FINLAND
(Declared independence
from Russia 1917)

Lake Ladoga

Petrograd

Gulf of Finland

FARTHEST AUSTRO-GERMAN PENETRATION 1918

Dvina R.

Mosco

RUSS

NORTH SEA

DENMARK

BALTIC SEA

EAST PRUSSIA

x MASURIAN LAKES

x TANNENBERG

IRELAND

UNITED KINGDOM

London

NETH.

Berlin

GERMAN EMPIRE

Visrula R.

Brest-Litovsk

English Channel

Brussels

BELGIUM

LUX.

GERMAN PENETRATION 1918

x VERDUN

Paris

Versailles

FRANCE

SWITZ.

ITALY

Vienna

AUSTRIA-HUNGARY

CARPATHIANS

x LEMBERG

Dniester R.

ROMANIA

BLAC
SEA

PREPARED BY
UNIVERSAL MAP, INC.

Central Powers Strategy

A two-front war was anticipated by the Germans, but they decided to concentrate a powerful offensive in the west (the Schlieffen plan). They planned to invade France through Belgium, sweep around the main French defenses, and encircle Paris from the south. After France capitulated, the Germans would reinforce the troops holding off the Russians on the eastern front.

Allied Strategy

The Allied plan also called for an offensive. French troops were to invade Germany through the province of Lorraine, ignoring the German threat on the Belgian border. The British were to sweep from the English Channel to Lorraine, and the Russians were to invade Germany on the eastern front.

WESTERN FRONT, 1914

August 4

Invasion of Belgium. Central powers victory. Proceeding according to the Schlieffen plan, German troops invaded Belgium, capturing Liège (Aug. 17) and Brussels (Aug. 20). By September, they had forced the Allies back to the Marne River, 15 miles from Paris.

August 14-25

French offensive. Central powers victories. In the area extending from the Ardennes Forest to the provinces of Alsace and Lorraine, the French tried to invade Germany. This offensive failed to dent the German lines.

EASTERN FRONT, 1914

August 17-September 15

Russian offensive in the north. Central powers victory. The Russians, at the request of France, had invaded East Prussia (Aug. 17) and pushed the Germans back to the Vistula River. But in a counter-offensive, the Germans routed the Russians at Tannenberg (Aug. 26-30) and the Masurian Lakes (Sept. 6-15), ending the Russian "steam roller" attack in East Prussia.

September

Russian offensive in Austria. Allied victory. While the Russians were losing battles in the north, they scored successes farther south, against Austrian troops. On Sept. 12, the Russians captured Lemberg (present-day Lvov) and forced the Austrians to abandon their lines in the south.

Western Front
1914-1918

September 5-12, 1914
First Battle of the Marne. Allied victory. An offensive ordered by French General Joseph Joffre halted the Germans, who fell back to the Aisne River.

October 20-November 22, 1914
First Battle of Ypres. Allied victory. Both Allied and Central powers troops raced toward the English Channel to secure ports. They clashed at Ypres, in the Flanders section of Belgium, and the Allies succeeded in holding the town. The western front established by the end of 1914 did not appreciably change during the next three years of fighting. It stretched from the English Channel to the French-Swiss border. All along this line, both sides dug trench defenses.

April 22-May 25, 1915
Second Battle of Ypres. Central powers victory. Using chlorine gas (the first use of poison gas as a military weapon), German troops scattered Allied defenders, but did not follow through on their assault. In May, the Germans decided to deploy some troops from the west to bolster the faltering Austrians. By September, Austro-German troops had crushed the entire Russian southern front. However, stalemate continued in France.

February-December 1916
Battle of Verdun. Drawn battle. The Germans launched a tremendous bombardment of the forts surrounding Verdun. The forts were captured in some of the bloodiest battles of the war; French casualties numbered 460,000 and the Germans lost 300,000 men. In October, French troops began a counteroffensive and by December, had recaptured the forts.

July-November 1916
Battle of the Somme. Allied victory. In a battle that yielded no strategic gain, the British introduced a new weapon, the tank.

November 21-December 3, 1917
Battle of Cambrai. Allied victory. Using tanks in mass formation for the first time, British troops broke through German lines, but were too exhausted to continue their advance.

March 21-June 4, 1918
German spring offensive. Central powers victory. The Treaty of Brest-Litovsk (March 3, 1918) ended Russian participation in the war, and the Germans brought most of their soldiers from the eastern front to the west. In three separate assaults—at the Somme River, the Lys River in Flanders, and the Aisne River—the Germans smashed through Allied defenses. They were within 27 miles of Paris when American troops helped stop the onslaught at the Battle of Château-Thierry (June 4).

May 28, 1918
Battle of Cantigny. Allied victory. United States troops (General John Pershing), who had arrived June 26, 1917, won their first clear-cut victory at Cantigny.

June 6-July 1, 1918
Battle of Belleau Wood. Allied victory. In bloody fighting, United States troops took a strategic German defense outpost.

July 15-August 7, 1918
Second Battle of the Marne. Allied victory. The Germans began another offensive aimed at Paris; French and American troops not only stopped them, they pushed the Germans back to the Vesle River. This marked a turning point in the war in favor of the Allies.

September 12-13, 1918
Battle of St. Mihiel. Allied victory. Supported by 1400 combat planes (Colonel William Mitchell), United States troops stormed and captured St. Mihiel, south of Verdun.

18th Infantry, 1st Division, Exermont, Ardennes, France, Oct. 7, 1918

Doughboys (the nickname for American soldiers) helped break the stalemated western front in 1918. The presence of fresh troops from the United States inspired the war-weary Allies to press on to victory. In the photographs on this page, American soldiers dodge enemy fire in a French town; rush through a barbed-wire entanglement where a tank has cleared an opening; and trudge across rough soil that has been churned by the shells of German artillery. On the opposite page, American gunners fire a barrage in a barren forest.

107th Infantry, 27th Division, Beauquesnes, Somme, France, Sept. 13, 1918

Somewhere between the lines, July 19, 1918

Meuse-Argonne

September 26-November 11, 1918
General Pershing planned a powerful frontal assault to break through the German lines. The main attack was to take place between the Meuse River and the western edge of the Argonne Forest, a 20-mile wide zone.

The defensive position was excellent: on the east were the heights of the Meuse River; on the west was the heavily wooded Argonne Forest; and a ridge running north and south was in the center. On this ridge were three heavily fortified positions: Montfaucon, Cunel, and Barricourt. Beyond this front line were three more German lines of defense, including strongly fortified points at natural obstacles such as woods and hills.

Pershing hoped to cut through all the defensive lines without loss of momentum. If all the defensive lines failed to fall in the initial assault, the attack would continue until the breakthrough.

First phase: The assault troops began to move (Sept. 26) after an artillery barrage that lasted three hours. By the end of the first day, the Americans had captured the forward German positions and had advanced everywhere except at Montfaucon and the Argonne Forest. Within the next few days, the first two defense lines were captured. However, the advance troops failed to break the third defense line and the American attack was halted.

Second phase: On Oct. 4, the Americans began a drive through the third defense line. The Germans brought troops in from other parts of the front and fought back stubbornly. Slowly, the Americans cleared the Argonne Forest of Germans and extended their attack east of the Meuse.

Third phase: On Nov. 1, the attack began again. The infantry moved forward, and by Nov. 7, they took the heights near Sedan. Pershing then planned to attack Montmedy. As troops were moving into position for the attack, the armistice came (Nov. 11).

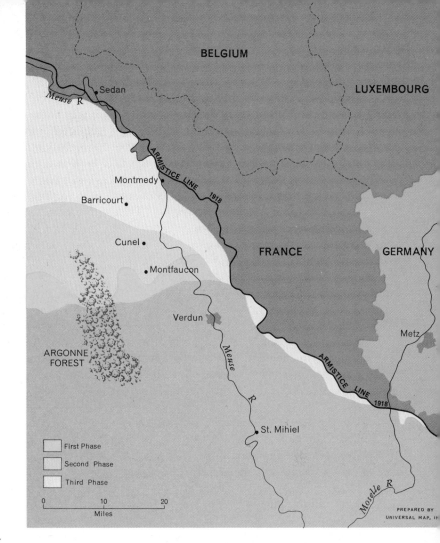

23rd Infantry, 2nd Division, 1918

As part of this offensive, the American army, fighting as an independent force, attacked the Germans in the region of the Argonne Forest and Meuse River. American casualties were especially high because the troops were inexperienced and reckless.

While the Meuse-Argonne battle was going on, the German government appealed to Wilson for peace on the basis of the fourteen points. The Allies accepted the request, with a few reservations. Meanwhile, Austria-Hungary collapsed, and signed an armistice with Italy on November 3, 1918. Germany signed an armistice on November 11 which brought an end to the war.

REVIEWING THE SECTION

1. Why did the people of the United States find it difficult to maintain an impartial attitude toward the belligerents? In what ways did the British violate the neutral rights of the United States?

2. How did German submarine warfare bring the United States into the war?

3. How was American industry mobilized for war? How were civil liberties restricted during the war?

4. What contribution did the United States make to the Allied victory? What were some of the provisions of Wilson's fourteen-point program for peace?

THE U.S. REJECTED THE LEAGUE OF NATIONS

When the Germans signed the armistice, not one Allied soldier had set foot on German soil. Some Americans, among whom were General Pershing and Theodore Roosevelt, did not want an armistice; they wanted a surrender. As a result, Roosevelt and other Republican leaders attacked the fourteen points during the armistice negotiations as allowing peace terms that were too soft. These critics demanded a Republican victory in the congressional elections of November 1918.

Upset by these attacks, Wilson made a blanket appeal to the voters to elect Democrats to Congress. "The return of a Republican majority to either house of the Congress," he said, "would ... be interpreted on the other side of the water as a repudiation of my leadership."

This appeal angered Republicans, many of whom had firmly supported Wilson's foreign policy. It also appeared to have little effect on the elections, for domestic grievances seemed to be more important to the voters than the question of who would control foreign policy. In any case, in November the voters gave the Republicans control of both houses of Congress by a narrow margin. Wilson had failed to make the elections a test of confidence in his conduct of foreign policy. The failure of his appeal had placed him in a difficult position in respect to the other Allied leaders, for these statesmen could think that the people of the United States had repudiated Wilson's leadership.

Wilson went to Paris

A week after the signing of the armistice, Wilson announced that he would himself attend the peace conference to be held in Paris. When he named the members of the American peace commission, Republicans were angered because he did not include a single prominent Republican.

Representatives from thirty-two nations which had fought on the Allied side were in attendance when the peace conference opened on January 18, 1919. Wilson, British Prime Minister David Lloyd George, French Premier Georges Clemenceau, and Italian Prime Minister Vittorio E. Orlando were known as the "big four." They handled the major problems at the conference and made the basic decisions.

Although all wanted a lasting peace, these statesmen quarreled over the means of achieving it. Wilson believed that the first and most important thing the conference could do was to adopt his plan for a league of nations. The French proposed that the peace treaties come first. Wilson had his way; the conference decided that a league of nations should be a part of the peace treaty.

Wilson drew up a constitution, which he called a covenant, for the league. In accordance with the covenant, the league would admit all nations as members. The league would consider all disputes between its members and try to settle them. Its two major bodies would be an assembly and a council. In the assembly, a kind of international congress, every member nation would have one vote. The council, or executive body, would be more powerful. There the "big five"—the United States, Britain, France, Italy, and Japan—would have permanent seats and could deal with questions of war and peace.

The "heart of the Covenant," according to Wilson, was the tenth article, which pledged all members to support the principle of collective security. This meant that the league would regard an attack on any one of its members as an attack on all of them; therefore, all would coöperate to defend the nation attacked.

After the conference had adopted the covenant of the League of Nations, the President returned to the United States to sign bills which had been passed by Congress during his absence. Before Congress adjourned, thirty-seven Republican senators and two senators-elect signed a statement rejecting Wilson's league. Then, on the last day of the session, Republicans prevented the passage of bills vital to the functioning of government. This made it necessary for the President to call Congress into special session before summer to consider those bills. By that time the Republicans would be in control of the new Senate and would deal with the league.

Wilson fought for the League of Nations and failed

In March, when Wilson returned to Paris to complete the peacemaking, he tried to make the covenant of the league more acceptable to Americans by having it amended. This led to bargaining in which the other statesmen tried to gain concessions from him.

The French, who felt the need for security against the Germans, wanted to get control of the west bank of the Rhine River. Wilson refused to allow this, but he did agree to the demilitarization of the west bank and its occupation by the Allies for fifteen years. He also agreed to the return of Alsace-Lorraine (which had been taken from the French after the Franco-Prussian War, 1870-1871), and to the reduction in size of Germany's army and navy. In addition, Wilson agreed to allow the Allies to take over Germany's colonies under mandates from the league. For security reasons, Wilson agreed to give Italy control of the Brenner Pass but he would not agree to give her a strip of land along the Dalmatian coast.

Germany lost about one seventh of her territory and was forced to agree to pay a large reparations bill for war damages, to admit guilt for starting the war, and to recognize the new states in eastern Europe that had been created when the Austro-Hungarian Empire broke up. Although Wilson made a number of concessions, he did manage to get the covenant of the League of Nations written into the peace treaty, the Treaty of Versailles.

While the President was in Paris, however, Republicans at home, led by Senator Henry Cabot Lodge of Massachusetts, planned to oppose the League of Nations. They considered the covenant, even as revised, unsatisfactory. William E. Borah of Idaho headed a small group of senators who were opposed to the league in any form. These senators, sometimes called "irreconcilables," were *isolationists,* men who believed the United States should avoid involvement in the politics of Europe.

Wilson called Congress into special session on May 19, 1919. The Republicans, who had a majority of two in the Senate, quickly organized their forces. They chose Lodge as majority leader and as chairman of the Committee on Foreign Relations.

On July 10, Wilson asked the Senate to approve the Treaty of Versailles. Although he was confident that the American people would support him, there was some opposition to the treaty. Wilson, therefore, decided to try to arouse public sentiment in favor of the treaty.

He decided to make an extensive speaking tour of the West and Midwest. After a speech at Pueblo, Colorado, on September 25, 1919, Wilson collapsed from exhaustion. He returned to Washington, and a few days later the President suffered a stroke that paralyzed his left side and incapacitated him for six months.

Lodge's committee, meanwhile, recommended approval of the treaty with many reservations, or changes, to the league covenant. Most of the changes were designed to protect the right of the United States to act independently of the league. Wilson thought the Lodge reservations would destroy the league rather than merely amend it. So he would not accept the reservations. Instead he urged the Democrats in the Senate to vote against the treaty with reservations.

The Democrats in the Senate voted as Wilson desired, but they did not have enough votes to gain a two-thirds approval of the treaty without changes. Most Republicans would have accepted the league, but only with changes. Only the irreconcilables wanted complete defeat of the league. Perhaps some compromise could have been worked out, but Wilson and the Republican leaders distrusted each other and compromise failed. The Senate voted on the Treaty of Versailles twice, once in November 1919, and the last time in March 1920. In each instance it was defeated. The result was defeat for the league and the shattering of Wilson's dream of establishing an effective system to maintain world peace.

The Democrats were defeated in the election of 1920

Wilson could not believe that his dream had been shattered and that his own people would remain outside the League of Nations he had helped to create. He thought that if the people could only be made to understand what was at stake they would reverse the decision of the Senate. He believed he could reach the people in the presidential election of 1920, and make it a national referendum on the league.

This was unrealistic. Wilson had not been able to keep in close touch with events since his breakdown, nor did he understand the mood of the American people. The people were tired of the squabbling over the league and were ready to express their resentment over domestic problems by voting against the party in power. The chances for a Democratic victory, and hence for saving the league, were slim.

Meeting in San Francisco, the Democratic convention ignored Wilson and chose James M. Cox, the governor of Ohio, as its candidate. Cox was not closely identified with Wilson, but the vice-presidential candidate, Assistant Secretary of the Navy Franklin D. Roosevelt was. The party platform called for approval of the Treaty of Versailles, and Cox and Roosevelt spoke out for the league.

The Republicans had held their convention in Chicago. Their platform promised a higher tariff, reduced taxes, and immigration restriction. It denounced Wilson's league, but promised an international agreement of some kind "to preserve the peace of the world." After two of the most popular candidates had deadlocked, a small group of senators decided that a fellow senator, Warren G. Harding of Ohio, should have the nomination. Another conservative, Governor Calvin Coolidge of Massachusetts, was chosen to run with Harding.

Republican campaign managers then decided that the less Harding said, the better his chance for victory. Harding accepted this decision and evaded practically all issues, but he did promise a return to "normalcy." Harding and the Republicans straddled the league issue, relying on their negative platform and on the people's resentment against the Democrats to bring them victory. Harding won the election in a landslide, carrying every state outside the Solid South.

On July 2, 1921, the new Republican Congress finally declared by joint resolution that as far as the United States was concerned, the war was formally over. In August, President Harding negotiated separate peace treaties with Germany, Austria, and Hungary.

Europe, 1922

The rejection of the League of Nations did not mean that the United States could ignore the events that had placed it near the center of the world stage since 1898. It was a world power; no matter how much some Americans yearned for a return to the less complicated days before 1898, that status could not be changed. But two great crusades were over—one to reform society at home, and the other to reform the world. Americans had entered an era of conservatism and isolationism.

REVIEWING THE SECTION

1. What were the main points of the covenant of the League of Nations? Why did the irreconcilables oppose the league?

2. What were some provisions of the Treaty of Versailles? How did the fight between Wilson and Republican leaders contribute to the defeat of the treaty in the Senate?

3. Why were the Democrats defeated in the election of 1920?

As a result of the Spanish-American War, the United States had acquired an empire in the Pacific which soon led to involvement in the politics of the Far East, especially in China. China had been carved up into spheres of influence by several European powers and in 1900 some Chinese called Boxers rebelled. They besieged the foreign legations in Peking and were finally driven off by an international army, which included American troops. In spite of this, the United States on the surface at least was more of a friend to the Chinese than were the other powers; it urged that the Open Door policy be maintained and that China's territorial integrity be respected.

With the interests of the United States now extending westward across the Pacific, the nation needed a way to shorten the trip (around the tip of South America) from its eastern shores to ports on the west coast. The French effort to build a canal across the Isthmus of Panama had failed. In 1902, therefore, Congress voted to construct a canal, preferably through Panama, a province of Colombia, or across Nicaragua. When European investors offered President Theodore Roosevelt the assets of the bankrupt French company, he decided to proceed with the Panama route. Colombia, however, was dissatisfied with the terms offered by the United States. The Panamanians, with American help, successfully rebelled against the Colombians and almost immediately accepted the American terms. The United States proceeded to build the canal.

As a result of these tactics, distrust of the United States by the nations of Latin America increased. That distrust increased even more when President Roosevelt announced his corollary to the Monroe Doctrine. Several Central and South American nations had borrowed money in Europe but had failed to pay it back. To forestall European intervention, Roosevelt announced that the United States would henceforth act as "policeman" of the Western Hemisphere. American intervention did bring some stability to the Caribbean but America's relations with her neighbors to the South deteriorated.

Elsewhere Roosevelt had successes in foreign policy. His diplomacy contributed to the peace settlement of the Russo-Japanese War and he helped prevent a war between France and Germany over Morocco.

Roosevelt's successor, William Howard Taft, followed a policy called dollar diplomacy. It encouraged United States investments abroad, but did nothing to improve relations with Central and South America, or to advance the interests of the United States in China.

Woodrow Wilson, Taft's successor, did not approve of the policies of his predecessors. He was soon embroiled in Mexico's problems, however, and was forced to send in troops in order to protect American lives and property.

Troublesome as the Mexican question was, it was minor in comparison to the troubles Wilson faced in Europe. A war between two opposing alliance systems was touched off in 1914 when the heir to the Austro-Hungarian throne was assassinated by a Serbian patriot. Austria-Hungary threatened Serbia; Russia came to the defense of Serbia; Germany sided with Austria-Hungary; Britain and France lined up on the side of Russia; and Turkey and Bulgaria sided with Germany and Austria-Hungary. A world war began.

The belligerents proclaimed blockades of each other's ports and searched neutral ships, including American ships. President Wilson protested. He protested even more angrily when the Germans resorted to submarine warfare, sinking ships without warning and killing passengers, some of them Americans. For a time, the Germans restricted submarine warfare. As the blockade tightened, however, the Germans again began sinking passenger ships. Germany's resumption of unrestricted submarine warfare, which indiscriminately destroyed American lives as well as property, led Wilson to ask Congress for a declaration of war. Although the United States was a latecomer to the war, American money, supplies, and, above all, manpower were decisive factors in the Allied victory. The fighting ended with an armistice on November 11, 1918.

President Wilson was determined to incorporate into the peace treaty his concept of collective security as embodied in the League of Nations. The other Allied leaders were more concerned with the spoils of war and with making Germany so weak she could not again threaten them. In order to get the league, Wilson compromised. Members of the United States Senate, however, opposed the league and refused to approve the Treaty of Versailles without changes in the covenant. Wilson refused to compromise and the Senate rejected the treaty, and the covenant it contained.

The Democrats tried to make the league an issue in the election of 1920, but were soundly defeated by the Republicans. Few people in the United States listened to the words of the dying Wilson in 1924 when he said: "We had a chance to gain the leadership of the world. We have lost it, and soon we shall be witnessing the tragedy of it all."

FOCUSING ON SPECIFICS

1. How did the Insular Cases (1901-1922) enable the United States to deny self-government to the inhabitants of American Samoa, Puerto Rico, and the Philippines?

2. How did the actions of the San Francisco school board cause tension between Japan and the United States?

3. How did the Lansing-Ishii Agreement change the Open Door policy?

4. In what ways did the Platt Amendment make Cuba a virtual protectorate of the United States?

5. What were the terms of the treaty of 1903 between the United States and Colombia? How did Colombia's rejection of the treaty lead to the Panamanian revolt?

6. Why did Wilson refuse to recognize Victoriano Huerta's government in Mexico?

7. What did the Zimmermann note propose? How did its publication affect public opinion?

8. How was the Committee on Public Information used to further the war effort?

9. How did Wilson anger many Republicans who were in favor of his foreign policy?

10. Why did Wilson call the tenth article the "heart" of the league covenant?

REVIEWING MAIN THEMES

1. How did the Roosevelt, Taft, and Wilson administrations promote the Open Door policy? How was this policy modified during the Taft and Wilson administrations?

2. How and why did the United States establish a protectorate in each of the following: Cuba, Panama, the Dominican Republic, Nicaragua, and Haiti?

3. In the early twentieth century, in what ways did the United States act as a mediator in the settlement of international disputes?

4. Why did the United States enter World War I? How did it contribute to the Allied victory? to the terms of peace?

EVALUATING THE ISSUES

1. Do you think the United States was justified in interfering with the sovereignty of Colombia, the Dominican Republic, Haiti, and Mexico?

2. The immediate cause of the United States entry into World War I was Germany's destruction of American ships. What other considerations influenced the United States to declare war on Germany? Do you think the United States had sufficient cause for entering World War I?

3. The historian Thomas A. Bailey has stated, "In the final analysis the treaty was slain in the house of its friends rather than in the house of its enemies. In the final analysis it was not the two-thirds rule, or the 'irreconcilables,' or Lodge, or the 'strong' and 'mild reservationists,' but Wilson and his docile following who delivered the fatal stab." Do you agree with Bailey's analysis of the Treaty of Versailles?

4. In 1900, should the United States have granted the people of the Philippines, Puerto Rico, and American Samoa the same rights as were granted Americans who were living in the territories of Arizona, New Mexico, and Oklahoma?

EXAMINING THE TIMES

1. Between 1895 and 1917, what new trends took place in philosophy, religion, art, literature, and journalism?

2. During this period, what social, educational, economic, and political reforms were made?

3. What attempts were made by Americans to control large corporations?

4. Between 1900 and 1920, what was the role of the United States in the affairs of Latin America, Asia, and Europe?

A Nation on the Move

The automobile revolutionized American life. It made possible the continued growth of cities and suburbs and led to the building of vast new highways and roads.

Modern scientific roadbuilding began around 1912. In 1916, the Federal Aid Road Act, the first of many such acts, provided for the improvement of roads and highways. In 1921 over a billion dollars was spent on highways; in 1928, over two billion was spent. At the turn of the century, France had had the best highway system in the world. Thirty years later the United States was far in the lead. Smooth, four-lane, divided highways like Route 23, Morris County, New Jersey (pictured in 1940), were commonplace.

Even before the highway construction boom, service stations like the Motor Car's Watering Trough in Kansas City, Missouri (pictured in 1910), provided for the needs of the automobile. As the number of cars and highways multiplied, the service station became big business and the crude structure gave way to the modern, gleaming complex of today.

As cities kept growing in size, new methods of transportation were needed to bring people to their jobs in the center of the city and to their homes on the edges of the city. The "elevated" went underground so that the city skyline would not be further marred. The first subway system in the United States was built in Boston. And the subway station, like that on the Boston Common at Tremont Street (pictured in 1904), became a common sight.

With cities getting more and more crowded, middle-class Americans began to flee to the suburbs, a move made possible by the new highways and automobiles. To carry these people from the central city, tall, graceful bridges like the George Washington Bridge (pictured in 1932), began to span wide rivers and add a new element to the landscape.

Route 23, Morris County, New Jersey, 1940

Motor Car's Watering Trough, Kansas City, Mo., 1910

George Washington Bridge from the New Jersey side, 1932

Subway Station at Tremont Street and Boston Common, Boston, Mass., 1904, Photograph by William H. Jackson

The Changing City

Park Avenue looking toward Grand Central Tower, New York, N.Y., c. 1936

The characteristic skyline of the American city as it is today took form early in the 20th century. It consisted of a single skyscraper (much like the Philadelphia Savings Fund Society building, built in 1931) or a group of skyscrapers or, in the larger cities, several groups of skyscrapers. The skyline of uptown Manhattan Island (pictured in 1939), was low along the river front; then it rose, as one writer put it, "in peaks of stone and steel, a jagged vision that is particularly American."

With improved means of transportation by car and improved commuter services, many wealthy people began to abandon their large town houses and build country homes; for the days they spent in the city they looked for luxurious apartments. Streets solidly lined with apartment buildings, like Park Avenue in New York (pictured c. 1936), became fashionable because they provided desirable, spacious apartments.

Efforts were made during this period to beautify the city. In addition to new residential areas, cities began to plan broad avenues with vistas. One of the most famous of these was the Benjamin Franklin Parkway in Philadelphia. Work began in 1910 on the tree-lined boulevard and, in 1918, construction began on the temple-like Philadelphia Museum of Art. Other cities, like Cleveland, placed their neo-classic art galleries and civic buildings in lush park-like settings.

Panorama of Uptown Manhattan Island, 1939

Cleveland Museum of Art, built in 1916

Philadelphia Savings Fund Society Building, Philadelphia, Pa., built in 1931

Philadelphia Museum of Art, Benjamin Franklin Parkway, c. 1918

Radburn, New Jersey, c. 1935

Residential Areas

As a result of the increasing number of automobiles, highways, and improved commuter service, many new, planned suburbs were built. Most of them were influenced by the garden city movement in England, an attempt to combine the best of town and country.

Radburn, New Jersey (pictured c. 1935), called itself "The Town of the Motor Age." In order to separate pedestrian and automobile traffic and add parkways to the town, the designers laid out dead-end streets with green walkways behind the houses. Radburn had single-family dwellings of uniform colonial design, some garden apartments, a small shopping center, and schools. Garden apartments, similar to the Queensboro Garden Apartments in Jackson Heights, New York (pictured in the 1920's), which faced interior gardens had a golf course and shops close by, became very popular in suburbs as the need for multiple dwellings grew.

Forest Hills Gardens, New York (pictured in the 1920's), was designed primarily for commuters, for wealthy commuters. Using the railroad station as a focal point, the planners laid out an orderly village, with tree-lined streets and single-family brick dwellings that resembled, on a smaller scale, the medieval castles of Europe. In addition, Forest Hills Gardens boasted one of the finest country clubs in the nation.

Medieval castles, Italian Renaissance villas, and other copies of European styles were very popular in the early 20th century. Wealthy men, able to commute or drive to the city easily, began to build themselves elaborate country villas like Villa Vizcaya in Miami, Florida. Whole rooms were brought from Europe to furnish Vizcaya. Indeed, there was such a craze for anything European that, according to one writer, Americans "launched perhaps the greatest plunder of the Continent since the sack of Rome."

Although many wealthy men insisted on living in copies of European castles, some preferred new and original styles like the prairie-style houses of architect Frank Lloyd Wright. The Robie House, one of his best known, consisted of a long low brick mass that clung to the earth and showed the architect's talent for "forcing space to flow as easily as water."

Villa Vizcaya, Miami, Florida, built in 1917

Robie House, Chicago, Illinois, built in 1908

Forest Hills Gardens, New York, in the 1920's

Queensboro Garden Apartments, Jackson Heights, New York, in the 1920's

Americans at Play

One of the major developments of the early part of the 20th century was the increased amount of leisure time available to most Americans. And, with the improvements in public transportation, such as the subway, and the increasing number of automobiles, most Americans no longer had to spend their leisure time close to home. During this period, too, most Americans had more money to spend—and they frequently spent it amusing themselves.

Since most Americans could not afford to live in a palace of their own, a movie palace, like Grauman's Chinese Theater (pictured in 1930) was the place to go. Many such movie houses were built in the center of the city, close to public transportation lines. To be popular, the movie palace only had to be "a little too big, a little too noisy, a little too bizarre." Any style —Chinese, Italian Renaissance, or Moorish—would do so long as it would "lend itself to grotesque overornamentation." One large movie palace was even perfumed for the benefit of the audience.

Although the movie palace was a fine place for an evening's entertainment, on weekends the family usually wished to go farther afield. By public transportation or by the family car, Americans by the thousands headed for amusement centers like Coney Island, New York. There they could go on rides at Steeplechase Park (pictured c. 1903), or go to the beach, or eat hot dogs and parade up and down in their finery.

Some cities became known as vacation centers. They consisted primarily of elegant, elaborate hotels, and offered facilities to please all kinds of travelers. One such vacation city was Atlantic City, New Jersey. There vacationers could bathe in the sea, or they could watch the attractions at the Steel Pier, or they could parade up and down the Boardwalk (pictured in 1920). The most elegant hotel in Atlantic City was the Traymore; like other hotels of the period, it was as ostentatious as the movie palaces of the day.

Opening night at Grauman's Chinese Theater, Hollywood, Calif., 1930

Steeplechase Park, Coney Island, New York, c. 1903

Steel Pier and Boardwalk, Atlantic City, New Jersey, 1920

The Great Depression of the 1930's was the worst economic crisis to strike the civilized world. It began, in 1929, in the United States with a crash in the stock market followed by a financial panic. Business could not sell their goods or obtain credit; wages dropped; and men lost their jobs. Yet it took two years for industry and the rest of the world to feel the full impact of the depression.

People everywhere felt the effect of the depression when Americans stopped buying goods from abroad, stopped investing, and withdrew money from Europe by selling their foreign investments. In Asia and in South America as well as in Europe, people saw American markets and dollars slip away. With far more goods for sale than there were buyers, prices fell. Many people could not pay their debts.

Testing a World Power

In May 1931, the largest bank in Vienna, the *Kredit Anstalt,* failed. It had creditors, mainly other banks, in western Europe and in the United States. It had investments scattered all over central Europe, so its collapse triggered many bankruptcies and business failures and helped spread depression throughout Europe.

In Germany, in the summer of 1931, several great banking houses failed. Germany's entire economy began to shake. The German government could not pay reparations, so other European governments were affected by the financial crisis.

From the continent, like a disease, the economic crisis descended on Britain. Britain could not sell enough manufactured goods to pay for the products she needed to import. As trade fell, unemployment rose and government tax revenues dwindled. So the British government had to dip into its reserves of gold to pay for imports. This gold drain weakened the pound sterling, which was backed by gold. In 1931, therefore, Britain went off the gold standard. This meant that the pound, long a symbol of stability in the world economy, had been cut in value and that foreigners could no longer obtain gold for their pounds sterling. Within two years, half the nations in the world, including the United States, went off the gold standard. Money could no longer cross borders and be easily converted to gold.

Unlike Britain, France for a while fought off the effects of the depression. The French were able to do so because their economy had a better balance between agriculture and industry than had Britain's. But by the winter of 1931-32 the French, too, found themselves unable to sell their goods at home and abroad. The government's resources were strained in caring for the unemployed.

Almost everywhere the problem of finding jobs for able-bodied men became so great that it resembled an epidemic that had gotten beyond control. In 1932, according to reliable statistics from industrial countries, 30 million people were unemployed. In addition, there were uncounted millions of unemployed in Asia and Africa.

Among the great powers only the Soviet Union seemed to have escaped the evils of unemployment. In 1928, the Communist government had launched the first of its Five Year Plans intended to build heavy industry without the use of loans. This planning began to transform the Soviet Union from a backward agricultural land to an advanced industrial society, and it helped overcome the cycle of boom and depression found in other countries. But the Soviets did not escape all the effects of the world-wide depression. The depression forced down the prices of food and other raw materials that the Soviets sold to buy machinery. So industrialization within the Soviet Union became more costly for the people than the planners had anticipated.

Reports of the relative employment stability in the Soviet Union and of the progress of the Five Year Plans reached the discontented in western capitalist countries. Many turned to communism as a way out of economic distress. Membership in the Communist party in European countries grew. In Britain and the United States Communist ideas made little headway. But many were attracted to the idea of economic planning.

Although conservatives shunned communism, they and men who had no jobs, who had lost what they owned, and who had lost hope for a stable, secure life joined movements and parties that preached violence and the overthrow of parliaments and other democratic institutions. Democracy, they argued, was suited only to rich countries. So in the 1930's, democracy survived only where democratic institutions were strong and deeply rooted, as in the United States, Britain, and France.

unit VII
1920-1941

What some of these disgruntled men turned to as an alternative to democratic government was a form of dictatorship called *totalitarianism*. It functioned on the idea of a permanent dictatorship that operated through a single political party that permitted no organized opposition. The totalitarian dictatorship despised democracy and subordinated the wishes of the people to the demands of the state. It crushed all opposition and demanded total commitment to the state. The totalitarians argued that the national state was in crisis and that extreme measures were therefore justified. But the totalitarian state operated as if society were in perpetual crisis.

The first of the totalitarian regimes began to emerge out of a great civil war in Russia in 1918-1922. There the Communists, under the leadership of Vladimir Lenin, imposed the Red Terror on the Russian people. The terror, carried out in part by the Cheka, a formidable secret political police organization, tried to root out all opposition to communism. Then Lenin and his followers set up a socialist state through the dictatorship of the proletariat, or of the working class. This meant, in fact, a dictatorship by the leaders of the Communist party, for no other party was allowed in the Union of Soviet Socialist Republics, Russia's official name from 1922 onward.

Lenin died in 1924 and was succeeded by Joseph Stalin, a dictator as determined, as single-minded in the use of power, and as brutal as any ruler Russia had known. Stalin introduced state planning and the idea of "building socialism in a single country," or a nationalistic emphasis in his dictatorship. He covered the country with a network of secret police and spies who had practically unlimited power to arrest, torture, and kill all those who opposed him. His reign of terror, often called Stalinism, exterminated practically all critics.

The next nation to succumb to dictatorship, and the only one in western Europe to abandon efforts to build a democratic society, was Italy. Although Italy had been on the winning side in World War I, the conditions in its society resembled those of a defeated country. The Italians were discontented and felt that they had been denied the spoils of war for which they had fought and sacrificed. Out of the disorder and agitation of postwar Italian society emerged Benito Mussolini, a fiery journalist and former socialist, to head a new political movement called fascism. The name came from the Latin *fasces*, the bound bundle of rods that had symbolized the power of the ancient republic of Rome.

In October 1922, Mussolini led his fascists, wearing black shirts, in a march on Rome. He was named premier, did away with the parliament, and made the Fascist party the sole organ of government. Mussolini became the first of the personal dictators of the totalitarian era, taking the title of *Duce* or leader. He ruled through use of sceret police, the crushing of individual liberty, and even the assassination of critics. Mussolini's dictatorship was based on the idea of the corporative state. Fascism placed the state in control of the economic life of the people within a structure of capitalism. Despite fascism's tight economic controls, when the Great Depression struck, Italy suffered severely from unemployment and other ills.

Other countries blighted by depression were attracted to Mussolini's experiment and set up dictatorships which came to be called by the Italian word, *fascist*. Germany established the most powerful, brutal, and feared fascist state.

While Mussolini was organizing his Black Shirts into the Fascist movement, in Germany, a defeated people was groping for stability. Various political groups plotted for the day when they could take power. One of these groups, called the National Socialist German Workers' Party, attracted to it a former corporal from the Austrian army, Adolph Hitler, a poorly educated man but one of shrewd intelligence and frenzied speaking ability. Hitler became the head of the Nazi party.

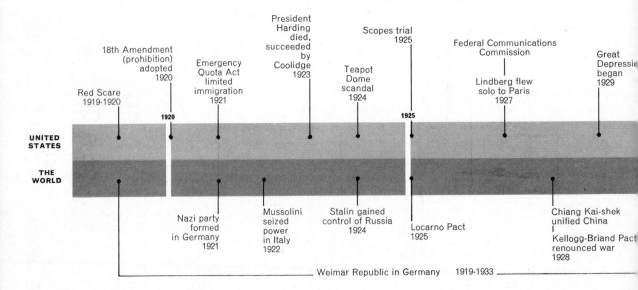

In 1923 Hitler and his Nazi Storm Troopers, wearing brown shirts, tried to imitate Mussolini's march on Rome and seize power through a "beer-hall *Putsch*" (a minor uprising) in Munich. They failed and Hitler himself might never have become anything more than another small-time politician if it were not for the Great Depression. That depression brought greater economic blight to Germany than to almost any other nation. The Nazis and the Communists made great gains. Finally, in January 1933, Hitler was named chancellor, the equivalent of prime minister.

Within a short time Hitler established a personal dictatorship and like Mussolini took the title of leader, or *Führer*. He did away with all parties except the Nazi party and governed through terror, brutality, and murder. A secret political police called the Gestapo rounded up opponents by the thousands and threw them into concentration camps. The Nazis unleashed a vicious campaign of persecution, torture, and murder against Jews. Under Hitler the state demanded total obedience.

Fascism and communism differed at first in their aims and principles. The Communists said they believed in the ideas of freedom and democracy. They did not at first glorify the national state as did the Fascists. Communists maintained that the dictatorship of the proletariat was temporary. Yet in time that dictatorship became as permanent as any in a Fascist state. Communists overthrew the capitalist system and established state ownership and control of property. Fascists retained at least an element of capitalism by leaving factories and farms in private hands.

Fascism and communism were both enemies of democracy. Both relied on terror and force; both had a monopoly of power through one party; both crushed individual liberty; and both ultimately appealed to the passions and prejudices of nationalism for support of policies that led to war. So it was that the decade of the 1930's, which opened with the economic chaos of the Great Depression, saw the rise of the totalitarian dictator. That decade closed in the flames of total world war.

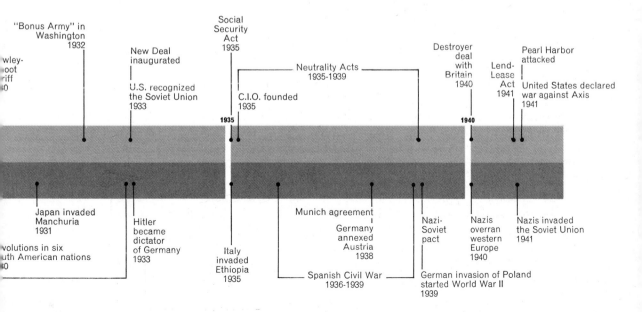

The Era of Conservatism

As the results of the election of 1920 indicated, many Americans wanted to forget the demands of the great crusade, other people's problems, and the responsibilities of power that the war had thrust upon their nation. They wished to return as quickly as possible to days of peace and comfort, or to what Harding called normalcy.

The break with the prewar past did not come suddenly. It began during the war years and continued during the debate over the League of Nations. Yet the break seemed sharp and sudden because peace came suddenly. As a result, the government had no plans for a smooth transition to a peacetime economy.

The postwar period was one of inflation. Manufacturers, farmers, and other producers tried to keep pace with the inflation by increasing their prices. Workers tried to keep up with the rising cost of living and to preserve wartime gains by striking for higher wages. Americans who lived on fixed incomes suffered the most and became bitter. They turned against the government, became hostile to organized labor and, at times, vented their resentments against minorities such as Negroes, Roman Catholics, Jews, and foreigners.

As a result, the years immediately following the armistice were filled with political, social, and economic unrest for some Americans, but were prosperous for most of them.

Since the good times continued for most Americans, the years of Calvin Coolidge's presidency were called the golden twenties. Although the nation as a whole prospered as never before, there were problems during the golden twenties. Farmers, for example, did not share in the prosperity. They faced an agricultural depression that triggered a rebellion against government policies favorable to business. The resentment against foreigners led to the restriction of immigration and increased intolerance. The spirit of intolerance was strong enough to make the election of 1928 one of the nastiest in the nation's history.

Finally, prosperity ended and Americans faced the longest and the deepest depression in the nation's history. Although President Herbert Hoover tried to revive the economy he was unable to do so. The nation, in despair, blamed him and the Republicans for the depression.

Even during the trying years between 1920 and 1932, the United States was unable to avoid the responsibilities of power. The government took part in disarmament conferences and in the movement to make war illegal. Relations with the nations of Latin America improved but American policy regarding the payment of war debts by the Allies alienated many Europeans.

When World War I ended, Americans had entered an era of conservatism and isolation. The conservative economic and social policies were shattered by the Great Depression, but the policies of isolation continued into the 1930's.

THE REPUBLICANS RETURNED TO POWER

The people of the United States were eager to return to the tasks of peace, but they could not shake off the attitudes that had been bred by the war. The wartime demands for conformity in thought and the intolerance against foreigners and radicals spilled over into the new era of peace. One result of this attitude was the hunt for radicals—called the Red Scare of 1919-1920—which overshadowed the problems of reconversion.

During the Red Scare, some government officials spread the story that radicals were stirring the Negroes to rebellion. When vicious race riots broke out in the summer of 1919, many Americans began to believe the story. But the radicals had not fomented the riots. They were caused, among other things, by the increasing intolerance toward Negroes.

It would be wrong, however, to assume that the Red Scare paralyzed constructive government action. Even though the government followed a policy of letting the people themselves deal with the problems of demobilization, Congress did try to meet some of the most pressing needs.

While Congress dealt with a few of the problems of demobilization, American workers fought for their livelihood against two foes—inflation and militant employers. Organized labor watched its wartime economic gains vanish as the cost of living climbed higher and higher. To retain those gains, and also to make new advances, labor struck.

When the Republicans returned to power, in March 1921, the new President was not equipped to handle the problems raised by the tensions of the transition from war to peace. Warren G. Har-

ding had been the owner and editor of a small-town newspaper. In 1914, the people of Ohio had elected him to the Senate. Although he did not want to be President, he gave in to pressure from friends and political bosses to accept the Republican nomination. His administration was remembered as much for scandal as for any accomplishment.

The Red Scare caused mass hysteria

Although the Red Scare was rooted in American problems, it was also connected with events in the Soviet Union which followed the Bolshevik Revolution of 1917. The Bolsheviks, or Communists, attacked the foundations of all other governments. They preached the idea of world-wide revolution by the *proletariat*, the workingmen. In other words, the Communists dedicated themselves to inciting class warfare whereby the workers would turn on their employers, seize property, and take control of the government.

Most Americans were shocked by Communist activities and the spread of communism. They were further upset when two Communist parties were formed in the United States in September 1919. The American Communists carried on an intensive propaganda campaign. They paraded, made violent speeches, distributed pamphlets, and demanded action to overthrow the capitalist system.

Many Americans denounced the Communists as foreigners and subversives. Businessmen and conservatives in general were alarmed, for they saw the threat of revolution in the activities of the radicals. Strikes, bombings, and even the surging inflation were taken as evidence that radicals were attacking the foundations of American society.

In reality, the threat from radicals was never great. In 1919, the membership of the Socialist party and of the two Communist parties in the United States was about two tenths of one per cent of the population. Yet, some radicals did resort to violence or to threats of violence.

Attorney General A. Mitchell Palmer conducted a nation-wide campaign against the Red menace.

On January 2, 1920, agents of the Bureau of Investigation of the Department of Justice, at Palmer's direction, raided Communist headquarters in thirty-three major cities in twenty-three states. In this one great roundup of Reds, more than 2700 people were hustled off to jails. Most of the people arrested during the Red Scare were released because they had committed no crime, but several hundred aliens were deported.

State officials, too, suppressed civil liberties. Many state legislatures passed restrictive laws designed to punish radicals. In April 1920, the New York legislature expelled five legally elected members for no other reason except that they were Socialists. After this act of intolerance, the Red Scare declined. People began to realize that it had been exaggerated.

Racial violence broke out

During World War I hundreds of thousands of Negroes had left the farms of the South for jobs in Northern cities. Although they gained a greater social and economic freedom than they had previously known, the Negroes encountered prejudice, hatred from unskilled workers who feared competition, and slum living as bad or worse than that of immigrants. Some 400,000 Negroes, moreover, had served in the army, half of them in Europe. There they had experienced a social freedom they had not known in the United States.

After the war, Negroes, like other workers, wanted higher wages but, in addition, they wanted to break down some of the barriers that had kept them at the bottom of American society. The National Association for the Advancement of Colored People actively worked for such improvements for the Negro.

Southern whites opposed this activity, and were determined to keep the Negro in his old subservient status. They revived the Ku Klux Klan. By 1919, it had grown from a small group to an organization with 100,000 members. In many Southern communities, night-riding Klansmen terrorized victims, most of whom were Negroes. Lynchings of Negroes increased and even included some men still in uniform.

In the North, Negroes attempted to escape from the slum areas of the central city. As they moved closer to white neighborhoods, resentment exploded. Race riots broke out in twenty-six towns and cities, including Washington, D.C. Before 1919 was over, hundreds were dead or maimed from the riots, and millions of dollars were lost in property damage.

The worst riot followed a fight between white and Negro teen-agers on July 27, 1919, on a Chicago beach. The fighting spilled over into the slum neighborhoods where the Negro population had more than doubled in the previous decade. For almost a week gangs roamed the streets, fighting, stabbing, shooting, and senselessly destroying property. The authorities were unable to subdue them. When the state militia finally restored order, there were 15 white and 23 Negro dead, well over 500 wounded, mostly Negroes, and more than 1000 people homeless.

As a result of these ordeals, many Negroes were ready to follow almost any leader who held out hope for a better life. One appeared—Marcus Aurelius Garvey, a mustached Jamaican immigrant with remarkable abilities as an organizer. He founded the Universal Negro Improvement Association, established himself in the Harlem district of New York City, and preached a Negro nationalism, or racial consciousness. Follow me back to Africa, he told the Negroes, and there we shall build a "free, redeemed and mighty nation."

By 1921, more than four million Negroes were paying dues into Garvey's organization. He gathered millions of dollars to buy ships to carry his followers to Africa, but the project never materialized. In 1923, a federal court convicted Garvey of using the mails to defraud, and sent him to prison (he was later deported). Garvey's huge following was evidence of the Negro's dissatisfaction with his place in American society.

Congress passed some Progressive laws

Immediately after the armistice, the government had to meet the cost of bringing United States soldiers back from France and caring for the sick and wounded. In addition, it gave relief to the starving people in Europe, and paid for ending the war program at home. To provide for these needs, Congress passed a war revenue bill, signed by President Wilson in February 1919.

Congress also had to decide what to do with the railroads, the communication facilities such as commercial radio, and the merchant marine—all of which the government owned or controlled. The Esch-Cummins Transportation Act, passed by Congress in 1920, was an attempt to solve both immediate and long-range problems of the railroads. This law returned control of the railroads to their private owners, but enlarged the powers of the Interstate Commerce Commission so that the government had effective control over rates, profits, and other aspects of operating the lines.

The government owned, rather than controlled, the huge merchant marine built during the war. In the Merchant Marine Act of 1920 Congress authorized the sale of some of the government's ships to private operators. This law also permitted the Emergency Fleet Corporation, a government corporation, to operate the shipping service at a loss, until private interests could take over. As a result, government subsidy and ownership kept a dwindling American merchant fleet afloat in the 1920's. At the same time, the government sold its radio stations to a private company, the Radio Corporation of America.

Two other laws passed in 1920 tried to protect public resources from exploitation by private companies. The General Leasing Act placed oil lands reserved for the navy beyond the reach of oil companies. It also permitted the government to lease other oil and mineral lands on terms that safeguarded the public interest. The Water Power Act established the Federal Power Commission to issue licenses for the construction and operation of dams and hydroelectric plants on rivers in government lands. The commission was also authorized to regulate rates.

These laws, all in the Progressive tradition, sought to solve problems through government regulation or assistance, and not through government ownership unless absolutely necessary.

Two measures advocated by the Progressives became law through amendments to the Constitution. The Eighteenth Amendment, prohibiting the manufacture, sale, or transportation of alcoholic beverages, went into effect in January 1919. The Nineteenth Amendment, which became law in August 1920, provided for woman suffrage.

Workers struck for higher wages

The businessman in the United States was in no mood to meet labor's demands for higher wages without a fight. He wanted to run his business as he saw fit. He believed that the workers' struggle for higher wages was the first stage of the class revolution plotted by Communists and he persuaded other Americans to believe it as well.

Public hostility toward organized labor was clearly recognizable in the reaction of the people to the steel strike of September 1919. Working conditions in the steel industry, as in many others, were wretched. The average workweek for the entire industry was just under sixty-nine hours. It was not difficult for the American Federation of Labor to organize many of the workers. When the United States Steel Corporation refused to negotiate with them, the workers went on strike.

The steel company succeeded in diverting public attention away from the real issues by claiming that the labor leaders were Communists. Public opinion then became so hostile toward the strikers that they could not hope to win. Although the strike dragged on until January 1920, the company had broken it earlier with the use of thousands of strikebreakers. The workers did not gain a single concession. The United States Steel Corporation emerged from the struggle as the champion of conservatism and the main industrial bastion against organized labor.

In November 1919, some 394,000 miners in the bituminous, or soft, coal industry left their jobs. They took this action even though Attorney General A. Mitchell Palmer obtained an *injunction,* or court order, prohibiting leaders of the United Mine Workers, such as John L. Lewis, from participating in the strike. Like many of the workers in other industries, the miners had genuine grievances. They had agreed not to strike during the war, but for two years, while the cost of living doubled, they had not received a wage increase.

Finally, when a second injunction was issued, Lewis canceled the strike. Many miners still refused to return to work. When President Wilson stepped in and promised a wage increase as well as an arbitral commission to investigate the workers' demands, the coal strike ended. The miners ultimately received a wage increase of twenty-seven per cent, but nothing else.

Scandals tarnished the government

President Warren G. Harding was kindly, friendly, and well liked by almost everybody who knew him, but he had no will power. He surrounded himself with old cronies, known as the "Ohio gang," who catered to his tastes but deceived him. Harding rewarded the leader of the Ohio gang, Harry M. Daugherty, with the post of attorney general. He gave another friend, Albert B. Fall of New Mexico, the job of secretary of the interior. Neither man was suited for his office.

Not all of Harding's appointments were bad, however. He had obtained three able and intelligent men in Charles Evans Hughes, secretary of state; Andrew Mellon, secretary of the treasury; and Herbert Hoover, secretary of commerce. They set the tone for the Republican restoration because Harding seldom made policy decisions. He presided over government with outward dignity, but left the making of policy to Congress and to his cabinet members.

Soon after Albert B. Fall took over as secretary of the interior, he persuaded Edwin N. Denby, the secretary of the navy, to transfer to the Department of the Interior control over oil lands held in reserve to meet the future needs of the navy. Even though a few of the navy's oil experts protested, the President agreed to the transfer. Fall then secretly leased the reserve at Elk Hills, California, to Edward L. Doheny of the Pan American Petroleum Company, and the reserve at Teapot Dome, Wyoming, to Harry F. Sinclair of the Mammoth Oil Company. For these favors Sinclair gave Fall over $200,000 in government bonds, $85,000 in cash, and other presents; and Doheny gave the secretary a "loan" of $100,000.

When Fall began to spend his sudden wealth, some senators became suspicious and investigated. Eventually the story was uncovered. In 1924, Doheny, Sinclair, and Fall were tried for conspiracy to defraud the government. All were acquitted, but in 1929, Fall was convicted of accepting a bribe, fined $100,000, and sentenced to a year in prison. Sinclair was fined $1000 and served nine months in jail for tampering with the jury, and for defying a Senate committee, but neither he nor Doheny was convicted of paying bribes. The Teapot Dome scandal brought shame and disgrace to the Harding administration.

Attorney General Daugherty also brought shame to the government. Senate investigators in 1924 found that he had sold liquor permits and pardons. He was forced to resign from office and, in 1927, was brought to trial for fraud. Daugherty refused to testify, and implied that he chose to remain silent rather than make revelations which might injure Harding's reputation. The jury failed to agree on Daugherty's guilt or innocence, and he went free.

In June 1923, as rumors of corruption in government began to spread, Harding began a speaking tour of the West. He became ill while returning from a vacation in Alaska. In San Francisco he developed pneumonia, and on August 2 he suffered a stroke and died. Not knowing of the scandals, the nation mourned him for the kindly man he was, and the statesman it thought he was.

Harding suspected that corruption had eaten into his administration, but he did not know the details. Before he started his trip he told a friend, "In this job I am not worried about my enemies. It is my friends that are keeping me awake nights." His friends had betrayed him to such an extent that, after his death, his reputation was destroyed.

REVIEWING THE SECTION

1. What caused the Red Scare? In what ways did the Red Scare interfere with civil liberties?

2. What conditions after World War I led to racial violence in both South and North?

3. In what ways did Congress attempt to meet the needs of the postwar period?

4. Why did miners and steel workers strike in 1919? What gains were made by the workers?

PROSPERITY BROUGHT PROBLEMS

On the night of Harding's death Vice President Calvin Coolidge was at his birthplace, his father's home, near Plymouth, Vermont. In the little living room at 2:47 A.M., with his hand on the open family Bible, Coolidge took the presidential oath. His father, a notary public, administered the oath by the light of kerosene lamps. This rural scene had tremendous appeal. To many people in the United States it suggested another chapter in the American dream. Another country boy had risen to occupy the White House.

Although Calvin Coolidge had not been poor, he had come from the country, and his career was that of a small-town politician who made good. Coolidge fitted the times. He was a conservative in almost everything. He favored legislation beneficial to big business because he believed business should run the country.

Coolidge was shy, aloof, and even austere. It was difficult for him to make friends and he spoke so seldom that he became known as "Silent Cal." Yet he was popular. People liked his folksy virtues. He had the qualities the Ohio gang lacked— old-fashioned honesty and understandable simplicity. As the elections of 1924 were to reveal, even the disclosure of the Harding scandals could not injure Coolidge and his party.

Businessmen controlled the Republican convention held in Cleveland, in June 1924. They gave Coolidge the nomination and framed a platform that promised to continue things as they were.

The Democrats were badly divided. At their convention in New York the urban and rural wings of the party could not agree on a presidential candidate. Finally, on the 103rd ballot after 16 days of sweltering heat, the Democrats nominated John W. Davis, a corporation lawyer as conservative as Coolidge.

Rebellious Republicans, labor leaders, and reformers, who resented Coolidge's conservatism, held a third convention in Cleveland. They organized a new Progressive party for the presidential campaign only and chose Robert M. La Follette to head their ticket. These Progressives gained most of their support from western farmers, organized labor, and Socialists. La Follette received nearly five million votes, a substantial number for a third party, but carried only the state of Wisconsin.

Farmers did not share in prosperity

Most farmers, particularly those who produced staple crops, did not share in the Coolidge prosperity. During the war farmers had made money, and they had spent it as though their prosperity would continue. Their prosperity ended in 1920 when foreign countries cut down their purchases of United States wheat, meat, and other products, and the federal government withdrew support for the price of wheat. Farmers now had an output that exceeded demand. An agricultural depression began that summer in some areas of the country and lasted all during the golden twenties.

Midwestern Republicans and Southern Democrats formed a farm bloc in Congress to combat the crisis. The farm bloc helped gain high tariff

King Oliver's Creole Jazz Band, Chicago, 1923

The broker

The jazz baby

The efficiency expert

The bootlegger

The Jazz Age, as the 1920's have been called, was a period of prosperity, optimism, and good times that many expected to last forever. Going to a "speakeasy," or night club, especially one which employed dixieland jazz musicians, became a fashionable thing to do. Some of the finest and most popular jazz artists were Negro musicians such as Louis Armstrong (center), who later became a nationally famous entertainer.

Many Americans were proud of their new prosperity and wanted to show it off. Eager to satisfy, automobile manufacturers built luxurious new models, and auto advertisements urged prospective customers to fulfill "their desire to own the best."

Life magazine of the 1920's was devoted to political satire and humor. In a fake advertisement, it invited the reader to "Let your sports sweater express your personality"—broker, "jazz baby," efficiency expert, or bootlegger. Artist John Held, Jr. effectively captured the spirit of the times in caricatures of a college type, a bobbed-hair type, a dandy, and others which appeared on the cover of *Life* in January 1925.

protection for farm products, and the Intermediate Credits Act of 1923 provided, among other things, government loans to growers of livestock. Yet the farm distress persisted.

Beginning in 1924, farmers supported the McNary-Haugen bill, which included a complicated plan for government aid to agriculture. This plan would establish a system whereby farm products would be sold for two prices—a low world price and a higher price in the United States. The government would buy the farm surpluses at the American price, sell them abroad at the world price, and recover its losses through a special tax on farmers.

The McNary-Haugen bill suffered its first of many defeats in the House of Representatives in June 1924, but was passed by Congress in revised form in 1927 and 1928. Coolidge vetoed it each time. Although the organized farmers gained a number of benefits from the government, they failed to get their most important measure. They failed primarily because the big business interests in the East, and the President, opposed the bill.

Immigration was restricted

While farmers were eager to dump their surpluses in foreign countries, many Americans were no longer willing to allow unrestricted immigration into the United States. Organized labor wanted to shut off immigration because it wished to keep the newcomers from competing for the available jobs. Many Protestants resented the influx of Roman Catholics and Jews from southern and eastern Europe. Even employers now favored restrictions because they believed that many of the new immigrants were radicals.

Pressure from these groups led to the passage of the Emergency Quota Act in May 1921 and the National Origins Act of 1924. These laws initiated a quota system by which the number of immigrants allowed from a given nation was based on the number of persons of that nationality already living in the United States. The immigration laws favored northwestern Europeans over the southern and eastern, because more persons of northwestern European descent already lived in the United States. Most Asians were completely barred, but immigrants from Latin America and Canada retained free access to the United States.

The effect of the two immigration laws was that discrimination, as well as restriction of immigration, became a national policy. People in other nations resented the discrimination, and by the late 1920's immigration had slowed down considerably. An historic policy, and one of the world's great mass migrations, had ended.

Intolerance became widespread

The hostility toward foreigners and the fear of radicals evident in the movement to restrict immigration was also evident in a murder case that stirred deep emotions during most of the 1920's. In April 1920, two men in South Braintree, Massachusetts, killed and robbed a factory paymaster and his guard. Nicola Sacco, an employee in a shoe factory, and Bartolomeo Vanzetti, a fish peddler, were tried and convicted of the murder. Both men were Italian aliens and both were anarchists. Webster Thayer, the trial judge, publicly expressed contempt for anarchism. Since the evidence against Sacco and Vanzetti was circumstantial, many people suspected that they had been judged guilty primarily because they were foreigners and radicals.

This suspicion, accompanied by protests all over the world against the decision, led to a special investigation of the case. The investigators said the judge had acted improperly, but they did not recommend a new trial. In August 1927, Sacco and Vanzetti died in the electric chair.

Much more sinister was the bigotry in American life as expressed in the continued growth of the Ku Klux Klan. After 1920, it spread from the South to other parts of the country, particularly to the small towns of the Midwest and the Far West. By the end of 1924, the Klan claimed six million members, but probably had four or five million.

Immigrants. Before the 1920's, families and individuals from all over the world came to the United States in search of better economic opportunities and to escape persecution, famine, or political turmoil in their homelands. Some Americans resented people whose look and customs were "different." After World War I, resentment increased and became widespread. As a result Congress in 1921 and 1924 passed laws to limit immigration. America's gates no longer were open to the world's "huddled masses."

Proclaiming itself the protector of "Anglo-Saxon" Protestant America, the Klan waged illegal war on foreigners, Negroes, Jews, and especially Roman Catholics. Its members wore their hoods and white sheets on brutal raids in which victims were beaten and sometimes murdered. The Klansmen announced their outrages by burning crosses.

In 1924, the political influence of the Klan was so great that it prevented the Democratic national convention from condemning its activities and caused a serious split in the party. In the following year a scandal exposed Indiana Klan leaders as immoral, dishonest, and corrupt. This disillusioned many of the rank-and-file members. By the end of the 1920's, this lawless organization was discredited and stripped of much of its influence.

Prejudice marred an election

Even though the Ku Klux Klan had declined, the spirit of intolerance remained and it affected the election of 1928. The difficulty began in Houston, Texas, when the Democrats nominated Alfred "Al" E. Smith, four times governor of New York, for the presidency.

Smith represented something new in national politics. Never before had either of the two major parties nominated such a man—a Roman Catholic with an immigrant background, educated in parochial schools. In addition, he was city-bred, raised on New York's East Side. He was a "wet" who sought repeal of prohibition.

Calvin Coolidge could have had the Republican nomination, but in the summer of 1927, he announced that he did "not choose to run for President in 1928." So the Republicans nominated Herbert Hoover, the distinguished secretary of commerce who had served in the cabinet of the two previous Republican administrations.

Hoover campaigned on a conservative platform that avoided important issues and stressed prosperity. Only a continuation of Republican policies, he repeated as a campaign theme, could make prosperity a lasting way of life. "We in America today

are nearer to the final triumph over poverty than ever before in the history of any land," he said in his acceptance speech.

Aside from prosperity, three issues dominated the campaign—Smith's religion, his big city background, and his opposition to prohibition. Everywhere the people who feared Roman Catholicism attacked him. In the South the opposition against him became almost a crusade. Vile stories about him were whispered or circulated on crude handbills. In Oklahoma City, where Smith denounced the Ku Klux Klan, fiery crosses greeted him.

So great was the opposition to Smith that Hoover broke the Solid South, the first Republican to do so since the Reconstruction period. Hoover, in fact, won by a landslide. Probably no Democrat could have won, for the people were satisfied with Republican prosperity. Yet prejudice had marred the election and left an ugly wound in American society, one that would heal slowly.

REVIEWING THE SECTION

1. What legislation did farmers promote to alleviate the agricultural depression of the 1920's?

2. Why was immigration restricted? Against whom did the laws discriminate?

3. What were the evidences of intolerance during the 1920's?

PROSPERITY ENDED IN A CRASH

As a poor orphan boy from the country who achieved wealth, fame, and power, Herbert Hoover had lived the American dream. He was born in the small town of West Branch, Iowa, and for eight years enjoyed boyhood in the country. He attended Stanford University, where he worked for his education, and then became a mining engineer. His profession took him over most of the world—to Australia, Asia, Africa, and Europe. In 1914, he claimed that he was probably the wealthiest of American engineers. After wealth came fame, particularly as chairman of the Commission for Relief in Belgium. Hoover the great engineer now became the great humanitarian. Then followed his appointment as Wilson's food administrator, and eight years as secretary of commerce.

Since the presidency was Hoover's first elective office, he lacked political experience, and he found it difficult to make the compromises demanded of a politician. He was a conservative who believed in efficiency and service and who distrusted the spread of governmental power.

Prohibition was evaded

Prohibition had been a bitter issue in the election campaign. Protestant rural America favored it. Prohibitionists believed that drinking was a vice of immigrants and corrupt city dwellers. The people who lived in the cities and industrial areas, where the drinking of liquor, wine, or beer was an accepted social custom, resented the Eighteenth Amendment as an invasion of their personal liberty.

People who wanted to drink did so regardless of the Constitution. Bootleggers, rumrunners, and others evaded the law and furnished a steady supply of alcohol to the "wets." Never, it has been said in jest, did private enterprise show greater efficiency in meeting consumer demand.

Enforcement of nation-wide prohibition was possible only if a majority of the people supported it. By law, the federal, state, and local governments all were responsible for enforcement. But in "wet" areas the local authorities did nothing and left enforcement to the federal government. Congress never appropriated enough money to do the job properly.

The enforcement of prohibition had become a farce by 1928. Shortly after Hoover entered the White House he appointed a commission, headed by former Attorney General George W. Wickersham, to investigate the whole problem of enforcement. Two years later, in January 1931, the Wickersham Commission reported evidence documenting what most Americans already knew—that prohibition was a failure. Yet the commission suggested no plan for attacking the problem.

Hoover strengthened the federal government's machinery for enforcement and did a better job than had Harding and Coolidge, but he too failed. His task actually became more difficult as opposition to prohibition grew. Finally, in August 1932, he announced that he favored repeal of the Eighteenth Amendment. Since the Democratic platform of that year had also come out for repeal, prohibition was doomed.

In February 1933, Congress submitted the repeal amendment to the states. In December, the Twenty-First Amendment, which repealed the Eighteenth Amendment, became law. The "noble experiment" was over.

Aid for farmers failed

When Hoover was inaugurated, the nation was enjoying a booming prosperity. During the campaign, Hoover had promised help to the farmers, who comprised one of the important segments of the population that was not making money. To redeem his promise, Hoover called Congress into special session to enact legislation to help farmers.

In June 1929, Congress passed the Agricultural Marketing Act to give aid to farmers through their own coöperative marketing organizations. This law set up the Federal Farm Board of nine members and provided a revolving fund of $500 million to make loans to coöperative associations so that they could store and sell agricultural surpluses more efficiently than in the past. In 1930, after the outbreak of a great world-wide economic depression, the Farm Board created the Grain Stabilization Corporation and the Cotton Stabilization Corporation. These two agencies tried to keep prices stable by buying up surpluses, but prices fell drastically anyway. Hoover's farm experiment had failed.

Hoover asked Congress to give farm products the same protection it had in the past given to manufacturers by raising the tariff on agricultural products. The Hawley-Smoot tariff bill, passed by Congress in June 1930, could scarcely be called an aid to the farmer. The rates on numerous manufactured products (which the farmer had to buy) were raised. The average duty on all taxable goods was increased to 55.3 per cent of their value.

People everywhere, including more than a thousand of the nation's professional economists, pleaded with the President not to sign the bill, saying it was economically unsound. Since businessmen and some farmers wanted the tariff, Hoover signed it. The Hawley-Smoot Tariff Act, the highest peacetime tariff in the nation's history, failed to help farmers. They actually suffered because they were exporters, and other nations retaliated with tariffs of their own against United States products. The Hawley-Smoot Tariff Act stimulated the growth of economic nationalism in the 1930's, and helped deepen the depression.

Prices plunged on the stock market

The depression in the United States was touched off by distress in the New York Stock Exchange. For several years the prices of stocks had been rising, and stocks had been selling for far more than was justified by the earning power of the companies that had issued them. Yet in the late 1920's, people bought the stocks because they thought they could get rich easily. They gambled on the stock market by buying on *margin,* buying on credit from brokers. This kind of speculation was all right only so long as stock prices continued to climb, as nearly everybody expected they would.

Outside the market there were signs that prosperity was weakening. Much of the prosperity had been founded on the construction and automobile industries. In 1925, the construction of homes had reached a value of five billion dollars; in 1929, the value fell to three billion. By 1929, too, sales of automobiles, and related products such as tires, had declined. Some stock operators began quietly to dispose of their holdings. In September 1929, the stock market broke and then recovered. On October 24, called "Black Thursday," prices broke violently and many investors lost money. On the following day, President Hoover assured the people that what had happened was not very serious.

Five days later, on Tuesday, October 29, the big crash came. In a day of wild trading, a day that turned out to be the most devastating in the history of the Stock Exchange, nearly 16.5 million shares of stock exchanged hands. The frenzied selling went on for two weeks, until the value of the stocks on the Wall Street Exchange had declined about forty per cent.

Leaders in government and business tried to bolster sagging spirits. When men everywhere were being wiped out financially, John D. Rockefeller, for example, came out with an optimistic statement. He said that the country was sound and added that "my son and I have for some days been purchasing sound common stocks." Many people applauded Rockefeller, but Eddie Cantor, a popular comedian, commented later, "Sure, who else had any money left?"

The mighty crash on Wall Street brought the prosperity of the golden twenties to a disastrous end. Although the crash did not cause the Great Depression that followed, the longest and most severe in the nation's history, it was a contributing factor.

Herbert Hoover fought the depression

When the depression struck, businessmen took the view that the various phases of the business cycle were inevitable and that, in time, prosperity would return. Some said the economy was sound, and that the only thing wrong was the people's lack of confidence.

No one could truly ignore the depression. It penetrated every aspect of life in the United States. A year after the crash, 6 million men walked the streets looking for jobs that did not exist. In 1931, unemployment in the nation rose to 9 million, and in 1932 climbed to about 15 million. Thousands of banks failed, prices dropped, foreign trade shrank, and business failures increased.

By the summer of 1932, steel plants were operating at twelve per cent of capacity. Many factories had shut down completely. People lost their savings; they could not make mortgage payments, so they lost their homes; charity soup kitchens opened in the cities, and long bread lines formed; the jobless slept where they could—on park benches or in the doorways of public buildings; many suffered from cold, starvation, and malnutrition.

Hoover did not go along with those who advised him to do nothing. He did more to fight the depression with the resources of the government than did any previous President in an economic crisis. He stepped up federal construction, such as public buildings and roads, to stem declining business activity and ease unemployment.

Beyond this limited use of government spending, Hoover would not go. He was opposed to direct use of federal money for relief for the unemployed. He believed that state and local governments, and private charities should provide relief. In general, he at first relied on the voluntary cooperation of business, labor, and local government agencies to fight the depression. But these measures were not enough. State and local governments ran out of money, and private charities proved inadequate to care for the hungry and the homeless.

Congress began to demand that Hoover abandon his reliance on voluntary measures and start some large-scale federal relief. Finally, after repercussions from a panic in Europe made the depression in the United States worse, the President asked Congress to create the Reconstruction Finance Corporation to lend money to banks, railroads, insurance companies, and other such businesses. Congress created that agency in January 1932, and before the year was over, the Reconstruction Finance Corporation loaned $1.5 billion to more than 5000 business concerns.

Hoover followed this action with other measures, such as the Federal Home Loan Bank Act of July 1932, which was designed to save home mortgages by helping building and loan associations. In the same month he vetoed a bill for direct federal relief and a huge public works program. Many people believed that he was willing to use government funds for business, but not for the relief of human suffering.

The President seemed to confirm that impression in his treatment of the "Bonus Army" that gathered in Washington in the spring of 1932. About 15,000 World War I veterans had come to demand immediate payment of a bonus that Congress had authorized in 1924. (The bonus was not due to be paid until 1945.) Congress voted down a bill for immediate payment, and over half of the bonus marchers left Washington. Several thousand remained. They had no jobs, no homes, and nowhere to go. The President ordered them evicted from government property. Finally, some units of the army, under the command of General Douglas MacArthur, drove the ragged veterans away with tanks and bayonets.

To many people it seemed as if both their business-trained President and capitalism had failed. While people went hungry, granaries spilled over with wheat no one could sell. Some Americans began to read Karl Marx with increased interest, some began flirting with radical ideas, and many were ready for a change.

REVIEWING THE SECTION

1. Which groups were in favor of prohibition in 1920? Why did prohibition fail?

2. What conditions led to the stock market crash in 1929? What is the evidence that the economy was basically unsound?

3. How did Hoover try to combat the depression? Why did many people turn against his administration?

AMERICANS SHUNNED WORLD LEADERSHIP

When World War I ended, the United States was committed to a policy of isolation. Despite that commitment, the United States in the 1920's did not shun all participation in world politics.

A naval rivalry had developed among three major powers—the United States, Britain, and Japan—as a result of World War I. That rivalry led to a conference to discuss differences among the nations as well as the problem of naval limitation. A strong peace movement in the United States led to a pact to make war illegal.

President Coolidge continued to support intervention in the affairs of the Caribbean republics but his successor, Herbert Hoover, did not. As a result, relations between the Latin-American nations and the United States improved. Hoover's economic policy and his attitude on the payment of war debts, were disliked by the nations of Europe.

The government sought disarmament

The naval rivalry was a result of World War I. When the war ended, the United States had the second largest navy in the world. If naval expansion continued, as Congress had authorized in July 1918, the United States Navy would soon surpass the British navy, then the largest in the world.

Japan had emerged from the war with the third largest navy. In 1919, her parliament had approved further naval expansion. In March 1921, Britain announced plans to build more warships in order to maintain her fleet as the world's largest. This announcement upset some statesmen in the United States as did rumors that Britain was planning to renew an alliance she had with Japan.

At the same time, there were movements in all three countries for disarmament as a step toward avoiding war. Statesmen in each of them wanted to find a way out of the costly naval race. The United States was the only one of the three nations that could afford unrestricted naval shipbuilding. This problem, as well as that of the Japanese alliance, bothered British statesmen.

In 1921, therefore, Britain's prime minister, David Lloyd George, asked the United States and Japan if they would be willing to participate in a conference to discuss the international problems of Asia and the Pacific, including the broader problem of naval limitation. This approach appealed to Republican leaders in the United States because they wanted to cut taxes, not raise them to pay for the building of a navy, and because they looked upon such a conference as a substitute for coöperation in the League of Nations.

President Harding and Secretary of State Charles Evans Hughes, responding to the demands of Congress and the people, issued invitations to a disarmament conference to be held in Washington. Since other powers were interested in the conference, they were invited, too. Altogether nine nations —the United States, Britain, Japan, France, Italy, Belgium, the Netherlands, China, and Portugal— attended the Naval Disarmament Conference that opened in Washington in November 1921.

On the opening day Secretary of State Hughes stunned the conference by proposing an immediate halt in the building of large warships. The delegates considered this proposal after they completed the Four-Power Pact, signed in December, in which the United States, Britain, Japan, and France agreed to respect each other's rights and territories in the Pacific. If any dispute arose among them, they agreed to discuss it in a conference. This agreement replaced the Anglo-Japanese Alliance.

Next the United States, Britain, Japan, France, and Italy worked on the Five-Power Naval Treaty, which they signed in February 1922. This agreement stopped the construction of large warships, such as battleships and battle cruisers, for ten years and called for the destruction of some of those ships that were already built. It established a ratio which allowed Japan 9 ships, and France and Italy 5 ships, for every 15 ships permitted the United States and Britain.

A third major agreement, the Nine-Power Open Door Treaty, was signed at the same time by all the delegates. It pledged all the powers to respect China's independence and territorial integrity and to uphold the Open Door principle.

The people wanted to insure peace

In the United States public support for the Washington conference had come from a peace movement stronger than any in the past. Even

PRESIDENTIAL ELECTIONS: 1920-1932

CANDIDATES: 1920

ELECTORAL VOTE BY STATE		POPULAR VOTE AND PERCENTAGE	
REPUBLICAN Warren G. Harding	404	16,143,407	
DEMOCRATIC James M. Cox	127	9,130,328	
MINOR PARTIES	—	1,454,333	
	531	26,728,068	

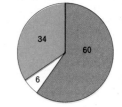

CANDIDATES: 1924

ELECTORAL VOTE BY STATE		POPULAR VOTE AND PERCENTAGE	
REPUBLICAN Calvin Coolidge	382	15,718,211	
DEMOCRATIC John W. Davis	136	8,385,283	
PROGRESSIVE Robert M. La Follette	13	4,831,289	
MINOR PARTIES	—	164,301	
	531	29,089,084	

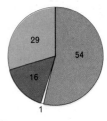

CANDIDATES: 1928

ELECTORAL VOTE BY STATE		POPULAR VOTE AND PERCENTAGE	
REPUBLICAN Herbert C. Hoover	444	21,391,993	
DEMOCRATIC Alfred E. Smith	87	15,016,169	
MINOR PARTIES	—	330,725	
	531	36,738,887	

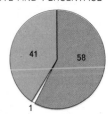

CANDIDATES: 1932

ELECTORAL VOTE BY STATE		POPULAR VOTE AND PERCENTAGE	
DEMOCRATIC Franklin D. Roosevelt	472	22,809,638	
REPUBLICAN Herbert C. Hoover	59	15,758,901	
MINOR PARTIES	—	1,153,306	
	531	39,721,845	

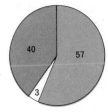

though Americans had rejected as a means of insuring peace the idea of collective security embodied in the League of Nations, the Republican administrations of the 1920's were willing to coöperate with other nations in disarmament conferences and in agreements in favor of peace. In time, the Republican leaders even came to accept the league itself as being of some importance to United States foreign policy.

After spurning the league, the Harding administration cautiously began to coöperate with it in 1922 by sending "unofficial observers" to conferences sponsored by the league. Coolidge and Hoover continued and expanded this coöperation but they did not officially join league agencies.

President Calvin Coolidge wanted to do something about the naval armaments race in cruisers, destroyers, and submarines. The Five-Power Treaty had curbed the construction of large warships, not of smaller ones. So Coolidge called another naval conference to meet in Geneva, Switzerland, in the summer of 1927. That conference, attended by American, British, and Japanese representatives, ended in failure.

The failure of the Geneva conference contributed to a loss of public confidence in disarmament as a means of insuring peace. But the peace crusaders had turned to another idea—a movement to outlaw war. A professor of history at Columbia, James T. Shotwell, persuaded Aristide Briand, the French foreign minister, to accept the idea. Briand, in turn, asked the United States government to join France in an antiwar treaty.

At first reluctant, President Coolidge and Secretary of State Frank B. Kellogg finally agreed to accept the suggestion, but only if the treaty outlawing war were expanded to include other nations. On August 27, 1928, the representatives of fifteen nations met in Paris to sign the Kellogg-Briand Pact, also known as the Pact of Paris. This treaty pledged the signers to renounce war "as an instrument of national policy" and to try to settle their disputes by peaceful means. Ultimately, sixty-two nations signed the pact.

Although President Hoover had faith in the antiwar treaty, he also believed that disarmament was necessary to "bring militarism under control." He, therefore, accepted an invitation from British Prime Minister Ramsay MacDonald to send a delegation in January 1930 to a naval conference in London. That conference produced the London Naval Treaty, signed in April, which extended the "holiday" on naval shipbuilding agreed to in the Five-Power Pact of Washington. The London treaty also applied limitations to the building of smaller warships, such as cruisers, destroyers, and submarines. This treaty, most of which was accepted by the five major naval powers—the United States, Britain, Japan, France, and Italy—was the first in the history of the modern world to limit all categories of ships.

War erupted in Asia

Although the United States and Japan had reached an accommodation on naval matters, tension between them had risen when Congress enacted the immigration law of 1924. While the act was under consideration, the Japanese had protested to the American government, saying that the new law would violate the Gentlemen's Agreement which they had carefully observed. Regardless of the Japanese protests, Congress went ahead with the law.

The ill will aroused by this law continued throughout the 1920's, but later in this period the area of difficulty with Japan shifted to the Chinese mainland. Beginning in 1925, the Chinese went through their second revolution of the twentieth century. The leader of this revolution was General Chiang Kai-shek, who had taken up the work of Sun Yat-sen, the founder of the Chinese Nationalist party.

Chiang clashed with the Soviets and the Japanese. In 1929, when Chiang's Nationalists tried to take over the Soviet Union's holdings in northern Manchuria, Soviet troops invaded the province and defeated the Chinese. Secretary of State Henry L.

Stimson tried to stop the fighting by invoking the Kellogg-Briand Pact, which both China and the Soviet Union had signed. The Soviets said the United States was not the enforcer of the pact and should mind its own business.

Japan was alarmed by Chiang's efforts to unify China and to control Manchuria. The Japanese blamed the Chinese for a mysterious explosion (September 18, 1931) on a Japanese railway near Mukden, Manchuria. The Japanese immediately invaded southern Manchuria, and within a few months, had conquered the province. In February 1932, Japan set it up as a puppet state called Manchukuo.

Shortly after the Japanese attack began, China had appealed to the United States, as sponsor of the Kellogg Pact, and to the League of Nations, under the covenant, to help keep the peace. Neither could do much. The league appointed a commission which investigated the dispute, and later condemned Japan as an aggressor. Secretary of State Stimson warned Japan that she was violating the Kellogg-Briand Pact and the Nine-Power Open Door Treaty. Then on January 7, 1932, he announced what has become known as the Hoover-Stimson Doctrine or the Stimson Doctrine. It said the United States would not recognize Japan's gains made in violation of the Open Door principle and the Kellogg-Briand Pact.

Neither the league's condemnation nor Stimson's nonrecognition doctrine stopped the Japanese. Japan retained her conquest and withdrew from the league.

United States relations with Latin America improved

Many Latin Americans were as hostile toward the United States as were the Japanese. They feared that the United States wanted to exploit and dominate them. Continued occupation of Nicaragua, Haiti, and the Dominican Republic, and friction with Mexico in the early 1920's added to Latin America's distrust of the United States. Under Coolidge, American troops also went into Honduras and Panama. In 1924, the United States exercised extensive control over the finances of most of the twenty Latin-American republics and had troops stationed in six of them.

Coolidge carried on a "private war" in Nicaragua. He supported one faction there with arms and American troops, while Mexico gave assistance to another warring faction. His troubles with Mexico increased in January 1927 when the Mexicans put into effect two laws that restricted the rights of foreigners, including Americans, who owned oil property in Mexico. These laws, as well as laws against the Roman Catholic Church, led many Americans to clamor once again for intervention in Mexico. Instead, Coolidge sent Dwight W. Morrow to Mexico as ambassador. Morrow turned out to be a fine diplomat, and helped overcome the major difficulties. Then in January 1928, Coolidge delivered the opening speech at the Sixth Pan-American Conference in Havana. This was only the second time a President of the United States had ever set foot in a Latin-American country. It indicated a new concern for relations with Latin America.

Herbert Hoover was more concerned about Latin America than was Coolidge. Late in 1928, as President-elect, Hoover made a good-will tour of eleven nations in Central and South America. In several of his speeches he told the Latin Americans that he disapproved of intervention, and that he wanted the United States to be their good neighbor. Later, his administration issued a memorandum on the Monroe Doctrine that repudiated the Roosevelt Corollary to the Monroe Doctrine.

Unlike his predecessors, Hoover did not start new interventions in Latin America. He denounced dollar diplomacy, and began to end existing interventions. He removed marines from Nicaragua, and began the evacuation of troops from Haiti. Although Latin Americans resented his signing of the Hawley-Smoot Tariff Act, which injured their trade, Hoover did improve relations with Latin America. His administration prepared the way for a stronger good neighbor policy.

United States economic policies alienated Europeans

Europeans were also upset by certain aspects of United States policy in the 1920's, particularly economic foreign policy. This economic policy was of tremendous importance to Europeans and others because the United States had emerged from World War I as the world's wealthiest power, greatest industrial nation, and most important market for raw materials and semifinished goods.

Between 1914 and 1919, the United States had also changed from a debtor to a creditor nation. European nations owed the United States some $10 billion for war debts.

Many European statesmen had thought the United States would consider the money it had loaned as part of its general contribution to the defeat of Germany and would cancel the debts. The American people and their representatives in Congress, on the other hand, expected full payment. They considered repayment a matter of national honor. In the 1920's, the United States government negotiated agreements with the debtor countries that called for repayment over a period of years. These agreements usually cut the interest rate, and hence reduced the debts.

The European debtors then began paying their American debts from reparations received from Germany. This system worked for a while because private American investors loaned money to German industries, and the Germans used most of this money to pay reparations. When the Great Depression struck, Americans stopped investing abroad, Germany halted her reparations payments, and the former Allies defaulted on their American debts.

These defaults caused anger in the United States. Europeans, on the other hand, were angered by the American insistence on payment. The Europeans felt that they had contributed far more blood on the battlefields of the war than the United States and that the United States, therefore, should be glad to contribute dollars. The Europeans also resented America's high tariff policy which they said prevented them from selling goods in the United States to earn dollars to pay the debts.

President Hoover tried to ease the debt crisis brought on by the depression. In June 1931, he announced that the United States would not demand payments on debts for one year if other nations would temporarily excuse German reparations and other debts owed them. The Hoover moratorium brought relief, but did not solve the debt crisis.

Early in 1933, Hoover wanted to renegotiate the debt agreements, but his successor would not bind himself to such a policy as Hoover desired, before taking office. So Hoover left the White House with the whole debt structure crumbling about him. Some nations made token payments, then even those were stopped. Only Finland, with a small postwar loan, continued to meet her payments. The United States has not forgiven these debts, and the European nations never have paid them.

REVIEWING THE SECTION

1. What efforts did the United States make between 1922 and 1930 to insure peace?

2. Why did relations with Japan deteriorate during the Coolidge and Hoover administrations?

3. What did Coolidge and Hoover do to improve Latin-American relations?

CHAPTER **22** CONCLUSION

When the Republicans returned to power, they faced a number of difficult problems. They faced social problems; the war had bred intolerance, and the Red Scare of 1919-1920 was one result of that

intolerance. The Negro, too, faced intolerance and not until race riots broke out did Americans stop to consider the problems of the Negro. Republicans also faced economic problems as a result of demobilization and labor troubles. Although they did manage to solve some of the problems, Warren G. Harding's administration became known for its corruption.

In spite of the scandals, business was satisfied with Republican rule. Other groups, the farmers in particular, were not. They did not feel that they were sharing in the prosperity of the times. Many Americans were convinced that the influx of immigrants was causing economic and social problems in the United States. They agitated until Congress passed a law restricting immigration. Intolerance continued to spread; it even marred the election of 1928.

Although Americans tried to avoid world leadership, the nation was actively involved in foreign affairs. In order to preserve peace, the nation took part in disarmament conferences, signed a treaty to outlaw war, and coöperated in some ways with the League of Nations. War did come, however; in 1929, the Chinese and the Soviets clashed, and in 1931, the Japanese invaded southern Manchuria.

At the beginning of the era of conservatism, Americans had sought normalcy. Now, at the end, which came with a crash, many sought change. They wanted social and economic reforms that would lead them out of the nightmare of depression. Since all of the old ideas had been tried and had failed, people seemed to be willing now, as they had not been in 1920, to experiment with new ideas. Herbert Hoover's failing lay in his rigidity, in his unwillingness to admit that the old way of doing things had failed, and that the leader of the nation must chart a new course.

Americans were not, however, seeking to change the nation's foreign policy. In spite of the failure to prevent war in the Far East, the nation continued its policy of isolation. Not until a second world war had broken out and the United States had been attacked, would Americans abandon that policy.

FOCUSING ON SPECIFICS

1. How did the Water Power Act continue the progressive tradition? the Esch-Cummins Transportation Act?

2. In what way was the Harding administration involved in the Teapot Dome scandal?

3. How was the McNary-Haugen plan intended to aid farmers?

4. Against which groups did the quota system of immigration discriminate?

5. Why did many people consider the Sacco-Vanzetti trial a miscarriage of justice?

6. Against which groups were the actions of the Ku Klux Klan directed in the 1920's?

7. What factors prevented the federal, state, and local governments from enforcing prohibition?

8. Why did Hoover oppose using federal money for the relief of the unemployed?

9. How did Hoover reinterpret the meaning of the Monroe Doctrine?

10. Why did Americans demand full payment of European war debts? Why did Europeans resent those demands?

11. How did Secretary of State Stimson react to the invasion of Manchuria by the Japanese?

REVIEWING MAIN THEMES

1. In the years following World War I, how did workers and farmers attempt to improve their economic position?

2. What events and issues indicate a conflict between urban and rural Americans in the 1920's? How did ethnic divisions in American society aggravate this conflict?

3. What conditions led to the stock market crash in 1929? How did Hoover deal with the problems of the Great Depression?

4. In what ways did the United States participate in world affairs during the 1920's?

EVALUATING THE ISSUES

1. In what ways did Hoover depart from tradition in his effort to deal with the depression? Yet, how did his commitment to traditional practices make it difficult for him to cope with the depression?

2. The Kellogg-Briand Pact, according to journalist Frank Simonds, was "the high water mark of American endeavors for world peace which consisted in undertaking to combine the idea of political and military isolation with that of moral and material involvement." What events and issues would support this statement?

The Depression and the New Deal

The actions taken by President Hoover to combat the depression were inadequate, and by election time, the Democrats felt certain of victory. The Democratic nominee for Vice President, John Nance Garner, told Franklin Delano Roosevelt that to win "all you have to do is to stay alive until election day." Roosevelt won the election of 1932 easily and the Democrats gained control of both houses of Congress.

During the interim between Roosevelt's election (November 8, 1932) and his inauguration (March 4, 1933), the "lame duck" period, economic conditions grew worse. By the time Hoover was ready to leave the White House, the economy appeared to be grinding to a halt. It was difficult to foresee how Roosevelt and his promised New Deal would meet the crisis.

The initial phase of the first New Deal (1933-1934) began with emergency acts passed by a special session of Congress to deal with the banking crisis, unemployment, and farm relief. This session (March 9-June 16, 1933) became known as the hundred days. The Emergency Banking Relief Act, the Federal Emergency Relief Act, the Agricultural Adjustment Act, the National Industrial Recovery Act, the Civilian Conservation Corps Reforestation Relief Act, and the Home Owners' Refinancing Act were passed during this period. These measures were aimed primarily at relief and recovery.

Some long-range reform legislation was also passed during the first New Deal. The Tennessee Valley Authority was established to develop the economic resources of the area; the Federal Securities Act was passed to protect investors against fraudulent practices; and the Glass-Steagall Act gave the federal government greater control of banking operations.

The second New Deal (1935-1939) consisted of measures designed to help the underprivileged of the nation. The Social Security Act and the Fair Labor Standards Act were passed during this phase. Since unemployment persisted, the Emergency Relief Appropriations Act of 1935 was passed. Under the powers granted by this act, the President established the Works Progress Administration, the Resettlement Administration, the Rural Electrification Administration, and the National Youth Administration.

Although the executive and legislative branches of the government seemed in agreement concerning the laws needed for recovery and reform, the Supreme Court was not. The Court declared several New Deal laws unconstitutional. Two of the best known were the Agricultural Adjustment Act and the National Industrial Recovery Act. The President was furious and proposed a plan to appoint additional justices to the Supreme Court who were friendly to the New Deal. The storm aroused over this "court-packing" plan caused him to abandon the idea. The Court, however, seemed to change its mind and, in 1937, upheld the constitutionality of some New Deal legislation. After 1937, resignations and death changed the membership of the Court; the new justices were favorable to the New Deal program. By 1941, Roosevelt had appointed seven of the nine justices.

There was a great deal of opposition to Roosevelt's policies outside the Court. Many people objected to allegedly "radical" New Deal laws. Yet in many ways Roosevelt's program was a continuation of the reform programs of the Populists and the Progressives. But Roosevelt's critics were at least partially correct. The New Deal represented a departure from the past; it gave the federal government a new, more direct role in the economy of the nation and in the lives of its citizens than it had played at any time in the past.

THE DEMOCRATS REGAINED CONTROL OF GOVERNMENT

The Democratic nominee for the presidency in 1932, Franklin Delano Roosevelt, was born on an estate on the Hudson River, near Hyde Park, New York. He received his basic education at a private boys' school, Groton in Massachusetts; was graduated from Harvard University in 1904; and then entered Columbia University Law School.

After graduation from Harvard, Franklin married a distant cousin, Anna Eleanor Roosevelt. The President of the United States, Theodore Roosevelt, who was the uncle of Eleanor and the fifth cousin of Franklin, gave the bride away.

Like his "Uncle Ted," Franklin had traveled abroad frequently. In 1910, after practicing law in New York City for about three years, Franklin accepted the Democratic nomination for a seat in the state senate. Although his district was solidly Republican, he won the election. Three years later President Wilson appointed him assistant secretary of the navy, a post held previously by his illustrious cousin. In this position, Roosevelt proved to be a capable administrator and a popular young Democrat in Washington, D.C.

This popularity, as well as support from important New York Democrats such as Alfred E. Smith, brought Franklin D. Roosevelt his party's nomination for the vice presidency in 1920. Although defeated, Roosevelt gained numerous new friends, absorbed invaluable political experience, and achieved national prominence.

In August of the following year, tragedy struck. He contracted infantile paralysis. For a while it seemed as if the disease had paralyzed his promising political career as well as his body. After several years spent in fighting the disease, Roosevelt taught himself to move about with the aid of crutches or the heavy steel braces which he had to wear for the rest of his life.

Roosevelt reëntered politics in 1924 when he nominated Alfred E. Smith for the presidency at the Democratic National Convention. Four years later, at Smith's insistence, Roosevelt ran for governor of New York and won. In 1930, he was easily reëlected. Two years later he was ready to run for the presidency.

Friends and critics alike agreed that Roosevelt —a man of wit, optimism, polished manners, and a smiling personality—had a magnetism that few could resist. Although not a man of high intellectual attainment, he had a warmth of personality that projected itself in political appeal, an appeal that became legendary even in his lifetime.

Franklin D. Roosevelt was elected President

Evidence everywhere indicated that the people of the United States were unhappy with President Hoover's policies. Yet the Republican party could not discard him. He represented the best of the kind of conservative business leadership that had been widely admired in the 1920's. He had, moreover, within the limits of his own political philosophy, fought a good fight against the Great Depression and the other problems of government. So in Chicago, early in June 1932, the Republicans renominated Hoover on the first ballot. They adopted a platform that praised him and his efforts to fight the depression.

The mood of the Democrats, who also met in Chicago, later in June, was different. They were excited and impatient, eager to grasp the victory they expected would be theirs. Franklin D. Roosevelt had emerged as the leading contender in 1930, when he won reëlection as governor of New York by a landslide. Al Smith and John Nance Garner, a Texan who was speaker of the House, were also contenders, but Roosevelt won the nomination on the fourth ballot.

Roosevelt immediately demonstrated that he would not let tradition bind him. He did not wait to be formally notified of his nomination. Instead, he quickly flew to Chicago and delivered his acceptance speech to the convention. "I pledge you, I pledge myself, to a new deal for the American people," he said. "This is more than a political campaign," he added, "it is a call to arms." So Roosevelt's program, which he had not yet constructed, got a name—the "New Deal."

Since the Democratic platform did not offer much that differed from the Republican platform, the major issue in the campaign was the depression and its causes. The Democrats blamed the Republicans for the depression, and the Republicans denied responsibility.

When the people went to the polls in November they turned overwhelmingly to Roosevelt and the Democrats. The people were tired of waiting for a prosperity that was "just around the corner." They were disillusioned with business leadership. Many just voted against the conservatism of the past and turned to the New Deal, no matter how vague, because they found little else to turn to.

Chaos threatened the nation

While the people waited for Roosevelt and the New Dealers to assume the leadership of the government, the country seemed to be drifting into chaos. Every day more men became unemployed, prices dropped, and business activity decreased. Everywhere banks were failing, while others were on the brink of failure. Frightened depositors even were withdrawing their funds from sound banks. To halt the stream of withdrawals and to prevent damage to the whole banking system, authorities in state after state closed banks for short "bank holidays."

In this crisis, President Hoover and the lame-duck Congress seemed paralyzed. An outgoing President usually hesitated to act because he had little time to carry out new policies, and he usually did not wish to tie the hands of the new President with old policies. In the past, such inaction in the lame-duck period had not done much harm. But with the nation in a severe depression, inaction might have been disastrous.

The Twentieth Amendment, which was to shorten the period of waiting for a new administration to take office, and thereby eliminate the lame-duck period, was not ratified until February 1933 and would not take effect until the following October.

Hoover believed he could not do anything effective to combat the deepening crisis without the coöperation of the President-elect. He appealed to Roosevelt to join him in an effort to restore public confidence. The action which Hoover suggested was to be based on his, not Roosevelt's ideas.

Hoover wanted the President-elect to accept his views on the depression, the bank panic, and a balanced budget.

On these issues Roosevelt had views of his own that he did not intend to abandon. Unlike Hoover, Roosevelt believed the depression grew out of domestic rather than international causes. He believed that the people had repudiated Hoover and his policies and that they demanded new policies, not a continuation of the old ones. Moreover, Roosevelt was unwilling to commit himself to policies before he had authority to carry them out himself. So Roosevelt refused to coöperate on President Hoover's terms.

Hoover admitted that if Roosevelt had accepted his proposals, it would have meant acceptance of the Republican program and "the abandonment of ninety per cent of the so-called 'new deal.'"

As the worried and exhausted Hoover made preparations to leave the White House, the nation's economy seemed about to collapse. Thirty-eight states had closed their banks; in the rest of the states, the banks were being operated on a restricted basis. Elsewhere, in stock exchanges and commodity exchanges, financial activity was badly crippled. Many Americans believed that something had to be done quickly to restore the morale of the people.

The New Deal took over

During this period of drift Roosevelt smiled, joked, and waved his cigarette holder—a gesture with which he became identified. He busied himself recruiting his cabinet. For secretary of state he chose Cordell Hull of Tennessee, a professional politician who was considered to be the most influential man in the Senate. The secretaries of agriculture and the interior came from the ranks of Progressive Republicans from the Midwest. They were Henry A. Wallace of Iowa, publisher of a farm newspaper, and Harold L. Ickes of Chicago, former supporter of Theodore Roosevelt. The new secretary of labor, Frances Perkins, a social worker

from New York, was the first woman to be given a cabinet post. The rest of the cabinet was composed of capable though not particularly well-known politicians.

Roosevelt also gave positions in government agencies and on the White House staff to a group of men who became his unofficial advisers. A number of these advisers were professors, most of them from Columbia University; hence, they came to be known as the "brain trust." The leader of the group was Raymond Moley, a shrewd and affable political scientist. Members of the brain trust were to have a hand in drafting the important New Deal measures that eventually would become federal laws.

The nation's economy was almost at a standstill when Roosevelt drove to the White House to pick up Hoover for the inauguration ceremonies. The day, March 4, 1933, was dark, chilly, and misty, but Roosevelt was far from despondent. He took his oath of office, and then he faced the crowds of people and the radio microphones to deliver his inaugural address.

Defying the gloomy weather and widespread despair the new President, his voice clear and ringing, announced that "This great Nation will endure as it has endured, will revive and will prosper . . . the only thing we have to fear is fear itself." Much needed to be done, he said, so that people could return to work, banks could reopen, and money could circulate. If Congress failed to provide means for meeting the crisis, he warned, he would seek "broad Executive power to wage a war against the emergency, as great as the power that would be given to me if we were in fact invaded by a foreign foe."

Although Roosevelt had offered no new way out of the crisis, his words, the very tone of his voice brought hope to millions of Americans listening around their radios. Within the next few days nearly a half million people sent laudatory letters to him. The people did not know what Roosevelt was going to do, but they sensed that he would take some positive action. This day would mark the beginning of a new era in the history of American life.

REVIEWING THE SECTION

1. Why did the Democrats win the election of 1932?

2. What conditions threatened the nation during the lame-duck period? Why did Roosevelt refuse to work with Hoover in combating the depression?

3. How did people react to Roosevelt's inaugural address?

ROOSEVELT'S PROGRAM UNFOLDED

There was no need for Roosevelt to demand emergency powers. The men who made up the Congress were so concerned about the economic crisis that they were willing to turn over to him power greater than any President ever had held in peacetime. Roosevelt was dedicated to the traditional American ideals. He believed in sound democratic government, in private ownership of property, and in the principles of the capitalistic system in general. But he did not believe that the federal government should remain aloof from the problems of the people if it could do something to help them. Unlike Hoover, Roosevelt believed that the federal government should take direct action to improve the day-to-day lives of Americans.

Roosevelt wasted no time. On the day he took office he issued orders to his advisers to act to avert a national economic collapse. On the following day he proclaimed a nation-wide bank holiday, closing all banks for four days, and a four-day embargo on the export of gold, silver, and currency. He called Congress into special session which convened on March 9, and it immediately began turning out laws to fight the depression. Congress remained at this task without letup until June 16, 1933. This period, one of great coöperation between the executive and legislative branches of the government, is known as the "hundred days."

During this period, Roosevelt and his advisers built the framework for the New Deal program. This was a time of limited experimentation with objectives that were to emerge with some clarity later. First of all, the New Dealers undertook to bring immediate relief to those who were in want. At the same time, wherever possible, they wanted to bring about economic recovery for farmers, manufacturers, and others by raising prices through cuts in production. At this point, the New Dealers believed in artificial, or planned, scarcity as a primary means of stimulating recovery. Over the long run, they wanted reforms that would provide safeguards against future depressions.

In its early stage the New Deal was relatively conservative and limited in the economic reforms it sought. Later, in response to popular demand, it embarked on a bold, far-reaching program of economic and social reform that transformed life in the United States. Most historians now believe that even the most far-reaching of these reforms were not so radical as they first seemed, or as the critics of the New Deal claimed.

New laws regulated banks and the stock market

As the New Deal program unfolded, it could be seen that, despite the haste and experimentation, the objectives of immediate relief, prompt recovery, and long-range reform were there. The very first measure of the hundred days was the Emergency Banking Relief Act of 1933. It was passed within four hours after Congress convened on March 9 and it brought prompt relief to the banking community. It gave the President broad, discriminatory power to regulate banks and the issuance of money and it provided means for the reopening of banks in sound condition. On the next day the President asked Congress for authority to cut government spending so that he could balance the budget. Within twenty-four hours Congress responded with the Economy Act.

On the night of Sunday, March 12, Roosevelt gave by nation-wide radio hookup the first of his reports to the people, the so-called fireside chats.

As an estimated sixty million Americans listened to their radios, he explained what his administration had done and assured the people that savings in the reorganized banks would be safe. On the following day, when banks began to reopen, people redeposited their money, and the banking crisis was brought under control.

In June, long-range reform was brought to the banking system with the Glass-Steagall Act, also known as the Banking Act of 1933. This law was designed to prevent bankers from speculating with depositors' money. To protect the depositor of small amounts of money, it created the Federal Deposit Insurance Corporation, which insured individual bank deposits up to $2,500. Later, accounts up to $15,000 were covered. With the passage of this act the man with limited funds was freed from the fear that a sudden bank failure could wipe out his savings. The government now guaranteed his savings. The Banking Act of 1935 completed Roosevelt's reform of banking and currency. It increased the federal government's control over the banking system, primarily through the Board of Governors of the Federal Reserve System, which could regulate interest rates on the money the reserve banks loaned to public banks.

Other laws brought stock market reforms to protect stock investors. The Federal Securities Act, or the "Truth-in-Securities Act," of 1933, was designed to eliminate fraud and deceit by requiring the sellers of new stocks to give the public information about them. In June 1934, the Securities Exchange Act brought federal regulation to the stock market through creation of the Securities and Exchange Commission.

These New Deal reforms stabilized banking and investing and helped the investor with limited funds. At the same time they angered businessmen who resented government controls.

Roosevelt experimented with the currency

Not all of Roosevelt's early reform measures were as successful as the banking laws. The Presi-

BUSINESS ACTIVITY 1920-1941

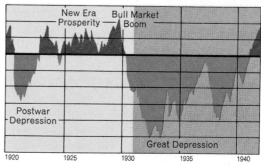

The prosperity of the twenties ended with the stock market crash of 1929. During the next decade, the United States suffered its most severe and prolonged economic crisis, which became known as the Great Depression. For the first time, the federal government sponsored extensive programs to help the economy recover from a serious depression. New Deal efforts to promote recovery from 1933 to 1936 were followed by limited business expansion, so economic activity increased unevenly. As gains were made, the government reduced its spending. So, from 1937 to 1938 a serious recession occurred. Then the government renewed its efforts to bolster the economy by resuming large-scale public works' programs, and other forms of spending. Nevertheless, the economy did not recover significantly until after the outbreak of the war in Europe in 1939, when economic activity again was generated. Full recovery did not come until the United States itself entered the war and mobilized its resources for the war effort.

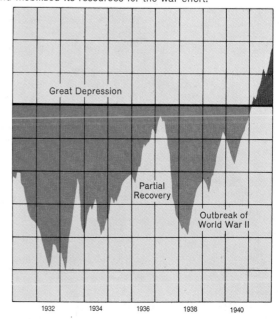

dent admitted that he expected some failures among his emergency measures. He told a radio audience: "I have no expectation of making a hit every time I come to bat." He made no hit when he experimented with the gold content of the dollar.

Many of the President's advisers believed that a program of deliberate, but controlled, inflation would stimulate recovery. And they believed that reducing the value of the dollar would lead to such inflation.

When Roosevelt became President, the nation was on the gold standard. This meant that the value of the dollar had a fixed relationship to gold and that anyone could exchange a paper dollar for that amount of gold. In April 1933, Roosevelt took the country off the gold standard. People could no longer convert their dollars into gold on demand. Soon, all debts that required payment in gold could be legally paid with paper money. When the country went off the gold standard, the value of the dollar dropped slightly.

Since the depression was world-wide and all major money systems had been affected by it, an international economic conference was called in London in June to try to bring some stability to money arrangements among countries. If an important nation such as the United States experimented independently with its money, it seemed obvious that the conference could accomplish little. The delegates wondered what Roosevelt would do. In a message to the conference early in July, he gave his view on monetary collaboration; the message "fell upon it like a bombshell." He said, in effect, that the United States would experiment with its money as it saw fit. As a result of Roosevelt's stand on the matter, the conference was a failure.

After the end of the conference, Roosevelt continued his policy of allowing the value of the dollar to go down in relation to gold and to other currencies. Since some of his advisers wanted more and faster inflation, after October he had the Treasury buy gold at increasingly higher prices. This had the effect of artificially lowering the value of the dollar. Then, in January 1934, after Congress had passed the Gold Reserve Act giving the President full control over devaluation of the dollar, Roosevelt set the price of gold in the United States at $35 an ounce; he set the gold content of the dollar at 59.06 per cent of its gold value before 1933.

Although prices rose slightly, Roosevelt's manipulation of the value of the dollar had little significant economic effect. But the devaluation alienated conservative Democrats and businessmen. Al Smith, for example, denounced the devalued currency as "baloney dollars."

The New Deal helped the unemployed

All this concern about inflation and the gold content of the dollar had little meaning for some fifteen million people who were unemployed in the spring of 1933. For many of them, the only thing with real meaning was immediate economic relief to keep them from hunger or starvation.

One of the New Deal's first and most popular relief measures tried to make use of human resources, particularly among the nation's unemployed youth, in the conservation of natural resources. Congress readily accepted this plan. Late in March it passed the Civilian Conservation Corps Reforestation Relief Act, which established the Civilian Conservation Corps. Congress appropriated $300 million for its use. Young men between the ages of eighteen and twenty-five who were unemployed could enroll in the Civilian Conservation Corps (CCC) and go to camps in mountains or forests where they would work on reforestation, road construction, flood control, and soil conservation projects. As compensation they received food, housing, and $30 a month, $25 of which had to be sent to their families. By 1941, when the program was ended, some 2.7 million young men had served in the corps, and they had completed more than half of all the forest replanting which had been done in the nation up to that time.

Even more pressing than the plight of unemployed young men were the needs of millions of other people who were on relief, receiving subsistence payments from local or state government agencies, but who faced hunger and a bitter winter because the resources of relief agencies were exhausted. In May, at the request of the President, Congress passed the Federal Emergency Relief Act with an appropriation of $500 million to be given to the states and towns for relief purposes. At the head of the Federal Emergency Relief Administration (FERA), the agency that distributed the money, Roosevelt placed Harry L. Hopkins, a zealous social worker from New York.

Roosevelt regarded the FERA as a temporary measure to give people some support until recovery came. Even for this purpose alone, Hopkins told the President, the program could not do enough, so in November, under powers authorized by the Federal Emergency Relief Act, Roosevelt authorized Hopkins to set up the Civil Works Administration (CWA). In this project the federal government did not work through the states. It provided relief directly to the people by giving them jobs at minimum wages. The federal government created jobs that would not compete with jobs already in existence. In all, the CWA project provided work for more than 4.2 million people who did everything from repairing county roads to teaching adult art classes.

The CWA was costly, and it fell under criticism from people who considered it wasteful and radical. As a result, the CWA was terminated in the spring of 1934. Once again, the main burden of relief fell on the FERA program.

Industry received help

While meeting some of the immediate needs of the unemployed, the New Deal also attempted to increase job opportunities and promote general recovery through its most dramatic and sweeping program for industry and labor, the National Industrial Recovery Act, (NIRA) of June 1933.

This law tried to help industry by ending unfair competition and by limiting the production of goods to amounts actually needed. The New Dealers believed that limited production would raise prices and bring an increase in profits. Labor would benefit because the work week would be reduced and wages would rise. At the same time, reduced hours would require more workers to achieve at least the same level of production, and unemployment would decline.

The government hoped to reach these goals through adoption of codes of "fair competition" by leaders in major industries. Since such agreements on prices and wages might violate the antitrust laws, the government suspended those laws. In section 7a of the NIRA, labor was given the specific right to organize and to bargain collectively with employers.

To carry out the National Industrial Recovery Act, Roosevelt established the National Recovery Administration (NRA). General Hugh Johnson, a gruff former cavalry officer with considerable administrative experience, was placed in charge. He was to supervise the drafting of the various codes and then the enforcement of them.

While the codes were being written, Johnson tried to drum up enthusiasm for the NRA. He sketched a blue eagle over the slogan "We Do Our Part," and this became the symbol of the NRA and the emblem for all who signed the fair competition codes. The blue eagle was displayed everywhere—on buttons, in factories, stores, elevators, books, and in NRA parades.

Johnson at first was successful; within a matter of months he was able to get from the representatives of approximately ninety-five per cent of the business interests of the country the adoption of satisfactory codes. The codes were then approved by the President and, to most Americans, seemed invested with the full force of law. These codes provided minimum wage scales and maximum hours of work and gave to each industry broad freedom to control production and prices.

Adherence to the codes was voluntary and many

men who had initially accepted them later chose not to follow them. Soon some businessmen complained that the codes had been written by the men of the giant corporations and that they offered few benefits to the small firms. Housewives moaned about higher prices, and labor felt dissatisfied with its position under the codes. When those businessmen who at first had supported the NRA also turned against it, failure seemed certain.

In May 1935, the Supreme Court declared the National Industrial Recovery Act unconstitutional. In *Schechter Poultry Corporation* v. *United States* (the "Sick Chicken" case) the Court ruled that Congress could not "delegate legislative powers" to the President. The Court ruled, moreover, that Congress' control over interstate commerce, as in the poultry code of the NRA, did not apply to a local poultry business, such as that of the Schechter brothers in Brooklyn, who brought the suit against the NIRA.

Until it was declared unconstitutional, the NIRA did provide jobs for about two million people. Some of the jobs came from one of the work programs, the Public Works Administration (PWA), established under the act. The PWA, with an appropriation of $3.3 billion, was headed by Secretary of the Interior Harold L. Ickes. He worked painstakingly and he searched through every proposal to make sure it would be useful. As a result, jobs were not created fast enough to have a solid impact on the economy.

Ultimately, Ickes spent more than $4 billion on some 34,000 government-sponsored projects. Many of these projects, such as schools, dams, and highways, were of lasting benefit to the nation. But the PWA failed to provide the prompt business recovery and unemployment relief needed at the time.

Farmers obtained help

To meet the problems of huge surpluses and low prices for farm products, the New Deal used the principle of limiting production, as it had in the NRA. This principle was embodied in the Agricultural Adjustment Act of May 1933, which established the Agricultural Adjustment Administration (AAA), under Secretary of Agriculture Henry A. Wallace.

Although the mechanics of the law were complicated, its purpose was not. It sought to bring about a balance between what farmers grew and what the people consumed so that the true income of farmers would rise to a level equal to that between 1909 and 1914—a favorable period for agriculture. The AAA tried to reach this goal by persuading farmers to cut their production of such staple crops as corn and cotton. In return, the government would give them cash as a subsidy for their crops. In this way surpluses would be reduced and the farmers would receive higher prices for their products; in addition, they would get cash from the government.

Money for the subsidies would come from taxes on processors, such as millers and operators of cotton gins. Since these processors would pass the increased cost on to the consumer, society would, in effect, be subsidizing farm income.

Before the AAA could swing into action, the nation's farms had bumper crops of most staples growing in the fields, ready for harvest. The government sent agents into the South and Southeast to urge farmers to uproot their cotton in return for benefit payments. To forestall a glut of pork in the nation's butcher shops, farm leaders convinced Wallace that it was necessary to order the slaughtering of more than six million pigs. This deliberate destruction of food when people were hungry aroused bitter comment, particularly from critics of the New Deal.

Despite the defects of the farm plan, it brought about some reduction in surpluses and a rise in farm prices. Then, in January 1936, when farm incomes were showing improvement, the Supreme Court declared unconstitutional the taxing and regulatory provisions of the Agricultural Adjustment Act. This decision terminated the first AAA.

A severe drought, which began in 1932 and

continued to 1936, increased the farmers' difficulties. In a vast area from the Texas Panhandle northward across the Great Plains to the Dakotas, farmers and sharecroppers were driven from their land by wind storms that blew away unanchored topsoil and left the land unfit for farming. These people, too, needed government help.

TVA transformed a region

Another region that suffered from nature's destructive forces was the Tennessee Valley. The area was made up of about forty thousand square miles in seven states and contained some 2.5 million people, many of them impoverished. For years, Progressives led by Senator George W. Norris of Nebraska had tried to obtain government operation of the Wilson Dam and power plant at Muscle Shoals, Alabama. Roosevelt not only went along with Norris' idea for government operation of the dam at Muscle Shoals, but he also had an even bigger plan. The President wanted to launch a huge regional experiment in social planning. He wanted to transform the valley's eroded and wasted land into rich farms and change the lives of the people there from the grinding monotony and hardship of poverty to the security of abundance.

In April 1933, Roosevelt asked Congress to create the Tennessee Valley Authority (TVA), an independent public corporation, to plan for the balanced development of the valley's resources. Congress quickly responded and provided liberal appropriations for the task.

The TVA built dams to control floods and to generate cheap, plentiful hydroelectric power. The charges which it made for the electricity would be used as a "yardstick" for measuring the reasonableness of rates charged by private power companies. TVA also produced phosphatic fertilizers which were then distributed to the farmers of the region.

Within a few years, the TVA became one of the most noted and most successful of the New Deal agencies. Its dams stopped floods in the Tennessee Valley, an area with one of the heaviest average annual rainfalls in the nation, and its conservation program ended soil erosion, reforested great sections, created clear, fresh lakes, and controlled malaria. TVA also attracted industry to the region, and brought the people social and cultural advantages, including improved recreational and educational facilities.

Despite these accomplishments, the TVA had many critics. Private power companies resented the yardstick method of determining fair rates; they claimed that TVA could offer low rates primarily because it paid no taxes and argued that it was illegal for the government to go into the business of selling electricity in competition with private companies.

Through a series of law suits, the power companies tried to block the sale of TVA electric power. Finally, in 1936, the Supreme Court ruled that all of TVA's activities were legal. In time, TVA became one of the nation's major producers of electric power. No other New Deal agency did so much to transform the economy, the lives, and the customs of an entire region.

REVIEWING THE SECTION

1. How did the Glass-Steagall Act regulate banks? How did the Federal Securities Act and the Securities Exchange Act regulate the stock market?

2. Why did Roosevelt lower the value of the dollar? Why did he refuse to collaborate with other nations at the London conference? What effects did his experimentation with the currency have on the economy?

3. How did the Civilian Conservation Corps, the Federal Emergency Relief Administration, and the Civil Works Administration aid the unemployed?

4. How was the National Recovery Administration intended to promote industrial recovery? Why was the National Industrial Recovery Act declared unconstitutional? What did the Public Works Administration accomplish?

Food for the hungry, Broadway, New York City, 1932

A destitute family, Tracy, California, c. 1933

5. How was the Agricultural Adjustment Administration intended to aid agriculture?

6. What did the Tennessee Valley Authority accomplish? Why was it criticized?

THE SECOND NEW DEAL LAUNCHED REFORMS

Historians usually divide the New Deal into two phases. They talk about a first and a second New Deal, though they do not agree on the precise nature of the differences between the two. In any case the first New Deal included the laws of 1933 and 1934 and it had the support of a loose alliance of businessmen, workers, and farmers. The second New Deal began in 1935, after this alliance fell apart.

In the 1934 congressional elections, the people of the United States gave Roosevelt and the Democratic party overwhelming support, even greater than they had given two years earlier. The voters, especially the poor and discontented among them,

wanted more social and economic reforms which would make jobs available and thereby improve their lot. However, business and industrial leaders turned more and more against the New Deal.

Roosevelt was disappointed because businessmen appeared to be abandoning his recovery program. In addition, he was alarmed by the appearance of demagogues who might mislead the people by urging them to demand more than the government possibly could provide. Hence he accepted leadership of a new political coalition. He gradually rid himself of his more conservative advisers and then launched a sweeping program of reform intended to help the underprivileged. This program and this new political alignment in 1935 are usually considered the substance of the second New Deal.

Organized opposition emerged

Organized opposition to the New Deal began to emerge in the summer of 1934, after the worst

The Great Depression. During the election campaigns of 1928, Americans were satisfied with Republican prosperity. Yet in less than a year, the longest and deepest depression in United States history had begun. By the end of 1932, 25 per cent of the nation's labor force was unemployed. In New York City, hundreds of hungry men lined up nightly to await their turn for a free sandwich and a cup of coffee. Such relief was insufficient for families with no source of income. Some lived in utter poverty, without hope for the future. Others sought better conditions in distant sections of the country. California was a common choice, but families often endured the hardships of travel in vain; California was also hard hit by the depression.

U.S. highway 99, "broke—baby sick—car trouble," 1937

phase of the depression had passed. Businessmen believed that the New Deal had become too radical and that it was a threat to personal liberty. So in August a group of them, led by executives of the Du Pont and General Motors corporations, worked with conservative Democratic and Republican politicians to form the American Liberty League. This organization campaigned against New Deal bureaucracy and reforms while emphasizing the need to preserve state rights.

The conservative revolt, though loud, did not have a large following. Roosevelt was more concerned about the rumblings from the disgruntled radical opposition on the left, which he considered more dangerous to his program. This opposition grew out of the discontent of sharecroppers, the unemployed, destitute old people, and others who felt the New Deal was not doing enough to help them. These people appeared willing to follow agitators who promised improvement through drastic social change.

One of these agitators, Dr. Francis E. Townsend, a country physician, made his home in Long Beach, California, where thousands of the elderly lived in impoverished retirement. He devised a scheme designed to lift these people out of poverty and the nation out of the depression. Under his plan the federal government would pay every nonworking citizen over sixty years of age a monthly pension of $200. One of the stipulations was that the $200 had to be spent each month, thereby stimulating the economy. Thousands of Townsend Clubs were organized across the nation. By 1935, these clubs claimed about five million members, a potent bloc of voters.

Charles E. Coughlin, a Roman Catholic priest from a parish in Royal Oak, Michigan, a suburb of Detroit, was a pied piper who had a larger following than Townsend. Father Coughlin gained his following by lacing his persuasive sermons, delivered over a nation-wide radio network, with comments on social and economic issues. At first, he had favored the New Deal but, by early 1935, he had become one of its harshest critics and an advocate of a vague program of "social justice." In 1934, he was reputed to be receiving more mail than anyone in the country, more even than the President. He was later silenced by his church superiors.

An anti-New Deal demagogue who seemed to pose the greatest threat to democratic government was a loud, flamboyant, but shrewd politician from Louisiana, Huey P. Long. People called him "King-fish," a name taken from one of the characters in a famous radio program of the time, "Amos 'n' Andy." First as governor and then as senator he set up a virtual dictatorship in Louisiana. When he said, "I am the law," nobody questioned him. Long gained a national following with his "Share-Our-Wealth" plan. He promised to make every man a king by confiscating large fortunes and by giving every family a home, a car, a radio, and a stable income. His organization, it was said, had a mailing list of 7.5 million people. In September 1935, when Long was at the height of his popularity, he was assassinated.

The reformers took over

Roosevelt feared that the campaigns of the demagogues might lure away his own following among the people. He also recognized that the New Deal had not yet grappled with some basic popular grievances. In his annual message to Congress in January 1935, he announced plans for a second New Deal. He proposed a huge program of emergency employment on public projects. Congress, also frightened by the left-wing rumblings, went along with the President. In April it voted for the Works Progress Administration (WPA) and other agencies, in order to give jobs instead of relief payments to men who were able to work but who were unemployed.

Harry Hopkins, former head of the FERA, was placed in charge of WPA. None of the jobs provided by WPA were to compete with regular jobs provided by government or by private industry. As a result, many of the agency's projects were in the nature of busy work that produced nothing of value. Critics, therefore, easily found fault with the wastefulness of the program.

Nonetheless, from 1935 until 1943, when it was brought to an end, the WPA employed more than 8.5 million people on 1.4 million projects, from airport repairs to puppet shows. During that time it spent about $11 billion. Since many people of talent and education were unemployed, Hopkins took the view that they should be given a chance to use their skills. The WPA created jobs and paid the wages of musicians, artists, actors, writers, circus performers, and even dance instructors. About seventy-eight per cent of the agency's money, however, went into the construction of hospitals, schools, and roads.

The New Dealers also experimented with social reforms intended to root out rural poverty. In April 1935, Roosevelt created the Resettlement Administration and placed Rexford Guy Tugwell, an agrarian reformer, in charge. Tugwell tried to move poor farmers and their families from submarginal land (land too poor to yield an adequate income) to better farms and provide them with adequate equipment and proper guidance. Congress opposed this program, so it never got beyond the stage of experimentation. Congress did support another reform agency, the Rural Electrification Administration (REA), established by executive order in May 1935. The REA was to provide electricity for rural areas not served by private power companies. In 1935, nine out of ten farms in the United States had no electric power; in 1941, partly as a result of the REA efforts, four out of ten farms were electrified; and by 1950, nine out of ten were so equipped.

The new works programs also provided something to help young people. Roosevelt doubled funds for the Civilian Conservation Corps and, in June 1935, created the National Youth Administration (NYA). In seven years the NYA gave jobs of various kinds to more than 600,000 college students, 1.5 million high school youths, and 2.6 million young people not in school.

Although the billions poured into WPA and allied agencies did not lead to the lasting reforms desired by some New Dealers, the works program overcame the despair of millions who had been on relief. They at least had some kind of job. They felt that the Roosevelt administration cared about them, and they were grateful.

Lasting reform on a nation-wide scale came with the Social Security Act of August 1935, a law that Roosevelt considered the New Deal's "supreme achievement." This law set up a system of old-age pensions; insurance for the unemployed; and government benefits for dependent mothers, children, and the crippled and the blind. Money for the program would come from a payroll tax levied on both the worker and his employer. With this measure most Americans accepted the principle that the government, as well as the individual, has an obligation to assist in matters concerning the welfare of the people.

Labor became a giant

While social security was under consideration, Congress passed and the President approved the National Labor Relations Act of July 1935, often called the Wagner Act because Senator Robert F. Wagner of New York had prepared it. This law reaffirmed the principle of section 7a of the National Industrial Recovery Act, which had been declared unconstitutional, and went further. The Wagner Act said that employers must allow workers to join unions of their own choosing and must bargain collectively with union members who legally represented the workers. The powerful, nonpartisan National Labor Relations Board (NLRB) of three men was given the authority to enforce the law. The Wagner Act, in effect, threw the weight of the federal government behind organized labor. It became the cornerstone of a revived strong labor movement.

Within the American Federation of Labor, a small group of men led by John L. Lewis of the United Mine Workers and Sidney Hillman of the Amalgamated Clothing Workers sparked the labor revival with demands for new efforts to gain union recognition from the mass-production industries, such as steel. These aggressive leaders wanted the A. F. of L. to charter industrial unions for the task. Most A. F. of L. leaders, however, still preferred to rely on unions organized along craft lines. Hence, in November 1935, Lewis and other rebel leaders formed, within the A. F. of L., the Committee for Industrial Organization. Three years later the C.I.O. broke away from the A. F. of L. to form a new organization which became known as the Congress of Industrial Organizations.

During this period of bickering within organized labor, the C.I.O. attempted to organize the steel workers and gain union recognition from the steel industry. The first objective in 1936 was the United States Steel Corporation, which Lewis called "the crouching lion in the pathway of labor." To everyone's surprise, the corporation refused to endure a costly strike. In March 1937, it recognized the steel workers' union. The C.I.O. had won a great victory; "Big Steel" was at last organized.

The C.I.O. organizers expected the other steel companies, known collectively as "Little Steel," to follow suit, but they were mistaken. Three of these companies fought back violently. Police killed ten strikers at the South Chicago plant of Republic Steel, in a skirmish known as the Memorial Day massacre of 1937. Finally, in 1941, after the National Labor Relations Board had compelled the companies to bargain collectively, "Little Steel" admitted defeat and the entire steel industry became unionized.

In December 1936, shortly after the drive against steel began, another C.I.O. union called a strike against plants of the General Motors Corporation in Flint, Michigan. The workers sat down by their machines and refused either to work or to leave. This was a technique known as the sit-down strike, which made it difficult to replace strikers with other workers. In February 1937,

General Motors recognized the United Automobile Workers and met most of the union's demands. Later that same year, other automobile companies, including Chrysler, also recognized the C.I.O. union as the representative of their workers, though Ford resisted until 1940.

By 1941, the workers, skilled and unskilled, in most of the large industries in the United States had unions representing them. With the help of the New Deal, organized labor had become a giant.

REVIEWING THE SECTION

1. Why did many businessmen turn against the New Deal? Why did Dr. Townsend, Father Coughlin, and Huey Long gain large followings?

2. What were the purposes of the Works Progress, the Resettlement, the Rural Electrification, the National Youth, and the Social Security administrations?

3. How did the Wagner Act help organized labor unions? What methods did the Congress of Industrial Organizations use to organize the steel and automobile industries?

THE NEW DEAL GRADUALLY FADED

As the 1936 elections approached, it was obvious that the New Deal reforms were immensely popular, except with businessmen and conservatives. Although slow, economic recovery was on the way; farm prices were up, employment had increased, and even the jobless were eating. No Republican seemed capable of shaking Roosevelt's hold on the people. Jubilant Democrats renominated him by acclamation and endorsed everything he had done.

The Republicans denounced the New Deal and nominated Alfred M. Landon, the governor of Kansas. Landon was no match for F.D.R. Even though more than two thirds of the nation's city newspapers supported Landon, he carried only two states, Maine and Vermont. With 27.8 million popular votes and 523 electoral votes to 16.7 million popular votes and 8 electoral votes for Landon, Roosevelt won a lopsided victory. The Democrats gained control of about two thirds of the seats in Congress.

This election saw two significant new developments. First, organized labor gave its support to one candidate, Roosevelt; second, a Democrat gained a majority of the Negro vote. Workers, white and Negro, obviously liked the New Deal and wanted it to continue. Roosevelt himself was prepared to fight for additional reforms.

Roosevelt attacked the Supreme Court

In his second inaugural address—delivered on January 20, 1937, instead of the traditional March 4 because the Twentieth (lame duck) Amendment had gone into effect—Roosevelt promised more reform. He wanted to help the "one-third of a nation" that was "ill-housed, ill-clad, ill-nourished." In his judgment the Supreme Court stood in the way of giving the help that was needed. In split decisions, the Supreme Court had wiped out a number of important New Deal laws. Five of the judges had shown themselves to be consistently hostile to New Deal reform measures.

Two weeks after his inauguration, therefore, Roosevelt asked Congress for a law that would allow him to reorganize the Supreme Court. His plan would have permitted him to appoint a new justice for each one who failed to retire within six months after reaching his seventieth birthday. The total number of justices, however, could not exceed fifteen. Six of the nine justices were at least seventy years old in 1937.

The President said he wanted to enlarge the Court because it was slow, inefficient, and behind in its work. He said that it needed new blood to catch up. Critics said that what Roosevelt really wanted was a change in the Court so that it would look favorably upon his reform program.

Although Roosevelt had expected opposition, he was stunned by the depth of feeling he had aroused. Critics violently denounced his "court-

THE NEW DEAL: THREE VIEWS

ALFRED E. SMITH

Governor of New York, 1919-1920, 1923-1928
Democratic candidate for President, 1928

[The first danger from the New Deal to fundamental principles upon which this government was organized] is the arraignment of class against class.... The next ... is the vast building up of new bureaus of government, draining the resources of our people, to pool and redistribute them, not by any process of law but by the whim of the bureaucratic autocracy....

Just get the platform of the Democratic party and ... the Socialist party and then study the record of the present administration ... and you will have your hand on the Socialist platform .... [You] can't mix socialism or communism with ... [a representative democracy]....

... Congress has overstepped its power, it has gone beyond ... constitutional limitation, and it has enacted laws that not only violate that, but violate ... the State's rights principle....

I would suggest that ... [the present administration] stop attacking all the forms ... of our government without recourse to the people themselves, as provided in their own Constitution which really belongs to the people. *(1936)*

NORMAN M. THOMAS

Six times Socialist candidate
for President

The reforms of the New Deal, while by no means negligible, were largely superficial. Perhaps the greatest contribution it made toward what we call recovery was that it suggested hope, confidence, action....

... Impressive as the list of its efforts ... may sound, there is nothing in it to warrant the argument that we have here a serious and successful attack upon the problem of poverty, insecurity, war, and the exploitation of workers. We have not had a reorganization of production and a redistribution of income to end near starvation in the midst of potential plenty. If we do not have such obvious "breadlines knee deep in wheat," as under the Hoover Administration, it is because we have done more to reduce the wheat ... than to end hunger....

N.R.A. and A.A.A. were far removed from the old laissez-faire individualistic capitalism, but assuredly they were not socialism. The President ... might talk much about the more abundant life, but they incarnated the inescapable capitalist doctrine that profit depends upon relative scarcity! *(1936)*

FRANCES PERKINS

Secretary of Labor,
1933-1945

[The] New Deal was not a plan, not even an agreement, and it was certainly not a plot .... Most of the programs ... arose out of the emergency which Roosevelt faced when he took office at the low point of the depression....

The NRA was a new, vigorous, and imaginative approach to the problem of reviving industry and overcoming unemployment....

Those who ... say that not enough consideration was given to these measures can hardly remember how gray and bleak and desperate were the people of this country .... It was a period of social danger ....

[Roosevelt] did not think we had discovered any panaceas.... [These] were temporary emergency measures. He once said ... about further expenditure for public works or WPA, "We have to do it. .... We haven't any more time."

... The speedy enactment of the program ... revived the faith of the people. It put us back on the upgrade. It gave us knowledge of industrial processes and complications which had never been in the possession of the government before. *(1946)*

packing" bill. They accused him of attempting to destroy the Constitution and trying to make himself a dictator. Roosevelt reluctantly abandoned the plan. Very shortly thereafter there was a change in the attitude of the Court. One of the conservative justices, Owen J. Roberts, switched sides. In a series of 5 to 4 decisions he voted with the more liberal judges to uphold a number of reform laws. In April 1937, for example, the Court found the Wagner Act constitutional, and in May it upheld the Social Security Act.

In June, one of the most conservative justices retired, and Roosevelt replaced him with a liberal. Two months later Congress passed a court-reform law that carried no provision for enlarging the Supreme Court. Thus, not long after his greatest victory at the polls, Roosevelt lost his first battle with Congress.

Later, other justices either died or retired, and Roosevelt appointed liberals in their places. In decision after decision, the Supreme Court then upheld reform laws and, with a broad interpretation of the Constitution, gave permanence to much of the New Deal legislation. Roosevelt later said that in his fight with the Supreme Court he had lost the battle but had won the war.

A recession stimulated more reforms

The battle over the Supreme Court disrupted the unity of the Democratic party, and gave new energy to conservatives in Congress. The angry and increasingly conservative Congress of 1937 refused to go along with some of Roosevelt's requests for reform, such as a law guaranteeing workers a minimum wage. Yet Congress did pass laws to help tenant farmers and to replace city slums with public housing.

In August 1937, there was a recession, and the mood of Congress began to change. The economic recovery of early 1937 had been built on government "pump-priming," meaning that the New Deal had poured money into the economy to get it going just as a little water is poured into a

pump to start it flowing. Roosevelt had reduced expenditures for WPA and other agencies in June, and the recession had followed.

This recession seemed to indicate to New Dealers that prosperity would not return without government spending. In October the President called Congress into special session to resume government spending and to continue New Deal reforms. When Congress met in November, Roosevelt asked for laws to aid farmers, abolish child labor, set minimum wages, control monopolies, and reorganize the executive department.

Frightened by the recession, Congress went along with the President and once again primed the pump with additional government expenditures; for example, $3 billion was appropriated to expand WPA. Congress also passed the Agricultural Adjustment Act of February 1938. The new agricultural act was more comprehensive than that of 1933 and was acceptable to the Supreme Court. It subsidized the farmers in an attempt to assure them purchasing power equal to what they had enjoyed in the favorable period 1909-1914, called the "parity" base. Thus the subsidies were termed parity payments. It also restricted crops and provided for government purchase and storage of surpluses. Farm prices soon rose, but real prosperity did not return to agriculture until after 1941, when war conditions increased demands for food.

During the recession, Roosevelt succeeded in wringing from a reluctant Congress his last important reform, the Fair Labor Standards Act or Wages and Hours Law (June 1938). This measure established an immediate minimum wage of 25 cents an hour, to be increased within eight years to 40 cents. It limited the work week to 44 hours, with a further reduction to 40 hours in three years and it forbade the employment of children in the making of goods sold in interstate commerce. So many exemptions were written into the law that it protected only part of America's poorest working people, but it struck a blow at sweatshops and exploiters of children.

Roosevelt put aside reform

As support for the New Deal in Congress faded in 1938, Roosevelt decided to strike back at the conservatives in his own party who had fought his program. He denounced his opponents in the Democratic party as "Copperheads," a contemptuous term used during the Civil War to describe Northerners who sympathized with the South. He openly campaigned against some of them in primary elections, particularly in the South. The President's "purge" failed. Conservative Southerners usually won. Furthermore, in the November elections the Republicans gained eighty seats in the House and seven in the Senate and for the first time since 1932, became a formidable force. Southern Democrats and Republicans, who were opposed to further New Deal reforms, could form a coalition that would dominate Congress.

The President decided that he could not alienate the Southerners because he needed their support on foreign policy. Late in 1938, large-scale war threatened in Europe and Asia. Roosevelt believed that these threats required a change in the nation's foreign policy away from isolationism and toward more coöperation with friendly non-aggressive nations.

Eastern Democrats were generally willing to support both an active foreign policy and measures for domestic reform. Southern Democrats, on the other hand, accepted the changed foreign policy, but rejected domestic reforms. Midwesterners usually favored domestic reforms but wanted an isolationist foreign policy. Since Roosevelt now considered the foreign danger more important than domestic problems, he put aside reform, partly to please Southerners. Then he tried to work with an alliance of Eastern and Southern Democrats in Congress to advance his foreign policy.

In his annual message of January 4, 1939, Roosevelt announced the end of the New Deal's "program of social reform." Then he talked about world affairs. But the needs of foreign policy and the growing opposition to the New Deal were not the only reasons for putting aside reform. The New Deal had reached most of its objectives, at least within the limits set by those who had planned it.

REVIEWING THE SECTION

1. Why did Roosevelt attempt to reorganize the Supreme Court? Why did he meet intense opposition? What was the result of his fight with the Court?

2. How did Congress attempt to combat the recession of 1937? What were the provisions of the Agricultural Adjustment Act of 1938 and the Fair Labor Standards Act?

3. Why did Roosevelt announce the end of the New Deal in 1939?

CHAPTER **23** CONCLUSION

In the view of most historians the successes and failures of the New Deal were mixed. It did not succeed in bringing full recovery. As late as 1941, six million Americans were still unemployed. This vast unemployment did not disappear until two years later, when the nation was at war. The New Deal did help raise national income, but it did not increase business activity to any great extent. It did not find a lasting solution to the farm problem, and the experiment in planning under the NRA was collapsing even before the Supreme Court declared it unconstitutional. The manipulation of the currency brought no tangible benefits, and even the pump-priming did not go far enough to bring permanent recovery.

On the other hand, the achievements of the New Deal were greater in extent and impact than those of

584

any previous period. It reformed banking, regulated the stock exchanges, created the TVA for vast regional development, brought guarantees to labor through the Wagner Act, protected the worker with a minimum-wage law, and helped many Americans by means of the social security system. To pay for these measures, the Roosevelt administration increased income and inheritance taxes. In this way, a redistribution of wealth was begun that reduced the most serious inequalities of the past. Even though many businessmen bitterly resisted innovations such as these, the New Deal could justifiably claim that its reforms blunted demands for more radical measures and that it saved the capitalistic system of private business enterprise.

The New Deal did not try to overturn the old social and economic system. Instead, without a planned design, it tried to reconstruct a shattered economy while at the same time it worked toward a more just society. Under the New Deal, minority groups made important gains; they not only received benefits, they also gained recognition as having a rightful and dignified place in an American society. When the illustrious Negro singer Marian Anderson was denied a concert hall in Washington because of her race, the secretary of the interior arranged to have her perform on the steps of the Lincoln Memorial. This reflected a growing concern for the dignity of the Negro.

This new concern for minorities and the underprivileged reflected a change in the nature of American politics under the New Deal. Social, economic, and racial issues became more important than they had been before 1932. Although this development alarmed conservative critics, it expanded the base of American democracy. Critics were also alarmed by the expansion of the power of the federal government. Roosevelt broadened the powers of the President and, for the first time, the federal government became an institution that many Americans felt had a direct effect on their lives. This happened, in part, because government had begun to accept a direct responsibility for the social and economic welfare of all its citizens.

The New Deal brought about its changes within the historic structure of American democracy. By showing the people that through democratic processes they could do something about their problems, the New Deal preserved democratic government in the United States at a time when it was being destroyed elsewhere in the world.

The New Deal can be credited with many achievements in preserving and broadening democracy and bringing a measure of justice to the poor, to the exploited, to the workers, and to other people who were underprivileged. Yet like the so-called Jeffersonian Revolution of 1800 and the Jacksonian Revolution of 1828, the New Deal left more unchanged than it changed. American society had only begun to deal with the problems of sharecroppers, big-city decay, migrant workers, and Negroes.

FOCUSING ON SPECIFICS

1. How did Roosevelt's attitude toward the role of the federal government differ from that of Hoover?
2. Why did New Dealers believe that cutting production would stimulate recovery?
3. What was the purpose of the Federal Deposit Insurance Corporation?
4. What was the purpose of the NRA codes? Why did many people object to the codes?
5. Why is the reform legislation of 1935 considered to have been a second New Deal?
6. How did Dr. Townsend propose to aid the elderly and bring the nation out of the depression?
7. What was Huey Long's "Share-Our-Wealth" plan?
8. Why was the Works Progress Administration criticized for being wasteful?
9. Why did the C.I.O. split with the A. F. of L.?
10. In general, how did the views of Eastern, Southern, and Midwestern Democrats differ in regard to domestic reform and foreign policy?

REVIEWING MAIN THEMES

1. How did New Deal legislation reform the stock market and the banking system?
2. How did the New Deal attempt to promote industrial recovery before 1935? after 1935?
3. How did the New Deal legislation aid farmers and workers?
4. What measures were passed to aid the unemployed?
5. Why was much New Deal legislation criticized? Why was the New Deal abandoned by 1939?
6. In what ways was New Deal legislation a failure? What were its achievements? In what ways was it a departure from the past?

1. In what way did legislation passed during the New Deal resemble that of the Progressive era? of Hoover's administration? In what way did New Deal legislation and policies differ from those of the earlier periods?

2. Was the National Recovery Administration a danger to democracy or was it a sensible attempt to plan the economy on a nation-wide scale without harsh controls over business? Explain.

3. Should the government subsidize farmers while other people who work in competitive industries are not subsidized? Why?

4. Should workers have participated in sit-down strikes to force employers to recognize unions? Explain your answer.

5. Historian Richard N. Hofstadter has stated, "The New Deal will never be understood by anyone who looks for a single thread of policy, a far-reaching, far-seeing plan. It was a series of improvisations, many adopted very suddenly, many contradictory. Such unity as it had was in political strategy, not economics." Do you agree? Explain your answer.

The Culture of Prosperity and Depression

In many ways the 1920's and the 1930's were decades of contrast. For most Americans the period before the great crash of 1929 was one of boundless hope and optimism. Writers have called these years of social ferment and frivolous fun the "Roaring Twenties," the "Golden Twenties," that "Era of Wonderful Nonsense," and the "Jazz Age," mainly because jazz music became a nation-wide mania. Despite the social tensions and the spottiness of prosperity, the people of the United States enjoyed more conveniences, comforts, and riches than had any people at any time, and they expected their wealth and comfort to increase. One of the songs they frequently listened to was "My God, How the Money Rolls In."

With the crash came a depression which hung over the 1930's like a black cloud. These were years of despair and frustration. "Brother, Can You Spare a Dime?" was the popular song that seemed to catch the mood of the people. On the last day of the 1930's a magazine writer summed up the long years of despondency by saying the "decade has been one of the gloomiest in modern history."

Despite the contrasts in mood, the 1920's and 1930's were alike in many respects. Both were decades of technological progress against a background of social and economic disorder. Both were periods of improvements in science and medicine that increased the life span of Americans. There were improvements in education and notable cultural advances were made. In addition, most Americans had more time for leisure and recreation.

Several of the major economic and social trends of the industrial era continued in the 1920's and 1930's. Big business grew bigger, existing cities continued to grow in size and population, and new cities were built. The farm population continued to decline, and the new middle class of white-collar workers increased in size and importance.

Some things changed in the 1920's and 1930's. For the first time in three centuries there was a decline in the rate at which the population grew. The birth rate began to drop in the 1920's, and in the 1930's it fell to its lowest point in the nation's history. The new laws restricting immigration also contributed to the declining rate of population growth. In some years more foreigners left the United States than came to it. In these decades the foreign-born became less and less important as social blocs in the population.

In 1920, the census showed that for the first time more than half of the people in the United States lived in towns or cities. On the farms, machinery replaced more and more of the laborers. As a result of this mechanization, fewer laborers tilling the same number of acres were able to increase production. During the early 1930's, the depression temporarily reversed the flow toward the city. Nearly two million of the nation's unemployed returned to homes on farms, where it was easier to find food.

Negroes continued their migration from South to North in both decades. As a result, an increasingly larger proportion of the Negro population spread over the country as a whole. Almost ninety per cent of the Negroes who migrated North went into the cities.

In the 1920's, many Americans moved westward. During the 1930's, this migration slackened but did not stop. Hundreds of thousands of the dispossessed and unemployed moved westward in search of jobs. Most of the Western states, and especially California, gained markedly in population. In the depression decade the population in the Eastern and Midwestern states grew but little. Some states in the southern part of the country actually lost population, especially Oklahoma and others in the Great Plains area which were struck by drought and dust storms.

Whether in prosperity or in depression, in these decades the people in the United States had to learn to live in a society of abundance, for they could produce more than they could consume and could do so with less work than before. Through the use of machines there was increased production of necessities as well as luxuries, but the number of jobs was reduced. The use of machines brought leisure and wealth to some Americans, but to others machines brought insecurity and fear of fewer job opportunities.

BIG BUSINESS CONTINUED TO GROW

Americans had to come to terms with the machine because it had become a central feature of their culture. The machine had led to the growth of big business, and in the 1920's business dominated most aspects of life in the United States.

The three Republican administrations in the 1920's coöperated closely with business leaders and followed policies favorable to the interests of big business. As could be expected from these businessmen's governments, there was none of the spectacular trust-busting activity of the Progressive era. Government officials practically ignored the Sherman and Clayton Antitrust laws. Encouraged by the friendliness of the government, businessmen went ahead with a program of large-scale industrial concentration. This was done primarily through the merging of companies engaged in the same or similar businesses.

At the same time, the variety of goods produced by industry and the volume of business activity increased tremendously. But the business boom was accompanied by a decrease in the number of firms doing business. In most industries, small companies began to disappear. Between 1919 and 1930, thousands of firms went out of business. Big businesses grew bigger, and their growth brought benefits as well as problems.

Competition in business changed

Both the benefits and the problems grew out of the changing nature of business competition. At the beginning of the century great industrialists tried to gain a monopoly, or exclusive control, of a product, and in this way snuff out competition. In the Progressive era antitrust suits broke up monopolies, or near monopolies.

In the 1920's, the rapid growth of production made it difficult for any one company to acquire

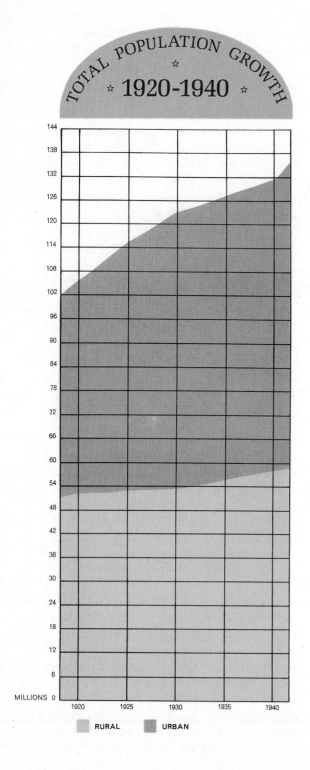

TOTAL POPULATION GROWTH
☆ 1920-1940 ☆

RURAL   URBAN

an industrial monopoly. Instead, it became common for a few large companies to dominate and control an industry. This kind of business situation is called *oligopoly.*

Oligopoly frequently led to intense competition among companies within an industry, and such competition led to benefits for the people in the form of low prices for goods. For example, by 1929, chain stores and great mail-order houses, such as Sears, Roebuck and Company, had come to control about twenty-five per cent of the nation's retail business. They extended their activities into small towns all over the United States, and brought the people a variety of quality goods at competitive prices. In so doing, they often destroyed the monopoly of the local merchant.

On the other hand, an oligopolistic situation could have the effect of destroying or limiting competition. When only a few big corporations controlled an industry, it was not difficult for them to agree on prices and thus avoid competition which could reduce profits. Uniform price schedules, not competitive ones, became the rule in many big industries. Frequently the largest corporation in an industry would set policy on prices. Smaller rivals would follow this price leadership. Competition would then shift from prices to improvements in quality and in advertising.

Another device used by businessmen to cut down competition was the *trade association,* a voluntary, coöperative, nonprofit organization composed of individuals (usually competitors) engaged in a particular industry. It was designed to help all businesses within that industry. Trade associations would collect and distribute information on prices, shipping problems, advertising, and various business practices. While many of the trade associations performed a useful service for their industry, some of them were responsible for unethical practices such as fraudulent advertising. Sometimes they were able to control prices, which often meant that prices for the consumer and profits for the manufacturers would be higher than in a competitive situation.

In 1920, only a small number of these trade associations were in operation. Harding, Coolidge, and especially Hoover encouraged their growth. In 1926, the Supreme Court ruled that their activities were legal. By 1933, when Hoover left the White House, more than two thousand trade associations were functioning. One of the most powerful of all was the National Association of Manufacturers. Later, in the 1930's, Franklin D. Roosevelt's administration set up codes for industries and used the trade association agreements as patterns.

Machines increased production and reduced labor

In the 1920's, there was increasing separation of business management from ownership. By the 1930's, the businessman was usually the manager, rather than the owner, of large factories or banks. The separation of management from ownership came about as more and more corporations sold stock to the public, and as numerous investors, rather than a few millionaires, became the owners of the large corporations. The separation was not absolute, however, because the managers, or executives, usually held stock in their companies.

Since many stockholders did not have the skill and knowledge to run the giant corporations, they left the making of important decisions to salaried executives. These salaried managers thus came to exercise great power over the United States economy.

These managers were the products of the continuing technological revolution that vastly increased industrial output in the 1920's. New machines, new sources of power, and new techniques in scientific management made it possible for each worker to produce more than ever before. Even though population and production increased, the number of workers employed in factories remained rather constant.

Most important in increasing production was industry's adoption of mass production by the assembly-line technique, used most successfully by Henry Ford in the automobile industry. Ford's use of the moving assembly line reduced the time required for a man to put together an automobile chassis from fourteen hours to less than two hours. Industrial research and improvements in working conditions in factories also contributed to industrial growth.

Even though industrial production in the 1930's was lower than in the 1920's, the technological revolution went on. Using the same number of workers in each year, industry could produce twenty per cent more goods and services in 1937 than in 1929.

New industries grew rapidly

Along with the change in competition in business and the increase in production, one of the significant developments in the 1920's and the 1930's was the growth of new industries or the rapid expansion of existing industries. The most important of these were automobiles, electric power, aviation, motion pictures, and radio.

Of all the new products, the one that had the greatest and swiftest influence on American life and culture was the automobile. It did much to supply the boom for the booming prosperity of the 1920's. Even during the depression years, when new car sales plummeted, the family automobile absorbed a good share of the people's incomes. During these years, it was said, Americans were the only people in history to ride to the poorhouse in automobiles.

Use of the automobile led to vast road construction and maintenance programs, and to growth in numerous allied industries, such as petroleum. In every town of consequence in the 1920's and 1930's, there were filling stations and garages for automobile repairs; many towns had motels (from *mo*torists' ho*tel*). The automobile manufacturers became the most important buyers of rubber, plate glass, nickel, and lead. They absorbed about fifteen per cent of the nation's steel production. Because of the automobile, there was a boom in the construction of country clubs, golf courses, and tourist hotels. The automobile also made possible the development of new suburbs farther from the central city. According to an estimate made in 1929, the use of the automobile gave employment, directly or indirectly, to 3.7 million people in the United States.

Before World War I, the electric power industry was inconsequential. After the war, it became one of the nation's industrial giants. In the 1920's, Americans used almost twice as much electric power as in all the years up to that time, and even in the 1930's, consumption continued to rise. At first, numerous small companies produced most of the power, but in the 1920's, the industry became the chief area for industrial mergers. By 1930, ten groups of holding companies controlled seventy-two per cent of the country's electric power.

One new industry where the businessman did not make an immediate profit in the 1920's was aviation. After the historic flight of the Wright brothers, in 1903, the airplane was used primarily for stunts and amusement. In World War I, airplanes were used for a number of things, including fighting. In 1924, government planes began regular transcontinental air-mail service from New York to San Francisco. Private aviation got a real boost the following year with the Air Mail Act, which permitted the federal government to make contracts with private companies for carrying mail. This was a form of government subsidy.

The airplane captured public imagination in May 1927 when a tall, shy, and handsome young pilot from the Middle West, Charles A. Lindbergh, Jr., in a single-engine plane, *The Spirit of St. Louis,* flew solo from New York to Paris. This flight of 33 hours and 39 minutes, the first of its kind, brought Lindbergh, "The Lone Eagle," a prize of $25,000, and world fame. He became the supreme hero of the jazz age. Upon his return to the United States, he was showered with a record eighteen hundred tons of ticker tape as excited New Yorkers acclaimed him.

Scheduled airline passenger service began in 1926, and during that first year commercial air-lines transported about 6000 passengers. In 1930, the airlines carried more than 400,000 passengers. During the 1930's, service was extended to new areas, and at the end of the decade, flights connected Europe and the United States. Americans could travel 200 miles an hour in planes with overnight sleeping accommodations on coast-to-coast flights. Statistics for 1940 show that airplanes transported about 3 million passengers and 14 million pounds of freight more than 120 million miles. The airplane had become a practical means of travel, and the United States had gained another major industry.

REVIEWING THE SECTION

1. In the 1920's, what devices were commonly used by businessmen to reduce competition?

2. What progress in industrial production was made during the 1920's and 1930's?

3. What major industries were developed in the 1920's and 1930's? Why was the automobile industry so important to the economy?

LITERATURE AND THE ARTS FLOURISHED

Many writers, artists, and other intellectuals rejected the culture of the businessman. Some isolated themselves into intellectual societies and lived in arty areas such as New York City's Greenwich Village. Others fled to Europe, especially Paris. Writers often described the drabness of life in communities of the Middle West. They attacked the machine as a menace to culture and criticized the United States for not building a culture to equal its industrial wealth. Never was a literary generation so critical of society in the United States as this one. In rejecting the United States, these intellectuals of the 1920's devoted themselves to art, primarily to their own art. But by the 1930's, many of them had returned to the United States with a new appreciation of their country. They began to write, paint, and talk about the problems they saw around them.

Novelists, poets, and dramatists of the 1920's

and 1930's showed new and sensitive creativity and gained world-wide fame. In addition, the American people showed a greater interest in the work of artists than they had in the past. Painting, sculpture, and art history became subjects of study in high schools and colleges, and new art museums were established in towns all over the country, not just in the cities of the East.

Novelists set new standards

Although new writers set the standards for the 1920's and 1930's, many were influenced by earlier writings, especially those by the naturalists Theodore Dreiser and Sherwood Anderson. Dreiser's first novel, *Sister Carrie,* went on sale in 1906. (However, it was not until 1925 that Dreiser published his most ambitious and best novel, *An American Tragedy.*) Anderson published his most outstanding book in 1919—*Winesburg, Ohio,* a collection of stories about the frustrations of life in a small town.

Sinclair Lewis, the first American author to win the Nobel Prize for literature, also attacked small-town life. In *Main Street* (1920), the book which made him famous, Lewis described the cultural poverty in small-town America. Lewis also aroused controversy with *Babbitt* (1922), a satire on the life of a self-satisfied businessman in a bustling city in the United States. "Babbitt" became a new word in the English language because Lewis' portrait of this middle-class type seemed accurate, though exaggerated in detail.

F. Scott Fitzgerald, who, like Lewis, was a native of Minnesota, touched off the revolt of the young intellectuals, and he became the symbol of the jazz age. Fitzgerald catapulted into fame with *This Side of Paradise* (1920), a novel based on his life as an undergraduate at Princeton University. He also captured the excitement of his age in *Tales of the Jazz Age* (1922), *The Beautiful and the Damned* (1922), and *The Great Gatsby* (1925).

Ernest Hemingway, a native of Illinois, who lived among the intellectual exiles in Paris, described that segment of the "lost generation" in *The Sun Also Rises* (1926). He was a writer of great talent who set a new standard of style which other young writers tried to imitate. His prose was simple, unadorned, and showed itself at its best in *A Farewell to Arms* (1929), a novel that dealt with the uselessness of modern war. His immensely popular novel *For Whom the Bell Tolls* (1940) also dealt with this theme.

Another Midwesterner by birth, John Dos Passos, wrote *Three Soldiers* (1921), one of the first novels to debunk the glory often associated with war. His major work was a trilogy, *U.S.A.,* which was composed of the novels *42nd Parallel* (1930), *1919* (1932), and *The Big Money* (1936). This trilogy, covering the first three decades of the twentieth century, presented characters from every class and a variety of occupations in American society. Early in his career, he condemned American business and society. Later, as he became conservative, he defended the United States and its past.

One of the finest writers of this period was William Faulkner, who wrote novels about life in his native Mississippi. In *The Sound and the Fury* (1929) he used the stream-of-consciousness writing technique with great success. The most widely read of his early novels was *Sanctuary* (1931). *Light in August* (1932) and *Absalom, Absalom!* (1936) contain some of his finest writing.

Faulkner was a naturalist, as were James T. Farrell, John Steinbeck, and Thomas Wolfe—other great novelists of the 1930's. Farrell wrote with brutal frankness about the lower middle-class Irish in Chicago, where he had grown up. His best-known work was the *Studs Lonigan* trilogy composed of *Young Lonigan: A Boyhood in Chicago Streets* (1932), *The Young Manhood of Studs Lonigan* (1934), and *Judgment Day* (1935).

Steinbeck was a Californian who wrote about the dispossessed farmers and the migratory workers of the depression era. His works, such as *Tortilla Flat* (1935), *In Dubious Battle* (1936), and

Of Mice and Men (1937), were varied in quality, but attracted attention. In 1939, he published *The Grapes of Wrath,* which told of the Joads, a farm family driven from Oklahoma by dust storms and the mechanization of the farms. The plight of the Joads, and their fight for survival among the migratory farm laborers in California had an epic quality. This book became one of the most widely-read novels of its time.

Like Farrell, Thomas Wolfe wrote in great detail about life as he had experienced it. He was a North Carolinian who went to New York City to seek success as a writer. His prose was undisciplined, but often beautiful. He died at the age of thirty-eight (1938), leaving behind him four huge novels (two of which were published posthumously): *Look Homeward, Angel* (1929), *Of Time and the River* (1935), *The Web and the Rock* (1939), and *You Can't Go Home Again* (1940). Among many other fine novelists of this period in American fiction was Willa Cather, who made use of realism in novels such as *One of Ours* (a Pulitzer prize-winner in 1922) and *Death Comes for the Archbishop* (1927).

The careers of some of these authors did not end in the 1930's. For instance, Hemingway won a Nobel Prize for Literature in 1954, awarded especially for his short novel *The Old Man and the Sea* (1952). Hemingway died in 1961. Faulkner continued to publish successful novels until his death in 1963. Dos Passos, Steinbeck, and Farrell made important literary contributions in the 1960's.

Poetry experienced a renaissance

The American renaissance in poetry began shortly before World War I. Ezra Pound, a native of Idaho who chose to live in Italy, was the first of a new school of poets called "imagists." Rejecting the traditional forms of verse, the imagists said poets should create impressions and feelings the way they are caught in a picture or image. In 1915, Amy Lowell, a New Englander, succeeded Pound as the leader of imagists.

A group of Chicago poets were particularly successful in breaking with the traditions of the past. Vachel Lindsay tried to capture the rhythms of the prairie, the beat of jazz and revival songs, and the sounds of the city and of the jungle in works such as *William Booth Enters Heaven and Other Poems* (1913), and *The Congo and Other Poems* (1914). In *Spoon River Anthology* (1915), Edgar Lee Masters laid bare the meanness and hypocrisy in a small town in Illinois. The following year Carl Sandburg published his first volume, *Chicago Poems.* He praised Chicago as a brawling city of hog butchers, wheat stackers, and freight handlers. Writing throughout the 1920's and 1930's, he became the poet of the people.

Edwin Arlington Robinson, a New Englander who lived in New York, also wrote about simple people, but in the traditional manner. His first success came in 1916 with *The Man Against the Sky.* Some of his later poems, such as *Tristram* (1927), sold better than did popular novels of the time. Another New England poet who wrote about people such as farmers and laborers was Robert Frost, who published his first book, *A Boy's Will* (1913), while in England. He returned to the United States after the publication of *North of Boston* (1914). Between 1915 and 1955, Frost published about fifteen volumes of verse and won four Pulitzer Prizes for his poetry.

One of the most gifted poets of these decades was Thomas Stearns (T. S.) Eliot, who was born in St. Louis, but lived most of his life in London. He believed that complex poetry was needed to reflect complex society. *The Waste Land* (1922), his first major work, deeply affected American poets. By 1925, he was recognized as the leading poet and critic both in Britain and the United States.

Other important poets of the period were Edna St. Vincent Millay, who wrote about love and youth; E. E. Cummings, who experimented with form; Stephen Vincent Benét, best known for his long narrative poem of the Civil War, *John Brown's Body* (1928); Robinson Jeffers, who reflected the naturalist approach of the novelists; Hart Crane, who sought a unified American tradition in *The Bridge* (1930); and Archibald MacLeish, who turned from personal discontent in the 1920's to social protest in the 1930's.

An important literary movement of the 1920's has often been called the "Harlem Renaissance," because during this time the writings of Negro authors and poets became popular. One of the most noted writers was Langston Hughes, whose sensitive poems and stories revealed the problems and pride of American Negroes. Other popular authors were Claude McKay, Countee Cullen, and James Weldon Johnson.

United States drama gained world-wide fame

As significant as the renaissance in poetry was the flowering of a truly American drama. In the 1920's, for the first time in the nation's history, drama became a vital form of literary expression. This movement began in 1915 in Provincetown, Massachusetts, where young intellectuals established the Wharf Theater. They later went on to New York City. Other little theaters sprang up elsewhere, and playwrights with serious ideas found outlets for their dramatic experiments.

The Provincetown group gave Eugene O'Neill his start. He experimented with psychological themes taken from the works of the Viennese physician Sigmund Freud, and wrote seriously to explore human nature, not solely to entertain. He expressed himself powerfully in plays such as *The Emperor Jones* (1920), *Desire Under the Elms* (1924), and *Strange Interlude* (1928).

In the early 1920's, other fine playwrights joined O'Neill, and it was then, seemingly overnight, that American drama became truly important as literature. This flowering of the drama began with *The Adding Machine* (1923), a modern allegory by Elmer Rice. In *Street Scene* (1929), he turned to realism and social protest. Social concern also marked the early work of Maxwell Anderson. In 1924, with Laurence Stallings, he wrote a war play, *What Price Glory*.

Anderson, according to many scholars of today, was one of the foremost playwrights of the 1930's. In plays about Elizabeth I of England, Mary Queen of Scots, and in *Winterset* (1935), he brought poetry back to the stage. He used verse to gain historical effect and to give special intensity to scenes in a modern setting.

In the plays *Our Town* (1938) and *The Skin of Our Teeth* (1942), Thornton Wilder explored human problems. Robert E. Sherwood condemned decadent society in *The Petrified Forest* (1934); in *Idiot's Delight* (1936) he denounced war; and in *Abe Lincoln in Illinois* (1938) he praised democracy. As the 1930's came to an end, American plays and their authors were known and respected all over the world.

Art and architecture attracted public interest

One of the events that aroused public interest in modern art was the Armory Show, held in New York in February 1913. That exhibit, designed in part to show the paintings of the American realists of the Ash Can School, also introduced the public to modern art from Europe by including the works of such artists as Paul Cézanne, Paul Henri Matisse, Henri de Toulouse-Lautrec, Vincent Van Gogh, and Pablo Picasso.

For the next several decades, two opposing concepts could be found in American painting. One was realism that showed scenes of American life. The other was abstract art which expressed the ideas and emotions of the artist through forms and color, often distorting actual shapes.

Neither the abstractionists nor the realists dominated American art, but in the 1920's, abstract art gained a significant following. Abstract artists like John Marin became popular. His imaginative interpretations of the Maine seacoast gave a new outlook to landscape painting. In 1929, a group of art collectors opened the Museum of Modern Art in New York City. In 1931, the Whitney Museum opened, the first museum devoted exclusively to American art.

Jack Curley's Dance Marathon, by Reginald Marsh, 1932

Scott's Run, West Virginia, By Ben Shahn, 1937, from the Collection of the Whitney Museum of American Art, N.Y.

Early Sunday Morning, by Edward Hopper, 1930, from the Collection of the Whitney Museum of American Art, N.Y.

Upper Deck, by Charles Sheeler, 1929

Stone City, by Grant Wood, 1930

United States Painting.

Using both abstract and realistic techniques, artists of the 1920's and 1930's developed highly individualistic styles. John Marin made extensive use of angular lines in his semi-abstract painting "Maine Islands." Grant Wood, who often painted mid-western scenes, emphasized round shapes in "Stone City." Charles Sheeler's fascination with precise geometrical patterns is evident in "Upper Deck." In a stark, realistic manner, Edward Hopper showed a city block in the pale sunlight of early morning.

Other painters recorded the social setting of the period. Ben Shahn's intense style was well suited for depression scenes with jobless workers, listless and bitter. Reginald Marsh depicted two bedraggled marathon dancers, barely able to stand up.

Maine Islands, by John Marin, 1922

In the 1930's, realism, particularly regional realism of artists from the Middle West, gained popularity. John Steuart Curry, Grant Wood, and Thomas Hart Benton painted brilliant scenes of life in Kansas, Iowa, and Missouri. At the same time, the federal government tried to help artists suffering from the hardships of the depression by employing them to paint murals in post offices, schools, and courthouses all over the country. This helped to acquaint the public with the work of many American artists.

Sculptors, too, felt the division between the realistic and the abstract approach, but realism was dominant in their work. William Zorach and Gaston Lachaise experimented with new forms, some of which were abstract. Among the sculptors who favored the realistic approach were Jacob Epstein and Gutzon Borglum, who is best known for his faces of the Presidents carved in the Black Hills of South Dakota.

Modernists were slow in influencing architecture in the United States. In the 1920's, traditional design prevailed, but in the 1930's, a modern style of straight, simple lines gained favor. This clean, uncluttered style was used in New York City's Rockefeller Center. The nation's most influential architect in these decades, Frank Lloyd Wright, carried on the tradition of his teacher, Louis H. Sullivan. Whether designing homes or factories, Wright applied a principle of integrating the form, the function, and the materials of a building with its site. His low, ranch-type houses have been termed "prairie" houses because they were designed for the flat Midwest terrain.

REVIEWING THE SECTION

1. What themes were treated in the novels of the writers of the 1920's and 1930's? How did these themes reflect trends in American life?

2. Give examples of outstanding poets of the 1920's and 1930's and the kinds of poetry they created.

3. What themes were expressed by American dramatists during this period?

4. What developments took place in art and architecture during the 1920's and 1930's?

NEW IDEAS CHALLENGED THE OLD

The belief that ideas in all fields were interdependent, which affected writers and artists, also affected other intellectuals. Historians, for example, switched from their almost exclusive concern with political institutions, and began probing the social, intellectual, and economic background of man. As colleges and universities grew, so did the quality and depth of historical scholarship. Historians in the United States studied the past of the world, not just of their own country, in greater depth than ever before. Sociologists, influenced by ideas from Europe, developed new techniques for the study of man and his reaction to his environment. Economists became less concerned with "laws" than with studies of how the economic system worked.

In the physical sciences, remarkable progress was made in astronomy and physics. Scientists gained acceptance for new theories on the structure of the universe and on the nature of matter and energy. Most of these ideas came from Europe, but in the 1930's, outstanding European scientists migrated to the United States. Advances in medical science had almost immediate practical effect. Techniques and drugs that reduced or wiped out disease improved the health of the people and extended their life expectancy.

At the same time, Protestant fundamentalism, which had always been strong in the rural areas, experienced a revival. Early in the 1920's, the fundamentalists launched a crusade against Darwin's theory of evolution. That crusade, however, faltered in many sections of the country, especially in urban areas.

The growth of scientific research in the United States, much of it in the universities, was evidence of change and improvement in American education. In the 1920's and 1930's, almost all Americans were literate. Illiteracy had dropped from 7.7

per cent of the population in 1910 to 4.3 per cent in 1930. By 1910, most American children had an opportunity to obtain free public education of some kind. By that time the democratic ideal of a common school, supported by public taxes and with doors open to all children, had not only been realized, but also it had become a part of American life. In the 1920's and 1930's, the primary task of education was to improve the schools, the quality of the teaching, and the courses offered.

Psychology influenced thought and behavior

Psychology was a relatively new social science, but in the 1920's, its influence was so great that it seemed to have become a national craze. One of the most popular psychologists, Dr. John B. Watson, said the mind was like an electric machine that received signals and automatically sent out established responses. He had explained this idea in his book *Behaviorism* (1914), but the theory did not become popular until the book's third edition (1925). Watson's idea had social implications. If man were only a machine, as he said, then environment and training would shape his conduct, and ultimately that of society.

More important were the ideas of Sigmund Freud. He developed a method for treating people who were mentally disturbed, and called the technique psychoanalysis. Freud assumed that many of man's normal mental activities were unconscious and irrational rather than conscious and rational. Men became emotionally upset when their unconscious wishes were repressed. Psychoanalysis could be used to help a patient discover the conflict in the mind caused by repression.

If, as Freud said, the motives in human conduct were largely unconscious, then accepted ideas, such as man being self-reliant and capable of making intelligent choices, were undermined. If, as Freud said, man's behavior were not entirely rational, then he could not entirely meet his own needs. These implications disturbed many intellectuals, but inspired others. Freud's ideas influenced fiction,

drama, the interpretation of history, the study of politics, and the views of religious thinkers.

Since many of the unconscious motives developed in early childhood, according to Freud, American mothers began paying special attention to childhood experiences and to the best means of rearing children who would be healthy in mind as well as body. In the 1930's, Freud's ideas and the findings of other psychologists, too, were put to practical use in the study of crime, juvenile delinquency, and behavior in jobs, in the army, and in other activities. Man could no longer be studied merely on the basis of his conscious behavior and motivation.

A Tennessee trial attracted attention

Many of the ideas of scientists and of the psychologists such as Watson and Freud were disturbing to some religious leaders. Some of these scientists expressed contempt for traditional Christian concepts. "No one," Watson said, "has ever touched a soul, or has seen one in a test tube." Nonetheless, by 1920, many church leaders had accepted some findings and ideas of science, such as evolution.

Some of the fundamentalists, however, wanted to prevent the theory of evolution from being taught in the schools. In the South, the crusade, headed by William Jennings Bryan, was fairly successful. In March 1925, the legislature of the state of Tennessee passed a law prohibiting those in the schools to teach

any theory that denies the story of the divine creation of man as taught in the Bible and to teach instead that man has descended from a lower order of animals.

A few months later John T. Scopes, a modest young high-school teacher in the mountain town of Dayton, Tennessee, decided to test the validity of the law. He proceeded to do so by discussing evolution in his classes; he was arrested, and in July went to trial. To his support came Clarence Darrow, an agnostic and the nation's most famous defense lawyer. Bryan served on the staff of prosecuting attorneys.

The trial attracted world-wide attention and reporters, evangelists, and the curious jammed themselves into Dayton, giving the trial the atmosphere of a circus. The judge even moved the proceedings to an empty lot to accommodate the crowds. The climax came when Bryan was questioned as an expert on the Bible. Under Darrow's ruthless grilling, Bryan was revealed as a man ignorant of science. Later, the anti-evolution campaign faded. Scopes was found guilty, for he admitted breaking the law. He was fined $100, a fine that was later rescinded on a technicality.

Church attendance was not affected adversely by the controversy. In the 1920's, attendance increased in the Protestant and Roman Catholic churches and in Jewish synagogues. But in the depression years of the 1930's, membership in all churches slumped.

Scientists advanced new theories

While fundamentalists were making a stand against old scientific ideas, scientists themselves were discarding or modifying old theories. New discoveries, particularly in physics and astronomy, led them to question the idea that the universe was governed by final and absolute laws. Using giant telescopes at observatories on Mt. Hamilton and Mt. Wilson in California, astronomers discovered clouds of new stars, or galaxies. In 1930, at Lowell Observatory near Flagstaff, Arizona, Clyde Tombaugh discovered a ninth planet, Pluto. Scientists began to speak of an expanding universe, not a fixed one.

These new ideas on the structure of the universe, and also on the nature of matter and energy, gained acceptance by American scientists in the 1920's, but most of the theoretical work was done by Europeans. Many of the ideas discussed in the 1920's stemmed from the work of a brilliant German physicist, Albert Einstein. In 1905, he advanced a theory of relativity, which he refined in later years. According to this theory, only the speed of light could be regarded as fixed or absolute. Everything else was relative to the motion and position of the observer. Part of this theory could be tested by the observations of astronomers.

Another part of Einstein's theory was later verified by experiments in physics. He said that matter and energy are equivalent, and he expressed that relationship in an equation for measuring energy locked up in an atom, or particle of matter. That formula was $E = mc^2$, which said that "E," or energy, equals "m," or mass, times "c²", or the velocity of light (186,326 miles a second) squared.

Scientists, primarily the ones in Europe, at first used Einstein's theories to unlock the atom, which had long been considered indivisible. In England in the 1920's for example, Ernest Rutherford, a New Zealander, began exploring the uranium atom. In the 1930's, Enrico Fermi in Italy used information from England to conduct important experiments of his own with uranium. At the same time, American physicists began atomic experiments of increasing significance. In 1932, Ernest O. Lawrence, a young physicist at the University of California, Berkeley, built the first practical cyclotron. This powerful machine was designed for use in the study of the nature of atoms.

To escape the tyranny of dictators, many of the fine European scientists migrated to the United States. Einstein and Nils Bohr, a leading theorist from Denmark, went to the Institute for Advanced Study at Princeton, New Jersey, and Fermi joined the faculty at Columbia University. By 1939, three of the world's greatest physicists were in the United States and were working with others such as Leo Szilard from Hungary, to make the United States a great center of scientific research.

By this time physicists all over the world were using machines to analyze the uranium atom, because it was capable of releasing an immense amount of energy. In 1939, news reached Bohr that scientists in Germany had actually split the uranium atom. This alarmed some scientists, including

The great "Monkey Trial"—*Tennessee* v. *John Thomas Scopes,* No. 5232—was held in Dayton, Tennessee, during twelve sweltering days in July 1925. The trial was concerned with the question: While states have had the unquestionable legal authority to regulate education, what are the moral and legal limitations to the curb that can be placed upon free speech and thought in the classroom? The defendant, John Scopes, was accused of unlawfully teaching evolution in a high school biology class. William Jennings Bryan was the attorney for the prosecution, and Clarence Darrow the attorney for the defense.

Bryan was the Great Commoner who had electrified the Democratic National Convention of 1896 with his "Cross of Gold" speech. Three times candidate for President, and secretary of state under Woodrow Wilson, he had become a Florida real estate salesman. Defender of the middle-class farmer against Wall Street and the railroads, he was still a hero to rural America and regularly toured the Chautauqua Bible circuit advocating a literal interpretation of the Holy Scripture.

Darrow was the country's most famous criminal lawyer. Deeply cynical and thoroughly aware of society's shortcomings, he had often engaged in legal battles involving freedom of speech, thought, and action.

"The right of the people speaking through the legislature, to control the schools which they create and support is the real issue," Bryan claimed. The people should not relinquish control of the schools to scientists or teachers. "The teacher is an employee and receives a salary; employees take directions from their employers, and the teacher is no exception to the rule."

There was only one scientist for every ten thousand people, and Bryan looked upon men of science as a "little oligarchy to put in control of the education of all the children." The science that wanted absolute freedom in the classroom was "the same science that manufactured poisonous gases to suffocate soldiers." Science had "no morality" and, therefore, had to be controlled.

Always a strong advocate of education, Bryan thought it should be controlled carefully. "The brain will plot a murder or plan a burglary as willingly as it will labor for the welfare of mankind. All, therefore,

MEN
IN
HISTORY

BRYAN AND DARROW

depends upon the heart behind the brain. . . . The sin of this generation is mind worship—a worship as destructive as any other form of idolatry." What America needed was "not more brains but more heart—not more intellect but more conscience."

Darrow believed that the public schools had degenerated into institutions that molded children to a particular pattern and made their minds sterile. The schools had failed in their primary purpose, which he maintained was to encourage students to think out questions for themselves. He believed in "the right of everyone to investigate for himself," and resented "the interference of the state in its efforts to forbid or control the convictions and mental attitudes of men."

The present trial was just another "peril" which confronted "the freedom of education." Although it concerned a scientific theory, it might just as easily have been a question of politics, economics, or social values. Darrow saw the "sharpshooters of bigotry . . . picking off . . . victims in . . . schools and colleges." The preservation of academic freedom, he said, depended upon saving educators from the pressure of fanatics.

"Reared . . . on books of science," Darrow placed great reliance on specialists and their accomplishments. "The future is with science and not with the law," he wrote. "If I were to begin my life again, and had a chance to choose, I would adopt scientific research."

The academic world, according to Darrow, was the particular domain of scientists, teachers, and other specialists. They had the right and deserved the freedom to propagate their findings. "Ideas are very slow in affecting the mass of mankind," he said. "They are held back by prejudice, by ignorance, by common conception until long after the intelligent specialist has thoroughly proved conditions and discovered remedies." Therefore, would it not be tragic if the "mass of mankind" could legally prevent a new idea from being introduced.

When the trial was ended, Scopes was found guilty and fined $100. Actually, the trial itself settled nothing. It had been conducted in the atmosphere of a circus. The fundamental issue was practically forgotten, and the defendant completely overshadowed by the two dramatic lawyers.

Einstein. In August, Einstein wrote to President Roosevelt, saying that

some recent work by E. Fermi and L. Szilard . . . leads me to expect that the element uranium may be turned into a new and important source of energy in the immediate future . . . [and] would also lead to the construction of bombs.

Einstein implied that soon scientists might be able to obtain a chain reaction among atoms as they split. This reaction would release in a fraction of a second the vast energy stored up in matter. He wanted the United States to build a bomb based on this principle before anyone else did.

Americans became better educated

Educators went about making improvements in the educational systems in the United States in two important ways. They put more and different courses in the schools, and they adopted many of John Dewey's ideas. Despite opposition from traditionalists, who insisted upon drills in basic subjects, such as reading and spelling, educators set up progressive, or child-centered, schools. There children were encouraged to experiment and to participate in the learning process. In the 1930's, the emphasis shifted to community-centered schools, where students worked more on social and economic problems.

High schools and colleges made the most significant progress. At one time high schools offered only academic courses that prepared students mainly for college. Colleges, in turn, had prepared students almost exclusively for professions. In the 1920's and 1930's, both high schools and colleges increasingly offered vocational courses. They trained young men and women for careers in industry and the sciences, as well as in the professions.

High-school education became widespread and popular. Employers began to insist on at least a high-school education for many jobs. A new institution, the junior college, met the need of many people who wanted to continue their studies beyond high school, but who could not go to a college or university. The establishment of junior colleges spread rapidly, especially in western states such as California. Despite the expansion of vocational subjects, professional training and higher research did not suffer. Graduate schools in universities often grew more rapidly than undergraduate schools.

In the prosperous 1920's, schools expanded. In the 1930's, some schools closed for lack of funds and many suffered from crowded classrooms, shortened time for instruction, and the inability to pay teachers. But even during the depression, high-school and college enrollments increased. Since they could not find jobs, many young men and women prolonged their education.

REVIEWING THE SECTION

1. How did the ideas of Sigmund Freud influence American thought?
2. Why did the Scopes trial attract world-wide attention?
3. How did new scientific theories and discoveries lead to a new conception of the universe? How did European refugees contribute to American science?
4. What changes were evident in the education of American students during the 1920's and 1930's?

MASS ENTERTAINMENT BECAME BIG BUSINESS

In the 1920's, Americans had more time for leisure than in the past and the money to pay for entertainment. As a result, manufacturers of sports equipment, movie makers, radio broadcasters, automobile manufacturers, promoters of sporting events, and entertainers of various kinds enjoyed a boom. The radio, the movies, the book clubs, and the chain newspapers reached Americans all over the country with the same songs, jokes, stories, and ideas. Popular culture became a nation-wide commodity.

Organized sports had long entranced Americans, but in the 1920's, such sports became practically a national obsession. This was the era of the "million dollar gate" in boxing and of nation-wide Saturday afternoon pilgrimages to college football stadiums. This was the era when big sports became as competitive as big business.

Like organized sports, the publishing of newspapers, magazines, and books in the period 1920 to 1940 became a bigger business than ever. At the end of the 1920's, about ninety-five per cent of the adults read newspapers, seventy-five per cent read magazines, and fifty per cent read books. The depression slowed the sale of books, but did not slow the interest in reading. Millions of jobless made use of public libraries, many of which served as clubs for men with little or no money.

America's foremost commercial amusement and the most glamorous form of popular entertainment in the 1920's and 1930's was the motion picture. It developed out of a device invented by Thomas A. Edison in 1896 called the kinetoscope. By peering into the kinetoscope, a person could see small figures move jerkily, thus the term motion picture. In a short time projectors were developed that threw flickering pictures on a screen which could be viewed by an audience. Soon crude theaters, called nickelodeons because they charged a nickel for admission, were set up all over the country. Thousands now flocked to the "flickers," to see short films that showed one incident, or episode.

A new instrument of news and education, the radio, changed the daily living habits of more Americans in the 1920's and 1930's than either the newspapers or the movies. Although invented earlier, radio did not begin to reach the people until 1919, when the government lifted a wartime ban on private radio facilities. The first fully licensed broadcasting station, KDKA in East Pittsburgh, began operation on the night of November 2, 1920, announcing returns in the Harding-Cox election. After that there were daily broadcasts, and a craze for radio surged over the nation.

In the early 1930's, the amount of money spent on sports and other entertainment decreased. Many people dropped their memberships in country clubs, gave up their baseball and football games, and instead participated more actively in sports. They tried to find ways to amuse themselves inexpensively, but entertainment remained a big business.

Spectator sports broke records

For the promoters of organized sports the 1920's were truly golden. Baseball teams, football teams, wrestling, boxing, and tennis matches drew huge crowds. Sports figures became national heroes. Robert T. "Bobby" Jones, who used a putter called "Calamity Jane," was considered the greatest golfer of all time. He climaxed his career in 1930 by winning the American and British amateur and open golf championships. In 1920, William T. Tilden became the first American man to win the world-famous tennis tournament held annually at Wimbledon, England. He dominated American tennis for a good part of the decade.

Knute Rockne, Notre Dame's football coach, became one of the most famous Americans. In 1925, Harold E. "Red" Grange, a football player at the University of Illinois who earned the title "Galloping Ghost," so captured the imagination of admirers that some of them circulated a petition seeking his nomination as a congressman, even though he was too young to hold office. So great was the prowess of George H. "Babe" Ruth of the New York Yankees that his fame helped boost baseball to a peak of popularity. Known as the mighty "Sultan of Swat," his string of home runs broke records. He hit 54 home runs in 1920, 59 in 1921, and 60 in 1927. World Series crowds broke records for attendance and gate receipts.

Jack Dempsey, known as the "Manassa Mauler," drew huge crowds to boxing matches, a brutal sport that achieved a tinsel glamor in the 1920's. In 1921, nearly 75,000 people paid more than $1.5 million to watch Dempsey knock out Georges Carpentier of France in four rounds. This was the first of the million-dollar gates. Six years later the era of frenzied spectator sports reached a climax in Chicago when Dempsey fought Gene Tunney for the heavyweight championship for the second time and lost. This fight attracted 145,000 spectators who paid a record gate of more than $2.6 million. Forty million heard a blow-by-blow account on the radio.

This craze for spectator sports diminished in the 1930's. Gate receipts in college football, boxing, and other sports also declined. Professional baseball continued to hold the interest of the public. The big star of the thirties was "Joltin Joe" DiMaggio of the Yankees. In boxing the king was Joe Louis, the "Brown Bomber" from Detroit. Track star Jesse Owens won four gold medals for the United States at the 1936 Olympic games held in Berlin.

Americans by the millions participated in sports such as golf, tennis, and basketball. Active participation in sports and other forms of recreation was more widespread in the 1930's than it had been in the 1920's. The government encouraged such activities by building—often as relief work projects —camp grounds, ski jumps, swimming pools, tennis courts, and playgrounds.

The tabloid invaded journalism

The trend of newspaper mergers that had started earlier in the century continued. As a result, there were fewer newspapers, but those which survived had larger circulations than in the past. Newspaper chains dominated the field. In the 1930's there were about sixty chains that published some three hundred newspapers with a total of more than one third of the daily circulation in the nation. Since the head office usually made policy for an entire chain, individual newspapers lost their former position as carriers of independent ideas. They became increasingly standardized with news from press associations, with opinions from syndicated columnists, and with features such as Sunday supplements compiled from a few central sources. The cable-car rider in San Francisco now read the same press dispatch and the same feature column as did the subway passenger in New York.

The most important newspaper development in this period was called "tabloid" journalism, a form of sensational journalism borrowed from England. The tabloid was a small, easy-to-handle newspaper, designed to appeal to the eye and to the emotions of the reading public. It made use of garish headlines printed in very large type and featured pictures, comic strips, and stories of violence and lust. The first American tabloid, the *New York Daily News,* was established in 1919. Five years later it had attained a circulation of 1.75 million, the largest in the country. Such success attracted numerous imitators. A survey of young people in New York in 1935 showed that two thirds of them read the tabloids, while one fifth of them read no other kind of newspaper.

Magazines, too, began to strive for appeal to the eye by making greater use of pictures combined with a short, simple narrative. Some serious magazines stopped publication during the depression. Magazines such as the *Saturday Evening Post,* and women's magazines which combined light fiction with some serious articles of contemporary interest continued to enjoy mass circulation. The big change began in 1923, when Henry Luce began publication of *Time,* a weekly digest of news presented in a crisp style with a conservative slant. In 1936, Luce introduced a picture magazine called *Life.* The success of these pioneer journals produced vigorous rivals in *Newsweek* and *Look.*

Book publishers found a key to the mass market through book clubs. This movement began with the Book-of-the-Month Club and the Literary Guild and became a vogue in the 1930's. "Experts" picked books which were sent by mail to thousands of club members, some of whom had never been inside a book store. Many club selections were of little value, but some were excellent; a few worthy books, therefore, received broad circulation. In addition, the book clubs helped increase the number of book buyers. In 1939, Pocket Books also helped widen the book market by publishing inexpensive, paperbound books that were sold in drug stores, train stations, and even in grocery stores.

Publishers continued to reach Americans with words and pictures. Newspapers, magazines, and books entertained as much as they informed.

Movies offered escape from reality

An important turning point came for motion pictures in 1915, when David W. Griffith produced *The Birth of a Nation*. Although this film about the Civil War and Reconstruction praised bigotry and did injustice to the Negro, it showed that movies could be a form of popular art. It gave the viewer panoramic shots of huge armies, battles, and mob scenes, and impressive close-ups of the actors. Others followed Griffith's technique, and movies became immensely popular. Hollywood, California, became the movie capital of the world, the source of a multimillion-dollar industry. By the middle of the 1920's, the movies, with a capital investment of $1.5 billion, ranked fourth among United States industries. By 1930, it was claimed that 100 million movie admissions were sold each week.

What the movie-goer usually got for his money was escape from reality into a land where everyone was rich, beautiful, and sophisticated, or where heroes were virile, strong, and always in the right. Women swooned when Rudolph Valentino, the "great lover" of the 1920's, breathed heavily or strode across the sands of the Sahara as a sheik. Other stars, such as Charlie Chaplin, Mary Pickford—"America's Sweetheart"—and Douglas Fairbanks, earned fabulous salaries, lived glamorously, and were popular idols.

The first full-length "all-talking, all-singing" movie, *The Jazz Singer,* starring Al Jolson, was shown in 1928. Even though movie attendance dropped during the depression, the talkies helped the motion-picture industry weather the hard times. In fact, the 1930's are considered Hollywood's golden decade. Even though most movies still concentrated on escape themes, many dealt with important social themes. In the 1930's, the movies often achieved a high technical quality. By 1935,

full color films were perfected. By 1939, attendance had risen, bringing receipts of nearly $700 million, an average of $25 per family for the year.

At its best, the motion picture brought art, fine drama, and splendid acting to the masses. At its worst it promoted intolerance and glorified a dream world. But most of the time it just brought entertainment.

Radio became a household gadget

Commercial radio came into existence when advertisers began sponsoring programs in 1922. Nation-wide network broadcasting started in 1926, when the National Broadcasting Company transmitted programs coast-to-coast over telephone lines. By 1930, over twelve million families, or more than forty per cent of the American people, had radios in their homes. The voice from the box could be heard everywhere, in crowded tenements as well as in secluded mansions.

In most other countries the national government owned the radio stations. People paid a tax to cover the costs of broadcasting. This system did away with annoying commercials, but it also offered opportunity for government propaganda and thought control. In 1927, when the American system of privately owned commercial stations threatened to become chaotic, Congress established the Federal Radio Commission to license stations, assign wave lengths, and establish hours for broadcasting. Seven years later the Federal Communications Commission took over the regulation of the radio industry.

Radio—through news, music, serial drama, comedy, sportscasts, and other features—brought the outside world into the parlors of millions. A crooner named Rudy Vallee was imitated in nearly every town in the country. Some radio serials became so popular they were almost national institutions. Many people believed that radio handled news more objectively than did newspapers, and they were probably right.

Even the depression failed to halt the growth of radio. In the 1930's, the average household had a radio blaring about four-and-a-half hours a day. By the beginning of 1940, some twenty-eight million homes—eighty six per cent of the population—had radios. The radio had become a household gadget.

Critics pointed out that much of what went out over the airwaves was trash, such as unending commercials and soap operas. There was also much that was fine, such as programs on the arts, current events, operas, and music.

REVIEWING THE SECTION

1. What spectator sports became popular among Americans during the 1920's and 1930's?
2. What trends were evident in the publishing industry during this period?
3. How did the motion-picture industry become one of major importance?
4. What developments took place in the commercial radio-broadcasting industry?

CHAPTER **24** CONCLUSION

In the 1920's business and the machine set the pace for American life. After the crash of 1929, the cult of the businessman lost much of its glamour and prestige, but business activity remained the most distinctive feature of American life. Even the blight of depression did not wipe out the broad streak of materialism that ran through American culture.

The technological revolution during the 1920's and 1930's led to the replacement of men in certain jobs by machines. Americans could now enjoy a richer life, with less back-breaking labor, than any people had known. In the booming 1920's men began working less and earning more than before. In the depression years, improvements in technology continued at a swift pace, but job opportunities diminished. This was one of many factors that kept the entire economy off balance. By the end of the 1930's, Americans were aware of this problem and wanted to do something about it.

In the 1920's, there arose for the first time in the nation's history a large, fairly distinct, and self-conscious body of intellectuals. Many writers, artists, and critics worked at their crafts as professionals, on a full-time basis. These young intellectuals rebelled against the traditions of the past, and were disillusioned with what they called the businessmen's culture. Feeling themselves cut off from the rest of the country, they considered themselves to be a "lost generation."

In the 1930's, the intellectuals lost their sense of alienation, and became less critical of society in the United States than they had been in the 1920's. Many returned from Paris far less rebellious than when they left, and with a new appreciation for life in the United States. The trials of the depression, which increased their resentment against the businessman's materialism, also gave them a feeling for social issues. Writers and artists concerned themselves with the common man and his problems.

The American writer and artist of the 1920's and 1930's had been influenced by new ideas in other fields of intellectual endeavor. These fields, in turn, showed that the intellectual world was international, not national, and that ideas had an interdependence in the physical and social sciences that made it difficult to speak of an American science as such.

Expanding sales in books, magazines, and newspapers reflected the growth of American population, and the increasing literacy of that population. These sales indicated, also, that in the 1920's and 1930's, Americans—a vast number of them, not just a small class—were better educated and had more time for leisure than ever before. This freedom from the grind of the job was one of the fruits of the industrial revolution that brought change into the daily lives of millions of Americans, and, as a result, entertainment for the masses became a big business.

Americans had always been a mobile people, but now in the 1920's and 1930's, the airplane and automobile helped make mobility a way of life. Along with radios, movies, consolidated schools, and churches, they helped break down the barrier between town and country. The culture of the United States was becoming the culture of the city. The splendid new literature, the arts, the books, the magazines, and even social attitudes now spread outward from the city. Language, manners, customs, and dress had national standards, set by radio announcers, movie actors, and others in the public eye. In the 1920's and 1930's, there was a nationalizing of American life on a massive scale. That trend was to continue in future decades.

FOCUSING ON SPECIFICS

1. How did the Republican administrations of the 1920's encourage industrial consolidation?

2. What techniques did businessmen use to control prices during the 1920's?

3. How did the federal government encourage the growth of the aviation industry?

4. Why were many American writers and artists of the 1920's critical of life in the United States?

5. How did the Great Depression influence American art and literature?

6. During the 1920's, how did many writers from the Midwest deal with Midwestern themes?

7. What was the contribution of the Armory Show (1913) to American art?

8. What changes took place in historical scholarship during the 1920's and 1930's? in the study of economics? in the study of psychology?

9. How did newspapers become more and more standardized during this period?

10. Why did the culture of the United States become the "culture of the city?"

REVIEWING MAIN THEMES

1. What changes took place in the distribution of the population in the 1920's and 1930's?

2. What trends were evident in United States industry during the 1920's and 1930's?

3. What developments took place in literature, art, and architecture during this period?

4. How did scientific achievements lead to new ideas in American thought?

5. What developments took place in the communications and entertainment industries?

EVALUATING THE ISSUES

1. In what ways can the 1920's be considered "conservative"? In what ways can they be considered "progressive"?

2. How do you account for the extraordinary creativity among writers of the 1920's and 1930's?

3. During the 1920's, mass communication led to the development of a mass culture. What was the significance of this development?

CHAPTER **25** 1932-1941

The End of Isolation

In his inaugural address on March 4, 1933, President Franklin D. Roosevelt had indicated that problems in world affairs would take second place to domestic affairs, especially to the problems of the depression. "I favor as a practical policy," he said, "the putting of first things first." He was, it seemed, determined to follow the traditional isolationist policies of the United States. While the New Deal experiments were taking place, however, the world was becoming increasingly troubled and before the end of his second administration, problems in world affairs overshadowed all domestic problems.

The President had indicated his isolationist attitude when he refused to coöperate in an attempt to stabilize the major money systems of the world at the International Economic Conference in London (June 1933). Secretary of State Cordell Hull, however, feared the effects of such economic nationalism. He finally convinced the President that the high tariff policy of the nation, which had resulted in trade wars against the United States, was slowing down economic recovery and causing unnecessary ill will toward the United States. The administration, therefore, proposed a series of reciprocal-trade agreements which Congress finally agreed to in June 1934.

Some Americans looked upon the program of the reciprocal-trade agreements as a means of combating the depression. With the same objective in mind, many Americans urged the recognition of the Soviet Union, hoping that this would increase trade with that nation. On November 16, 1933, the Soviets and the Americans exchanged notes that marked the formal recognition of the Soviet Union by the United States. Neither the evils nor the benefits that were supposed to follow recognition ever materialized.

In his first inaugural address, Roosevelt also had said: "In the field of foreign relations, I would dedicate this nation to the policy of the good neighbor." He applied that policy, essentially an expansion of Herbert Hoover's policy, to the nations of Latin America. This Good Neighbor policy, as it came to be known, eventually led to improved relations between the United States and Latin America. It also indicated a desire on the part of the United States to withdraw, to some extent at least, from active participation in the internal politics of the nations of the Western Hemisphere. The grant of conditional independence to the Philippines in 1934 has usually been interpreted by historians as indicating an attempted withdrawal by the Roosevelt administration from active participation in the international politics of Asia.

The continued belligerence of Japan in Asia, as well as the growing threat of war in Europe as a result of the rise of fascism and nazism there, strengthened the isolationist convictions of many, perhaps most, Americans. Americans wanted above all else, to keep out of war, and at first saw no real danger to themselves from the strutting dictators across the seas. Most Americans had become disillusioned and disappointed regarding the course of world affairs. Novels, movies, and histories all reflected this despair and disillusionment. Congress accepted the isolationist mood of the people and enacted laws designed to keep the country from being dragged into any foreign war.

By 1937, however, Roosevelt had become alarmed over the actions of Japan, Italy, and Germany. In a speech in Chicago in October, he condemned war, aggression, and "international lawlessness." When he said "there must be positive endeavors to preserve peace," he aroused a storm of protest from many Americans. It was clear that Americans would not easily abandon their chosen policy of isolation.

Events in Europe, however, increasingly threatened world peace. In the spring of 1938, Germany forcibly annexed Austria. At the Munich Conference several months later, Britain and France reluctantly agreed to German annexation of the Czechoslovakian Sudetenland in the hope of appeasing the Germans and averting a general war. In August 1939, Germany and the Soviet Union signed a nonaggression pact. With the fear of a two-front war removed, Germany, on September 1, 1939, invaded Poland. The long-anticipated and dreaded World War II had erupted.

The United States, fearful of being drawn into war once again, began to build up the nation's defenses. As the situation in Europe worsened for the Allies, American public opinion began to shift against Germany and Italy.

After his reëlection to an unprecedented third term, Roosevelt and his advisers worked out a plan for large-scale aid to Britain. By October 1941, the United States was firing on Nazi submarines and in November, Congress repealed the neutrality law. It was the Japanese attack on Pearl Harbor, however, which led Congress to declare war and to involve the American people in the world's greatest conflict.

ROOSEVELT MOVED SLOWLY IN FOREIGN AFFAIRS

Although President Roosevelt was determined to subordinate foreign problems to domestic problems, events which were taking place in Europe soon would make it difficult for him to do so.

About a month before Roosevelt became President, Adolf Hitler, a former corporal in the Austrian army who had been preaching doctrines of hate, war, and racism, became chancellor of Germany. Hitler headed the National Socialist German Workers party, popularly called the Nazi party, and in a few hectic weeks the Nazis swept away the remains of a crumbled German democracy, carried out revolutionary changes in German life, and made Hitler a dictator.

South of Germany, Italy already had fallen (1922) under a dark cloud of dictatorship. Like Hitler, Italy's dictator, Benito Mussolini, once had been a corporal. Although members of Mussolini's Fascist party were not committed to racial hatred as were the Nazis, they, too, used brutality, violence, and terror against their enemies. They, too, were enemies of democracy.

On the other side of the world, in Japan, military strong men were more and more shaping the nation to their will. Although they did not impose an absolute dictatorship on their nation, as Hitler and Mussolini had, they, too, preached ideas of violence, hatred, and war. About a week before Roosevelt's inauguration (March 4, 1933), the Japanese delegation defied world opinion and walked out of the League of Nations, never to return. Japan's military leaders were determined to consolidate their conquests in Manchuria and to embark on new ventures on China's mainland.

Of these three nations, Nazi Germany was the

most violent in its hatreds and the most powerful in the resources and technology of modern war; hence it was the most dangerous to democracies such as Britain, France, and the United States. While the United States Congress was passing laws in an effort to keep many Americans from starving and to restore their dignity as human beings, Nazi storm troopers were humiliating and beating up Jewish men, women, and children in the streets of German cities. The police just stood by and watched. Hitler soon withdrew Germany from the League of Nations and, even though he was forbidden to do so under the terms of the Treaty of Versailles, he began to rearm the nation and to rebuild the German armed forces.

At first, most Americans saw no great danger in the rise of the dictatorships, at least not to their own country, protected as it was by two great oceans. They wanted to be left alone and did not want their government to become involved in the troubles of other nations. In the early years of the New Deal, Roosevelt and many of his advisers shared this isolationist attitude. "Despite what happens in continents overseas," Roosevelt announced in October 1935, "the United States of America shall and must remain, as long ago the Father of our Country prayed that it might remain —unentangled and free."

For a while, Americans were able to minimize the importance of the events in Europe. The administration concerned itself primarily with domestic problems and in foreign affairs, dealt primarily with economic policy and relations with Latin-American nations.

Cordell Hull attempted to lower the tariff

After the International Economic Conference in London broke up, the nations of the world engaged in a kind of economic warfare. They raised tariff barriers against each other's goods and tried to solve economic problems only within their own national boundaries.

Roosevelt's economic nationalism and the failure of the International Economic Conference were severe blows to Secretary of State Cordell Hull, the head of the American delegation in London. He had devoted twenty-five years in Congress to a crusade for lower tariffs, and when he went to London he assumed the President supported his plan to work out agreements with other nations to lower tariffs on a reciprocal basis. Despite his disappointment, Hull did not give up his campaign to lower the traditional high-tariff policy of the United States through reciprocal-trade agreements.

Hull persisted in his efforts to lower tariff walls because he believed that increased international trade would keep peace. Economic warfare between nations, on the other hand, would lead to shooting wars. Despite the hostility of some of the early New Dealers to his views, Hull finally convinced the President that his idea was sound. In March 1934, Roosevelt asked Congress for authority to negotiate agreements with other nations for a mutual lowering of tariff duties.

Many businessmen objected because they feared competition from foreign goods if those goods came into the country easily. Republican congressmen objected because the President would gain added control over foreign policy. In the past, before approving trade agreements, Congress had discussed each one as though it were a treaty on a major issue. If the President got his way, Congress would give a blanket approval beforehand to reciprocal-trade agreements. Since the Democrats controlled both houses, Congress, in June 1934, passed the Reciprocal Trade Agreement Amendment to the Tariff Act of 1930.

This amendment permitted the President, with the advice of certain experts in the government, to make trade agreements with other nations without congressional approval, provided that the new duties did not vary from the existing duties by more than fifty per cent. Through a device called the most-favored-nation clause, any concession the United States granted to one nation would automatically extend to any other nation producing the item, if that nation had a trade treaty with the

United States and it did not discriminate against American goods.

By January 1940, the Roosevelt administration had concluded reciprocal-trade agreements with twenty-one countries. Even though these agreements touched sixty per cent of America's foreign trade, they never did achieve what Hull had expected of them. They did not greatly increase American trade, nor did they help keep the peace. They did help, however, in overcoming the international ill will toward the United States that had resulted from the Hawley-Smoot Tariff of 1930, and even won some good will in Latin America. This achievement, in a time of increasing economic nationalism and political tensions, may be considered significant.

The U.S. granted recognition to the Soviet Union

Since President Woodrow Wilson's time, every administration had refused to grant diplomatic recognition to the government of the Soviet Union. This policy was followed primarily because the Soviets had repudiated Russia's debts, confiscated private property, preached world revolution, and plotted the overthrow of capitalism.

Despite these obstacles, Roosevelt cautiously began to explore the basis for resuming relations with the Soviet Union. Two considerations apparently motivated him. First, he was willing to go along with the desire of businessmen to try to increase trade with the Soviet Union. Second, he saw that, in any showdown with Japan over her aggressive policies on the Asian mainland, it would be good to have the Soviet Union as a friend.

The Soviets accepted the American overtures and sent a negotiator, Maxim Litvinov, to Washington, D.C. With an exchange of notes on November 16, 1933, the United States formally recognized the Soviet Union. In return for recognition, the Soviet government promised, among other things, to extend religious liberty to Americans in the Soviet Union, to curb revolutionary activity in the United States, and to negotiate, at some future date, a settlement of the debts owed to Americans.

Critics argued that recognition of the Soviet Union would open a Pandora's box of evils. Actually, no real trouble grew out of the resumption of diplomatic relations with one of the world's great powers, a nation covering one sixth of the earth's land surface. On the other hand, few of the hoped-for benefits came from the new relationship. Trade with the Soviets did not increase; the Soviets continued their Communist propaganda; the debts were never settled; and no policy of coöperation against Japan was ever worked out during peacetime.

Roosevelt adopted the Good Neighbor policy

Roosevelt's recognition of the Soviet Union represented a reversal of one part of Hoover's foreign policy. To those Americans who advocated the continued application of the Roosevelt Corollary to the Monroe Doctrine, and to others, Roosevelt's Latin-American policy represented another such reversal. Although Roosevelt's policy did bring change—particularly in the spirit in which it was applied and in its obvious success—it was essentially a continuation and expansion of the policy Hoover had started. The United States, in order to become a "good neighbor," declared that it would not intervene in the affairs of Latin-American nations and that it would treat them as its equal in matters of common interest.

Latin Americans were not impressed by the first practical application of the Good Neighbor policy. In August 1933, the Cuban army overthrew a brutal dictator named Gerardo Machado. Another revolution followed, and a left-wing government under a university professor, Dr. Ramón Grau San Martín, gained power. Roosevelt sent warships to Cuban waters to stand by in case the lives of Americans were endangered by the revolution, but he did not order troops to land. At the same time, he refused to recognize the regime of Grau San Martín. In January 1934, this regime was overthrown and Roosevelt speedily recognized the conservative regime that followed.

Many Latin Americans believed that the use of warships and nonrecognition were forms of intervention in Cuba. Roosevelt, on the other hand, thought that his forbearance in the use of force was a practical application of the Good Neighbor policy. Later, in March 1934, he gave Latin Americans a more successful demonstration of the spirit of his Good Neighbor policy. He ended the Platt Amendment that gave the United States the right to intervene in Cuban affairs, but the United States retained its naval base at Guantánamo Bay, Cuba.

The Good Neighbor policy met its most difficult test in Mexico. From 1933 to 1936, the Mexican government quarreled with Roman Catholics and placed restraints on them. Some Roman Catholics in the United States demanded intervention, but Roosevelt refused. Then, in 1938, President Lázaro Cárdenas expropriated most of the foreign-owned oil companies in Mexico. Since the American companies involved believed the Mexican government would never compensate them, they demanded intervention by the United States government to regain their investments.

The United States government refused to intervene. It accepted Mexico's right to expropriate foreign property but insisted that payment for the property should be fair and prompt.

Finally, in November 1941, after long, bitter exchanges, the American and Mexican governments worked out a compromise settlement. Mexico accepted the American principle that expropriation required payment, but it paid the American oil companies far less than they demanded for their properties. Through all of the difficulties, Roosevelt clung to his Good Neighbor policy. He refused to intervene and even overlooked some of the claims of American investors in order to retain Mexico's good will.

Roosevelt's restraint in Mexico, Hull's reciprocal-trade policy, American renunciation of intervention at a conference in Montevideo, Uruguay, in December 1933, and the withdrawal of United States troops from Haiti in the following year—all contributed to the success of the Good Neighbor policy. Another less tangible reason for that policy's success was that the Latin Americans admired Roosevelt. They believed that in his New Deal at home he was showing a concern for the problems of the poor and oppressed and that this concern extended to them, for Latin America was a region where poverty and oppression never had been overcome. It was not surprising, therefore, that when Roosevelt visited Buenos Aires in 1936, more than half a million cheering Argentines greeted him.

REVIEWING THE SECTION

1. Why did the Roosevelt administration promote reciprocal-trade agreements?

2. Why had the United States refused before 1933 to grant recognition to the Soviet Union? Why did the Roosevelt administration grant this recognition?

3. In what ways did the Roosevelt administration apply the Good Neighbor policy?

THE UNITED STATES CLUNG TO ISOLATIONISM

In Asia, as in Latin America, Roosevelt followed essentially the same policy as his predecessor, Herbert Hoover. He refused recognition to Japan's puppet state, Manchukuo, and he coöperated in a limited way with the League of Nations on Asian matters. Some of his advisers wanted him to do more, to oppose Japan's expansion.

In March 1933, the same month Roosevelt took office, Japan annexed to Manchukuo the Chinese province of Jehol. Then the Japanese forced harsh truce terms on the Chinese. Most Americans disliked Japan's aggressive program and sympathized with China. They were not impressed when, in April 1934, a spokesman for the Foreign Office in Tokyo announced a "Japanese Monroe Doctrine" for Eastern Asia. Secretary of State Hull protested mildly and said that the United States would hold on to its treaty rights in China regardless of Japan's policy.

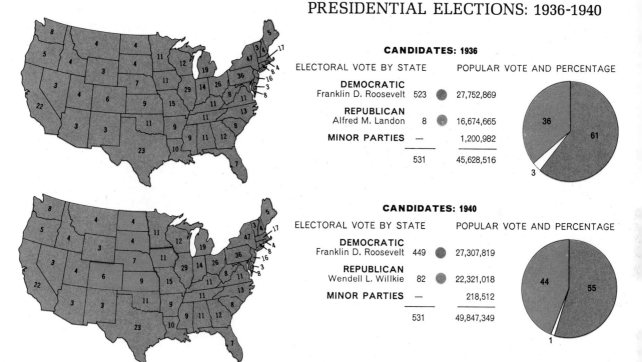

PRESIDENTIAL ELECTIONS: 1936-1940

CANDIDATES: 1936

ELECTORAL VOTE BY STATE	POPULAR VOTE AND PERCENTAGE
DEMOCRATIC Franklin D. Roosevelt 523	27,752,869
REPUBLICAN Alfred M. Landon 8	16,674,665
MINOR PARTIES —	1,200,982
531	45,628,516

CANDIDATES: 1940

ELECTORAL VOTE BY STATE	POPULAR VOTE AND PERCENTAGE
DEMOCRATIC Franklin D. Roosevelt 449	27,307,819
REPUBLICAN Wendell L. Willkie 82	22,321,018
MINOR PARTIES —	218,512
531	49,847,349

The Roosevelt administration did nothing more than to protest, partly because the American people were unwilling to support a stronger Far Eastern policy. They not only wanted to concentrate on the problems of the depression, but they also wanted to isolate themselves from the troubles in Asia. In addition, the President dealt cautiously with Japan because of his concern for the safety of the Philippine Islands and for other United States possessions in the Pacific Ocean.

The Philippines gained limited freedom

Almost from the moment of their acquisition the Philippines had been a source of concern to American policy-makers. As the years passed, it became increasingly evident that the islands could not be defended against Japan if that nation should decide to seize them. Many Americans considered the islands the key to increased trade with China, and these men had insisted on retaining possession

of the Philippines. The hoped-for trade was never realized, so, in the 1930's, more and more Americans were willing to allow the islands to become independent.

In January 1933, over President Hoover's veto, Congress passed the Hawes-Cutting Act, which offered independence to the Philippines after a ten-year period of transition from colonial status. In October, the Philippine legislature rejected the offer on the grounds that the real aim of the act was not to free the Philippines but to exclude Filipino laborers and products, such as tobacco and sugar, from the United States. The Philippine legislature was correct. Agricultural and labor pressure groups had agitated for the act because they wished to rid themselves of direct competition from Filipino products and workers.

In March 1934, Congress passed another law for Philippine independence, the Tydings-McDuffie Act, which was essentially the same as the earlier law except for a provision that called for the eventual removal of United States military posts and for the settlement by negotiation of the future status of United States naval bases there. Since the Philippine legislature could not obtain better terms, it accepted the Tydings-McDuffie Act. In November 1935, under a new government, the Commonwealth of the Philippines began to function as an almost independent state.

Historians have usually interpreted the Philippine policy of the Roosevelt administration as an effort to rid itself of a costly and indefensible burden, and as an attempt to modify or abandon the more aggressive Far Eastern policy of its predecessors. The effort to cling to isolation could not succeed primarily because the Philippines were not yet fully free; they were a part of Asia, and the United States had an obligation to protect them.

The dominant American mood was despair

As a result of the Great Depression, many Americans were bewildered and confused. In addition, most of them were disappointed and disillusioned about the state of world affairs. Woodrow Wilson's crusade to make the world safe for democracy obviously had failed, for democracies were crumbling or were on the defensive everywhere. The peacemakers of 1919 had not built a lasting peace. They had merely patched up a truce.

Novelists, political writers, and historians expressed this despair and thus intensified the isolationist mood. A school of historians who were known as revisionists—because they tried to revise traditional interpretations—investigated the causes of World War I. They concluded that considerable blame must be placed on the Allied side, that, in effect, American intervention on that side had been a mistake. The most popular of these revisionist histories was written by Walter Millis, a skilled newspaper man. His book *Road to War* (1935) cast doubt on the idea that Americans had fought for worthy ideals.

Others spread disillusion by implying that financiers and makers of munitions had brought on the war solely for personal profit. These men, one writer said, were "merchants of death."

Beginning in April 1934, a Senate committee headed by Gerald P. Nye, who was a Progressive Republican from North Dakota as well as an isolationist, investigated the armaments industry. During months of public hearings, the Nye Committee tried to establish the "merchants of death" thesis. Although there was no evidence to indicate that war profiteers had tricked the nation into war, many Americans believed the charge and concluded that intervention in World War I had been a mistake. They were determined that such a mistake should not be made again. They thought it could be prevented if the United States isolated itself politically from the rest of the world, if the possibility of making a profit from war were removed, and if the President's power to decide matters of war and peace were curbed.

Congress passed neutrality laws

Congress accepted the isolationist reasoning of its investigators and enacted laws designed to keep the nation from being dragged into any foreign war. The Neutrality Act of August 1935 provided for an embargo on arms to all belligerents as soon as the President proclaimed the existence of a state of war. The law also authorized him to discourage Americans from traveling on belligerent ships by warning them they would do so at their own risk.

In October 1935, Mussolini's Fascist troops invaded Ethiopia without a declaration of war. Roosevelt, nonetheless, proclaimed that a state of war existed, and he applied the Neutrality Act to both sides. The League of Nations condemned Italy as an "aggressor" and voted to impose *economic sanctions* (an embargo) against her. Roosevelt and Secretary of State Hull then attempted a one-sided "moral embargo" by urging that Americans voluntarily stop selling oil, steel, and other supplies (in addition to arms) to Italy. The moral embargo and the League sanctions failed to stop the Fascist conquest of Ethiopia.

In February 1936, Congress passed the second Neutrality Act. It extended the embargo provisions so as to include other materials besides arms and it prohibited loans to belligerents. A week later Hitler sent troops into the demilitarized zones of the Rhineland in violation of the Treaty of Versailles. No one tried to stop the Germans, for most European countries were concerned about the war between Italy and Ethiopia.

In July 1936, the Spanish army touched off a civil war in Spain. Since the neutrality law did not apply to a civil conflict, Roosevelt asked American exporters not to sell arms to either side in the Spanish war. This request changed a long-standing policy which had permitted legitimate governments—but not rebels—to buy arms from American companies. When the voluntary embargo failed, Roosevelt asked Congress to extend the neutrality law to include civil wars. This Congress did in January 1937.

Liberals in the United States were disappointed in Roosevelt's policy. The Spanish Civil War had become a miniature international war. Italy and Germany gave open aid to the army while the Soviet Union gave limited assistance to the Loyalist government. Liberals charged that, by failing to distinguish between victim and aggressor, American policy helped the enemies of democracy.

The danger from fascism appeared greater when, in 1936, Italy and Germany signed a treaty establishing a Rome-Berlin Axis and, in 1937, enlarged it with the addition of Japan. Although this Anti-Comintern Pact, or Rome-Berlin-Tokyo Axis, was supposedly directed against communism, it united three nations that were contemptuous of democracy and of peace.

At the same time, Congress made permanent the neutrality law, which was about to expire. The third Neutrality Act (May 1937) extended indefinitely most features of the old law and added two new provisions. It made illegal the travel of Americans on belligerent ships, and it permitted warring nations to buy goods in the United States only if they paid cash on delivery and carried those goods away in their own ships. This "cash and carry" provision was limited to two years.

Critics argued that the neutrality laws abandoned American rights at sea and, by making no distinction between friend and foe, actually endangered the security of the United States. Yet the laws were popular with the people at large. Isolationist America looked upon these laws as a safeguard against involvement in a great war.

Roosevelt challenged the isolationists

On the night of July 7, 1937, while tensions in Europe were still high, Japanese and Chinese troops clashed at the Marco Polo bridge, nine miles southwest of Peiping (Peking). A few weeks later Japanese soldiers invaded China, and war began. Japan refused to declare war, however, and referred to the conflict as the "China incident."

President Roosevelt—who, like most Americans, favored the Chinese—took advantage of Japan's refusal to declare war. He deliberately did not recognize a state of war in China. As a result, he did not have to invoke the neutrality law; and Americans continued, legally, to ship arms and other supplies to China.

Alarmed by Japan's warlike actions and by the Rome-Berlin Axis, Roosevelt wanted to awaken others to the danger he saw. In a speech on October 5, 1937, in Chicago, the center of isolationist sentiment, he warned Americans that no nation, not even the United States, was immune from attack. None could escape "through mere isolation or neutrality." He urged an international "quarantine" of the disease of lawlessness.

Those who believed in collective security were pleased, for they thought Roosevelt had broken with the isolationists. But isolationist leaders and many other Americans reacted to the speech with anger. Some of the President's closest advisers warned him that he had gone too far in challenging the isolationists. Roosevelt himself was so shocked by the vigor of the isolationist response that he gave up the idea of a quarantine.

As the President had warned, Americans were not immune from attack. On December 12, 1937, Japanese planes bombed, strafed, and sank the gunboat *Panay,* while it was escorting tankers of an American oil company on the Yangtze River in China. Two Americans were killed and thirty were wounded. The Japanese government quickly apologized and offered to pay for the damage inflicted. Even though the attack on one of their warships was deliberate, most Americans took the matter calmly, and the crisis in Japanese-American relations soon passed.

Fear that the crisis might lead to war speeded up action in Congress on a proposed amendment to the Constitution sponsored by Louis Ludlow, a representative from Indiana. The Ludlow amendment would have required majority approval, by a nation-wide vote, before the United States could go to war—except in case of an invasion of the United States or its territorial possessions. The amendment had wide support. Only intense pressure from Roosevelt prevented Congress from adopting the proposal and thus giving a victory to the isolationists who wished to curtail the President's power over foreign policy. The Ludlow proposal was made at the high tide of isolationist sentiment in the United States.

REVIEWING THE SECTION

1. Why did Congress decide to grant independence to the Philippines? Why did the Philippine legislature reject the first act granting the islands independence but reluctantly accept the second?

2. Why did many Americans believe that the United States entry into World War I had been a mistake?

3. How did the United States respond to the Italian attack on Ethiopia? to the Spanish Civil War? to the *Panay* incident?

THE UNITED STATES BECAME A NONBELLIGERENT

It became increasingly difficult for Americans to isolate themselves from the events in Europe.

In March 1938, Adolf Hitler again violated the Treaty of Versailles. He marched his Nazi troops into Austria and annexed that nation to Germany. No one tried to stop him, not even the Austrians.

Hitler next threatened Czechoslovakia, saying that the Sudetenland, the western region of Czechoslovakia where some three million Germans lived, must become a part of Germany. The Czechs, who had defensive alliances with France and the Soviet Union, refused to give up the Sudetenland without a fight. Tension built up everywhere in Europe. In September 1938, Europe seemed ready to plunge into another great war.

Roosevelt intervened in the crisis by pleading for peace in messages to the national leaders involved. The pleas seemed to have no effect on Hitler, who delivered an ultimatum to the Czechs: they could either surrender to his demands or fight for the Sudetenland. Hitler finally agreed to a conference, held at Munich on September 29 and 30, 1938. At that meeting Hitler, Mussolini, Prime Minister Neville Chamberlain of Britain, and Premier Edouard Daladier of France arranged the dismemberment of Czechoslovakia. (Poland and Hungary also seized parts of Czechoslovakia.) By thus appeasing Hitler, the western European democracies postponed war, but they failed to secure what Chamberlain optimistically said that they had obtained—"peace in our time."

Most Americans thought Munich's results meant peace. In November, Nazi brutality shattered the illusion. The Nazis, in retaliation for the assassination of a German diplomat by a young Jew in Paris, attacked Jews, burned their homes, synagogues, and stores. Roosevelt was appalled; all America was sickened. The President, to indicate his strong disapproval, recalled the United States ambassador from Germany.

Roosevelt opposed the aggressors

In October 1938, when the President announced that he was devoting a special sum of $300 million to armaments, he showed his concern for the safety

THE PRESIDENTS OF THE UNITED STATES

WARREN G. HARDING
(1865-1923)
IN OFFICE: 1921-1923

CALVIN COOLIDGE
(1872-1933)
IN OFFICE: 1923-1929

Republican from Ohio. The major achievement of the Harding administration was the limitation of naval armaments agreed upon at the international conference held in Washington, D.C., in 1922-1923. A short time after the death of Harding, the exposure of corruption involving some of his appointments damaged the reputation of his administration.

Republican from Massachusetts. During Coolidge's administration, the nation enjoyed a period of prosperity. Like his predecessor, Coolidge favored conservative business interests. He reduced tax rates and at the same time reduced the national debt. In 1928, the United States signed the Kellogg-Briand Pact which renounced war as a national policy.

HERBERT C. HOOVER
(1874-1964)
IN OFFICE: 1929-1933

FRANKLIN D. ROOSEVELT
(1882-1945)
IN OFFICE: 1933-1945

Republican from California. Because he was afraid that federal intervention would destroy individualism, Hoover hesitated to extend the role of the federal government in combatting the depression of 1929. However, in 1931, he requested that Congress establish the Reconstruction Finance Corporation to help industry recover. His efforts were not enough to restore prosperity.

Democrat from New York. Roosevelt's program to combat the depression shifted more power from the states to the central government. During his third term, the United States became involved in World War II (1939-1945). His decisions at various conferences during the war helped to determine national policies in the post-war world. He died soon after his election to an unprecedented fourth term.

of the nation. In his annual message to Congress, in January 1939, he gave clear evidence that he had given up any lingering attachment to isolationism. He told Congress that American action through "methods short of war" might help in curbing the aggressors. What he wanted from Congress was repeal of the neutrality law so that he could make American arms available to friendly nations. This request warned the aggressors that he was opposed to them.

Within a few months the dictators showed that Roosevelt's fear was well founded. In March 1939, only six months after saying he had no more territorial ambitions in Europe, Hitler's troops invaded and overran what was left of Czechoslovakia. In April, Mussolini took over Albania. Next, Hitler threatened Poland. This threat led Britain and France to abandon their appeasement of Hitler and to guarantee Poland's boundaries. War now seemed certain.

As the war crisis intensified, Roosevelt denounced the dictators and refused to recognize their easy conquests; then he asked the dictators to promise not to attack other nations. If they gave that pledge, he said, the United States would join other nations in efforts to ease international tensions. Hitler and Mussolini paid little attention to the President's appeal. On May 28, 1939, they concluded a military alliance. Roosevelt's diplomacy had accomplished nothing.

Meanwhile, Japan continued her assault on China and threatened French Indochina, the Philippines, and the Netherlands East Indies. Roosevelt had already registered his disapproval of Japan's actions by asking American manufacturers to place a voluntary moral embargo on war goods going to Japan. In July 1939, in response to pressure from Congress, he notified Japan that her commercial treaty of 1911 with the United States would expire in 1940 and would not be renewed. This notice cleared the way for economic sanctions against Japan.

At the same time, the President kept up pressure on Congress for repeal of the neutrality law.

Secretary of State Cordell Hull even predicted war in Europe by the end of summer. He pleaded that France and Britain desperately needed supplies that were denied them by the law. The isolationist sentiment was too strong to be overcome, however, and on August 4, 1939, Congress adjourned with the neutrality law unchanged.

During this time the British and French were trying to persuade Joseph Stalin, the pipe-smoking, iron-fisted dictator of the Soviet Union, to join them in stopping Hitler. Stalin distrusted them because he feared they wanted Russia to take the full impact of a Nazi attack. He also wanted concessions from Poland which the French and British were unwilling to seek. So, on August 23, 1939, to the surprise of the world, he concluded a nonaggression treaty with Nazi Germany. This pact freed Hitler of the fear of a Communist attack when he invaded Poland.

Hitler then demanded that Poland return territory that had once belonged to Germany. The Poles refused and, on September 1, 1939, German soldiers marched across the Polish frontier. Two days later, Britain and France declared war on Germany. At the last minute Roosevelt had pleaded with the dictators to save the peace and had offered himself as a conciliator. His efforts failed. Once again, war had come to Europe.

The neutrality law was changed

In a fireside chat soon after the war broke out, the President promised the people he would keep the nation out of the conflict. He then issued several proclamations of neutrality.

No one doubted the sentiments of the American people. Overwhelmingly, they blamed the Nazis for the war and wanted to see them defeated. Most Americans were also determined to stay out of the war but seemed to have a fatalistic fear that somehow they would be drawn into it.

This fear became evident when Congress, called into special session three weeks after Hitler attacked Poland, considered Roosevelt's renewed request for a revision of the neutrality law. Isolationists put up a stiff resistance but, after six weeks of debate, Roosevelt got what he wanted—a repeal of the embargo on arms. The new law, the Neutrality Act of November 1939, reëstablished the "cash and carry" provision, which had expired under the old law. Now, at least, the Allies could buy American guns and other equipment, if they could carry away their own purchases.

Since this fourth neutrality act retained many provisions of the old law, it still had appeal for the isolationists. One important new feature was a concession to the isolationists—the law designated certain areas as combat zones and prohibited American ships from going there. British and French ports were in the combat zones; the provision, therefore, had the effect of assisting a German blockade of those ports.

This aspect of the law became clear after Hitler crushed Poland in a *blitzkrieg,* a sudden, overpowering attack which resulted in almost immediate victory, and then divided that helpless country with Stalin, whose troops had moved in from the east. Hitler then began shifting his troops from Poland to confront the French and British in the west. During these winter months of 1939-1940, often called the period of the "phony war" because there was no serious fighting on the western front, Britain attempted a naval blockade of Germany. Hitler tried to strangle Britain, which needed imports in order to survive, with a submarine blockade. His submarines and magnetic mines, planted at the entrance to British harbors, destroyed many precious Allied ships, many of which were loaded with goods from the United States.

The combat zones provided for in the neutrality law were designed to insulate the United States from the war, as was a resolution passed at the first meeting of the Foreign Ministers of the American Republics at Panama, in September 1939. This Declaration of Panama announced sea safety zones around the Western Hemisphere, south of Canada. The belligerents were not supposed to undertake any naval actions in the zones. This

effort to insulate most of the Western Hemisphere never worked. The belligerents refused to accept the prohibition.

The ineffectiveness of the neutrality zone, violated by German and British warships in December 1939, was disturbing. Even more disturbing to most Americans was the Soviet Union's attack on Finland on November 30. The Finns put up a heroic resistance in what was called the "winter war." In March 1940, however, they were forced to surrender and meet Soviet demands. These demands included a surrender of some Finnish territory. Americans admired the Finns and wanted to help them, but the Finns received little more than sympathy from the United States.

The United States built up its defenses

In April 1940, a month after the end of the winter war in Finland, the phony war ended. Nazi forces invaded Denmark and Norway and quickly occupied those nations. A month later German armored columns sliced into Belgium, the Netherlands, and Luxembourg, and then pierced France's defenses. Britain's new prime minister, Winston Churchill, and France's premier, Paul Reynaud, begged Roosevelt for help but, because of the neutrality law, the President could do little.

On June 10, 1940, Italy joined the war on Germany's side and invaded France from the south. Twelve days later, in the same railroad car in the Compiègne forest where Germany had agreed to the armistice in 1918, France signed an armistice with Hitler. Under the terms of the armistice, France north of the Loire River and the entire Atlantic coast would be occupied and administered by the Germans; the remainder, later called Vichy France, would have some autonomy. The world was stunned by the tragedy of France, and by the overwhelming victory of the Germans. Americans awoke to a new sense of peril. Only Britain stood between them and Hitler's well-armed legions.

During the blitzkrieg the President asked for huge appropriations to mechanize the army and to create a massive air force. Congress responded quickly. When France fell, Roosevelt feared that Hitler might bring together the German, Italian, French, and—if he could bring them to surrender—the British fleets. This would permit him to overwhelm United States naval forces. In June, therefore, the President asked Congress for money to build a two-ocean navy, one that could meet both the Japanese and German threats. Congress appropriated more than $5 billion ($4 billion for the navy alone), a peacetime record for armaments. In June, Roosevelt set up the National Defense Research Committee to work on new weapons. It ran a race against time to build an atomic bomb, which German scientists were also trying to construct.

In this same fateful June of 1940, a bill was introduced in Congress calling for compulsory military service. In September, after months of debate, marked by bitter opposition from all over the nation, Congress passed the nation's first peacetime draft law.

After the fall of France, the Roosevelt administration took steps for defense of the Western Hemisphere. In the second meeting of the Foreign Ministers of the American Republics, held in Havana in July, the ministers were persuaded to adopt resolutions that their nations would coöperate in defending the hemisphere against outside attack. For the first time the Latin-American republics agreed to take responsibility for carrying out the defensive principle of the Monroe Doctrine.

On August 17, 1940, Roosevelt met Prime Minister William Lyon Mackenzie King of Canada at Ogdensburg, New York. On the next day the two leaders announced the formation of the Permanent Joint Board on Defense. By providing for the defense of the northern part of the Western Hemisphere, this agreement complemented the Havana declarations.

Roosevelt abandoned traditional neutrality

The need for time to build up the nation's defenses had prompted Roosevelt to move cautiously against Japan's "new order" in Asia. When the commercial treaty of 1911 expired in January 1940, for instance, he did not impose economic sanctions on the Japanese. Then Hitler's smashing victories in Europe made the Japanese grow bolder. They stepped up their war in China and menaced British, French, and Dutch colonies in Asia.

In July 1940, therefore, Roosevelt ordered an embargo on the shipment of airplane gasoline, scrap steel, and other war materials. This was the beginning of economic sanctions.

Japan protested but did not stop her army. In August, Japanese troops advanced into French Indochina and took over some bases there. The United States responded on September 26, 1940, with a complete embargo on the shipment of scrap iron and steel to Japan. The next day in Berlin, Japan's representative signed an alliance with Germany and Italy called the Tripartite Pact. Roosevelt and his advisors now assumed that the fighting in Asia and Europe were linked to form one war.

During this perilous summer of 1940, the United States declared economic war against Germany and Italy, as well as against Japan. American public opinion, as measured by polls, approved these actions designed to aid the Allies. Roosevelt switched from a policy of technical neutrality to one of nonbelligerency (helping Britain as the best means of defending the United States). A powerful American pressure group, the Committee to Defend America by Aiding the Allies, helped make this view popular.

Winston Churchill hoped this policy of nonbelligerency would soon lead to United States intervention in the war on the side of Britain. He hoped that the American people would be stirred into joining the war against Hitler when they learned about the destruction of British cities by wave after wave of Nazi planes in a pre-invasion attack. United States intervention did not come.

In July 1940, Churchill made a desperate plea for some old American destroyers left over from World War I to replace British destroyers lost to Nazi planes. Roosevelt wanted to give the ships but feared the legal and political consequences. He doubted that he had the authority to give them away, and he feared that isolationists would block any move on his part to gain that authority from Congress. Finally, he assumed he had the authority, and by-passed Congress.

In September 1940, in exchange for eight air and naval bases on British possessions from Newfoundland to South America, Roosevelt transferred to the British fifty of the old destroyers—some of them barely seaworthy. He did this by executive agreement instead of by treaty which would have required the Senate's approval. In addition to the domestic problems involved, the destroyers-for-bases agreement violated international law and made the United States virtually an ally of Britain.

Isolationists were so alarmed that the day after the President announced the transaction they formed the America First Committee. It soon became the most powerful isolationist organization. Despite isolationist opposition, most Americans apparently approved of the destroyers-for-bases agreement. They believed it was possible to give Britain "all aid short of war" and still avoid direct involvement in the war.

REVIEWING THE SECTION

1. Why did Roosevelt try to obtain the repeal of the neutrality law of 1937? Why did he fail?

2. What were the provisions of the Neutrality Act of 1939? How did it aid the Germans?

3. What actions taken during the summer of 1940 made the United States a nonbelligerent rather than a neutral?

THE U.S. ABANDONED ISOLATION

Roosevelt was so concerned over the course of the war that he had decided to challenge the tradition, established by George Washington, that no man should serve more than two terms as President. He kept this decision to himself until after the Democratic convention had opened in Chicago, in July 1940. This strategy prevented any other Democrat from building up a following impressive enough to win the nomination.

The battle for the Republican nomination, on the other hand, was wide open. The Republicans finally chose as their candidate Wendell Willkie of Indiana, a political novice who, as the president of a public utility company, had gained national prominence fighting the Tennessee Valley Authority. Willkie had been a Democrat and favored aid to Britain.

Democratic politicians and liberal New Dealers all wanted Roosevelt to seek a third term. The President pretended to give in to this pressure and to accept the nomination reluctantly.

Since both Roosevelt and Willkie were internationalists, isolationism was never a truly important issue in the campaign. Yet the campaign itself revealed that fear of war was widespread. Many Americans who were isolationists from deep conviction felt that they had no effective way of expressing their opposition to a foreign policy they believed would lead to war.

Willkie fought a tough campaign, but failed to dislodge "the old champ." Roosevelt, who promised to keep the nation out of war, won reelection to a third term with 27.3 million popular votes and 449 electoral votes. Willkie, with 22.3 million popular votes and 82 electoral votes, had made a better showing than any loser since 1916. In addition, Democrats lost seats in Congress so that their majorities were reduced. Regardless of the domestic implications of the election, Roosevelt chose to consider it as a mandate for his foreign policy.

The U.S. became an arsenal of democracy

Well before the election results were in, it was evident that Britain was nearly bankrupt, near exhaustion, and incapable of surviving without generous aid from the United States. After the election, Churchill asked Roosevelt for such help in a "decisive act of non-belligerency." The President was willing to do just that. In a fireside chat in

December 1940, he told the people that the United States "must be the great arsenal of democracy" and give more help to Britain, even at the risk of war. The fate of the United States, he explained to Congress a few days later, was linked to the struggle in Europe.

In working out a plan for large-scale aid, Roosevelt and his advisers remembered the bitterness of Americans over the war-debt payments in the 1930's. They wanted to prevent a similar difficulty in the future, so they presented a plan, the Lend-Lease bill, to Congress in January 1941. This bill would permit the President to lend or lease arms and other goods to America's friends. After the war, in theory, the guns and tanks could be returned and no payment would be required.

For two months, argument swirled around the bill. Isolationist groups, such as the America First Committee, did everything they could to defeat the measure, but they failed. It won approval in both Houses of Congress and became law in March 1941. Lend-Lease, deceptively titled "An Act to Promote the Defense of the United States," allowed goods to go to any nation the defense of which the President considered vital to the security of the United States. Lend-Lease was another unneutral act, an unofficial declaration of war against the Axis, and another link added to the unwritten alliance tying the United States to Britain.

Before Lend-Lease could go into effect, hard-pressed Britain suffered further setbacks. Late in October 1940, Mussolini's Fascists invaded Greece, but met humiliating defeats there as well as in North Africa against the British. Hitler came to the aid of his ally. In April 1941, German soldiers conquered Yugoslavia and Greece, pushed British forces out of Greece, and mounted punishing attacks on British troops in North Africa.

At the same time, Nazi U-boats stepped up attacks on British shipping in the Atlantic to break the flow of American supplies to Britain. The submarines attacked in swarms called "wolf packs" and sank ships much faster than the British could replace them. To help the British reduce their losses, Roosevelt ordered American naval vessels to help the British in antisubmarine patrols. This action led to clashes between United States destroyers and Nazi U-boats.

In April 1941, the President signed an agreement with Denmark, temporarily placing Greenland, a Danish possession, under American control so that American ships could patrol the sea routes near there. It became clear that if ships carrying lend-lease goods were to get to Britain in quantity, the United States Navy would have to convoy ships carrying them, but the Lend-Lease Act prohibited United States convoys. Roosevelt got around this prohibition for a while by calling American ships on antisubmarine duty "on patrol." By the end of June 1941, the United States Navy was actively protecting the shipment of goods to Britain.

Americans fought an undeclared naval war

While becoming more deeply involved in the war in the Atlantic, Roosevelt also took bolder action against the Japanese. He increased aid to China, but would not agree to an alliance with China and Britain, requested by Chiang Kai-shek, China's ruler, to counterbalance the Tripartite Pact. The United States government did apply economic sanctions against Japan bit by bit in the hope that the ever-tightening restrictions would keep the Japanese from further expansion without provoking immediate war. The government also built up defenses in the Philippines and Guam and made plans with the British and French for the defense of their colonial possessions in the Pacific against Japanese attack.

Japan's leaders prepared for a showdown with the United States. In April 1941, Japan signed a neutrality treaty with the Soviet Union that would protect her northern frontiers in case of war with the United States and Britain. At the same time the Japanese ambassador in Washington, D.C., Admiral Kichisaburo Nomura, held conversations with Secretary of State Cordell Hull in an apparent effort to avoid war.

These talks went on for months; and by June 1941, they were stalemated. Basically, the United States wanted Japan to get out of China and to promise not to attack lands in the Southwest Pacific, such as the Netherlands East Indies. Japan wanted the United States to end its economic sanctions and to recognize Japan's conquests in China.

At this point, a startling event changed the course of the war in Europe. On June 22, 1941, Hitler sent his armored columns roaring into the vast plains of the Soviet Union. This attack changed the American outlook on world affairs. Now Americans no longer feared the immediate collapse of Britain from a Nazi assault. The Nazi invasion also increased the possibility of a Japanese attack against lands in Southwest Asia, because the Japanese now were certain that the Soviet Union would be too busy to threaten Japan from the north.

To buy time for building up defenses, Roosevelt sent aid, and ultimately lend-lease supplies, to the Russians, who were putting up a stiff resistance against the Nazi invaders. In July 1941, he pushed the United States defense zone far out into the Atlantic by occupying Iceland with United States troops. As a result, the United States Navy could protect British and American ships more than halfway across the sea.

A month later Prime Minister Churchill traveled across the sea for a secret meeting with Roosevelt on a warship at Placentia Bay, Newfoundland. There the two men arranged a convoy system for British and United States ships in the North Atlantic. They also issued a declaration of principles called the Atlantic Charter, which stated that both nations were opposed to aggression and would work for a better postwar world. More important than the highly publicized principles was the fact that the charter announced a common purpose behind the increasingly intimate, but unwritten, Anglo-American alliance.

Roosevelt had to find some way to tell the people about the decision to use American ships to escort the convoys without arousing isolationist opposition. His opportunity came on September 4, 1941, when a harassed German submarine fired on a United States destroyer, the *Greer,* near Iceland. On September 11, he announced that he had ordered convoy escorts and that ships of the United States Navy would shoot Axis ships, "rattlesnakes of the Atlantic," on sight.

In October, United States warships and Nazi submarines exchanged fire, and the shooting war began. In November 1941, Congress repealed, by a slim margin, the ineffective neutrality law. United States merchant ships could now be armed, and with the end of combat zones they could deliver guns and planes right to British ports. The United States had entered a state of undeclared naval war in the Atlantic.

Japan attacked Pearl Harbor

The final decision for all-out war did not come in the Atlantic, as many Americans feared it would, but in the Pacific. After the Nazi invasion of the Soviet Union, Japan's militarists decided that the time had come for massive expansion southward. Since American naval cryptographers, in operation "Magic," had broken Japan's secret diplomatic code, Roosevelt and a few of his closest advisers were able to follow, in many instances, the inner workings of Japanese policy-making.

In July 1941, much to America's displeasure, Japan demanded that France allow her to occupy southern French Indochina. Helpless, France's government at Vichy gave in. Next, Japan menaced the Netherlands East Indies, British Malaya, and the Philippines. Roosevelt, supported by Britain, her dominions, and others, retaliated with drastic economic sanctions. This extensive embargo cut off essential supplies, such as oil, for Japan's war machine. Japan's leaders, faced with economic ruin, had to decide whether to stop their expansion, as America desired, or go on to conquer lands which held the materials they needed.

The militarists wanted war, which would mean a strike against the United States because it stood

MAJOR EVENTS IN UNITED STATES FOREIGN AFFAIRS: 1920-1941

1920-1935 (From the end of World War I to the neutrality legislation of 1935)

STATEMENTS OF POLICY

1921-1924 *Immigration. Emergency Quota Act* and *National Origins Act* greatly restricted immigration of southern and eastern Europeans. Most Asians were completely barred by the law of 1924 which superseded the Gentlemen's Agreement of 1907-1908 with Japan. These laws reversed the traditionally liberal U.S. immigration policy.

1929-1935 *Good Neighbor policy* toward Latin America was initiated by Hoover, who denounced dollar diplomacy and returned to the traditional policy of recognizing national governments in effective control. He disapproved of interventions and began removal of troops from Nicaragua and Haiti. Roosevelt expanded Hoover's policy of nonintervention in Latin America. U.S. declared that it would treat Latin-American nations as its equal in matters of common interest. In 1934, U.S. abrogated the Platt Amendment of 1901, relinquishing the right to intervene in Cuban affairs. Cuba ceased to be a protectorate. Upon withdrawal of remaining troops from Haiti (1934), for the first time since 1915 there were no U.S. troops in Latin America.

1930 *Clark memorandum on the Monroe Doctrine,* issued by Hoover to support his policy of nonintervention, repudiated the Roosevelt Corollary of 1904. Thus U.S. intervention in Latin America no longer could be justified under the Monroe Doctrine.

1932 *Hoover-Stimson Doctrine.* U.S. refused to recognize Japan's conquest of Manchuria made in violation of the Open Door principle and the Kellogg-Briand Pact, which Japan had signed.

1933 *U.S. recognition of the Soviet Union.* Recognition had been delayed since 1917.

1935 *Neutrality Act of 1935,* first of a series of neutrality laws, provided for an arms embargo against all belligerents, whenever the President declared that a state of war existed. The act was applied when Mussolini invaded Ethiopia.

TERRITORIAL SETTLEMENTS AND ACQUISITIONS

1934 *Tydings-McDuffie Act* provided for independence of the Philippine Islands after a 10-year transition period as a commonwealth.

ECONOMIC POLICY AND COMMERCIAL TREATIES

1931 *Hoover Moratorium.* A 1-year suspension of payments on debts among Allies of World War I and on German reparations—proposed by the President during the world-wide depression. Hoover hoped to renegotiate the debt agreements, but no formal settlement was ever made.

1932 *St. Lawrence Seaway Treaty,* signed by the U.S. and Canada, provided for joint construction of waterway from the Gulf of St. Lawrence to inland ports on the Great Lakes, contem-

plated as early as 1920. The treaty was not confirmed by the Senate.

1933 *International Economic Conference* met at London in an attempt to stabilize the world's major money systems. But Roosevelt adopted a policy of economic nationalism, placing domestic recovery before international financial coöperation, and the conference failed.

1934 *Reciprocal Trade Agreement Amendment* to the Tariff Act of 1930 authorized the President to make agreements with other nations for a mutual adjusting of tariff duties. This act was the beginning of a more liberal U.S. tariff policy and cleared the way for many reciprocal trade agreements up to the 1960's.

DIPLOMACY OF WAR PREVENTION

1921-1922 *Washington Naval Disarmament Conference*—participated in by U.S., Britain, Japan, France, Italy, China, Belgium, the Netherlands, and Portugal—resulted in the first international agreement for naval limitation and in treaties endeavoring to settle problems in the Far East. *Five-Power Treaty* (1922) halted the building of large warships for 10 years and limited the ratio the number of ships allowed the leading naval powers—U.S., Britain, Japan, France, and Italy. *Four-Power Pact* (1921) bound U.S., Britain, Japan, and France to respect each other's rights and possessions in the Pacific and to discuss in conference any future problems concerning them. *Nine-Power Open Door Treaty* (1922) bound all the participating nations to respect the Open Door principle in China and China's independence and territorial integrity.

1922-1935 *League of Nations.* At first, the U.S. sent unofficial observers and, later, official representatives in an advisory capacity to league conferences. Coöperation continued under Coolidge, Hoover, and Roosevelt, but the U.S. never officially joined the league.

1928 *Kellogg-Briand Pact* (Pact of Paris) pledged U.S. and 14 other nations to renounce war "as an instrument of national policy" and to try to settle disputes by peaceful means. Open to all, 62 nations ultimately signed the pact.

1930 *London Naval Conference,* attended by U.S., Britain, Japan, France, and Italy, produced a treaty that broadened the suspension of shipbuilding outlined in the Five-Power Pact to include all categories of warships and extended the suspension for 5 years. An earlier naval-limitations conference, held at Geneva in 1927, failed.

1933 *Pan-Americanism. The 7th Pan-American Conference,* held at Montevideo, Uruguay, adopted a pact, supported by the U.S., which declared that "no state has the right to intervene in the internal or external affairs of another." This renunciation of the right of unilateral intervention by the U.S. made Roosevelt's good neighbor declarations toward Latin America definite U.S. policy.

1935-1941 (From the neutrality legislation of 1935 to U.S. involvement in World War II)

STATEMENTS OF POLICY

1935-
1941   *Good Neighbor policy.* In 1936, the U.S. gave up its right to intervene in the affairs of Panama and relinquished it as a protectorate. By the treaty, as ratified, the U.S. retained the right to defend the canal. Roosevelt refused to intervene when the Mexican government expropriated U.S.-owned oil properties in 1938. In 1941, a compromise settlement of claims was reached.

1936-
1941   *Neutrality Acts. The Neutrality Act of 1936* extended for one year the law of 1935, added materials other than arms to the embargo, and required the President to apply the embargo to any new nation entering a war. It also prohibited loans to belligerents. In 1937, during the Spanish Civil War, the neutrality law was made applicable to civil wars. *The Neutrality Act of 1937* made "permanent" the major provisions of the previous acts; it forbade American travel on belligerents' ships and permitted warring nations to buy U.S. goods, for 2 years, only on a cash-and-carry basis. *Proclamation of Neutrality* was issued after Germany invaded Poland in September 1939. *The Neutrality Act of 1939* (November) repealed the arms embargo, reëstablished cash-and-carry, and retained some other features of the old law. It prohibited U.S. ships from entering designated combat zones. With the repeal of most restrictions in November 1941, merchant ships could be armed and enter ports of belligerents.

1937   *Quarantine speech.* In Chicago, Roosevelt warned Americans that no nation was immune from attack and that none could escape through neutrality. He urged an international quarantine of the disease of the lawless. The idea was abandoned because of public opposition.

1941   *Lend-Lease Act* permitted the President to lend or lease arms or other equipment and supplies to any nation if its defense were considered vital to the defense of the U.S.

EXECUTIVE AGREEMENTS

1940   *Destroyers-for-bases agreement* between Roosevelt and Churchill. The U.S. traded 50 old destroyers to Britain in exchange for 8 sites for air and naval bases, making the U.S. virtually an ally of Britain.

PERSONAL DIPLOMACY

1941   *Atlantic Charter.* A declaration of principles was issued by Roosevelt and Churchill in August, announcing a common purpose behind the unofficial Anglo-American alliance and stating postwar aims.

ECONOMIC POLICY AND COMMERCIAL TREATIES

1940   *Economic sanctions against Japan* were imposed by the U.S., beginning in July. In January, U.S. had allowed its commercial treaty of 1911 with Japan to expire.

World War II began in Europe when the Germans invaded Poland on September 1, 1939. France and Britain declared war on Germany. The Soviet Union invaded from the east and within a month the Poles had been overwhelmed. Warsaw, the Polish capital, was nearly destroyed in the fighting. Events in Europe led the U.S. to revise its neutrality legislation.

Germans battle Warsaw snipers, September 23, 1939

DIPLOMACY OF WAR PREVENTION

1936   *London Naval Conference.* Italy and Japan refused to adhere to a new naval treaty signed by U.S., Britain, and France and soon the structure of naval limitations, built up since 1922, collapsed.

1938-
1940   *Pan-Americanism. Declaration of Lima* (1938) of the 8th Pan-American conference provided for consultation of foreign ministers of the American republics in the event of an outside threat to one of them. For the first time, the American republics had agreed to work as a unit in meeting certain international problems. *Declaration of Panama* (1939), made at the

first ministers' conference, decreed a safety zone around the Western Hemisphere south of Canada—an effort to avoid involvement in the European war. *Resolutions of Havana* (1940). At the second ministers' meeting it was declared that an attack on one American state by an outside state would be considered an act of aggression against all and that the republics would coöperate in defending the hemisphere.

1940   *Permanent Joint Board on Defense,* formed by U.S. and Canada, provided for defense of the northern part of the Western Hemisphere.

in the way of further conquests and was now the only power capable of stopping them. Before taking this final step, other leaders, such as Prime Minister Fuminaro Konoye, wanted to try to reach an agreement with the United States that might permit Japan to attain her territorial objectives without clashing with Americans. With this objective in mind, Konoye resumed the talks in Washington, D.C., but nothing came of them.

In October, Hideki Tojo, a tough general, succeeded Konoye as prime minister. Tojo and his advisers agreed that if the United States would not come to terms within several weeks and lift the embargo, there would be war. To stress the urgency of the crisis, Tojo sent a "trouble shooter," Saburo Kurusu, to Washington, D.C., to take part in the Hull-Nomura talks. At the same time Tojo's government made plans for an attack on American and British bases. The United States cryptographers learned of the Japanese plans but did not find out where the strikes would come.

In Washington, D.C., the negotiators got nowhere. Step by step the Japanese war plan went into action. A carrier task force left the fog-enshrouded Kuril Islands and approached Hawaii undetected as planes zoomed from carrier decks. Then, at 7:55 A.M. (local time), Sunday, December 7, 1941, the first wave of Japanese bombers appeared over the United States fleet anchored at Pearl Harbor and dropped their bombs; they were followed by other planes. The attack, a complete surprise, ended about 9:45 A.M. More than 2400 servicemen were killed, practically every plane on the island of Oahu was destroyed, and six battleships—the heart of the American fleet—were sunk, or disabled. Fortunately, three aircraft carriers were outside the harbor and were safe.

Japan also attacked the Philippines, Thailand, British Malaya, and other places and, after her sneak attack, declared war on the United States. On the next day Roosevelt told Congress that Sunday, December 7, was a day "which will live in infamy," and asked for a declaration of war. Congress made the declaration against Japan in less than an hour. On December 11, 1941, Germany and Italy declared war on the United States, and on that same day Congress declared war on them. Many sincere men who wanted to stay out of the war now admitted that isolationism was shattered. The United States had been drawn into World War II.

REVIEWING THE SECTION

1. What was the purpose of the Lend-Lease Act? How did Roosevelt evade the provision prohibiting United States convoys?

2. How did Japanese-American negotiations reach a stalemate in June 1941?

CHAPTER **25** CONCLUSION

Up to the moment the bombs fell on Pearl Harbor, most Americans had hoped that somehow the final step to all-out war would never have to be taken. Even as they built their elaborate system of neutrality laws, designed to prevent what actually happened, many Americans had had little faith in the laws or in their leaders as barriers to involvement in a great war. They had seemed to assume that fate had decided that America should once again fight in distant lands.

Actually the decisions of many men had brought the United States into the war. Roosevelt and the New Dealers had not wanted war. They had started out as believers in America's isolationist tradition and were far more concerned about the domestic crisis, the Great Depression, than about world affairs. They accepted the disillusionment of the 1930's over the failure of collective security and the seeming failure of democracies abroad. Even the most successful part of Roosevelt's early foreign policy, the Good Neighbor policy, at first seemed more like an effort to insulate the Western Hemisphere rather than to bring it into the mainstream of world politics.

Many historians have considered Roosevelt's quarantine speech in October 1937 the turning point from isolationism to an attitude of internationalism. But no great change in foreign policy followed that speech. The change came much less abruptly, more as a series of reactions to specific developments, such as the Nazi-Soviet Pact and Germany's invasion and dismemberment of Poland in 1939.

The President had to move away slowly from his former isolationist position, for he believed that public opinion remained largely isolationist. Following the fall of France in the summer of 1940, he and the people became truly alarmed for the safety of the nation. Yet most Americans still wanted to avoid war. At the same time, they believed the government should do all it could to keep Britain from collapsing. They also approved of efforts—short of war—to stop Japan's conquests in Asia.

After his reëlection in 1940, Roosevelt came to the conclusion that an Axis victory was a greater evil than possible involvement in the war. So, step by step, he took actions that were not neutral and involved the United States indirectly in the conflicts in Europe and Asia. The destroyers-for-bases agreement, lend-lease, the patrols in the North Atlantic, and economic sanctions against Japan, all in one way or another could have provoked war. Yet the danger was real, and seemed to justify the risk. If the Axis powers defeated Britain, the Soviet Union, and China, their power would then have been irresistible. The enemies of the Axis were able to continue to resist only with help from the United States.

When the Americans refused to curtail their assistance, the Japanese struck. The attack on Pearl Harbor ended the great debate over isolationism and internationalism. It united the American people as they had never before been united.

FOCUSING ON SPECIFICS

1. In what way did Roosevelt intervene in the affairs of Cuba?

2. How did Roosevelt attempt to gain the good will of Mexico?

3. Why did many Americans believe the Philippines should be independent?

4. Why did many people charge that the United States neutrality laws aided Fascists in the Ethiopian and Spanish wars?

5. What methods did the United States use after July 1940 in an attempt to stop Japanese expansion?

6. What was the purpose of the destroyers-for-bases agreement?

REVIEWING MAIN THEMES

1. How did the United States use diplomacy as a means to increase its foreign trade?

2. How did the aftermath of World War I influence American attitudes toward foreign policy?

3. Between 1933 and 1939, how did the United States attempt by means of neutrality laws to avoid entanglement in foreign wars?

4. After the war broke out in Europe, what steps did the United States take to build up its defenses?

5. Before its entry into the war, how did the United States aid the British and the Soviet Union?

6. In what ways did Roosevelt by-pass Congress in order to aid the British?

7. What issues led to the involvement of the United States in a war with Germany? with Japan?

EVALUATING THE ISSUES

1. Was Roosevelt correct in by-passing Congress to lead the nation slowly into an alliance with Britain and a war with Germany?

2. Should an amendment be passed similar to the Ludlow amendment requiring a national referendum for a declaration of war except in time of invasion?

3. By placing an embargo on oil and metal exports to Japan, the United States placed Japan in the position of having to choose between abandoning the conquest of China or attempting a quick victory before its war supplies were depleted. Should the United States have compromised to avoid war?

EXAMINING THE TIMES

1. Compare the federal government's domestic and foreign policies of the 1930's with the policies of the 1920's.

2. What trends were evident in population distribution, industrial growth, literature, and mass communications during the 1920's and 1930's?

Expansion into the Countryside

With the mass production of automobiles and the development of vast highway systems, the suburb, once the home of the wealthy, became the home of many more Americans. As more people moved to the suburbs, it became necessary to find new and faster ways to get them in and out of the city. New, long bridges (like the Verrazano-Narrows Bridge) were built, and vastly more complex highway systems with complicated interchanges (like the California Freeway Interchange) were added to the landscape.

The automobile, however, did far more than carry people to and from their jobs in the city; it also took them out into the country for fun and sport. The only requirement was ample space for parking (as at Jones Beach).

The travel industry grew to tremendous proportions. Almost overnight it seemed, simple cabins appeared along the new highways, but these soon gave way to lush, modern resort areas. At the Broadwater Beach Hotel, for example, the traveler had on the premises a swimming pool, a golf course, and a marina (for the docking of boats). Once, the vacationer would choose his destination, get there as quickly as he could, and stay there until it was time to return home. With the new complexes along the highways (which included motels, restaurants, and service stations), the vacationer now could stop at scenic spots along the way or plan a vacation that consisted only of sightseeing.

At one time, trailer camps appeared on the roadside to accommodate what one writer called the "tin-can nomads." But some Americans found that trailers or mobile homes provided them with excellent low-cost housing. Trailer camps, once rather crude, developed rapidly. They were frequently located in beautiful settings (like the one at Black Meadows on Lake Havasu) and provided many services.

By the middle of the 20th century, the automobile had so changed life in the United States that "the pursuit of happiness," as one writer commented, "had become the happiness of pursuit."

Verrazano-Narrows Bridge from Staten Island, New York, N.Y.

Trailer Camp at Black Meadow on Lake Havasu in California

Jones Beach, Long Island, New York, 1959

California Freeway Interchange, Los Angeles, Calif.

Broadwater Beach Hotel,
Biloxi, Mississippi

Contour-planted pineapple fields around Lanai City, Hawaii, 1959

The Changing Countryside

New communities, most of them planned, continued to appear on the United States landscape. Some of them were built by private enterprise, some were built by the federal government, and some were built with the help of the government.

The federal government began building communities during the Great Depression when private enterprise was unable to provide funds for such projects. While Grand Coulee Dam was being constructed (beginning in 1933), for example, low-cost housing was needed for the construction workers, and after completion of the dam, housing was needed for the personnel of the dam. That housing was provided by the government. During World War II, when housing was needed for workers in war industries, private enterprise (with the help of the government) was able to build orderly, attractive communities like Channel Heights, California.

Some of the communities that appeared in the postwar period, like those of the past, were built around a single industry or by a single industry or by a single company. Lanai City, Hawaii, for example, was constructed to provide housing for the employees in the nearby pineapple fields.

With the increasing affluence of Americans in the postwar years, private enterprise was able to finance and build many new communities. Levittown, Long Island, New York, for example, was only one of many such communities designed, as one writer put it, to provide "wall-to-wall housing" for those middle-class Americans who liked working in the city and living in a suburb.

A completely new kind of planned community—the retirement community—was a phenomenon of the 20th century. The retirement community (such as Sun City, Arizona) provided the elderly with various kinds of housing, organized recreational activities, and all the other services needed to care for the elderly.

Levittown, Long Island, New York, 1949

Sun City, Arizona

Channel Heights, California, 1950

Grand Coulee and Grand Coulee Dam, Washington

Diversity in Housing

By the middle of the 20th century, the cities of the United States had become a mixture of different styles and different periods. Although there was a tremendous amount of new construction going on, there developed all over the nation a desire to preserve the old along with the new. And it was this combination of the old and the new which gave a great many American cities (such as San Francisco, California) their charm.

Some cities began to restore whole sections in order to achieve this combination. When completed, the restored areas (like the Strand in New Castle, Delaware) provided Americans with a tranquil retreat from the frantic pace of the 20th century.

The city, however, was also eager to provide new kinds of housing in order to lure people back from the suburbs. One type of building, which became extremely popular, was the

The Strand, an old colonial street in New Castle, Del

Marina City, Chicago, Illinois

self-contained community within a building. These structures provided luxurious apartments, garages, stores, restaurants, laundries, cleaners, and, frequently, a bank. Some of them, like Marina City in Chicago, Illinois, offered unique features such as a marina and a theater.

New communities, however, continued to grow in spite of the efforts to bring people back to the city. Some (like Cape Coral, Florida) simply provided facilities, like a marina with every residence, which most cities could not match. Others (like Reston, Virginia) provided everything the American family needed or wanted—and more. Reston, for example, provided town houses and apartments, shopping centers, nurseries, parks, schools, restaurants, a theater, and a museum. And, to help the suburbanite avoid the inevitable traffic jam going to and from work in the city, Reston made plans to bring industry to the community.

Cape Coral, Florida

San Francisco, California

Lake Anne Village, Washington Plaza, Reston, Virginia

Detroit, Michigan

Urban Redevelopment

The State House, Raleigh, North Carolina

In order to provide much-needed housing in the city and to make the city more attractive, whole sections were torn down and redeveloped.

In cities where there was an acute housing shortage and there was little room in which to expand, private interests began to build taller and taller apartment buildings—high-density housing. Parkchester, Bronx, New York (opened in 1940), was one of the earliest such developments.

With many areas of the central city deteriorating into slums, slum clearance and redevelopment projects were begun, often with the help of the federal government. In some areas, the slum buildings were replaced by new low-cost housing (as in the Mayor Wright housing development in the Liliha district, Honolulu, Hawaii); in others the slum buildings were replaced by industry or by new schools (such as the University of Illinois Chicago Circle Campus).

In addition to tearing down slum buildings, many cities began to rebuild blighted commercial areas. In Detroit, Michigan, for example, the waterfront area, once a collection of old and ugly buildings, became one of the showcases of the city. In other cities, the blighted areas were replaced by modern buildings (like the State House in Raleigh, North Carolina), which gave a new look to government complexes.

The Library and University Hall, University of Illinois Chicago Circle Campus

The Mayor Wright housing development in the Liliha district, Honolulu, Hawaii

Parkchester, New York, New York, 1940

Intalco Aluminum Corporation (foreground) and the Mobil Oil Refinery (background), Ferndale, Wash.

Offices of CIBA, Summit, New Jersey

Industrial Areas

Since the United States is one of the most highly industrialized nations in the world, industrial areas have long been an important part of the United States landscape.

Most Americans think of industrial areas as spoilers of the landscape—massive buildings with tall smokestacks (like the steel mills in Pittsburgh, Pennsylvania) intruding on the skyline. Modern industry, however, is making an attempt to integrate with the landscape. Intalco (in the foreground) in Ferndale, Washington, for example, has buff and green buildings designed to blend in with the surrounding countryside. The Mobil Refinery (in the background) has built a system to render harmless the waste material it discharges into the waters.

At one time it was necessary to locate stores close to the central city. With the coming of the automobile, however, stores could be built anywhere. And, as people began moving away from the central city, the retail industry moved with them. Today, shopping centers (like Oak Brook Shopping Center, Oak Brook, Illinois) are a common sight in suburban areas and on the edge of the city. These centers provide for almost all of the needs of the family and —most important—they provide ample parking space for the family car.

Since the 20th century has often been called the "age of technology," perhaps research companies (like CIBA) are the best representatives of the age. Their primary function is to find new products, new methods of production, new uses for old products —and find them all in a hurry.

Advanced technology and the need for speed in the 20th century has revolutionized the transportation industry. Where once the automobile and the railroad were the most popular means of going long distances, now most Americans find it faster and more convenient to travel to vacation cities such as Miami Beach, Florida, by plane—by jet. As a result, large airports (like O'Hare International Airport, Chicago, Illinois) and small airports have appeared at the edges of cities all over the country.

Miami Beach, Florida

Steel Mills, Pittsburgh, Pennsylvania

Oak Brook Shopping Center, Oak Brook, Ill.

O'Hare International Airport, Chicago, Ill.

Recreation for Americans

In the middle of the 20th century, with more Americans having more leisure time available to them, recreational facilities became an increasingly important part of the United States landscape.

Elaborate resorts such as Sun Valley, Ketchum, Idaho, were built for winter sports enthusiasts. New stadiums (like the one in Atlanta, Georgia) were built for baseball, football, basketball, and other sports activities. And new, elaborate amusement centers, like Disneyland in Anaheim, California, were built to accommodate visitors from all over the United States.

Americans, however, did not only seek fun and amusement during their leisure time. Such repertory theaters as the Tyrone Guthrie Theatre in Minneapolis, Minnesota, found that audiences would flock to see performances of new, experimental plays as well as the classics. As a result, theaters were no longer limited to the largest city in a region or to the major cities along the eastern coast of the United States.

Many of the smaller cities of the nation found that museums, too, were attracting large numbers of people. They began building new, modernistic ones like the Eisenhower Museum in Abilene, Kansas, which contrasted sharply with the classical structures, such as the Cleveland Museum of Art, built in the major cities of the nation during previous periods.

The desire of Americans for varied activities during their leisure time and during their vacations even changed the existing resort cities. A "sun city" like Tucson, Arizona, for example, had always been a vacation center. By the middle of the 20th century, however, such cities could offer far more to the vacationer than a good climate. The resort city provided fine hotels, fine restaurants, theaters, museums, and sometimes an amusement park and facilities for such sports as skiing and boating.

The stadium in Atlanta, Georgia

Tyrone Guthrie Theatre, Minneapolis, Minn.

Disneyland, Anaheim, California, 1958

Eisenhower Museum, Abilene, Kansas

Tucson, Arizona

Sun Valley, Ketchum, Idaho

On the morning of August 6, 1945, an American airplane dropped a single bomb on Hiroshima, a commercial city and military center in central Japan. That bomb had the power of more than 20,000 tons of TNT, the explosive used in ordinary bombs, and flattened seven square miles of the city. Three days later another American plane dropped another bomb on Nagasaki, one of Japan's important industrial cities, and caused similar devastation. These were atomic bombs and these were the first and only times they were used as military weapons against human beings.

Problems of a World Power

The world was stunned. Except for a handful of scientists and high government and military officials, no one had thought man capable of setting off explosions of such magnitude. It is true that in the past the use of new weapons, such as cannons, had changed the nature of warfare. But atomic bombs were different from new weapons developed in the past. They appeared late and suddenly in a great war without having gone through any period of known experimentation before being used in battle. They seemed so effective and so destructive that they almost immediately revolutionized the thinking of military men on the nature of war and of statesmen on the nature of diplomacy.

Sole possession of the secret of making atomic bombs gave the United States a unique position in the world. It was powerful, secure, rich and capable of destroying enemies without itself being seriously injured. The United States could and did use its possession of atomic weapons to protect friends, such as allies in Europe, and to awe its enemies, such as the Soviet Union.

The period of America's monopoly lasted only four years. In September 1949, the Soviet Union exploded an atomic device. This achievement came as a shock to most Americans. They believed, or had been led to believe, that at the earliest the Soviets could not produce an atomic bomb for another six years. Equally shocking, or almost so, were disclosures that the Soviets had established successful spy rings in the United States and Britain to steal atomic secrets.

Now the relationship of the United States to Russia had changed. To retain its lead in armaments and its ability to shield its allies, the United States embarked on a nuclear armaments race with the Soviet Union. President Harry Truman and his advisers made a grim decision. They decided to go ahead at full speed to develop a thermonuclear superbomb, or hydrogen bomb. After overcoming a number of obstacles, scientists developed the new weapon.

All work on the hydrogen bomb had been carried on in secret and so were preparations for its first test. That test took place on the morning of November 1, 1952, on a tiny coral spit called Elugelab out in the Pacific Ocean. When the device was detonated a huge bluish-white fireball lit up hundreds of miles of sky in the Pacific. The fireball itself was more than three miles in diameter. It completely destroyed Elugelab. All that remained was a cavity in the coral one mile wide and 175 feet deep.

This thermonuclear explosion had the power of twelve million tons of TNT, or of twelve megatons. The bomb itself was, however, too big and bulky for military use. Seventeen months later American scientists produced and tested a hydrogen bomb capable of being transported for military use. Meanwhile, in August 1953, the Soviets had exploded their first hydrogen device. Now the United States and the Soviet Union stepped up their race to build bigger and bigger arsenals of nuclear fire. There seemed to be no limit to the destructiveness of the new superbombs.

The development of the hydrogen bomb was as revolutionary in its impact on warfare and foreign relations as was the explosion of the first atomic bombs. The difference in explosive power between a hydrogen bomb and an atomic bomb was about as great as that between an atomic bomb and a TNT "blockbuster" of World War II. Since the destructive force of the new thermonuclear weapons was discussed everywhere, in books, newspapers, magazines, and on television, everyone knew that one superbomb was capable of destroying any large city in the world.

unit VIII
1941-1960

Men now talked about war being outmoded and about international relations being held in a delicate balance of terror. The superbombs, some said, were not truly weapons of war. They were instruments of terror, psychological weapons that could be used to frighten and terrorize whole populations.

The attitude of fright increased in the Western world after October 1957, when the Soviets flung *Sputnik I,* the world's first space satellite, into orbit. Before this time the United States, which had more nuclear weapons than the Soviet Union and better means of delivering them, was reasonably free from fear of sudden Russian nuclear attack. This security had also added to the security of its allies, most of whom had no nuclear weapons of their own. These allies had taken comfort in the thought that their protector, the United States, was beyond the enemy's reach and was always capable of fighting with nuclear weapons. This sense of security and protection shrank with the knowledge that the Soviets had a lead in long-range ballistic missiles. A rocket capable of putting *Sputnik* into orbit could carry a nuclear warhead 5000 miles in almost a half hour and deliver it to almost any place on the globe.

Men everywhere were horrified by the idea of a nuclear war. Some argued that total nuclear war would bring the end of civilization. Others maintained that there would be survivors and man would rebuild from the ruins of war as he has always done. Regardless of these differences, it was obvious that thermonuclear war would cripple civilization so badly that such a war would be folly. Even military thinkers such as General Douglas MacArthur insisted that no one could win a nuclear war. "Global war has become a Frankenstein to destroy both sides," he said in 1961. "It contains now only the germs of double suicide."

Despite their horror of nuclear war, men failed to control the use of thermonuclear weapons. They did not even change the basis of their international relations to cope with the danger of nuclear conflict. In the fifteen years following the Hiroshima explosion it became clear that nuclear weapons as instruments of diplomacy had limitations. Unless it had been willing to defy the feelings of the rest of the world, the United States could not use its nuclear weapons in offensive war. Even if it threatened to use them, it did so mainly to keep an enemy from acting. It did not seek to destroy an opponent with atomic fire.

The American and Soviet possession of nuclear weapons had the effect of contributing to a *status quo* in relations between the Western allies and the Soviet bloc. The small nations of the world, and others without nuclear weapons, tended to follow the lead of one of the two great nuclear powers. And those powers stuck to their own policies without much bending, but they approached each other cautiously whenever there was danger of a big conflict.

Yet the possession of nuclear weapons did not in itself enable either the United States or the Soviet Union to dominate or paralyze other nations. Nor did such possession give those big nations the means to prevent or control little wars by

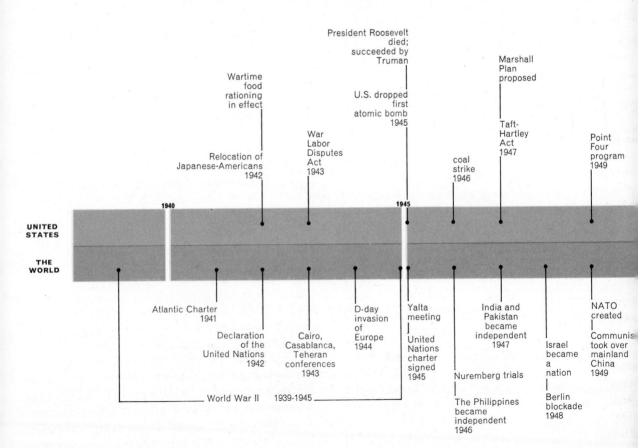

small nations. Using conventional weapons, the minor powers, as in the Middle East, continued to quarrel and fight. Communists, as in Cuba, continued to fight for power and to challenge a great nuclear nation such as the United States.

In Asia and Africa people who had thrown off the yoke of colonialism acted as if awesome nuclear bombs did not exist. America's possession of nuclear weapons did her no good in China, which became Communist, or in Korea where she fought a long war solely with conventional weapons. But President Dwight D. Eisenhower claimed that his threat to use atomic bombs in the Korean War helped to end it.

What is clear about nuclear weapons is that in big issues their possession and the capability of using them has been important. They may deter war or other violent action by a nation without such weapons. In civil wars or small international conflicts the possession of nuclear weapons has been of limited value. In a quarrel with Egypt in 1956, for example, Britain's possession of atomic weapons did her no good. As instruments of diplomacy nuclear weapons cannot be ignored. They are weapons of incalculable destructive power that have been used cautiously but with the knowledge that as instruments of foreign policy, they have limitations.

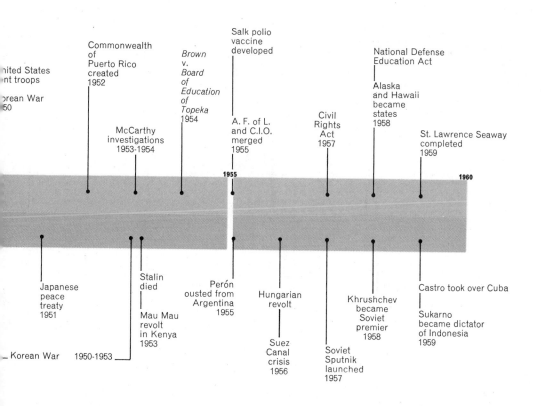

Commonwealth of Puerto Rico created 1952

Brown v. Board of Education of Topeka 1954

Salk polio vaccine developed

National Defense Education Act

Alaska and Hawaii became states 1958

ited States nt troops

rean War 50

McCarthy investigations 1953-1954

A. F. of L. and C.I.O. merged 1955

Civil Rights Act 1957

St. Lawrence Seaway completed 1959

1955

1960

Japanese peace treaty 1951

Stalin died

Perón ousted from Argentina 1955

Hungarian revolt

Khrushchev became Soviet premier 1958

Castro took over Cuba

Mau Mau revolt in Kenya 1953

Sukarno became dictator of Indonesia 1959

Korean War 1950-1953

Suez Canal crisis 1956

Soviet Sputnik launched 1957

The World in Conflict

With the attack on Pearl Harbor, the United States became a full-fledged belligerent. Foreign policy was no longer a public issue; most Americans knew only that their country had been attacked and that they must fight to defend themselves. Almost every American could foresee a long, hard pull against foes who were now triumphant almost everywhere. Among America's allies, only Britain seemed beyond the reach of Axis armies.

Germany's armies were deep inside the Soviet Union. In the north they were pounding at the gates of Leningrad; in the central area they were trying to pull down the defenses of Moscow; and in the south they were driving toward Stalingrad. Although the Soviets had put up an inspired resistance, few Americans expected them to survive renewed Nazi onslaughts.

In North Africa, too, an Axis victory seemed imminent. A German army, aided by Italians, held the region from northern Tunisia to Egypt, and appeared capable of seizing the Suez Canal and closing the Mediterranean Sea to Allied shipping.

In the Atlantic, deadly German submarines were blasting Allied merchant ships to bits faster than replacements could be built. The British were losing desperately needed supplies.

On the other side of the world, the United States fleet had been so badly mauled that it appeared incapable of offering meaningful resistance to the Japanese. The United States Army could do even less than the navy. The striking power of the British navy in the Pacific had been crippled when the Japanese had sunk the battle cruiser *Repulse* and the battleship *Prince of Wales*. The Japanese had used torpedo planes and bombers to sink these ships and the British, without adequate air cover, had been helpless. Japanese forces captured Wake Island, Guam, Singapore, Hong Kong, British Malaya, Burma, Thailand, the Netherlands East Indies, and swarmed over the Philippine Islands.

The only source of inspiration in the gloomy winter of 1941-42 came from the rocky peninsula of Bataan and the fortified island of Corregidor, guarding the entrance to Manila Bay. There, outnumbered American and Filipino defenders held off the Japanese for five months before surrendering. Before their capitulation, their commander, General Douglas MacArthur, was ordered out of Corregidor to take command of Allied forces in the Southwest Pacific. When he landed in Darwin, Australia, he announced dramatically that Americans would retake the Philippines. "I came through," he said, "and I shall return."

Despite the sweep of the Axis conquests, the position of the United States was not hopeless; it entered the global struggle better prepared for war than at any time in its history. Although its fleet had been crippled, it had not been destroyed. As a result of peacetime conscription, the army began the war with a nucleus of half a million men and that nucleus was quickly expanded.

United States resources, such as oil, steel, and other strategic materials, were greater than those controlled by the Axis. American industrial capacity dwarfed that of all the belligerents. What the United States needed most was time to adapt its superior technology to the demands of war. Allied troops bought that time by fighting and retreating, and then by taking a stand when successful resistance and counterattack were possible.

GOVERNMENT MOBILIZED THE HOME FRONT

Modern warfare required virtually all of the nation's industrial resources, manpower, and scientific knowledge to be mobilized so that they could be turned against the enemy with the greatest possible effectiveness. This requirement meant that the government would have to assume broad powers affecting the lives of all Americans. This it did, but with far less damage to individual liberties than in World War I.

Democratic liberties suffered small damage because few Americans opposed the war. Most of them knew why they were fighting. Their nation had been attacked and, as loyal citizens, they were striking back at the attackers. Beyond this, they talked little about ideals, such as making the world safe for democracy. War was a grim, necessary business and they wanted to bring it to an end as quickly as possible.

Soon after the attack on Pearl Harbor, the American people set about building huge armies and fleets, producing the tools of war, fixing controls over the economy to curb inflation and to assure a reasonably fair distribution of available goods, and finding ways to pay for the war.

Industry went to war

The shift of industry from the production of civilian goods to the production of war materials had begun in 1940, after the Nazi victory over France. In January 1942, President Roosevelt created the War Production Board and gave authority over the nation's production to Donald M. Nelson, the board's director and a former business executive. After that, even though there were serious lags and shortages in production, American industry responded to the more exacting demands of World War II with greater and more remarkable results than in World War I.

In 1940, Roosevelt asked for fifty thousand new planes a year, a demand that critics called preposterous. In 1942, American factories turned out 47,000 planes, and in 1944, more than 96,000. Similarly spectacular results were achieved in the building of other war materials.

In at least one instance, almost overnight, the government created a new industry and operated plants itself. In 1942, the government established a special agency within the War Production Board, the Rubber Administration, to produce synthetic rubber. By that time Japan had overrun the major sources of natural rubber and the rubber shortage had become critical. By the end of 1943, the new synthetic rubber industry was turning out more rubber than the entire nation had been using before the war.

When the manufacture of civilian goods interfered with war production, the flow of the civilian products was cut off or curtailed. Even so, civilians did not truly suffer any serious shortages in essential goods. Despite the great demands of the war, two thirds of American industry continued to turn out goods for the civilian market.

All during the war, the United States functioned as an arsenal for its allies. Without American trucks and tanks, for example, the Russians probably could not have mounted their successful offensives against the Germans. By the beginning of 1944, the production of American factories

644

amounted to more than twice that of all the Axis nations as a whole. The industrial capacity of the United States contributed as much to the winning of the war as did its armies and fleets.

Workers and farmers prospered

Manpower, as well as machines, made possible the miracle of wartime production. The armed forces, the war industries, the farms, and the producers for the home front all competed for manpower and created a labor shortage. First call on available manpower went to the armed forces. Draft boards registered thirty-one million men. Altogether, including draftees and volunteers, the fighting services enrolled fifteen million men and women. The women served in the armed forces on a volunteer basis, performing noncombatant duties. From 1940 to 1945, the civilian working force expanded from 46.5 million to 53 million people. Many of these new workers were women, elderly men and women, or very young people who took jobs normally held by the men who were now in the armed forces.

Money, as well as patriotism, lured many workers into the war plants. The money came less from rising wages than from increased hours of work. Shipyards and important war plants went on around-the-clock shifts, and the workweek increased from 40.6 to 45 hours. When laborers worked beyond 40 hours they received time-and-a-half pay. As a result, many workingmen became prosperous and enjoyed a standard of living higher than they ever had known.

In April 1942, the government established the War Manpower Commission to assure the proper and efficient use of all workers. The commission shifted workers, on a voluntary basis, into areas where there were shortages or critical needs. The government never resorted to the drafting of workers or to the assigning of jobs.

Labor unions coöperated faithfully in the war effort. In December 1941, the major unions pledged themselves not to strike during the war,

to settle disputes by peaceful means, and to "produce without interruption." In the following month, to help settle serious disputes and to try to avoid strikes, the government established the National War Labor Board. It ultimately had the authority to set wages and hours for workers, and conditions for maintaining union membership.

Most union leaders kept the no-strike pledge, but as prices and profits rose, some strikes occurred. Though such strikes were usually brief, many people criticized the strikers and were particularly upset by the action of the United Mine Workers under the leadership of John L. Lewis. In May 1943, when the mine operators refused to grant a wage increase, the miners refused to work. The following month, Congress passed the Smith-Connally Anti-Strike Act. This law, passed over the President's veto, required unions to give thirty days' notice before striking, and it permitted the President to seize plants threatened by strikes.

Despite the public attention the small strikes received, only one ninth of one per cent of labor's working time was affected by them. Labor performed well during the war. Its performance and its prosperity led to an increase in union membership from 10.5 million workers in 1942 to nearly 15 million at the end of the war.

More than a million Negroes migrated from the South to industrial areas all over the nation in search of jobs and an improved social and economic status. They continued to suffer from various kinds of discrimination, but they found jobs—especially after June 1941, when President Roosevelt forbade, by executive order, discrimination in plants working under government contract and established the Fair Employment Practices Committee (FEPC) to investigate cases of discrimination because of race.

Farmers, too, enjoyed a booming wartime prosperity. From 1940 to 1945, farm prices doubled, and they would have gone higher if the President had not acted to stabilize them. There was a fourfold increase in the net cash income of farmers during that period. They cut down their mortgage debts by $2 billion, enjoyed a higher standard of living, and piled up $11 billion in savings.

During the war farm population dropped seventeen per cent, but the output of the individual farm worker, profiting from increased use of machinery and better fertilizers, reached a level almost double that established in the years preceding World War I. The farmers met the food needs of the armed forces, of a growing domestic market, and even of some liberated areas overseas where people were near the point of starvation.

The government fought inflation and raised money

When the prosperity of Americans was combined with a cutback in goods that civilians could buy, inflation was a logical consequence. People had more money available for spending than the nation had goods for sale and, as a result, the prices of available goods went up. All during the war, the income of individual Americans amounted to at least one third more than the value of goods and services available to civilians. The government wanted to control inflation because it would increase the cost of the war and cause discontent and suffering on the home front. In addition, the government had to find ways to pay for the war.

In January 1942, Congress passed the Emergency Price Control Act. This act placed responsibility for curbing inflation in the Office of Price Administration (OPA), headed by Leon Henderson. Henderson's efforts failed to stop inflation and at the President's insistence Congress, in October 1942, passed a law designed to bring stability to the cost of living. This anti-inflation law froze food prices, wages, and rents all through the nation.

Another part of the effort to curb inflation was the rationing of scarce goods. The government rationed automobile tires, gasoline, meat, canned food, sugar, coffee, butter, shoes, and other items. People could purchase these commodities if they had enough stamps from ration books issued by the government. Some people cheated by going to "black markets," where goods were sold illegally

at high prices. Despite the cheating and the unpopularity of price controls and rationing, the economic controls of World War II assured most Americans a fairer share of available goods than had the uncontrolled economy of World War I.

In addition to controls, the government sold war bonds and imposed new and higher taxes to fight inflation, primarily by trying to drain off some of the people's buying power. The money obtained from the war bonds and the taxes would be used to help pay for the war. The government launched eight war-bond drives that brought more than $100 billion into the treasury. Everyone, from the factory worker to the millionaire, was encouraged to buy the war bonds which paid a fixed rate of interest and which the treasury would redeem in later years. The government raised even more money through taxes, which took big jumps upward. For the first time, as a result of the Revenue Act of October 1942, the income tax became a "mass tax." Millions of Americans with incomes as low as $625 a year, who never before had filed a return, now were required to do so. To make collection simple and easy, Congress, in June 1943, passed a payroll deduction law which provided for the withholding of money for income taxes—a pay-as-you-go plan. During the war the government raised $138 billion from taxes.

Government imposed restrictions on civil liberties

In addition to manipulating prices and taxes, the government tampered with civil liberties. On the whole, however, the United States had a good record regarding civil liberties during World War II. Unlike the witch hunts during and after World War I, violations of free speech and personal liberty were few. There were few organized hate campaigns against Italian and German aliens.

In February 1942, the President authorized the army to exclude all persons of Japanese ancestry from "military areas" on the West coast. Later, the commanding general on the Pacific coast ordered these people uprooted and placed in special

346

camps guarded by barbed wire and soldiers. Within the year some of the Japanese born in the United States, called Nisei, were permitted to leave the camps to go to college, to harvest crops, to resettle in the Middle West, and even to volunteer for duty with the army. The "all Japanese" 100th Infantry Battalion and the 442nd Regimental Combat team, which were in time combined into one unit, fought in some of the bloodiest battles in Italy. This unit received widespread praise. Some military observers said it was "probably the most decorated unit in United States military history."

In the case of *Korematsu* v. *United States,* in December 1944, the Supreme Court ruled, in effect, that "military necessity" permitted the government to deny a citizen of the United States the protection of the Bill of Rights. After the war many Americans came to look on this decision with alarm. If the civil rights of Japanese-Americans could be violated in time of war, they reasoned, then the individual rights of all Americans could be taken away.

Scientists worked against time

Like businessmen, workers, and farmers, the scientists contributed their knowledge and skill to the struggle against the Axis powers. Although the power of science had grown immensely in the 1930's, the United States government had made little use of scientific research for military purposes. Germany, on the other hand, had used scientists to produce a number of new and powerful weapons.

The fear of German scientific developments had led President Roosevelt to set up, in June 1941, the Office of Scientific Research and Development with Dr. Vannevar Bush, president of the Carnegie Institution in Washington, as director. This organization mobilized scientists and they began a race against time to develop and perfect the devices needed to win the war.

Allied scientists forged ahead in the use of an electronic instrument called "radar" (*ra*dio *detect*ing *a*nd *r*anging). This invention, perfected and

put into effective use by the British, detected airplanes and ships by means of a radio beam. That beam could also be used to guide shells against the enemy craft. Americans made use of radio in another important invention, the proximity fuse. With this fuse, essentially a miniature radio in the nose of a shell, it was not necessary for gunners actually to hit a target—the shell exploded when near the target.

The most devastating weapon of all was the atomic bomb. The building of such a bomb became technically possible on December 2, 1942. (It had long been theoretically possible.) On that day, under the stadium at Stagg Field of the University of Chicago, Enrico Fermi and other physicists achieved the first self-sustaining nuclear chain reaction.

Under the direction of Dr. J. Robert Oppenheimer, a physicist from the University of California, other scientists at Los Alamos, New Mexico, harnessed the power of a chain reaction and built a bomb. The bomb was moved to an air force base at Alamogordo, New Mexico. At 5:30 A.M., on July 16, 1945, on a steel tower above the white sands of the surrounding desert, the world's first atomic bomb was detonated. Mankind had entered the new era of atomic wonders—and fears.

REVIEWING THE SECTION

1. How did the government direct American industry during the war?

2. In what ways was the civilian labor force affected by the war?

3. How did the government attempt to control wartime inflation?

4. During World War II, how did the government restrict civil liberties?

5. How did scientific advances contribute to the war effort?

THE ALLIES CONCENTRATED ON EUROPE FIRST

As soon as the United States had declared war against the Axis powers, Prime Minister Churchill crossed the Atlantic to talk to President Roosevelt about world-wide military strategy. Churchill feared that the sneak attack on Pearl Harbor, which had aroused and infuriated Americans, might cause them to concentrate on the destruction of Japan rather than on Nazi Germany. Churchill knew that alone his exhausted nation could not continue the fight against the Nazis.

Churchill had good reason for concern. Millions of Americans considered Japan the major enemy. Military commanders in the Pacific, such as General MacArthur, believed that the war against Japan should receive priority over Hitler's defeat.

Fortunately for Churchill, Roosevelt and his closest advisers agreed that Germany was the more dangerous foe. Hitler controlled more manpower and greater resources than Japan. Germany, as time would show, had the capability of developing atomic bombs and guided missiles which, in time, could conceivably have made her victorious.

Roosevelt and Churchill decided to give China only limited help and to fight a holding action in the Pacific. They would pour most of their troops, guns, planes, and tanks into the European theater of the war in an effort to crush Hitler first.

Nazi submarine and air threats were overcome

If Germany were to be defeated, the United States had to get its guns, planes, and soldiers across the Atlantic. Hitler was determined to prevent that. Soon after the United States entered the war, Germany shifted its U-boats across the Atlantic. Wolf packs, with eight to twenty submarines in a group, began sinking American and British merchant ships within sight of the American shore.

Allied shipping losses were staggering, but the U-boats suffered very few losses. During the first ten months of 1942, the Allies lost more than five hundred ships to submarines. Slowly the United States Navy, in coöperation with the British, was able to curb the submarine menace. The navy used a host of small ships, some of them converted

yachts, to escort convoys along the coast. It sent out airplanes, dirigibles, and specially equipped destroyers to hunt for the undersea killers. Two instruments for detecting submarines—the sounding device called "sonar" (sound navigation ranging) and radar—proved especially effective in the battle of the Atlantic sea lanes.

By the spring of 1943, the United States and British navies were destroying U-boats in large numbers, and Allied shipyards were turning out merchantmen faster than they were being sunk. The convoys brought supplies and men to Britain to prepare for an attack on Europe.

The United States Army Air Force joined the British in August 1942 in the attempt to destroy Hitler's Europe. Bombs fell both day and night on German cities. The British took over the night bombings and the Americans carried out the daytime raids. By the time the war ended the two air forces had dropped 2.6 million tons of bombs on enemy targets.

Despite the devastation they left behind them, the great air strikes did not succeed in destroying German war production. As time went on, the constant bombing did affect German morale. In addition, the Allies eliminated the German *Luftwaffe* as an effective opponent and gained command of the air over Europe. Without such control, there could be no land assault on the continent.

The Allies invaded North Africa and Italy

In 1942, the American and British leaders, in spite of Stalin's pleas to open a second front, felt that their forces in Britain were not strong enough to invade Europe. So the Allied leaders decided to launch the first great offensive in the Atlantic theater of the war against a weakly protected region—French North Africa, held by the Vichy government of France.

The Allies assembled three expeditionary forces. A huge fleet of more than eight hundred ships converged on the African shore and, on November 8, 1942, American and British soldiers under the

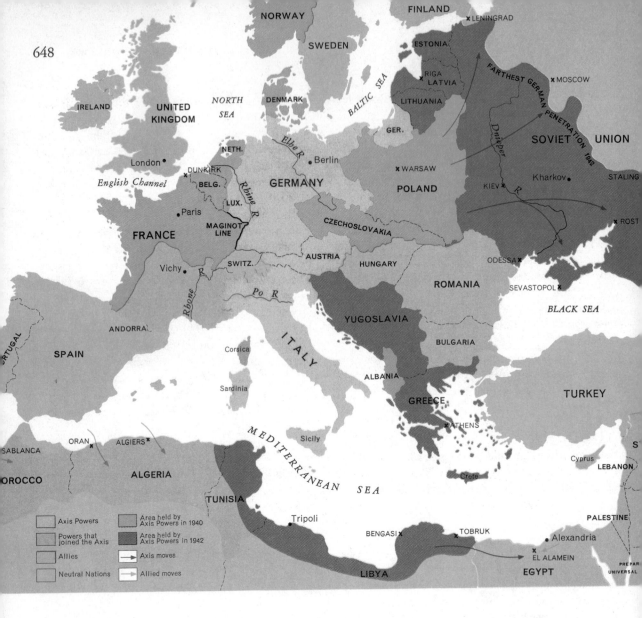

overall command of General Dwight D. Eisenhower of the United States, splashed through the surf at Casablanca, Oran, and Algiers. French resistance was slight; but the Germans reacted swiftly. They ferried troops to Tunisia from Sicily and flew others in from bases in Italy and France. These soldiers, joined by German and Italian armored forces in the *Afrika Korps,* led by the German field marshal, Erwin Rommel, inflicted heavy losses on inexperienced American troops.

For a while the battle of North Africa moved back and forth across the desert. Then, in May 1943, as veterans of Britain's Eighth Army closed in from the east and other Anglo-American troops pressed from the west to capture Tunis and Bizerte, the battered Axis forces surrendered. In the campaign, the Axis powers lost over a quarter of a million men, valuable equipment, a foothold in Africa, and control of the Mediterranean.

Since the prolonged fighting in Africa had made

World War II

EUROPEAN THEATER, 1939-1942

September 1-27, 1939
Invasion of Poland. Axis victory. Germany's invasion and occupation of Poland marked the beginning of World War II. With the fall of the capital, Warsaw, organized Polish resistance came to an end.

April 9-June 10, 1940
Invasion of Denmark and Norway. Axis victories. German troops occupied Denmark without meeting formal resistance. Although organized Norwegian resistance was broken April 30, sporadic fighting continued until June 10.

May 10-June 4, 1940
Invasion of Belgium, the Netherlands, and Luxembourg. Axis victories. Luxembourg was occupied by the Germans (May 10), the Netherlands capitulated (May 14), and Belgian resistance ended (May 26). British and French troops who had rushed to the aid of Belgium were seemingly trapped, as the Germans forced them back to the English Channel. With the help of an armada of small ships from England, the Anglo-French troops were evacuated from Dunkirk, France, (May 28-June 4).

June 5-22, 1940
Fall of France. Axis victory. The Germans, flanking the Maginot Line (a line of defenses along the German border), invaded France (June 5). Italy joined in the attack (June 10). The Germans occupied Paris (June 14) and France capitulated (June 22). A puppet French government was established at Vichy, while a Free French force was organized in London.

August 8-October 31, 1940
Battle of Britain. Allied victory. In an attempt to weaken and demoralize Britain, the German air force began a series of bombing raids on British cities, particularly London. The Germans hoped to invade Britain, but British planes gained dominance in the skies, and the Germans were forced to abandon the plan.

November 20, 1940-March 1, 1941
Additional nations joined the Axis: Hungary, Nov. 20; Romania, Nov. 23 (after having been occupied by the Germans Oct. 8); and Bulgaria, March 1.

April 6-April 27, 1941
Invasion of Yugoslavia and Greece. Axis victories. Yugoslavia surrendered April 17. Greece was forced to sign an armistice April 23, and four days later, Athens was occupied. The Greeks and Yugoslavs formed underground movements to fight the German occupation.

June 22, 1941-September 14, 1942
Campaign in the Soviet Union. Axis victories. The Germans attacked the Soviets along an 1800-mile front from the Baltic to the Black seas. By the end of 1941, the Germans had overrun much of the Soviet territory, capturing Riga (July 2), Kiev (Sept. 19), Odessa (Oct. 16), and Rostov (Nov. 22). In addition, sieges of three great cities had commenced: Leningrad (Sept. 4), Moscow (late October), and Sevastopol (Nov. 15). Although the Soviets launched a counteroffensive during the winter of 1941-1942, the Germans were able to continue their advance the following summer. Sevastopol was finally taken (July 2, 1942). An attack on Stalingrad began Aug. 22, and by Sept. 14, the Germans had begun to enter the city.

May 27-October 23, 1942
North African Campaign. Since 1940, battles between the British and German-Italian forces had seesawed back and forth. Cities like Bengasi and Tobruk in Libya had been taken by the British, recaptured by the Germans, and retaken by the British. The Germans launched a heavy offensive in May 1942. They again captured Tobruk (June 21) and were not stopped until they had almost reached El Alamein in Egypt. On Oct. 23, the British began a drive to regain their lost territory.

November 8-13, 1942
Invasion of North Africa. Allied victory. An invasion force of American and British troops landed on the North African coast near Casablanca, Oran, and Algiers. By Nov. 13, an armistice had been signed with the Vichy French in North Africa. The invasion force planned to move eastward and eventually meet the British army moving westward from El Alamein.

an invasion of France in 1943 an impossibility, the Allies decided to strike at Sicily. On July 10, 1943, American and British forces swarmed over Sicily's beaches, where they met only slight opposition from the Italians. German troops put up stiff rear-guard resistance, but after thirty-eight days of hard fighting, the Allies had complete control of the island.

The conquest of Sicily triggered a crisis in the Italian government. King Victor Emmanuel III and many of his political advisers decided that the war was lost and that they must get rid of Mussolini. Mussolini appealed to Hitler for help against the Allies, but the German "Führer" offered little more than advice. Mussolini was overthrown by Marshal Pietro Badoglio, and the new government immediately sued for peace. After some fumbling efforts to bargain, Italy signed the document of unconditional surrender on September 3, 1943. Then Italy joined the Allied side as a cobelligerent.

World War II

EUROPEAN THEATER, 1943-1945

January 24-May 13, 1943

The Campaign in North Africa. Allied victory. The fall of Tripoli to the British (Jan. 24) was a major success in the two-pronged drive to clear North Africa of Axis troops. Inexperienced American troops were delayed in their drive by fierce fighting at Kasserine Pass in Tunisia (Feb. 14-23). Finally, the Axis troops were forced into a pocket on the Cape Bon peninsula. They surrendered at Bizerte on May 7, and on the same day, the British captured Tunis. Axis troops in North Africa formally surrendered on May 13.

July-November 1943

Soviet offensive. Allied victories. Allied bombings of factories had dealt a severe blow to Germany's wartime production. Meanwhile Soviet production had greatly increased. With their new power, the Russians began an offensive in July and, by October, had pushed the Germans back to the Dnieper River. Kiev was liberated Nov. 6.

July 10-August 17, 1943

Invasion of Sicily. Allied victory. An Anglo-American invasion force (British General Bernard Montgomery and American General George Patton) overran the island of Sicily in five weeks, with major victories at Palermo (July 24) and Messina (Aug. 17).

September 3, 1943-June 4, 1944

Invasion of Italy. Allied victory. Montgomery's British troops crossed into the Italian Peninsula from Messina (Sept. 3). American troops

(General Mark Clark) landed at Salerno (Sept. 9) and met strong resistance from German troops that had occupied Italy. By December, the Allied forces controlled about half the peninsula.

On Jan. 22, 1944, the Allies made an amphibious landing at Anzio, 30 miles south of Rome. Pushing into the interior, they captured a German stronghold at Cassino (May 18). Allied soldiers marched into Rome on June 4.

January-May 1944
Soviet offensive. Allied victories. On Jan. 29, the Russians announced that German troops had been expelled from the Moscow and Leningrad areas. The Russians went on to recapture Odessa (April 10) and Sevastopol (May 9).

June 6, 1944
"D-day" invasion of Normandy. Allied victory. Under an air cover of 11,000 planes and preceded by paratroopers, Allied troops (General Eisenhower) stormed French beaches in Normandy province. After securing beachheads, the Allies took Cherbourg (June 27), Caen (July 9) and St. Lô (July 25). The occupation of St. Lô opened important routes for the liberation of France. By July, about one million men had landed in Normandy.

August 15, 1944
Invasion of southern France. Allied victory. Allied forces landed near Toulon and drove northward along the Rhone River. On Sept. 15, these forces joined the Normandy invaders at Dijon, France.

August 25, 1944
Liberation of Paris. Allied victory. Sweeping across France, the Allies, including Free French forces, rode triumphantly into Paris.

October 20, 1944
Fall of Belgrade. Allied victory. While western Europe was being liberated, Russian forces swept into eastern Europe. They were aided by Yugoslav partisans when they captured Belgrade.

December 16-26, 1944
Battle of the Bulge. Allied victory. This battle was named for a 50-mile bulge created in the Allied lines by a surprise German offensive at the Belgium-Luxembourg border. A heroic stand by American troops at Bastogne robbed the Germans of a victory in this their last offensive of the war.

March 7, 1945
Crossing the Rhine. Allied victory. Swiftly crushing all resistance, Allied troops pushed into Germany. They crossed the Rhine River via Remagen Bridge, which the Germans had hoped to destroy before the arrival of the Allies.

April 25, 1945
Meeting at the Elbe. Russian troops, who had pushed eastward through Germany, met United States forces near Torgau, southwest of Berlin.

May 1, 1945
Fall of Italy. Allied victory. Two Allied columns headed toward northern Italy. One made its way north on the peninsula; the other came south from Germany. The two columns met at Brenner Pass, where German troops surrendered.

Berlin, Germany, 1946

May 2, 1945
Fall of Berlin. Allied victory. Russian forces announced that Berlin was completely in their control.

May 8, 1945
V-E Day. Allied victory. Fighting with the Germans ceased, and the Allies celebrated victory in Europe.

Nuremberg, Germany, 1945

This surrender did not give the Allies control of the Italian peninsula. Aware of the surrender maneuvers, the Nazis had swiftly moved troops into northern and central Italy. At the same time, the British invaded the Italian peninsula from Sicily, and a combined force of British and American troops struck at Salerno south of Naples.

Allied leaders assumed that they could conquer Italy without great difficulty. They were wrong; Italy's hills and mountains gave the advantage to the defenders. With relatively few divisions, skillfully entrenched, the Germans held back the American and British armies. The Allied forces did not enter Rome until June 4, 1944. Northern Italy was yet to be conquered.

Great offensives crushed Germany

While weary American and British soldiers were slogging toward Rome, the Allies brought together more than 2.8 million men and 2.5 million tons of supplies in Britain for a direct assault on France. For six weeks in the spring of 1944, American and British bombers pounded airplane factories, oil refineries, bridges, roads, and railroads in France, Germany, and other areas held by the Nazis.

Late in the night of June 5, 1944 more than 100 huge gliders and 900 airplanes began leaving British airfields. Soon after they crossed the English Channel they dropped thousands of troops behind the German lines in France in what was the largest airborne invasion yet launched. Then, as the dawn broke, the American and British air forces pounded the German defenses with thousands of tons of bombs. Shortly after dawn on June 6, 1944, a great armada, guarded by an umbrella of airplanes, moved across the English Channel and deposited some 120,000 Allied soldiers on a sixty-mile strip of beach on the Normandy coast of France. General Eisenhower, supreme commander of the Allied expeditionary force, and his advisers had avoided the French ports because the Nazis had strong defenses there. Allied forces ran into formidable underwater

obstacles, mines, barbed wire, tank traps, deadly crossfire from pillboxes, and shelling from protected German artillery. Slowly, the Allied soldiers overcame this opposition and built up their beachheads. Within two weeks, more than a million American and British troops with heavy equipment were in Normandy. After seven weeks of hard fighting in the beach areas, an American army broke through the German defenses around Saint-Lô, a transportation hub that opened roads into the heart of France, and headed for Brittany.

On August 15, 1944, an American army and a French army landed on the southern coast of France between Nice and Marseilles and opened new lines of supply for the Allied forces. Ten days later Paris fell to the Allies. French partisans helped to liberate Paris, and all over France they rose to attack the Nazis and aid the Allies. By October, the Germans had been swept out of France.

On the eastern front, the Nazis were suffering even greater losses. Beginning with a great counterattack in 1943, which destroyed a German army at Stalingrad, the Red army began moving west.

With its armies falling back, both in the east and west, Germany's situation seemed hopeless. Some of the German generals wanted to negotiate peace but first they had to overthrow Hitler, who insisted that the fighting must go on. The German Führer not only survived an attempt to kill him, but destroyed the generals involved in the plot against him.

In December 1944, with the Allied advance in the west stalled, Hitler tried a desperate gamble. At a sector of the front near Belgium and Luxembourg, where the American troops were thinly spread, he launched a counteroffensive designed to split the Allied armies. Nazi tank columns broke through the defenses and created a "bulge" fifty miles deep in the Allied lines. In the Battle of the Bulge it seemed for a while as if German armor might slice through to the center of France. Finally, stubborn American paratroopers at Bastogne stopped this last Nazi offensive.

Soon the Allies put pressure on the Germans

and forced them to retreat. In March 1945, American troops captured a bridge across the Rhine River at Remagen. Four American divisions quickly crossed the bridge and spread out over Germany. In April, near Torgau on the Elbe River, American and Russian soldiers met for the first time.

In this hour of triumph the Allied soldiers uncovered evidence of a barbarism that hardly seemed possible among civilized men. At Buchenwald, Dachau, and elsewhere, the Allies found concentration camps in which Nazis had systematically tortured and murdered Jews, Poles, and political prisoners of many nationalities. In time of war, propagandists usually exaggerate the evils of an enemy, but Allied reports of Nazi deeds proved to be pallid in comparison with the horrors of the reality.

Hitler had claimed that in defeat "we shall drag a world with us—a world in flames." He and his loyal followers tried to do just that. They put Germany to the torch and fought to the death. As Russian soldiers battled toward his bomb-proof bunker under the Reichschancellery in Berlin, Hitler committed suicide (April 30).

A day or so earlier Italian partisans had captured and killed Mussolini. On May 1, 1945, German resistance in Italy ended. On May 2, 1945, the Russians captured Berlin. On May 7, at General Eisenhower's headquarters at Reims, Alfred Jodl, one of Hitler's generals, signed the document of unconditional surrender. At midnight, May 8, 1945, fighting stopped. The war in Europe, the most devastating conflict that continent ever had known, was over. Now Japan was the only enemy still fighting.

REVIEWING THE SECTION

1. How did the Allies destroy the effectiveness of the U-boats?

2. Why did the Allies launch an offensive in North Africa? How did their success in that campaign enable them to launch an attack on Sicily and Italy? How did the conquest of Sicily lead to the overthrow of Mussolini and Italy's surrender?

3. What great offensives enabled the Allied forces to defeat Germany?

NAVAL POWER WAS DECISIVE IN THE PACIFIC

Even though Roosevelt and Churchill had stuck to their decision to devote most of their resources to the conquest of Europe, this strategy did not mean that the war against Japan had been neglected until Hitler was defeated. In fact, as Japan's conquests expanded, the American attitude toward the war had shifted, and so had American strategy. Instead of merely holding off the Japanese, American military leaders decided that it would be possible to fight an aggressive two-front war. To carry out this strategy, Roosevelt even had some equipment, such as landing barges and troop transports, diverted from the Atlantic to the Pacific.

The President's military advisers argued that United States forces had to strike at the Japanese before the latter could exploit their conquests and become firmly entrenched in their advanced positions. The nature of the war in the Pacific made possible such offensive action with limited resources. Japan's conquests, spread over vast distances of the Pacific Ocean, were vulnerable to naval attacks on isolated outposts.

Americans did almost all of the fighting and made almost all of the decisions in the war against Japan. American commanders, such as General MacArthur and Admiral Ernest J. King, who were eager to strike back at the Japanese, were able to influence policy as well as military strategy. While the army built up its resources and new ships were being built, the navy gave a boost to national morale by attacking the Japanese as well as defending itself. American morale received a special boost on April 16, 1942, when a squadron of sixteen army planes under the command of Lieutenant Colonel James H. Doolittle bombed targets in the Tokyo area. Eventually, in coöperation with marine and army forces, the navy worked out a pattern of amphibious warfare that permitted assaults on Japanese strong points, one by one.

Navy pilots stopped the Japanese

Early in 1942, after their easy conquests elsewhere, the Japanese decided to strike at Port Moresby in southern New Guinea. If this outpost fell, Australia would be open to attack and invasion. In May, a Japanese fleet moved southward into the Coral Sea toward Port Moresby. The United States Navy, which had broken Japan's secret code, knew of the planned attack. It sent two aircraft carriers and some cruisers against the invaders. Before any of the ships could see each other, planes from the carrier decks of both sides struck. The Japanese lost one carrier and suffered damage on two others, while the Americans lost one carrier and had another one crippled.

Even though both fleets suffered heavy damage, the Battle of the Coral Sea (May 7-8, 1942) ended as an American victory. The Japanese retreated without even trying to land troops at Port Moresby. Australia was saved by the first sea battle in history in which surface ships did not engage enemy ships, where all the fighting was done by carrier-based planes.

Right after the Battle of the Coral Sea, Admiral Isoroku Yamamoto, the commander of Japan's combined fleet, decided to capture Midway, a tiny island more than 1100 nautical miles northwest of Hawaii. He wanted to make Hawaii useless as a naval base and to destroy what remained of the United States fleet in the Pacific. So Yamamoto brought together a huge armada of over two hundred ships, including eight aircraft carriers and eleven battleships. Admiral Chester W. Nimitz, in command of American naval forces in the Pacific, had only three aircraft carriers and no battleships to use against the Japanese. But he had Midway Island, which he could use as an unsinkable aircraft carrier.

Nimitz threw his torpedo planes, dive bombers, and marine fighter planes at the Japanese carriers. At the end of the Battle of Midway, most of which was fought on June 4, 1942, Yamamoto's once magnificent fleet limped away in retreat with one fourth of its ships, including his four best carriers, sunk or damaged. Although this American victory was costly, it saved Hawaii. The Japanese fleet had lost its offensive punch and Japan's advance across the central Pacific was checked. The Battle of Midway also showed that a fleet of ships could be defeated by concentrated air power.

Two months later United States Marines landed at Guadalcanal, one of the Solomon Islands which were part of a larger chain of islands used by Japan as a shield to protect her conquests. For six months United States and Japanese troops fought a brutal, bloody war in an almost impenetrable jungle. At the same time, the navy fought off every Japanese counterattack. In the Battle of Guadalcanal, fought in November 1942, the United States gained another costly victory. Finally, in February 1943, the Japanese pulled their forces out of the southern Solomons. The United States had ceased to think in terms of holding the Japanese at bay; it had become the attacker.

Americans "leapfrogged" toward Tokyo

Japan's defenses were spread over thousands of miles and crisscrossed hundreds of small islands. Before Americans could attack these fortified islands, military leaders had to work out a strategy that would bring victory without excessive losses. If they tried to advance toward Tokyo by attacking each island stronghold, the fighting would be long and costly. So they devised a plan that would permit American forces to avoid much of the island fighting and approach Tokyo in great leaps. This "leapfrog" strategy would permit American forces to attack carefully selected Japanese key spots and to neutralize others which would become isolated by American sea and naval power.

Control of the air and of the sea lanes made possible the leapfrog strategy. But Americans had to wait for about eight months after the conquest of Guadalcanal before they could strike because they were short of aircraft carriers. The first leapfrog offensive came in November 1943, when ma-

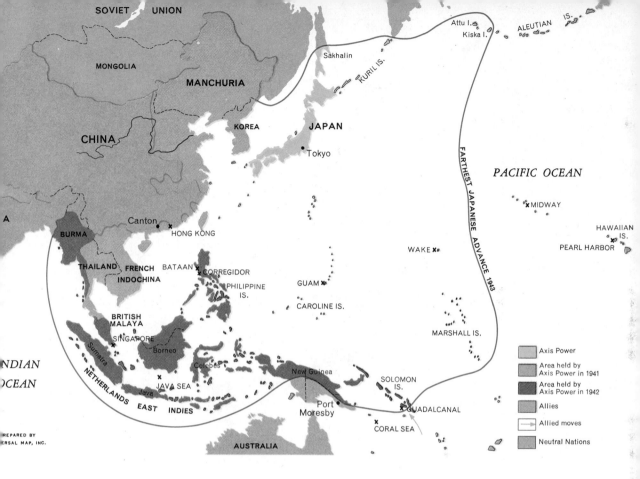

World War II
PACIFIC THEATER, 1941-1943

December 7, 1941
Raid on Pearl Harbor. Axis victory. In a surprise attack, Japanese bombers devastated the Pearl Harbor naval base in Hawaii. During the two-hour raid, 19 American ships were sunk or disabled, 150 planes were destroyed, and 2400 servicemen were killed. Simultaneously the Japanese assaulted Wake Island, the Philippines, Guam, and the Malay Peninsula.

January-May 1942
Japanese conquests in the Pacific and Asia. Axis victories. Advancing on many fronts, the Japanese took British Malaya (Jan. 31), Singapore (Feb. 15), Burma (March 9), and Java (March 9). The Battle of the Java Sea (Feb. 27-Mar. 1) was a severe loss for the Allies.

May 6, 1942
Fall of the Philippines. Axis victory. United States forces (General Douglas MacArthur) had retreated to Bataan peninsula, where they were trapped. On President Roosevelt's orders, MacArthur was evacuated to Australia (March 17). The Japanese overran Bataan on April 9, leaving only the off-shore island of Corregidor in United States hands. The 72,500 Filipino and United States troops on Bataan were forced on an 85-mile death march to prison camps. Corregidor, with 61,000 men, finally surrendered a month later (May 6).

May 7-8, 1942
Battle of the Coral Sea. Allied victory. Attempting to establish a base from which to attack Australia, a Japanese fleet headed toward Port Moresby in southern New Guinea. In a sea battle that involved not ships but carrier-based planes, American pilots thwarted the Japanese plan.

June 3-6, 1942
Battle of Midway. Allied victory. A relatively small United States force (Admiral Chester W. Nimitz) staved off a major Japanese attack on the Midway Island naval base. Four Japanese aircraft carriers and 275 planes were destroyed, thus restoring the balance of naval power in the Pacific.

August 7, 1942-February 9, 1943
Invasion of Guadalcanal. Allied victory. United States marines landed on the island of Guadalcanal in the Solomon Islands and captured an airport. Allied military experts wanted to make Guadalcanal a base from which they could launch an offensive in the Pacific. The naval Battle of Guadalcanal (Nov. 12-15) prevented the Japanese from landing reinforcements to aid against the marines. The Japanese evacuated Guadalcanal Feb. 9, 1943.

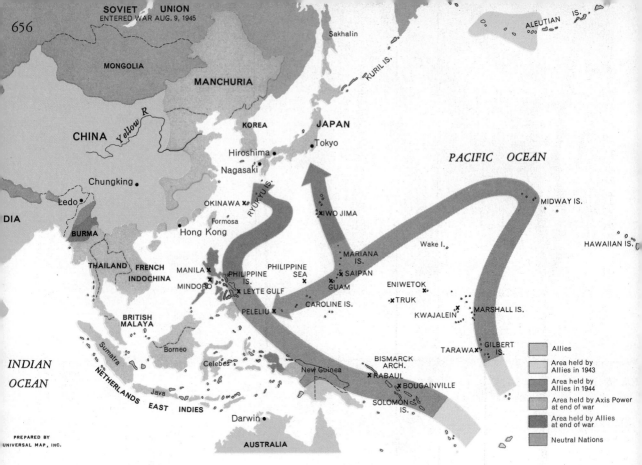

SOVIET UNION
ENTERED WAR AUG. 9, 1945

Sakhalin

MONGOLIA

MANCHURIA

KURIL IS.

ALEUTIAN IS.

CHINA

Yellow R.

KOREA

JAPAN

Tokyo

Hiroshima

Nagasaki

PACIFIC OCEAN

Chungking

Ledo

OKINAWA

RYUKYUS

IWO JIMA

MIDWAY IS.

DIA

Formosa

Hong Kong

BURMA

Wake I.

HAWAIIAN IS.

THAILAND

FRENCH INDOCHINA

MANILA

PHILIPPINE IS.

MINDORO

LEYTE GULF

PHILIPPINE SEA

SAIPAN

MARIANA IS.

GUAM

ENIWETOK

TRUK

CAROLINE IS.

KWAJALEIN

MARSHALL IS.

BRITISH MALAYA

PELELIU

Sumatra

Borneo

NETHERLANDS

Celebes

INDIAN OCEAN

New Guinea

BISMARCK ARCH.

RABAUL

BOUGAINVILLE

TARAWA

GILBERT IS.

Java

EAST INDIES

SOLOMON IS.

Darwin

AUSTRALIA

PREPARED BY
UNIVERSAL MAP, INC.

Allies

Area held by Allies in 1943

Area held by Allies in 1944

Area held by Axis Power at end of war

Area held by Allies at end of war

Neutral Nations

World War II

PACIFIC THEATER, 1943-1945

ALLIED STRATEGY

Because Japan's strategic island outposts were so far-flung, United States military experts decided to attack the most vulnerable islands and "leapfrog" toward the Philippines and Tokyo. The tactic was successful, and the United States won all the campaigns listed here.

July-November 1943

Solomon Islands campaign. After a series of naval victories (July-October 1943) that cleared the waters around the central Solomon Islands, United States marines landed at Bougainville (Nov. 1). From this base MacArthur directed the conquest of the Solomons.

November 1943-September 1944

Central Pacific campaign. Another thrust at the Japanese island perimeter was led by Admiral Chester Nimitz in the central Pacific. First fell the Gilbert Islands (Nov. 24) where the bloody battle of Tarawa cost the lives of 913 United States marines.

Next the marines invaded the Marshall Islands, with significant battles at Kwajalein (Feb. 6) and Eniwetok (Feb. 17-22). The marines went on to the Mariana Islands, taking Saipan (June 15) and Guam (July 21). With the landing on Peleliu Island (Sept. 15), the central Pacific forces were ready to invade the Philippines.

January-September 1944

New Guinea campaign. MacArthur's forces proceeded up the northeast coast of New Guinea, and Japanese resistance ended in September. These troops joined the forces under Admiral Nimitz in the liberation of the Philippines.

October 25, 1944-February 23, 1945

Liberation of the Philippines. The United States Navy prepared the way for a Philippines landing by virtually wiping out the Japanese fleet in the Battle for Leyte Gulf (Oct. 25). Landing on Mindoro Island (Dec. 15), United States troops overcame Japanese resistance and took the Philippine capital, Manila, Feb. 23.

February 10-March 17, 1945

Battle of Iwo Jima. At the cost of 6000 American lives, marines occupied this strategic island, only 660 nautical miles from Tokyo.

April 1-June 21, 1945

Invasion of the Ryukyu Islands. The threshhold to Japan itself was the Ryukyu Island group. It took almost three months of fighting to occupy the main island of Okinawa.

August 15, 1945

V-J Day. Following atomic bomb attacks on Hiroshima (Aug. 6) and Nagasaki (Aug. 9) the Japanese government unconditionally surrendered and victory in Japan was proclaimed.

Hiroshima, 1946—4/10 mile from atomic bomb impact

rines invaded Bougainville, the northernmost island in the Solomon chain. Within a few months a series of American victories in this area made it possible for planes and ships to encircle and neutralize Rabaul, Japan's stronghold nearby in the Bismarck Archipelago.

At the same time, far to the north in the central Pacific, American naval forces struck at the Caroline Islands. In capturing the small atoll of Tarawa in the Gilbert Islands, the marines suffered heavy losses fighting the Japanese.

Late in January 1944, Admiral Nimitz unleashed the first truly large amphibious attacks in the Pacific theater, against the Marshall Islands, where marines took the tiny island of Kwajalein. By the end of February, the great Japanese naval base at Truk, in the Caroline Islands, had been neutralized. Japan's outer defensive perimeter had been pierced. The next attack, launched in June 1944, cracked the inner perimeter at the Mariana Islands.

On June 15, marines assaulted the beaches of Saipan, one of the largest of the Marianas, only 1350 nautical miles from Tokyo.

The invasion of Saipan forced the Japanese to bring out their fleet, which had been rebuilt and retrained. An American task force, under Admiral Raymond A. Spruance, was waiting. In the Battle of the Philippine Sea on June 19 and 20, 1944, Spruance's planes wiped out the Japanese air groups. The Japanese also lost three carriers and other ships. Long-range bombers from Saipan now could strike at the industries and the flimsy, highly inflammable buildings on Japan's home islands.

While the navy and marines were doing most of the leapfrogging, General MacArthur's soldiers had fought their way northward from southern New Guinea. In some of the bitterest fighting of the war, through jungle swamps infested with malaria-carrying mosquitoes, the army conquered New Guinea (September 1943). Then, in October

1944, the navy and the army invaded Leyte, a central island in the Philippines. When General MacArthur waded ashore he announced, "People of the Philippines, I have returned."

The Japanese decided to commit their entire fleet to the destruction of the invaders and their ships. In the Battle of Leyte Gulf, three separate naval engagements on October 25, 1944, the Americans met the Japanese navy and destroyed it. The American losses were light; the Japanese lost three battleships, four carriers, nine cruisers, and eight destroyers. During the next few months, the army proceeded with the conquest of the Philippines and the navy blasted its way toward Tokyo.

Japan was forced to surrender

Only on the mainland of Asia was Japan able to hold on to much of what it had conquered, but there too, it suffered some setbacks. Although Japanese forces had isolated China from its Allies, Americans managed to send some supplies into China in 1943 from India. With an army of Chinese, Indians, and a few Americans, General Joseph W. Stilwell of the United States Army fought his way through northern Burma and built the Ledo Road, which went into operation in January 1945. It met the Burma Road and provided a route into China's rugged Yunnan province. Although the road eased the supply problem, China remained outside the main struggle against Japan.

While the fighting went on in China, Burma, and the Philippines, United States Marines scrambled ashore at Iwo Jima, a volcanic island only 660 nautical miles from Tokyo. In March 1945, after weeks of some of the bloodiest fighting in the war, the marines captured the island. This gave the Americans airfields for fighter planes to protect the huge bombers sent to raid Japan.

On April 1, 1945, soldiers and marines invaded Okinawa, largest of the Ryukyu Islands, which were a part of the Japanese homeland, and only 317 nautical miles from Tokyo. The battle for Okinawa took a frightful toll of men and ships.

Japanese pilots of the *Kamikaze,* the "Divine Wind," Corps (trained to fly just one mission and never return), were sent to dive at American ships, crash into them, and sink them. So effective were the suicidal Kamikaze attacks that, by June 22, when the battle for Okinawa ended, the Kamikaze pilots had sunk thirty-six ships and seriously damaged several hundred.

The deadly resistance at Okinawa convinced American military planners that a direct assault on Japan's main islands would be prolonged and costly. Japan now had almost no ships and only a few planes capable of stopping the American bombers which were daily attacking Japanese cities and reducing them to rubble. Moderate Japanese civilian leaders realized that their country had lost the war, but fanatical military leaders were determined to continue fighting. They were well prepared; they had an army of two million men and a force of five thousand planes for Kamikaze attacks against an invasion.

In July 1945, Allied statesmen issued an ultimatum calling on Japan to surrender or face destruction. The emperor, the premier, and other civilian leaders were willing to seek peace; Japan's military leaders rejected the ultimatum. On August 6, therefore, an American plane, the *Enola Gay,* droned over the city of Hiroshima, released a single bomb, and turned away. Fifty seconds later there was a blinding flash, an earsplitting roar, and a huge mushroom cloud. The first atomic bomb used in a war had just destroyed every building within a four-mile radius and had killed more than seventy thousand people.

Three days later, the Soviet Union joined the war against Japan and attacked Manchuria. On that same day, August 9, a few hours after the Soviet declaration of war, a second American atomic bomb leveled Nagasaki and killed tens of thousands of people. On August 14, after frantic negotiations, the Japanese agreed to surrender, and the fighting stopped. General MacArthur, as supreme commander for the Allied powers, imposed the final terms of surrender on September 2, 1945, on the deck of the battleship *U.S.S. Missouri*, anchored in Tokyo Bay. At last World War II was over. It had taken the lives of 325,000 Americans and brought injury to more than a million others.

REVIEWING THE SECTION

1. Why were the battles of the Coral Sea, Midway, and Guadalcanal important victories for the Allies?

2. How did the United States apply a leapfrog strategy to break through Japanese defenses?

3. Why did American military planners become convinced that an invasion of Japan would be extremely difficult?

WAR STRATEGY SHAPED DIPLOMACY

As soon as the United States had entered the war, the government reorganized the entire economy for the purpose of winning the war as quickly as possible. American statesmen conducted their wartime diplomacy with the same goal in mind. This meant that they often permitted military strategy rather than long-term political goals to shape the nature of their diplomatic decisions.

What American statesmen said and did was important for the whole world because, from the beginning, the United States took the dominant position in the shaping of war strategy and international diplomacy. It could do so because it was the strongest and wealthiest of the Allied nations. In one way or another all of the Allies depended on the United States for some form of help.

The other major Allies, Britain and the Soviet Union, did not subordinate political objectives to military objectives. Britain wanted to preserve her influence in the Mediterranean area. The Soviet Union sought territory in central Europe and in Asia. The United States desired no territory or area of special influence. Government leaders in the United States wanted to destroy fascism and militarism and to build a system of collective security that would preserve peace. They thought they could deal with political issues after the defeat of the Axis powers and plan for a postwar world free of military pressures. They were wrong. The political decisions could not wait. Furthermore, war strategy could not be separated from political and diplomatic considerations which would shape the postwar world.

A grand alliance was formed

The commitment to active participation in the international diplomacy of the war began at the White House on New Year's Day, 1942. There, President Roosevelt, Prime Minister Churchill, Ambassador Maxim Litvinov of the Soviet Union, and representatives of twenty-three other nations at war with the Axis powers signed the Declaration of the United Nations. This agreement forged a grand alliance against the Axis. The signers pledged to uphold the principles of the Atlantic Charter and not to make a separate armistice or peace with the enemies.

Almost immediately it became clear that the alliance would not work smoothly. Before Hitler had invaded the Soviet Union, the Soviets had absorbed the three small Baltic states of Lithuania, Latvia, and Estonia, the eastern part of Poland, a segment of Finland, and portions of Romania. The Soviets announced that they intended to keep these territories, but Roosevelt and Churchill refused to give legal recognition to these conquests.

Military strategy also became a source of friction between the Soviet Union and its Anglo-American allies. In 1942, the Red armies had suffered appalling losses as they took the heaviest of blows from Hitler's war machines. The Russians wanted help from the United States and Britain in the form of a second fighting front in Europe. Roosevelt sympathized with the Soviets, but the British and American leaders believed they did not have the men and equipment to open such a front. All Roosevelt could offer was a promise for a second front in the future. This promise did not satisfy the Soviets. The Russians, on the other hand, turned aside American requests for immediate cooperation against Japan. Joseph Stalin, always suspicious of his allies, feared that the United States was trying to incite the Japanese to attack Siberia.

Winston Churchill opposed a direct invasion of Europe as the Soviets desired. But he agreed with Roosevelt that the Anglo-American allies should take some kind of offensive action against the Axis powers in 1942, to help the Soviets avert disaster on the eastern front. This desire, as well as the German and Italian threat against Egypt, had led Roosevelt to agree to the Anglo-American invasion of North Africa in November 1942.

Roosevelt demanded unconditional surrender

In January 1943, after most Axis resistance in North Africa had been crushed, Roosevelt and Churchill and their staffs met at Casablanca to discuss future war strategy. This high-level personal diplomacy among Allied leaders became a major characteristic of the international politics of the war. Although it might delay the direct invasion of France desired by the Soviets, the British proposal to invade Sicily was accepted by Roosevelt.

The British accepted a proposal by the United States for a policy of unconditional surrender toward the Axis enemies. Roosevelt's critics later condemned the policy of unconditional surrender as one of the great mistakes of the war. They argued that it stiffened Axis resistance and hence prolonged the war. Actually, the policy of unconditional surrender was not applied rigidly, but permitted Allied leaders to offer terms, even concessions, to an enemy considering surrender. Roosevelt adopted the policy of unconditional surrender because he remembered the bitterness and misunderstanding that had grown out of the surrender terms of World War I. He wanted to avoid similar misunderstandings following World War II and to strengthen the will of the Allies to fight on to victory. Later, Stalin accepted the policy of unconditional surrender.

Roosevelt had long wanted to talk to Stalin. After the surrender of Italy, the President urged a meeting of the Big Three—Roosevelt, Churchill, and Stalin—to discuss world-wide strategy. Since Stalin refused to travel far from his homeland, the President reluctantly agreed to go to distant Teheran, Iran, to meet with him and Churchill.

Late in November 1943, on his way to Teheran, Roosevelt stopped at Cairo for several days to confer with Chiang Kai-shek and Churchill on China's place in global strategy. The most important result of this conference was the Declaration of Cairo, announced on December 1, after the Soviets had approved. It said the Allies would strip Japan of its possessions and would restore to the Chinese all the territories, such as Manchuria and Formosa, which Japan had taken. Korea ultimately would be made independent.

From Cairo Roosevelt flew to Teheran, where he met Stalin, and where the Big Three talked each day and evening from November 28 to December 2, 1943. In the Declaration of Teheran, released on December 1, Roosevelt and Churchill promised that the long-awaited invasion of France would come in the spring. Stalin reiterated an earlier promise that the Soviet Union would join the war against Japan after Germany's defeat. The Big Three also discussed the possible dismemberment of Germany and the nature of a postwar system of collective security. They parted with Roosevelt believing victory would come soon and that Allied coöperation would continue after the war. Teheran marked the high point of cordial coöperation with the Russians.

Yalta marked a turning point

In September 1944, while British and American armies were smashing Hitler's European fortress from the west and Russian armies were crushing it from the east, Roosevelt and Churchill and their staffs met in Quebec. They agreed on plans for final victory in Europe and Asia, and for the future control of Germany. Churchill and the American statesmen were alarmed by the actions of the Soviet Union and feared that as Red armies

MEN
IN
HISTORY

ROOSEVELT, CHURCHILL, AND STALIN

Yalta was once a vacation resort of tsars. It is located at the tip of the Crimean Peninsula, which juts out into the Black Sea. The leaders of the United States, Britain, and the Soviet Union met in Yalta in February 1945, when it was one of the few convenient showplaces of the battle-scarred Soviet Union. World War II was going well for the three nations, and the three heads of state were meeting to plan for the future.

As Franklin Delano Roosevelt arrived at the conference, some expressed concern for his physical condition. He appeared to be in poor health. He claimed to feel fine, and decisions did not seem to burden him, but he tired when discussions were prolonged, and he sought to avoid sustained argument.

A master politician, Roosevelt nevertheless had found the Soviet Union baffling, Stalin humorless, and Churchill alternately amusing and irritating. He admitted his confusion to his assistants. "I don't understand the Russians," he said. "I don't know a good Russian from a bad Russian." Still, Roosevelt thought of the conference as a family affair, and he liked to characterize relations among the three nations in family terms.

Winston Churchill arrived at the conference barely recovered from a near fatal siege of pneumonia. In fact, the meeting had been postponed so that Churchill could recuperate. Visualizing the great possibilities of the future, Churchill felt that the job of the leaders was to bring the world's people into a condition of peace and happiness. He said that such a prize was nearer mankind's grasp than it had been at any time in history. Churchill thought that if the prize of peace should slip away, history would be unforgiving.

For Churchill it seemed strange to be in the Soviet Union, conferring with the world's leading Communist. Earlier, at the moment when Britain had become allied with the Soviet Union, Churchill had said: "No one has been a more persistent opponent of communism that I have been for the last twenty-five years. I will unsay no word that I have spoken about it . . . . " Yet Churchill was aware that the alliance was necessary, though temporary.

Joseph Stalin, the host of the conference, arrived hale and hearty. Formerly the servant of a rebellious people, he had become their master. Efficient propaganda had made him the symbol of the Russian Bolshevik Revolution through all its phases. Purger of his own party, Stalin had built a contradictory half-conservative and half-revolutionary empire. He who was responsible for Russia's disastrous defeats at the beginning of the German invasion, who blamed later German advances toward Stalingrad and the Caucasus on the failure of his allies to invade France, was now carrying the Communist banner beyond his country's frontier.

Stalin said that it was not hard to maintain wartime unity since the Allies had a common aim clear to everyone. He predicted that a difficult time would come after the war when different interests would tend to divide the Allies. He contended that the three men had a duty to see that relations among them in peacetime would be as strong as they were in war.

Among the three men, Churchill and Stalin presented the greatest contrast. Churchill was a descendant of the Duke of Marlborough; Stalin a descendant of serfs. One was born in a palace, the other in a one-room hovel. A product of the climate of Victorian and Edwardian England, whose heritage he was guarding, sat opposite a survivor of underground rebellious groups and secret Politburo intrigue. A colorful lover of foods, wine, words, was confronted by a colorless distruster of words. Churchill represented the aristocratic right in class consciousness and feared he had an empire to lose. Stalin was the extreme left in class consciousness and had an empire to win.

Roosevelt presented an aristocratic background and middle-class reform attitude. He came from a family of land owners and industrialists who had established a political tradition, and he had spent his entire life in law, party politics, and government. He was the leader of a nation that had been spared the worst violence of class struggles and foreign wars. He had the most pragmatic outlook of the three.

And so it was that the three world leaders, representing three different political systems, came together at Yalta. The confrontation had begun.

moved into and occupied nations formerly held by the Nazis, the Soviets would forsake coöperation with their Allies and make the occupied countries Communist satellites. Churchill therefore urged another Big Three conference right after the Quebec meeting, but Roosevelt refused to leave the United States while he was involved in a campaign for election to a fourth term.

The wartime election campaign had started in June 1944, a few weeks after the Allies had launched their cross-channel invasion of France. At that time the Republicans had given the presidential nomination to Governor Thomas E. Dewey of New York, a vigorous young politician who favored a foreign policy of international coöperation. For Vice President they had chosen Governor John W. Bricker of Ohio, an isolationist.

Three weeks later, Roosevelt received his fourth nomination from the Democrats. Since he was aging and appeared to be ill, considerable interest swirled around the choice for Vice President. The convention bypassed the incumbent Vice President, Henry A. Wallace, and accepted a senator from Missouri, Harry S. Truman, as a compromise candidate. The Democratic platform, like that of the Republicans, promised international leadership in the future, as well as more social legislation.

Although Dewey conducted a vigorous campaign, he could not shake the people's confidence in Roosevelt. The President won decisively and although the Democrats lost one Senate seat, they gained twenty seats in the House. All over the world people saw Roosevelt's victory as a commitment by the American people to a policy of leadership in world affairs.

After the election, Roosevelt took up Churchill's plea for another meeting of the Big Three and agreed to confer, following his inauguration in January, with Churchill and Stalin at Yalta, a resort on the Black Sea in the Russian Crimea. When the Big Three met, from February 4 to 11, 1945, dissension threatened to split the grand alliance. With the hour of final victory near, the Allies were beset with fear and distrust of each other.

The Yalta conference, the most controversial and momentous of the war, covered four main topics: the problems of Asia, the governments of Poland and of the other nations of eastern Europe, the future of Germany, and the basis for a new league of nations.

In return for his promise to bring the Soviet Union into the war against Japan, Stalin obtained agreement from Roosevelt and Churchill that the Soviet Union could have Japan's Kuril Islands, control over Outer Mongolia, return of the southern half of Sakhalin Island, and recovery of the privileges she had had in Manchuria before the Russo-Japanese War (1905). This agreement was kept secret because officially the Soviet Union was still at peace with Japan.

Roosevelt and Churchill also reluctantly agreed that the Soviet Union could keep a part of eastern Poland. As compensation for this loss the Poles were to receive territory carved from eastern Germany. Roosevelt and Churchill refused to give definite approval to Poland's new western frontier. They also refused to recognize a Polish government set up by the Russians at Lublin, in eastern Poland. Finally, the western leaders accepted a compromise. The Lublin (Communist) government would be reorganized to include democratic Poles from home and abroad, and free elections would be held in Poland after the war.

As agreed upon earlier, the Big Three worked out a division of Germany into four zones. Each of the Big Three and France would occupy a zone. All agreed that Nazi war leaders should be tried as war criminals. But the Big Three disagreed on the matter of reparations. The United States asked for none, and the British mainly sought some German equipment with which to repair war damage. The Soviets demanded that the Germans be made to pay a total reparations bill of $20 billion of which the Soviet Union would receive half. Roosevelt and Churchill would not agree to this amount, but they accepted the Soviet terms as a basis for future discussion of the reparations question.

Although unenthusiastic about the postwar

United Nations Organization that Roosevelt hoped to establish, Stalin agreed that the Soviet Union would be a part of it. He also accepted a voting procedure and a pattern of membership in the organization previously opposed by the Soviets.

Eight days of tense bargaining and discussion put a strain on Roosevelt, who was ill, but he returned home believing the Big Three had laid the foundation for a firm peace. He said that the Yalta conference was a turning point in history. It proved to be a turning point, but not the kind he had in mind.

Stalin did not honor his pledges, and disillusionment over the diplomacy at Yalta quickly followed. Most Americans felt, in retrospect, that Roosevelt's concessions, when measured against Stalin's unkept promises, were unwise. Roosevelt probably counted too much on Soviet good faith. Yet except for the Kurile Islands, he and Churchill had not promised more than the Red army was in a position to take on its own. Although many Americans found them objectionable, the decisions at Yalta reflected the strength of the Soviet Union in a new balance of power being created out of the chaos of war.

Harry S. Truman became President

Franklin D. Roosevelt never experienced the disillusionment over Yalta. On the afternoon of April 12, 1945, while in Warm Springs, Georgia, trying to regain his strength for a forthcoming conference on the United Nations Organization, he suddenly died of a cerebral hemorrhage. Roosevelt's death struck millions of Americans with the force of a personal loss. They seemed to recognize, almost intuitively, that an era had ended.

The loss seemed particularly great to Harry S. Truman who quickly took the presidential oath of office. On the next day he told reporters:

Boys, if you ever pray, pray for me now...when they told me yesterday what had happened, I felt like the moon, the stars, and all the planets had fallen on me.

Truman had cause to be worried. As Vice President he had not been kept informed of what Roosevelt was doing. He was not prepared, therefore, to take over the awesome responsibility for ending the war and guiding the diplomacy that could affect the course of events in the postwar world. Nothing else in his life—neither his formal education, which did not go much beyond high school, nor his political career—had prepared him for such responsibilities. His childhood had been spent on a farm in Jackson County, Missouri, not far from Kansas City. When World War I came along, he served in the army as an artillery officer. He returned home, went into the men's clothing business, and failed.

In 1922, Harry Truman entered politics. He worked closely with the Democratic boss of Kansas City, Tom Pendergast. Despite the smell of corruption that surrounded Pendergast, everyone knew that Truman was inflexibly honest. In 1934, the people of Missouri elected Truman to the United States Senate, and reëlected him in 1940. There, he gained the attention of President Roosevelt through his work as chairman of a special committee that investigated war production. Truman consistently supported the New Deal, had a reputation for political moderation, and had many friends in Congress; he had been a logical compromise choice for Vice President in 1944.

The Allies met again at Potsdam

As quickly as he could, President Truman tried to learn all that he could about his new job from those cabinet officers and advisers who had been particularly close to Roosevelt. At the same time, Truman assured everyone he would continue Roosevelt's policies and carry out his wartime agreements. When Churchill expressed concern about increasing friction between the Soviet Union and the Anglo-American allies and urged another meeting of the Big Three to discuss mutual problems, Truman agreed.

This last of the high-level wartime conferences

took place at Potsdam, Germany, from July 17 to August 2, 1945. At the beginning, Truman, Churchill, and Stalin represented the Big Three, but during the conference, Clement R. Attlee, who had become prime minister when the Labour party won an election in Britain, replaced Churchill. Though the formalities seemed pleasant, uneasiness lurked under the surface politeness at Potsdam.

The Big Three squabbled over reparations to be obtained from Italy and Germany and over the Yalta agreements on eastern and central Europe. Finally they agreed on details for occupying and governing Germany and on a compromise for handling reparations. They could not agree on where Poland's western boundary should be, so they put that issue aside. But Germany's eastern provinces remained under Polish control. The Big Three also agreed to establish a council of foreign ministers which would represent themselves and France, to prepare peace treaties for Italy, Hungary, Bulgaria, Romania, and Finland. Truman and Attlee sponsored the Potsdam Declaration, the ultimatum that demanded Japan's surrender.

REVIEWING THE SECTION

1. Why did friction arise between the Soviet Union and its Anglo-American allies?

2. Why did Roosevelt adopt a policy of unconditional surrender? What policy decisions were made at the Cairo and Teheran conferences?

3. What decisions were made at the Yalta conference? Why were these decisions later criticized?

4. What agreements were made at Potsdam? Over what issues did the Allies quarrel?

CHAPTER **26** CONCLUSION

The attack on Pearl Harbor united the nation in a determination to meet and overcome the crisis. Industry, agriculture, and labor were mobilized to support the armed forces and to supply goods and equipment to the allies of the United States in the war against the Axis nations.

Within a year after Pearl Harbor, the United States had produced $47 billion worth of war goods, and by the spring of 1943, the United States had converted its peacetime industries into the greatest arsenal the world had ever seen. That job was supervised by the War Production Board, with Donald Nelson as chairman. The manufacture of many peacetime commodities was either curtailed or prohibited so as to facilitate war production.

Farmers, in spite of some difficulties, managed to meet the extraordinary demands for food. To supply the armed forces and the Allied nations with sufficient food required careful planning, since farmers were faced with a dwindling labor force and a lack of new machines and machine parts. Consumption of food at home was partly controlled through a system of rationing imposed by the Office of Price Administration. The entire food problem was under the supervision of a food administrator appointed by the President.

In order to meet the constantly increasing demands from the armed forces, more and more men were drafted. And, many men and women volunteered to serve their country. The armed forces were increased from half a million men in 1941 to more than fifteen million men and women in 1945. Many women enlisted for noncombatant work in every branch of the military service.

Organized labor generally refrained from striking early in the war. In 1943, when labor troubles did occur, Congress passed the Smith-Connally Anti-Strike Act, prohibiting strikes in plants working on war contracts and authorizing the President to seize plants where labor troubles impeded defense production. The production record for labor from 1940 to 1944 surpassed any previous record in the nation's history. Incomes rose while the workweek increased. At the end of the war, organized labor was stronger than it had ever been.

Although Americans were not personally as restricted as were people in other nations during the war, some Americans did suffer. In February 1942,

President Roosevelt authorized the secretary of war to exclude people from designated military areas. Under this order, more than 100,000 Japanese-Americans were relocated from the West coast to inland centers.

The United States had to find some way to pay for the war. So the government created new taxes, added new taxpayers to its lists, and sold war bonds and war stamps. By the end of the war, the national debt had increased from approximately $47 billion in 1941 to $247 billion in 1945.

On the European front, the Allies invaded Africa and Italy to prepare the way for landings in 1944 in France. The Germans fought stubbornly, and managed one large counteroffensive in the west, but were defeated within a year of the Normandy landings by the military power of the Allied forces, east and west. The defeat of Japan, hastened by the use of atomic bombs, followed several months later.

During the course of the war, the major leaders of the Allied nations held conferences. At these conferences, they planned military strategy, decided on the terms to be imposed on the defeated nations, and made plans for the postwar period.

The destruction caused by war, especially by air bombardment, was tremendous. Food, fuel, and clothing were in short supply in all the war-torn nations of Europe. The defeated nations were prostrate but some of the victors were in little better shape. In 1939, it had been possible to count seven great powers—Britain, France, Italy, Germany, the Soviet Union, Japan, and the United States. By 1945, there were only two truly great powers left—the United States and the Soviet Union.

FOCUSING ON SPECIFICS

1. Why did the Allied position seem particularly desperate in the winter of 1941-1942?

2. How did the government promote the efficiency of the industrial labor force during the war?

3. Why did the government ration many items during the war?

4. What principle was established in the case of *Korematsu* v. *United States*?

5. Why did the United States decide to concentrate on defeating Germany before defeating Japan?

6. How does the Battle of Midway show the importance of air power in naval warfare?

7. How did World War II change the international balance of power?

REVIEWING MAIN THEMES

1. How did the government mobilize the economy to support the war?

2. How were civil liberties affected by the war?

3. What factors enabled the Allies to defeat Italy and Germany?

4. What strategy enabled American forces to defeat Japan?

5. What decisions were made at the following conferences: Casablanca, Cairo, Teheran, Yalta, Potsdam? On what points did the Allies agree? On what points did they disagree?

EVALUATING THE ISSUES

1. The foreign policy expert George F. Kennan has concluded, "In Europe and Asia, Western democracy had become militarily outclassed. The world balance of power had turned decisively against it.... Together, [Germany and Russia] ...could not be defeated at all. Individually, either of them could be defeated only if the democracies had the collaboration of the other. But such collaboration...would mean the relative strengthening of the collaborating power and its eventual appearance as a greedy implacable claimant at the peace table.... As things stood in 1939 ...the Western democracies were already under the handicap of being militarily the weaker party. They could hardly have expected to avoid paying the price. Theirs were no longer the choices of strength. The cards were so stacked against them that any complete, unsullied democratic victory in a...world war was practically impossible to foresee." Discuss how the problems arising from the Yalta and Potsdam conferences reflect the accuracy of Kennan's statement.

2. To what extent did Germany's decision to attack the Soviet Union and Japan's decision to attack the United States make possible the defeat of the Axis? Is it possible that the Axis powers would have been victorious without those decisions? Explain.

The Search for Security

Americans greeted the end of World War II with joy. None of them felt more deeply the desire to forget about killing, power politics, and military problems than did the soldiers and sailors who had fought the war. Most of them were civilians who had put on uniforms just long enough to help their country in a time of need.

With the end of the war the nation's fighting men went home. Demobilization was accomplished swiftly and smoothly. Twelve million servicemen and women returned to civilian life without disrupting the economy or the social structure.

The rapid reduction in the armed forces affected the position of the United States in world affairs. When the war ended, the United States had the greatest navy, the greatest air force, and one of the two greatest armies in the world. It was the wealthiest nation on earth, and it alone possessed the secret of the atomic bomb. This immense power brought with it great responsibilities. The United States had to leave soldiers to occupy Italy, Germany, and Japan, and sailors in bases and on ships scattered around the world. It became increasingly difficult for the United States to carry out these postwar responsibilities when its armies were being disbanded.

Even though many Americans did not understand the full extent of the responsibilities that went with their great power, they felt that the United States must retain its position of leadership in world affairs. They did not want their nation to return to self-centered isolationism, as it had done after World War I. In 1945, many Americans hoped that in the postwar world they could help shape a new order that would overcome international tension by means other than war.

This dream of a peaceful world remained only a dream. The postwar years saw increasing tension between the United States and the Soviet Union, the second most powerful nation to emerge from the war. Distrust marked almost all relations between the two nations. American statesmen immersed themselves, as never before in the nation's past, in the domestic and international politics of Europe, Asia, and the Middle East. Usually these statesmen acted to counter the expansion or threatened expansion of communism. Americans learned, unhappily, that leadership in world affairs brought peril, uneasiness, and new problems.

Although world affairs affected domestic politics as they seldom had in the past, the postwar era in the United States was one of comfort and prosperity such as few of the people ever had known. Yet many Americans were haunted by memories of the Great Depression and feared that the new prosperity would not last. People who could not erase memories of Nazi barbarism lost their faith in the belief that man was living in an ever-improving world. Millions of Americans were seized by a fear of Communist infiltration in government agencies and other public institutions and supported a vicious attack on civil liberties and political nonconformists.

For millions of America's large middle class the postwar society revolved around automobiles, improved highways, neighborhood shopping centers with acres of paved parking, and one-family ranch houses. These Americans knew that they would be secure only when all the people of the world were secure from another war—a war which could exterminate mankind.

AMERICANS ACCEPTED COLLECTIVE SECURITY

The United States government had made plans to exercise leadership in a system of postwar collective security well before the end of World War II. Secretary of State Cordell Hull actually began the planning early in 1942 although he had started thinking about the problem earlier. In 1942, he established the Special Advisory Committee on Postwar Foreign Policy to guide the President as he worked with Allied leaders. President Roosevelt and Secretary Hull wanted to avoid the mistakes made in 1919, so they included Republicans as well as Democrats on the committee and sought Republican support in their planning.

Leaders of the Republican party coöperated with the Roosevelt administration. In September 1943, some of the most important of those leaders met at Mackinac Island, Michigan, and unanimously adopted a declaration that announced the Republican party would support American participation in a postwar system of collective security.

At the same time both houses of Congress officially announced that they stood behind American plans to retain leadership in organizing the postwar world. In September and November 1943,

the House and the Senate approved resolutions placing Congress behind the idea of collective security. With the President, both political parties, and Congress committed to coöperation with other nations, no one had to fear a repetition of the isolationism of 1919.

Roosevelt planned an international organization

Franklin D. Roosevelt encouraged postwar planning by Congress, but he had ideas of his own as to what the new system of collective security should be. He believed the world could have peace if the wartime coalition of allied powers would carry its coöperation into the postwar era. In any new world organization he wanted power over important decisions, such as in matters of war and peace, placed in the hands of the wartime Big Four—the United States, Britain, the Soviet Union, and China. This idea required Soviet coöperation, and Roosevelt sought that coöperation.

Although the Soviets coöperated grudgingly, they did send representatives to a special conference in August 1944, at Dumbarton Oaks, an estate outside Washington, D.C. There American, British, Soviet, and Chinese delegates discussed the structure of a new postwar system of collective security. They also debated the question of voting power within the system, which would determine who would have the greatest political power in any new world organization. The Soviets demanded sixteen memberships, one for each of the republics within the Soviet Union. They also insisted on the right of an absolute veto.

The United States dealt patiently with the Soviet demands, but would not accept them. When the Dumbarton Oaks Conference ended in October, the Big Four had agreed on a tentative charter for a new permanent international organization for maintaining world peace and security. (It ultimately became known as the United Nations.) The delegates had been unable to agree on the voting problems, however. These questions were left for later settlement.

THE LEAGUE OF NATIONS: THREE VIEWS

WILLIAM E. BORAH	**HENRY CABOT LODGE**	**ROBERT LANSING**
Senator from Idaho, 1907-1940	*Senator from Massachusetts, 1893-1924*	*Secretary of State, 1915-1920*

I want a league of nations. . . . [But what] have we got? . . . a political alliance and nothing more. . . .

. . . I object to submitting the good faith of the United States . . . to a council of nine members, of which we have one. . . .

. . . [I] reject any treaty which contains a provision that gives to foreign nations any possible control over the United States. . . .

. . . [This] political alliance, as it stands, will . . . cause more wars than would have ever come without it. . . . [It] will endanger the welfare, the sovereignty, and the independence of the United States.

We can do more . . . strong, free, disinterested, than . . . by tangling . . . in every petty broil in Europe. *(1919)*

When this league . . . is formed four great powers . . . will rule one-half of the inhabitants of the globe as subject peoples—rule by force . . . . If we stay with our contract, we will come in time to declare with our associates that force . . . [is] the true foundation upon which must rest all stable governments. . . .

[We] are told that this treaty means peace. . . . Peace upon any other basis than national independence . . . can not last. [Your] treaty does not mean peace . . . it means war. . . . [You] ask this Republic to . . . abandon the creed under which it has grown to power and accept the creed of autocracy, the creed of repression and force. *(1919)*

The American people . . . should be the last to reject any instrumentality which gives promise of preserving amity between nations . . . . It is my unqualified judgment that the league of nations should be fully tested in its present form . . . if for no other reason than that to reject it would be to discourage future attempts to obtain unity of action among the nations in the effort to avoid international conflicts. We can not as an influential power . . . assume such a responsibility. . . .

. . . If, after a fair trial, the league fails to accomplish its objects, then is the time by amendment to make the convenant more efficient. *(1919)*

The settlement came after Roosevelt raised the questions with Stalin at Yalta. There, the Communist dictator accepted the American view that the power of veto in the United Nations would not apply in "procedural matters." This was only a small concession; on the big issues the veto power was absolute.

An awkward compromise settled the membership problem. Instead of sixteen memberships in the United Nations, the Soviet Union obtained three—one for itself and one each for the Ukraine and Byelorussia (White Russia). Stalin and Churchill assured Roosevelt that if the United States desired three votes, or memberships, in the United Nations, it, too, could have them.

At Yalta the Big Three had agreed that they and China should sponsor a special conference to draw up the final charter for the United Nations. Roosevelt persuaded the others that the conference should be held in the United States. Invita-

THE UNITED NATIONS: THREE VIEWS

JOHN T. WOOD
Representative from Idaho, 1951-1953

BURTON K. WHEELER
Senator from Montana, 1923-1947

ARTHUR H. VANDENBERG
Senator from Michigan, 1928-1951

This charter expresses the maximum of agreement possible among the great victor powers in this war. ... [Being], as it is, a declaration of pious intentions and designed as it is for purposes not yet known to the American people, I will reluctantly —very reluctantly—vote for it. ...

... I hope that the Charter will work .... If it does not work ... we shall be in a state of chaos. One who reads the history of what has taken place in the past cannot be very confident ... [it] will work much better than previous efforts. ... [Its success] depends upon whether Russia, England, and the United States can get along together. ... If they [cannot] ... it will not work. *(1945)*

[The United Nations] was a made-to-order trap for the Communists to bring into being a one-world government, a Communist world state, and a pliable instrument for Soviet aggression. ...

... [We] have been the world's most gullible Nation, blinded by our inherent love for peace, to the Communist menace which has been set up within our own borders by ... the United Nations. ...

... [The] Charter was never ... dedicated to ... [universal peace]. It has always been an instrument of force .... [Even] a cursory reading of the Charter will demonstrate that a solid backbone of military power occupies almost one-third of the body of the Charter. *(1951)*

We must have collective security to stop the next war ... before it starts; and ... collective action to crush it swiftly if it starts in spite of our organized precautions. ...

You may tell me that I speak of the millennium. ... You may tell me that some of the signatories to this charter practice the precise opposite of what they preach even as they sign. You may tell me that the aftermath of this war seems to threaten the utter disintegration of these ideals at the very moment they are born. I reply that the nearer right you may be ... the greater is the need for the new pattern which promises at least to try to stem these evil tides. *(1945)*

tions went out to forty-six other governments then at war with the Axis powers to meet at San Francisco on April 25, 1945, for the United Nations Conference on International Organization.

Seeking to avoid the difficulties of 1919, Roosevelt had separated the peacemaking from the building of a collective security organization. He also tried to overcome political troubles beforehand by appointing prominent Republicans, as well as Democrats, to the United States delegation.

The United Nations was established

Roosevelt died before the opening of the San Francisco conference, but his plans were carried on. President Harry Truman immediately announced that the conference would go on as planned and that membership in the United States delegation would remain as Roosevelt had named it.

The attention of people in all parts of the world was focused on San Francisco when the

670

United Nations conference opened. It was hoped that there men would create an organization of nations that would bring enduring peace.

The diplomacy of the conference did not reflect mankind's hopes. From its beginning, and for two months thereafter, the United States and the Soviet delegates bickered over voting procedure, the membership of nations such as Argentina, and the place of regional organizations within the world-wide United Nations. Finally, on June 26, 1945, after many compromises, the fifty allied nations signed the charter of the United Nations.

Despite the compromises made by statesmen of the United States and other nations, the United Nations Charter grew out of American ideas and plans. In its basic features it differed little from the old League of Nations Covenant.

All member nations of the United Nations were represented in the central body, the General Assembly. There, each nation had one vote and could discuss any matter within the scope of the United Nations. But the General Assembly could not make decisions that would legally bind its members and it did not have the authority to enforce its decisions.

More power was given to the Security Council, composed of eleven members. Five of these members—the United States, the Soviet Union, Britain, France, and China—were given permanent seats. The other six were to be elected by the General Assembly for two-year terms. The Security Council could make decisions, even on matters of war and peace, binding on all members of the United Nations. But, because of the veto power, important decisions could be made only if all of the Big Five powers agreed. Within the broad structure of the United Nations, there were several other important bodies, but these usually did not deal with political issues.

This time Congress and the people gave overwhelming approval to United States participation in the world-wide collective security organization. The Senate gave its consent to the United Nations Charter on July 28, 1945, by a vote of eighty-nine to two. This quick action made the United States the first nation to accept the charter.

Congress also passed a joint resolution inviting the United Nations to make its permanent headquarters in the United States. The world organization accepted the invitation and chose New York City for its center. From there the United Nations' activities would spread throughout the world.

Peacemaking did not bring security

Although peace was the basic objective of the United Nations, it did not have responsibility for the peacemaking that followed the end of the war. The great powers decided to keep the peacemaking in their own hands by entrusting it to the Council of Foreign Ministers (from the United States, Britain, the Soviet Union, France, and China) established at the time of the Potsdam Conference.

Germany, the most powerful of the former enemy states, was the one which would raise the most difficult problems in peacemaking. The Council of Foreign Ministers, therefore, decided to put aside the peace treaty for Germany until the other peace treaties were completed. As had been decided at Potsdam by the Big Three, Germany was divided and occupied by the United States, the Soviet Union, Britain, and France. By the beginning of 1947, coöperation between the former Allies had broken down, and Germany was divided into two hostile areas. Western Germany was held by three of the Allies, and eastern Germany was controlled by the Soviet Union.

Like Germany, Austria was divided and occupied by the former Allies. The United States wanted to make a peace treaty with Austria to end the occupation and establish its independence, but the Soviet Union refused to do so. For ten years after the war, Austria remained occupied because no peace treaty was made.

For the five other European nations which had allied with Germany—Italy, Hungary, Romania, Bulgaria, and Finland—peacemaking also proved difficult. The United States and its friends wanted these states to function as independent nations with democratically chosen governments. The Soviets, especially in the neighboring nations of eastern Europe, wanted nations with Communist governments that they could control. In a speech at Fulton, Missouri, in March 1946, Winston Churchill described the existing situation in Europe. He said the Communists had dropped an "iron curtain" across the continent of Europe. To the east all those behind the curtain had no freedom; they were controlled from Moscow.

These differences between Russia and the United States and its allies became so great that men such as Churchill called for a "get-tough" policy against the Soviets. Many feared that Churchill's suggested policy would wreck the United Nations and lead to war with the Soviet Union.

Nonetheless, the peacemaking slowly went on. In the summer of 1946, twenty-one of the nations which had fought in the European war held a peace conference. Work on the proposed peace treaties was not completed, however, until February 1947, after the foreign ministers had held another conference in New York. Four of the treaties—with Hungary, Romania, Bulgaria, and Finland—confirmed the armistice terms the Soviets had imposed. These treaties assured Soviet control of eastern Europe.

The treaty with Italy was more complicated. It stripped Italy of all its colonies and its fleet, gave small strips of Italian territory to France and Yugoslavia, and awarded $100 million in reparations to the Soviet Union. Italians considered the peace treaty harsh and particularly resented the loss of territory around Trieste to the Yugoslavs.

Although aware they contained flaws, the Senate finally approved the peace treaties with Italy, Hungary, Romania, Bulgaria, and Finland in June 1947.

REVIEWING THE SECTION

1. On what points concerning the organization of the United Nations did the United States and the Soviet Union disagree?
2. How was the United Nations organized?

3. What difficulties confronted the Allies in making peace treaties? By 1947, what agreements had been made between the Soviet Union and the other Allies?

THE UNITED STATES ENTERED A COLD WAR

The difficulties over Germany and peacemaking showed that the wartime coalition had broken down. The United Nations itself became a stage for bitter arguments between the Americans and the Soviets. Americans were alarmed by what they considered to be Soviet obstructionism in efforts to bring nuclear weapons under control. The failure to resolve this problem increased the existing tensions between the two nations.

The United States clashed with the Soviet Union over the expansion of communism in the Middle East. To obtain much-needed oil, the Soviets tried to take over Iran. Through direct military pressure and the use of Communist parties within Greece and Turkey, the Soviets sought control of those nations. If Turkey and Greece slipped behind the iron curtain, the eastern Mediterranean would be in Communist hands.

The problems in the Middle East were not unique. In some European nations, economic and political instability were an invitation to subversion. Communism was making gains there.

To control the spread of communism, the United States embarked on a program of military and economic aid to enemies of communism. This program brought the United States into conflict with the Soviet Union, fighting with political and diplomatic weapons instead of guns. This became known as the "Cold War." In fighting the Cold War, the Truman administration followed the diplomatic strategy of "containment," or of trying to restrain Soviet expansion.

East-West tensions increased rapidly

The destruction caused by the atomic bomb in World War II led to a movement for putting the manufacturing of nuclear weapons under tight international control. In January 1946, the Soviets agreed when the General Assembly created the United Nations Atomic Energy Commission. Six months later, Bernard M. Baruch, the American member of the commission, offered a plan that would place all control over atomic activities in an international agency. Ultimately, no more atomic bombs would be made and all atomic weapons in existence would be destroyed. The agency was to have power to inspect any national territory in searching for violators of the international ban on atomic weapons.

The Soviets, who regarded the plan as a device for keeping the secret of making atomic bombs solely in America, would not allow inspection of their land, and the Baruch plan failed. While the effort toward international control was blocked, the Soviets worked feverishly to build an atomic bomb, and succeeded. On September 23, 1949, President Truman announced that the Soviets had exploded an atomic device. America's nuclear monopoly had ended.

Even before the United Nations' efforts to control atomic weapons had failed, the United States had quarreled with the Soviet Union over Iran, Turkey, and Greece.

During the war, the Soviet Union and Britain had occupied Iran. After the war, the British withdrew their troops, but the Soviets increased their forces. They threatened to take over Iran and make it another Communist satellite.

At the first session of the United Nations Security Council in London in January 1946, the Iranians charged the Soviets with meddling in their affairs. The Iranians also appealed to the United States for help. President Truman took a strong stand against the Soviets. Faced with American firmness and hostile world opinion, the Soviets, in May, withdrew their forces.

From Turkey the Soviets demanded the provinces of Kars and Ardahan, and control over the Dardanelles and the Bosporus. With American and British support the Turks defied the Russians.

In Greece the situation was more complicated, for a civil war raged there. Greek Communists, supported by Communists in neighboring Yugoslavia, Albania, and Bulgaria, threatened to destroy the Greek monarchy which was supported by British troops. In February 1947, the drain on manpower and money became so great that the British decided they must withdraw from Greece. They also decided they could no longer afford to give help to Turkey. If Britain withdrew, Greece and Turkey appeared certain to fall to communism.

President Truman decided that the United States should assume the burden borne by the British. On March 12, 1947, he told Congress "that it must be the policy of the United States to support free peoples who are resisting attempted subjugation by armed minorities or by outside pressures." This policy later became known as the Truman Doctrine. The President also asked Congress for $400 million for aid to Greece and Turkey and authority to send civilian and military advisers there. After considerable debate, Congress voted to support the President's request.

The Marshall Plan helped Europe

Many people of western Europe suffered from cold, hunger, and misery in the winter of 1947. Throughout western Europe, and particularly in Italy and France, Communist parties were becoming stronger. While Congress was debating the Truman Doctrine, the President's advisers decided that the people of Europe needed more than fuel and food. They needed money, machinery, and farm equipment to help them make a sound economic recovery from the devastation of war. That recovery, it was felt, would itself contain the spread of communism in Europe.

Instead of helping each nation on a piecemeal basis, the President and his advisers hit upon the idea of helping Europe as a whole, or at least a large part of it. They decided that the European nations should get together, work out a recovery program that cut across national boundaries, and

Europe, 1952

ICELAND

NORWAY
SWEDEN
FINLAND
Oslo
Stockholm
Helsinki

NORTH SEA

IRELAND
Dublin
UNITED KINGDOM
DENMARK
Copenhagen
BALTIC SEA
Moscow

ATLANTIC OCEAN

London
NETH.
The Hague
Brussels
BELGIUM
Bonn
LUXEMBOURG
WEST GERMANY
EAST Berlin
GERMANY
POLAND
Warsaw

UNION OF SOVIET SOCIALIST REPUBLICS

Paris
Prague
CZECHOSLOVAKIA

FRANCE
Bern
SWITZ.
LIECHT.
Vienna
AUSTRIA
Budapest
HUNGARY
ROMANIA
Belgrade
Bucharest

CASPIAN SEA

Lisbon
PORTUGAL
Madrid
SPAIN
ANDORRA
MONACO
SAN MARINO
Corsica (Fr.)
Rome
ITALY
Sardinia (It.)
ADRIATIC SEA
YUGOSLAVIA
BULGARIA
Sofia
BLACK SEA

BALEARIC IS. (Sp.)
Tiranë
ALB.
Ankara
IRAN

(Sp.)
MEDITERRANEAN
Sicily
GREECE
AEGEAN SEA
TURKEY

MOROCCO (Fr.)
Malta (U.K.)
SEA
Athens
SYRIA
IRAQ

TUNISIA (Fr.)
Crete
DODECANESE IS.
Cyprus (U.K.)
LEBANON

ALGERIA (Fr.)
ISRAEL
JORDAN

PREPARED BY UNIVERSAL MAP, INC.
LIBYA
EGYPT
SAUDI ARABIA

present their needs to the United States. Secretary of State George C. Marshall made this idea the theme of a speech he gave at Harvard University on June 5, 1947; thus it became known as the Marshall Plan.

The Soviet Union and the nations of the Communist bloc refused to participate in the Marshall program, and Spain—because of her Fascist government—was not invited to participate. The other sixteen nations of western Europe quickly accepted

Marshall's offer. Congress supported the European Recovery Act, as the Marshall Plan was known officially, with an appropriation of $17 billion in March 1948. Later, Congress voted additional billions for aid to Europe.

European countries rebuilt their economies on sound foundations. Within four years, Europe's farms and factories were producing more than before the war. Communists everywhere, especially those in Italy and France, lost voting strength.

With help from the United States, the western Europeans had contained communism.

Western Germany, which had been included in the Marshall Plan, also recovered some of its pre-war strength. Since it had factories and manpower, western Germany would make a valuable ally in the Cold War. In June 1948, therefore, the United States, Britain, and France agreed to establish a West German government by uniting their zones of occupation.

This plan angered the Soviets. They retaliated by throwing a land blockade around Berlin, which was occupied by American, British, French, and Russian troops even though it was about 110 miles within the Soviet zone. Faced with the prospect that the Russians might start shooting if the Allies tried to force their way into Berlin, a massive American and British airlift, called "Operation Vittles," was organized to supply Berlin's western zones with food and fuel. Finally, in May 1949, the Soviets ended the blockade.

In May 1949, the West Germans proclaimed the German Federal Republic and the East Germans proclaimed the German Democratic Republic. As a result, there were now two German states, one democratic and the other communistic. At about this time, Yugoslavia had a disagreement with the Soviet Union and withdrew support from the Greek Communists. The Greek national army then crushed the rebels. By October 1949, the Marshall Plan and the Truman Doctrine had succeeded in containing communism in western Europe and in the eastern Mediterranean.

The NATO alliance was formed

The Truman administration wanted further to strengthen containment with a system of military alliances in western Europe. In June 1948, Congress had agreed to support participation in military alliances. President Truman then went ahead with plans for a regional alliance with the nations of western Europe, Iceland, and Canada, which covered the North Atlantic area. The alliance was forged on April 4, 1949, when the foreign ministers of twelve nations met in Washington, D.C., and signed the North Atlantic Treaty. Other nations later joined the alliance, but the original signatories were Belgium, Canada, Denmark, France, Britain, Iceland, Italy, Luxembourg, the Netherlands, Norway, Portugal, and the United States.

The heart of the treaty, Article 5, said that an attack against any one of the allies would be considered an attack against all. Congress approved the treaty in July 1949. For the first time since the French alliance of 1778, the United States had formally allied itself with Europeans. Thus the treaty, and the North Atlantic Treaty Organization (NATO) which stemmed from it, was a radical departure from established foreign policy in the history of the United States.

The Middle East attracted American interest

Another change in United States foreign policy in the postwar years was a growing concern for the Middle East. Prior to World War II, the world of the Arab and the Moslem had attracted little attention from the United States. After the war, the Middle East became important to American policy-makers because of its vast oil fields and its strategic importance in the policy of containment.

United States policy first encountered difficulty in the Middle East not because of containment but because of entanglement in a bitter rivalry between Arab and Jewish aspirations. Jews had long dreamed of building a national home in Palestine, a concept known as Zionism. In 1917, the British, who controlled Palestine, promised to help the Jews build such a home. But the British had also promised independence to Arabs in lands they controlled. As Jews streamed into Palestine, particularly in the 1930's, to escape Nazi brutalities, the Arabs in Palestine protested and then attacked Jewish settlements. When the British restricted Jewish immigration, the Jews fought the British and the Arabs.

The United States became deeply involved in

this problem because it had become the center of the world Zionist movement during World War II. The Jews in Palestine obtained most of their money and other support from people in the United States. President Truman sympathized with the Jews, who had been the victims of some of the worst persecution of all time, and supported the idea of a Jewish state in Palestine.

The British found themselves unable to police the Middle East without assistance, and they asked Truman to help solve the problem of Arab and Jewish hostility. The President refused to become directly involved, and in February 1947, the British turned the Palestine problem over to the United Nations. After deliberation, the United Nations recommended the partition of Palestine into Arab and Jewish states. This recommendation infuriated the Arabs, who looked upon Palestine as theirs. They began guerrilla warfare against the Jews.

In May 1948, when the British withdrew the last of their troops from Palestine, the Jews proclaimed the independent state of Israel. The Arabs immediately launched full-scale war. Eleven minutes after Israel came into existence, Truman officially recognized it.

The Jews defeated the Arabs, but the war dragged on until July 1949. At that time Dr. Ralph J. Bunche, a distinguished American diplomat employed by the United Nations, worked out a truce. In the following year the United States, Britain, and France, agreed to guarantee the armistice between Israel and the Arab nations.

Latin America joined an alliance

Unlike the Middle East, Latin America always had been an area of concern to the United States. During the war, all the Latin-American nations except Argentina supported the United States against the Axis. In March 1945, Argentina declared war on Germany and Japan. This action brought only temporary unity to the Western Hemisphere. In 1946, the United States used its influence to interfere in Argentina's presidential election, seeking the defeat of Colonel Juan D. Perón. He won the election; the state department's intervention antagonized Argentinians; and the United States lost some of the good will that had been created by the Good Neighbor policy.

In the following year the Truman administration adopted a less hostile attitude toward Argentina. The United States agreed to attend the Inter-American Conference for the Maintenance of Continental Peace and Security at Petrópolis, just outside Rio de Janeiro. There, on September 2, 1947, twenty American republics signed a permanent defensive military alliance, the Inter-American Treaty of Reciprocal Assistance, usually known as the Rio Pact. This alliance was the first regional defense arrangement made under the charter of the United Nations and set the pattern for the North Atlantic Treaty.

In April 1948, the American republics held a conference at Bogotá, Colombia, where they created the Charter of the Organization of American States, frequently called the Bogotá Charter. The Organization of American States (OAS), the new name for the inter-American system which began functioning in December 1951, established a permanent body to help bring peace and security to the Western Hemisphere.

REVIEWING THE SECTION

1. Why did the Soviets refuse to accept the Baruch plan for control of atomic weapons?

2. What was the purpose of the Marshall plan? Why did the United States support the creation of a West German government?

3. Why was NATO formed? In what way was NATO a departure from traditional American foreign policy?

4. What was the purpose of the Rio Pact and the OAS?

A SHOOTING WAR ERUPTED IN ASIA

During the immediate postwar years, no part of the world seethed with greater discontent and unrest than Asia. There, the Japanese had spread a slogan which had wide appeal: "Asia for Asians." When the Japanese withdrew from the lands they had conquered, there arose nationalist movements that sought independence and the end of foreign control. This was anticolonialism.

Both Franklin D. Roosevelt and Harry S. Truman sympathized with this anticolonialism. Their attitude toward the Philippines reflected the United States friendliness toward Asian nationalism.

During the war—to strengthen Filipino resistance to the Japanese—President Roosevelt had promised that once Japan was defeated a fully independent Republic of the Philippines would be established. President Truman carried out this pledge. On July 4, 1946, when the Republic of the Philippines was proclaimed, the United States surrendered all control over its former colony. Special treaties bound the United States and the Philippines together for purposes of defense, but the Filipinos ran their own government.

Although the United States had met the problems of Philippine nationalism skillfully, it encountered tragedy in dealing with the national aspirations of China. When the Japanese withdrew from China, the Nationalist government of Chiang Kai-shek found itself too weak to take over. It asked for help from the United States. In helping Chiang, the United States angered the Chinese Communists who controlled most of the countryside. When Chiang was forced to leave the mainland, the United States found itself without a major ally in the Far East.

The problem of Japan also remained unsolved. At first, the United States, which had conquered and occupied Japan, had intended to reduce that nation to a second-rate power and at the same time, build up China as a great power. After the Communist victory in China, however, United States policy-makers encouraged Japan to rebuild its industries. By 1950, as a result of Cold War tensions, Japan had been changed from a former enemy under occupation to an informal partner of the United States.

Like Japan, Korea, formerly a colony of Japan, was occupied by foreign troops, but she was a divided nation. In 1945, the United States and the Soviet Union had stationed troops in Korea; they divided the nation between them along the thirty-eighth parallel, the Soviets occupying the northern part and the United States the southern part. Soon, this line became a zone of tension. When the Communists in North Korea attacked South Korea, the Cold War had turned into a shooting war.

Communism triumphed in China

Soon after Japan surrendered, in order to help Chiang Kai-shek remain in power, huge American transport planes moved Nationalist troops into cities such as Shanghai and Nanking. In the north, however, Communists swarmed through farms and villages. They seized Japanese guns and other equipment, particularly in Manchuria where the Soviets were in control.

In December 1945, President Truman tried to mediate the quarrel by sending General George C. Marshall on a special mission to China. Marshall recognized the Nationalist regime as "the only legal government in China," but he also sought to persuade that government to work out some kind of an agreement with the Communists that would avert civil war. Marshall failed; by the end of 1946, when he was called home, one of the world's great civil wars had broken out in China.

Despite great quantities of military equipment and money from the United States, the Nationalists could not stem the Communist tide. Critics of the administration demanded massive intervention against the Chinese Communists. Insisting that containment could not work in a land so large and populous as China, the Truman administration refused to go beyond its aid program.

The Communists, headed by Mao Tse-tung, sealed their triumph on October 1, 1949 by proclaiming the People's Republic of China (Red China). In December, Chiang Kai-shek fled to the island of Taiwan (Formosa) and set up his Nationalist government there. Many nations, including Britain, recognized the Communist government of China, but the United States refused to do so and blocked Red China's efforts to get into the United Nations.

In February 1950, Red China and the Soviet Union signed a thirty-year alliance and mutual assistance agreement. Since both nations were hostile to the United States, this led the United States to turn to Japan, its recent enemy, as its major ally in Asia.

Japan became an anchor in United States policy

General Douglas MacArthur, Supreme Commander for the Allied powers, headed the occupation forces in Japan which were almost wholly American. He was also responsible for carrying out American policy. Under General MacArthur, Japan's educational system was reorganized and a program of political reform was carried out. In a new constitution the Japanese people agreed to renounce war.

Since the Soviets wanted to keep Japan weak, the United States would not call a peace conference that would permit the Soviets to have a decisive role in making a peace treaty for Japan. This attitude became firmer in 1949, when Mao Tse-tung took control of China. The United States, which wanted a strong Japan for an ally in the Cold War in Asia, now urged the Japanese to rebuild their industries.

To further strengthen the Japanese position in the Far East, American policy-makers wanted to negotiate a peace treaty and end the enemy status of Japan. To overcome fears of danger from a revived Japan, the United States signed two defense treaties in August and September 1951, one with the Philippines and the other with Australia and New Zealand. Then, on the evening of September 4, 1951, President Truman opened a peace conference in San Francisco's Opera House with representatives from fifty-two nations in attendance. This conference was called to accept or reject the

terms of a treaty already worked out by representatives of the United States and Japan. Four days later, the delegates of forty-nine nations signed the Japanese peace treaty. The Soviet Union and two of its satellites refused to sign it.

Although the treaty reduced Japan's sovereignty to include only her home islands, it was generous. It imposed no fixed reparations and no restrictions on the Japanese economy. The same day that the Japanese peace treaty was signed in San Francisco, a United States-Japanese treaty was signed by which Japan gave the United States the right to maintain armed forces in Japan.

Americans fought a war in Korea

As the Cold War became more and more intense, the United States and the Soviet Union found it increasingly difficult to settle their differences.

Korea was still divided, and the United States and the Soviet Union finally put aside efforts for unifying it and reëstablishing its independence. To break the stalemate, the United States turned over to the United Nations the problem of Korean unification. The Russians refused to go along with the plans of the United Nations; so elections were held only in South Korea and, in August 1948, the South Koreans set up the Republic of Korea. Then the North Koreans established the Democratic People's Republic of Korea, a Communist state. Within a year the Soviet Union and the United States withdrew their occupying forces.

Since the president of South Korea, Syngman Rhee, threatened to try to unify the nation by force, the United States equipped his army only with light weapons. The Russians, on the other hand, gave the North Koreans heavy equipment, such as tanks, and trained them well as soldiers.

Early Sunday morning, June 25, 1950, the well-drilled North Korean army, spearheaded by Russian-made tanks, smashed across the thirty-eighth parallel. The surprised and lightly armed South Koreans retreated in panic.

As soon as news of the Communist attack

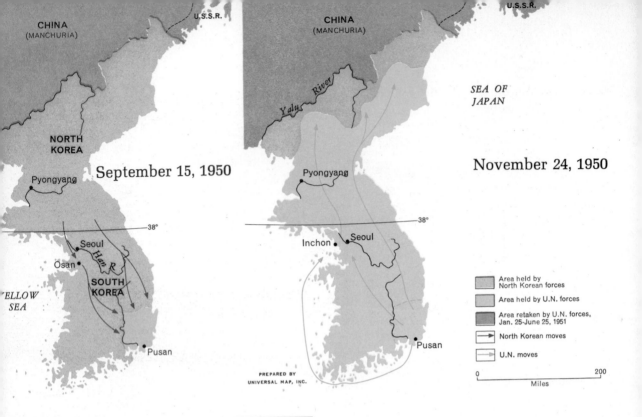

CHINA
(MANCHURIA)

U.S.S.R.

NORTH
KOREA

September 15, 1950

Pyongyang

38°

Seoul

Osan

Han R.

SOUTH
KOREA

YELLOW
SEA

Pusan

CHINA
(MANCHURIA)

U.S.S.R.

Yalu River

SEA OF
JAPAN

November 24, 1950

Pyongyang

38°

Inchon

Seoul

Pusan

Area held by
North Korean forces

Area held by U.N. forces

Area retaken by U.N. forces,
Jan. 25-June 25, 1951

North Korean moves

U.N. moves

0   200
Miles

PREPARED BY
UNIVERSAL MAP, INC.

Korean War, 1950-1953

June 25, 1950
Invasion of South Korea. Communist victory. A North Korean army crossed the 38th parallel into South Korea on June 25 and three days later entered Seoul, the South Korean capital. The troops then crossed the Han River. The South Korean army retreated in disorder, leaving most of its equipment behind. The use of United States troops to help the South Koreans was authorized on June 30. On July 2, a few Americans were sent to Osan, 30 miles south of Seoul, to fight a delaying action until more troops could be brought in. The United Nations Security Council asked the United States to form a unified command, which was established in late July under General Douglas MacArthur.

August 5-September 15, 1950
Battle of the Pusan Beachhead. United Nations victory. By August, American and South Korean troops were cornered on the southeast tip of the Korean peninsula. They were ordered to make a final stand along a 140-mile perimeter around Pusan. The North Koreans hammered at the thinly held line for more than six weeks, but failed to break it. During this time, troops from other nations came to South Korea and MacArthur began to build strength for a counterattack. During the war, troops from fifteen members of the United Nations participated in the fighting.

September 15-November 24, 1950
Inchon landing. United Nations victory. A daring amphibious landing at Inchon (Sept. 15) ended North Korean domination of the penin-

sula. The same day, UN troops broke out of the Pusan perimeter and moved northward while the Inchon invaders swept eastward. Seoul was recaptured Sept. 26. The North Korean capital, Pyongyang, fell Oct. 20 as the UN army headed toward the Yalu River on the Manchurian border. An end-the-war offensive began Nov. 24 in hopes that fighting would cease by Christmas.

November 26, 1950-January 1951
Chinese intervention. Communist victory. Small numbers of Chinese soldiers had crossed into Korea as early as Oct. 26, but the Chinese waited until Nov. 26 to launch a massive attack. Caught unprepared, UN forces retreated. They abandoned Pyongyang (Dec. 5), fell back to the 38th parallel, and finally established a line south of Seoul.

January 25-June 25, 1951
United Nations offensive. United Nations victory. Cautiously moving north once again, UN troops recaptured Seoul. By March 19, they held a line that divided Korea near the 38th parallel, but UN troops were not allowed to penetrate North Korea. During two years of off-and-on peace talks, limited but fierce fighting continued for strategic ridges and hills.

July 27, 1953
Armistice. The main problem that had delayed an armistice was repatriation of war prisoners. The North Koreans insisted that all captured Communists must be returned to them. However, many Communist prisoners did not want to return, and the United Nations command refused to force them to do so. This problem was solved when it was agreed that both sides would have a chance to convince their captured men to return home. The armistice was signed at Panmunjon July 27.

CHINA
(MANCHURIA)

U.S.S.R.

SEA OF
JAPAN

Pyongyang

July 27, 1953

ARMISTICE LINE

Panmunjon

38°

Seoul

Han R.

YELLOW
SEA

Pusan

United States soldiers in Seoul, Sept. 20, 1953

The Korean War raged up and down the peninsula during the first ten months. Seoul, the South Korean capital, changed hands four times. After the armistice (July 1953), prisoners-of-war were repatriated in "Operation Big Switch." As late as the 1960's, military officers still had to thresh out border complaints.

Operation Big Switch, Aug. 13, 1953

Demilitarized zone, Sept. 5, 1963

reached New York, the Security Council of the United Nations went into emergency session. Since the Soviet Union was boycotting the United Nations at the time and could not use her veto, the Council declared the North Korean attack "a breach of the peace" and ordered the North Koreans to cease fire and withdraw their troops. Then, in response to a South Korean plea, President Truman sent naval and air assistance to the South Koreans. When the Security Council urged members of the United Nations to help South Korea, the United States sent ground troops into Korea.

Another Security Council resolution authorized the use of the blue United Nations flag in Korea and permitted President Truman to name General MacArthur the commander of United Nations forces. Although sixteen United Nations members eventually sent some forces to Korea, Americans and South Koreans did most of the fighting. But the United States never formally declared war on North Korea.

At first, the fighting went badly for the United States. The raw, untrained recruits, rushed from occupation duty in Japan, could not stop the Communists. In August 1950, the United Nations forces ended their retreat and established a perimeter 140 miles in length on the southeastern tip of Korea, near the port city of Pusan. On September 15, General MacArthur surprised the Communists with an amphibious attack on Inchon, on the western coast of Korea, far behind North Korean lines. This attack trapped thousands of North Koreans and caused others to flee north.

Pleased by the impressive victory, American policy-makers permitted MacArthur's forces to cross the thirty-eighth parallel and attempt to unite Korea. As the United Nations troops approached the banks of the Yalu River, the border between Red China and Korea, the Chinese became increasingly alarmed. In November 1950, Red Chinese troops, which had been pouring into Korea, crashed through MacArthur's lines. In their offensive the Red Chinese pushed the United Nations troops far south of the thirty-eighth parallel.

MacArthur wanted to launch diversionary attacks on China. The President and his advisers opposed this course, fearing it would bring the Soviet Union into the conflict and touch off a third world war. In April 1951, after MacArthur had publicly criticized the administration's foreign policy, Truman dismissed him for insubordination. The dismissal created a political furor. When MacArthur returned to the United States he was given a hero's welcome and a chance to defend his views before Congress. But Truman's Korean policy and the principle of civilian supremacy in government remained unchanged.

On the battlefield, meanwhile, American forces had driven the Chinese out of South Korea and the war settled into a stalemate with Chinese and American armies slugging at each other in the hills north of the thirty-eighth parallel. In July 1951, the Americans and the Communists began truce talks which dragged on for two years. Finally on July 27, 1953, after American policy-makers implied that they might use tactical atomic bombs if necessary, the Communist negotiators agreed to an armistice. That night the fighting stopped.

Neither side could claim victory. The demilitarized zone which divided North and South Korea now ran slightly north of the thirty-eighth parallel for most of its distance but dipped south of that line in the west. Yet, for the first time, no matter how limited the commitment, the United Nations had tried to use force on a large scale. Americans could at least say they had contained communism in Korea without bringing on a third world war.

REVIEWING THE SECTION

1. What attempts did the United States make to prevent a Communist victory in China? How did the United States respond to the Communist victory?

2. How did the United States attempt to make Japan an ally in the Cold War?

3. How did different attitudes toward fighting the Korean War lead to Truman's dismissal of MacArthur?

THE NATION SHIFTED TO A PEACETIME ECONOMY

Americans fought the Korean War without a massive mobilization of manpower, industry, or agriculture, without the rationing of consumer goods, and with only limited controls over prices and wages. They had had enough of stringent controls during World War II. When that war ended in 1945, so great was everyone's desire to return to the ways of peace that the government used every available ship to return soldiers, sailors, and marines to their families. Within nine months of Japan's surrender the army had discharged more than 6 million men, reducing its strength from 8 to less than 2 million men.

The Servicemen's Readjustment Act, known as the G.I. Bill of Rights, helped the returning veteran adjust to the peacetime economy. The letters *G.I.* stood for "government issue," but during the war American soldiers had called themselves G.I.'s and the veterans had retained that name. Under the G.I. bill, anyone who had served in the armed forces for ninety days or more and was honorably discharged could get help from the government in securing a job, in acquiring an education, or for buying a house, farm, or business.

Veterans were particularly attracted to the educational benefits. By the summer of 1956, when the educational provisions of the G.I. bill ended, more than 7.8 million veterans had received some form of education at government expense. Of these, some 2.2 million had crowded into college and university classrooms.

Economic controls collapsed

Everyone, it seemed, had agreed on giving help to the veterans, but Americans could not agree on the means of reconverting the economy to the ways of peace. When the war ended, prices soared because the people had money to spend but goods were scarce.

The government lifted most of the controls, such as rationing, that it had imposed on the economy. Most Americans apparently were pleased with

BUSINESS ACTIVITY 1941-1964

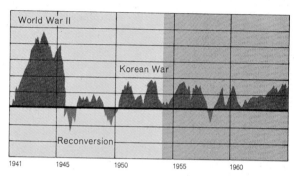

Some depressions, such as those between 1945 and 1964, have been short, mild drops in business activity, and therefore were really recessions. In the Great Depression of the 1930's, the federal government began to intervene directly in the economy in an effort to build and sustain the prosperity. Even in the prosperity of the 1940's and after, unemployment remained a problem, owing in part to increased mechanization in agriculture, automation in industry, and the inability of many workers to meet the demands for new kinds of skills. Although unemployment persisted, the national average of family incomes showed an increase of almost one third in the years following World War II. During that time, incomes rose faster than ever before. In spite of five recessions in the twenty years immediately following the war, this was the longest unbroken period of prosperity ever experienced in the United States.

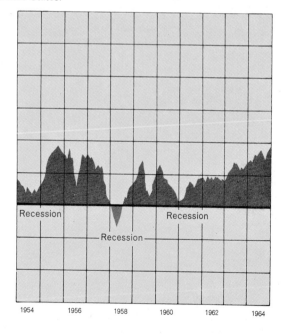

that step, but they wanted an end to all controls that prevented them from using their money as they desired. There were few who agreed with the government economists who advised continued controls over wages and prices to curb inflation. Businessmen argued that the best weapon against inflation was an increase in production. When supplies met the demand, they said, prices would become stable.

Impressed by the desire of the businessmen and reluctant to carry the President's swollen wartime powers into peacetime, Congress limited the power of the Office of Price Administration in 1946 when price controls were continued for another year. Truman had asked for tight controls, but Congress would not go along with him. With weak price controls, inflation soared.

By the end of 1946, the businessmen who had wanted to get rid of all controls had won the battle. Americans went on a buying spree, bidding for scarce refrigerators, stoves, and other appliances. Prices continued to rise unchecked, and inflation remained a major problem.

Strikes angered the public

Inflation made living a real struggle for many of the nation's workers. With the end of the war, many of them found their buying power sharply reduced by their loss of overtime pay and by the shrinking value of the dollars they took home. To compensate for their losses they demanded wage increases. Fearing cutbacks in profits as they reconverted, industrialists resisted labor's demands. Labor then tied up various parts of the economy with a series of strikes. Before the strikes were settled, the economy found itself caught in a "wage-price spiral"; each time the workers got a raise, prices went up.

A strike that posed the most serious threat to the nation's economy involved the railroad unions. They threatened for the first time in the nation's history to stop all rail traffic in the country. So on May 17, 1946, in order to keep the trains running,

President Truman seized the railroads. Then the government offered labor and management a compromise settlement. All but two of the railroad brotherhoods—the Locomotive Engineers and the Railway Trainmen—accepted the government wage solution. On May 23 the two unyielding brotherhoods went on strike.

On the next day, after the strikers turned down his pleas to go back to work, Truman explained the crisis to the nation by radio and threatened to draft "all workers who are on strike against their government." The army would then run the trains. On May 25, as Truman asked a joint session of Congress for emergency legislation to cope with the strike, the two unions accepted the government's proposal and ordered their members to return to work.

Many Americans were angered by the strikes. Some felt that the Wagner Act of 1935 was a main source of labor's belligerence. They thought it gave too much power to labor and should be revised. Republicans and conservative Democrats in particular wanted to curb labor's power.

In the congressional campaigns of 1946, Republicans promised to take action against organized labor. Using the slogan "Had Enough? Vote Republican" to capitalize on various dissatisfactions with the Truman administration, the Republicans swept the nation. For the first time since 1931, they gained majorities in both houses of Congress.

A strike by John L. Lewis' United Mine Workers in November 1946, made it easier for Republicans in the Eightieth Congress, which convened the following January, to carry out the campaign pledge for a new labor law. The government had seized the bituminous coal mines, but the miners defied a court order against a strike and closed the mines for seventeen days. They did not return to work until after a federal judge had fined Lewis and his union.

Convinced that labor was abusing its power, Congress, in June 1947, passed the Taft-Hartley Labor-Management Relations Act. This law, passed over President Truman's veto, banned the closed shop—the exclusive hiring of union men—and some other union practices. The law made unions liable to damage suits and required them to publish annual financial statements. The law also provided for a sixty-day cooling-off period before unions could go on strike.

Production of atomic energy was regulated

Congress was so concerned with strikes and other problems of reconversion that it gave little attention to President Truman's recommendations for new social and economic legislation. He had first outlined what he was later to call his "Fair Deal" in a message to Congress in September 1945. His program, he explained, would expand "the progressive and humane principles of the New Deal." A coalition of conservative Republicans and Southern Democrats had had enough of New Deal experiments. They were determined to block the Fair Deal.

Since many Americans still feared the possibility of another depression, Congress did not block all economic legislation. In February 1946, Congress adopted the Employment Act that established the three-man Council of Economic Advisers to help the President "formulate and recommend economic policy." Significantly, the law stated that the government had a responsibility "to use all practicable means . . . to promote employment, production, and purchasing power." Although the economy was relatively free of controls, Americans could expect the government to regulate economic activity to avoid unemployment.

Nowhere was government control over the use and development of a product more absolute than in the area of atomic energy. Democrats and Republicans agreed that until some form of international control was devised the nation's security demanded that the government hold on to the secrets of atomic research and production. A related issue—whether to place peacetime control of atomic energy in military or civilian hands—aroused heated disagreement.

Debate swirled around a bill introduced by Senator Brien McMahon of Connecticut that would give civilians exclusive control over atomic energy policies. Ultimately Congress passed a revised version of the McMahon bill, which the President signed on August 1, 1946. The Atomic Energy Act placed complete control of research and production of all fissionable materials, such as uranium, in the hands of the Atomic Energy Commission. Under this law, only the President could order the explosion of atomic bombs in case of war.

The defense establishment was reorganized

Despite the coöperation between Democrats and Republicans on laws such as the Atomic Energy Act, bitter quarrels marked the relationship between President Truman and the Eightieth Congress. His foe in most instances and the most influential Republican in Congress was Senator Robert A. Taft of Ohio. This brilliant conservative, the son of a former President, was opposed to many of the progressive social reforms of the New Deal and the Fair Deal.

Taft and his fellow Republicans had promised to cut the high wartime taxes. Truman vetoed two tax bills, claiming the reductions would help the rich and promote inflation, but Congress enacted a third tax-reduction bill into law over his veto in April 1948.

Many Americans were concerned about the breaking of the long-established precedent for limiting a President to two terms in office. That precedent was broken when Franklin D. Roosevelt was elected to four consecutive terms. In March 1947, Congress adopted a proposal that prevented any man—except Truman, then President—from serving more than two terms in the presidency. When ratified by the required thirty-six state legislatures in February 1951, that proposal became the Twenty-Second Amendment to the Constitution.

Past experience also led to the passage of the

National Security Act in July 1947. The new law created the National Security Council to coordinate military and foreign policy and the National Military Establishment, later called the Department of Defense, to unify the armed forces. The offices of secretary of war and secretary of the navy were dropped from the cabinet and placed under the control of the secretary of defense, as was a new secretary of the air force. The office of secretary of defense was given membership in the cabinet.

Another agency created by the National Security Act was the Central Intelligence Agency (CIA), which became especially important in fighting the Cold War. It was responsible for the collection, analysis, coördination, and interpretation of secret information from all over the world. Previously, this work had been done by various government agencies, particularly those which had special use for the information such as the army or navy. Under the new law, all intelligence information dealing with national security, which was obtained by other agencies, would be correlated by CIA experts. The National Security Council and the President would make use of that information when determining policy.

REVIEWING THE SECTION

1. Why did most people want a rapid end to government controls on wages and prices?

2. Why was there a wave of strikes after the war? How did the Taft-Hartley Act limit the power of labor unions?

3. What was the purpose of the Employment Act? the Atomic Energy Act?

THE FAIR DEAL HAD TROUBLES

Truman's troubles with Congress, fights with his cabinet officers, and the results of the 1946 congressional elections gave encouragement to the Republican National Convention which met in Philadelphia in June 1948. There, for the first time, television cameras brought the circus-like atmosphere surrounding the nomination of a presidential candidate into millions of American homes. Confident of victory, the Republicans adopted a platform that promised to continue some of the social and economic programs of the Democrats, and they nominated Thomas E. Dewey of New York and Governor Earl Warren of California as their presidential and vice presidential candidates.

In July, gloomy Democrats also met in Philadelphia. Almost everyone there, with the exception of Harry Truman, who captured the presidential nomination, seemed resigned to defeat. For the vice presidential candidate the Democrats chose Alben W. Barkley, a seventy-one-year-old senator from Kentucky.

Dewey apparently was convinced by the public opinion polls, the newspaper accounts, and the prophecies of politicians that he would win in a landslide. He carried on a conservative, confident campaign and limited his speeches to vague general statements.

The odds against Truman were great. His party did not have much money for the campaign and the funds were split three ways. Henry A. Wallace, who had disagreed with Truman on issues of foreign policy, headed the ticket of a new Progressive party. That party attracted unhappy former New Dealers, pacifists, and left-wingers of various persuasions. Southern Democrats, angered by a civil-rights plank in the party platform that called for federal laws to prevent discrimination in employment, penalize lynching, and kill poll taxes, walked out of the convention. They organized a States' Rights Democratic (Dixiecrat) party and chose Governor J. Strom Thurmond of South Carolina as their presidential candidate.

Truman ignored the odds and launched a slashing campaign against the record of the Republicans of the Eightieth Congress. The President stumped the country, and at practically every "whistle stop," in earthy, twangy, extemporaneous speeches he denounced the "do-nothing" Congress.

On election day the pollsters were stunned. Truman won and the Democrats also captured control of both houses of Congress. Truman had scored the biggest political upset in the nation's history. As for Dewey, no man, a quipster said, had ever so deftly snatched defeat from the jaws of victory.

The President asked for social reforms

In his State of the Union message in January 1949, President Truman asked Congress to enact what he now confidently announced as his Fair Deal program. He requested new laws in support of public housing, full employment, higher minimum wages, subsidies for farmers, a broadening of the social security system, and regional development of major river valleys, similar to that in the Tennessee Valley. Despite the Democratic victories at the polls, only a small part of this program could get by the bloc of Republicans and Southern Democrats who still dominated Congress.

Minority groups, such as the Negroes, particularly needed the help of reform laws. Late in 1946, Truman had appointed the Committee on Civil Rights to investigate "all areas of racial and religious discrimination." He used the committee's report to ask Congress, in February 1948, to give the nation laws that would provide everyone with an equal opportunity to get a job, buy a home, and go to a decent school; Congress ignored his request. Truman then issued an executive order ending segregation in the armed forces and he also took other steps, such as using the Justice Department to help private individuals in civil rights cases, to improve the status of the Negro.

Truman's farm program, proposed by Secretary of Agriculture Charles F. Brannan, also could not get approval from Congress. The Brannan Plan stressed high farm income for farmers through direct federal payments to farmers rather than high prices for many agricultural products. Men who did large-scale farming, and others as well, called the plan "socialistic." Truman, therefore, accepted the Agricultural Act of October 1949 that set up a system of flexible price supports, or supports that would range from seventy-five to ninety per cent of parity, for farm commodities.

In July 1949, Congress passed the National Housing Act. It set aside large sums to help cities clear slums and build low-cost public housing. In 1949, under an extension of the Fair Labor Standards Act, Congress raised the minimum wage from forty to seventy-five cents an hour. In 1950 and 1952, Congress amended the Social Security Act to include an additional 10.5 million people. People already receiving social security benefits were given increased payments to meet the higher cost of living.

Truman also brought reform to governmental administration. Under the chairmanship of former President Herbert Hoover, a special committee studied the executive branch of the government and recommended simplifications in the structure. In June 1949, Congress acted upon the Hoover reports and passed the Reorganization Act. Truman carried out more than half of the Hoover recommendations and thereby improved the operating efficiency of the government.

Loyalty became a political issue

Upset by the events of the Cold War, some Americans believed that the executive branch of the government had been infiltrated by Communists and needed purging as well as reorganizing. Aware of this feeling and of Communist efforts to steal atomic secrets, in 1947 President Truman ordered the Federal Bureau of Investigation and the Civil Service Commission to investigate the loyalty of all persons employed in the executive departments of the government. These probes led to the dismissal of a small number of employees whose loyalty seemed doubtful.

At the same time the House Committee on Un-American Activities was trying to uncover evidence of Communist subversion and espionage. In August 1948, Whittaker Chambers, a former Communist and a senior editor of *Time* magazine, testified before the committee. He accused Alger

Hiss, a former official in the Department of State, of being a Communist agent who had passed secret government documents to the Soviets in 1938. Hiss denied the charges and was then tried for perjury (the statute of limitations on espionage had run out). Chambers produced some stolen secret documents from a scooped-out pumpkin on his farm and linked them to Hiss. After two trials, Hiss was found guilty in January 1950 and sentenced to five years in a federal prison.

The Hiss case made the nation acutely conscious of Communist subversion and set off an anti-Communist crusade. Republicans who wanted an effective political issue now charged the Democratic party with being "soft on communism." But the man who exploited and abused the Communist issue in a spectacular way was Joseph R. McCarthy, a senator from Wisconsin. His demagoguery introduced a new word into the American language: *McCarthyism,* the making of indiscriminate and irresponsible charges of political disloyalty.

McCarthyism began, in February 1950, in Wheeling, West Virginia, when the senator claimed that the Department of State was "thoroughly infested with Communists." He never proved his charges, but over a period of four years he accused and frightened many men with his unproven accusations. Because of his unscrupulous methods and careless accusations, the McCarthy committee stirred up broad controversy, and many people expressed alarm.

Many Americans believed that even though McCarthyism threatened the loss of traditional civil liberties, the danger from Communist subversion was greater. The courts, too, cracked down on Communists. In 1940, the Smith Act, which prohibited the teaching of the overthrow of the government by force, had become law. In 1949, the government convicted eleven leaders of the Communist party of violating the Smith Act. In 1951, in the case of *Dennis* v. *United States,* the Supreme Court declared the law constitutional and upheld the convictions.

At the same time, the government struck at Soviet spies. An espionage trial in England, in 1950, revealed that Dr. Klaus Fuchs, an atomic physicist who had worked on the American bomb project, had been slipping nuclear secrets to the Russians. Fuchs' conviction led to the arrest of several key spies in the United States. The case of Ethel and Julius Rosenberg created the greatest stir. The Rosenbergs were convicted of espionage and given the death penalty.

Congress reacted to the spy trials and the Communist exposures by passing the McCarran-Nixon Internal Security Act of 1950. This complex law required all Communist and Communist-linked organizations to register with the government. It also made it unlawful for anyone to conspire to perform any act that would "substantially contribute" to the establishment of a dictatorship in the United States. "In a free country," Truman said when he vetoed the bill, "we punish men for the crimes they commit, but never for the opinions they have." Congress, nevertheless, overrode his veto.

Two years later, Congress overrode another of Truman's vetoes to pass the McCarran-Walter Immigration and Nationality Act of June 1952, the first major revision of immigration laws since 1924. This new law did away with the exclusion of Asians. It placed them on a small quota and permitted them to become citizens through naturalization. Yet it continued the discriminatory features of the old quota system against southern and eastern Europeans. It even tightened some discrimination because of a desire by Congress to strike at communism. These features of the bill had led President Truman to veto it and others to lament its passage.

REVIEWING THE SECTION

1. What were the goals of Truman's Fair Deal program? What social and economic reforms were made during Truman's second administration?

2. Why did the question of loyalty become a political issue? What measures were taken by the government to prevent Communist subversion?

CHAPTER **27** CONCLUSION

The Truman portion of the Democratic era saw the successful end of World War II, the nation's full acceptance of collective security through membership and leadership in the United Nations, and the emergence of the Cold War. In fighting the Cold War the Truman administration devised the foreign policy of containment, carried out the Truman Doctrine, and put western Europe on the road to prosperity with the Marshall Plan. Under Truman, the United States formally abandoned its tradition of nonentanglement in foreign relations by adhering to the Rio Pact of 1947 and the North Atlantic Treaty. In Asia, the policy of containment was not successful. Communism triumphed in China and was held at bay in Korea only when troops from the United States and other nations once again went off to war. In all, Truman's record in foreign policy was one of major accomplishment.

Social reformers, and Truman himself, realized that in domestic affairs the Fair Deal fell short of its goals. Yet Truman proved himself a leader as dedicated to reform and social justice as were the New Dealers who had preceded him. In the area of civil rights he did more to advance the concept of equality for minorities than did the New Dealers. At a time of tension over the Cold War, the hot war in Korea, and the anti-Communist hysteria at home, the total accomplishments of the Truman administration were much more impressive than its shortcomings.

FOCUSING ON SPECIFICS

1. What was the policy announced in the Truman Doctrine?

2. Why did the Soviet Union blockade Berlin in 1948? How did the Americans and British respond to the blockade?

3. Why did the United States abandon its plan of reducing Japan to a second-rate power?

4. Why, despite the Soviet Union's membership on the Security Council, was the United Nations able to send troops into Korea?

5. How did the government aid returning veterans? How did veterans' benefits affect higher education in the United States?

6. Why did Congress pass the Taft-Hartley Act?

7. Why was the campaign of 1948 a difficult one for the Democrats?

8. What were the provisions of the McCarran-Nixon Internal Security Act?

REVIEWING MAIN THEMES

1. How did American participation in world affairs after World War II differ from American participation after World War I?

2. What efforts did the United States make to contain communism during the Truman administration?

3. What social and economic problems did the United States experience during the Truman administration? What efforts did the President and Congress make to solve these problems? What successes did they achieve? In what areas did they fail?

EVALUATING THE ISSUES

1. Do you agree with Truman that the McCarran-Nixon Internal Security Act punished men for opinions rather than crimes? Why or why not?

2. Why did the United States restrict the freedom of political parties such as the Communist party which advocate the overthrow of the government by force? Should such parties be outlawed or should they be given the same opportunity to voice their opinions as have other political parties?

3. Explain why the United States did not recognize the Communist government of China once it had taken power.

The Eisenhower Years

In the prosperous United States of the 1950's most Americans were moderate in their political and economic views. They enthusiastically supported Dwight D. Eisenhower, a President with basically conservative ideas. Most Americans wanted to preserve the social and economic gains they had made during the Roosevelt and Truman administrations; they appeared uninterested in new programs or new ideas.

There were times when it seemed as if the deeply conservative Republican and Southern Democratic leaders in Congress did not agree with Eisenhower's more moderate conservatism. There were times also when the businessmen who took a leading part in his administration did not agree with his philosophy either.

It was not surprising, therefore, that the President's popularity did not extend to his party. In the 1952 election, for example, his vote ran ahead of his party's vote by fifteen per cent. Although the Republicans gained control of both houses of Congress, they lost that control to the Democrats two years later. In the presidential election of 1956, Eisenhower won easily, but he was unable to carry his party with him. Since 1848, Presidents had always carried at least one house of Congress with them; for a President as popular as Eisenhower to fail to carry even one house was unprecedented.

The problems of foreign policy, the rivalry with the Communist bloc, overshadowed all others during the Eisenhower administration. Basic United States policy toward the Soviet Union had already been determined by the beginning of the 1950's. United States policy toward Red China had been established earlier but had hardened during the Korean War. Since the popular discontent with the foreign policy of the Truman administration had contributed to Eisenhower's election victory, the new administration tried to formulate a new and more dynamic policy. The Eisenhower policy, however, did not solve the differences between East and West.

One aspect of the rivalry between the United States and the Communist bloc continued to center on the race for superiority in nuclear weapons. Although the Soviets had exploded an atomic bomb in 1949, the United States maintained a sufficient lead in nuclear weapons to deter the Communist nations if they gave thought to launching a full-scale war to advance their interests.

After the Korean War, Secretary of State John Foster Dulles had committed the Eisenhower administration to a policy which appeared to promise the liberation of the satellite nations from Communist rule. He soon was forced to back down and adopt a less aggressive tone. He did, however, warn the Communist bloc that the United States would meet aggression with "massive retaliation." The Eisenhower administration was determined to contain the Soviet Union through reliance on nuclear weapons rather than on huge land armies and conventional weapons. The Soviets reacted with a policy of trying to narrow the American lead in nuclear weapons, especially in the means of delivering nuclear bombs. By the end of the Eisenhower administration, the Soviet Union appeared in some categories, mainly in long-range guided missiles, to be ahead of the United States.

CONSERVATISM RETURNED TO THE WHITE HOUSE

Dwight D. Eisenhower was born on a farm and grew up in the Middle West. From 1915, when he was graduated from the United States Military Academy at West Point until he became President, he spent all of his time in the military service, except for a short period from the spring of 1948 to December 1950 when he was actively president of Columbia University.

Eisenhower gained national prominence in 1943, after President Roosevelt had appointed him commander of the Allied forces in North Africa. His successes there and in Sicily brought Eisenhower the supreme command of Allied forces in Europe. Long before the war ended, Eisenhower had become a national hero; he was known as "Ike" to millions of Americans. At the request of President Truman late in 1950, he took over command of the defense forces under the North Atlantic Treaty Organization (NATO) in Europe. He resigned that command in 1952 to campaign for the presidency.

Prior to the 1952 campaign, Eisenhower had had no political experience, local or national. He admitted at that time that he was "a political novice." Yet Dwight "Ike" Eisenhower had positive views on government. In domestic affairs his attitude was conservative. He believed that the government should not direct or experiment with controls over the lives of the people, particularly in economic matters. He considered himself a moderate, the leader of modern Republicanism. In foreign affairs Eisenhower was an internationalist, a supporter of collective security. He considered isolationism outdated and dangerous.

Eisenhower was elected President

President Truman had denounced the congressional Communist investigations as being a political "red herring." The Republican Communist hunters, he implied, were building up the idea of an internal Red conspiracy in a desperate effort to win votes with an emotional issue. However, the atomic-spy cases persuaded many voters that Communist subversion was a real menace and that the Democratic party might be incapable of dealing with the Reds. When added to public discontent over the Korean War and disgust with a number of minor scandals within the executive departments, this attitude suggested that the Democrats would have difficulty in the 1952 elections.

The Republicans were divided into two factions. One faction, composed of conservatives and party stalwarts supported Robert A. Taft, hailed everywhere as "Mr. Republican." But Republicans with internationalist leanings believed Taft was still an isolationist, so they rallied behind General Dwight D. Eisenhower. Early in 1952, Eisenhower publicly acknowledged that he was a Republican and after that battled the Taft forces to win the Republican presidential nomination. Taft's bitterly disappointed followers were partially appeased when Eisenhower chose a conservative young senator from California, Richard M. Nixon, as his running mate. Their campaign gained strength when Eisenhower denounced corruption and "creeping socialism" at home and promised to end the war in Korea.

Since Truman had decided not to run again, the Democrats drafted Adlai E. Stevenson, the governor of Illinois, as their candidate. A man of wit, intelligence, and remarkable eloquence, Stevenson had great appeal for intellectuals and liberals. He campaigned vigorously on a platform that endorsed the Truman policies.

Eisenhower won in a landslide; he received 33.9 million popular votes while Stevenson garnered 27.3 million. In the electoral college the vote was 442 to 89. The Republicans gained narrow majorities in Congress.

During the campaign, Eisenhower had gathered around him a group of advisers. As President-elect, he turned to his advisers and together they began constructing his cabinet, but only after he had visited the Korean battlefields, as he had promised in his campaign to do. The majority of the cabinet officers had been executives in big business. For example, Charles E. Wilson, the president of General Motors, became secretary of defense. Only one man, Martin P. Durkin, president of a plumbers' union who was appointed secretary of labor, could be considered a spokesman for the nation's working millions, but he resigned within a year.

This businessmen's cabinet did more to set the tone of government than had the cabinets of preceding Presidents. Eisenhower relied heavily on the cabinet for advice and gave each department head considerable power. Secretary of State John Foster Dulles, a lawyer from New York, became the most powerful member of the cabinet; he not only advised the President but he also usually shaped foreign policy.

When Eisenhower entered the White House, he took with him not only a conservative view of government but also of the position of the President in that government. Under Roosevelt and Truman, he believed, the power of the President had swollen to such proportions that it endangered the concept of three separate but equal branches of government. He wanted to restore balance to government by limiting his own power and by encouraging Congress to make policy.

The new President and his close advisers also disliked the government's deep involvement in the economy and its commitment to certain welfare programs. They wanted to return to what they called the principles of free enterprise. They felt that government should act decisively, but at the smallest possible expense, in three main areas: to ensure a stable dollar, to balance the budget, and to maintain the nation's defenses. Eisenhower believed that his moderate program, which he called modern Republicanism, would appeal to millions of Americans who traveled the middle of the road politically.

Old guard Republicans, who were far more conservative than Eisenhower, wanted him to abandon the reforms and welfare programs left over from the New Deal and the Fair Deal. The President refused to turn back the clock, but he tried to placate conservatives in Congress by working closely with Senator Taft, until Taft's death in July 1953. At times, however, old guard Republican opposition to some measures, combined with that of conservative Southern Democrats, proved as frustrating to Eisenhower as it had to Truman.

Republicans finally lowered taxes

Republican campaigners had promised the voters that, when elected, they would bring prosperity and stable prices. This stability would come through balanced budgets, lower taxes, and the removal of government restrictions on the economy. As soon as the Republicans took over, they set out to redeem their promises, but they quickly found themselves unable to balance the budget and at the same time reduce taxes.

Through executive orders in February 1953, President Eisenhower eliminated the weak controls over rents, wages, and prices the Truman administration had imposed on the economy after the outbreak of the Korean War. He and the secretary of the treasury, George M. Humphrey, a conservative steel industrialist from Ohio, decided they would try to put down inflation by curbing credit rather than by wage and price ceilings. With the help of the Federal Reserve System, Humphrey

PRESIDENTIAL ELECTIONS: 1944-1956

CANDIDATES: 1944

ELECTORAL VOTE BY STATE			POPULAR VOTE AND PERCENTAGE
DEMOCRATIC Franklin D. Roosevelt	432		25,606,585
REPUBLICAN Thomas E. Dewey	99		22,014,745
MINOR PARTIES	—		200,612
	531		47,821,942

46 53 1

CANDIDATES: 1948

ELECTORAL VOTE BY STATE			POPULAR VOTE AND PERCENTAGE
DEMOCRATIC Harry S. Truman	303		24,105,182
REPUBLICAN Thomas E. Dewey	189		21,970,065
STATES' RIGHTS Strom Thurmond	39		1,169,063
MINOR PARTIES	—		1,442,667
	531		48,686,977

45 50 3 2

CANDIDATES: 1952

ELECTORAL VOTE BY STATE			POPULAR VOTE AND PERCENTAGE
REPUBLICAN Dwight D. Eisenhower	442		33,936,234
DEMOCRATIC Adlai E. Stevenson	89		27,314,992
MINOR PARTIES	—		290,959
	531		61,542,185

44 55 1

CANDIDATES: 1956

ELECTORAL VOTE BY STATE			POPULAR VOTE AND PERCENTAGE
REPUBLICAN Dwight D. Eisenhower	457		35,590,472
DEMOCRATIC Adlai E. Stevenson	73		26,022,752
Walter B. Jones	1		—
MINOR PARTIES	—		194,166
	531		61,807,390

42 57 1

established a tight-money policy in which money became more difficult for most people to obtain because the cost of borrowing went up.

In an effort to balance the budget Eisenhower tried to cut government spending, but this was not of much help because almost two thirds of the budget was allotted to national defense, and the President would not let the drive for economy endanger the national security. Despite efforts to economize, Eisenhower's first budget showed a deficit of $3.1 billion.

Despite the deficit, which continued in Eisenhower's second budget, Republicans in Congress wanted to reduce taxes. At first, the President refused to put a tax cut ahead of a balanced budget, but in 1953-1954, the nation experienced a mild recession. Fearing that a depression with mounting unemployment might follow, Eisenhower and his advisers eased their tight-money policy and changed their stand on a tax cut. The President allowed some emergency taxes to expire and recommended further tax reductions.

In the summer of 1954, Congress responded with the Internal Revenue Act, the first major revision of the tax laws in many years. The law provided some tax reductions for farmers, businessmen, and investors. Another law reduced many excise taxes. Although the tax cuts in 1954 amounted to $7.4 billion, critics charged that they benefited primarily those with relatively high incomes.

Farmers continued to receive subsidies

Farmers demanded more than tax relief. Even during the prosperity of the early 1950's, the prices of their products fell while the prices of other goods rose. Like his Democratic predecessors, Eisenhower had to deal with a farm problem that seemed to defy solution.

Secretary of Agriculture Ezra Taft Benson, a political conservative with uncompromising faith in free enterprise, was convinced that government price supports encouraged farmers to overproduce. Those supports, therefore, led to the farm surplus that kept prices down. He proposed a plan that would free the government from high, rigid price supports and would replace them with flexible supports on a sliding scale. He hoped to lower the supports gradually so that, in time, farm prices would respond to supply and demand in a free market. Benson's plan appealed to the President because it appeared to hold out hope for getting the government out of farm economics and for saving the government money.

Many farmers expressed alarm over the plan. They feared it would lower their already declining incomes. Nonetheless, Congress in August passed the Agricultural Act of 1954 that established the program Benson wanted. In August, Congress also passed the Agricultural Trade Development and Assistance Act. This law permitted the government to dispose of surplus agricultural products in foreign countries in exchange for goods of strategic value to the American economy.

These laws were of some help to the farmers, but basically Benson's plan did not work. In 1955, the surplus was huge; farm income continued to decline; and the cost of government subsidies rose by about $1.5 billion. Benson became the most unpopular man in the cabinet. Farmers and politicians from both parties demanded his resignation, but Eisenhower, who believed in Benson's policy, stuck by him.

Eisenhower then tried to attack the farm problem with another scheme, one that Benson did not like. Under the new plan, the government would pay farmers if they voluntarily would not grow certain crops. This plan also included the idea of a *soil bank,* a plan for taking out of production some farm land to lie uncultivated. The President persuaded Congress to pass two more agricultural acts —one in 1956 and another in 1957—that embodied subsidies for farmers who reduced their crops.

Even though farm income rose in 1958, none of the plans, as Eisenhower admitted, "really got at the roots of the farm problem." The agricultural surplus continued to grow and the cost of price supports to the taxpayer continued to rise.

Free enterprise was encouraged

Eisenhower's devotion to the free-enterprise system, an economy with little regulation by the government, can be seen in his attitude toward the use of natural resources. Many Americans believed that oil resources in tidelands, such as those lying off the California coast near Santa Barbara and off the Louisiana shore, should be developed by the federal government and be the property of the nation. Eisenhower and the modern Republicans did not. In May 1953, he signed a law that turned the tidelands over to the states, a law that pleased both the states involved and the private oil companies. He considered this an act against "the implacable expansionism of the federal government."

The President and his advisers also wanted to stop the expansion of federal power projects such as the Tennessee Valley Authority, which he called "creeping socialism." Yet Eisenhower did not favor complete abandonment of federal help. If private or local groups could not finance a power plant, he was willing to use government money for such a project. What he preferred was the "partnership idea." Under this scheme, a local unit of government or a private corporation could build and pay for a power project. The federal government would join as a partner if needed.

Since the Eisenhower administration wanted to break the government's monopoly over nuclear power, it used the partnership idea to allow private corporations to enter the atomic-energy industry. The Atomic Energy Act of 1954 permitted private utility companies, under license from the Atomic Energy Commission, to own and operate atomic reactors for the production of electric power for commercial use. By 1960, several privately owned and operated nuclear-power plants were in operation.

McCarthyism declined

Eisenhower was confident that he was following a policy of moderation in issues concerning civil liberties just as he thought his policy was a moderate one in issues involving natural resources. Although he disliked Senator Joseph McCarthy's methods, Eisenhower tried to placate the senator. He stepped up the hunt for subversives in government and dismissed employees who were considered security risks, or not trustworthy enough to have access to classified documents. Congress also took an active part in the campaign against the Reds. In August 1954, it passed the Communist Control Act that outlawed the Communist party.

Many people criticized the Eisenhower administration for some of its security policies, but some extreme conservatives—particularly McCarthy—claimed the administration did not go far enough. Two months after his inauguration, Eisenhower had an indirect clash with McCarthy over the appointment of Charles E. Bohlen as ambassador to the Soviet Union. McCarthy accused Bohlen of being a "security risk." The Senate, however, approved Bohlen's nomination as Eisenhower desired. In December 1953, McCarthy attacked Secretary of the Army Robert T. Stevens for allegedly shielding Communists in the army and clashed sharply with the Eisenhower administration.

In April 1954, after the army accused McCarthy of seeking special treatment for one of his assistants who had been drafted, Congress held hearings on charges made by McCarthy and by the army. For more than a month the hearings were broadcast on nation-wide television. Millions of Americans watched McCarthy bully and insult witnesses, among whom were some high-ranking army officers.

McCarthy began to lose his hold on the public imagination, and in December 1954, the Senate itself turned against McCarthy. It condemned him, by a vote of 67 to 22, for conduct unbecoming a senator and Eisenhower expressed public satisfaction with this blow at McCarthyism. The senator's influence dropped abruptly. It was soon learned that the senator was in poor health, and he died in 1957, without regaining his influence on the people of the nation.

Even without McCarthy anticommunism did not attract votes as politicians hoped it would. In the congressional elections of 1954, Vice President Nixon spoke all over the United States in behalf of Republican candidates, stressing that Democrats were "soft on communism" and should not be elected. Despite his efforts, the Republican party lost control of both houses of Congress.

Welfare legislation slowed down

Eisenhower took as moderate an approach toward social welfare laws as he had toward civil liberties. Although basically conservative, he did not attempt to erase the welfare laws of the Democratic past. He allowed the Reconstruction Finance Corporation, established during the Hoover administration, to die, but he went along when Congress boosted the minimum wage to $1 an hour, and he established a new Department of Health, Education and Welfare. During his administration, millions of Americans gained new or additional social security benefits as a result of amendments to the original law. Although Congress passed a number of laws to help cities build public housing and to help people buy their own homes, the Eisenhower administration did little to meet effectively a pressing housing problem.

The modern Republicans did more for the nation's highways. Originally, Eisenhower wanted a system of self-financing toll highways that would make possible, he said, "speedy, safe transcontinental travel; inter-city communications; access highways and farm to market movements." In June 1956, Congress passed the Federal Aid Highway Act, the largest road-building project in the nation's history. It provided for the construction of a 41,000 mile interstate highway system, linking all major cities with a population of 50,000 or more. The cost over thirteen years would be nearly $33.5 billion. This project also had a partnership feature. Although the federal government provided most of the costs, the states had to pay a share, too.

Two of the most pressing and controversial social problems of the 1950's were the future of American education and the need for adequate medical care for all Americans. Since the building of schools and the paying of teachers were local matters, the quality of education America's children received varied; some of it was excellent and some of it was poor. With a booming population a crisis had come. State and local governments were running out of money to build schools; they could not keep up with the needs of the nation's children. Most educators and others welcomed federal aid, but many conservatives resisted the idea, and Eisenhower did not try to overcome the resistance.

In support of college and university education Congress, in 1958, passed the National Defense Education Act. It provided, among other things, for federal aid to improve the teaching of science, mathematics, and languages, to extend guidance and counseling, and to provide loans and graduate fellowships for students preparing for college teaching careers. The impact of this measure was limited, for it did not provide the scholarships educators desired and did nothing about the larger problem of classroom shortages over the nation.

Conservatives offered even greater resistance to a workable program of federal assistance to improve the health of Americans. Millions of elderly people and others from middle and low income families could not afford the high costs of hospital and medical care. The partnership Medical Care Act of September 1960 was of little help, although it offered some federal assistance to the states to meet the medical needs of the elderly.

REVIEWING THE SECTION

1. Why were many voters discontented with the Democrats in 1952? What was Eisenhower's view of the responsibilities of the federal government?

2. Why did the Eisenhower administration have difficulty in balancing the budget? What changes did it make in the tax laws?

3. What efforts to solve the farm problem were made by the Eisenhower administration?

CONTAINMENT REMAINED AMERICA'S POLICY

Eisenhower held strong views on the nature of the government's role in domestic affairs, but he felt himself better able to deal with foreign affairs. Most people of the United States looked upon him as a capable, patriotic American with considerable experience in the affairs of the world. Yet he delegated much responsibility for initiating foreign policy to Secretary of State John Foster Dulles.

Eisenhower followed Dulles' advice because he and the secretary of state held similar views on foreign policy. During the presidential campaign the Republicans had promised to provide better leadership than had the Democrats. Republican speakers bitterly denounced the policy of containment and promised a new, positive foreign policy.

When the Republicans took over responsibility for carrying out foreign policy, they acted as cautiously as had the Democrats. Instead of abandoning containment, the Republicans continued it. Actually, the transition from Truman to Eisenhower brought no significant change in foreign policy but Eisenhower did bring a healing influence to deep divisions in foreign policy among Americans. His prestige was so great that he could make concessions to the Soviets which might ease international tension and yet not be charged with being "soft on communism." Under Eisenhower America's commitment to leadership in international affairs became, through a network of alliances, more extensive than it had been under the Democrats.

Anti-Americanism spread in Asia

Before he had entered the White House, Eisenhower took the first steps in his promised dynamic foreign policy. He went to Korea for three days in December 1952 in search of peace. Then, after his inauguration, he "unleashed" General Chiang Kaishek from Truman's restriction that kept Chiang tied to Taiwan and unable to attack the Chinese mainland. The Nationalists proved to be too weak to attack, so nothing happened.

This policy of encouraging Chiang to fight infuriated the Chinese Communists who spread anti-American feeling in other parts of Asia. Anti-American nationalism took an especially strong hold in Indochina. In one of the states created out of that colony—Vietnam—Ho Chi Minh, an able Communist trained in the Soviet Union, led a nationalist group, the Vietminh, which fought the French who were trying to regain control. The Eisenhower administration helped the French against the Vietminh. The President justified this help on the theory that if the Communists took over Vietnam, all the states of Southeast Asia, like a row of dominoes, would fall to the Reds.

Despite American help, the French suffered a series of defeats. In the spring of 1954, the Vietminh trapped a large French force in a remote northern fortress called Dienbienphu. The French pleaded for United States intervention in the civil war to relieve the fortress. Eisenhower and his advisers were, for the most part, willing to intervene, but the President would not do so without support from allies such as Britain. When Britain refused support, the idea of intervention collapsed.

In April 1954, a few weeks before Dienbienphu fell, the French attended a peace conference in Geneva to discuss Vietnam. The Soviet Union and Red China represented the Communist world and France and Britain negotiated for the democratic nations. Dulles participated in the discussion on Korea but he boycotted the negotiations on Indochina. The settlement divided Vietnam at the seventeenth parallel. The northern state became the Communist-controlled Democratic Republic of Vietnam and the southern region became the National State of Vietnam. This Geneva agreement injured American prestige and displeased President Eisenhower, even though the United States had not signed it.

To prevent the further expansion of communism in Asia, Secretary of State Dulles organized a loose alliance, signed in September 1954 by representatives of Australia, France, Britain, New Zealand, Pakistan, the Philippines, Thailand, and

MAJOR EVENTS IN UNITED STATES FOREIGN AFFAIRS: 1941-1960

1941-1945 (From U.S. entry into World War II to the establishment of the United Nations)

EXECUTIVE AGREEMENTS

1942 *Declaration of the United Nations,* drafted by Roosevelt and Churchill and signed by representatives of 26 nations, formed an alliance against the Axis. Each pledged to uphold the principles of the Atlantic Charter (1941) and not to make a separate armistice or peace.

PERSONAL DIPLOMACY

1943 *Casablanca Conference.* The policy of demanding unconditional surrender from the Axis countries was proposed by Roosevelt and approved by Churchill. Stalin later agreed.

Declaration of Cairo, made by Roosevelt, Churchill, and Chiang Kai-shek, stated Allied purpose to strip Japan of its overseas possessions and to restore territory to China.

Teheran Conference. At first Big Three war conference. Roosevelt, Churchill, and Stalin discussed the future of Germany and the nature of a postwar system to keep the peace.

1945 *Yalta Conference.* Major decisions were reached by the Big Three on the division and occupation of Germany; the government and boundaries of Poland; and support of freely elected postwar governments in the other liberated states of eastern Europe. The Soviets agreed to participate in the world peace organization. For concessions in Europe and Asia, Stalin secretly agreed to enter the war against Japan.

The Potsdam Declaration, made after a conference attended by Truman, Churchill (later Attlee), and Stalin, demanded Japan's immediate and unconditional surrender.

WARS AND PEACE TREATIES

1941-1945 *U.S. in World War II.* With an immediate declaration of war following the Japanese attack on Pearl Harbor, the U.S. became an active belligerent. War was declared on Germany and Italy 3 days later. Italy surrendered on September 3, 1943, and joined the Allies. On May 7, 1945, Germany surrendered unconditionally. Japan agreed to final terms of surrender on September 2, 1945.

DIPLOMACY OF WAR PREVENTION

1944 *Dumbarton Oaks Conference.* U.S., Britain, Soviet Union, and China agreed on a tentative charter for a permanent international peace and security organization.

1945 *United Nations Conference on International Organization* at San Francisco. Delegates of 50 nations signed the U.N. Charter. The U.S. became the first nation to accept the charter.

1945-1953 (From the end of World War II to the end of the Korean War)

STATEMENTS OF POLICY

1945-1949 *Chinese Nationalist regime* recognized by Truman in 1945. In 1949, the U.S. blocked efforts of Red China to obtain membership in the United Nations.

1947 *Containment of communism* has been the major U.S. foreign policy since World War II, and in expressing containment the *Truman Doctrine* stated: "that it must be the policy of the U.S. to support free peoples who are resisting attempted subjugation by armed minorities or by outside pressures."

1952 *Immigration. McCarran-Walter Act* removed the ban excluding Asians and placed them on a quota; it continued the quota system for southern and eastern Europeans.

WARS AND PEACE TREATIES

1947 *Peace treaties with Italy, Bulgaria, Finland, Hungary, and Romania,* negotiated by the great powers, were reluctantly ratified by the U.S. because the Soviets were assured control of eastern Europe.

1950-1953 *Korean War.* When Communist-controlled North Korea invaded the Republic of South Korea, the U.N. for the first time committed military forces to enforce its resolution against armed aggression. Truce talks initiated in July 1951 began a stalemate that lasted 2 years. In 1953, an armistice was signed. No peace treaty was signed and the nation has remained divided.

1951 *Peace treaty with Japan* was signed by U.S. and 48 other nations. The treaty officially ended World War II. U.S. and Japan also signed a mutual security treaty.

TERRITORIAL SETTLEMENTS AND ACQUISITIONS

1946 *Republic of the Philippines* was proclaimed on July 4. U.S. surrendered all control over its former colony.

ECONOMIC POLICY AND COMMERCIAL TREATIES

1947 *Marshall Plan* (European Recovery Act) gave aid in a broad European recovery program that cut across national boundaries. It furthered the success of the U.S. policy of containment.

1948-1949 *Allied airlift.* In response to Soviet land blockade of West Berlin, a 321-day shuttle service by U.S. and British planes provided food, clothing, fuel, and medical supplies.

DIPLOMACY OF WAR PREVENTION

1946 *League of Nations,* which had become ineffective before World War II, was disbanded.

1946-1947 *Baruch Plan* for control of atomic energy activities by an international agency failed because the Russians, who were working to build an atomic bomb, refused to allow inspection.

1947-1948 *Pan-Americanism. Rio Pact* (Inter-American Treaty of Reciprocal Assistance). By a permanent defensive military alliance 20 republics of the Western Hemisphere agreed to resist an attack on any member nation. The first regional defense arrangement as sanctioned under the U.N. Charter, it became the model for the North Atlantic Treaty. The *Organization of American States* (OAS), which superseded the Pan-American Union, was formed at Bogota in 1948.

1949   *North Atlantic Treaty,* a regional military alliance signed by 12 nations, was an effort to strengthen containment. The treaty said that an attack on one member would be considered an attack on all members. For the first time since 1778, the U.S. formally allied itself with Europeans.

1951   *Mutual defense treaties* bound the U.S. in security arrangements with Australia and New Zealand and with the Philippines.

1953-1960 (From the end of the Korean War to the beginning of the Castro regime in Cuba)

STATEMENTS OF POLICY

1954-1955   *Nationalist China* was promised U.S. support against attack by Red China. *Formosa Resolution* (1955) gave advance congressional support to any presidential action in regard to Formosa Strait.

1957   *Eisenhower Doctrine* was a warning that the U.S. would help defend the Middle East against Communist aggression. Congress approved and voted economic and military aid to the Middle East. The U.S. responded to Lebanon's request for protection with a 4-month occupation of strategic areas there.

WARS AND PEACE TREATIES

1955   *West German peace protocol.* The Senate ratified the Paris treaties (signed in 1954) giving full sovereignty to the Federal Republic of Germany, or West Germany, and admitting it as a full member of NATO.

TERRITORIAL SETTLEMENTS AND ACQUISITIONS

1952   *Puerto Rico* became a self-governing commonwealth associated with the U.S.

ECONOMIC POLICY AND COMMERCIAL TREATIES

1954-1959   *St. Lawrence Seaway* and power project were completed in 1959 by U.S. and Canada following approval by Congress in 1954.

1960   *Restrictions on trade with Cuba.* Embargo on importation of Cuban sugar was imposed in July. In October, U.S. embargoed all exports to Cuba except for food and medical supplies.

Fidel Castro's victorious revolution in Cuba at first was hailed in the U.S., and his regime was promptly recognized by the U.S. government. It soon became apparent that Cuba was drifting toward the Communist bloc and its ties with Red China and the Soviet Union were in defiance of hemispheric security. In 1960, Kennedy said that the island had become a "Communist satellite."

Fidel Castro speaking to his followers

DIPLOMACY OF WAR PREVENTION

1953-1957   *Atoms-for-Peace plan* to make atomic material available for peaceful uses was proposed to U.N. by Eisenhower. U.S.S.R. refused to coöperate. *International Atomic Energy Statute,* signed in 1957 by 80 nations including the U.S. and U.S.S.R., authorized work to harness the atom for peaceful purposes.

1954   *Geneva Conference on Indochina and Korea,* attended by U.S., Soviet Union, Britain, France, Red China, and lesser powers. U.S. withdrew from discussions on Vietnam, then reluctantly accepted the settlement which divided the country.

Southeast Asia Treaty Organization (SEATO) for collective defense, organized by U.S., included U.S., Australia, Britain, France, New Zealand, Pakistan, Philippines, and Thailand.

1955-1959   *Middle East Treaty Organization* (METO), sponsored by U.S., allied Turkey, Iraq, Britain, and Pakistan for defense. By a declaration of collective security in 1958, the U.S. was committed to coöperate with the member nations, and through executive action the U.S. assumed the obligations of the METO alliance. In 1959, with the withdrawal of Iraq, the name was changed to Central Treaty Organization (CENTO).

1956-1957   *Suez Canal crisis* developed between Egypt and Anglo-French-Israeli interests over nationalization of the canal by Nasser. U.S. called for a cease-fire and withdrawal of foreign troops from Egypt. Order was restored by the U.N., but the canal remained under Egyptian control.

1958   *Nuclear arms race.* Representatives from the U.S.S.R. and from the West met at Geneva to explore ways to achieve a nuclear control agreement. U.S. and U.S.S.R. suspended testing of nuclear weapons and negotiated for 3 years.

the United States. Burma, Ceylon, India, and Indonesia refused to join. The alliance developed into a regional organization called the Southeast Asia Treaty Organization (SEATO). Unlike NATO, this alliance had little power; in case of a Communist threat the members were bound only to consult each other.

As the SEATO arrangements were being completed, a crisis erupted in Formosa Strait. The Chinese Communists shelled and threatened to invade a string of small islands along the China coast, most of which were held by Chiang's Nationalist troops. To bolster Chiang's morale, Dulles signed an alliance with the Nationalist government in December 1954 in which the United States promised to come to the aid of Nationalist China, if the Reds attacked it. This pledge did not apply to the islands along the Chinese mainland from Quemoy northward to Shanghai, already attacked. In January 1955, Congress passed the Formosa Resolution which supported beforehand any action the President might take in Formosa Strait. This crisis, Dulles said later, brought the United States to the "brink of war."

Relations with Latin America deteriorated

Anti-Americanism was rising in the Latin-American republics of the Western Hemisphere as well as in Asia. In June 1953, the President sent his brother Dr. Milton Eisenhower, president of Pennsylvania State University, to investigate conditions in South America. When Dr. Eisenhower returned home, he reported that economic coöperation with the Latin-American nations would help improve relations with them. Before action could be taken on this recommendation, the President acted to uproot Communist penetration in Guatemala.

When Colonel Jacobo Arbenz Guzmán became president of Guatemala in 1951, Communists gained important posts in the government. When Arbenz Guzmán confiscated plantations belonging to the United Fruit Company, a North American corporation, the Department of State protested.

State department officials were convinced that Communists were behind Arbenz Guzmán's policy. At the Tenth Inter-American Conference, in March 1954, at Caracas, Venezuela, Secretary of State Dulles gained approval of a resolution declaring communism a threat to the peace of the Americas. If a state fell under Communist control, the resolution stated, the other nations would consult with one another.

In May, when Guatemala began importing guns from Communist Czechoslovakia, Dulles announced that "Communist colonialism" had taken over in Guatemala and endangered the peace of the Western Hemisphere. The United States sent arms to Nicaragua and Honduras and made them available to Colonel Carlos Castillo Armas, an exiled Guatemalan army officer. On June 18, 1954, leading a small ragtag and bobtail army, Castillo Armas invaded Guatemala from Honduras. He overthrew Arbenz Guzmán and established a conservative regime.

Many Latin Americans denounced Eisenhower's aid to Castillo Armas as intervention in Guatemala's internal affairs and as a revival of "big stick" diplomacy. Anti-Yankee feeling swept over many parts of Latin America.

Relations with Canada were better despite difficulties over the building of a seaway from the Gulf of St. Lawrence to inland ports in the Middle West. Many Americans and Canadians had long wanted such a seaway, but political problems had always blocked the project.

Eisenhower favored construction of the seaway. In May 1954, Congress yielded to the President's pressure and passed the Wiley-Dondero Seaway Act, which established a special corporation to finance, construct, and operate the United States portion of the seaway. The St. Lawrence Seaway and the St. Lawrence power project were completed in partnership with Canada in April 1959. It strengthened the bonds of friendship between the two nations. It increased the tonnage shipped out of Great Lakes ports, and brought millions of dollars in revenue to those ports.

Europe was urged to unify

American policy-makers had helped set up machinery for the military integration of western Europe through the North Atlantic Treaty Organization (NATO). American military aid helped Europe to rearm. American leaders hoped that western Europe would become strong enough to stand on its own feet if its peoples overcame old hatreds and created a political and economic union. A union of western European states was at the heart of American foreign policy when Eisenhower became President.

Eisenhower, who had been in command of the NATO forces in Europe in 1951-1952, supported European unity, particularly a plan called the European Defense Community. He also announced a change in military policy that committed the United States to rely primarily on its atomic "deterrent" rather than on land armies for defense of western Europe. This policy, as well as a relaxation of tension after the death of Stalin, the Russian dictator, in March 1953, led many Europeans to desire "peaceful co-existence" with the Soviets. This attitude and the fear of a strong, rearmed Germany within a unified Europe led France to break up the European Defense Community in August 1954. Dulles considered this act a major setback for United States foreign policy.

French fears were overcome with a new plan called Western European Union which was put into a treaty of October 1954, signed by Europe's leading NATO nations and West Germany. Separate agreements restored West Germany's sovereignty by ending the Allied occupation and admitted her to membership in NATO. Western European Union covered a system of alliances based on national armies and the rearmament of West Germany. In May 1955, in answer to western alliances, the Soviets signed an alliance with Europe's Communist nations, the Warsaw Pact.

Some Americans, particularly members of the Republican party, did not like America's deepening involvement in Europe. They also disapproved

of Eisenhower's efforts to increase foreign trade through lower tariffs and his defense of the President's power over the making of treaties. Senator John W. Bricker, a Republican from Ohio, sponsored an amendment to the Constitution that would have prohibited "executive agreements," such as those made at Yalta, without the approval of Congress. So strong was isolationist support for the Bricker amendment that when the Senate voted on it, in February 1954, it failed to pass by only one vote.

One aspect of Eisenhower's early views of international affairs that had pleased many conservative Americans was his announcement that his administration would replace "containment" with a policy of "liberation" of the peoples behind the iron curtain. In Hungary, in October 1956, students rioted against their Communist masters. Soon others joined the revolt, including units from Hungary's Communist army. The rebels demanded the end of Communist rule, denounced the Warsaw Pact, and tried to take Hungary out of the Communist bloc. This effort at self-liberation brought in the Soviet army with heavy tanks and big guns. Although the Hungarians fought for Budapest block by block, the Russians crushed them and imposed a new Communist government on Hungary.

President Eisenhower pleaded with the Soviets to allow Hungary to decide her own fate, but he would not intervene to aid the Hungarian rebels for fear of starting a nuclear war. Hungarians expressed bitter disappointment because they received no help from the West. Critics charged Eisenhower and Dulles with encouraging captive peoples to revolt against hopeless odds, a charge both men denied.

Fighting broke out at Suez

During the Hungarian revolt, the Eisenhower administration had also been involved in a crisis in the Middle East. The difficulties grew out of Egypt's policy of anticolonialism and its desire to become the leader of the Arab world.

In 1951, the United States and its western allies had worked out a plan for a collective security organization in the Middle East to protect the region against a Communist attack. Egypt refused to participate and demanded that British troops guarding the Suez Canal zone get out. This tension over Suez, as well as internal problems, led to a bloodless revolution in Egypt. In July 1952, the corrupt Egyptian king, Farouk, was overthrown; ultimately, Gamal Abdel Nasser, a nationalistic young colonel was brought to power. In October 1954, with the assistance of the United States, Nasser succeeded in making an agreement with Britain that led to the withdrawal of its troops from the base at Suez.

Britain and the United States hoped Nasser would bring Egypt into a new Middle East alliance that Secretary of State Dulles was attempting to organize. This alliance, known later as the Middle Eastern Treaty Organization (METO), included Turkey, Iraq, Britain, Pakistan, and Iran. Egypt would not join. The United States sponsored the alliance but did not join it.

In December 1955, the United States and Britain agreed to help build a high dam at Aswan on the Nile River, about 800 miles south of Cairo.

Nasser delayed acceptance of the United States and British offers to help finance the dam, apparently hoping to get better terms from the Soviet Union. In July 1956, Dulles withdrew the American offer, and the British withdrew theirs. In retaliation, Nasser announced that he would take over the Suez Canal, owned primarily by British and French stockholders, and would use the tolls to defray the expenses of the dam construction.

Nasser's seizure outraged the British and French, who threatened to take back control of the canal by force. Dulles urged restraint but, on October 29, 1956, the Israelis, alarmed by Nasser's threats, invaded the Gaza strip and the Sinai Peninsula, east of the canal. Within a few days British and French forces occupied Port Said at the western end of the canal. The Egyptians made the canal useless by sinking ships in it, and elsewhere Arabs blew up oil pipelines, forcing western Europeans to ration oil.

Eisenhower was surprised and shocked by the assault on Egypt. He joined the Russians in condemning the attack and through the United Nations asked for a cease-fire and withdrawal of foreign troops from Egypt. The Soviet Union threatened to use missiles to help Egypt, but the United States said it would block such interference. Faced with the opposition of their major ally, of the Soviet Union, and of the United Nations, the British and French withdrew from Egypt, and finally, the Israelis withdrew, too. In April 1957, the Suez Canal was opened to traffic, after it had been cleared by a United Nations salvage operation.

The Eisenhower stand in the Suez crisis won favor in the Arab world and elsewhere. It also revealed a gulf between the United States and its two major allies, Britain and France—one that threatened the solidarity of NATO.

REVIEWING THE SECTION

1. What actions of the Eisenhower administration led to increased anti-American feeling in Asia?

2. Why did the United States intervene in Guatemala in 1954? Why did many Latin Americans criticize the intervention?

3. How did the Eisenhower administration promote the defense of western Europe?

CIVIL RIGHTS BECAME A MAJOR ISSUE

The Suez and Hungarian crises burst into the newspaper headlines as Americans were winding up a presidential campaign. Even though Eisenhower, in the space of a year, had suffered a heart attack and had undergone major surgery, he ran for a second term. The Republicans again nominated Richard M. Nixon for Vice President. The Republican platform praised four years of Republican peace, progress, and prosperity, and promised more of the same for the future.

The Democrats once again chose Adlai E. Stevenson to head their ticket, so the contest of

1956 resembled that of 1952. Eisenhower's personality and immense popularity dominated the campaign. Nothing Stevenson did could match Eisenhower's popular appeal. Again Eisenhower won a smashing victory, the greatest since that of Franklin D. Roosevelt in 1936.

Of the 61.8 million Americans who went to the polls, 35.6 million of them voted for Eisenhower and 26 million for Stevenson. The electoral votes were split 457 to 73. Eisenhower was much more popular than his party; the Democrats retained control of both houses of Congress. Two years later the Democrats increased their margin of control in Congress and won many state offices. As a result, during his second term Eisenhower was a Republican President with tremendous popular support, but he had to work with a Democratic Congress.

The Supreme Court ruled against segregation

During Eisenhower's second term the civil rights question, primarily involving discrimination against the Negro, became a foremost issue in American life. States in the South long had enforced segregation of Negroes from whites on trains and buses, in restaurants, and in schools. The Supreme Court's decision of *Plessy* v. *Ferguson* (1896) gave legal status to this "separate but equal" doctrine. In fact, however, the segregated schools which the Negro children attended were seldom truly equal to those of the white children.

For a number of years after World War II the Supreme Court had made decisions that removed some of the discriminations against the Negro and gave him some of the civil liberties guaranteed by the Fourteenth Amendment. This trend culminated, in May 1954, in the decision in the case of *Brown* v. *Board of Education of Topeka.* Unanimously, the justices ruled that separate facilities in public education were by their nature unequal and that they kept the Negro from enjoying his rights on terms equal with whites. A year later, the Supreme Court required the Southern states to integrate their schools "with all deliberate speed."

In border states such as Delaware, Kentucky, Maryland, Missouri, and Oklahoma and in some of the large cities, authorities began desegregation and admitted Negro and white children to the same schools, but in most of the South the decision met with bitter resistance. Most Southern governors and legislatures were opposed to integration and tried to prevent it. Southern resistance to the school ruling finally led to a crisis. In Clinton, Tennessee, in September 1956, a white mob tried to prevent twelve Negro students from attending a high school that formerly had been segregated, and the National Guard had to maintain order.

The most severe crisis developed in September 1957, in Little Rock, Arkansas. Governor Orval Faubus of Arkansas challenged the authority of the federal government by using all means available to him to keep Negro students out of previously all-white Central High School in Little Rock. When local authorities did not control rioting there, President Eisenhower ordered paratroopers to Central High to protect the Negro students and enforce the order of the federal court. "Mob rule," he told the people, "cannot be allowed to override the decisions of our courts." Even though the President used the army to enforce the federal court decision and to uphold the Constitution, Faubus continued to resist integration. Desegregation of schools in Arkansas was delayed for several years.

Other Southern states followed a policy of "token desegregation," allowing only a few Negroes to enter white schools but segregating most Negro children. By the beginning of 1961, a small portion of the three million Negro children in the South were attending integrated classes, but no legal doctrine blocked further integration.

Negroes took direct action

The slowness in achieving integration and other civil rights spurred Negro leaders to take action on their own. In the North, as well as in the South, they reacted against discrimination in housing, employment, and in other areas of life. They used their political power in the North and their rising economic power in the South to secure some changes.

President Eisenhower encouraged improvement in the status of the Negro. As Truman before him had done, Eisenhower ordered the armed forces to operate on the principle of racial equality. He also ordered government officials to follow that principle in hiring; and he appointed Negroes to several prominent positions in the government. The most important was the post of Assistant Secretary of Labor filled by J. Ernest Wilkins. Eisenhower's administration also asked Congress for a civil rights law that would put the power of the federal government behind the Negro's right to vote.

The Civil Rights Act of 1957 was the first such law enacted since the days of reconstruction and marked a turning point in the struggle for civil rights, but its effects were limited. Since the law permitted federal judges to punish state and local officials who interfered with the Negro's right to vote, it did bring some openings in the barrier against Negro political activity in the South.

This slow action against racial discrimination did not satisfy the younger generation of Negroes, particularly their better-educated leaders. To combat segregation, they used a strategy called "nonviolent" protest or direct action. They refused to obey city and state laws that they believed were based on racial discrimination in violation of the Constitution. The man who emerged as the outstanding leader of this movement was Dr. Martin Luther King, Jr., a young, well-educated Negro clergyman from Montgomery, Alabama.

In December 1955, when authorities in Montgomery arrested and fined a Negro woman for having refused to move from the white to the Negro section of a bus, King organized a peaceful boycott of the bus company. He urged Negroes to walk or to ride in car pools rather than use segregated buses. The boycott, which lasted more than a year, was almost wholly successful. It ended when, late in 1956, the Supreme Court ruled that bus segregation was illegal.

Encouraged by the Montgomery success, Dr. King formed an alliance of church groups, the Southern Christian Leadership Conference (SCLC), to conduct protests in other cities. Other organizations, such as the Congress of Racial Equality (CORE), adopted King's strategy of nonviolence.

Not all Americans were prosperous

In addition to segregation, one of the most difficult problems for the Negro to overcome was that of economic disability. While most Americans were growing increasingly prosperous in an expanding economy, the unskilled Negro worker found it difficult to earn an adequate living. Automation struck hard at the opportunity for the Negro to earn a livelihood. Many Negroes were unskilled and poorly educated, and there seemed to be few places for them in an economy where more refined skills and higher levels of education were being demanded.

This rapid change in the way most Americans earned a living had a decided impact on labor organizations. The source of their membership was shrinking. This meant that in time their power would also decline. In December 1955, the labor leaders appeared to recognize their dilemma when they muffled old rivalries. The American Federation of Labor and the Congress of Industrial Organizations merged to form a new organization, the AFL-CIO. George Meany, the president of the new union, as well as other union leaders, were concerned about the economic slumps of the 1950's, each of which left larger pockets of unemployment in industrial centers such as Detroit and Cleveland.

During the recession of 1957, which lasted nine months, industrial production decreased 14.3 per cent and unemployment increased by about 4.6 per cent, but the personal income of Americans fell only .3 per cent. In some parts of the country, even after economic recovery, unemployment remained a serious problem. Labor leaders urged the government to establish a public works program to create jobs, but the Eisenhower administration took no interest in this.

IMMIGRATION TO THE UNITED STATES, 1920-1963

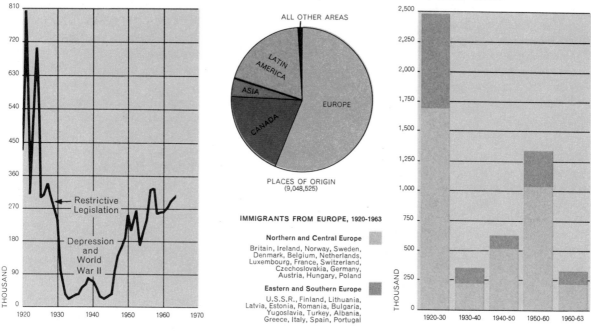

ALL OTHER AREAS

LATIN AMERICA

ASIA

CANADA

EUROPE

PLACES OF ORIGIN
(9,048,525)

IMMIGRANTS FROM EUROPE, 1920-1963

Northern and Central Europe
Britain, Ireland, Norway, Sweden,
Denmark, Belgium, Netherlands,
Luxembourg, France, Switzerland,
Czechoslovakia, Germany,
Austria, Hungary, Poland

Eastern and Southern Europe
U.S.S.R., Finland, Lithuania,
Latvia, Estonia, Romania, Bulgaria,
Yugoslavia, Turkey, Albania,
Greece, Italy, Spain, Portugal

Restrictive Legislation

Depression and World War II

THOUSAND

At this time, moreover, many congressmen and others were hostile to certain labor unions because of publicity concerning corruption and racketeering in connection with members' funds. In 1959, Congress enacted the Landrum-Griffin Labor-Management Reporting and Disclosure law to help clean up the internal affairs of unions and to outlaw abuses by union officials.

REVIEWING THE SECTION

1. How did the decision in *Brown* v. *Board of Education of Topeka* strike against segregation?

2. How did the Eisenhower administration promote integration and civil rights for Negroes?

3. What measures did Negroes take against continued segregation?

THE UNITED STATES FACED WORLD DISCONTENT

One of the methods used by the Eisenhower administration to end the brief recessions of the

1950's was to increase government spending for defense. This spending upset Eisenhower's plans for achieving economy in government. He and his advisers cut down expenditures for conventional weapons for the army, navy, and air force to save money. They relied on nuclear weapons for the nation's main line of defense. Such weapons, they said, could be used in massive retaliation against a foe and cost less than the support of huge armies and navies.

Some prominent military and political leaders criticized this "new look" in defense policy. They argued that tensions of the Cold War required the United States to maintain a balanced military force, one that could quickly fight a small war with conventional weapons as well as a war that could destroy an enemy with nuclear weapons.

Other critics charged that the government was delaying the development of guided missiles. They claimed that the Soviet Union's missile program was ahead of the American program. This concern became nation-wide after October 1957, when the Soviets launched their *Sputnik,* the first earth satellite. As a result, for much of Eisenhower's second term, Americans carried on a public debate about whether or not the United States had to overcome a "missile gap" to catch up with the Russians.

Many of the most serious world problems the United States faced did not stem from Soviet missile technology but from the discontent of hungry peoples and from the rising nationalism in many of the so-called backward areas of the world.

The Eisenhower Doctrine was announced

In no part of the world did local tensions mixed with Communist agitation prove more perplexing to United States policy-makers than in the Middle East. After the Suez crisis, the Soviets moved into the Middle East with enhanced prestige and appeared capable of filling the power vacuum left by the retreat of Britain and France. To counter the Soviet moves, the President decided to issue a unilateral warning, which became known as the Eisenhower Doctrine, that said the United States would help defend the nations of the Middle East threatened by Communist aggression.

In March 1957, at the President's request, Congress approved by joint resolution the Eisenhower Doctrine. It also approved the spending of $200 million for economic and military assistance for nations in the Middle East. By deeply involving the United States in the politics of the Arab world, the Eisenhower Doctrine marked another new departure in United States foreign policy.

Various crises in the Middle East, such as an Egyptian threat to destroy the small Arab kingdom of Jordan, kept the United States Sixth Fleet on the alert in the eastern Mediterranean. The crisis that led the administration to invoke the Eisenhower Doctrine grew out of a civil war in Lebanon. Lebanon's ruler, Camille Chamoun, charged President Nasser of the United Arab Republic (which had been created by combining Egypt and Syria) with fomenting the revolt. At the same time, Nasser flooded Iraq with Arab nationalist propaganda. Suddenly, in July 1958, a group of army officers overthrew Iraq's monarchy, proclaimed a republic, and allied their nation with the United Arab Republic. Iraq later withdrew from the Middle Eastern Treaty Organization supported by the United States.

Fearing a similar *coup,* Lebanon's President Chamoun appealed to the United States government for help. Eisenhower responded by sending 5000 marines to Beirut, Lebanon's chief port. Soon the United States force increased to 14,000, and British troops went into Jordan. Both Britain and the United States felt that these interventions were necessary to protect the independence of Lebanon and Jordan from outside revolutionaries.

Despite the protests of Nasser, Nikita Khrushchev of the Soviet Union, and others, the United States troops remained in Lebanon until October 1958, when United Nations observation teams began patrolling the borders to prevent infiltration of Communists and other political extremists. Although world-wide reaction to intervention of the United States in the Middle East was unfavorable, the President and his advisers felt that they probably had prevented a dangerous situation from getting out of hand. They did not assume that they had brought any lasting solutions to the problems of Arab nationalism in the Middle East.

The "good partner" policy failed

Problems of poverty, Communist agitation, and a turbulent nationalism affected the policies of the Eisenhower administration in Latin America as they did in the Middle East. After the furor created by the indirect intervention of the United States in Guatemala had died down, Eisenhower tried to improve relations with the Latin-American countries through his policy of the "good partner," by asking them to join the United States in an inter-American partnership.

Eisenhower sent Vice President Richard M. Nixon and his wife on a good-will tour of eight

South American nations. The tour began in April 1958, and from the beginning, the Nixons encountered hostile demonstrations. Everywhere Nixon bore the brunt of an exploding anti-Americanism. Bitter students swore and spat on the Vice President. Finally, in Caracas, a mob attacked him in his car, and he ended his trip and returned home.

Nixon reported that Latin America required more attention from the United States, particularly in the form of economic aid. Eisenhower and Secretary of State Dulles agreed. In 1959, the United States joined an inter-American development bank to provide credit and other help for the nations which needed it.

Anti-Americanism was an outlet for the violent nationalism and the yearning for economic and social reform among many Latin Americans. That yearning led to revolution in Cuba. In January 1959, after five years of plotting and fighting, the revolutionary movement led by Fidel Castro overthrew the conservative dictatorship of Fulgencio Batista. At first, many Americans were sympathetic toward Castro's efforts. However, it soon became evident that Castro intended to carry through an extensive social revolution that would bring Cuba into the Communist camp. When Castro began confiscating United States property and establishing a left-wing dictatorship, public opinion in the United States turned against him.

After Castro made a deal with the Soviet Union for the sale of Cuban sugar, the Eisenhower administration became truly alarmed. With the approval of Congress, it imposed an embargo on the importation of Cuban sugar. After Castro recognized Red China in 1960, announced his acceptance of the protection of the Soviet Union, and imported Soviet arms, the United States government (in October) imposed an embargo on all exports to Cuba except food and medical supplies.

Earlier, in February 1960, Eisenhower had made a good-will tour of Argentina, Brazil, Chile, and Uruguay, where he was warmly received. He found little evidence of the violent anti-American sentiment experienced by the Nixons two years earlier.

Yet his good-partner policy had not been successful. Castro's Cuba had brought Latin America into the politics of the Cold War.

The involvement in Asia deepened

Concern over the spread of communism drew the United States deeply into the politics of nationalism and anticolonialism in Asia. That concern once again entangled the United States in a crisis with Red China over Quemoy and Matsu.

In August 1958, after three years of calm, the Red Chinese suddenly began bombarding those islands again. This time Eisenhower said he would repel any Communist attack in the Formosa Strait. Khrushchev warned that he would support his Chinese ally. Many Americans feared that war might follow. After a few months the crisis passed. Dulles persuaded Chiang Kai-shek to remove some of his troops from Quemoy, and the Eisenhower administration changed its policy of supporting Chiang's desire to invade the Chinese mainland. The Reds stopped their bombardment.

During the crisis over Formosa Strait, the Republic of India, the most important of the new Asian nations, expressed displeasure over American policy. India followed a policy of "neutralism" in the Cold War, in which she sided with neither the Soviet Union nor the United States. More often than not Indian statesmen opposed United States policies in Asia. India's attitude began to change in 1959, when Communist China brutally suppressed a rebellion in Tibet and Chinese soldiers clashed with Indian soldiers on Tibet's borderlands. President Eisenhower tried further to improve relations by visiting Asia in December 1959, and his good-will tour took him to eleven nations.

The President had also planned a good-will visit to Japan after the United States government, in January 1960, had signed a new alliance with the Japanese government. Many Japanese, particularly the Socialists and the Communists, opposed the alliance because it permitted the United States to continue to station troops in Japan. Anti-American demonstrations forced the Japanese government to withdraw the invitation it had extended to President Eisenhower to visit there. The Japanese government finally ratified the treaty, but the prestige of the United States in Japan was weakened. Although disappointed, Eisenhower continued on another good-will tour of other Asian nations.

Eisenhower's deepest Asian involvement came in Laos, a nation that was formerly a part of French Indochina. In 1959 and 1960, the Pathet Lao there, a nationalist movement that received Communist support, fought conservative governments that received United States military aid. The Pathet Lao, claiming to represent the people, accused the United States of opposing national self-determination. Although the Pathet Lao was winning the civil war, the Eisenhower administration would not intervene with United States troops and risk a war with Red China, which supported the Pathet Lao.

African nationalism entered world politics

Emergence of nationalism in Africa in the 1950's made American policy-makers increasingly concerned about United States policy toward that continent. In Africa, a large number of independent states which had formerly been colonies of European nations were being established. These new nations were committed to a policy of anticolonialism that would end all remnants of foreign control over their continent. Their attitude toward the United States seemed to be governed by its policy toward colonialism. The Communists—Russian and Chinese—claimed to be violently anticolonial, and they tried to win the African nations to their side of the Cold War.

The first open struggle between the Soviets and Americans for the allegiance of an African nation occurred in the Belgian Congo. Frightened by the possibility of a racial revolution, Belgium abruptly gave the colony its independence in June 1960, without having prepared the Congolese for self-government. Almost immediately, the Congolese army began slaughtering its white officers and Belgian settlers. Belgian forces intervened. The Russians threatened a counter-intervention, and the United States warned it would block Soviet troops if they attempted to enter. Finally, the United Nations sent in troops to try and bring order to the Republic of the Congo.

In September 1960, at the fifteenth session of the General Assembly of the United Nations in New York, the Congo crisis topped the agenda. The world organization at that time had twenty-six African nations as members, and a still larger bloc of Afro-Asian nations carried great weight. The Soviets and the Americans competed to win over the Afro-Asians. Khrushchev himself attended the session and persuaded many other heads of government to attend.

President Eisenhower addressed the General Assembly. He offered a program of aid to Africa through the United Nations. When Khrushchev talked to the delegates he attacked European colonialism and demanded its abolition everywhere. This approach had great appeal. The General Assembly voted for a resolution, put forth by the Afro-Asians, that asked for those nations which held colonies to take immediate steps toward giving them independence.

In most instances, the Eisenhower administration tried to avoid commitments on anticolonialism. It did not wish to offend allies, such as Britain and France, which still held a few colonies.

The Cold War continued

Britain and France, America's principal European allies, had been badly shaken by Eisenhower's opposition to the Suez war. In 1957, United States and European statesmen worked to mend the North Atlantic alliance. The need for strengthening the alliance seemed urgent in the face of the Soviet Union's demonstrated ability to launch long-range missiles with nuclear war heads and her threat to the Allied foothold in Berlin.

In November 1958, Khrushchev demanded that

THE PRESIDENTS OF THE UNITED STATES

HARRY S. TRUMAN
(1884-   )
IN OFFICE: 1945-1953

DWIGHT D. EISENHOWER
(1890-   )
IN OFFICE: 1953-1961

Democrat from Missouri. Truman, in order to shorten the war, authorized the first use of an atomic bomb (on Hiroshima, Japan, Aug. 1945), soon after he took office. His administration was largely concerned with the politics of the Cold War. The threat of Communist aggression led to the Truman Doctrine, the Marshall Plan, and the Point Four Program. The Korean War began during his second term.

Republican from New York. Eisenhower was the first Republican President in twenty years and the first professional soldier to serve in that office since U. S. Grant. During his administration, the Korean War was ended (1953), the McCarthy hearings (1953-1954) attracted national attention, and the Supreme Court declared school segregation unconstitutional (1954).

the United States, Britain, and France get out of West Berlin within six months. Since the Allies, who had about 10,000 troops in Berlin, refused to withdraw, another blockade seemed in the offing. Khrushchev finally removed the six-month deadline but asked for a meeting with Eisenhower and other heads of state to discuss the status of Berlin.

Secretary of State Dulles was opposed to diplomatic conferences by heads of state—the so-called summit meetings. After Dulles' death in May 1959, President Eisenhower began to take a more direct part in diplomacy. He came to feel that perhaps the tense situation in Berlin could be improved through high-level discussion. In July, therefore, Eisenhower invited Khrushchev to the United States "to melt a little of the ice" of the Cold War, and said that he would be willing to travel to the Soviet Union. The Soviet Premier arrived in September and made a whirlwind trip across the United States. In conversations with

Eisenhower at Camp David, Maryland, Khrushchev removed any threat of a time limit for negotiations on the status of Berlin. Eisenhower then agreed to a summit meeting of the Big Four heads of state from the United States, the Soviet Union, Britain, and France.

On May 1, 1960, fifteen days before Eisenhower was scheduled to go to the summit meeting in Paris, a United States plane, with only the pilot aboard, was damaged by a Russian anti-aircraft missile and forced down over Sverdlovsk, an industrial city about twelve hundred miles inside the Soviet Union. It was a reconnaissance plane, equipped with infrared cameras and other sensitive photographic equipment. This plane, called the U-2, and others like it had been making reconnaissance flights over the Soviet Union for almost four years, but the Soviets had been unable to bring them down prior to this time because they flew so high that they could not be intercepted.

At first, the United States government denied that the U-2 plane had been engaged in spying activities. But when the Russians announced that they were holding a U-2 pilot captive, the President at last acknowledged that he had authorized the flight. Khrushchev was furious; he then used the U-2 incident to disrupt the Paris summit meeting and he withdrew his invitation to Eisenhower to visit the Soviet Union. "The Russian people would say I was mad," he explained, "to welcome a man who sends spy planes over here." Eisenhower bore Khrushchev's abuse in Paris with dignity, and his behavior there won for him widespread admiration. Yet his effort to ease the tensions of the Cold War has been thwarted. Crisis still marked United States relations with the Soviets.

Equally discouraging were the results of efforts to control the nuclear arms race between the United States and the Soviet Union. People all over the world wanted these two nations to stop their testing of nuclear weapons so that all of mankind might not be irreparably harmed by radioactive fallout. In the summer of 1958, Western and Soviet scientists and diplomats met in Geneva to explore the bases for a nuclear agreement. Both nations suspended the testing of nuclear weapons and carried on negotiations in Geneva for over three years. They talked about disarmament but they could not even agree to stop nuclear testing permanently.

REVIEWING THE SECTION

1. What was the aim of the Eisenhower Doctrine? Why and how was it applied? In what way was it a departure from traditional foreign policy?

2. How did the United States attempt to gain the good will of Latin-American nations? How did the United States respond to the Cuban revolution?

3. How did the United States attempt to win the good will of India and Japan? How did it respond to the civil war in Laos?

4. How did the Soviet Union and the United States come into conflict over the Congo? How did the United Nations respond to the Congo crisis?

5. How did the Eisenhower administration attempt to improve relations with the Soviet Union?

CHAPTER **28** CONCLUSION

Under the leadership of Dwight D. Eisenhower, the Republicans won the elections of 1952 and 1956. Many conservatives were disappointed when the President refused to attack either the New Deal or Fair Deal laws. In fact, social legislation was extended during his administration. Almost ten million people were added to the list of those who received social security benefits and the benefits were increased. In 1955, the minimum wage in covered employment was raised to $1 an hour.

During the Eisenhower administration, the issue of civil rights divided the nation. The division, however, was along sectional, not party lines. The Supreme Court decision to end segregation in public schools in 1954 (*Brown* v. *Board of Education of Topeka*) received support from moderates in both parties. In addition, moderates supported the civil rights legislation of 1957.

In foreign affairs, the Eisenhower administration continued the Truman policy of containment. New alliances, such as the SEATO alliance, were formed. As British power declined in the Middle East, the United States assumed more and more responsibilities in that area. Following the Suez crisis, President Eisenhower asked Congress to grant funds for economic and military assistance for the nations of the Middle East and to permit the use of United States troops to resist Communist aggression in that area. This policy became known as the Eisenhower Doctrine.

During his second administration, President Eisenhower began to exert more leadership over his party and the Congress. Since the Republicans had lost control of both houses of Congress in the mid-term election of 1954, the President had to gain Democratic support for his program. With the help of the Democrats, he was able to get much of his program enacted.

As his administration ended, President Eisenhower decided to leave a few words of advice to the new generation that followed him. Like America's first soldier-President, George Washington, Eisenhower gave his fellow Americans an important farewell address. On January 18, 1961, three days before leaving office, he summarized the achievements of his administration over radio and television. He stressed what had been the theme of his administration—moderation and balance. There should be, he said, a balance between the demands of the government and those of the individual.

Most important, Eisenhower warned against the growth of something new in American society—"a permanent armaments industry of vast proportions." He urged Americans not to allow this "military-industrial complex" to gain a commanding influence in government and upset the idea of balanced government. Eisenhower did not claim he had brought lasting peace but did point out that war had been avoided. In the perilous 1950's, that was an accomplishment of considerable merit.

FOCUSING ON SPECIFICS

1. What was the policy of "massive retaliation"? How did it affect American defense strategy?

2. What was Eisenhower's "partnership idea" regarding federal sponsorship of power plants? How did he attempt to put this idea into practice?

3. Why were Chinese Communists infuriated by Eisenhower's policy toward the Nationalists?

4. How did the commitments of members of SEATO differ from commitments to NATO?

5. How did the Bricker amendment aim to restrict the power of the President?

6. How did the Civil Rights Act of 1957 attempt to protect the Negro's right to vote?

7. How did Negroes use the strategy of non-violent protest to combat segregation?

REVIEWING MAIN THEMES

1. In what ways did the Eisenhower administration continue to support domestic, foreign, and military policy established by the Roosevelt and Truman administrations? In what ways did it depart from Democratic precedents?

2. What actions did the Eisenhower administration take to prevent Communist take-overs of nations in the Middle East, Latin America, and the Far East? How did the United States promote the defense of western Europe?

3. During the Eisenhower administration, what efforts were made to eliminate segregation and restore civil rights to Negroes? What successes were achieved?

EVALUATING THE ISSUES

1. During the Eisenhower administration, the United States was involved frequently in the internal politics of nations in Latin America, Asia, Africa, and the Middle East in order to prevent Communist take-overs. Does the fear of Communist take-overs in foreign countries justify American intervention in the internal affairs of foreign governments?

2. Why has it been so difficult for the United States and the Soviet Union to reach agreement on nuclear disarmament?

3. Was Eisenhower justified in ordering troops to Little Rock during the school integration crisis?

EXAMINING THE TIMES

1. In what ways did the administrations of Truman and Eisenhower continue to promote domestic reforms initiated during the New Deal? In what ways did they go beyond these reforms?

2. How did the aftermath of World War II create new demands on American foreign policy?

3. In what ways did the Eisenhower administration continue the foreign policy established during the Truman administration?

The American Countryside

Rice fields and taro patches, Hanalei Valley on Kauai, Hawaii

When the Europeans came to the New World, they found little more than a wilderness. Only occasionally could they see the dwellings of the Indians on the landscape. As more and more settlers came, the landscape began to be filled in. Yet today, more than 350 years later, there are areas that look much as they did then despite the many changes that have taken place. And, the nation has grown from a strip of land along the eastern coast to one that stretches from the Atlantic to the Pacific and to islands beyond the continental limits. Across the country, wheat fields, rice fields, and orchards stretch almost as far as the eye can see, the view unbroken except for an occasional farm building. Small villages are set in the midst of rich farm land or nest in the mountains, on coastal islands, and in deserts. As some of these small villages, cities, and towns continue to grow, the countryside is beginning to disappear.

East Corinth, Vermont

Monhegan Island, Maine

Countryside near Eldorado, Iowa

Taos, New Mexico

Orchards and grain fields near Grandview, Washington

De Kalb, Illinois and Northern Illinois University

A farm from Sugar Hill in the White Mountains near Franconia, N.H.

A farm in North Dakota

The American City

Manhattan skyline, New York, N.Y.

The disappearance of the countryside is due, in part, to the continuing growth of cities. The cities and suburban communities have combined to form sprawling urban areas so that one can often drive for hundreds of miles without seeing anything except city, suburb, town, and village.

In the more than 350 years since the first settlers arrived, the nucleus of these urban areas, the city, has changed from a European replica to one which is uniquely American. That uniqueness lies partly in the cultural diversity still reflected in the city and partly in its appearance. The homes, libraries, museums, industrial and commercial buildings—be they classic, medieval, renaissance, or modern skyscraper—somehow have become the American city. And this, together with the countryside, is the United States landscape.

The Capitol and downtown, Denver, Colo.

The old Capitol and new State Office Building, Indianapolis, Ind., 1963

Downtown Houston, Texas

Anchorage, Alaska, 1965

Capitol Hill, Nashville, Tenn., 1965

Oil refinery and skyline, Tulsa, Okla.

Virginia Street, Reno, Nevada

Los Angeles, California

A red and white striped parachute wafted down through the air and splashed a United States spaceship into the Atlantic Ocean. Its pilots soon learned that theirs was the first splashdown to be seen on the television sets of millions of Americans and Europeans. The television coverage had been transmitted from the spacecraft's rescue ship by another United States space vehicle, the *Early Bird* communications satellite. This event, the descent of *Gemini 9,* occurred in June 1966, only nine years after the beginning of man's so-called space age.

Responsibilities of a World Power

Since October 1957, when the Soviet Union launched into orbit the first man-made satellite, space exploration has proceeded in two parallel programs. The first was designed to probe space with unmanned vehicles. These relayed information on the nature of outer space, of the moon, and of distant planets.

The second program placed men in spacecraft with the objective of landing them on the moon. Such a landing might be considered the first step in an enlarged age of space exploration that would send men to other planets.

Space exploration has depended on the development of rockets, or self-contained propulsion engines. Rocket propulsion has a history of more than 2000 years, but the use of rockets was limited mainly to military weapons until after World War I. In the 1920's, Robert A. Goddard of Worcester Polytechnic Institute in Massachusetts carried out experiments that greatly improved the performance of rockets. Up to that time, rockets were slow and their direction could not be accurately controlled. Goddard experimented with the use of a liquid propellant, or fuel, to replace the conventional solid explosive powder propellant.

In 1926, Goddard fired the world's first liquid-propellant rocket a distance of 184 feet at 60 miles per hour. He continually improved his rockets, and in 1935, one of them climbed 7500 feet at over 700 miles an hour.

Meanwhile, scientists in other parts of the world were also thinking about possible uses for rockets. Hermann Oberth, a German, wrote *Rocket to Outer Space* in 1923, advancing the idea of using an artificial satellite for scientific research. Four years later, the German Society for Space Flight was formed. It began experiments with liquid-fuel rockets. The Nazi army became interested in the experiments and, beginning in 1936, constructed costly facilities for building and testing rockets.

By 1942, the Germans had constructed the V-2 rocket, which was larger than any previous model. It stood more than five stories tall and weighed nearly fourteen tons. After two earlier failures, a V-2 rocket was fired in October 1942. It rose more than fifty miles above the earth and soared through space for nearly two hundred miles, traveling at a speed more than twice that of a rifle bullet.

The world became aware of the power of the new rocket in September 1944.

A V-2, equipped with a self-guidance system, crashed a ton of explosives down on London. (Such long-range, guided rockets have come to be called guided missiles.) This attack revealed that the Germans were well ahead of the United States in rocket research. Americans had been concentrating on rockets to help lift heavy airplanes. After the V-2 success, the United States rocket program was expanded to include high altitude exploration.

When World War II ended, American and Soviet troops occupied some German rocket facilities. After experimenting with captured V-2's, Americans built similar rockets of their own, called *Vikings,* for space research. The Soviets began to develop huge rockets to be used as weapon-carrying guided missiles. During this period, the United States relied on airplanes to carry atomic bombs. Only in 1954, after developing lightweight nuclear weapons, did the United States begin work on long-range missiles. Because the Soviets had developed more powerful rockets, they were able to launch larger satellites and spaceships for longer periods of time. However, within the first ten years of the space age, the United States had caught up with, if not surpassed, the Soviet Union in space achievements.

The first Soviet satellite, *Sputnik I,* was a sphere 23 inches in diameter and weighing 184 pounds. In November 1957, a month after *Sputnik I,* the Soviets sent aloft a live dog named Laika in *Sputnik II.*

The United States entered the "space race" on January 31, 1958, with the launching of *Explorer I.* It was a cylinder 6 inches in diameter and 80 inches long, and it weighed 30.8 pounds. In 1958, Congress created the National Aeronautics and Space Administration (NASA) to handle all aspects of space science. American space scientists began planning a program which they hoped would result in the United States becoming the first nation to land men on the moon.

On April 12, 1961, a Soviet airman, Yuri A. Gagarin, became the first man to fly in space and the first to orbit the earth. He circled the earth once in the spaceship *Voskhod I* (10,418 pounds) in a flight that lasted one hour and forty-eight minutes. On August 6, another cosmonaut (a Soviet astronaut) went aloft; Gherman S. Titov, in *Voskhod II,* orbited the earth 17 times.

The United States manned space program began more modestly. First in space for the United States was Alan B. Shepard who, on May 5, 1961, flew 115 miles high at 5160 miles an hour, but he did not circle the earth. This was accomplished for the United States by John H. Glenn, Jr. on February 20, 1962. Glenn orbited the earth three times in four hours and fifty-five minutes in his spaceship *Friendship* 7.

During 1962, other American astronauts and Soviet cosmonauts made orbital flights. The United States and the Soviet Union also launched numerous satellites equipped with cameras, radios, and other instruments to probe space. The satellites sent back remarkable pictures clearly showing the outlines of continents and of storm clouds forming in the earth's atmosphere. Close-up pictures of the moon were received on July 31, 1964, from cameras on United States spaceship *Ranger 7.* A year later, on July 14, 1965, the world received its first "close-up" pictures of another planet when *Mariner 4* passed within 6118 miles of Mars.

During 1963 and 1964, both the United States and the Soviet Union launched larger and larger spaceships, and the length of the space trips was extended. But again it was the Soviets who scored the next sensational space feat. Cosmonaut Aleksei A. Leonov floated outside his spaceship for about ten minutes on March 18, 1965, thus becoming the first man to "walk" in outer space. Eleven weeks later, on June 3, astronaut Edward H. White, III, while tethered to his ship by a twenty-five-foot cord, maneuvered in space for twenty minutes with the aid of a jet-propulsion gun. His performance far surpassed that of Leonov.

Although the Soviets had scored spectacular space firsts, the United States had always designed more maneuverable spacecraft than the Russians. It was this planning that led the United States to a major triumph in late 1965. American astronauts carried out a rendezvous in space, in which two teams of astronauts maneuvered their two separate spaceships in a nose-to-nose position while orbiting the earth. This event was a prelude to the even more complex space docking accomplished by the United States in March 1966. A two-man spacecraft *(Gemini 8)* was joined to an unmanned vehicle *(Agena 8)*. Although technical difficulties forced a speedy uncoupling of this first docking, in July the exercise was carried off with "textbook" perfection during the *Gemini 10* flight.

Meanwhile, lunar exploration by camera was being advanced by both the Soviet Union and the United States. A Soviet craft, *Luna 9,* achieved the first "soft landing"

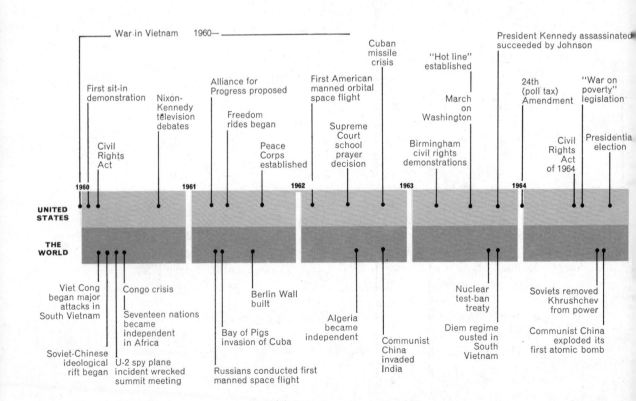

on the moon in February 1966. *Luna 9* did crash into the moon with considerable force, but only after it had jettisoned cameras which transmitted to earth the first on-surface pictures of the moon. Continuing this program, the Soviets in April 1966 accomplished the first lunar orbit when *Luna 10* circled the moon.

When the United States accomplished a soft landing on the moon in June 1966, it was technically more advanced than was the earlier Soviet landing. *Surveyor I* spacecraft itself descended to the moon at about three miles per hour. After nestling on the moon's surface, *Surveyor I* began transmitting remarkable pictures until the two-week lunar "night." Even after this dark period, the cameras were in good enough condition to reactivate themselves and again start transmitting pictures. In August 1966, a United States satellite called *Lunar Orbiter* circled the moon transmitting pictures of possible landing sites.

Thus by 1967, the goal of landing a man on the moon did not seem very remote at all, as it had ten years earlier. The cosmonauts and astronauts had shown that man not only could survive in space, but also that he could maneuver while in orbit. Although the rockets were not powerful enough to send men directly to the moon and back, space docking procedures to allow refueling had been accomplished. And a soft-landing vehicle had been constructed and successfully tested. Yet no one knew whether the first man on the moon would be American or Soviet.

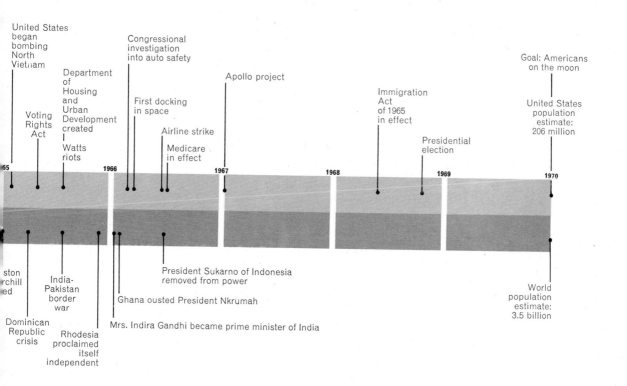

United States began bombing North Vietnam

Congressional investigation into auto safety

Goal: Americans on the moon

Department of Housing and Urban Development created

Apollo project

Voting Rights Act

First docking in space

Immigration Act of 1965 in effect

United States population estimate: 206 million

Watts riots

Airline strike

Medicare in effect

Presidential election

65   1966   1967   1968   1969   1970

ston rchill ed

India-Pakistan border war

President Sukarno of Indonesia removed from power

Ghana ousted President Nkrumah

World population estimate: 3.5 billion

Dominican Republic crisis

Rhodesia proclaimed itself independent

Mrs. Indira Gandhi became prime minister of India

The Age of Technology

In his farewell address, President Eisenhower advised the nation against allowing a military-industrial complex to gain a commanding influence in government. His warning came because the use made of science and technology in American life in the 1950's and early 1960's threatened to upset the nation's social and economic institutions. So high had the status of the scientist and the engineer risen in these decades that many people spoke of the "age of science" or the "age of technology."

Change had always been a major theme in United States history, and technology had been an important instrument in that change. But never before had so much change—primarily through science and technology—come in so short a time as in the decades following World War II. Almost everything in American society—from baby foods measured, packed, and labeled by machines to personal checks counted, scanned, and registered by electronic computers—revolved around the products of the technological age.

Man sent to the moon rockets carrying cameras which were controlled by computers and which transmitted pictures to earth. In schools, children were using "teaching machines" and their tests and personalities were being analyzed by computers. Sculptors were using acetylene torches to create,

out of steel scrap, what they called new art forms. Painters known as "pop" artists were glorifying everyday products of technology, such as cans of soup. And musicians were experimenting with sounds produced electronically. Music and other forms of entertainment now reached the public primarily through two mass-produced instruments of technology—television and the transistor radio.

Not many Americans could grasp the significance of science and technology in their lives. Businessmen knew from past experience that technology contributed to industrial improvement and profit. Millions of Americans realized vaguely that science made possible a life much more comfortable than their parents had known. Others, especially industrial workers, feared that technology was taking or would take their jobs. One thing almost all knowledgeable people knew—scientific and technological experimentation were enormously expensive. Such experimentation flourished in the postwar United States because the nation was big, rich, and prosperous enough to take advantage of what science offered.

A zooming population stimulated economic growth and technological expansion. In the 1930's, immigration had been cut off, and the birth rate had declined. In the 1940's, the birth rate skyrocketed and continued to do so through most of the 1950's, though it then began to decline. As population expanded, its nature changed. Improvements in medicine, nutrition, and sanitation made possible a longer life for the average American. In 1900, his life expectancy was 49 years; in 1950, it was 68 years; and in 1964 it was slightly over 70 years. The rising birth rate and the increasing longevity resulted in a population consisting of a higher proportion of both the very young and the very old. This meant that the people in the productive middle years had to bear the heavy burdens of paying for schools and for old-age pensions and medical care.

Since the great increase in population had come without much immigration, the proportion of foreign-born to native-born Americans dropped. As more and more sons and daughters of immigrants married children of old-stock Americans, the white population of the 1960's became remarkably homogeneous. In 1960, only five per cent of the population was foreign-born, and few Americans belonged to families that had not lived at least two generations in the United States.

The Negro population also increased. But Negroes were no longer seen most often in the South; by the 1960's, Negroes lived in all parts of the country. New York had the largest Negro population in the Union. New York City, Chicago, and other northern cities had Negro sections as well as mixed areas of whites and Negroes.

By the 1960's, the melting pot had done its work among the whites. Regardless of the national origin of his name, the white American was likely to be the offspring of a mixture of European peoples. Regardless of racial or ethnical background, Americans of the technological age had come to think of themselves mainly as Americans.

THE ECONOMY BOOMED

Many economists had predicted that there would be a serious depression after World War II. Twenty years after the war, such a depression had yet to come. Although there were a number of short setbacks or recessions, Americans experienced the longest, dizziest boom of prosperity in the history of the modern world.

Numerous factors contributed to this amazing prosperity. After World War II, industry in the United States had to grow fast to keep up with the demands of consumers. In 1955, the United States contained about six per cent of the world's population, yet its factories were pouring out almost fifty per cent of the world's goods. This tremendous production brought wealth that promoted technological development and the creation of still more wealth. After 1955, when the nations of western Europe and Japan got their industries functioning at full capacity, America's economic growth, while still increasing, declined in comparison with that of several other nations.

Yet prosperity in the United States continued, and a number of industries made greater and greater profits. General Motors, for example, the nation's largest corporation, broke its own records in 1964 and again in 1965. In 1964, the company's sales of cars and trucks brought a profit of $1.7 billion; the next year, $2.1 billion. The profits of General Motors and other corporations came from unprecedented sales to private consumers and to the federal government, which kept up its defense spending because of the Cold War, the Korean War, and a war in Vietnam.

Americans were a people in motion

Americans had always been a mobile people, but in the age of technology they seemed to be in motion constantly. They moved from one neighborhood to another, from one town to another, and from one part of the country to another. There were many causes for this, but for the years after 1940 a few stand out: the shifting of men in the armed forces and their dependents in three wars, the economic prosperity that made it possible for millions to pay for moves, the widespread ownership of automobiles, and most important of all, the attraction of new and better jobs.

Increasingly, Americans sought the warmth of the sun. More and more of them made their homes in California, Florida, and the states of the Southwest. California's growth was most remarkable. In 1965, its population was estimated at 18.75 million. California, with an annual growth of three per cent, was the most populous state in the Union. Some observers spoke of a "western tilt," implying that the North American continent was tilted westward so as to draw people from east to west.

The shift in population changed the geographical pattern of political power, especially as reflected in the distribution of seats in the House of Representatives. After the census of 1960, the Far West together with Hawaii and Alaska gained seats in the House while the East, the Middle West, and the South lost seats there.

Prosperity also stimulated tourist travel, within the United States and abroad. In 1963, about 95 million Americans took vacation trips in 34 million automobiles. They spent approximately $20 billion, a figure that includes food, lodgings, gasoline, and other needs. Tourism had become a major industry. That year, for the first time, air travel exceeded railroad and bus travel.

As in the past, Europe attracted more tourists from the United States than from any other part of the world. In 1963, more than 1.1 million Americans visited Europe where they spent $755 million. In summer the piazzas of Rome, the boulevards of Paris, and the parks of London swarmed with Americans. The Americans who traveled were no longer only the millionaires and the teachers. Businessmen, stenographers, lawyers, students, contractors, and others from the prospering middle class traveled, too. Thus a great many Americans were able to learn something about the rest of the world.

Mergers highlighted industrial growth

American industry had long been growing bigger and bigger, and some men had been increasing-

ly concerned over the concentration of wealth and power in fewer and fewer giant corporations. Despite various antitrust laws, industrial concentration continued in the years after World War II. Changes in technology stimulated this trend.

Airplanes that traveled faster than sound, ships that were powered by atomic fuel, automatic equipment that produced steel, and automobile factories governed by electric computers—these were extremely expensive to produce, too expensive for small businesses. In 1903, the Wright brothers had assembled an airplane in a bicycle shop. In the 1960's, the construction of subsonic and supersonic jet airplanes required armies of skilled technicians and millions of dollars. These were resources that only the largest of corporations could afford.

Giant corporations often were the result of mergers of two or more corporations. Banks, railroads, publishing firms, chains of department stores, and automobile manufacturers all were a part of the trend toward mergers. In 1966, there remained only three giant corporations producing automobiles at considerable profit—General Motors, Ford, and Chrysler. American Motors' sales and profits had declined, and Studebaker had discontinued car manufacturing.

Under these conditions, competition in the old-fashioned sense could scarcely survive. Manufacturers argued that they continued to compete in quality, service, and design. But competition in prices could not easily be found, and one, two, or three large companies tended to set a pattern for an entire industry.

Yet never before had United States industry tried so hard to woo and to please the customer as in the 1950's and 1960's. Market surveys were conducted to measure his whims, as well as his needs, and advertising sought by ingenious ways to persuade him to buy on the basis of whim, fashion, or mere impulse.

Credit buying became the most frequent means used by Americans to purchase the goods advertised in the newspapers, magazines, and television commercials. In 1960, Sears, Roebuck and Com-

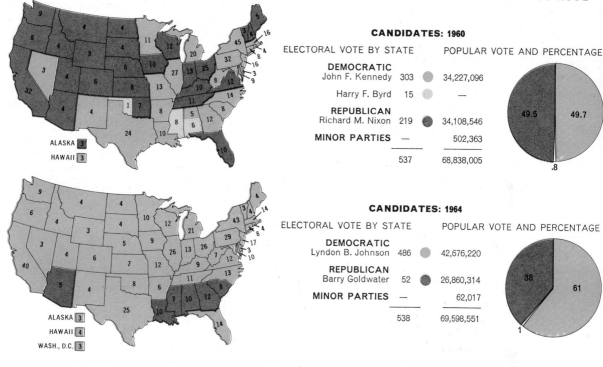

PRESIDENTIAL ELECTIONS: 1960-1964

CANDIDATES: 1960

ELECTORAL VOTE BY STATE		POPULAR VOTE AND PERCENTAGE
DEMOCRATIC		
John F. Kennedy	303	34,227,096
Harry F. Byrd	15	—
REPUBLICAN		
Richard M. Nixon	219	34,108,546
MINOR PARTIES	—	502,363
	537	68,838,005

49.5   49.7   .8

CANDIDATES: 1964

ELECTORAL VOTE BY STATE		POPULAR VOTE AND PERCENTAGE
DEMOCRATIC		
Lyndon B. Johnson	486	42,676,220
REPUBLICAN		
Barry Goldwater	52	26,860,314
MINOR PARTIES	—	62,017
	538	69,598,551

38   61   1

ALASKA 3
HAWAII 3

ALASKA 3
HAWAII 4
WASH., D.C. 3

pany, the nation's largest retailing corporation, announced that it had over ten million credit accounts, or one for every five families in the country. Credit had become part of the American way of life. Americans could get credit cards for almost everything—for trips to Europe, for dining in restaurants, for lodging in hotels or motels, and for many other luxuries as well as necessities. In the year ending in August 1964, consumer credit in the United States rose by $6.8 billion or 10.2 per cent.

The businessman's attitude toward society changed

Despite the enormous concentration of wealth and power in a few giant corporations, no demand arose among the people for the breakup of the industrial empires. The emergence of a new attitude toward society on the part of the businessman was partially responsible for this. The men who ran the great corporations often owned little or no

stock in them. Most of the corporation executives were highly trained professionals who were well educated, understood economics and the problems of technological change, and often had a sense of social responsibility not found in most of the earlier captains of industry.

The old fear that bankers would control the corporations almost disappeared. So great were profits that many of the giant corporations were able to pay for expansion and for new equipment from their own funds. They no longer needed credit from bankers and other financiers.

Even the power of the stockholder ceased to be an effective check on the managers of the giant corporations. Ownership of stock had become so widely diffused among thousands of small stockholders—stockholders who were often unversed and disinterested in the intricacies of business—that control lay in the hands of the executives.

Since the new managerial class wielded enormous power and could seriously affect the welfare of the nation, the question arose as to who would control the managers. In the 1960's, it became clear that government was regulating the corporation through an elaborate system of restraints on advertising, prices, wages, credit, and other matters. Although most of the government's controls were indirect, economic policy, on the whole, had become part of national policy. Only giant government, it seemed, could cope with the power of giant business.

REVIEWING THE SECTION

1. What changes took place in the distribution of population in the United States after World War II?

2. How did technological change stimulate the growth of giant corporations? How did this trend affect competition among companies?

3. How was the great power wielded by managers of giant corporations kept under control?

LIVING AND WORKING PATTERNS CHANGED

Affluence and technology affected the way Americans lived and earned a living. The long-term trend of population movement from the country to the city continued. In the 1950's, the population of cities went up twenty-nine per cent while that on the farms and small towns barely held its own. By 1960, almost seventy per cent of the people in the United States lived in urban areas, and the trend appeared to be irreversible, with each census reporting a further decline in the rural population.

Yet not all cities grew during these years. Many older cities, such as New York, Chicago, Philadelphia, and Detroit, actually lost population. Newer cities in the West and Southwest, such as Los Angeles, San Diego, Houston, and Dallas continued to grow. But the population of all cities grew much more slowly than the population of the suburbs that surrounded them. People were becoming concentrated in great metropolitan areas, such as those comprising New York City and its suburbs and Los Angeles and the surrounding communities. In the 1960's, more than one out of every six Americans lived in a suburb.

Millions of people worked in the cities and lived in the suburbs. Since stores, banks, and even some industries followed them into the suburbs, a new pattern of living developed for middle-class Americans. On weekdays, they clogged the highways and public transportation into the city, and they spent their week ends in their suburban communities, where they mingled socially with others of a similar economic level. Frequently, the suburbanite felt little sense of pride in the city or its institutions. This alienation of the middle classes from the cities became a problem of national concern in the 1960's.

The central city continued to decay

Middle-class Americans fled the central cities primarily because they sought in the suburbs a better life for themselves and their children. For many of them, the city represented high rent or taxes, polluted air, dirt, crime, crowded streets, and inadequate schools. Some looked upon the shift to the suburbs as a move upward on the social scale, a move made possible by prosperous times.

The city suffered because of this shift in population. The neighborhoods vacated by the middle class were soon occupied by lower-income families, many of whom were Negroes, Puerto Ricans, and Mexicans. These people could not afford high rents and were forced to huddle in crowded apartments. Nonexistent or poorly enforced building and housing codes, haphazard zoning laws, and negligence, as well as the profits to be made from slum real estate, contributed to a decline in the central city. Once-respectable neighborhoods became slum areas. Empty stores, shabby buildings, and closed factories were common, and crime and juvenile delinquency increased.

City governments often felt powerless to combat the decay in their central districts. The newcomers could not find jobs easily and often went on relief. They needed all kinds of services, such as good public transportation, sound schools, and public health facilities, but they could not pay the taxes necessary for providing them.

The federal government provided funds to help restore the centers of cities through a program of urban renewal. It permitted town and city governments to rehabilitate slums and blighted areas by land clearance and new construction or by renovation of existing structures.

City planners hoped to make the cities so attractive that at least some of the middle-class people who had gone to the suburbs would return. In the mid-1960's, some suburbanites did move back into the city, attracted by the many new "high-rise" apartment buildings and their promise of glamorous living. But the centers of most cities still were occupied by people who seldom tasted affluence.

Workers feared automation

Many of the people who lived in the central city were unemployed. A great number of them could not get jobs because they had no skills, and the technological society needed fewer and fewer unskilled workers. In 1900, there had been eleven million common laborers at work; in 1950, even though there had been a vast increase in population, there were only six million. And the number of unskilled workers continued to decline into the 1960's. Automation and mechanization accounted in large part for the shrinkage in jobs for unskilled laborers.

Automation meant the use of machines to do the work of human hands, and sometimes human minds as well. The most advanced machine was the computer, which could be programmed to make decisions, to interpret information, and even to play chess. Computers could be used to control the machines that made automobile engines and other complex products. This use of computers in automation has been termed *cybernation,* an invented term derived from the Greek word for steersman.

For the businessman, a cybernated industry had many advantages. It produced goods of uniform quality swiftly and at low cost. It reduced the labor force and hence labor problems, and it eliminated many human errors. For the workers, however, cybernation meant the threat of fewer jobs. For the economy, it meant an increased power to produce and the need for a larger market.

Organized labor tried to meet the threats of automation and cybernation in various ways, frequently by resorting to *featherbedding,* or the forcing of employers to maintain positions no longer of any use. Featherbedding solved no problems; it merely delayed the impact of the new technology.

Unions faced a membership crisis

As the number of blue-collar workers diminished, organized labor had difficulty maintaining its membership. In 1945, there were about 14.5 million union members, almost 36 per cent of the workers. In 1962, there were about 16.5 million, but these members comprised less than 30 per cent of the work force. If the American labor movement were to keep pace with the changing technology, some union leaders believed they would have to recruit among white-collar workers, teachers, and other professional people. In 1964, the American Federation of Teachers, an affiliate of the AFL-CIO, made strong efforts to attract public-school teachers in a number of cities. It won bargaining rights for teachers in New York, Chicago, Detroit, and other cities.

Despite the failure to grow and expand, the union movement prospered and enjoyed a comfortable stability in the 1950's and 1960's. Organized labor suffered some embarrassment as the result of exposures of graft, corruption, and racketeering in some unions—notably in the largest and most powerful of all, the Teamsters union. In 1957, the AFL-CIO expelled the Teamsters. In this way unions sought to preserve a reputation for responsible behavior.

As unions won an increasing number of "fringe benefits" for their members, they became more and more conservative in their social and political attitudes. At the bargaining table with employers they obtained pension plans, medical plans, paid vacations, and welfare funds. Since these benefits, as well as wage increases, pleased union members, there was seldom cause for violent strikes. Labor leaders openly defended capitalism. In 1950, David Dubinsky, head of a garment union, said, "trade unionism needs capitalism like a fish needs water."

In the 1960's, whenever a major labor dispute threatened the national economy, national security, or even the political situation, the government stepped in to work for a settlement. Since powerful unions could have an impact on the whole nation if they struck, government treated them as it did industry. It considered labor policy a part of national economic policy.

Yet, in January 1966, a strike of subway and bus workers crippled the city of New York for twelve days, and in July and August 1966, a strike by mechanics against some major airlines stranded travelers and caused great economic loss. Some Americans expressed alarm over the vulnerability of transportation facilities and of cities in the United States to what they called a "misuse of union power."

REVIEWING THE SECTION

1. What caused the central city to decay during the postwar years? What efforts were made to alleviate the problems of the cities?

2. Why did it become more and more difficult for many unemployed people to find work? How did automation and cybernation affect the nation?

3. Why did labor unions fail to grow in proportion to the expanding work force? Why did they become more politically conservative?

NEGROES SOUGHT A BETTER LIFE

As technology boosted production higher and higher, the real income of most workers shot up.

About two thirds of the working class gained a substantial share of affluence. These people worked fewer hours each day than in the past, had leisure time for sports and entertainment, lived in comfortable houses and apartments, and bought what had formerly been considered luxury items, such as new cars, refrigerators, and television sets. Laborers and their children wore good clothes, enjoyed vacations, and the children frequently went to the best colleges.

Few could deny that these conditions represented a considerable overall improvement in the life of the American workingman. Yet, many of the nation's working people lived in poverty, if not squalor. The census of 1960 showed that more than thirteen per cent of America's families had a yearly income of less than $2000, an amount below what was considered the subsistence level. Many of these families were white, but most were Negro, Puerto Rican, or Mexican. These minority families had incomes averaging only about fifty-four per cent of those of white families.

Unemployment and discrimination were, in part, responsible for the poverty among Negroes. In one big-city slum of 125,000 people, for example, seventy per cent of the Negro boys and girls between the ages of sixteen and twenty-one were out of school and had no jobs. These young people desperately wanted jobs, and cars, and good homes. Yet they knew that discrimination in employment and housing kept many of these advantages out of their reach.

Civil rights became a crusade

Most minority groups, particularly immigrant groups from Europe, had managed, in time, to escape the misery of slums. They became assimilated in American society, and many second- and third-generation sons and daughters of immigrants gained middle-class status. Even though Negroes had been in America since colonial days, few of them had been able to advance socially and economically, as had the descendants of immigrants.

Primarily because of prejudice, Negroes remained outside the mainstream of American life even in the 1960's.

In the South the white people, through customs and laws, erected barriers that kept Negroes from being treated on equal terms with the whites. For years, most Negroes in the rural South accepted their position of inferiority without consistent or loud protest. Negroes began to shed their submissiveness as a result of two trends. One was the continued migration of millions of Negroes to the North and the other was the concentration of Negroes in cities, North and South. In the twenty years after 1940, the Negro population of the North almost tripled whereas that of the South barely held steady.

When the Negroes went North, they found no promised land. Instead, they found *de facto,* or actual, segregation and other forms of discrimination—though not the "Jim Crow" laws of the South that enforced segregation in public places such as bus stations. Yet in the North Negroes gained the right to vote in fact as well as in law. As their numbers increased, they elected men of their own race to city offices, to judgeships, to state legislatures, and to Congress. Men with special talent often had a chance to develop it.

It became difficult for politicians seeking Negro votes to deny them their basic civil rights. It became difficult, too, for Negro officeholders, intellectuals, and others in positions of leadership to accept only the rights that white men saw fit to give. In the 1950's, a new generation of Negroes became impatient with the slow, careful struggle of the National Association for the Advancement of Colored People (NAACP), which appealed to the courts to gain decisions against voting and school discrimination.

The new generation of Negroes took it upon itself to fight actively for equality in fact as well as in theory. Supported by the national conscience, the courts, and many whites, the Negroes launched a mass crusade against racial discrimination in all forms.

Freedom riders invaded the South

Negro students from middle-class backgrounds started one part of this crusade. On February 2, 1960, four students from a Negro college sat down on stools at a lunch counter in a five-and-ten-cent store in Greensboro, North Carolina. No one would serve the young Negroes because they had challenged a practice of long standing. In drug and variety stores in the South, it was the custom to provide seats at lunch counters for whites but standing room only for Negroes. The action of the Negro students in Greensboro that day was a protest against this form of discrimination. Their action was also the beginning of the "sit-in," a form of peaceful civil disobedience.

The Greensboro sit-in inspired similar demonstrations throughout the South. Usually, the local authorities arrested the protesters for breaking the peace or trespassing on private property. Nevertheless, the sit-in demonstrations—together with nationwide boycotts of chain stores whose Southern outlets practiced discrimination—finally brought an end to segregation at lunch counters.

In May 1961, a group of young Negroes and whites from the North, under the sponsorship of the Congress of Racial Equality (CORE), rode buses into the South to see how effectively federal laws against segregation in interstate buses and stations were being enforced. In Anniston and Birmingham, Alabama, mobs descended on the "freedom riders," beat several of them severely, and destroyed one of the buses with a firebomb. Violence also greeted the "freedom riders" in Montgomery, Alabama. Attorney General Robert F. Kennedy ordered federal marshals into Montgomery to restore the peace and to protect the travelers. In September 1961, the attorney general asked the Interstate Commerce Commission to prohibit segregation in all interstate travel facilities.

Riots erupted in Northern cities

In 1963, the one hundredth anniversary of the

Emancipation Proclamation, the civil rights crusade picked up in intensity. On August 28, about 200,000 Negroes and white sympathizers gathered in Washington, D.C., and staged the largest civil rights demonstration ever seen. As television cameras brought their protest into millions of homes, the demonstrators marched from the Washington Monument to the symbol of their cause, the Lincoln Memorial. There, speakers cried out for justice, equality, and freedom—now. Not one act of violence disturbed this massive demonstration, but elsewhere in the nation rising racial tension, violence, and bloodshed accompanied the civil rights struggle.

To help increase the registration of Negroes as voters in the South, civil rights leaders plunged into a stronghold of segregationists. In March 1965, more than twenty-five thousand Negroes and whites singing "We Shall Overcome," the song of the civil rights crusade, staged a "freedom march." It covered fifty-four miles from Selma to Montgomery, Alabama, and lasted five days. Out of it came a murder that shocked the nation: Mrs. Viola Gregg Liuzzo, a white civil rights worker from Detroit, was shot and killed. At a federal trial, it became apparent that Ku Klux Klan members were involved in the episode. The march itself had a great impact on Americans, especially on members of Congress who were considering a new civil rights bill.

In some areas of the South, extremists and members of racist organizations such as the Klan were bombing Negroes' homes and churches. In Alabama and Mississippi they murdered Negro and white civil rights workers in cold blood. In some towns, police used dogs and high-powered water hoses against demonstrators, and in others such as Cambridge, Maryland, whites and Negroes fought in the streets.

Widespread violence erupted in the Negro sections of Northern cities in 1964, "the long hot summer" of Negro discontent. Trouble began in New York City after an off-duty policeman had struggled with a Negro youth and killed him.

Negroes immediately protested against what they called "police brutality." From the scene of the shooting, the demonstrations spread, leading to riots in Harlem, the nation's largest Negro section, and to the Bedford-Stuyvesant section of Brooklyn where bands of young, unemployed Negroes smashed windows and looted and ransacked stores. Similar outbreaks followed in Rochester, New York; Jersey City, Elizabeth, and Paterson, New Jersey; in Philadelphia; and in Dixmoor, a suburb of Chicago.

During the following summer, racial tensions became hotter. On August 11, 1965, a California highway patrolman arrested, for drunken driving, a young Negro in Watts, a sprawling Negro community of forty-five square miles in Los Angeles. The fairly neat-looking homes and lawns in Watts seemed to contradict the community's problems. The density of population was four times as great as the rest of Los Angeles. There was a high rate of unemployment.

After the arrest, word of "police brutality" spread through Watts. Almost a week of rioting, looting, burning, and shooting followed. Roving bands of Negroes smashed store windows, looted under the lenses of news cameras shooting pictures from helicopters, and set fire to hundreds of buildings. When firemen tried to put out the blazes, snipers fired at them. Some of the rioters spoke of making all-out war on whites.

Los Angeles police were powerless to cope with the uprising, so the governor sent thirteen thousand national guardsmen into Watts. Using tear gas, bayonets, rifles, and machine guns, the troops finally suppressed the riot. The toll was high: thirty-six were dead—most of them Negroes—and about nine hundred people were injured. Some four thousand persons were arrested, and damage was estimated at $47 million.

During the same week, there were also Negro riots in Chicago and in Springfield, Massachusetts, but the Watts riot was by far the worst—one of the worst in the nation's history.

Most of the rioters were the rootless, bitter, un-

THE
CHANGING STATUS
OF THE
AMERICAN NEGRO

From 1898

1898

In the case of *Williams* v. *Mississippi*, the Supreme Court upheld literacy tests as requirements for voting.

1915

The Supreme Court, in the case of *Guinn* v. *United States*, declared unconstitutional the "grandfather clause," which had exempted from literacy voting tests persons whose ancestors had been able to vote prior to Reconstruction. Thus most white persons had been exempted, but most Negroes had to take tests.

1917

In the Selective Service Act, Congress removed the quota that had restricted the number of Negroes allowed to serve in the armed forces. The policy of segregated Negro military units continued.

1941

President Roosevelt ordered a policy of non-discrimination in employment in defense industries and established the Fair Employment Practices Commission.

1944

The "white primary" was declared unconstitutional in the Supreme Court case of *Smith* v. *Allwright*.

1946

President Truman established the Committee on Civil Rights.

1947

Jackie Robinson became the first Negro to play in major league baseball.

March on Washington
August 28, 1963

1957 and 1960

Two Civil Rights Acts, the first since Reconstruction, gave the federal government new powers to aid Negroes in their attempts to secure the right to register and vote. The 1957 act also established the Commission on Civil Rights.

1961

In an executive order, President Kennedy announced that nondiscrimination clauses would be required in all government contracts. The order also established the Committee on Equal Employment Opportunity. By 1964, thirty state governments had passed some form of fair employment practice law.

1962

President Kennedy issued an executive order prohibiting discrimination in federally assisted housing. During the 1960's, "open occupancy" demonstrations took place in many cities.

1963

More than 200,000 persons participated in a March on Washington, D.C., to dramatize the accomplishments of the civil rights movement and the determination to continue the drive for equal rights.

1964

The Twenty-Fourth Amendment to the Constitution outlawed the use of poll taxes in any federal election.

1964

The comprehensive Civil Rights Act of 1964 outlawed discrimination and segregation in restaurants, concert halls, sports arenas, and hotels. Also, most businesses, labor unions,

1948

An executive order by President Truman ended segregation in the armed forces.

1954

In a major case, *Brown* v. *Board of Education of Topeka*, the Supreme Court ruled that segregated public schools constituted a denial of equal rights. In the 1960's, Negro leaders complained of both "token" desegregation and *de facto* segregation.

1955

In Atlanta, Georgia, Negroes boycotted a bus company that required them to sit or stand at the rear of buses. By 1962, all forms of segregated transportation facilities had been declared illegal.

and employment agencies were prohibited from racial discrimination in hiring practices, working conditions, and wages.

1965

Through the Voting Rights Act, the federal government was authorized to register any qualified voter who had been denied the right to vote because of his race. This act applied only where discrimination was found to be evident in registration practices.

1966

When Robert Weaver was sworn in as secretary of the Department of Housing and Urban Development, he became the first Negro to serve on a President's cabinet.

employed Negroes who had had no contact with the civil rights leaders of their own race. They rebelled violently against the slum conditions that trapped them. Even though city, state, and federal government agencies tried to overcome the Negroes' despair, it persisted. Watts was again the scene of rioting in March 1966, when two persons were killed. In July 1966, national guard troops were needed to stop rioting and looting in Negro sections of Chicago and Cleveland. Unrest was apparent in other cities across the nation. To help the Negroes in city slums, the civil rights crusade had to gain more than legal freedoms and equal voting rights; it also had to provide Negroes with vastly better employment opportunities.

REVIEWING THE SECTION

1. Why did Negroes have difficulty advancing socially and economically? How did the migration of Negroes to Northern cities affect the Negro civil rights movement?

2. What measures were taken by Negroes to end segregation in the South?

3. Why did outbreaks of violence accompany the struggle for civil rights?

SCIENCE AND EDUCATION ENLARGED MAN'S KNOWLEDGE

Social issues, such as civil rights, often filled the newspaper and television reports in the 1950's and 1960's. Sometimes, however, scientific and technological accomplishments were so spectacular that they overshadowed all else. In the years following World War II, science became as much a part of the American cultural scene as art, music, literature, and history.

Since science required experimentation, the universities were the chief contributors to its development. They trained scientists and carried out experiments, sometimes under contract for the federal government. Government and private industry, employing many of the scientists educated at the universities, applied scientific ideas to prac-

tical projects, such as the building of ships and power plants to be run by nuclear energy.

Government, industry, and various private foundations gave large sums of money to the universities to support research. In 1950, the government established the National Science Foundation to coördinate and intensify its activities in scientific research and education, especially through scholarships to students and through various research projects.

Scientific change was swift and varied

In no period in the nation's history was there greater and swifter changes in science and technology than in the decades of the 1940's, 1950's, and 1960's. Physicists, with their work on the atom, achieved the most spectacular results. Not only did their work lead to the making of atomic and other nuclear bombs but also to peaceful uses of atomic energy. Such energy came to be used in the treatment of cancer, in bringing electricity to towns and cities, in seeking a cheap way to remove the salt and make ocean water drinkable, and in powering ships and submarines.

In 1954, the United States launched the *Nautilus,* the world's first nuclear-powered submarine. Four years later, in August 1958, that vessel undertook and completed an underwater journey from the Pacific Ocean to the Atlantic. It was the first submarine to make the voyage under the ice cap covering the North Pole, a feat no ordinary ship or submarine could accomplish.

Nuclear energy permitted ships to travel great distances without refueling. In the past, ships were always limited by the amount of fuel they could carry, or by the proximity of fueling stations. In the summer of 1964, the United States Navy's first nuclear task force took a world cruise. During the entire voyage of thirty thousand miles, the ships did not have to refuel.

Great advances were also made in the biological sciences and in medicine. Many diseases that man had long dreaded, such as typhoid fever and malaria, were brought under control with drugs and vaccines. One of the most dramatic scientific struggles against disease was the one against poliomyelitis, long a dreaded crippler of children. Two American researchers, supported by funds from private foundations, developed vaccines offering protection against the disease. Dr. Jonas Salk discovered a killed-virus vaccine, and Dr. Albert B. Sabin worked out a live-virus vaccine. By the early 1960's, these vaccines had almost wiped out polio.

Since scientific change was often accompanied by social change, many Americans came to feel that the scientist should not pursue his work without giving thought to its ultimate place in society. Bombs that could destroy mankind, computers that could do the work of men, and energy that could serve the needs of all mankind evolved from the work of scientists. Some men argued that the power of scientists, like the power of the giant corporations and unions, must be controlled by society.

Men explored outer space

No other feat of the scientists and engineers gripped the public imagination as did the exploration of outer space. The work of many scientists, as far back as Sir Isaac Newton in the 1680's, laid the basis for fulfilling man's old dream of flying through the emptiness of airless space.

What some writers have called the "space age" began on October 4, 1957, when the Soviet Union launched *Sputnik I*, a satellite of 184 pounds, in orbit around the earth. A month later the Russians sent *Sputnik II,* a larger capsule, carrying a live dog, hurtling around the earth. In January 1958, the United States sent up its first satellite, *Explorer I.* Then Russians and Americans launched satellites that sent back to earth photographs and radio messages with scientific information.

Many Americans were upset by the Soviet lead in space science and technology. The Soviets had gained their advantage after World War II by concentrating research on fuels and engines capable of boosting the heavy and bulky weapons their rockets had to carry. The United States had relied on planes to carry its big bombs. It did not begin serious work on space rockets until after it had developed lightweight nuclear weapons in 1954. It entered the field of space science with a heavy commitment in July 1958, when Congress created the National Aeronautics and Space Administration (NASA). This agency was given responsibility for scientific investigation and exploration of space. The armed forces continued to carry on their own missile program for defense purposes.

The space accomplishments of the United States were impressive, but those of the Soviet Union were more spectacular. In April 1961, the Soviets shot *Voskhod I*, a spaceship weighing 10,414 pounds, into space. Inside was the young cosmonaut Major Yuri A. Gagarin, the first man to orbit the earth and return safely. In February 1962, the United States hurled its first astronaut, Lieutenant Colonel John H. Glenn, Jr., into orbit around the earth. Glenn's space ship, *Friendship 7,* was smaller than the Russian capsules, and he circled the earth only three times though another Soviet cosmonaut had done so seventeen times. Yet Americans were thrilled. They now thought their scientists could compete in the "space race."

After these feats, both the Soviets and the Americans sent more and larger manned spacecrafts into space for longer periods. The Russians launched their ships in secret; the Americans did so in a glare of publicity. Television cameras covered the launchings and recoveries. Millions of Americans shared the excitement and fears of each flight into space of their astronauts.

In 1963, the Soviets sent the first woman cosmonaut into space, and in March 1965, one of their cosmonauts, Aleksei Leonov, became the first man to "walk" in space; he walked for ten minutes while tethered to the spaceship *Voskhod II.* Two months later, in June 1965, Major Edward H. White stepped outside the capsule *Gemini 4* for twenty minutes and became the first American to walk in space. The space walks of Leonov and White proved that man, with proper clothing and equipment, could survive in space and could even control his own movements.

By this time America's missiles were beginning to approach those of the Soviets in thrust. In December 1965, the United States, achieved a great triumph in space technology. It sent *Gemini 7* into orbit at 17,500 miles an hour and, several days later it hurled *Gemini 6* into space in a 1400-mile chase. *Gemini 6* caught *Gemini 7,* and the spaceships maneuvered to within ten feet of each other 185 miles from earth. *Gemini 7* remained in flight fourteen days, a new record.

In spring and summer of 1966, the United States space program concentrated on "docking" exercises in which a crew of two astronauts would maneuver their capsule into proper position and link it with an unmanned rocket also orbiting in space. Although there were some failures, successful docking was accomplished several times.

Both the United States and the Soviet Union had sent capsules crashing into the moon and, in February 1966, the Soviet *Luna 9* succeeded in making a "soft landing." Cameras in a package ejected from the ship sent back clear pictures of the moon's surface. In June of that year the United States *Surveyor I* made a "soft landing" and cameras aboard televised thousands of pictures from the moon to earth.

Space research was tapping the resources of almost every field of science. The pioneer stage of space flight had been concluded. Through the instruments of science and technology, men had made outer space something of a laboratory.

Technology made new demands on education

Americans realized that continuing progress in space science, and in all fields of knowledge, depended on a sound educational system. They had always shown faith in education as an important part of life. In the 1950's and 1960's, they expressed a more intense interest in schools, teachers, and ideas concerning learning than they had at any time in their history.

Education became increasingly important to almost every American family as the machines of the age of technology became more and more complicated. Almost every year in the postwar decades saw a new record in school enrollments. In the fall of 1965, there were 54 million students in the nation's schools, colleges, and universities. This figure amounted to an increase of about 2.1 per cent over the previous year. By the middle of the 1960's, more than one fourth of all Americans were enrolled in a program of formal education.

An increasingly larger proportion of the population went on to college. In 1930, one million Americans were enrolled in colleges; in 1965, nearly five and a half million were enrolled. College degrees were required for more and more jobs, and graduate degrees were needed for most of the professions.

Although schools were superior to those available before 1940 and teachers were better trained than in earlier years, school administrators in the postwar decades had difficulty in maintaining and raising standards. Teachers' salaries were low and, in many parts of the country, school buildings were overcrowded and inadequate. Richer states, such as California and New York, could afford well-equipped schools and reasonably good salaries for teachers. But poorer states could not spend nearly so much per child, even though some of these states spent a large part of their total income on education. Americans who believed that the education of children was everybody's obligation argued that only the use of federal funds in schools would give the poorer states educational systems comparable to those in the richer states.

Even in the richer states many Americans were not satisfied with the quality of public education. In 1957, after the Soviets had launched their first sputniks, critics argued that a superior educational system had made possible the Soviet space lead. These critics claimed that American elementary and secondary education had neglected basic intellectual skills such as reading, writing, and arithmetic. Some attacked progressive education and

Astronaut Edward H. White III maneuvering in space, Gemini 4, June 1965

The flight to the moon. The United States lunar spaceship *(Apollo)* will consist of three parts: a three-man capsule, or command module; an augmented target docking adapter (ATDA); and a lunar excursion module (LEM). When the spaceship achieves an orbit around the moon, the LEM will separate from the spaceship and carry two of the astronauts to the moon. After the astronauts explore the moon's surface, the LEM will transport them back to the orbiting spaceship. The ATDA, which has been used in space docking exercises, is a service module that will provide extra power to the command module as it travels from an earth orbit to a lunar orbit and back again.

rendering of three lunar excursion modules landing on the moon's surface

augmented target docking adapter in space during Gemini 8 flight, March 1966

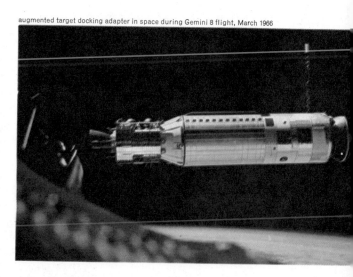

John Dewey's ideas of learning. The purpose and quality of American education became the subject of nation-wide debate.

Colleges and universities also felt the sting of criticism. Critics charged that higher education had become much too narrow and too specialized. Some contended that professors were so immersed in their own narrow fields of research that they neglected students. In November 1964, when students at the Berkeley campus of the University of California revolted against regulations restricting political activity, this unrest was taken as evidence of student dissatisfaction with university teaching. Actually, knowledge had become so broad and complex that schools and colleges had difficulty in keeping up with it and at the same time giving personal attention to hordes of students.

REVIEWING THE SECTION

1. What peaceful uses for atomic energy were developed after World War II?

2. What advances in the exploration of outer space were made by the United States and the Soviet Union?

3. What changes took place in American education during the postwar years? What criticisms were made regarding the quality of education?

CULTURAL ACTIVITY BECAME WIDESPREAD

The tremendous expansion in education all over the United States in the years after 1940 stimulated activity in all areas of culture. Not only did the cultural ground swell of the 1920's and 1930's continue, but it also spread and became stronger.

For millions of Americans, the center of cultural life was the church. More of them than ever before joined churches, as religion experienced an impressive revival. In the 1960's, about two thirds of the population went to church. According to figures compiled in 1965, some 123.3 million Americans were church members, an increase of more than 2.3 million over the previous year. About 55 per cent belonged to various Protestant

denominations, 37 per cent to the Roman Catholic Church, and 4.5 per cent to the Jewish faith.

Among Protestants, differences in ritual became less important than in the past, and many denominations worked toward Christian unity. In 1950, twenty-five Protestant and five Eastern Orthodox church bodies formed the National Council of Churches of Christ to coördinate their missionary, educational, and welfare programs.

Roman Catholics and Jews suffered far less from discrimination than in the past. Leaders from these faiths carried on dialogues with each other and with Protestant clergymen. The efforts of Popes John XXIII and Paul VI to bring the Roman Catholic Church up to date led to these dialogues. Neither anti-Catholicism nor anti-Semitism had entirely disappeared, yet never before had there been so cordial a relationship among the Protestant, Roman Catholic, and Jewish religious leaders as in the 1960's.

The printed word retained vitality

Some observers of the American scene had feared that the hypnotic influence of television would keep people away from churches and from bookstores. But it did not do so.

Television began to take a strong hold on the American people in 1947. Television sets, much improved, became as common as radios in American homes. Since television shows needed mass audiences to please advertisers, they often concentrated on low-grade spy thrillers and westerns. Such programming led one critic to call television a "wasteland" of culture. At times, however, when dealing with current events such as political conventions or an astronaut's splashdown, television could be excellent. When it presented serious drama or opera, it also became a vitally important means of spreading culture on a mass scale. Television also became a significant instrument in formal education.

Even though enthralled by television and radio, Americans continued to be avid newspaper readers.

Newspaper circulation rose as the population increased, but the number of newspapers continued to decline. Magazines, too, jumped in circulation but fell in numbers. Serious monthlies or quarterlies had small audiences and often survived only because of subsidies from universities. The mass market was dominated by the picture magazines—*Life* and *Look*—and by women's magazines such as *McCall's. Time* and *Reader's Digest* numbered their readers in the millions.

Book publishing went through a revolution. Inexpensive paperback books were sold everywhere—in drugstores, supermarkets, and railway stations. Many of those paperbacks offered tales of violence, sex, and horror. Many publishers, however, offered reprints of historical, scientific, and literary works, and these were bought by the thousands. To some extent, the concern for reprints reflected the state of American literature in the postwar decades.

As in the past, the novel remained the American writer's major form of expression. Critics generally agreed that the postwar novel had vitality even though it may have lacked freshness and imagination. One of the best war novels, Norman Mailer's *The Naked and the Dead* (1948), depicted war realistically, as grim and futile.

Saul Bellow, another of the better novelists of the period, also stressed realism in his *The Adventures of Augie March* (1953) and *Herzog* (1964). Other writers followed themes that saw man as a hopeless creature because of his own weakness or because of circumstances. One of the most widely read books of the period, especially by high school and college students, was J. D. Salinger's *The Catcher in the Rye* (1951), a story about a confused adolescent boy. Robert Penn Warren, a Southern writer of considerable skill, brought philosophical insight to historical themes. His *All the King's Men* (1946) was a novel based on the career of Huey Long of Louisiana.

Another talented young Southerner, Truman Capote, who moved to New York, wrote imaginatively, in *Grass Harp* (1951), about poorly adjusted people who were searching for understanding in a disinterested world. Later, in what he called a "nonfiction novel," *In Cold Blood* (1966), he told the factual story of two murderers and their victims.

In poetry such giants of the past as Robert Frost and E. E. Cummings, were still active in the 1950's and early 1960's. The new younger poets, among them Robert Lowell and Karl Shapiro, had so complex an approach to poetic expression that many people could not easily understand them. Yet they had something worthwhile to say to readers with the patience to decipher their poems.

Creative art gained large audiences

Opera performances on television, heavy sales of classical and serious modern music on records, popular new art museums in cities such as Los Angeles, travel to the great art galleries of Europe, and an increasing demand for serious paintings by private buyers—all indicated that America of the 1950's and 1960's had an increasingly large audience capable of appreciating creative art on a high level. This stepped-up public interest in art, as well as the general affluence of society, removed the American painter from the role of the impoverished bohemian living in a garret. Now he could often sell his paintings for a decent price, or he could sometimes find a post on a college faculty that would permit him to do creative work as well as teach. In this era, the college and the university often became the patron of the artist, the composer, and the musician, as well as the writer.

Few of the young painters portrayed life in terms that even approached realism. They experimented with pure abstraction, with canvases filled with geometric patterns and splashes of color. Some artists threw paint on canvas without any pattern at all; they painted to express emotion and feeling. Others adopted a technique called "surrealism," in which realistic objects were combined in startling, exaggerated ways.

In the early 1960's, a new art trend in Britain

Water of the Flowery Mill, by Arshile Gorky

United States Painting. After World War II, the techniques of abstract painting broke free of practically all traditions. "Water of the Flowery Mill" is an example of abstract expressionism, a free and spontaneous style of painting. "Ready-to-wear" is an arrangement of more definite shapes; the artist may have had a dress pattern in mind. "The Map" is an abstract representation of a map of the United States. The Great Lakes are in the upper right. The artist also has included recognizable shapes—hands, flags, a motorcycle, and a few letters. In the "op" art painting "Spiral Illusion," a three-dimensional effect is created by geometrical patterns of dots.

Other painters creatively used realistic techniques. "The Rock" is an example of surrealism, in which realistic objects and figures are arranged in a dream-like, symbolic setting. The sharp-focus detail of "Young America" distinguishes Andrew Wyeth's realistic style.

Young America, by Andrew Wyeth, 1950

Ready-to-wear, by Stuart Davis, 1955

The Rock, by Peter Blume, 1948

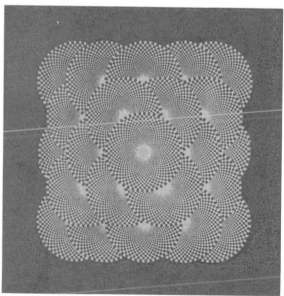

Spiral Illusion, by Tom Strobel, 1965

The Map, by Roy Schnackenberg, 1964

and the United States seemed to be a reaction against more than a decade of formlessness. The trend was called "pop" art, a new form of realism that stressed themes taken from popular culture, such as comic strips. In another art form, called "op" art, geometric patterns were combined to give optical illusions.

Architecture, while experimental, never lost touch with the people who had to live and work in the buildings that architects designed. American architects broke away from earlier European styles. In the 1940's, a severe functional style seemed to prevail. When expressed in huge office buildings and housing projects, it often appeared oppressively monotonous. In the late 1950's and early 1960's, architects such as Eero Saarinen, Edward D. Stone, and Minoru Yamasaki designed buildings that retained functional lines but also had some ornamentation.

Experimentation, some of it original and fascinating, marked work in the American theatre also. None of the new generation of playwrights, however, scaled the heights reached by Eugene O'Neill. The works of Tennessee Williams and Arthur Miller had dramatic force and impact. Williams often dealt with themes of decay and degeneracy, as in *The Glass Menagerie* (1944) and *A Streetcar Named Desire* (1947). Miller, too, was pessimistic and dealt with characters defeated by circumstances, as in *Death of a Salesman* (1949). Both Williams and Miller concerned themselves with psychological analyses of human behavior.

Musical plays generally were more successful than serious drama. Two smash hits, *Oklahoma* (1943) and *South Pacific* (1949), by Oscar Hammerstein II and Richard Rodgers, were fresh and original. The most successful musical of the 1950's, *My Fair Lady* by Alan Jay Lerner and Frederick Loewe, ran on Broadway in New York City for more than six years. Its story and dialogue were adapted from the British playwright George Bernard Shaw's *Pygmalion. Hello, Dolly!*, based on Thornton Wilder's farce *The Matchmaker,* became a "smash hit" in 1964.

A new interest in serious music was demonstrated among American composers and audiences. Men such as Aaron Copland, Roger Sessions, Walter Piston, and Lukas Foss wrote compositions that gained recognition both in the United States and abroad. Although born in Italy, Gian-Carlo Menotti was an American and wrote operas on American themes to be sung in English. American jazz continued to have followers all over the world. Most composers themselves were seeking a new definition or synthesis of the various musical styles arising in the twentieth century. The new "abstract" experimental music, however, often was difficult for the general public to understand.

REVIEWING THE SECTION

1. What changes took place in the mass communications industries during the postwar years? What themes were dealt with by the major novelists of this period?

2. What were the trends in American art, music, and architecture during the postwar years?

CHAPTER **29** CONCLUSION

Probably no people enjoyed so many material and cultural benefits as did the people of the United States in the age of technology. Although a few recessions left pockets of unemployment, the economic boom that began with World War II continued through the 1960's and showed no signs of slackening. Even the farmer, whose surpluses often could not be marketed at a profit, was enjoying a solid prosperity by the mid-1960's.

The technological revolution that had shaken the foundations of agriculture had also helped reshape farming into a modern industry. America's millions needed great quantities of food, and with prosperity they had plenty of money to pay for it. In 1966, the government was also exporting huge shiploads of food, such as wheat. Some of it went to starving millions in India and Egypt. These and other factors reduced the grain surpluses in government warehouses to manageable proportions. In some instances the surpluses disappeared.

There was fear that the family farm would disappear as farming became a big business requiring expensive machinery and huge acreage. This fear was not realized. Technology did almost take over the farm as machines replaced men, but as farms became larger, machines also made it possible for one man or one family to run farms of large acreage and make a profit. The combining of acreage and the removal of sub-marginal farms from cultivation led to a fifty per cent reduction in the number of farms from 1939 to 1967. Yet production increased, and in the last five years of this period farm income rose faster than income for the rest of the population.

While farming gained new strength, the city was being eaten by decay in an era of abundance. The technology that produced such an affluent middle class left behind in the heart of American cities many who were unemployed and some who were unemployable. Since many of these poor were Negroes or uneducated whites who had never known the security of a job, some observers saw unemployment for the first time as a class and racial issue.

Negroes were acutely aware of their plight. In their civil rights crusade they did not seek anything more unusual than justice. They wanted what most Americans wanted—a job, a respectable home, and adequate schooling for themselves and their children. Even though the turmoil of the civil rights crusade captured most of the headlines, the statistics that showed a steady growth in the size of the Negro middle class were equally important. Old barriers, especially in the North, that kept Negroes out of America's mainstream were crumbling. The chances for a Negro to attain what he desired in the United States, while not rosy, were better in the 1960's than at any time in the past.

Just as Americans were learning to adjust to the changes brought about by the civil rights crusade, they learned to accept the swift transformations brought by science and technology. Color television sets, travel

by jet airplane, and the use of computers to run businesses and factories had become accepted as part of everyday life. Even children talked easily about space travel, and almost everyone seemed concerned about science and its place in culture.

The traditional forms of culture had considerable support. Good music, good books, good theatre, and good art were more readily available to Americans than ever before. Abundance also gave some Americans the time and money to learn to appreciate the arts. Technology and vigorous creativity by the individual were not incompatible. It seemed possible for Americans, through the use of science and technology, to build a richer cultural as well as a richer material life.

FOCUSING ON SPECIFICS

1. By the 1960's, what changes in the ethnic composition of the American people had become evident?

2. Why did many people move to the suburbs during the postwar years? How did this movement affect the central city?

3. How were sit-in demonstrations used to challenge segregation in the South?

4. What were the trends in religious activity among Americans in the postwar years?

5. What were the major developments in the newspaper and magazine industries? in the book-publishing industry?

REVIEWING MAIN THEMES

1. What trends were evident in the growth and technology of American industry? How did these trends affect government policy, industrial workers, and the American people as a whole?

2. During the postwar years, what efforts to end discrimination were made by Negroes?

EVALUATING THE ISSUES

1. How do you account for the development of a strong civil rights movement among American Negroes after World War II?

2. The authors state: "Only giant government, it seemed, could cope with the power of giant business." Do you agree with this statement? How else might giant corporations be kept under control?

30

The Politics of Power

On November 22, 1963, John F. Kennedy became the fourth United States President to die from an assassin's bullet. (The others were Lincoln, 1865; Garfield, 1881; and McKinley, 1901.) Quite soon it became clear that Kennedy's assassination was an isolated incident, the irrational act of an unstable person. The people's feelings of fear or insecurity were short-lived; they soon gave way to the greater feeling of mourning for a popular leader. Americans relied on their government to provide an orderly transfer of power with no interruption in the keeping of national security. They retained their faith in the democratic processes established by the Constitution some 170 years before.

Just three years previous to the assassination, Americans had elected their first Roman Catholic President. They had also brought a new generation of young men to power, men who had known only the wars, the depressions, and the industrial affluence of the twentieth century. The election seemed to promise a government of youthful "vigor," to use one of Kennedy's favorite terms.

The slogan "New Frontier" had been coined to characterize Kennedy's campaign and his hopes for the future. He saw his program as a successor to the New Deal and the Fair Deal. In his inaugural address, delivered in a distinctive Boston accent, he asked his fellow Americans to work with him on the New Frontier to "explore the stars, conquer the deserts, eradicate disease, tap the ocean depths, and encourage the arts and commerce."

In his brief administration, Kennedy managed to score well with a number of accomplishments. A campaign promise that soon became reality was a peace corps to work on a down-to-earth level with citizens in other countries. Amazing achievements highlighted his continuing support for the space program. He issued a housing order aimed at giving people in minority groups a freer choice than in the past in deciding where to live. A treaty outlawing atmospheric testing of nuclear weapons seemed to indicate a possible break in the Cold War.

Kennedy's successor, Lyndon B. Johnson, was totally different in appearance and style, but not in political attitude. He pledged to carry out Kennedy's program of social betterment, and fulfilled this pledge in the area of civil rights by guiding through Congress the Civil Rights Act of 1964. This act included many of Kennedy's proposals, and it guaranteed that public accommodations and public facilities would be accessible to all persons, regardless of race or national origin. In addition, Johnson initiated a "war on poverty" to eliminate a cause of social disparity in the United States.

Once elected in his own right, in 1964, Johnson further extended the principles of the New Frontier to his own program, which he called the Great Society. Johnson, who had been a senator for twelve years, had great skill in persuading Congress to enact his programs.

The first congressional session after the presidential election of 1964 was the most productive in thirty years. Its laws made possible broad social advances that profoundly affected the character of life in the United States. These laws, which touched practically every American, brought many of the goals of Johnson's Great Society within realization. Politicians and students of government were so impressed by Johnson's success with Congress that they called him a legislative miracle worker.

Among the important new measures were laws providing federal aid to education, financial assistance to help pay medical costs for aged persons, and increased social security benefits.

Both the Kennedy and Johnson administrations had to deal with a series of crises in foreign nations where the United States had special involvement. Situations in Berlin, Cuba, Panama, and the Dominican Republic all required attention and action. But by late 1966, the overriding problem in foreign affairs was in Southeast Asia, where the country of South Vietnam, caught in a long civil war, was also fighting Communists. Through a gradual build-up of troops in South Vietnam, the United States became the main force in this Asian "hot" war against communism.

Both domestic and foreign situations during the 1960's frequently demanded positive presidential action. Presidents Kennedy and Johnson were able to provide such action.

THE NEW FRONTIER TOOK SHAPE

Although the youngest man ever to have been elected President, John Kennedy at age forty-three brought considerable political experience to the presidency. His father, Joseph P. Kennedy, had

been ambassador to Britain and both his grandfathers had been prominent Boston politicians. John Kennedy was educated at Choate, an exclusive New England preparatory school, and at Harvard University. During World War II, he was commander of a torpedo boat, and when enemy action destroyed his boat, he emerged a combat hero.

Right after the war, in 1946, he won the first of three successive elections as a United States representative from the state of Massachusetts. In 1952, in an impressive, though narrow, victory, he defeated Henry Cabot Lodge, Jr., Eisenhower's campaign manager, and became a senator from Massachusetts.

While recuperating from surgery in 1954, he wrote *Profiles in Courage,* which won the Pulitzer prize for biography in 1957. Even admirers admitted that Kennedy's record as a congressman had been undistinguished. But after a serious illness in 1954, he gained a deeper sense of purpose than in the past. His book showed his serious concerns, his talent as a writer, and his sense of history, qualities which could be put to good use in the presidency.

In 1956, Kennedy narrowly missed winning the Democratic vice presidential nomination. Two years later, he won reëlection to the Senate. After that, with the assistance of the dynamic, wealthy, and large Kennedy family, and with the help of his many friends, he planned carefully the campaign that brought him the Democratic presidential nomination in 1960.

Kennedy won a close election

World-wide turmoil, cold war tension, and fear of a depression in a time of affluence provided the background for the presidential election of 1960. Since the still-popular Eisenhower could not run for a third term (because of the Twenty-Second Amendment), the Democrats had high hopes for victory when they met in Los Angeles in July to choose a candidate. The young senator from Massachusetts, John F. Kennedy, captured the nomination on the first ballot. For his running mate, he chose his most powerful rival, Lyndon B. Johnson of Texas, the majority leader in the Senate. The platform criticized Eisenhower's domestic policies and promised a program of welfare measures.

Two weeks later in Chicago, the Republicans nominated the most obvious candidate, Vice President Richard M. Nixon. For geographic balance, he selected Henry Cabot Lodge, Jr., of Massachusetts, the ambassador to the United Nations, for the vice presidential spot. The Republican platform defended the Eisenhower policies, called for "business-like methods" in government, and supported an "internationalism," which did not differ much from the foreign policy of the Democrats.

But foreign policy became a major issue. The Republicans claimed Nixon to be more mature and more experienced than Kennedy in world affairs. The important underlying issue was religion. Kennedy tried to overcome the prejudices against having a Roman Catholic President by bringing the issue into the open. Both men conducted vigorous campaigns.

Nation-wide television emphasized the matter of personality. The candidates held four television "debates," really confrontations, which some 65 to 75 million Americans saw and heard. These debates worked to Kennedy's advantage because he became as well known as Nixon. Kennedy's impressive performance helped dispel the myth of his immaturity.

Nonetheless the election was so close that virtually a hair's breadth separated the two men. Out of 68.8 million votes Kennedy obtained only 118,550 more than Nixon. In the electoral college, however, Kennedy was well ahead with 303 votes to Nixon's 219. Later analyses of the election showed that the Protestant rural areas went massively for Nixon and that Kennedy did exceptionally well in urban areas where Roman Catholics, Negroes, and other minority groups were concentrated. Both houses of Congress remained in Democratic hands by substantial majorities, but conservative Southern Democrats held most of the key committee posts.

Kennedy had looked forward to choosing his cabinet officers and other important advisers. He sought men of talent who could both think and act, and he was reasonably successful in finding them. Two of the three top cabinet posts were filled by Republicans; Robert McNamara became secretary of defense and Douglas Dillon became secretary of the treasury. McNamara, a former executive of Ford Motor Company, quickly became the strong man of the cabinet. Dillon, a banker, had been Eisenhower's under secretary of state for economic affairs and had contributed money to Nixon's campaign fund. The secretary of state was Dean Rusk, a former Rhodes scholar, professor of political science, and president of the Rockefeller Foundation. Kennedy's most controversial appointment was that of his younger brother Robert to the post of attorney general.

Kennedy promoted economic reform

When Kennedy took office, the nation was in the midst of another recession, one which struck some parts of the nation hard but barely touched others. Also, there were still pockets of poverty in certain areas. During the campaign, he had urged that the economic growth of the nation be stepped up. He hoped for a boost of at least five per cent in the nation's rate of production so that there would be a job for nearly everyone.

Kennedy felt that something had to be done immediately about unemployment. A few weeks after Kennedy entered the White House, 8.1 per cent of the working people were unemployed, a figure which economists considered dangerously high. On February 2, 1961, the new President sent a special message to Congress in which he asked for an extension of insurance payments to the unemployed, an increase in the minimum wage rate to $1.25 an hour, an increase in social security payments, and funds to clear away slums and replace them with public housing. Congress turned these requests into laws. It also passed the Area Redevelopment Act, which made federal aid available to bring industries into "distressed" areas with chronic unemployment. In 1962, Congress supplemented this act with the first accelerated public works program since the New Deal experiments.

Before the end of 1961, the economy again began to move forward, but Kennedy ran into difficulty getting congressional support for the long-range economic reform that was a part of his program. In the affluent society those who did not experience or even see unemployment were almost unaware of it. Furthermore, the old coalition of Southern Democrats and conservative Republicans controlled powerful positions in Congress. This coalition opposed much of Kennedy's program.

The New Frontiersmen felt that their program of economic reform would be endangered if prices and costs went up at the same rate that the economy grew. Kennedy, therefore, was determined to prevent such inflationary trends.

The President considered prices and wages in steel a bellwether for all industry. Early in 1962, when officials of the steel industry and the steelworkers union were negotiating a new contract, Kennedy intervened. He asked industry to keep prices down and asked labor to keep its wage demands in line with increases in productivity. Both sides seemed to accept the President's views. The settlement provided for no general wage increase but did give workers fringe benefits that raised costs about ten cents an hour, or 2.5 per cent. New Frontiersmen did not consider this an inflationary rise in cost.

On April 10, 1962, after the last major wage contract had been signed, Roger Blough, chairman of the board at the United States Steel Corporation, in a private conference presented to the President a mimeographed press release announcing that his corporation was going to raise the price of steel by $6 a ton. This figure represented an increase four times as great as the cost of the wage settlement.

Kennedy reacted with anger. He felt that he had been deceived, that the unions had been misled, and that the office of the President had been used

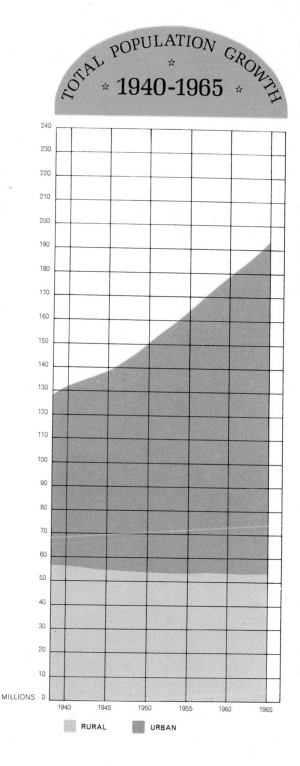

TOTAL POPULATION GROWTH ☆ 1940-1965 ☆

MILLIONS

RURAL   URBAN

in the deception. The workers and much of the public also felt that the steel men had shown bad faith, for on the next day five other steel companies raised prices.

At a televised press conference the next day the President, with controlled anger, denounced the "tiny handful of steel executives" for placing profit above public responsibility. Blough and other business leaders defended the price increases, but the New Frontiersmen struck back. The Department of Defense shifted its purchases of steel to those companies that had not yet raised prices, and the Department of Justice announced it would investigate to see if the steel companies had violated the antitrust laws by agreeing on price increases.

Several smaller steel companies were persuaded to hold out against the price increase in an effort to force United States Steel and others to bring their prices back down to meet the competition. This strategy worked. By the afternoon of April 13, all major steel companies had rescinded their increases, and the fight was over.

The steel fight showed that the government and the people had a stake in the bargaining between capital and labor and that the President would not stand aside when the result might affect the national welfare.

Tax reform was planned

Although the rate of economic growth had continued to improve into 1962, by the middle of the year it had slowed down. Much unemployment persisted. Administration leaders were particularly concerned over a severe drop in the stock market.

The situation seemed to suggest a developing recession. The President's economic advisers urged him to ask Congress for an emergency cut in taxes that would put more money in circulation and stimulate the economy. Kennedy accepted this advice, even though a tax cut without a decrease in expenditures would lead to another deficit in the budget. But he wanted to include, along with the tax cut, a reform of the income tax structure to close some of the loopholes in the tax laws.

Many businessmen objected to a cut in taxes without a cut in expenditures. The President therefore gave up the idea of a major tax bill in 1962, but he promised a major cut in taxes for the following year. Before the end of 1962, Congress passed a "little" tax bill, which brought some benefits to business without decreasing government revenues.

During the tax debate, Kennedy defied his political advisers, who did not want him to campaign in the mid-term elections of 1962. "It is," he replied, "a responsibility of the President of the United States to have a program and to fight for it." He campaigned vigorously for those Democrats who supported his program. The election results pleased him. The Democrats lost two seats in the House, but in the Senate they picked up four new ones. For the first time since 1934, the party in power had managed to avoid a loss of seats in mid-term congressional elections. Kennedy took this result as evidence of popular approval of the New Frontier.

In January 1963, Kennedy asked Congress to enact a broad program to give the people more social security and health benefits and to train young men who were out of school and out of work. He also urged a tax cut of $10 billion. But Congress did not pass a tax law in 1963; that reform had to wait.

Kennedy championed civil rights

To Kennedy, the most important domestic reform of all was one to give the Negro his share of democratic rights. He had received overwhelming support from Negroes; without their votes he could not have been elected President. He encouraged the Negroes' drive for equality not merely for political advantage; he sympathized with Negroes and was deeply distressed by their plight.

During the first two years of his administration, he tried to improve the status of the Negro through executive action rather than new legislation. In March 1961, he established the Committee on Equal Employment Opportunity. Headed by Vice President Lyndon B. Johnson, this committee sought to persuade firms holding government contracts to provide equal job opportunities for all employees. Kennedy appointed more Negroes to high offices such as federal judgeships and ambassadorships than had any previous President. Early in 1962, he urged Congress to pass laws that would end the use of literacy tests and poll taxes as means of preventing Negroes from voting. In August, Congress responded by passing a constitutional amendment that prohibited any state from requiring a citizen to pay a poll tax in order to vote in federal elections. After thirty-eight states had ratified the amendment, in January 1964, it became the Twenty-Fourth Amendment to the Constitution. In November 1962, the President finally issued the long-awaited Housing Order that banned racial discrimination in housing financed with federal funds.

Shortly before issuing the Housing Order, Kennedy had to uphold federal authority in what was probably the most serious clash with state authority since the Civil War. The Supreme Court had ordered the all-white University of Mississippi to admit a qualified Negro resident of that state, James H. Meredith. In September 1962, when Meredith, accompanied by federal marshals, arrived at the campus at Oxford, Mississippi, Governor Ross R. Barnett personally blocked his registration at the university. To overcome this defiance, the President sent federal marshals to Oxford. Despite precautions, on the night of September 30, rioting broke out on the campus. Two men were shot and killed by rioters, and two hundred others were injured. To restore order, the President ordered federal troops to Oxford. Also, the Mississippi National Guard was federalized to remove it from the governor's control. The troops protected Meredith as he registered and attended classes.

Desegregation at Oxford left the University of Alabama as the only state university in the Union without some integration. In 1963, a federal judge ordered the university at Tuscaloosa to admit two Negroes to its summer session. Governor George C. Wallace, a diehard segregationist, defied the court

order and a request from the President not to interfere. Wallace personally tried to block the Negroes and federal marshals when they appeared on the campus in June. Kennedy promptly federalized part of the Alabama National Guard and secured admittance for the students.

On television the President told the people they should accept the Negroes' crusade and help make it constructive and peaceful. That June, he also sent to Congress a civil rights bill, the most comprehensive in the nation's history. On November 21, 1963, just as he was preparing for a speech-making trip into Texas, Kennedy learned that this bill was beginning to make progress in Congress.

REVIEWING THE SECTION

1. What were the major issues in the presidential campaign of 1960? Which groups voted for Kennedy? which for Nixon?

2. In what ways did Kennedy promote economic reform? How did he try to prevent inflation?

3. How did the Kennedy administration attempt to promote economic growth?

4. How did Kennedy, by means of executive action, attempt to overcome discrimination against Negroes? What legislation was passed to achieve this end?

THE GREAT GOAL WAS PEACE

Foreign affairs were President Kennedy's chief interest, and they took most of his time and attention. For him, the search for peace came before all else. Without peace, the great domestic reforms could not go forward.

Kennedy's deep concern for peace became apparent during the presidential campaign in 1960. He announced the idea of a "peace corps" in a speech at the University of Michigan in Ann Arbor. Members of the corps would receive brief, intensive training and then be sent to underdeveloped countries, he explained. Following Kennedy's suggestion, in September 1961, Congress established the Peace Corps. This agency aroused considerable enthusiasm at home and abroad. In Asia, Africa, South America, and elsewhere corps volunteers served as teachers, engineers, nurses, and agricultural experts. They accepted the standard of living of the people they served, and worked with the people to improve education, health, and sanitation.

Disarmament also received special attention. In September 1961, with the approval of Congress, Kennedy established the Arms Control and Disarmament Agency, the first government body of its kind concerned with full-time planning for peace and disarmament. He also continued United States participation in a disarmament conference at Geneva, sponsored by the United Nations.

The Soviets at Geneva demanded the abolition of all armies and weapons over a period of four years. The United States urged disarmament in stages over a longer period, with international inspection of the arms retained by each nation. Since the Soviets and Americans could not agree, especially on the matter of inspection, disarmament remained only a hope.

During Kennedy's administration crises simultaneously occurred in many areas of the world. For the most part, he handled these crises with forthright action.

The Berlin issue flared again

Shortly after Kennedy became President, he and Soviet Premier Khrushchev agreed to meet in Vienna to discuss some of the differences between their two countries. At the two-day meeting in June, Kennedy found out how tough an adversary Khrushchev could be. Kennedy said that if the United States and the Soviet Union went to war, the whole world would suffer. "My ambition," he told the Soviet premier, "is to secure peace." But the two men reached no important agreement. Kennedy described the two-day meeting as "somber."

At the meeting Khrushchev revived the crisis over Berlin. He demanded an immediate settlement of the status of the city on Soviet terms, and even spoke of being willing to risk war to gain his end.

Kennedy accepted the challenge, saying the United States and its allies would defend their rights at any cost. He called reserve units into active service and built up United States combat forces in Europe. Kennedy's actions convinced Khrushchev that the Western Allies intended to remain firm.

This crisis sent a flow of East German refugees into West Berlin. By early August, more than two thousand people were streaming across the border each day. But on August 13, 1961, the Communists began sealing off their sector of the city, first with barbed wire and then with a concrete-block wall twenty-eight miles long. The wall stopped the flow of refugees and permitted Khrushchev to retreat from his maximum demands. On October 17, he withdrew his six-month deadline for a showdown, and the crisis ended. But the deadlock continued on the question of German unification.

In June 1963, Kennedy visited West Berlin and was received with joy when he told the people, gathered to hear him speak from the steps of the city hall, that the United States would defend the city.

Africa and Southeast Asia were trouble spots

Problems in Africa and Asia did not pass as quickly as had the Berlin crisis. When Kennedy took office, there was conflict and bloodshed in the Congo, Laos, and South Vietnam. The United States was involved with each nation.

The Kennedy administration followed a policy of supporting the anticolonialism of new nations in Africa. This represented a shift from the Eisenhower position. In the Congo, however, the Eisenhower policy was continued and expanded. The United States wanted to keep out Communist influence and thought this could be done if the Congo remained united and independent.

Maintaining unity proved difficult. In February 1961, Congolese enemies murdered Patrice Lumumba, a young revolutionary who had served briefly as premier. A civil war was averted, but the nation seethed with unrest and several provinces

Food for the starving, New Delhi, India

Aid to foreign nations. In addition to economic and military assistance, food shipments have played an important part in the United States government's foreign aid program. For example, tons of surplus wheat have been sent to Jordan to relieve that nation's food shortage. Privately, Americans have helped promote welfare abroad through voluntary organizations such as the Cooperative for American Remittances to Everywhere, or CARE. In New Delhi, food from CARE packages helped feed hungry Indian children. Through MEDICO, a division of CARE, Americans have given medical assistance in other nations.

Medical assistance for Malaysia

Aqaba, Jordan, 1965

threatened secession. When Moise Tshombe, whom many Africans considered a tool of neocolonialism, led the province of Katanga—rich in copper and other metals—on an independent course, the United Nations used troops to combat the secession.

In December 1961, the United Nations forces carried out an offensive against Tshombe. The United States helped the United Nations forces with money and equipment. This aid from the United States angered the British, the French, the Belgians, and the Portuguese, who favored Tshombe. Nevertheless, the Kennedy administration persisted in its policy. Finally, the United Nations forces ended Katanga's secession.

The United States was involved more directly in Southeast Asia than in Africa. Kennedy accepted the line of containment against communism that had been drawn in 1954 across the peninsula of Indochina at the seventeenth parallel between North and South Vietnam. But in Laos, he abandoned the Eisenhower policy of helping pro-Western regimes in anti-Communist wars. Kennedy accepted a British plan for a cease-fire in the civil war in Laos and for a neutralist government that would be neither pro-Western nor Communist.

The Soviets, too, accepted this plan. In May 1962, however, it looked as if Communists might overrun the nation. President Kennedy reacted with a show of strength. He ordered the Seventh Fleet into adjacent waters and landed more than five thousand combat troops in neighboring Thailand. The Communist offensive ceased. In June, fourteen nations, Communist as well as Western, signed agreements guaranteeing independence and neutrality for Laos.

Across the border in South Vietnam, the Western position was even shakier. In March 1960, the Communist guerrillas there, known as the *Viet Cong,* established the National Liberation Front, which called for the liberation of South Vietnam from United States "imperialism." The Communists of North Vietnam supported this movement. Viet Cong guerrillas spread over the countryside and, in October 1961, began a series of attacks on the large towns and cities in South Vietnam.

United States policy-makers were divided over proper policy in South Vietnam. Some wanted to step in with extensive military aid, including troops, against the Viet Cong. Others believed that South Vietnam President Ngo Dinh Diem ought to liberalize his dictatorial regime and thus gain popular support against the Communists. The United States government increased the size of its military mission, which was used mainly to advise and train Diem's army. But Diem resisted reform. Early in November 1963, some young generals seized the government and assassinated him. This coup failed to bring stability to the strife-ridden land.

By this time, too, the United States became more deeply involved. When Kennedy became President, two thousand United States military advisers were in South Vietnam. By the end of 1963, there were sixteen thousand troops, including combat units.

The U.S. faced Latin-American problems

During his campaign discussions of foreign policy, Kennedy had indicated that he would give special attention to Latin America, where continuing poverty and unrest encouraged Communist agitators to seek a foothold. When he entered the White House, the most pressing Latin-American problem centered on Cuba. Two weeks earlier President Eisenhower had broken off diplomatic relations with Fidel Castro's regime there. Upon taking office, Kennedy learned that Eisenhower also had supported a plan for Cuban exiles to invade their homeland and overthrow Castro's government. Some members of Kennedy's staff advised him to drop the idea, but others encouraged him to support this plan, believing that an invasion would trigger a large-scale Cuban rebellion.

In April, Kennedy took his first decisive step against Castro's Cuba. The Department of State issued a white paper, or a statement of policy, denouncing Castro as a threat to peace in the Americas. In the following week, Cuba became the scene of sabotage and guerrilla warfare.

Then, on April 17, an invasion force of about fourteen hundred Cuban exiles from training bases in Guatemala landed at the Bay of Pigs, on Cuba's southern coast. These men expected people living in Cuba to rise in revolt against Castro, but they failed to do so. The exile brigade lacked adequate air cover or naval support and, though the exiles fought bravely, they were no match for Castro's force of about twenty thousand. Within seventy-two hours, Castro had killed or captured the invaders.

Although the government of the United States at first denied involvement, various sources soon made it clear that the exile volunteers had been trained, armed, transported, and directed by the Central Intelligence Agency (CIA). As a result, the United States lost the confidence of many nations, particularly in Latin America. At the United Nations Castro charged the United States with aggression, and he emerged from the affair with his political position greatly strengthened. United States participation was severely criticized, and finally, President Kennedy took full responsibility for the fiasco. On May 1, 1961, Castro proclaimed Cuba a socialist state. Later he admitted he was himself a Communist, and he established a Communist dictatorship.

Kennedy tried to contain Castro's Communist revolution in Cuba and to build up aid to the rest of Latin America. He had announced on March 13, 1961, at a White House reception for Latin-American diplomats, a broad program of economic aid for the American republics. He called his program the Alliance for Progress, and he wanted it to be as effective as the Good Neighbor policy had been. In August, at Punta del Este, a fashionable resort in Uruguay, economic experts from the Latin-American republics met for the first conference on the Alliance for Progress.

All of the Latin-American nations except Cuba signed the official charter for the Alliance and agreed on a minimum fund of $20 billion spread over a ten-year period to fight poverty, disease, illiteracy, and unemployment. More than half of this money was to come from the United States government, the remainder from private investors.

War over Cuba was averted

The Alliance for Progress excluded Cuba from its benefits, and the United States declared an embargo on trade with Cuba. Since Castro had committed his nation to economic coöperation with the Communist nations, the embargo was not effective.

In the fall of 1962, President Kennedy learned from photographs taken by surveillance planes that Soviet technicians were installing missile bases on Cuba. From such bases, nuclear missiles could have destroyed cities such as Washington, Detroit, and St. Louis. On October 22, in a nation-wide television address the President announced a naval quarantine, or a limited blockade, to prevent weapons from reaching Cuba. He warned that if nuclear missiles were launched from Cuba against any nation in the Western Hemisphere he would regard the attack as coming from the Soviet Union. The United States would immediately order a full retaliatory blow against the Soviet Union. The world stood on the brink of nuclear war. People everywhere were apprehensive.

President Kennedy insisted that the Soviets must dismantle the missile bases on Cuba. If this were not done, he said, United States bombers would level the installations. European allies of the United States supported this position, and so did the Organization of American States. United States and Soviet armed forces went into combat readiness, and everywhere people waited uneasily for the Soviet response to Kennedy's challenge. United States planes observed Soviet ships, loaded with weapons, steaming toward Cuba with submarine escorts. But instead of testing the blockade, the Soviet ships turned back. People everywhere breathed easier, especially after Khrushchev himself backed down. In an exchange of letters with Kennedy, the Soviet leader promised to remove offensive weapons from Cuba and to permit inspection by the United Nations to verify the removal. In return, he asked the United States to lift its blockade and not to invade Cuba. Kennedy agreed.

The Soviets withdrew their missiles and bombers and dismantled the launching sites, but Castro refused to permit inspectors on Cuban soil. So the United States carried out its own inspection by aerial surveillance. On November 22, 1962, Kennedy lifted the quarantine. The great nuclear confrontation and one of the most dangerous crises in the nation's history was over.

An improvement in Soviet-American relations began after the Cuban missile crisis. Diplomats called this relaxation of tension a *détente*. In April 1963, the Soviet Union and the United States agreed to establish a direct and uninterrupted tele-type communication—a "hot line"—between Moscow and Washington. The purpose was to help reduce the danger of accidental nuclear war.

A nuclear test-ban treaty was signed

President Kennedy was always concerned with the problem of accidental war—what he called war by miscalculation. He wanted to lessen this danger through nuclear disarmament. A first step, he thought, could be a treaty that prohibited the testing of nuclear weapons in the atmosphere. Moreover, there was increasing world-wide concern over the danger of radioactive fall-out. It poisoned the atmosphere with substances such as strontium 90, which fell to earth with rain and fog. The health of people for generations to come might be endangered.

Unseen death from the skies seemed probable after September 1961, when the Soviets broke an unofficial moratorium on nuclear testing in the atmosphere. In two months they exploded some fifty nuclear devices and increased radioactive contamination of the atmosphere. These Soviet explosions led to the break-up of negotiations for a test-ban treaty. The United States resumed nuclear testing in April 1962, and in August, the Soviets

conducted some additional nuclear tests.

President Kennedy and Prime Minister Harold Macmillan of Britain still hoped for a test-ban treaty. Finally, in June 1963, Khrushchev grudgingly agreed to receive United States and British emissaries in Moscow to discuss such an agreement. On June 10, Kennedy announced the coming negotiations and called for a fresh start on "a treaty to outlaw nuclear tests." On July 25, 1963, American, Soviet, and British negotiators signed a test-ban treaty, which prohibited nuclear testing in the air, in space, and underwater, but not underground.

More than one hundred other nations signed the same pledge. Red China, France, and Cuba refused to sign. The Senate approved the test-ban treaty in September 1963. Kennedy considered the treaty an important step toward world peace.

REVIEWING THE SECTION

1. How did the Kennedy administration become involved in the affairs of the Congo? What action did the United States take to preserve a neutralist government in Laos? How did the United States become involved militarily in South Vietnam?

2. What attempts were made to help improve economic conditions in some of the nations in Latin America?

3. How did Kennedy persuade the Soviet Union to retreat from its plan to establish missile bases in Cuba?

4. What were the provisions of the 1963 test-ban treaty?

THE HELM CHANGED HANDS

After the Senate's approval of the test-ban treaty, Kennedy felt that that step toward world peace was a political asset that could help him in his campaign for reëlection in 1964. In Texas the Democratic party was split, and many there disliked his stand on civil rights and the *détente* with the Soviet Union. He decided to visit Texas to try to strengthen his own position and that of his party in the coming election.

MEN
IN
HISTORY

COLUMBUS AND GLENN

Two voyages took place nearly five hundred years apart. One lasted two months and covered about 3000 miles. The other journey was over in five hours but traversed 81,000 miles. Preparations for the 3000-mile voyage took several months; those for the longer trip took several years. Both voyages ended in the Bahama Islands off the coast of North America.

Each voyage was an undertaking of the world's most powerful nation. Though rivaled by Italian and Portuguese traders, and threatened by Moorish invaders, Spain was approaching her zenith when she sent three small sailing ships beyond the horizon. The Mercury capsule which orbited the earth was the product of the most advanced scientific and industrial nation, the United States of America, a nation rivaled by the rising scientific capability of the Soviet Union.

Both voyages involved unique men. Christopher Columbus, admiral of the Spanish fleet was "tall and well built." Possessed by a mystical belief that God intended him to make great discoveries, Columbus was thought to be arrogant and tiresome by many people. Some regarded him as a fanatic. Yet his voyages mark him as one of the greatest seamen of all time.

John Glenn, pilot of the space capsule, was a man of determination. A veteran marine combat flyer, he had felt handicapped by age and lack of a college degree when Project Mercury was announced. However, his outstanding record and highly stable personality helped him win a place as an astronaut over 110 other carefully screened candidates.

The preparation for both journeys shows the extent of technological development over the last five centuries.

Columbus' ships carried stone ballast to insure an upright position in the water. They were fastened with wood pins and covered with pitch beneath the water line to discourage barnacles. The instruments of navigation were so crude that Columbus relied on dead reckoning—plotting his course and position on a chart from the three elements of direction, time, and distance. Time was measured by a half-hour glass turned by a boy and recorded by an officer marking a stroke on a slate. Columbus merely guessed his speed, consistently erring by nine per cent. The com-

pass was a circular card of 32 points mounted on a pin with a lodestone under the north point. To maneuver, Columbus' ships had heavy tillers attached directly to the rudder head and tended by the helmsman standing below deck.

The preparation before John Glenn's flight in *Friendship 7* was long and arduous. The Mercury capsule represented the ultimate in metal fabrication and electronic gear. Systems to sustain life, to navigate, and to communicate were perfected. In the interests of safety, such systems were backed up once or even twice by additional systems. The astronaut underwent years of physical and mental training to prepare for the orbital flight. Glenn was required to draw up a detailed plan of his mission, listing the precise time sequence of each act he was to perform or monitor during the flight. Through the use of a plastic ball on which the position of the stars had been plotted, he familiarized himself with every constellation he would see in order to keep track of his position on the dark side of the earth. Once the voyage was underway, Glenn maneuvered his capsule by squirting jets of gas through fine nozzle openings.

Exploration always has been an expensive venture for mankind. It took Columbus several years to find a financial backer for his expedition. Finally, Queen Isabella of Spain gave her husband, King Ferdinand, an I.O.U. for most of the money required. Additional financial aid came from wealthy merchant families. The town of Palos, Spain, provided a ship. Altogether, about $14,000—a large sum for the time—was required to fit out Columbus' entire fleet.

The total bill for Project Mercury, of which John Glenn's flight in *Friendship 7* was but one part, added up to $384,000,000. Furthermore, Project Mercury was only a part of the total United States commitment to space exploration and a small fraction of the nation's budget.

Two years after his voyage John Glenn wrote, "Like Columbus, it is difficult for anyone to foresee the full benefits of such ventures into the unknown." Certainly, if the benefits of the "space race" equal those of the "westward route to the Orient," the advances of the next 500 years are impossible even to imagine.

On the afternoon of November 22, 1963, after speaking at Fort Worth about his desire for world peace, the President flew the short distance to Dallas. As the presidential motorcade moved from the airport through the city, shots were fired from a building alongside the route. Bullets struck the President in the head and also struck Governor John B. Connally, Jr., of Texas, who was seated just in front of Kennedy in the open limousine. Both men were rushed to a Dallas hospital. There the President died.

Later in the day, Dallas police captured the alleged assassin, Lee Harvey Oswald, an unstable man who at one time had defected to the Soviet Union. Two days later, a Dallas night club owner, Jack Ruby, shot and killed Oswald as he was being transferred from the city jail to the county jail. Millions of people who were watching a live television broadcast of the events in Dallas saw the shooting of Oswald.

After Lyndon Johnson became President, he appointed a commission headed by Chief Justice Earl Warren to investigate the circumstances surrounding the assassination. The commission reported that Oswald alone had planned and carried out the murder of President Kennedy.

From all over the world people expressed their grief at the tragic death of the President. Statesmen gathered from everywhere to attend the funeral services for President Kennedy in Washington, D.C. As a memorial, the British government deeded to the United States an acre at Runnymede, site of the signing of the Magna Charta. The memorial at Runnymede was dedicated in 1965, the 750th anniversary of the signing of the charter. For the people of the United States, an eternal flame burning at the grave in Arlington National Cemetery became the symbol for the thousand days of John F. Kennedy's presidency.

Lyndon B. Johnson became President

When Kennedy was shot, Vice President Lyndon Baines Johnson was riding just two cars behind.

Under heavy security guard, he was rushed to Love Field, Texas. There, in the cabin of the presidential airplane, *Air Force One,* less than two hours after Kennedy's death, Johnson took the oath of office of the President of the United States. Thirty people, including Mrs. Johnson and the late President's widow, observed the brief ceremony. Then the new President gave the order and the plane climbed into the dusk, carrying the body of President Kennedy and the grief-stricken passengers back to Washington, D.C. The flight to Washington with a new President at the head of the United States symbolized the strength of the nation; continuity of leadership had not been broken.

As soon as he landed in Washington, Johnson indicated that there would be continuity in policies, too. He asked all of President Kennedy's cabinet members and White House advisers to remain on the job and assist him in running the government.

No Vice President had been better prepared than Johnson to take the helm of the government in an emergency. Kennedy had kept him fully informed of important developments, decisions, and details of all emergency planning that had been adopted by the President. Unlike Harry Truman who as Vice President had not been kept informed, Johnson knew what was expected of him and what resources he could command as President.

Johnson, who became President in his fifty-fifth year, was a man of action and tremendous energy rather than a man of contemplation as Kennedy had been. He was warm and hospitable and his manner was direct. He brought to the White House many of the attitudes of the people of central Texas where he was born and reared, near the small village of Stonewall. Johnson's forebears were Texas frontiersmen who had fought Indians to hold their dry, mesquite-covered land. Following his graduation from high school at age sixteen, he roamed for two years, taking various jobs. He returned home, he said, with "empty hands and empty pockets." He entered Southwest State Teachers College at San Marcos, Texas, in 1926, and after graduation, he taught school.

In 1931, Johnson made speeches supporting Richard M. Kleberg, a Democratic candidate for Congress. When Kleberg was elected, he brought Johnson to Washington as his secretary. Two years later, Johnson married a Texas girl, Claudia "Lady Bird" Taylor. In 1935, President Roosevelt made him Texas state administrator of the National Youth Administration, an important New Deal agency, and Johnson displayed considerable ability in this job. Politics had begun to fascinate Johnson, and in 1937, he sought and won a seat in the House of Representatives. He was reëlected for five additional terms.

During World War II, Johnson served for several months as a lieutenant commander in the navy, on duty in the South Pacific. When President Roosevelt ordered congressmen in the armed forces to return to Washington, Johnson's military career ended. In 1948, he tried for one of Texas' seats in the Senate, a prize that had eluded him in 1941. This time he won the run-off of the Democratic primary by the slender majority of eighty-seven votes out of the nearly 900,000 votes cast. Five years later, he became minority leader in the Senate. In 1954, he was reëlected, and since the Democrats had gained control in the election, he became majority leader. In this position, he was a virtuoso in negotiation and compromise, the outstanding legislative leader of his time.

In 1960, after losing the Democratic presidential nomination to Kennedy, Johnson surprised almost everyone by accepting the vice presidential nomination. He was a tireless campaigner, even though he had suffered a heart attack in 1955. Without Johnson on the ticket, Kennedy probably would have lost Texas and perhaps one or two other Southern states, and with them the election.

Many liberals distrusted Johnson, primarily because of his record in the Senate. Actually, Johnson was a New Deal liberal, and he was also a shrewd and seasoned politician, who had learned how to coax Congress into action in support of his party's policies. In the 1950's, the mood of the country was conservative and the people in Texas who could make or break him were even more conservative, so he played down his liberalism.

Congress responded to the new leader

When Kennedy died, some of the bills he most desired to be enacted were stalled in the Congress. On November 27, 1963, just five days after taking over, President Johnson asked a special joint session of Congress for action on the program of the New Frontier. He pointed out:

No memorial oration or eulogy could more eloquently honor President Kennedy's memory than the earliest possible passage of the civil-rights bill for which he fought so long.

Johnson also urged Congress to enact the tax-reduction bill. He sought a continuation of the Kennedy program, and he kept Congress in session well into the December holiday season to gain the action he desired.

Before adjourning briefly in December, Congress enacted a number of laws, including the foreign-aid bill. Kennedy had asked for an appropriation of $4.5 billion. Although Johnson accepted $3 billion, this was a victory in the light of congressional opposition to continuation of the program.

Johnson then used his influence with Congress to pull the tax-reduction bill out of the committees that were delaying its consideration. With pressure, promises, and persuasion, he guided it through both houses of Congress. Republican critics argued that any tax cut should be matched by reduced government spending. Johnson met this argument by reducing Kennedy's proposed budget by $500 million, saying he could cut the cost of government without depriving the people of vital services. In February 1964, Congress responded by enacting the tax cut and reform bill.

Action on the civil rights bill came with less speed. The measure was passed by the House of Representatives, in February 1964, by a vote of more than two to one, but it ran into a Southern filibuster in the Senate. The debate continued for more than eighty days; it was the longest filibuster in history. On June 10, Northern Democrats and Republicans voted in favor of *cloture,* an action bringing an end to the debate and calling for an immediate vote on the question. (Cloture restricts each member to one hour of debate on the bill under consideration. The Senate seldom has made use of cloture because of a cherished tradition of unlimited debate.) This was the first time the senators had ever voted for cloture on a civil rights filibuster. On June 19, by a vote of 73-27, the Senate passed the Civil Rights Bill of 1964, and Johnson signed it into law on July 2.

This law placed the power of the federal government behind Negro demands for equal treatment. It prohibited discrimination in voting, in public facilities such as hotels and restaurants, and in jobs, and it authorized the attorney general to take action against discriminatory practices, as in schools. Johnson's leadership, aided by many groups and leaders in Congress, had gained a civil rights law even stronger than Kennedy had proposed.

In August, Congress passed the first major piece of legislation proposed by Johnson himself—the Economic Opportunity Act of 1964. This law set up a number of agencies to fight a "war on poverty." The Job Corps and the Volunteers in Service to America (VISTA), a domestic version of the Peace Corps, were created to help the underprivileged break out of social and economic conditions that kept them in a "cycle of poverty."

Under Johnson's prodding, Congress also passed laws to aid higher education, to help cities with mass transportation, to preserve wilderness sanctuaries in federal lands, and to improve other aspects of life in the United States. In the brief period of less than a year, Johnson achieved a remarkable record in dealing with Congress. Few, if any, Presidents could match his knowledge of ways to manipulate Congress. Now, it seemed clear, he could still use that knowledge effectively from the White House. His record gave him confidence in the presidential campaign of 1964.

1. How had Johnson helped Kennedy win the presidency?

2. What features of Kennedy's program were enacted soon after Johnson became President? What were the provisions of the Civil Rights Act of 1964? What new legislation proposed by Johnson was enacted by Congress during 1964?

THE GREAT SOCIETY BECAME THE CHALLENGE

Within the Republican party the presidential campaign of 1964 brought to the top many of those conservatives who had long been discontented with the course of United States politics. They claimed that Republican moderates such as Wendell Willkie, Thomas Dewey, and Dwight Eisenhower had not offered the voters a clear alternative to the Democratic candidates. They argued that a true conservative candidate would not only sweep the nation but would also save the nation from being devoured by big government and subverted by Communists.

At the Republican convention in San Francisco in July 1964, the conservatives took command and nominated Senator Barry M. Goldwater of Arizona for President and, for Vice President, Representative William E. Miller from upstate New York. The Republican platform reflected Goldwater's conservative views, and he went to the people saying he offered "a choice not an echo." He claimed that the federal government had unjustifiably invaded the rights of the states. In foreign affairs he called for a more aggressive policy against communism.

A month later, the Democrats met in Atlantic City and, as expected, they nominated Johnson. They also accepted his choice for Vice President, Senator Hubert H. Humphrey of Minnesota. The Democratic platform warmly endorsed the Kennedy-Johnson policies and promised more of the same.

Johnson made few specific campaign promises, but he did pledge to continue the program he had

THE PRESIDENTS OF THE UNITED STATES

JOHN F. KENNEDY
(1917-1963)
IN OFFICE: 1961-1963

LYNDON B. JOHNSON
(1908-   )
IN OFFICE: 1963-

Democrat from Massachusetts. Kennedy won the presidency in the closest election since 1884. He was the first Catholic and the youngest man ever elected to that office. During his administration, the first American was launched into space (1961), the U.S.S.R. was forced to remove its missiles from Cuba (1962), and a nuclear test ban treaty was signed (1963).

Democrat from Texas. Succeeding to the presidency upon the assassination of Kennedy, Johnson continued the domestic programs initiated under the previous administration. A "war on poverty" was declared and anti-poverty legislation passed; civil rights legislation was enacted; federal aid to education was increased; and space flights were continued with some spectacular successes.

taken over. In a speech in May at the University of Michigan, he had given this program his own label. He called it "the Great Society" which would rest on "abundance and liberty for all," would end poverty and racial injustice, and would be "a challenge constantly renewed."

Goldwater's somewhat inconsistent arguments confused and frightened many voters. He gave the impression of being opposed to government participation in social betterment and of being too willing to risk nuclear war with the Soviet Union. The result of the campaign was a rout. Johnson received 43 million popular and 486 electoral votes. Goldwater received 27 million popular and 52 electoral votes and carried only six states. The Democrats gained 38 seats in the House and 2 in the Senate. Johnson's decisive victory was one of the most sweeping in the nation's history. Except for the deep South, the nation turned solidly against Goldwater's conservatism.

Broad social advances were made

President Johnson interpreted his victory as an overwhelming endorsement of his program for the Great Society, and he moved quickly to get the program off to a sound start. When Congress convened in January 1965, he outlined the kind of laws that would move the nation toward the Great Society.

Congress responded quickly and favorably. The many legislators who had ridden to victory on Johnson's coattails had helped break the conservative Southern Democratic and Republican coalition, which had long blocked or delayed social reforms. As a result, Congress passed eighty-six major laws requested by Johnson.

Four of the most important measures that went through Congress dealt with federal aid for education, medical care for old people, federal support for voting rights, and revision in immigration policy. In the Elementary and Secondary Education Act of April 1965, Johnson solved the problem of direct help to parochial schools, a problem that had knocked out earlier plans for federal aid to education. This new law provided funds for the purchase of educational materials for all eligible pupils whether in public or parochial schools.

The Social Security Amendments of July 1965 provided Medicare, or health insurance, for people sixty-five and over to help them to meet doctors' bills and the cost of hospitalization and nursing care. The battle for Medicare had been long and intense. Old people, labor unions, and President Kennedy had been for it, but the American Medical Association and other groups had fought it as a first step toward "socialized" medicine.

In August, the government's toughest measure against discrimination, the Voting Rights Act of 1965, became law. It abolished literacy tests for voters and authorized representatives of the federal government to register voters in precincts where less than fifty per cent of the people of voting age were registered. This law was expected to give Negroes far more votes in the South and hence change the political structure of the region. By 1966, compliance with the law had added thousands of Negroes to the lists of registered voters.

In October, at the foot of the Statue of Liberty, President Johnson signed into law the far-reaching Immigration and Nationality Amendments of 1965. This act abolished the policy, which had been in effect since 1921, of placing quotas on immigrants according to their national origins. The new standards gave preference to close relatives of residents in the United States, and to people with special talents, such as artists, professional people, and to skilled workers. It set an annual limit of 170,000 on immigrants from all nations outside the Western Hemisphere. Immigration from nations of the Western Hemisphere, previously unrestricted, was to be limited to 120,000 annually after 1968.

Congress also created a new executive department, the Department of Housing and Urban Development, designed to handle federal involvement in housing problems, such as urban renewal, and other matters pertaining to city life. A law was passed in September, but Johnson waited until January 1966 to appoint the head of the department, Robert C. Weaver, the first Negro to serve in the President's cabinet.

The President, like many other Americans, was concerned about the ugliness of roads and highways cluttered with garish advertising and auto junkyards. The humorist Ogden Nash, in a parody of Joyce Kilmer's poem "Trees," caught the spirit of this concern. Nash wrote:

> I think that I shall never see,
> A billboard lovely as a tree.
> Perhaps unless the billboards fall,
> I'll never see a tree at all.

At Johnson's request, Congress passed the Highway Beautification Act of 1965. It restricted advertising and auto junkyards along interstate and primary highways.

The economy was stimulated and restrained

Social reforms were expensive. They could be best accomplished when the economy was strong and growing. Johnson became President during an economic boom, which in January 1965 he called "the greatest upward surge of economic well-being in the history of any nation." To keep the boom going, he continued the economic policy of budget deficits and tax cuts. He wanted to stimulate the economy and reduce unemployment. By February 1966, a long-standing aim of both Kennedy and Johnson became a reality. Unemployment fell to four per cent of the working force, a figure that the President's economic advisers looked upon as signifying, for all practical purposes, full employment. Later in 1966, this figure fell below four per cent.

Yet unemployment among Negroes, teen-agers, and others in depressed areas remained higher. Congress had passed a number of laws to combat poverty and unemployment within these groups.

These laws provided for more federal, financial, and technical help in public works programs. In the Appalachian Regional Development Act of 1965, $1.1 billion was appropriated by Congress for economic improvement in the eleven-state Appalachian Mountain region stretching from Pennsylvania into the deep South. The Public Works and Economic Development Act of the same year authorized the appropriation of $3.3 billion for economic help to depressed areas. In June 1965, Congress followed up the economic stimulant of the previous year's tax cut with the Excise Tax Reduction Act. This law eliminated or reduced many taxes that had been in effect since World War II.

As the stimulant of the tax cuts took effect, as unemployment declined, and as factories functioned at near capacity, there was pressure to raise prices and wages.

Because of these inflationary trends, Johnson asked industry not to increase prices and labor not to seek wage increases above a 3.2 per cent guideline. Despite government efforts, the pressure for inflation mounted. The cost of the war in Vietnam kept increasing, and the government was forced, in March 1966, to reinstate some of the excise taxes that had been cut in the previous year.

The steel industry put through a price increase in 1966 and the government did not protest as it had in 1962. And, in the summer of 1966, the airline mechanics were granted a wage increase well above the old guideline. It was obvious that the 3.2 per cent guideline would have to be revised in the light of the rising cost of living.

REVIEWING THE SECTION

1. What major reform legislation was passed during 1965?

2. What efforts did the Johnson administration make to stimulate the economy and reduce unemployment?

FOREIGN AFFAIRS DEMANDED ATTENTION

When Lyndon B. Johnson took over the presi-
dency, domestic politics interested him most. This had been the area of his most extensive experience. Since it offered him the greatest opportunity to use his political skills, he hoped to concentrate on domestic reforms. But he did not realize this hope. Troubles all over the world demanded his attention. Soon he was devoting more of his time to matters of foreign policy than to domestic concerns.

Johnson continued the basic features of Kennedy's foreign policy but changed the manner of conducting it. He maintained fairly good relations with the Soviet Union even after a change in Soviet leadership. In October 1964, Khrushchev suddenly was removed from power. Two other Soviet leaders took over—Aleksei N. Kosygin as premier, and Leonid Brezhnev as first secretary of the Communist party.

In that same week, the world learned that Communist China had exploded its first atomic device and thus had become the world's fifth nuclear power. This development gave new urgency to the need for some international agreement on the control of nuclear weapons. The Soviet Union recognized this need, but China did not. These two Communist nations had not only drifted apart but were also engaged in bitter controversy. The United States profited from this controversy. On the other hand one of its major allies, France, led by a haughty, capable, and determined president, Charles de Gaulle, was contesting American leadership in Europe. These problems and others, such as a war between India and Pakistan (in 1965), all required attention from American policy-makers.

The U.S. intervened in Latin America

Johnson confronted his first sudden crisis in foreign policy seven weeks after he became President. Early in January 1964, as the result of action by United States high school students in raising a United States flag at their school in the Canal Zone, Panamanian students demonstrated. In the riots that followed, United States soldiers fired on the attackers. In all, twenty-five people were killed,

Cutting a New Britain "rug," July 13, 1944

American influences in the world. Foreign interest in United States culture for many years was focused primarily on the frontier. For example, at meetings of the Munich Westerners, a club formed in 1913, German "squaws" performed Bavarian folk dances for "braves" and "cowboys."

After World Wars I and II, the continued presence of United States troops gave Europeans, Asians, and Americans a chance to find out more about each other's customs. Having watched an exhibition of tribal dances of New Britain, United States marines performed their own native dance, the jitterbug.

Several years after the war, as American tourism increased and better communications spread information faster and farther, the American way of life became known all over the world. At the same time, war-torn nations in Europe and Asia began to recover. Eventually they looked to the United States for ways to use their new wealth. Such American conveniences as supermarkets began to appear all over the world. The downtown sections of large cities, such as Tokyo, assumed the flamboyant look of bright lights and glaring advertisements typical of cities in the United States. Even fads such as the hula-hoop (popular in the 1950's) quickly spread from the United States to other lands.

including four United States soldiers, and many were injured.

The Republic of Panama broke off diplomatic relations and demanded renegotiation of the treaty of 1903 that gave the United States special rights in the Canal Zone. After a period of bitter exchange, President Johnson agreed to Panama's terms. Since United States aircraft carriers and huge tankers could not squeeze through the Panama Canal's locks, he announced plans for a new, wider canal. In September 1965, both nations announced that the treaty of 1903 would be abrogated, and a new treaty would recognize Panama's sovereignty over the Canal Zone.

The action of the United States in the Canal Zone aroused considerable criticism from Latin Americans. They were even more violent in their denunciations of the United States as the result of political turmoil in the Dominican Republic.

In 1961, the tyrannical dictatorship of Rafael Leónidas Trujillo ended after 31 years. The next year the Dominicans held their first free elections

in thirty-eight years and elected as their president a social reformer with leftist leanings, Juan Bosch. He was overthrown in seven months, and an army *junta*—a group of officers—ruled the nation. On April 24, 1965, Bosch's followers tried to bring him back into power with a mass uprising.

The fighting appeared to endanger Americans in the capital city of Santo Domingo. So, on April 28, President Johnson dispatched four hundred marines to protect American lives and property there, the first such armed intervention in Latin America in thirty years. The next day he sent in paratroopers and other soldiers, ultimately building up the United States forces there to about thirty thousand. On May 2, he said on nation-wide television that "a band of Communist conspirators" had taken over the rebel movement in Santo Domingo. He explained that another Communist government must not be permitted in the Western Hemisphere.

Bosch and others denied Johnson's charge. Latin Americans, even in friendly nations such as Mexico and Chile, also considered the concern of the

The Ginza district, Tokyo, 1965

A waiter in Cairo using a hula-hoop, January 4, 1959

Munich "Westerners," September 22, 1950

Tokyo supermarket, 1965

United States over communism exaggerated and Johnson's intervention hasty and ill-advised. Many criticized the United States for violating the Charter of the Organization of American States, which forbade intervention in the internal affairs of a member republic.

The OAS relieved the United States of some embarrassment by voting to establish the Inter-American Peace Force to maintain order in Santo Domingo. That force included a few units from Latin-American nations. In March 1966, the intervention was continued with a peace force of eight thousand men, six thousand of them from the United States. After negotiating with leaders of different factions, OAS mediators established a provisional government.

On June 1, 1966, after eight months of provisional rule, the Dominicans held national elections, Joaquín Balaguer, a conservative, defeated Bosch to become the next president of the Dominican Republic. When Balaguer was inaugurated on July 1, Vice President Hubert Humphrey attended the ceremonies. A few days earlier the first United States troops began leaving the country to end the intervention.

Americans went to war again

Johnson's major concern in foreign policy was Southeast Asia, particularly the war in South Vietnam. In 1964, the Viet Cong stepped up their attacks against the forces of the South Vietnamese government. By May, the Viet Cong's victories indicated that the Communists soon might be able to take over the country. President Johnson and his advisers feared that all of Southeast Asia would then fall into Communist hands. So he gradually increased United States aid to South Vietnam and built up the number of United States troops there.

In August 1964, some patrol boats from Communist North Vietnam twice launched torpedo attacks at United States destroyers in the Gulf of Tonkin. In response, the President ordered jet bombers from aircraft carriers to bomb gunboat bases and oil storage tanks in North Vietnam. On August 7, after the retaliatory attack, Congress responded to a request from Johnson. The legislators overwhelmingly passed a resolution supporting "all necessary measures" to repel the attacks and also to "prevent further aggression." The President said, during his campaign that fall, that he had no intention of broadening the war by turning it into an attack on North Vietnam.

Early in 1965, it became clear that the Viet Cong could not be stopped without greater United States involvement. Johnson sent more troops to South Vietnam for the purpose of fighting full-scale battles. In February, he ordered navy and air force planes to bomb bridges, military installations, and other objectives in North Vietnam. He explained that his aim was to force the Communists to negotiate a settlement. He said he was willing to open "unconditional discussions" with any powers which could end hostilities. The Communist nations—the Soviet Union, China, and North Vietnam—rejected his terms.

Despite Johnson's claim that he sought peace if only the Communists would stop their aggression and negotiate, peoples all over the world criticized United States policy, in friendly nations as well as in Communist lands. In the United States, intellectuals, especially in colleges and universities, expressed disapproval of United States involvement in the Vietnam war. In Congress, too, critics were vocal. But most members of Congress and most Americans apparently supported Johnson's policy. Some wanted an even bigger war to crush communism.

Early in 1966, Johnson halted the bombing of North Vietnam for thirty-seven days while intensive efforts were made to move the Vietnamese conflict to the conference table. When bombing was resumed the President asked the United Nations Security Council to help in the continuing "pursuit of peace."

Peace eluded its pursuers. In South Vietnam, Buddhists demonstrated violently against a military dictatorship and the Viet Cong seemed to be gaining strength. So late in June 1966, to cripple the North Vietnamese who were aiding the Viet Cong, President Johnson ordered air strikes against oil depots around Hanoi and Haiphong, North Vietnam's principal cities. Almost everywhere, but especially in Asia and Africa, people protested this stepping-up of the war. Rumors circulated that the Soviet Union or Communist China might intervene when the bombing increased in intensity.

Few could doubt that the United States was now fighting a major war against a stubborn and elusive enemy. By mid 1966, the United States had some 300,000 troops in South Vietnam and planned to send 100,000 more by the end of the year. These soldiers were engaged in daily combat with the Viet Cong and each week the American casualty lists grew. People everywhere feared that the war would become fiercer and more brutal before peace would come.

REVIEWING THE SECTION

1. How did Johnson respond to the crisis over the Panama Canal? Why did he send United States troops to the Dominican Republic?

2. Why did Johnson increase the number of United States troops in South Vietnam? Why did he authorize the bombing of North Vietnam? Why did many people criticize Johnson's escalation of the war in Vietnam? What efforts did he make to negotiate a peace?

CHAPTER **30** CONCLUSION

The United States in the era of the New Frontier and the Great Society was a land of affluence and of impressive social and economic advances. It was also a land of racial turmoil, of pockets of poverty, despair, violence and crime. Kennedy, a popular President, was the fourth man in that office to be assasinated in less than one hundred years.

In the 1960's, Congress passed the most advanced civil rights laws in the history of the United States. Efforts were made to help underprivileged persons everywhere. With the Peace Corps, the people of the United States helped the poor in foreign lands. At home, the federal government worked out a program of medical care for old people. Many Americans gradually overcame their resistance to federal aid to education and Congress got around religious obstacles to bring better learning opportunities to all children. The United States government changed discriminatory immigration laws. To overcome problems of inflation and unemployment, it also took a hand in economic affairs.

In foreign affairs, policy-makers continued to move from one crisis to another. When the Soviet Union threatened war in an effort to change the status of Berlin, the United States stood firm. When Castro created in Cuba the first Communist government in the Western Hemisphere, Kennedy supported a plan to remove Castro by force. The plan failed. Later, when Khrushchev planted missiles in Cuba, Kennedy did not flinch from the possibility of nuclear war and forced the Soviets to remove the missiles. Finally, after much talk and little accomplishment, the United States, the Soviet Union, and other nations signed a treaty forbidding the testing of nuclear bombs except underground. Yet as additional nations, such as Communist China and France, became capable of making atomic weapons, the threat of nuclear annihilation lurked behind every major international crisis.

The containment of communism remained a basic policy of the United States. So concerned was President Johnson with the spread of communism that he sent troops into the Dominican Republic. But his most serious foreign problems, and those of the American people as well, were in Southeast Asia. Step by step, the United States became involved in an undeclared war in Vietnam. This war led to intense debate in the United States, showing that a vocal and increasingly large minority was unhappy about United States foreign policy. This uneasiness also showed that a nation of great power and influence, such as the United States, did not have an easy role in world politics.

Many Americans feared that the war in Vietnam—

which took young lives, stimulated inflation, and led to tax increases—would push aside the planned reforms of the Great Society. President Johnson was aware of this fear. In his third annual State of the Union message, delivered in January 1966, he suggested that some domestic reforms might be slowed but insisted that they would not be abandoned. "We will continue to meet the needs of our people," he said, "by continuing to develop the Great Society."

Social and economic mobility—the chance for any man to move ahead—had always been a distinctive feature of American life. It was still so in the 1960's. The United States remained a nation of great vitality, vast energy, and stunning economic growth. Increasingly better education was accessible to more and more Americans. The United States in the 1960's in many ways was what it had been in the days of the Founding Fathers—a land of opportunity—but now there was an opportunity for a much larger number of people.

FOCUSING ON SPECIFICS

1. What was the purpose of the Committee on Equal Employment Opportunity? the Housing Order?

2. How did the Kennedy administration help Negroes gain admittance to the universities of Mississippi and Alabama?

3. What was the function of the Peace Corps? the Alliance for Progress?

4. Why did the invasion of Cuba prove to be a fiasco?

5. What measures were taken by the United States against the Soviet establishment of missile bases in Cuba?

6. How did continued nuclear testing endanger life? What steps were taken to end testing in the atmosphere?

7. How did the Immigration and Nationality Amendments of 1965 reverse long-standing policies on immigration?

REVIEWING MAIN THEMES

1. What did the Kennedy administration do to promote economic stability and social reform?

2. In what ways did the Kennedy administration continue the foreign policy of previous administrations? What efforts did it make to limit Communist power in Cuba and Southeast Asia?

3. What reform legislation promoted by Kennedy was passed during the Johnson administration? In what areas did legislation passed during the Johnson administration go beyond that promoted by Kennedy?

EVALUATING THE ISSUES

1. Why did United States policy-makers consider events in Southeast Asia to be of vital interest to the security of the United States?

2. Why was extensive reform legislation passed during the Kennedy and Johnson administrations?

EXAMINING THE TIMES

1. What attempts have been made by administrations since the end of World War II to end poverty, reduce unemployment, and maintain economic growth?

2. What efforts have been made since the end of World War II to end discrimination against Negroes?

3. In what ways have the Kennedy and Johnson administrations had foreign policies similar to those of Truman and Eisenhower?

Atlas of the Modern World

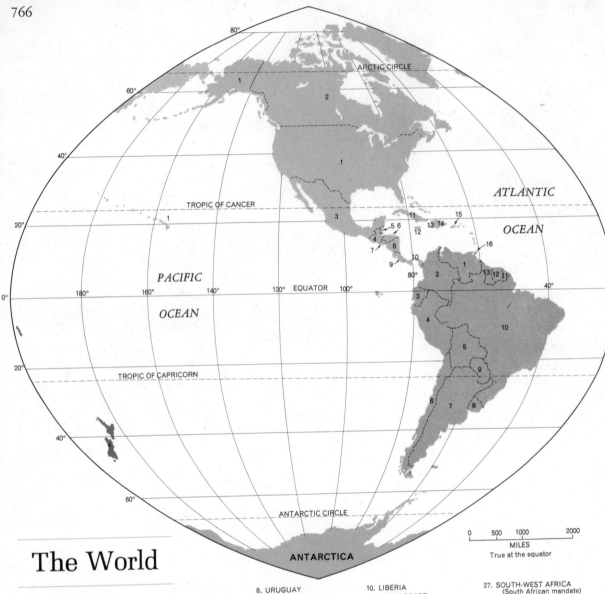

The World

ARCTIC CIRCLE

ATLANTIC

OCEAN

TROPIC OF CANCER

PACIFIC

OCEAN

EQUATOR

TROPIC OF CAPRICORN

ANTARCTIC CIRCLE

ANTARCTICA

0 500 1000 2000
MILES
True at the equator

NORTH AMERICA

1. UNITED STATES
   ALASKA
   HAWAII
2. CANADA
3. MEXICO
4. GUATEMALA
5. BRITISH HONDURAS
6. HONDURAS
7. EL SALVADOR
8. NICARAGUA
9. COSTA RICA
10. PANAMA
11. CUBA
12. JAMAICA
13. HAITI
14. DOMINICAN REPUBLIC
15. PUERTO RICO (U.S.A.)
16. TRINIDAD AND TOBAGO

SOUTH AMERICA

1. VENEZUELA
2. COLOMBIA
3. ECUADOR
4. PERU
5. BOLIVIA
6. CHILE
7. ARGENTINA
8. URUGUAY
9. PARAGUAY
10. BRAZIL
11. FRENCH GUIANA
12. SURINAM (Neth.)
13. GUYANA

AFRICA

1. MOROCCO
2. IFNI (Sp.)
3. SPANISH SAHARA
4. MAURITANIA
5. SENEGAL
6. GAMBIA
7. PORTUGUESE GUINEA
8. GUINEA
9. SIERRA LEONE
10. LIBERIA
11. IVORY COAST
12. MALI
13. UPPER VOLTA
14. GHANA
15. TOGO
16. DAHOMEY
17. NIGERIA
18. NIGER
19. CHAD
20. CENTRAL AFRICAN REPUBLIC
21. CAMEROON
22. EQUATORIAL GUINEA (Sp.)
23. GABON
24. CONGO REPUBLIC
25. REPUBLIC OF THE CONGO
26. ANGOLA, CABINDA (Port.)
27. SOUTH-WEST AFRICA (South African mandate)
28. SOUTH AFRICA
29. BASUTOLAND (U.K.)
30. SWAZILAND (U.K.)
31. BECHUANALAND (Br. prot.)
32. MALAGASY
33. MOZAMBIQUE (Port.)
34. RHODESIA (U.K.)
35. ZAMBIA
36. MALAWI
37. TANZANIA
38. BURUNDI
39. RWANDA
40. UGANDA
41. KENYA
42. SOMALIA
43. FRENCH SOMALILAND

PREPARED BY
IVERSAL MAP, INC.

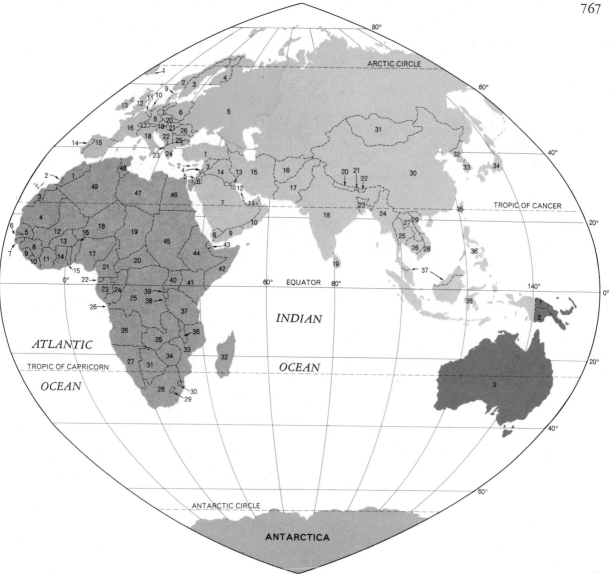

ARCTIC CIRCLE

TROPIC OF CANCER

EQUATOR

INDIAN

OCEAN

ATLANTIC

TROPIC OF CAPRICORN

OCEAN

ANTARCTIC CIRCLE

ANTARCTICA

44. ETHIOPIA
45. SUDAN
46. UNITED ARAB REPUBLIC
    (Egypt)
47. LIBYA
48. TUNISIA
49. ALGERIA

EUROPE

1. ICELAND
2. NORWAY
3. SWEDEN
4. FINLAND
5. UNION OF SOVIET
   SOCIALIST REPUBLICS
6. POLAND
7. EAST GERMANY

8. WEST GERMANY
9. DENMARK
10. NETHERLANDS
11. BELGIUM
12. UNITED KINGDOM
13. IRELAND
14. PORTUGAL
15. SPAIN
16. FRANCE
17. SWITZERLAND
18. ITALY
19. AUSTRIA
20. CZECHOSLOVAKIA
21. HUNGARY
22. YUGOSLAVIA
23. ALBANIA
24. GREECE

25. BULGARIA
26. ROMANIA

ASIA

1. TURKEY
2. CYPRUS
3. SYRIA
4. LEBANON
5. ISRAEL
6. JORDAN
7. SAUDI ARABIA
8. YEMEN
9. ADEN (Br. prot.)
10. MUSCAT AND OMAN
11. TRUCIAL OMAN
12. QATAR
13. KUWAIT

14. IRAQ
15. IRAN
16. AFGHANISTAN
17. WEST PAKISTAN
18. INDIA
19. CEYLON
20. NEPAL
21. SIKKIM
22. BHUTAN
23. EAST PAKISTAN
24. BURMA
25. THAILAND
26. CAMBODIA
27. LAOS
28. SOUTH VIETNAM
29. NORTH VIETNAM
30. CHINA

31. MONGOLIA
32. NORTH KOREA
33. SOUTH KOREA
34. JAPAN
35. TAIWAN
36. PHILIPPINES
37. MALAYSIA
38. INDONESIA

AUSTRALIA

1. TERRITORY OF
   NEW GUINEA (Australia)
2. TERRITORY OF PAPUA
   (Australia)
3. AUSTRALIA
4. NEW ZEALAND

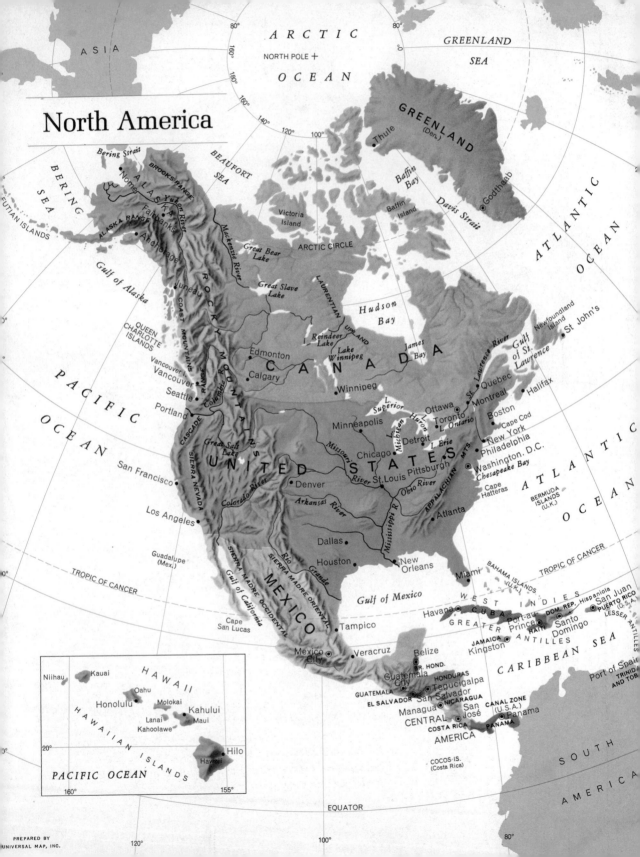

North America

ASIA

ARCTIC
NORTH POLE +
OCEAN

GREENLAND
SEA

GREENLAND
(Den.)

Thule

ATLANTIC

Godthaab

Baffin
Bay

OCEAN

Bering Strait

BEAUFORT
SEA

BROOKS RANGE

ALASKA

Nome Fairbanks
Yukon River

Baffin
Island

Davis Strait

BERING

SEA

ALASKA RANGE

Anchorage

Victoria
Island

ARCTIC CIRCLE

ALEUTIAN ISLANDS

Gulf of Alaska

Mackenzie River

Great Bear
Lake

Juneau

ROCKY

Great Slave
Lake

LAURENTIAN

Hudson
Bay

Newfoundland
Island

St. John's

QUEEN
CHARLOTTE
ISLANDS

COAST

Reindeer
Lake

UPLAND

Gulf
of St.
Lawrence

PACIFIC

Vancouver I.
Vancouver

MOUNTAINS

Edmonton

CANADA

James
Bay

St. Lawrence River

Seattle

Calgary

Lake
Winnipeg

Quebec

Halifax

Portland

COLUMBIA

RANGE

Winnipeg

L.
Superior

Montreal

OCEAN

CASCADE

Great Salt
Lake

L.
Michigan

Ottawa
L. Huron

Boston

Cape Cod

SIERRA NEVADA

Minneapolis

Toronto
L. Ontario

New York

San Francisco

UNITED

Chicago

Detroit
L. Erie

Philadelphia

Washington, D.C.

Denver

Missouri
River

STATES

Pittsburgh

APPALACHIAN MTS.

Chesapeake Bay

Los Angeles

Colorado River

St. Louis

Ohio River

Cape
Hatteras

ATLANTIC

Arkansas River

Atlanta

BERMUDA
ISLANDS
(U.K.)

OCEAN

Guadalupe
(Mex.)

SIERRA MADRE OCCIDENTAL

Dallas

Mississippi R.

TROPIC OF CANCER

Houston

Rio Grande

New
Orleans

TROPIC OF CANCER

Gulf of California

MEXICO

SIERRA MADRE ORIENTAL

Miami

BAHAMA
ISLANDS
(U.K.)

Gulf of Mexico

WEST INDIES

Cape
San Lucas

Tampico

Havana

CUBA

GREATER

Port-au-
Prince
HAITI

DOM. REP.

Hispaniola
San Juan
PUERTO RICO
(U.S.A.)

ANTILLES

LESSER

Mexico
City

Veracruz

Belize
BR. HOND.

ANTILLES

Santo
Domingo

Guatemala
City

JAMAICA
Kingston

CARIBBEAN SEA

Port of Spain
TRINIDAD
AND TOBAGO

GUATEMALA
EL SALVADOR

HONDURAS
Tegucigalpa
San Salvador

Managua
NICARAGUA

CANAL ZONE
(U.S.A.)

CENTRAL

COSTA RICA

San
José

Panama
PANAMA

AMERICA

COCOS IS.
(Costa Rica)

SOUTH

EQUATOR

AMERICA

Hawaii inset

Niihau

Kauai

HAWAII

Oahu

Honolulu

Molokai

Lanai
Kahoolawe

Kahului

Maui

HAWAIIAN ISLANDS

20°

Hilo

Hawaii

PACIFIC OCEAN

160°

155°

PREPARED BY
UNIVERSAL MAP, INC.

South America

90°   75°   60°   TROPIC OF CANCER   45°   30°

15°

CARIBBEAN SEA

CENTRAL

AMERICA

Barranquilla

Maracaibo   Caracas

Lake Maracaibo

Medellín

Bogotá

Buenaventura

Cali

COLOMBIA

Orinoco R.

VENEZUELA

L L A N O S

PACARAIMA MTS.

Georgetown   Paramaribo

GUYANA

SURINAM (Neth.)   Cayenne

FRENCH GUIANA

GALAPAGOS ISLANDS (Ecuador)

Quito

ECUADOR

Guayaquil

Negro R.

EQUATOR

Iquitos

Napo R.

Amazon R.

Manaus

Amazon River

Belém

Ucayali R.

Juruá R.

Madeira R.

Tapajoz R.

Xingú R.

Callao

Lima

PERU

A N D E S

Lake Titicaca

La Paz

BRAZIL

B R A Z I L

Recife

Arequipa

Sucre

BOLIVIA

Araguaia R.

Brasília

São Francisco R.

BRAZILIAN HIGHLANDS

Salvador

Belo Horizonte

TROPIC OF CAPRICORN

Antofagasta

Paraguay R.

MATO GROSSO

CHACO

GRAN

PARAGUAY

Asunción

São Paulo

Santos

Rio de Janeiro

PACIFIC

Tucumán

ATACAMA DESERT

C H I L E

Salado R.

Paraná River

Uruguay R.

OCEAN

Córdoba

Mendoza

Valparaíso

Rosario

URUGUAY

Montevideo

Santiago

PAMPAS

Buenos Aires

Rio de la Plata

ATLANTIC

ARGENTINA

Valdivia

Colorado R.

Bahía Blanca

OCEAN

Chubut R.

PATAGONIA

Punta Arenas

Strait of Magellan

FALKLAND ISLANDS (U.K.) (Claimed by Argentina)

TIERRA DEL FUEGO

Cape Horn

PREPARED BY
UNIVERSAL MAP, INC.

90°   75°   60°   45°   30°

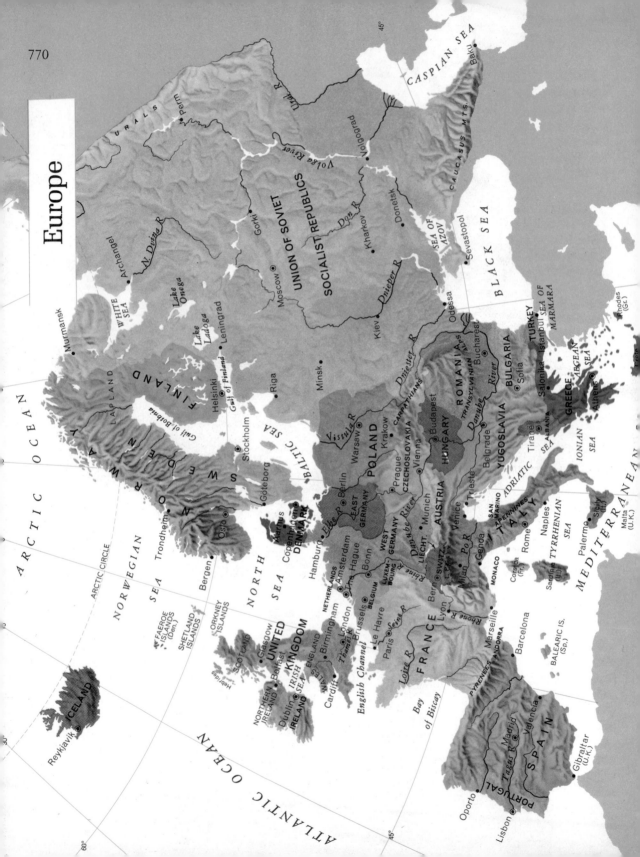

Asia

ARCTIC OCEAN

PACIFIC OCEAN

EQUATOR

60°

TROPIC OF CANCER

Kamchatka Peninsula

KURIL ISLANDS

NEW SIBERIAN ISLANDS

LAPTEV SEA

EAST SIBERIAN SEA

BARENTS SEA

KARA SEA

LENA River

Yenisei River

Ob River

Irtysh River

ARCTIC CIRCLE

Magadan

Sakhalin

SEA OF OKHOTSK

Hokkaido

JAPAN

Tokyo

Yokohama

Osaka

Honshu

Shikoku

Kyushu

SEA OF JAPAN

RYUKYU ISLANDS

PHILIPPINE SEA

WEST IRIAN (Indon.)

New Guinea

TIMOR

ARAFURA SEA

BANDA SEA

CELEBES SEA

CELEBES (SULAWESI)

Makassar

Diakarta

SULU SEA

Mindanao

PHILIPPINES

Quezon City

Luzon

Manila

BORNEO (SABAH)

BRUNEI

SARAWAK

Jesselton

Kuching

BORNEO (KALIMANTAN)

I N D O N E S I A

MALAYSIA

SINGAPORE

Kuala Lumpur

SUMATRA

Malay Peninsula

SOUTH CHINA SEA

Hainan

Canton

HONG KONG (U.K.)

Victoria

Taipei

TAIWAN (FORMOSA)

EAST CHINA SEA

Shanghai

Nanking

Hankow

Chungking

Yangtze River

Yellow River

Peking

Tientsin

YELLOW SEA

Seoul

SOUTH KOREA

NORTH KOREA

Pyongyang

Vladivostok

Harbin

MANCHURIA

Amur River

Chita

Irkutsk

Lake Baikal

YABLONOVY

STANOVOI

Novosibirsk

Omsk

U N I O N   O F   S O V I E T   S O C I A L I S T   R E P U B L I C S

MONGOLIA

Ulan Bator

GOBI (DESERT)

ALTAI MTS.

Lake Balkhash

TIEN SHAN

TAKLA MAKAN (DESERT)

KUNLUN MTS.

C H I N A

Tashkent

Syr Darya R.

ARAL SEA

Amu Darya R.

KARA KUM (DESERT)

AFGHANISTAN

Kabul

PLATEAU OF IRAN

TIBET

PLATEAU OF TIBET

Lhasa

HIMALAYAS

NEPAL

Katmandu

BHUTAN

Thimbu

SIKKIM

Gangtok

BRAHMAPUTRA

Brahmaputra R.

BURMA

Mandalay

Rangoon

THAILAND

Bangkok

LAOS

Vientiane

NORTH VIETNAM

Hanoi

SOUTH VIETNAM

Saigon

CAMBODIA

Pnom Penh

Mekong R.

Salween R.

ANNAM MTS.

ANDAMAN SEA

Bay of Bengal

ANDAMAN ISLANDS (India)

NICOBAR ISLANDS (India)

CEYLON

Colombo

Madras

EASTERN GHATS

WESTERN GHATS

Cape Comorin

LACCADIVE ISLANDS (India)

MALDIVE ISLANDS

Bombay

I N D I A

Calcutta

DACCA

Dacca

Ganges R.

Delhi

New Delhi

Amritsar

Rawalpindi

PAKISTAN

Karachi

KASHMIR

INDIAN OCEAN

ARABIAN SEA

Gulf of Oman

MUSCAT AND OMAN

Muscat

OMAN (Br. prot.)

TRUCIAL OMAN

Sharjah

Gulf of Oman

Persian Gulf

Doha

QATAR

Riyadh

S A U D I   A R A B I A

Mecca

Sana

YEMEN

ADEN (Br. prot.)

Aden

Gulf of Aden

Socotra (Aden prot.)

RED SEA

AFRICA

CASPIAN SEA

Teheran

I R A N

Baghdad

Tigris R.

Euphrates R.

IRAQ

Kuwait

KUWAIT

NEUTRAL ZONE

Ankara

TURKEY

BLACK SEA

EUROPE

Nicosia

CYPRUS

LEBANON

Beirut

SYRIA

Damascus

ISRAEL

Jerusalem

Amman

JORDAN

EQUATOR

URALS

Australia

120° 130° 140° 150° 160°

EQUATOR

EQUATOR

BISMARCK ARCH.

TERRITORY OF NEW GUINEA (Austr.)

New Ireland

Rabaul

TERRITORY OF PAPUA (Austr.)

New Guinea

New Britain

Lae

Bougainville

Kieta

ARAFURA SEA

Salamaua

Torres Strait

Port Moresby

SOLOMON IS. (Br. prot.)

Honiara

Guadalcanal

Cape York

Great Barrier Reef

CORAL SEA

NEW HEBRIDES (U. K. and Fr. admin)

TIMOR SEA

Darwin

Gulf of Carpentaria

ARNHEM LAND

Wyndham

NORTHERN

10°

Broome

Normanton

Townsville

New Caledonia (Fr.)

Nouméa

TERRITORY

Roebourne

GREAT SANDY DESERT

MACDONNELL RANGES

WESTERN AUSTRALIA

GREAT DIVIDING RANGE

Rockhampton

TROPIC OF CAPRICORN

HAMMERSLEY PLATEAU

GIBSON DESERT

Alice Springs

ARUNTA DESERT

QUEENSLAND

20°

AUSTRALIA

MUSGRAVE RANGES

Charleville

Brisbane

GREAT VICTORIA DESERT

Lake Eyre

PACIFIC OCEAN

SOUTH AUSTRALIA

FLINDERS RANGE

Broken Hill

Perth

Fremantle

NULLARBOR PLAIN

NEW SOUTH WALES

Newcastle

0°

Great Australian Bight

Darling R.

Sydney

Albany

Port Lincoln

Spencer Gulf

Adelaide

Murray R.

Canberra

AUSTRALIAN CAPITAL TERRITORY

30°

VICTORIA

TASMAN SEA

Melbourne

Bass Strait

INDIAN OCEAN

TASMANIA

Launceston

North Cape

Auckland

North Island

Hobart

NEW ZEALAND

Cook Strait

Wellington

South Island

Christchurch

40°

Dunedin

110° 120° 130° 140° 150° 160° 170° 180°

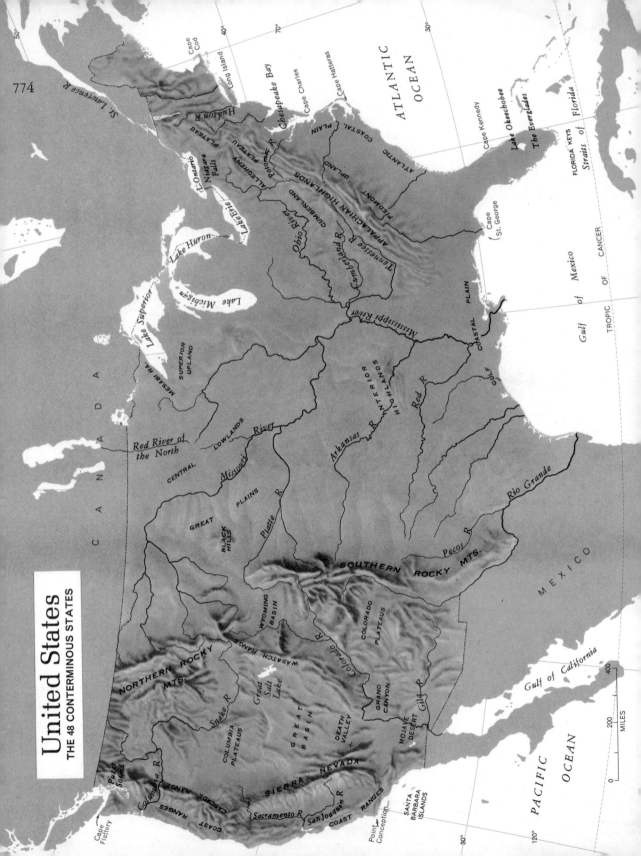

United States
THE 48 CONTERMINOUS STATES

774

CANADA

ATLANTIC OCEAN

PACIFIC OCEAN

Gulf of Mexico

MEXICO

Gulf of California

TROPIC OF CANCER

St. Lawrence R.

Cape Cod

Long Island

Cape Charles

Chesapeake Bay

Cape Hatteras

Hudson R.

Niagara Falls

L. Ontario

Lake Erie

Lake Huron

Lake Superior

Lake Michigan

ALLEGHENY PLATEAU

PLATEAU

Potomac R.

ATLANTIC COASTAL PLAIN

PIEDMONT UPLAND

APPALACHIAN HIGHLANDS

CUMBERLAND

Ohio River

Tennessee R.

Cumberland R.

Mississippi River

Cape Kennedy

Lake Okeechobee

The Everglades

Florida

FLORIDA KEYS

Straits of Florida

Cape (St. George)

COASTAL PLAIN

GULF

MISSABI RANGE

SUPERIOR UPLAND

Red River of the North

CENTRAL LOWLANDS

River

Missouri R.

INTERIOR HIGHLANDS

Arkansas River

Red R.

Rio Grande

Pecos R.

GREAT PLAINS

BLACK HILLS

Platte R.

SOUTHERN ROCKY MTS.

WYOMING BASIN

WASATCH RANGE

COLORADO PLATEAU

Colorado R.

Great Salt Lake

NORTHERN ROCKY MTS.

Snake R.

COLUMBIA PLATEAUS

GREAT BASIN

DEATH VALLEY

GRAND CANYON

Gila R.

MOJAVE DESERT

SIERRA NEVADA

CASCADE RANGE

COAST RANGES

Puget Sound

Columbia R.

Cape Flattery

Sacramento R.

San Joaquin R.

COAST RANGES

Point Conception

SANTA BARBARA ISLANDS

0 200 400

MILES

50° 40° 70° 30°

120° 30°

MAINE
Augusta
Montpelier
VT. N.H.
Concord Boston
MASS.
Providence
CONN. R.I.
New York
Albany
Hartford
Trenton
N.J. Philadelphia
NEW YORK
Dover
DEL.
Buffalo
PENNSYLVANIA
MD.
Pittsburgh
Harrisburg Baltimore
Washington, D.C.
Richmond
W. VA. Annapolis
Norfolk
VIRGINIA
Cleveland
Columbus
OHIO
Charleston
Dayton
Frankfort
Detroit
INDIANA
Cincinnati Louisville
Toledo
Indianapolis
KENTUCKY
NORTH
CAROLINA
Raleigh
Lansing
MICHIGAN
Nashville
TENNESSEE
Columbia
SOUTH
CAROLINA
Charleston
Savannah
Jacksonville
FLORIDA
Miami
Tampa
TROPIC OF CANCER
Birmingham
ALABAMA
GEORGIA
Tallahassee
Atlanta
Montgomery
Mobile
Memphis
MISSISSIPPI
New Orleans
Baton Rouge
LOUISIANA
Jackson
Shreveport
Houston
Galveston
ARKANSAS
Little Rock
Milwaukee
Chicago
Madison
ILLINOIS
WISCONSIN
Springfield
St. Louis
Jefferson City
MISSOURI
Kansas City
Duluth
St. Paul
MINNESOTA
Minneapolis
IOWA
Des Moines
Topeka
Wichita
KANSAS
Tulsa
Oklahoma City
OKLAHOMA
Ft. Worth
Dallas
TEXAS
Austin
San Antonio
Omaha
Lincoln
NEBRASKA
Bismarck
NORTH DAKOTA
Pierre
SOUTH DAKOTA
Denver
Pueblo
COLORADO
Santa Fe
Albuquerque
NEW MEXICO
El Paso
Cheyenne
WYOMING
Casper
Billings
MONTANA
Great Falls
Helena
IDAHO
Boise
Salt Lake City
UTAH
Spokane
WASHINGTON
Seattle
Olympia
OREGON
Salem
Portland
NEVADA
Carson City
Las Vegas
ARIZONA
Phoenix
CALIFORNIA
Sacramento
Oakland
San Francisco
Los Angeles
San Diego
CANADA
MEXICO

PREPARED BY

National Capital
State Capital
Other Cities

MILES
0   200   400

50°   40°   70°   30°   120°   30°   90°

776

United States
(ALASKA AND HAWAII)

ARCTIC OCEAN

Barrow • Point Barrow

Colville R.

BROOKS RANGE

Ft. Yukon •

Fairbanks •

Tanana R.

ALASKA RANGE

CHUGACH MTS.

Valdez •

Anchorage •

Juneau •

Kenai

Seward •

Kenai Peninsula

Sitka

ALEXANDER

ARCHIPELAGO

Ketchikan

CANADA

ARCTIC CIRCLE

Kotzebue Sound

Bering Strait

Seward Peninsula

Nome •

St. Lawrence I.

Norton Sound

McGrath •

Kuskokwim R.

Yukon River

U.S.S.R.

60°

St. Matthew I.

Nunivak I.

Bethel •

Lake Iliamna

Cook Inlet

Shelikof Strait

Kodiak •

Kodiak Island

Gulf of Alaska

BERING SEA

Bristol Bay

PRIBILOF ISLANDS

Alaska Peninsula

ALEUTIAN RANGE

BEAR ISLANDS

Kiska I.

RAT IS.

ANDREANOF ISLANDS

ALEUTIAN ISLANDS

FOX ISLANDS

Unimak I.

Unalaska I.

Umnak I.

ISLANDS OF THE FOUR MTS.

50°

180°   170°   160°   150°   140°

| 0 | 200 | 400 |
MILES

◉ State Capital   • Other Cities

180°   170°   160°   150°

Kure I.

MIDWAY IS.   • Gambia Shoal

Pearl and Hermes Reef

LEEWARD

Lisianski I.

Laysan I.

Maro Reef

Dowsett Reef

Gardner Pinnacles

Brooks Shoal

ISLANDS

French Frigate Shoal

Necker I.

TROPIC OF CANCER

Nihoa I.

MAIN ISLANDS

Lehua

Kauai

Niihau

Oahu

Molokai

Kaula

Honolulu ◉

Lanai

Maui

Kahoolawe

Hilo

PACIFIC OCEAN

Hawaii

180°   170°   160°   150°

Bibliographies

UNIT ONE   THE PATH TO INDEPENDENCE

Adams, James Truslow. *The Founding of New England.* Little, Brown.*

Adams, James Truslow. *Provincial Society: 1690-1763.* (*A History of American Life,* vol. 3) Macmillan, 1938.

Alden, John R. *The American Revolution: 1775-1783.* Torchbooks.*

The American Heritage Book of the Revolution. By the Editors and Bruce Lancaster. American Heritage, dist. by Simon and Schuster, 1958.

Barbour, Philip L. *The Three Worlds of Captain John Smith.* Houghton Mifflin, 1964.

Boorstin, Daniel J. *The Americans: The Colonial Experience.* Vintage.*

Bradford, William, ed. *Of Plymouth Plantation.* Intro. by Harvey Wish. Abr. Capricorn.*

Chitwood, Oliver P. *A History of Colonial America.* 3rd ed. Harper and Row, 1961.

Cooper, James Fenimore. *The Last of the Mohicans.* Signet.*

De Voto, Bernard. *The Course of Empire.* Sentry.*

Fleming, Thomas J. *The Story of Bunker Hill.* Collier.*

Franklin, Benjamin. *The Autobiography, and Other Writings of Benjamin Franklin.* Dodd, Mead, 1963.

Gallman, Robert E. *Developing the American Colonies, 1607-1783.* (Economic Forces in American History) Scott, Foresman, 1964. (booklet)*

Jefferson, Thomas. *Notes on the State of Virginia.* Harper and Row, 1964.*

Lancaster, Bruce. *From Lexington to Liberty: the Story of the American Revolution.* Doubleday, 1955.

Morgan, Edmund S. *The Birth of the Republic: 1763-1789.* University of Chicago Press.*

Morison, Samuel Eliot. *The Story of the "Old Colony" of New Plymouth.* Knopf, 1956.

Morris, Richard B. *The New World: Prehistory to 1774.* (The Life History of the United States, vol. 1) Time, Inc., dist. by Silver Burdett, 1963.

O'Meara, Walter. *Guns at the Forks.* Prentice-Hall, 1965.

Parkman, Francis. *Discovery of the Great West: La Salle.* Holt, Rinehart and Winston.*

The Parkman Reader. Ed. by Samuel Eliot Morison. Little, Brown.*

Peare, Cathrine Owens. *William Penn: A Biography.* Lippincott, 1957.

Peckham, Howard H. *The War for Independence: A Military History.* University of Chicago Press.*

Roberts, Kenneth. *Northwest Passage.* Crest.*

Rutman, Darrett Bruce. *Winthrop's Boston; Portrait of a Puritan Town.* Univ. of North Carolina Press, 1965.

Scheer, George F. and Rankin, eds. *Rebels and Redcoats.* Mentor, 1957.*

Smith, Bradford. *Captain John Smith.* Lippincott, 1956.

Thane, Elswyth. *Washington's Lady.* Dodd, Mead, 1960.

Van Alstyne, Richard. *Empire and Independence: The International History of the American Revolution.* Wiley.*

Van Doren, Carl. *Benjamin Franklin.* Compass.*

Vaughan, Alden T. *New England Frontier; Indians and Puritans, 1620-1675.* Little, Brown, 1965.

Wahlke, John C. *The Causes of the American Revolution.* Amherst, 1962.*

Wright, Louis B. *The Cultural Life of the American Colonies: 1607-1763.* Torchbooks.*

UNIT TWO   THE ESTABLISHMENT OF A NEW NATION

Bakeless, John. *Lewis and Clark: Partners in Discovery.* Apollo.*

Bauer, Frederick E., Jr. *Liberty and Power in the Making of the Constitution.* Heath, 1963.*

Bowers, Claude. *The Young Jefferson, 1743-1789.* Houghton Mifflin, 1945.*

Brown, Stuart Gerry. *Thomas Jefferson.* Washington Square Press.*

Chidsey, Donald Barr. *The Birth of the Constitution: An Informal History.* Crown, 1964.

Corwin, Edward S. *The Constitution and What It Means Today.* Atheneum.*

DeConde, Alexander. *Entangling Alliance: Politics and Diplomacy Under George Washington.* Duke, 1958.

DeConde, Alexander. *The Quasi-War: The Politics and Dipomacy of the Undeclared War with France, 1797-1801.* Scribner, 1966.

Dillon, Richard H. *Meriwether Lewis; A Biography.* Coward-McCann, 1965.

Dos Passos, John. *Men Who Made the Nation.* Doubleday, 1957.

Forester, C. S. *The Age of Fighting Sail.* Doubleday, 1956.

Jefferson, Thomas. *The Autobiography of Thomas Jefferson.* Capricorn.*

Koch, Adrienne. *Adams and Jefferson: Posterity Must Judge.* Rand McNally, 1963.*

Krout, John A. and Fox, Dixon R. *The Completion of Independence: 1790-1830.* (*A History of American Life,* vol. 5) Macmillan, 1944.

Miller, John C. *The Federalist Era, 1789-1801.* Torchbooks.*

North, Douglass C. *Decision That Faced the New Nation, 1783-1820.* (Economic Forces in American History) Scott, Foresman, 1964 (booklet).*

*paperback

Padover, Saul K. *The Living United States Constitution.* Mentor, 1963.*

Paine, Ralph D. *The Fight for a Free Sea: A Chronicle of the War of 1812.* Yale Univ. Press, 1921.

Perkins, Bradford, ed. *The Causes of the War of 1812: National Honor or National Interest?* Holt, Rinehart and Winston, 1962.*

Roberts, Kenneth. *Captain Caution.* Crest.*

Rutland, Robert A. *Birth of the Bill of Rights, 1776-1791.* Collier.*

Rutland, Robert A. *The Ordeal of the Constitution: the Antifederalists and the Ratification Struggle of 1787-1788.* University of Oklahoma Press, 1965.

Schrag, Peter. *The Ratification of the Constitution and the Bill of Rights.* Heath, 1964.*

Tomkins, Calvin. *The Lewis and Clark Trail.* Intro. by Stewart Udall. Harper and Row, 1965.

Tully, Andrew. *When They Burned the White House.* Popular Library.*

Taylor, George Rogers. *The War of 1812: Past Justifications and Present Interpretations.* Amherst, 1963.*

Van Doren, Carl. *The Great Rehearsal.* Compass.*
An account of the Constitutional Convention.

White, Patrick T. C. *A Nation on Trial: America and the War of 1812.* Wiley.*

Van Every, Dale. *Men of the Western Waters.* Houghton Mifflin, 1956.

Van Every, Dale. *Ark of Empire: the American Frontier, 1784-1803.* Mentor.*

UNIT THREE   PROBLEMS OF A GROWING NATION

Anderson, S. F. and Korg, J. *Westward to Oregon.* Amherst, 1958.*

Bristow, Gwen. *Jubilee Trail.* Crowell, 1950.
Fiction.

Commager, Henry Steele. *The Era of Reform, 1830-1860.* Van Nostrand, 1960.*

Current, Richard N. *Daniel Webster and the Rise of National Conservatism.* Little, Brown.*

Current, Richard N. *John C. Calhoun.* Washington Square Press.*

Brown, Richard H. *The Missouri Compromise: Political Statesmanship or Unwise Evasion?* Heath, 1964.*

Dana, Richard Henry. *Two Years Before the Mast.* Bantam.*
Fiction.

De Voto, Bernard. *Across the Wide Missouri.* Sentry.*

De Voto, Bernard. *The Year of Decision: 1846.* Sentry.*

Edmonds, Walter D. *Rome Haul.* Award.*

Gerson, Noel B. *Old Hickory.* Doubleday, 1964.

Guthrie, A. B., Jr. *The Big Sky.* Pocket Books.*

Hawkins, Hugh. *The Abolitionists: Immediatism and the Questioning of Means.* Amherst, 1964.*

Henry, Robert Selph. *The Story of the Mexican War.* Ungar, 1961.

James, Marquis. *Andrew Jackson: Portrait of a President.* Universal Library.*

James, Marquis. *The Raven: A Biography of Sam Houston.* Paperback Library.*

Johnson, William Weber. *The Birth of Texas.* Houghton Mifflin, 1960.

Lavender, David. *Westward Vision: The Story of the Oregon Trail.* McGraw-Hill, 1963.*

Lord, Walter. *A Time to Stand: the Story of the Alamo.* Pocket Books.*

Monaghan, Jay, ed. *The Book of the American West.* Messner, 1963.

Parker, William N. *Commerce, Cotton, and Westward Expansion, 1820-1860.* (Economic Forces in American History) Scott, Foresman, 1964 (booklet).*

Parkman, Francis. *The Oregon Trail.* Signet Classic;* Washington Square.*

Perkins, Dexter. *A History of the Monroe Doctrine.* Little, Brown.*

Rappaport, Armin. *The War with Mexico, Why Did It Happen?* Rand McNally, 1964.*

Remini, Robert V. *The Election of Andrew Jackson.* Preceptor.*

Ruiz, Ramón Eduardo, ed. *The Mexican War: Was It Manifest Destiny?* Holt, Rinehart and Winston, 1963.*

Schlesinger, Arthur S., Jr. *The Age of Jackson.* Abr. Mentor.*

Sellers, Charles. *Andrew Jackson, Nullification and the State-Rights.* Rand McNally, 1963.*

Stegner, Wallace. *The Gathering of Zion: The Story of the Mormon Trail.* McGraw, Hill, 1964.

Tinkle, Lon. *The Alamo.* Signet.*

Turner, Frederick Jackson. *The Frontier in American History.* Holt, Rinehart and Winston.*

Van Deusen, Glyndon G. *The Jacksonian Era, 1828-1848.* Torchbooks.*

Van Every, Dale. *The Final Challenge: The American Frontier, 1804-1845.* Mentor.*

Weisberger, Bernard A. *Abolitionism: Disrupter of the Democratic Process or Agent of Progress?* Rand McNally, 1963.*

UNIT FOUR   DIVISION AND REUNION

Angle, Paul M. ed. *The Nation Divided: The Civil War: Before and After.* Fawcett, 1960.*

The American Heritage Picture History of the Civil War. By the Editors; narrative by Bruce Catton. American Heritage, dist. by Doubleday, 1960.

Benét, Stephen Vincent. *John Brown's Body.* Holt, Rinehart and Winston, 1941.

Bishop, Jim. *The Day Lincoln Was Shot.* Harper and Row.*

Buckmaster, Henrietta. *Freedom Bound: A Handbook of Negro Liberty.* Macmillan, 1965.

Catton, Bruce. *The Coming Fury.* (Centennial History of the Civil War, Vol. 1) Doubleday, 1961.

Catton, Bruce. *A Stillness at Appomattox.* (The Army of the Potomac, vol. 3) Pocket Books.*

Catton, Bruce. *This Hallowed Ground.* Pocket Books.*

Churchill, Winston. *The Crisis.* Washington Square.*
Fiction.

Commager, Henry Steele. *The Defeat of the Confederacy.* Van Nostrand, 1964.*

Cramer, Kenyon C. *The Causes of War: The American Revolution, The Civil War, and World War I.* (Scott Foresman Problems in American History) Scott, Foresman, 1965.*

Crane, Stephen. *The Red Badge of Courage.* Bantam.*

Current, Richard N. *Lincoln and the First Shot.* Preceptor.*

Current, Richard N., ed. *Reconstruction (1865-1877).* Prentice-Hall, 1965.*

Freeman, Douglas Southhall. *Lee of Virginia.* Scribner, 1958.

Greeley, Horace. *An Overland Journey From New York to San Francisco.* Knopf, 1963.

Kantor, MacKinlay. *Andersonville.* Signet.*

Leech, Margaret. *Reveille in Washington.* Universal.*

McKitrick, Eric L., ed. *Slavery Defended: the Views of the Old South.* Prentice-Hall, 1963.*

McWhiney, Grady. *Reconstruction and the Freedman.* Rand McNally, 1963.*

Mitchell, Margaret. *Gone With the Wind.* Pocket Books.*

Nevins, Allan. *The War for the Union.* 2 vols. Scribner, 1959-60.

Parrish, Anne. *A Clouded Star.* Popular Library.*
Biographical Novel.

Roland, Charles P. *The Confederacy.* University of Chicago Press.*

Rozwenc, Edwin C. *Reconstruction in the South.* Amherst, 1952.*

Rozwenc, Edwin C. *Slavery As A Cause of the Civil War.* Amherst, 1963.*

Sandburg, Carl. *Abraham Lincoln: The Prairie Years and The War Years.* 3 vols. Dell.*

Semmes, Raphael. *The Confederate Raider, "Alabama."* Fawcett, 1962.*

Stampp, Kenneth M. *Era of Reconstruction, 1865-1877.* Knopf, 1965.

Stammp, Kenneth M., ed. *The Causes of the Civil War.* Prentice-Hall, 1965.*

Stern, Philip Van Doren, ed. *Soldier Life in the Union and Confederate Armies.* Fawcett, 1961.*

Stowe, Harriet Beecher. *Uncle Tom's Cabin.* Collier;* Dolphin;* Washington Square.*

The Union Sundered, by T. Harry Williams and the Editors. (*The Life History of the United States,* vol. 5: 1849-1865). Time, Inc., 1963.

UNIT FIVE   PROBLEMS OF AN INDUSTRIAL NATION

Addams, Jane. *Twenty Years at Hull House.* Signet Classics.*

Aldrich, Bess Streeter. *A Lantern in Her Hand.* Tempo.*
Fiction.

Angle, Paul M., ed. *The Making of a World Power: Golden '90's to Depression Years.* Fawcett, 1960.*

Billington, Ray A. *The Far Western Frontier: 1830-1860.* Torchbooks.*

Bingham, E. R. *California Gold.* Amherst, 1959.*

Broehl, Wayne G. *The Molly Maguires.* Harvard Univ. Press, 1964.

Cather, Willa. *My Antonia.* Sentry.*

Davis, Lance E. *The Growth of Industrial Enterprise, 1860-1914.* (Economic Forces in American History) Scott, Foresman, 1964. (booklet)*

Ferber, Edna. *Cimarron.* Bantam.*

Freidel, Frank. *The Splendid Little War.* Dell.*
The Spanish-American War.

Glad, Paul W. *McKinley, Bryan, and the People.* Preceptor.*

Green, Constance. *The Rise of Urban America.* Harper and Row, 1965.

Greene, Theodore P. *American Imperialism in 1898.* Amherst, 1955.*

Handlin, Oscar. *The Uprooted.* Universal Library.*

Hawkins, Hugh. *Booker T. Washington and His Critics: The Problem of Negro Leadership.* Amherst, 1962.*

Hoogenboom, Ari. *Spoilmen and Reformers.* Rand McNally, 1964.*

Iman, Raymond S. and Koch, Thomas W. *Labor in American Society.* (Scott, Foresman Problems in American History) Scott, Foresman, 1965.*

Josephson, Mathew. *The Robber Barons.* Harcourt, Brace and World.*

Kennedy, Gail. *Democracy and the Gospel of Wealth.* Amherst, 1949.*

Kennedy, Gail. *John D. Rockefeller: Robber Baron or Industrial Statesman?* Amherst, 1949.*

Lewis, Arthur H. *Lament for the Molly Maguires.* Harcourt, Brace and World, 1964.

Morgan, Wayne H. *America's Road to Empire: The War with Spain and Overseas Expansion.* Wiley, 1965.*

Morison, Samuel Eliot and Commager, Henry Steele. *The Growth of the Republic.* Vol. 2. 5th ed. Oxford Univ. Press, 1962.

Rölvaag, Ole Edvart. *Giants in the Earth.* Perennial Library;* Torchbooks.*

Schlesinger, Arthur M. *The Rise of the City: 1878-1898.* (*A History of American Life,* vol. 10) Macmillan, 1933.

Taylor, George Rogers. *The Turner Thesis: Concerning the Role of the Frontier in American History.* Amherst, 1956.*

Stone, Irving. *Adversary in the House.* Doubleday, 1947.
A fictional biography of Eugene V. Debs.

Unger, Irwin. *Populism: Nostalgic or Progressive?* Rand McNally, 1965.*

Warne, Colston E. *William Jennings Bryant and the Campaign of 1896.* Amherst, 1953.*

Wister, Owen. *The Virginian.* Pocket Books.*

Wolff, Leon. *Lockout: The Story of the Homestead Strike of 1892.* Harper and Row, 1965.

UNIT SIX   THE EMERGENCE OF A WORLD POWER

Aaron, Daniel. *Men of Good Hope: A Story of American Progressives.* Galaxy.*

Adams, Henry. *The Education of Henry Adams: An Autobiography.* Sentry.*

Allen, Frederick Lewis. *Great Pierpont Morgan.* Perennial.*

Baldwin, Hanson W. *World War I: An Outline History.* Black Cat.*

Beale, Howard K. *Theodore Roosevelt and the Rise of America to World Power.* Collier.*

Congdon, Don, ed. *Combat: World War I.* Dell.*

Cramer, Kenyon C. *The Causes of War: The American Revolution, The Civil War, and World War I.* (Scott, Foresman, Problems in American History) Scott, Foresman, 1965.*

Dos Passos, John. *Mr. Wilson's War.* Doubleday, 1962.*

Falls, Cyril. *The Great War, 1914-1918.* Capricorn.*

Faulkner, Harold U. *The Quest for Social Justice: 1898-1914.* (*A History of American Life,* vol. 11) Macmillan, 1931.

Harbaugh, William. *The Life and Times of Theodore Roosevelt.* Collier.*

Hart, Robert A. *The Great White Fleet; Its Voyage Around The World, 1907-1909.* Little, Brown, 1965.

Hofstadter, Richard. *The Age of Reform.* Vintage.*

Hofstadter, Richard, ed. *The Progressive Movement (1900-1915).* Prentice-Hall, 1963.*

Iman, Raymond S. and Koch, Thomas W. *Labor in American Society.* (Scott Foresman Problems in American History) Scott, Foresman, 1965.*

Leech, Margaret. *In the Days of McKinley.* Harper and Row, 1959.

Leuchtenburg, William E. *The Perils of Prosperity: 1914-1932.* University of Chicago Press.*

Link, Arthur S. *Woodrow Wilson and the Progressive Era: 1910-1917.* Torchbooks.*

Lorant, Stefan. *The Life and Times of Theodore Roosevelt.* Doubleday, 1959.

Lord, Walter. *The Good Years.* Bantam.*

Lyons, Thomas T. *Realism and Idealism in Wilson's Peace Program.* Heath, 1965.*

Mann, Arthur, ed. *The Progressive Era: Liberal Renaissance or Liberal Failure?* Holt, Rinehart and Winston, 1963.*

Millis, Walter. *The Martial Spirit.* Compass.*
The Spanish-American War.

Norris, Frank. *The Octopus.* Bantam; Signet Classics.*

The Progressive Era, May, Ernest R. and the Editors of *Life.* Time, Inc., 1964.

Remarque, Erich Maria. *All Quiet on the Western Front.* Crest.*

Riis, Jacob. *How the Other Half Lives.* American Century.*

Sinclair, Andrew. *Era of Excess: A Social History of the Prohibition Movement.* Colophon.*

Steffens, Lincoln. *The Autobiography of Lincoln Steffens.* Abr. ed. Harcourt, Brace and World, 1936.

Tuchman, Barbara. *The Guns of August.* Dell.*

Tuchman, Barbara. *The Proud Tower: A Portrait of the World Before the War, 1890-1914.* Macmillan, 1966.

Washington, Booker T. *Up From Slavery.* Dell;* Bantam.*

Udall, Stewart L. *The Quiet Crisis;* intro. by John F. Kennedy. Avon.*

UNIT SEVEN   TESTING A WORLD POWER

Allen, Frederick Lewis. *Only Yesterday.* Harper and Row.*

Angle, Paul M., ed. *The Uneasy World: New Deal to New Frontier.* Fawcett, 1960.*

Burns, James M. *Roosevelt: The Lion and the Fox.* Harvest.*

Cronon, E. David. *Labor and the New Deal.* Rand McNally, 1963.*

Dos Passos, John. *U.S.A.* Sentry.*

Gunther, John. *Roosevelt in Retrospect: A Profile in History.* Pyramid.*

Handlin, Oscar. *Al Smith and His America.* Little, Brown, 1958.

Iman, Raymond S. and Koch, Thomas W. *Labor in American Society.* (Scott, Foresman, Problems in American History) Scott, Foresman, 1965.*

Keller, Morton, ed. *The New Deal: What Was It?* Holt, Rinehart and Winston, 1963.*

Lawrence, Jerome and Lee, Robert E. *Inherit the Wind.* Bantam.*

Leuchtenburg, William E. *Franklin D. Roosevelt and the New Deal, 1932-1940.* Torchbooks.*

Lewis, Sinclair. *Babbitt.* Signet Classics.*

Lewis, Sinclair. *Main Street.* Signet.*
Fiction.

Lindberg, Charles A. *The Spirit of St. Louis.* Scribner.*

Lyons, Eugene. *Herbert Hoover; A Biography.* Doubleday, 1964.

Lyons, Thomas T. *Presidential Power in the New Deal.* Heath, 1963.*

McDougall, Duncan. *World Power and New Problems, 1914-1930.* (Economic Forces in American History) Scott, Foresman, 1964. (booklet)*

MacLeish, Archibald. *The Eleanor Roosevelt Story.* Houghton Mifflin, 1965.

Merrill, Edward H. *Responses to Economic Collapse: The Great Depression of the 1930's.* Heath, 1964.*

Mowry, George E., ed. *The Twenties: Fords, Flappers and Fanatics.* Prentice-Hall, 1963.*

Parks, E. T. and L. F., eds. *Memorable Quotations of Franklin D. Roosevelt.* Crowell, 1965.

Payne, Robert, ed. *Civil War in Spain.* Premier.*

Perkins, Dexter. *The New Age of Franklin Roosevelt: 1932-1945.* University of Chicago Press.*

Roosevelt, Eleanor. *This is My Story.* Dolphin.*

Schary, Dore. *Sunrise at Campobello.* Signet.*

Schlesinger, Arthur M., Jr. *The Coming of the New Deal.* (*The Age of Roosevelt,* Vol. 2). Sentry.*

Schlesinger, Arthur M., Jr. *The Crisis of the Old Order, 1919-1933.* (*The Age of Roosevelt,* Vol. 1). Sentry.*

Schlesinger, Arthur M., Jr. *The Politics of Upheaval.* (*The Age of Roosevelt,* Vol. 3). Houghton Mifflin, 1960.

Smith, Gene. *When the Cheering Stopped: The Last Years of Woodrow Wilson.* Bantam.*

Smolensky, Eugene. *Adjustments to Depression and War, 1930-1945.* (Economic Forces in American History) Scott, Foresman, 1964. (booklet)*

Steinbeck, John. *The Grapes of Wrath.* Bantam;* Compass.*

Waller, George M. *Pearl Harbor; Roosevelt and the Coming of the War.* Amherst, 1965.*

Warne, Colston E. *The Steel Strike of 1919.* Amherst, 1963.*

UNIT EIGHT   PROBLEMS OF A WORLD POWER

Angle, Paul M., ed. *The Uneasy World: New Deal to New Frontier.* Fawcett, 1960.*

American Heritage. *D-Day, The Invasion of Europe.* Perennial.*

Babian, Haig. *Problems of Prosperity and Leadership, 1945–.* (Economic Forces in American History) Scott, Foresman, 1964. (booklet) *

Baruch, Bernard. *Baruch: My Own Story.* Pocket Books.*

Beech, Edward L. *Run Silent, Run Deep.* Pocket Books.*

Bradley, Gen. Omar. *A Soldier's Story.* Popular Library.*

Churchill, Sir Winston. *The Second World War.* 6 vols. Bantam.*

Congdon, Don, ed. *Combat: Pacific Threater—World War II.* Dell.*

Congdon, Don, ed. *Combat: World War I.* Delacorte, dist. by Dial, 1964.

Donovan, Robert J. P. *PT Boat 109.* Crest.*

Eisenhower, Dwight David. *Crusade in Europe.* Dolphin.*

Eisenhower, Dwight David. *Mandate for Change, 1953-1956; The White House Years.* Signet.*

Eisenhower, Dwight David. *Waging Peace: The White House Years, 1956-1961.* Doubleday, 1965.

Faber, Harold. *Soldier and Statesman: General George C. Marshall.* Farrar, Strauss and Giroux, 1964.

Fenno, Richard F., Jr. *The Yalta Conference.* Amherst, 1955.*

Forester, C. S. *Sink the Bismarck!* Bantam.*

Horvath, David. *D-Day: The Sixth of June, 1944.* McGraw-Hill.*

Lamont, Lansing. *Day of Trinity.* Atheneum, 1965.

MacArthur, Douglas. *Reminiscences.* McGraw-Hill, 1964. Crest.*

Lord, Walter. *Day of Infamy.* Bantam.*

Merrill, James M. *Target-Tokyo: the Halsey-Doolittle Raid.* Rand McNally, 1964.

Michie, Allan A. *The Invasion of Europe; The Story Behind D-Day.* Dodd, Mead, 1964.

Middleton, Harry J. *The Compact History of the Korean War.* Hawthorn, 1965.

Morison, Samuel Eliot. *The Two-Ocean War.* Little, Brown, 1963.

Newcomb, Richard F. *Iwo Jima.* Holt, Rinehart and Winston, 1965.

Potter, E. B. and Nimitz, Chester W., eds. *The Great Sea War; The Story of Naval Action in World War II.* Prentice-Hall, 1960.

Potter, E. B. and Nimitz, Chester W., eds. *Triumph in the Pacific: The Navy's Struggle Against Japan.* Spectrum.*

Potter, Charles E. *Days of Shame.* Coward-McCann, 1965.

Pyle, Ernie. *Brave Men.* Popular Library.*

Rovere, Richard. *Senator Joe McCarthy.* Meridian.*

Ryan, Cornelius. *The Longest Day: June 6, 1944.* Crest.*

Söderberg, Sten. *Hammarskjöld: A Pictorial Biography.* Viking, 1962.

Toland, John. *But Not in Shame: The Six Months After Pearl Harbor.* Signet.*

Tregaskis, Richard. *Guadalcanal Diary.* Popular Library.*

Wise, David and Ross, Thomas B. *The U-2 Affair.* Random House, 1962.

UNIT NINE   RESPONSIBILITIES OF A WORLD POWER

Abel, Elie. *The Missile Crisis.* Lippincott, 1966.

Adler, Bill, ed. *The Kennedy Wit.* Bantam.*

Belfrage, Sally. *Freedom Summer.* Viking, 1965.

Bishop, Jim. *A Day in the Life of President Kennedy.* Bantam.*

Block, Herbert. *Straight Herblock.* Simon and Schuster, 1964.

Brown, Stuart Gerry. *Adlai E. Stevenson, Shaper of History.* Barron's.*

Burns, James M. *John Kennedy: A Political Profile.* Avon.*

Carter, Richard. *Breakthrough: The Saga of Jonas Salk.* Trident, 1966.

Farmer, James. *Freedom—When?* Random House, 1966.

Ford, Gerald and Stiles, John R. *Portrait of the Assassin.* Simon and Schuster, 1965.

Humphrey, Hubert H. *The War on Poverty.* McGraw-Hill, 1964.

Johnson, Lyndon B. *A Time for Action.* Atheneum, 1964.

Kennedy, John F. *The Burden and the Glory* . . . Ed. by Allan Nevins; foreword by Lyndon B. Johnson. Popular Library.*

King, Martin Luther. *Why We Can't Wait.* Signet.*

Lieberson, Goddard, ed. *John Fitzgerald Kennedy as We Remember Him.* Atheneum, 1965.

Lord, Walter. *The Past That Would Not Die.* Harper and Row, 1965.

Luce, Iris, ed. *Letters From the Peace Corps.* McKay, 1964.

McClellan, Grant S., ed. *Civil Rights.* (The Reference Shelf, v. 36, no. 6) Wilson, 1964.

Meyer, Karl E. and Szulc, Tad. *The Cuban Invasion: The Chronicle of a Disaster.* Praeger.*

Morris, Willie, ed. *The South Today, 100 Years After Appomattox.* Harper and Row, 1965.

Newman, Bernard. *Background to Vietnam.* Roy, 1966.

The Official Warren Commission Report on the Assassination of President John F. Kennedy. Bantam.*

Ross, Lillian. *Adlai Stevenson.* Lippincott, 1966.

Salinger, Pierre and Vanocur, Sander, eds. *A Tribute to John F. Kennedy.* Dell.*

Schlesinger, Arthur M., Jr. *A Thousand Days: John F. Kennedy in the White House.* Houghton Mifflin, 1965.

Settel, T. S., ed. *The Wisdom of JFK.* Dutton, 1965.

Sidney, Hugh. *John F. Kennedy, President.* Crest.*

Sorensen, Theodore C. *Kennedy.* Harper and Row, 1965.

Steiner, Paul, ed. *The Stevenson Wit and Wisdom.* Hawthorn Books, 1965.

Sullivan, George. *The Story of the Peace Corps.* Fleet, 1964.

United Press International. *Gemini: America's Historic Walk in Space.* Prentice-Hall, 1965.

Walsh, William B. *A Ship Called "Hope."* Dutton, 1964.

White, Theodore H. *The Making of the President 1960.* Pocket Books.*

White, Theodore H. *The Making of the President 1964.* Atheneum, 1965.

The Declaration of Independence in Congress, July 4, 1776

THE UNANIMOUS DECLARATION OF THE THIRTEEN UNITED STATES OF AMERICA,

WHEN in the Course of human events, it becomes necessary for one people to dissolve the political bands which have connected them with another, and to assume among the powers of the earth, the separate and equal station to which the Laws of Nature and of Nature's God entitle them, a decent respect to the opinions of mankind requires that they should declare the causes which impel them to the separation.—We hold these truths to be self-evident, that all men are created equal, that they are endowed by their Creator with certain unalienable Rights, that among these are Life, Liberty and the pursuit of Happiness. —That to secure these rights, Governments are instituted among Men, deriving their just powers from the consent of the governed,—That whenever any Form of Government becomes destructive of these ends, it is the Right of the People to alter or to abolish it, and to institute new Government, laying its foundation on such principles and organizing its powers in such form, as to them shall seem most likely to effect their Safety and Happiness. Prudence, indeed, will dictate that Governments long established should not be changed for light and transient causes; and accordingly all experience hath shewn, that mankind are more disposed to suffer, while evils are sufferable, than to right themselves by abolishing the forms to which they are accustomed. But when a long train of abuses and usurpations, pursuing invariably the same Object evinces a design to reduce them under absolute Despotism, it is their right, it is their duty, to throw off such Government, and to provide new Guards for their future security.—Such has been the patient sufferance of these Colonies; and such is now the necessity which constrains them to alter their former Systems of Government. The history of the present King of Great Britain is a history of repeated injuries and usurpations, all having in direct object the establishment of an absolute Tyranny over these States. To prove this, let Facts be submitted to a candid world.—He has refused his Assent to Laws, the most wholesome and necessary for the public good.—He has forbidden his Governors to pass Laws of immediate and pressing importance, unless suspended in their operation till his Assent should be obtained; and when so suspended, he has utterly neglected to attend to them.—He has refused to pass other Laws for the accommodation of large districts of people, unless those people would relinquish the right of Representation in the Legislature, a right inestimable to them and formidable to tyrants only.—He has called together legislative bodies at places unusual, uncomfortable, and distant from the depository of their public Records, for the sole purpose of fatiguing them into compliance with his measures.—He has dissolved Representative Houses repeatedly, for opposing with manly firmness his invasions on the rights of the people.—He has refused for a long time, after such dissolutions, to cause others to be elected; whereby the Legislative powers, incapable of Annihilation, have returned to the People at large for their exercise; the State remaining in the mean time exposed to all the dangers of invasion from without, and convulsions within.— He has endeavoured to prevent the population of these States; for that purpose obstructing the Laws for Naturalization of Foreigners; refusing to pass others to encourage their migration hither, and raising the conditions of new Appropriations of Lands.—He has obstructed the Administration of Justice, by refusing his Assent to Laws for establishing Judiciary powers.— He has made Judges dependent on his Will alone, for the tenure of their offices, and the amount and payment of their salaries.—He has erected a multitude of New Offices, and sent hither swarms of Officers to harass our people, and eat out their substance.—He has kept among us, in times of peace, Standing Armies without the Consent of our legislatures.—He has affected to render the Military independent of and superior to the Civil power.—He has combined with others to subject us to a jurisdiction foreign to our constitution, and unacknowledged by our laws; giving his Assent to their Acts of pretended Legislation:—For quartering large bodies of armed troops among us:—For protecting them, by a mock Trial, from punishment for any Murders which they should commit on the Inhabitants of these States:—For cutting off our Trade with all parts of the world:—For imposing Taxes on us without our Consent:—For depriving us in many cases, of the benefits of Trial by jury:—For transporting us beyond Seas to be tried for pretended offenses:—For abolishing the free System of English Laws in a neighbouring Province, establishing therein an Arbitrary government, and enlarging its Boundaries so as to render it at once an example and fit instrument for introducing the same absolute rule into these Colonies:—For taking away our Charters, abolishing our most valuable Laws, and altering fundamentally the Forms of our Governments:—For suspending our own Legislatures, and declaring themselves invested with power to legislate for us in all cases whatsoever.—He has abdicated Government here, by declaring us out of his Protection and waging War against us.—He has plundered our seas, ravaged our Coasts, burnt our towns, and destroyed the lives of our people.—He is at this time transporting large Armies of foreign Mercenaries to compleat the works of death, desolation and tyranny, already begun with circumstances of Cruelty & perfidy scarcely paralleled in the most barbarous ages, and totally unworthy the Head of a civilized nation.—He has constrained our fellow Citizens taken Captive on the high Seas to bear Arms against their Country, to become the executioners of their friends and Brethren, or to fall themselves by their Hands.—He has excited domestic insurrections amongst us, and has endeavoured to bring on the inhabitants of our frontiers, the merciless Indian Savages, whose known rule of warfare, is an undistinguished destruction of all ages, sexes and conditions. In every stage of these Oppressions We have Petitioned for Redress in the most humble terms: Our repeated Petitions have been answered only by repeated injury. A Prince, whose character is thus marked by every act which may define a Tyrant, is unfit to be the ruler of a free people. Nor have We been wanting in attentions to our British brethren. We have warned them from time to time of attempts by their legislature to extend an unwarrantable jurisdiction over us. We have reminded them of the circumstances of our emigration and settlement here. We have appealed to their native justice and magnanimity, and we have conjured them by the ties of our common kindred to disavow these usurpations, which, would inevitably interrupt our connections and correspondence. They too have been deaf to the voice of justice and of consanguinity. We must, therefore, acquiesce in the necessity, which denounces our Separation, and hold them, as we hold the rest of mankind, Enemies in War, in Peace Friends.—

WE, THEREFORE, THE REPRESENTATIVES OF THE UNITED STATES OF AMERICA, in General Congress, Assembled, appealing to the Supreme Judge of the world for the rectitude of our intentions, do, in the Name, and by authority of the good People of these Colonies, solemnly publish and declare, That these United Colonies are, and of Right ought to be FREE AND INDEPENDENT STATES; that they are Absolved from all Allegiance to the British Crown, and that all political connection between them and the State of Great Britain, is and ought to be totally dissolved; and that as Free and Independent States, they have full Power to levy War, conclude Peace, contract Alliances, establish Commerce, and to do all other Acts and Things which Independent States may of right do.—And for the support of this Declaration, with a firm reliance on the protection of divine Providence, we mutually pledge to each other our Lives, our Fortunes and our Sacred Honor.

JOHN HANCOCK

Button Gwinnett	W^m. Paca	Robt Morris	Wm Floyd	Saml Adams
Lyman Hall	Thos. Stone	Benjamin Rush	Phil. Livingston	John Adams
Geo Walton.	Charles Carroll of	Benj^a. Franklin	Fran^s. Lewis	Robt Treat Payne
Wm Hooper	Carrollton	John Morton	Lewis Morris	Elbridge Gerry
Joseph Hewes,	George Wythe	Geo Clymer	Rich^d. Stockton	Step Hopkins
John Penn	Richard Henry Lee.	Ja^s. Smith	Jno Witherspoon	William Ellery
Edward Rutledge.	Th Jefferson	Geo. Taylor	Fra^s. Hopkinson	Roger Sherman
Thos Heyward Junr.	Benj^a Harrison	James Wilson	John Hart	Sam^{el} Huntington
Thomas Lynch Junr.	Thos Nelson Jr.	Geo. Ross	Abra Clark	W^m. Williams
Arthur Middleton	Francis Lightfoot Lee	Caesar Rodney	Josiah Bartlett	Oliver Wolcott
Samuel Chase	Carter Braxton	Geo Read	W^m. Whipple	Matthew Thornton
		Tho M: Kean		

The text of the Constitution, which is printed in the left-hand column, is taken from the "literal print" issued by the Department of State. Portions of the text within brackets [.....] have been affected by an amendment. The number of the amendment is given after the final bracket, so][16]. In the right-hand column is printed an explanation of the Constitution, paragraph by paragraph. The explanation and the headings are not a part of the Constitution.

Constitution of the United States of America

THE PEOPLE ESTABLISH THE UNION

WE THE PEOPLE of the United States, in Order to form a more perfect Union, establish Justice, insure domestic Tranquility, provide for the common defence, promote the general Welfare, and secure the Blessings of Liberty to ourselves and our Posterity, do ordain and establish this Constitution for the United States of America.

WE CITIZENS of the United States adopt this Constitution in order to:

Form a better, more coöperative union of our states (better than the one provided by the Articles of Confederation).

Give fair treatment to everybody.

Secure peace in all our states.

Defend ourselves and our country against any enemies.

Enjoy good living conditions.

Possess liberty for ourselves and for our children.

THE LEGISLATIVE DEPARTMENT • CONGRESS

ARTICLE. I.

SECTION. 1. All legislative Powers herein granted shall be vested in a Congress of the United States, which shall consist of a Senate and House of Representatives.

Laws for our country shall be made by Congress. Congress is made up of two parts (called "houses"), a Senate and a House of Representatives.

THE HOUSE OF REPRESENTATIVES • REPRESENTATIVES SHALL BE ELECTED BY THE PEOPLE

SECTION. 2. The House of Representatives shall be composed of Members chosen every second Year by the People of the Several States, and the Electors in each State shall have the Qualifications requisite for Electors of the most numerous Branch of the State Legislature.

Representatives shall have two-year terms and shall be elected by the voters of each state. If a state's laws allow a citizen to vote for state representatives, he may vote for a representative in the national House of Representatives. (The right of each state to make laws about voting is recognized here.)

QUALIFICATIONS OF REPRESENTATIVES

No Person shall be a Representative who shall not have attained to the Age of twenty-five Years, and

A Representative must be at least twenty-five years old, a citizen of the United States for at least seven

been seven Years a Citizen of the United States, and who shall not, when elected, be an Inhabitant of that State in which he shall be chosen.

years, and live in the state which he represents, but not necessarily in the district he represents.

REPRESENTATION IS BASED ON POPULATION

Representatives and [direct Taxes]16 shall be apportioned among the several States which may be included within this Union, according to their respective Numbers, [which shall be determined by adding to the whole Number of free Persons, including those bound to Service for a Term of Years, and excluding Indians not taxed, three fifths of all other Persons.]14 The actual Enumeration shall be made within three Years after the first Meeting of the Congress of the United States, and within every subsequent Term of ten Years, in such Manner as they shall by Law direct. The Number of Representatives shall not exceed one for every thirty Thousand, but each State shall have at Least one Representative; and until such enumeration shall be made, the State of New Hampshire shall be entitled to chuse three, Massachusetts eight, Rhode Island and Providence Plantations one, Connecticut five, New-York six, New Jersey four, Pennsylvania eight, Delaware one, Maryland six, Virginia ten, North Carolina five, South Carolina five, and Georgia three.

The number of people in a state determines the number of Representatives the state shall have. (The original method of counting population is not important today since slavery is abolished.) The first count of the people shall be made within three years after 1789 (actually the first census was taken in 1790) and then every ten years afterwards. Congress shall decide how the count shall be made and the number of Representatives from each state, except that the number of people shall not be less than 30,000 for each Representative. Each state shall have at least one Representative even if the population is smaller than 30,000. (The first House of Representatives consisted of 65 members, two and one-half times as large as the first Senate.)

VACANCIES ARE FILLED BY ELECTION

When vacancies happen in the Representation from any State, the Executive Authority thereof shall issue Writs of Election to fill such Vacancies.

If a state does not have its full number of Representatives, the governor of the state shall call an election to fill any vacancy.

SELECTION OF SPEAKER • IMPEACHMENT

The House of Representatives shall chuse their Speaker and other Officers; and shall have the sole Power of Impeachment.

The House of Representatives shall select its Speaker (presiding officer) and other officers. (The Speaker has always been a member of the House.) The House of Representatives alone has the power to demand that high executives and judicial officers be removed from office for serious misbehavior. (An impeached official is tried before the Senate, which acts as a court and decides whether the official is guilty of wrongful acts in office or not.)

THE SENATE

SECTION. 3. The Senate of the United States shall be composed of two Senators from each State, chosen [by the Legislature thereof,]17 for six Years; and each Senator shall have one Vote.

The Senate is made up of two Senators from each state. (Senators are now elected by the voters.) Each Senator is elected for a term of six years and has one vote. (In the Congress of the Confederation each state had one vote no matter how many members it had in the Congress.)

WHEN SENATORS ARE CHOSEN • VACANCIES

Immediately after they shall be assembled in Consequence of the first Election, they shall be divided as equally as may be into three Classes. The Seats

The terms of Senators in the first Congress shall be arranged so that in the future one third of the Senators will be elected every two years. When a

of the Senators of the first Class shall be vacated at the Expiration of the second Year, of the second Class at the Expiration of the fourth Year, and of the third Class at the Expiration of the sixth Year, so that one third may be chosen every second Year; and if Vacancies happen by Resignation, or otherwise, [during the Recess of the Legislature of any State, the Executive thereof may make temporary Appointments until the next Meeting of the Legislature, which shall then fill such Vacancies.][17]

vacancy occurs, the governor of the state shall arrange for the people to elect a Senator and, if state laws permit, the governor may appoint one to serve until the people elect one.

QUALIFICATIONS OF SENATORS

No Person shall be a Senator who shall not have attained to the Age of thirty Years, and been nine Years a Citizen of the United States, and who shall not, when elected, be an Inhabitant of that State for which he shall be chosen.

A Senator must be at least thirty years old, a citizen of the United States for at least nine years, and live in the state he represents.

OFFICERS OF THE SENATE

The Vice-President of the United States shall be President of the Senate, but shall have no Vote, unless they be equally divided.

The Senate shall chuse their other Officers, and also a President pro tempore, in the Absence of the Vice President, or when he shall exercise the Office of President of the United States.

The Vice-President shall preside at Senate meetings. He votes only when there is a tie vote.

The Senate chooses its other officers, and may select a presiding officer when the Vice-President is absent.

IMPEACHMENTS

The Senate shall have the sole Power to try all Impeachments. When sitting for that Purpose, they shall be on Oath or Affirmation. When the President of the United States is tried the Chief Justice shall preside: And no Person shall be convicted without the Concurrence of two thirds of the Members present.

Judgment in Cases of Impeachment shall not extend further than to removal from Office, and disqualification to hold and enjoy any Office of honor, Trust or Profit under the United States: but the Party convicted shall nevertheless be liable and subject to Indictment, Trial, Judgment and Punishment, according to Law.

The Senate is given the power to try officials who are impeached by the House of Representatives. The Senators must take an oath to try the case fairly. If the President is tried, the Chief Justice presides over the Senate at the trial, but in other cases the Vice-President presides. To convict an official, two thirds of the Senators present must vote him guilty.

The penalty for the convicted official shall not be more than the loss of his office and his right ever to hold another United States government office. But he may still be tried in the regular courts for any crimes that caused his loss of office and be punished if found guilty.

ELECTIONS AND MEETINGS OF THE CONGRESS

SECTION. 4. The Times, Places and Manner of holding Elections for Senators and Representatives, shall be prescribed in each State by the Legislature thereof; but the Congress may at any time by Law make or alter such Regulations, except as to the Places of chusing Senators.

The Congress shall assemble at least once in every Year, [and such Meeting shall be on the first Monday

The states may make laws about when, where, and how elections for Senators and Representatives in Congress are held. But Congress may change the state laws. (Congress, for example, has fixed the first Tuesday after the first Monday in November of even-numbered years as the date for election of Senators and Representatives. Representatives must be elected from districts by secret ballot. Senators are now elected at the same voting places as other officials.)

Congress must meet at least once a year. The date of regular meeting is set by the Constitution unless

in December, unless they shall by Law appoint a different Day.][20]

Congress passes a law setting a different day. (The date now fixed by the Twentieth Amendment is January 3.)

ORGANIZATION AND RULES OF CONGRESS

SECTION. 5. Each House shall be the Judge of the Elections, Returns and Qualifications of its own Members, and a Majority of each shall constitute a Quorum to do Business; but a smaller Number may adjourn from day to day, and may be authorized to compel the Attendance of absent Members, in such Manner, and under such Penalties as each House may provide.

The House of Representatives and the Senate each has the right to decide if its own members are entitled to be in Congress. (Both have kept out members who met the qualifications of the Constitution but who were thought by more than half the House or Senate to be undesirable persons.) Neither House nor Senate can hold meetings for business unless more than half the members are present (but often the absence of a quorum is not noticed). Less than half the members may adjourn until the next day and may make absent members attend. The Senate and the House of Representatives can each make rules and fix penalties for not attending meetings.

Each House may determine the Rules of its Proceedings, punish its Members for disorderly Behaviour, and, with the Concurrence of two thirds, expel a Member.

The House and the Senate may each make its own rules for conducting its business. They may punish their own members for not following these rules. In either the House or the Senate two thirds of the members present must agree if they wish to expel a member. (It is easier to keep a member out of Congress than to put him out.)

Each House shall keep a Journal of its Proceedings, and from time to time publish the same, excepting such Parts as may in their Judgment require Secrecy; and the Yeas and Nays of the Members of either House on any question shall, at the Desire of one fifth of those Present, be entered on the Journal.

The House of Representatives and the Senate must each keep a record of what is done at its meetings. (Not only are proceedings recorded, but most of what is said and much that is not said is printed in the big *Congressional Record.*) The record is to be printed unless the members decide to keep some matters secret (which they have not done since 1929). If one fifth of the members present wish, the record must show how each member voted on any question.

Neither House, during the Session of Congress, shall, without the Consent of the other, adjourn for more than three days, nor to any other Place than that in which the two Houses shall be sitting.

While Congress is meeting, neither the House nor the Senate shall let three days pass without holding a meeting, unless the other agrees. Both must meet in the same city.

CONGRESSIONAL PRIVILEGES AND RESTRICTIONS

SECTION. 6. The Senators and Representatives shall receive a Compensation for their Services, to be ascertained by Law, and paid out of the Treasury of the United States. They shall in all Cases, except Treason, Felony and Breach of the Peace, be privileged from Arrest during their Attendance at the Session of their respective Houses, and in going to and returning from the same; and for any Speech or Debate in either House, they shall not be questioned in any other Place.

Senators and Representatives shall be paid out of the Treasury of the United States according to the law which fixes their salaries (now $30,000 a year, plus an allowance not taxed as income).

Congressmen attending meetings of Congress, or going to and from meetings, shall not be arrested except for treason, serious crime, or breaking the peace. (This protects them only from interference in doing their duty.) They cannot be held responsible for anything they say in their meetings, no matter how criminal it may be, except by the house to which they belong.

No Senator or Representative shall, during the

Senators and Representatives cannot hold other

Time for which he was elected, be appointed to any civil Office under the Authority of the United States, which shall have been created, or the Emoluments whereof shall have been encreased during such time; and no Person holding any Office under the United States, shall be a Member of either House during his Continuance in Office.

United States government offices while they are members of Congress. During the time for which they have been elected they cannot take any government position which has been created during that time, or any position for which the salary has been increased during that time.

LAWMAKING • TAX BILLS MUST ORIGINATE IN THE HOUSE

SECTION. 7. All Bills for raising Revenue shall originate in the House of Representatives; but the Senate may propose or concur with Amendments as on other Bills.

Only members of the House of Representatives may propose bills that levy taxes. But the Senate may amend such bills (and always does). (In fact, the Senate often substitutes a wholly different bill.)

THE PRESIDENT'S VETO POWER

Every Bill which shall have passed the House of Representatives and the Senate, shall, before it become a law, be presented to the President of the United States; If he approve he shall sign it, but if not he shall return it, with his Objections to that House in which it shall have originated, who shall enter the Objections at large on their Journal, and proceed to reconsider it. If after such Reconsideration two thirds of that House shall agree to pass the Bill, it shall be sent, together with the Objections, to the other House, by which it shall likewise be reconsidered, and if approved by two thirds of that House, it shall become a Law. But in all such Cases the Votes of both Houses shall be determined by Yeas and Nays, and the Names of the Persons voting for and against the Bill shall be entered on the Journal of each House respectively. If any Bill shall not be returned by the President within ten Days (Sundays excepted) after it shall have been presented to him, the Same shall be a Law, in like Manner as if he had signed it, unless the Congress by their Adjournment prevent its Return, in which Case it shall not be a Law.

A bill that has passed both the House of Representatives and the Senate shall be sent to the President. If he approves, he shall sign it and the bill becomes law. If he does not approve the bill, the President shall send it back, without his signature, to the house that first passed it. The President shall also give his reasons for not approving it, and these reasons must be put in the record of proceedings. The members of that house must vote on the bill again. If two thirds of the members present agree to pass the bill, it is sent, together with the President's objections, to the other house. If two thirds of that house favor the bill, it becomes a law without the President's approval. The records of Congress must show how each member voted.

The President has ten days (not counting Sundays) after receiving a bill to consider it. If he keeps it longer, it becomes a law without his signature, provided Congress has not adjourned. If Congress has adjourned, the unsigned bill does not become a law. (This is called the "pocket" veto.)

THE PRESIDENT'S CONSENT TO OTHER ACTS

Every Order, Resolution, or Vote to which the Concurrence of the Senate and House of Representatives may be necessary (except on a question of Adjournment) shall be presented to the President of the United States; and before the Same shall take Effect, shall be approved by him, or being disapproved by him, shall be repassed by two thirds of the Senate and House of Representatives, according to the Rules and Limitations prescribed in the Case of a Bill.

If either the House of Representatives or the Senate takes action which needs agreement by the other (except adjournment and constitutional amendments), the matter must be sent to the President for approval. If the President agrees, it shall take effect. If the President does not agree with what is proposed, both Senate and House must pass the measure again by a two-thirds vote before it shall be carried out. (This prevents Congress from making laws without the consent of the President by calling them something else.)

POWERS GRANTED TO CONGRESS • REGARDING TAXES

SECTION. 8. The Congress shall have the Power To lay and collect Taxes, Duties, Imposts and Excises,

Congress has the power to get money by taxing. Such income can be used (1) to pay the debts of

to pay the Debts and provide for the common defence and general welfare of the United States; but all Duties, Imposts and Excises shall be uniform throughout the United States.

the national government, (2) to defend the country, and (3) to provide services for the good of all our people. All national taxes in the form of charges on imported goods and on privileges, occupations, and sale of things, such as tobacco, must be the same in all parts of the country.

BORROWING MONEY

To borrow Money on the credit of the United States;

Congress has the power to borrow money for the government to use, by exchanging promises to pay for cash. (There is no constitutional limit to the amount.)

REGULATING COMMERCE

To regulate Commerce with foreign Nations, and among the several States, and with the Indian Tribes;

Congress has the power to make laws to control trade, transportation, communication, and related transactions with other countries, among the states, and with the Indian tribes.

NATURALIZATION, BANKRUPTCY LAWS

To establish an uniform Rule of Naturalization, and uniform Laws on the subject of Bankruptcies throughout the United States;

Congress has the power to say how people born in other countries can become citizens of the United States. Congress has the power to make for the entire country a legal way in which a person can escape his debts by giving his property to those whom he owes.

COINING MONEY, FIXING WEIGHTS AND MEASURES

To coin Money, regulate the Value thereof, and of foreign Coin, and fix the Standard of Weights and Measures;

Congress has the power to coin money and say how much it is worth and to put a value on foreign money. (Combined with the power to borrow money, this power enables Congress to issue paper money and make it legal in payment of all debts.) Congress has the power to define weights and measures so they will be the same everywhere.

PUNISHING COUNTERFEITERS

To provide for the Punishment of counterfeiting the Securities and current Coin of the United States;

Congress has the power to make laws to punish persons who make imitation government bonds, stamps, or money.

ESTABLISHING A POSTAL SERVICE

To establish Post Offices and post Roads;

Congress has the power to provide post offices and roads.

ISSUING PATENTS AND COPYRIGHTS

To promote the Progress of Science and useful Arts, by securing for limited Times to Authors and Inventors the exclusive Right to their respective Writings and Discoveries;

Congress has the power to help science, industry, and the arts by making laws under which inventors, writers, and artists may receive patents and copyrights on their work and so have exclusive right to profit from their creations.

ESTABLISHING COURTS

To constitute Tribunals inferior to the supreme Court;

Congress has the power to establish national courts that are not supreme (lower in authority than the Supreme Court of the United States).

PUNISHING CRIMES AT SEA

To define and punish Piracies and Felonies committed on the high Seas, and Offences against the Law of Nations;

Congress has the power to make laws which declare certain acts committed on the seas or oceans anywhere to be crimes and to say how the crimes are to be punished. Congress also has the power to make laws to punish those who break laws which are recognized by all nations (international law).

DECLARING WAR

To declare War, grant Letters of Marque and Reprisal, and make Rules concerning Captures on Land and Water;

Congress has the power to declare war, to permit persons to capture or destroy ships and goods of enemy nations without being guilty of piracy (this power given up in 1856), and to make rules about seizing enemy property on land or sea.

MAINTAINING ARMED FORCES

To raise and support Armies, but no Appropriation of Money to that Use shall be for a longer Term than two Years;

To provide and maintain a Navy;

To make Rules for the Government and Regulation of the land and naval Forces;

Congress has the power to raise armed forces (army, navy, and air) and supply them by any means and to any extent necessary. But Congress may not provide money for the Army for more than two years at a time. (There is no time limit on appropriations for the Navy because it is not so dangerous to liberty as a permanent army.) Congress also has the power to make rules for the organization and control of the armed services.

REGARDING THE MILITIA

To provide for calling forth the Militia to execute the Laws of the Union, suppress Insurrections and repel Invasions;

Congress has the power to call out the able-bodied men (militia) to (1) enforce the national laws, (2) put down rebellion, and (3) drive out enemies who attack us.

To provide for organizing, arming, and disciplining, the Militia, and for governing such Part of them as may be employed in the Service of the United States, reserving to the States respectively, the Appointment of the Officers, and the Authority of training the Militia according to the discipline prescribed by Congress;

Congress has the power to provide ways and means for states to have civilian soldiers and to make rules for using these soldiers for the whole country. But the states have the right to select the officers of the militia and to see that the militia is trained according to rules made by Congress. (The organized militia is the National Guard.)

MAKING LAWS FOR THE DISTRICT OF COLUMBIA

To exercise exclusive Legislation in all Cases whatsoever, over such District (not exceeding ten Miles square) as may, by Cession of particular States, and the Acceptance of Congress, become the Seat of the Government of the United States, and to exercise like Authority over all Places purchased by the Consent of the Legislature of the State in which the Same shall be, for the Erection of Forts, Magazines, Arsenals, dock-Yards, and other needful Buildings;—And

Congress has the power to make all laws for the District of Columbia, which includes the national capital (Washington, D. C.). Congress shall govern all places bought from the states for use as forts, arsenals, navy yards, and public buildings.

MAKING LAWS TO CARRY OUT POWERS

To make all laws which shall be necessary and proper for carrying into Execution the foregoing Powers, and all other Powers vested by this Consti-

Congress has the power to make laws that are needed in order to use the powers which it is given, or powers which are given to the government of the

tution in the Government of the United States, or in any Department or Officer thereof.

United States, by this Constitution. (This is the power which allows Congress to choose the means of exercising its specific powers, but it does *not* permit Congress to do *everything* that Congress might think desirable.

SECTION. 9. The Migration or Importation of such Persons as any of the States now existing shall think proper to admit, shall not be prohibited by the Congress prior to the Year one thousand eight hundred and eight, but a Tax or duty may be imposed on such Importation, not exceeding ten dollars for each Person.

Congress could not forbid the bringing in of "persons" (here the Constitution means "slaves") before 1808, but could levy a tax as high as $10 on each one brought in.

The Privilege of the Writ of Habeas Corpus shall not be suspended, unless when in Cases of Rebellion or Invasion the public Safety may require it.

Only when the country is in danger from rebellion or invasion can Congress stop the courts from issuing papers called "writs of habeas corpus." (A writ of habeas corpus compels a jailer or other person to bring a man into court so that the prisoner can have a judge decide if he is being held lawfully.)

No Bill of Attainder or ex post facto Law shall be passed.

Congress cannot pass a law convicting or punishing a particular person.

Congress cannot pass a law that makes unlawful something that has already been done legally.

No Capitation, [or other direct,][16] Tax shall be laid, unless in Proportion to the Census or Enumeration herein before directed to be taken.

Congress shall not levy "head" taxes or poll taxes unless all persons (men, women, and children) in the United States are taxed the same. Other direct taxes (except on incomes, according to the Sixteenth Amendment) must also be based on population instead of value, size, or any other factor. (The cost of a direct tax cannot be passed along to someone else by the original taxpayer.)

No Tax or Duty shall be laid on Articles exported from any State.

Congress shall not tax goods or products for being sent out of any state.

No Preference shall be given by any Regulation of Commerce or Revenue to the Ports of one State over those of another: nor shall Vessels bound to, or from, one State, be obliged to enter, clear, or pay Duties in another.

Congress shall not make any laws which favor one state or one city more than another in matters of trade or commerce. Ships from any state may enter the ports of any other state without paying charges.

No Money shall be drawn from the Treasury, but in Consequence of Appropriations made by Law; and a regular Statement and Account of the Receipts and Expenditures of all public Money shall be published from time to time.

Government money can be spent only if Congress passes a bill for that purpose. An account of money taken in and spent must be made public.

TITLES OF NOBILITY

No Title of Nobility shall be granted by the United States: And no Person holding any Office of Profit or Trust under them, shall, without the Consent of the Congress, accept of any present, Emolument, Office, or Title, of any kind whatever, from any King, Prince, or foreign State.

The United States shall not give a title (such as duke, earl, etc.) to anyone. No one in the service of the United States can accept a title, a present, or a position from another country without permission of Congress. (This prevents foreign governments from corrupting our officials.)

POWERS DENIED TO THE STATES

SECTION. 10. No State shall enter into any Treaty, Alliance, or Confederation; grant Letters of Marque and Reprisal; coin Money; emit Bills of Credit; make any Thing but gold and silver Coin a Tender in Payment of Debts; pass any Bill of Attainder, ex post facto Law, or Law impairing the Obligation of Contracts, or grant any Title of Nobility.

States cannot make treaties with foreign countries. States cannot grant permits for private citizens to fight other countries. States cannot coin their own money or issue paper money. States cannot pass laws which allow materials other than gold and silver to be used as money. States cannot pass laws declaring a particular person guilty of a stated offense and describing his punishment. States cannot pass laws which would punish a person for something that was not against the law when it was done. States cannot pass laws which excuse people from carrying out lawful agreements. States cannot give titles of nobility.

No State shall, without the Consent of the Congress, lay any Imposts or Duties on Imports or Exports, except what may be absolutely necessary for executing it's inspection Laws: and the net Produce of all Duties and Imposts, laid by any State on Imports or Exports, shall be for the Use of the Treasury of the United States; and all such Laws shall be subject to the Revision and Controul of the Congress.

No State shall, without the Consent of Congress, lay any Duty of Tonnage, keep Troops, or Ships of War in time of Peace, enter into any Agreement or Compact with another State, or with a foreign Power, or engage in War, unless actually invaded, or in such imminent Danger as will not admit of delay.

States cannot tax goods entering or leaving a state unless Congress agrees. But states may charge an inspection fee if necessary. Any profit from state import or export taxes approved by Congress must go into the United States Treasury, and these state tax laws may be changed by Congress. Without the consent of Congress, states may not tax ships, or keep troops (except civilian soldiers—militia) or warships in time of peace. States cannot make alliances with other states or with foreign countries unless Congress agrees. States cannot go to war without the consent of Congress unless invaded or in such great danger that delay is impossible.

THE EXECUTIVE DEPARTMENT • THE PRESIDENT AND THE VICE-PRESIDENT

ARTICLE. II.

SECTION. 1. The executive Power shall be vested in a President of the United States of America. He shall hold his Office during the Term of four Years, and, together with the Vice President, chosen for the same Term, be elected as follows

The leader and manager of our national government shall be the President. He shall have a four-year term of office. The Vice-President shall have the same term of office.

ELECTORS AND THEIR DUTIES

Each State shall appoint, in such Manner as the Legislature thereof may direct, a Number of Electors, equal to the whole Number of Senators and Representatives to which the State may be entitled in the Congress: but no Senator or Representative, or Person holding an Office of Trust or Profit under the United States, shall be appointed an Elector.

The President shall be elected by electors chosen by each state in the way the state legislature decides. Each state chooses as many electors as it has Representatives and Senators in Congress. No Senator or Representative in Congress or anyone holding a national government position may be an elector.

ORIGINAL METHOD OF ELECTING PRESIDENT AND VICE-PRESIDENT

[The Electors shall meet in their respective States,

(This paragraph was changed by the Twelfth

and vote by Ballot for two Persons, of whom one at least shall not be an Inhabitant of the same State with themselves. And they shall make a List of all the Persons voted for, and of the Number of Votes for each; which List they shall sign and certify, and transmit sealed to Seat of Government of the United States, directed to the President of the Senate. The President of the Senate shall, in the Presence of the Senate and House of Representatives, open all the Certificates, and the Votes shall then be counted. The Person having the greatest Number of Votes shall be the President, if such Number be a Majority of the whole Number of Electors appointed; and if there be more than one who have such Majority, and have an equal Number of Votes, then the House of Representatives shall immediately chuse by Ballot one of them for President; and if no Person have a Majority, then from the five highest on the List the said House shall in like manner chuse the President. But in chusing the President, the Votes shall be taken by States, the Representation from each State having one Vote; A quorum for this Purpose shall consist of a Member or Members from two thirds of the States, and a Majority of all the States shall be necessary to a Choice. In every Case, after the Choice of the President, the Person having the greatest Number of Votes of the Electors shall be the Vice President. But if there should remain two or more who have equal Votes, the Senate shall chuse from them by Ballot the Vice President.][12]

Amendment. See that Amendment for the way electors now choose the President and Vice-President.)

DATE OF PRESIDENTIAL ELECTION

The Congress may determine the Time of chusing the Electors, and the Day on which they shall give their Votes; which Day shall be the same throughout the United States.

Congress has the power to set the day for choosing electors and the day when the electors shall vote —the latter shall be the same day for all states. (The date set for choosing electors is the first Tuesday after the first Monday in November. The electors cast their votes on the first Monday after the second Wednesday in December.)

QUALIFICATIONS FOR PRESIDENT

No Person except a natural born Citizen, or a Citizen of the United States, at the time of the Adoption of this Constitution, shall be eligible to the Office of President; neither shall any Person be eligible to that Office who shall not have attained to the Age of thirty five Years, and been fourteen Years a Resident within the United States.

To be President, a person must be born in the United States or have parents who were citizens of the United States at the time of his birth (this matter has never raised a question in the case of a candidate) or be a citizen at the time the Constitution was adopted. Such a person must be at least thirty-five years old and must have lived in the United States at least fourteen years.

SUCCESSION TO THE PRESIDENCY

In Case of the Removal of the President from Office, or of his Death, Resignation, or Inability to discharge the Powers and Duties of the said Office, the Same shall devolve on the Vice President, and

If the President dies, resigns, is removed from office, or is unable to perform his duties, the Vice-President shall have charge. Congress may pass a law to decide who shall act as President in case both

the Congress may by Law provide for the Case of Removal, Death, Resignation or Inability, both of the President and Vice President declaring what Officer shall then act as President, and such Officer shall act accordingly, until the Disability be removed, or a President shall be elected.

the President and Vice-President cannot carry out the duties of the office. This person will perform the duties until the President (or the Vice-President) can take charge again or until a new President is elected. (Although the person who takes office if both President and Vice-President are dead or incapable only *acts* as President, the Vice-President *becomes* President when the President dies, but would be only acting President if the President were temporarily unable to perform his duties.)

PRESIDENT'S SALARY

The President shall, at stated Times, receive for his Services, a Compensation, which shall neither be encreased nor diminished during the Period for which he shall have been elected, and he shall not receive within that Period any other Emolument from the United States, or any of them.

The President shall be paid a salary which cannot be raised or lowered during his term of office. While in office, he cannot receive any other salary from the national government or from any state. (His salary is now $100,000 a year.)

PRESIDENTIAL OATH OF OFFICE

Before he enter on the Execution of his Office, he shall take the following Oath or Affirmation:—"I do solemnly swear (or affirm) that I will faithfully execute the Office of President of the United States, and will to the best of my Ability, preserve, protect and defend the Constitution of the United States."

Before he takes the office of President, the person elected must promise to do his work faithfully and see that the Constitution is obeyed.

POWERS OF THE PRESIDENT • MILITARY AND CIVIL

SECTION. 2. The President shall be Commander in Chief of the Army and Navy of the United States, and of the Militia of the several States, when called into the actual Service of the United States; he may require the Opinion, in writing, of the principal Officer in each of the executive Departments, upon any Subject relating to the Duties of their respective Offices, and he shall have Power to grant Reprieves and Pardons for Offences against the United States, except in Cases of Impeachment.

The President is the head of the country's armed forces, including the state militia when it is called into national service.

The President may ask for reports from the chief officers in charge of executing the laws.

The President may pardon or postpone the sentences of those convicted in the national courts, but he cannot interfere in cases of impeachment.

MAKING TREATIES • APPOINTING OFFICERS

He shall have Power, by and with the Advice and Consent of the Senate, to make Treaties, provided two thirds of the Senators present concur; and he shall nominate, and by and with the Advice and Consent of the Senate, shall appoint Ambassadors, other public Ministers and Consuls, Judges of the supreme Court, and all other Officers of the United States, whose Appointments are not herein otherwise provided for, and which shall be established by Law: but the Congress may by Law vest the Appointment of such inferior Officers, as they think proper, in the President alone, in the Courts of Law, or in the Heads of Departments.

The President shall have Power to fill up all Vacancies that may happen during the Recess of the

The President has the power to make treaties with foreign countries if the Senate approves by a two-thirds vote of those present.

The President has the power to appoint persons to represent the United States in other countries, provided the Senate approves of them by a simple majority vote. He also has the power to appoint, with the Senate's approval, the justices of the Supreme Court and other government officials, unless the Constitution provides a different way.

Congress may pass laws giving the President, the courts, or heads of government departments, the right to select people for certain government positions.

The President may appoint persons to fill vacancies that occur when the Senate is not meeting. These

Senate, by granting Commissions which shall expire at the End of their next Session.

appointments hold good until the end of the next meeting of the Senate.

OTHER PRESIDENTIAL POWERS

SECTION. 3. He shall from time to time give to the Congress Information of the State of the Union, and recommend to their Consideration such Measures as he shall judge necessary and expedient; he may, on extraordinary Occasions, convene both Houses, or either of them, and in Case of Disagreement between them, with Respect to the Time of Adjournment, he may adjourn them to such Time as he shall think proper; he shall receive Ambassadors and other public Ministers; he shall take Care that the Laws be faithfully executed, and shall Commission all the Officers of the United States.

The President shall inform Congress about the condition of our country (which he always does at the beginning of each session of Congress). He must recommend laws that he thinks are needed, and advise Congress about desirable changes or improvements in the government.

In emergencies the President may call meetings of the House of Representatives, the Senate, or both.

If the two houses of Congress disagree about ending their meetings, the President may end them. (This has not yet happened.)

The President deals with representatives of other countries.

It is the President's duty to see that the laws of the country are followed.

The President must sign the papers which show the right of officers to hold their positions.

IMPEACHMENT

SECTION. 4. The President, Vice President and all civil Officers of the United States, shall be removed from Office on Impeachment for, and Conviction of, Treason, Bribery, or other high Crimes and Misdemeanors.

The President, Vice-President, and other officers of the national government (except Congressmen and military officers) can be removed from office after being accused by the House of Representatives and then convicted by the Senate of treason (aiding our country's enemies), of taking bribes, or of committing other crimes.

ARTICLE. III.   JUDICIAL DEPARTMENT • JUDICIAL POWER • JUDGES

SECTION. 1. The judicial Power of the United States, shall be vested in one supreme Court, and in such inferior Courts as the Congress may from time to time ordain and establish. The Judges, both of the supreme and inferior Courts, shall hold their Offices during good Behaviour, and shall, at stated Times, receive for their Services, a Compensation which shall not be diminished during their Continuance in Office.

The Supreme Court of the United States is the final authority in matters of law. Congress may establish other national courts with less power than the Supreme Court.

Judges of all national courts hold office for life, or until they are proved guilty of wrongful acts. They are paid a salary which cannot be lowered while they hold office.

CASES HEARD IN UNITED STATES COURTS

SECTION, 2. The judicial Power shall extend to all Cases, in Law and Equity, arising under this Constitution, the Laws of the United States, and Treaties made, or which shall be made, under their Authority;—to all Cases affecting Ambassadors, other public Ministers and Consuls;—to all Cases of admiralty and maritime Jurisdiction;—to Controversies to which the United States shall be a Party;—to Controversies between two or more States;—[between a State and Citizens of another State;][11]—between Citizens of different States,—between Citizens

The national courts settle disputes which have to do with the Constitution, with laws of the United States, with treaties, and with laws about ships and shipping. These courts also settle disputes in which representatives of foreign countries, the national government, or two or more state governments are interested. (The next part has been changed by the Eleventh Amendment.)

National courts may also settle disputes between people of different states, disputes in which

of the same State claiming Lands under Grants of different States, and between a State, or the Citizens thereof, and foreign States, Citizens or Subjects.

people of the same state claim lands in other states, and disputes between a state or citizens of a state and a foreign country or citizens of a foreign country.

JURISDICTION OF THE COURTS

In all Cases affecting Ambassadors, other public Ministers and Consuls, and those in which a State shall be Party, the supreme Court shall have original Jurisdiction. In all the other Cases before mentioned, the supreme Court shall have appellate Jurisdiction, both as to Law and Fact, with such Exceptions, and under such Regulations as the Congress shall have.

If the representative of a foreign country is in the dispute, or if a state is in the dispute, the trial may go directly to the Supreme Court. All other disputes mentioned above can be tried in a lower national court first. Decisions in such cases may be appealed to the Supreme Court after being tried in the lower court. Congress has the power to make further rules about these cases.

CRIMINAL TRIALS ARE BY JURY

The Trial of all Crimes, except in cases of Impeachment, shall be by Jury; and such Trial shall be held in the State where the said Crimes shall have been committed; but when not committed within any State, the Trial shall be at such Place or Places as the Congress may by Law have directed.

Anyone, except an impeached official, accused of a crime by the national government has a right to a trial by jury.

The trial shall be held in the state where the crime was committed. If the crime was not done in any state (for example, a crime done at sea), the trial shall be held in a place Congress has chosen by law.

TREASON

SECTION. 3. Treason against the United States, shall consist only in levying War against them, or in adhering to their Enemies, giving them Aid and Comfort. No Person shall be convicted of Treason unless on the Testimony of two Witnesses to the same overt Act, or on Confession in open Court.

The Congress shall have Power to declare the Punishment of Treason, but no Attainder of Treason shall work Corruption of Blood, or Forfeiture except during the Life of the Person attainted.

Treason is carrying on war against the United States or helping the enemies of the United States.

No one can be punished for treason unless he confesses in court, or unless at least two witnesses say he committed a treasonable act.

Congress has the power to fix the punishment for treason. (It is now death or imprisonment and fine.) The family of a person guilty of treason cannot also be punished for his crime.

ARTICLE. IV.

RELATIONS OF THE STATES • ACTS, RECORDS, AND PROCEEDINGS

SECTION. 1. Full Faith and Credit shall be given in each State to the public Acts, Records, and judicial Proceedings of every other State. And the Congress may by general Laws prescribe the Manner in which such Acts, Records and Proceedings shall be proved, and the Effect thereof.

All states must accept as legal and binding the laws, records, and court decisions of other states. Congress has the power to make laws which say how these laws, records, and decisions must be presented for acceptance.

RIGHTS OF CITIZENS IN OTHER STATES

SECTION. 2. The Citizens of each State shall be entitled to all Privileges and Immunities of Citizens in the several States.

A Person charged in any State with Treason, Felony, or other Crime, who shall flee from Justice, and be found in another State, shall on Demand of the Executive Authority of the State from which he fled, be delivered up, to be removed to the State having Jurisdiction of the Crime.

[No Person held to Service or Labour in one State,

A citizen of another state has the same rights as the citizens of the state where he happens to be. (But he can be denied privileges that resident citizens enjoy, such as voting in elections.)

Anyone accused of crime who is found in another state shall be sent back for trial, if the governor of the state where the crime was committed requests it. (But there is no legal way to compel a governor to return such a refugee.)

Slaves do not become free by escaping to a free

under the Laws thereof, escaping into another, shall, in Consequence of any Law or Regulation therein, be discharged from such Service or Labour, but shall be delivered up on claim of the Party to whom such Service or Labour may be due.][13]

state, but must be sent back to their owners. (This part is no longer in effect.)

NEW STATES AND TERRITORIES

SECTION. 3. New States may be admitted by the Congress into this Union; but no new State shall be formed or erected within the Jurisdiction of any other State; nor any State be formed by the Junction of two or more States, or Parts of States, without the Consent of the Legislatures of the States concerned as well as of the Congress.

Congress has the right to add new states to the United States. (There is no way for a state to leave the Union.)

No state can be divided to make another state without the consent of the original state and Congress. (Two such states have been formed from existing states: Maine from Massachusetts in 1820; and West Virginia from Virginia in 1863. The law admitting Texas to the Union provided that it could later be divided into five states.)

A new state cannot be made from parts of two or more states without the agreement of the legislatures of the states and of Congress. (None has been formed this way.)

The Congress shall have Power to dispose of and make all needful Rules and Regulations respecting the Territory or other Property belonging to the United States; and nothing in this Constitution shall be so construed as to Prejudice any Claims of the United States, or of any particular State.

Congress has the power to make rules about all government lands and property. (This Constitution did not try to settle conflicting claims of states to western lands.) The government of territories before they become states is determined by Congress.

PROTECTING THE STATES

SECTION. 4. The United States shall guarantee to every State in this Union a Republican Form of Government, and shall protect each of them against Invasion; and on Application of the Legislature, or of the Executive (when the Legislature cannot be convened) against domestic Violence.

It is the duty of the national government to see that every state has a government in which the people rule and that each state is protected from invasion. Help must be sent a state to put down riots if the state legislature asks it, or if the governor asks when the legislature is not meeting. (The President can also send troops into a state without the request of state officials if necessary to enforce national law and maintain peace.)

AMENDING THE CONSTITUTION

ARTICLE. V.

The Congress, whenever two thirds of both Houses shall deem it necessary, shall propose Amendments to this Constitution, or, on the Application of the Legislatures of two thirds of the several States, shall call a convention for proposing Amendments, which, in either Case, shall be valid to all Intents and Purposes, as Part of this Constitution, when ratified by the Legislatures of three fourths of the several States, or by Conventions in three fourths thereof, as the one or the other Mode of Ratification may be proposed by the Congress; Provided that no Amendment which may be made prior to the Year One thousand eight hundred and eight shall in any Manner affect the first and fourth Clauses in the Ninth Section of

If two thirds of the Senate and two thirds of the House of Representatives think it necessary, the Congress may suggest amendments to the Constitution. If legislatures of two thirds of the state request it, Congress must call a meeting of specially elected persons to suggest amendments. If amendments are proposed in either of these two ways, they become a part of the Constitution if legislatures of three fourths of the states agree, or if three fourths of the states have special meetings which agree to the amendments. Congress may decide which of these two ways of approving amendments is to be used.

No amendment could be made before 1808 that would stop the bringing in of slaves to the United

the first Article; and that no State, without its Consent, shall be deprived of it's equal suffrage in the Senate.

States or allow direct taxes without distributing the burden according to the population of the states. And no amendment can take away a state's right to have the same number of Senators as other states, unless the particular state agrees to this change.

NATIONAL SUPREMACY

ARTICLE. VI.

All Debts contracted and Engagements entered into, before the Adoption of this Constitution, shall be as valid against the United States under this Constitution, as under the Confederation.

This Constitution, and the Laws of the United States which shall be made in pursuance thereof; and all Treaties made or which shall be made, under the Authority of the United States, shall be the supreme Law of the Land; and the Judges in every State shall be bound thereby, any Thing in the Constitution or Laws of any State to the Contrary notwithstanding.

The Senators and Representatives before mentioned, and the Members of the several State Legislatures, and all executive and judicial Officers, both of the United States and of the several States, shall be bound by Oath or Affirmation, to support this Constitution; but no religious Test shall ever be required as a Qualification to any Office or public Trust under the United States.

Promises to repay money borrowed and agreements made by Congress before the adoption of the Constitution shall be as binding on the United States as they were before this Constitution was put into effect.

This Constitution, the laws made by Congress as permitted under this Constitution, and treaties made by the United States shall be the highest law of the United States. Judges must follow this law, even if state laws contradict it. (This is the rule which makes the federal system of government work. No state law contrary to national law can be enforced.)

All national government and state government officials must promise to follow this Constitution.

National officials and employees cannot be required to take any kind of religious test in order to hold office. (The states could still require their officials to meet religious standards.)

RATIFICATION

ARTICLE. VII.

The Ratification of the Conventions of nine States, shall be sufficient for the Establishment of this Constitution between the States so ratifying the Same. done in Convention by the Unanimous Consent of the States present the Seventeenth Day of September in the Year of our Lord one thousand seven hundred and Eighty seven and of the Independence of the United States of America the Twelfth In Witness whereof We have hereunto subscribed our Names.

When nine states have held meetings and agreed to this Constitution, government under the Constitution shall begin in the states which have agreed to it. (This method of changing the form of government was contrary to the existing Articles of Confederation, which required consent of all thirteen states. Special conventions were required because they would be more likely to accept the new Constitution than the people or the state legislators. Within a year nine states had ratified the new Constitution.)

The states represented in the Constitutional Convention on September 17, 1787, agreed to the Constitution as a plan of government to be proposed. (Rhode Island refused to take part in the Convention. The other twelve states selected sixty-five men to go to the Convention; and fifty-five of them attended meetings. Forty-two were present the day the Constitution was signed, but only thirty-nine signed it.)

The signers were:

Gº Washington—Presidt.

Attest WILLIAM JACKSON Secretary
and deputy from Virginia

| New Hampshire | { John Langdon
Nicholas Gilman | Massachusetts | { Nathaniel Gorham
Rufus King |

Connecticut	{ Wm. Saml. Johnson Roger Sherman	Maryland	{ James McHenry Dan of St Thos. Jenifer Danl. Carroll
New York	{ Alexander Hamilton		
New Jersey	{ Wil: Livingston David Brearley Wm. Paterson Jona: Dayton	Virginia	{ John Blair James Madison Jr.
Pennsylvania	{ B Franklin Thomas Mifflin Robt Morris Geo. Clymer Thos. FitzSimons Jared Ingersoll James Wilson Gouv Morris	North Carolina	{ Wm. Blount Richd. Dobbs Spaight Hu Williamson
Delaware	{ Geo: Read Gunning Bedford jun John Dickinson Richard Bassett Jaco: Broom	South Carolina	{ J. Rutledge Charles Cotesworth Pinckney Charles Pinckney Pierce Butler
		Georgia	{ William Few Abr Baldwin

AMENDMENTS TO THE CONSTITUTION

The first ten Amendments, adopted in 1791, are frequently called the Bill of Rights

RELIGIOUS AND POLITICAL FREEDOM

AMENDMENT 1.

Congress shall make no law respecting an establishment of religion, or prohibiting the free exercise thereof; or abridging the freedom of speech, or of the press; or the right of the people peaceably to assemble, and to petition the Government for a redress of grievances.

Congress cannot pass laws which make any religion the official religion of the country, or laws which prevent people from following their own religion; or laws which prevent people from speaking and printing what they wish (if it is not slanderous or seditious); or laws that prevent people from meeting peaceably, or from asking the government to right any wrong.

THE RIGHT TO BEAR ARMS

AMENDMENT 2.

A well regulated Militia, being necessary to the security of a free State, the right of the people to keep and bear Arms, shall not be infringed.

Because people have a right to protect themselves with armed men (militia), Congress cannot pass any laws which prevent men from keeping and carrying firearms for military purposes. (Congress can and has restricted the possession of sawed-off shotguns and concealed weapons for private purposes.)

QUARTERING OF SOLDIERS

AMENDMENT 3.

No Soldier shall, in time of peace be quartered in any house, without the consent of the Owner, nor in time of war, but in a manner to be prescribed by law.

In peacetime, citizens cannot be compelled to give either room or board to soldiers in their homes. In wartime, this may be done if Congress passes a law providing for it.

SEARCHES AND SEIZURES

AMENDMENT 4.

The right of the people to be secure in their persons, houses, papers, and effects, against unreasonable searches and seizures, shall not be violated, and no Warrants shall issue, but upon probable cause, supported by Oath or affirmation, and particularly describing the place to be searched, and the persons or things to be seized.

A man's house cannot be searched or his property or papers taken except in ways that are according to law. Courts cannot issue search warrants unless convinced there is good reason for doing so. Whoever asks for a search warrant must give the reasons and explain exactly where the search is to be made and what is to be taken. (This put an end to "writs of assistance," which were general warrants used by the British chiefly to catch smugglers.)

THE RIGHT TO LIFE, LIBERTY, AND PROPERTY

AMENDMENT 5.

No person shall be held to answer for a capital, or otherwise infamous crime, unless on a presentment or indictment of a Grand Jury, except in cases arising in the land or naval forces, or in the Militia, when in actual service in time of War or public danger; nor shall any person be subject for the same offence to be twice put in jeopardy of life or limb; nor shall be compelled in any criminal case to be a witness against himself, nor be deprived of life, liberty, or property, without due process of law; nor shall private property be taken for public use, without just compensation.

No one can be tried in a national court for a serious crime unless a grand jury makes an accusation, except in the case of men in our armed forces in times of war or public danger.

No one can be tried a second time for an offense of which a court has once declared him innocent. (But if the offense is a crime under state law, the person can be tried again in a state court. Or if the offense hurts someone the person can be made to pay for damages though innocent of a crime.)

No one can be forced to say anything in a national court that would help convict himself of a crime.

No one shall lose his life, his freedom, or his property except in the exact ways laid down by law. (The Fourteenth Amendment applies this rule to the states, too.)

The government cannot take a man's property without paying a fair price for it (and then only if it is to be used for the benefit of everybody).

PROTECTION IN CRIMINAL TRIALS

AMENDMENT 6.

In all criminal prosecutions, the accused shall enjoy the right to a speedy and public trial, by an impartial jury of the State and district wherein the crime shall have been committed, which district shall have been previously ascertained by law, and to be informed of the nature and cause of the accusation; to be confronted with the witnesses against him; to have compulsory process for obtaining witnesses in his favor, and to have the Assistance of Counsel for his defence.

A man accused of crime must be given prompt trial in public. His guilt or innocence must be decided by a jury chosen from the state and the district where the crime was committed. He must be told what he is being tried for. He must be present when witnesses speak against him in court. He can have witnesses called to testify for him. He can have a lawyer to defend him. (This Amendment applies only to national courts but the states follow nearly the same rules.)

CASES AT COMMON LAW

AMENDMENT 7.

In Suits at common law, where the value in controversy shall exceed twenty dollars, the right of trial by jury shall be preserved, and no fact tried by a jury, shall be otherwise re-examined in any Court of the United States than according to the rules of the common law.

In disputes over property worth more than twenty dollars, either party to the dispute can insist on having a jury trial, or both can agree not to have a jury. (This applies only in law suits under Common Law, not under acts of Congress or in equity cases such as an action for an injunction.)

After a jury's decision, a matter of fact cannot be brought up again in a higher court unless before a jury.

BAIL, FINES, PUNISHMENTS

AMENDMENT 8.

Excessive bail shall not be required, nor excessive fines imposed, nor cruel and unusual punishments inflicted.

To get out of jail, a man accused of crime cannot be forced to put up an extra large sum of money or property as bail to make certain he will not run away to escape trial. Courts cannot fine persons too much for the crime done, or punish convicts in cruel or unusual ways (such as branding with a hot iron). (But death is not considered a cruel or unusual punishment for very serious crimes like treason, if the convict is not tortured in the process.)

AMENDMENT 9. ALL OTHER RIGHTS

The enumeration in the Constitution of certain rights, shall not be construed to deny or disparage others retained by the people.

The mention of certain rights in the Constitution does not mean that these are the only rights that people have or does not make the other rights less important. (These unnamed rights probably meant "pursuit of happiness"—rights so vague that no law has ever been thought to violate them.)

AMENDMENT 10. POWERS RESERVED TO STATES AND PEOPLE

The powers not delegated to the United States by the Constitution, nor prohibited by it to the States, are reserved to the States respectively, or to the people.

All powers not given by the Constitution to the national government, and all powers not denied to the states by the Constitution are kept by the states or by the people of the states. (This guarantees state rights, but not state supremacy.)

AMENDMENT 11. (1798) SUITS AGAINST A STATE

The Judicial power of the United States shall not be construed to extend to any suit in law or equity, commenced or prosecuted against one of the United States by Citizens of another State, or by Citizens or Subjects of any Foreign State.

Citizens of other states or of foreign countries cannot sue a state in the national courts.

AMENDMENT 12. (1804) ELECTION OF PRESIDENT AND VICE-PRESIDENT

The Electors shall meet in their respective states, and vote by ballot for President and Vice-President, one of whom, at least, shall not be an inhabitant of of same state with themselves; they shall name in their ballots the person voted for as President, and in distinct ballots the person voted for as Vice-President, and they shall make distinct lists of all persons voted for as President, and of all persons voted for as Vice-President, and of the number of votes for each, which list they shall sign and certify, and transmit sealed to the seat of the government of the United States, directed to the President of the Senate;—The President of the Senate shall, in the presence of the Senate and House of Representatives, open all the certificates and the votes shall then be counted;—The person having the greatest number of votes for President, shall be the President, if such number be a majority of the whole number of Electors appointed; and if no person have such majority, then from the persons having the highest number not exceeding three on the list of those voted for as President, the House of Representatives shall choose immediately, by ballot, the President. But in choos-

The electors meet in their own states and cast separate ballots for President and Vice-President. (Before 1804 each elector had voted for two persons for the two offices without distinguishing between them.) At least one of the candidates they vote for must live in another state. After the vote, the electors make a list of the persons voted for as President and another list of the persons voted for as Vice-President. On each list they write the total votes cast for each person and then sign their names, seal the lists, and send them to the president of the Senate in Washington.

In a meeting of all members of Congress, the president of the Senate opens the lists from all the states, and the votes are counted. The person having the most votes for President shall be President if the number of votes received is more than half of the total number of all electors. (Now 266 or more.) If no person has more than half of this total, the House of Representatives selects the President from the candidates who have the highest number of electoral votes, but no more than the three highest can be considered. (Before 1804 the House could

ing the President, the votes shall be taken by states, the representation from each state having one vote; a quorum for this purpose shall consist of a member or members from two-thirds of the states, and a majority of all the states shall be necessary to a choice. And if the House of Representatives shall not choose a President whenever the right of choice shall develop upon them, before the fourth day of March next following, then the Vice-President shall act as President, as in the case of the death or other constitutional disability of the President.—The person having the greatest number of votes as Vice-President, shall be the Vice-President, if such number be a majority of the whole number of Electors appointed, and if no person have a majority, then from the two highest numbers on the list, the Senate shall choose the Vice-President; a quorum for the purpose shall consist of two-thirds of the whole number of Senators, and a majority of the whole number shall be necessary to a choice. But no person constitutionally ineligible to the office of President shall be eligible to that of Vice-President of the United States.

choose any one of the five highest.) Each state has one vote, no matter how many Representatives it has. Two thirds of the states must be represented when this vote is cast. The candidate who receives a majority of the votes of the state shall be President. (Only twice has the House of Representatives elected the President—Jefferson in 1800 and Adams in 1824.)

If the House of Representatives does not elect a President before the date set for the new President to take office, the Vice-President shall act as President. (The President's term now begins on January 20.)

The person who receives the most electoral votes for Vice-President becomes Vice-President if he has over half of the electoral votes. If no person has over half, the Senate votes for one of the two highest on the list of Vice-Presidential candidates. Two thirds of all the Senators must be present when the vote is taken. To be elected Vice-President, the candidate must receive the votes of more than half (49 or more out of 65 or more) of all the Senators.

A person who does not have the qualifications for President of the United States cannot be Vice-President. (This corrected an oversight in the original Constitution.)

ABOLISHING SLAVERY

AMENDMENT 13. (1865)

SECTION. 1. Neither slavery nor involuntary servitude, except as a punishment for crime whereof the party shall have been duly convicted, shall exist within the United States, or any place subject to their jurisdiction.

SECTION. 2. Congress shall have power to enforce this article by appropriate legislation.

Slavery shall not be allowed in the United States or in any lands under our control. No one shall be compelled to work against his will unless a court has given that punishment for committing a crime. (Henceforth neither the states nor the nation could permit slavery.)

Congress has the power to make laws which will put this amendment into effect.

CIVIL RIGHTS IN THE STATES

AMENDMENT 14. (1868)

SECTION. 1. All persons born or naturalized in the United States, and subject to the jurisdiction thereof, are citizens of the United States and of the State wherein they reside. No State shall make or enforce any law which shall abridge the privileges or immunities of citizens of the United States; nor shall any State deprive any person of life, liberty, or property, without due process of law; nor deny to any person within its jurisdiction the equal protection of the laws.

SECTION. 2. Representatives shall be apportioned among the several States according to their respective numbers, counting the whole number of persons in each State, excluding Indians not taxed. But when the right to vote at any election for the choice of

All persons born in the United States and under our laws or those who have been naturalized are citizens of the United States and of the state where they live. (This defined national citizenship and wiped out the Dred Scott decision of the Supreme Court in 1857, which denied that Negroes were citizens.)

States cannot make laws or enforce laws which are already made that prevent any citizen from enjoying his rights. States cannot take anyone's life, liberty, or property except in ways which the courts say are legal and proper. Anyone living in any state is entitled to that state's protection and the benefit of its laws. (This did not add to existing rights of citizens but did forbid the states to take away any rights,

electors for President and Vice President of the United States, Representatives in Congress, the Executive and Judicial officers of a State, or the members of the Legislature thereof, is denied to any of the male inhabitants of such State, being twenty-one years of age, and citizens of the United States, or in any way abridged, except for participation in rebellion, or other crime, the basis of representation therein shall be reduced in the proportion which the number of such male citizens shall bear to the whole number of male citizens twenty-one years of age in such State.

SECTION. 3. No person shall be a Senator or Representative in Congress, or elector of President or Vice President, or hold any office, civil or military, under the United States, or under any State, who, having previously taken an oath, as a member of Congress, or as any officer of the United States, or as a member of any State legislature, or as an executive or judicial officer of any State, to support the Constitution of the United States, shall have engaged in insurrection or rebellion against the same, or given aid or comfort to the enemies thereof. But Congress may by a vote of two-thirds of each House, remove such disability.

SECTION. 4. The validity of the public debt of the United States, authorized by law, including debts incurred for payment of pensions and bounties for services in suppressing insurrection or rebellion shall not be questioned. But neither the United States nor any State shall assume or pay any debt or obligation incurred in aid of insurrection or rebellion against the United States, or any claim for the loss or emancipation of any slave; but all such debts, obligations and claims shall be held illegal and void.

SECTION. 5. The Congress shall have power to enforce, by appropriate legislation, the provisions of this article.

particularly to prevent Negroes from enjoying them.)

All people, except untaxed Indians (none now) shall be counted in order to determine how many Representatives in Congress each state shall have. (This changes Article 1, Section 2, which declared that only three fifths of the slaves should be counted.)

If men citizens, who are twenty-one and have not committed crimes which keep them from voting, are not allowed to vote by any state, that state's representation in the House of Representatives may be cut down according to the number of people deprived of their vote. (This was a means of forcing states to allow Negro men to vote, but it has never been used though there have been many opportunities.)

Persons who have sworn to uphold the government and the Constitution in taking either a state or a national government office, and then rebelled against the government, or helped the government's enemies, cannot again hold government office. But Congress by a two-thirds vote of both houses may allow such a person to hold office again. (This was to prevent any Confederate leader from having any political rights. It was withdrawn on June 6, 1898.)

Money borrowed by the United States government, including money for soldier pensions and other expenses made because of the War Between the States, is a lawful debt of the United States and shall not be questioned. The United States will not and the states must not repay any money borrowed to help fight against the government. Neither the United States nor any state shall pay owners for slaves who have been freed.

Congress has the power to make laws that will put this amendment into effect.

AMENDMENT 15. (1870) **NEGRO SUFFRAGE**

SECTION. 1. The right of citizens of the United States to vote shall not be denied or abridged by the United States or by any State on account of race, color, or previous condition of servitude—

SECTION. 2. The Congress shall have power to enforce this article by appropriate legislation—

Neither the United States nor any state has the right to keep a citizen from voting because of his race or color, or because he was once a slave.

Congress has the power to make laws that will put this amendment into effect.

AMENDMENT 16. (1913) **INCOME TAXES**

The Congress shall have power to lay and collect taxes on incomes, from whatever source derived, without apportionment among the several States, and without regard to any census or enumeration.

Congress has the power to levy and collect income taxes from the people. In levying such a tax, Congress does not have to apportion it among the states or divide the taxes according to the population. (If it were not for this amendment the income tax, like other direct taxes, would have to be levied so that the amount collected from each state would be in proportion to the population.)

DIRECT ELECTION OF SENATORS

AMENDMENT 17. (1913)

The Senate of the United States shall be composed of two Senators from each State, elected by the people thereof, for six years; and each Senator shall have one vote. The electors in each State shall have the qualifications requisite for electors of the most numerous branch of the State legislatures.

When vacancies happen in the representation of any State in the Senate, the executive authority of such State shall issue writs of election to fill such vacancies: *Provided,* That the legislature of any State may empower the executive thereof to make temporary appointments until the people fill the vacancies by election as the legislature may direct.

This amendment shall not be so construed as to affect the election or term of any Senator chosen before it becomes valid as part of the Constitution.

The Senate shall be made up of two Senators from each state, elected by the people of the state (not by the state legislature) for six-year terms. Each Senator has one vote. Citizens entitled to vote for representatives in the state legislatures may vote for Senators.

The governor of a state shall call an election to fill a vacancy among that state's Senators. But the state legislature may allow the governor to appoint someone to fill the Senate vacancy until the election is held. (Most vacancies are filled by temporary appointments.)

This amendment did not affect any election that had been held or the term of office of any Senator in the Senate at the time the amendment was adopted.

NATIONAL PROHIBITION

AMENDMENT 18. (1919)

SECTION. 1. After one year from the ratification of this article the manufacture, sale, or transportation of intoxicating liquors within, the importation thereof into, or the exportation thereof from the United States and all territory subject to the jurisdiction thereof for beverage purposes is hereby prohibited.

SECTION. 2. The Congress and the several States shall have concurrent power to enforce this article by appropriate legislation.

SECTION. 3. This article shall be inoperative unless it shall have been ratified as an amendment to the Constitution by the legislatures of the several States, as provided in the Constitution, within seven years from the date of the submission hereof to the States by the Congress.

One year after this amendment is ratified it shall become illegal to make, sell, or carry in the United States or its territories, intoxicating liquors for drinking purposes. It shall be illegal to send such liquors out of the country and its territories or to bring such liquors into them. (This amendment was declared in force on January 29, 1919.)

Congress and the states have the power to make laws needed to make this amendment effective.

This amendment will not become a part of the Constitution unless ratified by the legislatures of the states within seven years.

WOMAN SUFFRAGE

AMENDMENT 19. (1920)

The right of citizens of the United States to vote shall not be denied or abridged by the United States or by any State on account of sex.

Congress shall have power to enforce this article by appropriate legislation.

Neither the United States nor any state has the right to keep a citizen from voting because she is a woman.

Congress has the power to make laws that will make this amendment effective.

PRESIDENTIAL AND CONGRESSIONAL TERMS OF OFFICE

AMENDMENT 20. (1933)

SECTION 1. The terms of the President and Vice President shall end at noon on the 20th day of January, and the terms of Senators and Representatives at noon on the 3d day of January, of the years

The terms of office of President and Vice-President shall end at noon, January 20, and the terms of office of Senators and Representatives shall end at noon, January 3, of the same years they would have

in which such terms would have ended if this article had not been ratified; and the terms of their successors shall then begin.

SECTION. 2. The Congress shall assemble at least once in every year, and such meeting shall begin at noon on the 3d day of January, unless they shall by law appoint a different day.

SECTION. 3. If, at the time fixed for the beginning of the term of the President, the President elect shall have died, the Vice President elect shall become President. If a President shall not have been chosen before the time fixed for the beginning of his term, or if the President elect shall have failed to qualify, then the Vice President elect shall act as President until a President shall have qualified; and the Congress may by law provide for the case wherein neither a President elect nor a Vice President elect shall have qualified, declaring who shall then act as President, or the manner in which one who is to act shall be selected, and such person shall act accordingly until a President or Vice President shall have qualified.

SECTION. 4. The Congress may by law provide for the case of the death of any of the persons from whom the House of Representatives may choose a President whenever the right of choice shall have devolved upon them, and for the case of the death of any of the persons from whom the Senate may choose a Vice President whenever the right of choice shall have devolved upon them.

SECTION. 5. Sections 1 and 2 shall take effect on the 15th day of October following the ratification of this article.

SECTION. 6. This article shall be inoperative unless it shall have been ratified as an amendment to the Constitution by the legislatures of three-fourths of the several States within seven years from the date of its submission.

ended if this amendment had not been made. (The former date was March 4.) The new officials' terms begin then.

Congress must meet at least once a year. The meeting must begin at noon, January 3, unless another date is selected by law. (The former date was the first Monday in December.)

If the person elected President dies before he takes office, the person elected Vice-President shall become President. If a President has not been chosen by January 3, or if the person chosen is not qualified to be President, then the person elected Vice-President shall act as President until a President has qualified. Congress may pass a law to determine who shall act as President if neither the person elected President nor the one elected Vice-President qualifies for the position. Congress may decide how this person shall be chosen. (But Congress has not yet done so.)

Congress has the power to make a law which tells the House of Representatives what to do in case it must select a President and one of the candidates has died. Congress also has the power to make a law which tells the Senate what to do in case it must select a Vice-President and one of the candidates has died. (See Amendment 12.)

Sections 1 and 2 of this amendment become law on October 15 after three fourths of the states have agreed to this amendment. (This amendment was declared to be ratified on February 6, 1933.)

This amendment will not become a part of the Constitution unless the legislatures of three fourths of the states agree to it within seven years.

AMENDMENT 21. (1933)   REPEAL OF NATIONAL PROHIBITION

SECTION. 1. The eighteenth article of amendment to the Constitution of the United States is hereby repealed.

SECTION. 2. The transportation or importation into any State, Territory, or possession of the United States for delivery or use therein of intoxicating liquors, in violation of the laws thereof, is hereby prohibited.

SECTION. 3. This article shall be inoperative unless it shall have been ratified as an amendment to the Constitution by conventions in the several States, as provided in the Constitution, within seven years from the date of the submission hereof to the States by the Congress.

This amendment made the Eighteenth Amendment of no effect, so that the national government could no longer prohibit the manufacture, sale, or transportation of intoxicating liquor.

(But if a state forbids bringing liquor for drinking purposes across its boundaries for use in that state, such carrying of liquor is a crime against the United States as well as against the state.)

Congress required this amendment to be ratified by assemblies specially elected for that purpose. (It is the only amendment adopted in this way.)

This amendment will not become a part of the Constitution unless agreed to by assemblies in three fourths of the states within seven years. (It was declared to be in force on December 5, 1933.)

TERMS OF OFFICE OF THE PRESIDENT

SECTION. 1. No person shall be elected to the office of the President more than twice, and no person who has held the office of President, or acted as President, for more than two years of a term to which some other person was elected President shall be elected to the office of the President more than once. But this article shall not apply to any person holding the office of President when this article was proposed by the Congress, and shall not prevent any person who may be holding the office of President, or acting as President, during the term within which this article becomes operative from holding the office of President or acting as President during the remainder of such term.

SECTION. 2. This article shall be inoperative unless it shall have been ratified as an amendment to the Constitution by the legislatures of three-fourths of the several States within seven years from the date of its submission to the States by the Congress.

No person can have more than two terms as President. Holding the office of President, or acting as President, for more than two years will be considered as one full term. This article does not apply to the President holding office at the time this amendment was proposed by Congress. This article cannot prevent the person holding the office of President, or acting as President, when the article is ratified, from finishing his term of office.

This amendment becomes part of the Constitution if the legislatures of three-fourths of the states agree to it within seven years. (This amendment was declared to be ratified on March 1, 1951.)

PRESIDENTIAL ELECTORS FROM DISTRICT OF COLUMBIA

AMENDMENT 23. (1961)

SECTION 1. The District constituting the seat of Government of the United States shall appoint in such manner as the Congress may direct:

A number of electors of President and Vice President equal to the whole number of Senators and Representatives in Congress to which the District would be entitled if it were a State, but in no event more than the least populous State; they shall be in addition to those appointed by the States, but they shall be considered, for the purposes of the election of President and Vice President, to be electors appointed by a State; and they shall meet in the District and perform such duties as provided by the twelfth article of amendment.

SECTION 2. The Congress shall have power to enforce this article by appropriate legislation.

This amendment to the Constitution gave the District of Columbia the right to take part in the election of the President and Vice President of the United States. Congress enacted the requisite legislation which provided for the direct election of electors by residents of the District. The number of electors was limited to no more than the number of electors from the state with the smallest population. In this way, the District was given three votes in the Electoral College.

This amendment did not provide for representation in Congress or for a system of home-rule municipal government for the District.

BARRING POLL TAX IN FEDERAL ELECTIONS

AMENDMENT 24. (1964)

SECTION. 1. The right of citizens of the United States to vote in any primary or other election for President or Vice President, for electors for President or Vice President, or for Senator or Representative in Congress, shall not be denied or abridged by the United States or any State by reason of failure to pay any poll tax or other tax.

SECTION. 2. The Congress shall have the power to enforce this article by appropriate legislation.

This amendment prohibits any national or state law making the payment of a poll tax or any other tax a requirement for voting in a primary or general election of national officers, namely, President, Vice President, electors of these, Senators, and Representatives in Congress.

AMENDMENT 25. (1967)

SECTION. 1. In case of the removal of the President from office or his death or resignation, the Vice President shall become President.

SECTION. 2. Whenever there is a vacancy in the office of the Vice President, the President shall nominate a Vice President who shall take office upon confirmation by a majority vote of both houses of Congress.

SECTION. 3. Whenever the President transmits to the President Pro Tempore of the Senate and the Speaker of the House of Representatives his written declaration that he is unable to discharge the powers and duties of his office, and until he transmits to them a written declaration to the contrary, such powers and duties shall be discharged by the Vice President as Acting President.

SECTION. 4. Whenever the Vice President and a majority of either the principal officers of the executive departments or of such other body as Congress may by law provide, transmit to the President Pro Tempore of the Senate and the Speaker of the House of Representatives their written declaration that the President is unable to discharge the powers and duties of his office the Vice President shall immediately assume the powers and duties of the office as Acting President.

Thereafter, when the President transmits to the President Pro Tempore of the Senate and the Speaker of the House of Representatives his written declaration that no inability exists, he shall resume the powers and duties of his office unless the Vice President and a majority of either the principal officers of the executive departments or of such other body as Congress may by law provide, transmit within four days to the President Pro Tempore of the Senate and the Speaker of the House of Representatives their written declaration that the President is unable to discharge the powers and duties of his office. Thereupon Congress shall decide the issue, assembling within 48 hours for that purpose if not in session. If the Congress, within 21 days after receipt of the latter written declaration, or, if Congress is not in session, within 21 days after Congress is required to assemble, determines by two-thirds vote of both houses that the President is unable to discharge the powers and duties of his office, the Vice President shall continue to discharge the same as Acting President; otherwise, the President shall resume the powers and duties of his office.

This amendment fills two voids in the original Constitution: *(1)* It provides for filling the office of Vice President in case of a vacancy in that office—through appointment by the President subject to confirmation by a vote of Congress, and *(2)* It determines the existence and duration of the inability of the President to fulfill the powers and duties of his office.

It provides that a President shall notify Congress of his inability to perform his official duties, whereupon the Vice President takes over to serve as Acting President. If a disabled President is unable or unwilling to notify Congress of his incapacity, the Vice President with approval of a majority of the Cabinet shall make such a declaration and he shall then become Acting President.

When the President recovers from his disability, he may so notify Congress and resume the powers and duties of his office.

If the President's recovery appears doubtful, then the Vice President with approval of a majority of the Cabinet (or of some other body designated by Congress) may challenge the President's declaration. The issue then goes to Congress, to be acted upon speedily. If two thirds or more of each house votes against the President, the Vice President continues to serve as Acting President; otherwise, the President resumes his office.

Map Index

The following index lists the major place-names appearing on the maps in *United States History,* exclusive of those in the Atlas Section. An asterisk following an entry indicates that the entry also appears on many other maps.

Index

Acknowledgments

The editors of *United States History* are particularly indebted to the following persons and institutions for their assistance in obtaining illustrations for this book.

Anselmo Carini, Publications Editor, and the staff of the library, Art Institute of Chicago
Adolf K. Placzek, Librarian, Avery Memorial Architectural Library
Walter Muir Whitehill, Director and Librarian, Boston Athenaeum
Edward A. Ruesing, Public Relations Officer, City Art Museum of St. Louis
Dean A. Fales, Jr., Director, Essex Institute
Mrs. S. P. Phillips, Registrar, Gibbes Art Gallery, Carolina Art Association
R. N. Williams, 2nd, Director, Historical Society of Pennsylvania
Henry E. Huntington Library
Mrs. Edwin B. Worthen, Jr., Curator, Lexington Historical Society
Virginia Daiker; Milton Kaplan, Library of Congress
John D. Kilbourne, Librarian; Thomas S. Eader, Assistant Librarian, Maryland Historical Society
Joseph Thomas, National Archives
Newberry Library
Ralph W. Thomas, Curator, New Haven Colony Historical Society
James J. Heslin, Director, The New-York Historical Society, New York City
Karl Kup, Chief; Elizabeth E. Roth, First Assistant, Prints Division, New York Public Library
Lewis M. Stark, Chief; Mrs. Philomena C. Houlihan, Professional Assistant; Mrs. Maud D. Cole, First Assistant, Rare Book Division, New York Public Library
Mrs. Frances R. Raynolds, Curator of Fenimore House, New York State Historical Association
Merrick B. Carpenter, Curator, Old Academy Museum, Wethersfield Historical Society
Louise Wallman, Registrar, Pennsylvania Academy of the Fine Arts
Dr. Carl S. Dentzel, Director, Southwest Museum

Positions of illustrations are shown in abbreviated form as follows: (t) top, (c) center, (b) bottom, (l) left, (r) right.

THE UNITED STATES LANDSCAPE:
COLONIAL BUILDING

70 Stokes Collection, New York Public Library
71 Courtesy of The New-York Historical Society, New York City (t); Museo Naval, Madrid, Courtesy of John Howell Books, San Francisco (b,l); From the *Sunset Book, The California Missions* (b,r)
72 Old Academy Museum, Wethersfield Historical Society
73 The New Haven Colony Historical Society (t); Courtesy of The New-York Historical Society, New York City (c,l; b,l); Redrawn from Edwin Whitefield, *Homes of Our Forefathers*, 1880-1886 (c,r); Thomas Anburey, *Travels Through the Interior Parts of America*, 1789, (b,r)
74 From the Collections of the Maryland Historical Society (t); The Metropolitan Museum of Art, Gift of Edgar William and Bernice Chrysler Garbisch, 1963, Courtesy American Heritage Publishing Co. (b)
75 From the Collections of The Historical Society of Pennsylvania (t); From "A Charleston Sketchbook 1796-1806," by Charles Fraser, Collection of the Carolina Art Association, Charleston, S.C. (c); From the Collections of the Maryland Historical Society (b)
76 From the Collections of The Historical Society of Pennsylvania (t,l); The Boston Athenaeum (t,r); The Pennsylvania Academy of the Fine Arts (b)
77 From the Collections of The Historical Society of Pennsylvania (t); The Metropolitan Museum of Art, Rogers Fund, 1942 (b)

THE UNITED STATES LANDSCAPE:
BUILDING THE NATIONAL CAPITAL

162 Copyright White House Historical Association, photograph by the National Geographic Society
163 Coast and Geodetic Survey, U.S. Department of Commerce
164 Stokes Collection, New York Public Library
165 Stokes Collection, New York Public Library (t); The Library of Congress (b)
166 The Library of Congress (t)
167 The Library of Congress (t,b)
168 Capitol Photo Service
169 The Commission of Fine Arts, Washington, D.C., (t); Capitol Photo Service (b)

637 Josef Muench (t); Fred Bond—Publix Pictorial Service (b)

THE UNITED STATES LANDSCAPE:
TODAY

710 Werner Stoy—Freelance Photographers Guild
711 Fred Ragsdale—Freelance Photographers Guild (t); John Lewis Stage—Photo Researchers (b,l); Patricia Caulfield—Photo Researchers (b,r)
712 Jack Zehrt—Publix Pictorial Service (t); George Hunter—Shostal (b,l); James Ballard (b,r)
713 A. C. Shelton—Publix Pictorial Service (t); H. Armstrong Roberts (b)
714 Israel—Freelance Photographers Guild
715 H. Armstrong Roberts (t); Ellis-Sawyer—Freelance Photographers Guild (b)
716 Steve McCutcheon, Ketchikan, Alaska (t,l); Ellis-Sawyer—Freelance Photographers Guild (b,l); Bradley Smith—Photo Researchers (t,r); Bill Driver—Nashville Housing Authority (c,r); Josef Muench (b,r)
717 Ellis-Sawyer—Freelance Photographers Guild

UNIT ONE
37 The Library of Congress; 46 Emmet Collection, New York Public Library; 47 From the Collections of The Historical Society of Pennsylvania; 51 The Library of Congress; 57 The Connecticut Historical Society (t); The Lexington Historical Society (c;b)

UNIT TWO
92 Victor Collot, *Voyage dans l'Amerique . . .*, 1826, Rare Book Room, New York Public Library; 131 Franklin D. Roosevelt Library, Hyde Park, New York; 153 Courtesy of The New-York Historical Society, New York City

UNIT THREE
185 William A. Crafts, *Pioneers in the Settlement of America,* 1876, Courtesy of the Newberry Library (t); Tulane University News Service (c); Courtesy Harry Shaw Newman, The Old Print Shop (b); 206 James Jerome Hill Reference Library, St. Paul, Minnesota; 224 City Council Chambers, Charleston, S.C. (t); From *George Caleb Bingham: River Portraitist,* by John Francis McDermott (b,l); City Art Museum of St. Louis (b,r); 225 Essex Institute, Salem, Massachusetts (t); The Walters Art Gallery (b,l); The Metropolitan Museum of Art, Gift of Edgar William and Bernice Chrysler Garbisch, 1962 (b,r); 228 The Library of Congress; 251 George Wilkins Kendall, *The War Between the United States and Mexico,* 1851, Courtesy of the Newberry Library

UNIT FOUR
276 From the Permanent Collection of Everson Museum of Art, Syracuse, New York (t); Yale University Art Gallery, Mabel Brady Garvan Collection (b,l); Farm and Industrial Equipment Institute (b,r); 278 *Ballou's Pictorial Drawing-Room Companion,* April 12, 1856, Courtesy of the Newberry Library (t); William Bollaert, *Observations on the Geography of*

Texas, 1850, Courtesy of the Newberry Library (b); 279 The Harry T. Peters Collection, Museum of the City of New York; 291 American Antiquarian Society; 295 Historical Pictures Service (t,l; b,c); Brown Brothers (t,r); 333 The Library of Congress (t); Commonwealth Club, Richmond (b); 344 Brown Brothers (l); Culver Pictures, Inc. (r); 345 Culver Pictures, Inc. (l); Brown Brothers (r); 352 The Library of Congress

UNIT FIVE
393 *The Century Magazine,* July 1891, Courtesy of the Newberry Library (t,l); The Metropolitan Museum of Art, Gift of Several Gentlemen, 1911 (t,r); The Thomas Gilcrease Institute of American History and Art, Tulsa, Oklahoma (b); 403 *Harper's Weekly,* August 29, 1891, The Library of Congress; 417 Culver Pictures, Inc.; 426 The Library of Congress; 438 Collection of Mrs. Vincent Astor, Courtesy American Heritage Publishing Co. (t); *Harper's Weekly,* July 27, 1889, The Library of Congress (b); 439 Culver Pictures, Inc. (t); Courtesy of the Chicago Historical Society (b); 442 Culver Pictures, Inc.; 447 The Library of Congress (t); *McClure's Magazine,* October 1898, Courtesy of the Newberry Library (b,l); *Leslie's Official History of the Spanish American War,* 1898, Courtesy of the Newberry Library (b,r); 451 Culver Pictures, Inc.

UNIT SIX
475 The Metropolitan Museum of Art, Bequest of Edith Minturn Stokes, 1938 (l); Collection of Dr. and Mrs. Irving Frederick Burton (t,r); Roland P. Murdock Collection, Wichita Art Museum, Wichita, Kansas (b,r); 482 Courtesy of Jefferson Medical College of Philadelphia, photographed by the Philadelphia Museum of Art (t); The Addison Gallery of American Art, Phillips Academy, Andover, Massachusetts (b); 483 The Phillips Collection (t); The Art Institute of Chicago, Alfred Stieglitz Collection (b); The Detroit Institute of Arts (r); 510 The Library of Congress; 526 U. S. Signal Corps Photos, National Archives (t,l; t,r); War Department General Staff, National Archives (b); 527 U. S. Signal Corps Photo, National Archives

UNIT SEVEN
552 Culver Pictures, Inc. (all); 553 Culver Pictures, Inc. (all); 555 Culver Pictures, Inc. (all); 576 Wide World Photos (l); Farm Security Administration, Library of Congress (r); 577 Farm Security Administration, Library of Congress, photo by Dorothea Lange; 581 Culver Pictures, Inc. (t,l; b,c); Brown Brothers (t,r); 594 From the Permanent Collection of Everson Museum of Art, Syracuse, New York (t,l); Collection of the Whitney Museum of American Art, New York (t,r; b,l); Courtesy of the Fogg Art Museum, Harvard University, Louise E. Bettens Fund (b,r); 595 Collection of the Joslyn Art Museum, Omaha, Nebraska (t); The Phillips Collection (b); 623 Wide World Photos

UNIT EIGHT
651 Freelance Photographers Guild (both); 657 Wide World Photos; 668 Brown Brothers (t,l); The Granger Collection (b,c); Culver Pictures, Inc. (t,r); 669 Wide World Photos

(t,l); Brown Brothers (b,c; t,r); **679** United States Army (all); **697** Andrew St. George—Magnum

UNIT NINE
731 United Press International; **735** NASA (all); **738** The Metropolitan Museum of Art, George A. Hearn Fund, 1956 (t); The Pennsylvania Academy of the Fine Arts, Courtesy American Heritage Publishing Co. (b,l); The Art Institute of Chicago, Gift of Mr. and Mrs. Sigmund W. Kunstadter and Goodman Fund (b,r); **739** The Art Institute of Chicago, Gift of Edgar Kaufmann, Jr., (t); Devorah Sherman Gallery, Chicago (b,l); Main Street Galleries, Chicago (b,r); **749**

United Press International (t,l; b,l); Courtesy of MEDICO; **760** United Press International; **761** Freelance Photographers Guild (t,l); Wide World Photos (t,r); United Press International (b,l); Peter Gridley—Freelance Photographers Guild (b,r)

EDITORIAL DIRECTION AND PRODUCTION

Landon Risteen, Alice Kay, Philip O'Neil, Jeanne Amann, Mary Chase, Elaine Fandell, Nancy Huelsman, Frederic Kempster, Ida McCain, Janet Shagam, Virginia Valker, Jean Van Gerpen

W9-CBO-312

HENRY DAVID THOREAU

Natural History Essays

HENRY DAVID THOREAU

Natural History Essays

GIBBS SMITH

TO ENRICH AND INSPIRE HUMANKIND

Revised Edition
19 18 17 16 15   5 4 3 2 1

Introduction © 2015 Gibbs Smith

Published by
Gibbs Smith
P.O. Box 667
Layton, Utah 84041

1.800.835.4993 orders
www.gibbs-smith.com

Cover designed by Seth Lucas
Printed and bound in the China

Gibbs Smith books are printed on either recycled, 100% post-consumer
waste, FSC-certified papers or on paper produced from sustainable PEFC-
certified forest/controlled wood source. Learn more at www.pefc.org.

The Library of Congress has cataloged the earlier edition as follows:

Thoreau, Henry David. 1817–1862.
Natural history essays.

(Peregrine Smith literary naturalists)
1. Natural history. 2. Natural history—Massachusetts. I. Title. II. Series.
QH81.T6122   1988   917.44'02   88-34468
ISBN: 0-87905-298-8 (first edition)

ISBN: 978-1-4236-2228-4 (updated edition)

"Huckleberries" is reprinted, with permission, from Henry David
Thoreau, *Huckleberries*, edited, with an introduction, by Leo
Stoller, preface by Alexander C. Kern (The Windhover Press of the
University of Iowa and The New York Public Library, 1970) The
New York Public Library, Astor, Lenox, and Tilden Foundations.

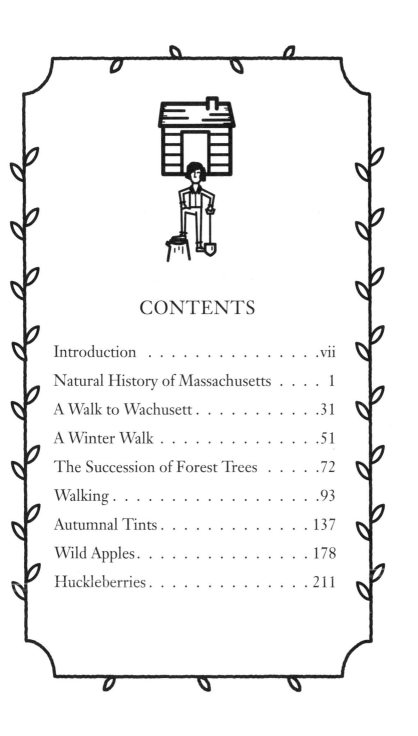

CONTENTS

INTRODUCTION

Ever since the first explorers sent back to Europe enthusiastic and distorted accounts of the natural wonders of the new continent, natural history writers have played a large role in defining the nature of American experience. The underlying mythology of the eras of exploration and settlement made the American an Adam-like figure, given a new world and and the opportunity to make himself and society over without the Old World's traditionary weaknesses. The naturalist's role was no less than a new version of Adam's charge in paradise: to name and describe each living thing man was to have dominion over. On a less mythological level, natural history writing provided Americans with an inventory of their riches and a forum for important debate about the relations of man to nature and about the nature of nature itself in the New World. Two of the finest works concerned with natural history in the eighteenth century, for example, William Bartram's *Travels* and Thomas Jefferson's *Notes on the State of Virginia*, used their subject matter to construct sophisticated visions of the character and potential of life in America — Bartram's purpose being to dramatize an Enlightenment Quaker's reasoned rapture at the works of God, and Jefferson's being to defend American nature (and by extension Americans themselves) from the prevailing European theory asserting the inferiority and degeneracy of natural products in the New World. Nineteenth and twentieth century classics such as John Wesley Powell's *Report on the Lands of the Arid Regions of the United States,* Aldo Leopold's *Sand County Almanac,* and Rachel Carson's *Silent Spring* contained powerful critiques of some fundamental American assumptions about the uses to which nature may be put, and have had a significant impact on the shaping of laws and public policy. The sheer fact of nature itself — its overwhelming presence, its difference from familiar European norms, its seemingly limitless extent — has always been a major component of national self-definition. The naturalist's challenge has been not merely to describe this massive and protean phenomenon but to interpret its significance for civilization and ultimately render it meaningful to human consciousness.

Yet the naturalist has also been a comic or even a suspicious figure in America. Dr. Battius in Cooper's *The Prairie* was a caricature of the early naturalist, absently endangering himself and others in an addled quest for new species, and spouting unintelligible Latin phrases from the new Linnaean taxonomic system. At a deeper level, though, the naturalist's pursuits could even be subversive of the social and economic order. In a pragmatic, expanding society whose major enterprises were clearing, settling, farming, and building, the destruction of habitat and the displacement if not the extinction of native species was inevitable. In this environment the naturalist was doubly suspect because he was concerned about wild plants and animals, and — perhaps even more disturbingly — because he seemed to do no work. His studies necessitated the kind of patient observation of often minute phenomena which could only seem trivial to the mass of his contemporaries.

Although the prevalent atmosphere of Concord, Massachusetts, was probably more tolerant than that of most places in mid-nineteenth century America, Henry Thoreau came in for his share of this distrust and antagonism. He even wrote *Walden*, in part, to answer his neighbors' inquiries about what seemed to them an idle way of life for a young man whose family had sacrificed to send him to Harvard College. And in "Life Without Principle," an essay which dealt in a more concentrated way with the problem of making a living without losing one's soul, he put the problem succinctly: "If a man walk in the woods for love of them half of each day, he is in danger of being regarded as a loafer; but if he spends his whole day as a speculator, shearing off those woods and making earth bald before her time, he is esteemed an industrious and enterprising citizen."

Americans in the late twentieth century, who work very hard at cultivating leisure, are probably more willing than Thoreau's contemporaries were to grant him the broad margin of free time that he required; and his advocacy of the wild as a necessary complement to civilized life has made him something of an environmental oracle, whose words embellish countless calendars, posters, and collections of photographs. Moreover, in a curious turn of events for a writer who was largely ignored in his own time, his work has become a mark against which later writers are inevitably judged and usually found lacking: it is almost as fatal for a naturalist with literary pretensions to be compared to Thoreau as it is for a humorist to be compared to Mark Twain.

Still, this popularity and preeminence is largely based on just a few episodes in Thoreau's life — his two-year stay at Walden Pond and his one-night stay in jail — and on the widespread familiarity of certain sentences from *Walden* and the essay "Walking": "The mass of men lead lives of quiet desperation," for example, or "In Wildness is the preservation of the World." The actual records of his lifelong attention to natural history — his voluminous Journal, his travel books *Cape Cod* and *The Maine Woods*, and the essays included in this volume — are comparatively little studied. In fact, Thoreau's natural history writing and his abilities as a naturalist have frequently even been denigrated, and the concensus of critical opinion on this aspect of his career is a puzzling paradox, most clearly evident in Sherman Paul's pronouncement in *The Shores of America* that "In spite of his gifts for nature study, Thoreau was not a good naturalist . . . " (p. 277). How and why this odd state of affairs came to be can only be understood in the context of Thoreau's development as a natural historian and of the popular understanding of the mission and methods of science in his day and ours.

The foundation of Thoreau's interest in natural history was his passionate affection for his native environment. Concord was a rural village, and Thoreau's boyhood pursuits were those of most of his fellows — hunting and fishing, boating, berry-picking — augmented by his family's cultivation of outdoor activities. With his older brother John, especially, he ranged the countryside, collecting Indian artifacts and watching birds. The two built their own boat, and in 1839 they took it on a two-week trip down the Concord and up the Merrimack Rivers, after which they hiked overland to Mt. Washington in the White mountains. Years later, after John's sudden death in 1842, Thoreau would commemorate the journey in his first book, *A Week on the Concord and Merrimack Rivers*. In a Harvard classbook entry, Thoreau described his youth in Wordsworthian terms, saying: "Those hours that should have been devoted to study, have been spent in scouring the woods, and exploring the lakes and streams of my native village." And as a young man he so impressed Emerson and Hawthorne with his boating skill and knowledge of riparian life that both wrote enthusiastic accounts in their journals of excursions in his company on Concord streams.

By the philosophical currents of his age and his own intellectual training, however, Thoreau looked on nature as much more than the source of recreation or picturesque scenery: it was the phenomenal medium through which divinity and truth were communicated to man. Even more insistently than other

nineteenth century philosophical and religious movements, the Transcendentalists were preoccupied with
the great question of the age — in the words of
Nature, Emerson's important manifesto of the movement, "to what end is nature?" Although the notion
that nature provided a link with divinity might seem
to ally Thoreau in spirit to earlier naturalists like
William Bartram or Gilbert White, who saw in nature the wonderful harmony and balance of God's
creation revealed, a crucial difference existed. To the
earlier naturalists (and to many of their descendants
today) nature was the *evidence* of design in the universe; by studying the details and organization of
nature one could discover its universal laws and even
infer the attributes of its creator, in much the same
way that anthropologists might try to reconstruct
the culture of a prehistoric people by studying its
fossil artifacts. Natural history was a tool, frequently, of what was called Natural Theology, where
students expected to find, as the title of a popular
book on geology expressed it, *The Foot-Prints of
the Creator.*

Thoreau, like many other Romantics, was intensely interested in science, but he was less interested in the footprints of the Creator than he was
in creation itself. He was disposed to find in nature
not the result of some previous plan but a phenomenon continually expressive of creation; not the evidence of design but design itself. Nature was the
medium through which spirit manifested itself, and
Thoreau was quite in earnest when he proclaimed in

the climactic "Spring" chapter of *Walden* that "The earth is not a mere fragment of dead history, stratum upon stratum like the leaves of a book, to be studied by geologists and antiquaries chiefly, but living poetry like the leaves of a tree, which precede flowers and fruit, — not a fossil earth, but a living earth."

The essays in which Thoreau reported his investigation of nature and the natural history of New England fall naturally into two groups. The first are apprentice and exploratory pieces growing out of his earliest engagement with nature and the writer's craft. The essays in the second group were quarried from lectures and unfinished longer studies near the end of his life, and represent that portion of his late work he was able to put in shape for publication before his death in 1862. The reader interested in the overall development of Thoreau's natural history should bear in mind that in between these two distinct groups of essays lie Thoreau's two books — *A Week on the Concord and Merrimack Rivers* and *Walden* — and his book-length collections of travel and natural history essays — *The Maine Woods* and *Cape Cod*.

After Thoreau graduated from Harvard in 1837 he thought of himself (during the hours he could spare from schoolteaching) as an apprentice man of letters, and at first he tried the conventional literary forms of criticism, poetry, and the familiar essay. His efforts in these fields, however, met with little success, even from the sympathetic editors and readers of the Transcendentalists' magazine, *The*

Dial, where they were published. His mentor Emerson saw more clearly than Thoreau at this time the bent of his young friend's genius, and one of his first acts upon assuming the editorship of *The Dial* in 1842 was to ask Thoreau to review several volumes of surveys of the flora and fauna of Massachusetts that had recently been commissioned and published by the state. He explained to Thoreau "the felicity of the subject to him, as it admits of the narrative of all his woodcraft boatcraft & fishcraft."

Thoreau accepted the commission, and produced for the July 1842 issue "Natural History of Massachusetts," his first essay on the subject which was increasingly to absorb his energies for the rest of his career. "Natural History of Massachusetts" is patently an apprentice work which neither finds a structure of its own nor actually reviews the volumes named. But Thoreau blithely admits to having placed the surveys at the beginning of the essay "with as much license as the preacher selects his text," and the interest and energy of the ensuing discourse derive chiefly from self-discovery. Although Thoreau begins by stressing, scholar-like, the winter activity of reading about natural history, this imposed distance from his subject quickly disappears as his rambling catalogue of New England sights and scenes begins. Most important for his future as a naturalist and as a writer, however, is his concluding formulation about the nature of natural history, a passage which really amounts to a kind of prologomena to his life's work, and which sets forth the

challenge facing the Transcendentalist as would-be
scientist:

> "The true man of science will know nature bet-
> ter by his finer organization; he will smell, taste,
> see, hear, feel, better than other men. His will
> be a deeper and finer experience. We do not
> learn by inference and deduction and the appli-
> cation of mathematics to philosophy, but by
> direct intercourse and sympathy. It is with
> science as with ethics, — we cannot know truth
> by contrivance and method; the Baconian is as
> false as any other, and with all the helps of
> machinery and the arts, the most scientific will
> still be the healthiest and friendliest man, and
> possess a more perfect Indian wisdom."

Behind the tone of youthful self-assurance in this
passage lies a crucial, though perhaps not an apparent, distinction. When Thoreau asserts that "the
Baconian is as false as any other," he may seem to
be dismissing casually the whole revered inductive
superstructure of what we have come to think of as
the Scientific Method, in favor of some undefined
and possibly mystical "Indian wisdom." But what he
actually says, of course, is that "the Baconian *is as
false as any other*." This is a statement of principle — a fundamental assumption — that no theory
of nature or way of representing nature should be
mistaken for nature itself. No result produced by
"contrivance and method," no matter how attractive
or useful, should be confused with nature's essence.

The challenge Thoreau set for himself at the beginning of his career, one he would respect if not always be comfortable with for the rest of his life, was how to contribute legitimately to the natural history of New England without succumbing to the lure of method and material results.

Thoreau was encouraged enough by this first effort to turn almost immediately to similar projects. He wrote "A Walk to Wachusett," based on a trip he made in July of 1842, during the following fall. He began "A Winter Walk" at the same time, although he did not complete the essay until June 1843. The sophistication of his natural history did not increase significantly in these essays, but he did mature greatly as a writer and begin to master the skills which would serve as the basis of his later work. He made strides to correct the anecdotal and rambling character of "Natural History of Massachusetts" in "A Walk to Wachusett" by employing a narrative rather than discursive form, and by subordinating the mere observation of nature to an archetypal pattern — the quest — which deepened the significance of what was observed. The specific quest of "A Walk to Wachusett," to see if nature is capable of sustaining the imaginative significance with which the narrator invests it, has perhaps a foregone conclusion. But the pattern enabled Thoreau to place his observation of nature in its true context of spiritual aspiration. Henceforth the universal and timeless patterns of the journey out and back, and the ascent and descent of mountains, together with the diurnal and seasonal cycles, would provide him with both structural principles and a symbolic dimension for his writing about nature.

Thoreau still tended to see nature, however, through European conventions of landscape description. "A Walk to Wachusett" focuses less on specific natural detail than on sweeping and sometimes painterly descriptions of broad panoramas or of the picturesque occupations — cultivating hops, for instance — of the country people. "A Winter Walk," on the other hand, is much closer in tone and spirit to his mature work, for in it he began to concentrate on the particular and even minute details of his environment, and to make this newly-sharpened perception into a kind of tacit source of value, through a central image or conceit running through the whole essay: the idea of feeling summer warmth in winter.

Emerson almost rejected "A Winter Walk" for *The Dial* because of this theme of finding warmth in cold, which he considered to be no more than a perverse mannerism of Thoreau's, a symptom of his unfortunate fondness for paradox. But this motif is absolutely essential to the charge of meaning with which Thoreau wishes to endow the process of sense perception. Nature is cold and dead this winter morning, until the narrator's imagination, fueled by the flow of sense perception, begins to generate an "increased glow of thought and feeling." If there is a "slumbering subterranean fire in nature" which not even the intensest cold can extinguish, it is because this warmth answers to the "subterranean fire . . . in each man's breast." The reciprocity of nature and man's imagination produces the warmth by which life is maintained. Characteristically, Thoreau finds an apparent paradox to be his most effective way of expressing this truth, for it is always the inside of the outside he seeks to reveal, and "our vision does not penetrate the surface of things," as he put it in *Walden*.

A corollary of this emphasis on clarity of perception is his discovery — analogous to Faulkner's discovery of an epic world in his poor northern Mississippi county — that the smallest details of nature may tell the most important stories. Many years later in the introduction to his lecture on "Huckleberries" he would quote Pliny approvingly: *In minimis Natura praestat* — Nature excels in the least things. He began to pay attention to this important truth in "A Winter Walk," noting in almost microscopic detail the "submarine cottages of the caddiceworms," the "tiny tracks of mice around every stem," and the chip of wood which "contains inscribed on it the whole history of the woodchopper and his world."

Yet, on balance, these early essays testify that Thoreau was still an admirer of nature whose enthusiasm and gifted amateur eye masked the fact that he actually knew relatively little systematic natural history. Additionally, the familiar essay was less than ideally suited to his talents at this stage in his life. In the process of composition his imagination worked slowly and accretively, normally requiring years to raise the structures of his works, and the quickly turned out magazine piece was rarely a suitable form for him. Both his education and his craft required long seed times.

The next decade of his life was devoted to the experiment at Walden Pond (1845-1847), to the writing of *A Week on the Concord and Merrimack Rivers* (1849) and *Walden* (1854), and to the acquisition of something approaching a professional competence as a naturalist. He began to botanize systematically, acquired a basic library of botanical guides, and learned taxonomy. He corresponded with and collected specimens for Louis Agassiz of Harvard, America's leading scientist. He also knew the work of Asa Gray, Harvard's other eminent natural scientist, destined to become Agassiz's rival in the American debate over Darwin's theory of evolution. He made a study of limnology and of the fishes of Concord rivers and ponds. He read Kirby and Spence and others on insects, and struck up a professional acquaintance with Thaddeus Harris, a prominent entomologist and the librarian of Harvard College. He had been interested in ornithology since boyhood (a family album of bird sightings survives, dating from the 1830s and containing entries by Henry, his brother John, and his sister Sophia), and he compiled a large collection of birds' nests and eggs. In 1850 he was elected a corresponding member of the Boston Society of Natural History, to which he contributed specimens and various

written accounts over the years, and whose library
and collections he used regularly in pursuing his
studies. (His own extensive collections of Indian
artifacts, birds' nests and eggs, and pressed plants
went to the Society after his death.) In his work as
a surveyor he made a more intimate acquaintance
with the farms, swamps, and woodlots of Concord.
Gradually his townsmen, who had generally looked
askance at his activities, began to come around for
help in identifying plants and animals, and to bring
him new items for his collections.

In addition to his more systematic reading and collecting, the most important factors in his growth as
a careful observer were his daily stints of walking
and journal writing. As he states in "Walking," he
averaged at least four hours a day in the field in all
weathers, after which he carefully recreated from
records kept in pocket notebooks the accounts of his
excursions which began to swell the Journal. The
bulk of this systematic observation came after 1850,
so that thirteen of the fourteen published volumes of
the Journal cover only the last eleven years of his
active life, from 1850 to 1861.

The vast quantity of observation and raw data
in the late Journal has led most critics to see in
Thoreau's increasing attention to the collection of
facts a loss of creative power. But this conclusion
is based on a kind of false statistic, for there is still
about the same amount of reflection and contemplation of ideas in the late Journal as the early Journal; it only appears to be more scattered because

Thoreau now used the Journal for the additional purpose of making detailed records of his various natural history observations. In the same way commentators point to Thoreau's occasional moments of concern or despondency over becoming too absorbed in detail, ignoring the larger fact that he worked happily and with increasing energy on these studies until his final illness, when he prepared as many of his papers as possible for publication.

At any rate, the results of his new diligence and competence as a naturalist were manifest in his writings — the "Concord River" chapter of *A Week*, the exquisite miniatures as well as the larger studies of the pond itself in *Walden*, and in his accounts of the northern wilderness and the wild seashore in the chapters of *The Maine Woods* and *Cape Cod* that were published serially in the 1840s and 1850s. And as far as Thoreau himself was concerned, the real danger to his career lay not in becoming too scientific, but in becoming estranged from the scientific community itself. By continuing in the midst of his detailed studies to hold to a vision of a humane science which would not treat nature merely as matter to be manipulated, he realized that he was stemming an ever-strengthening tide of belief to the contrary. When he was proposed for membership in the Association for the Advancement of Science in 1853, he was asked to complete a form describing his particular field of study, and he realized to his dismay what would happen if he told the truth: "Now, though I could state to a select few that department of human inquiry which engages me, and should be rejoiced at an opportunity to do so, I felt that it would be to make myself the laughing-stock of the scientific community to describe or attempt to describe to them that branch of science which specially interests me, inasmuch as they do not believe in a science which deals with the higher law."

Nevertheless, Thoreau did attempt to explain himself, usually by lecturing to local lyceums in New England. All his later natural history essays, in fact, began as lectures, and he did not put them into essay form until near the end of his life. His most concerted attempt to set forth the rationale of his way of life and to explain why civilization could not afford to cut itself off from its wild heritage is "Walking," an essay which he spliced together from two lectures, "Walking" and "The Wild," which he gave many times during the 1850s.

"Walking" is one of Thoreau's better-known essays today because its advocacy of the wild is the philosophical cornerstone of twentieth century movements to preserve wilderness tracts in America. Yet Thoreau did not think of the wild — or of walking either — as a special preserve. It was not for recreation so much as it was for re-creation; it was a particular quality of life that had to be actively cultivated. The spirit of the walk and not the specific route makes one a true saunterer (*Sainte-Terrer*, Holy-Lander, in his not entirely fanciful etymology), because the walk undertaken rightly denotes a commitment to the highest uses to which

thought and observation may be put. Even Thoreau's paean to the West — jingoistic as it may
appear at first — is primarily in praise of man's
capacity to imagine and live according to his vision
of a fairer world. "Westward I go free" may have
the ring of pioneer travel about it, but Thoreau had
to travel no farther than the Old Marlborough Road
in Concord to find his West.

Similarly, the wild has less to do with actual wilderness areas (for that Thoreau went to Maine)
than it does with a habit of mind which recognizes
the balance of mutually dependent forces in life.
The avowed "extreme statement" on behalf of the
wild is not atavism or even primitivism, but an attempt to redress an imbalance in our way of thinking about life in nature. The wild is a reminder of
an original attachment to the sources of life, and
points back to a time and a state where nature and
man's consciousness were not separate entities, and
where nature was not an object to be learned and
mastered for the sake of material knowledge and
power. Hence Thoreau's proposal, at once earnest
and ironic, for a "Society for the Diffusion of Useful
Ignorance," for he argues that it is only when we
become wise enough to forget that we "know" nature
that we can participate in what he calls "Beautiful
Knowledge." The historical result of increasing knowledge in the scientific sense has been an increased
separation and loss of harmony between man and
nature, a loss, as Thoreau points out, that can be
demonstrated by history and language itself: "We

have to be told that the Greeks called the world
Κοσμος, Beauty, or Order, but we do not see clearly
why they did so, and we esteem it at best only a curious philological fact." The wild is valuable and necessary insofar as it enables us to imagine, however
fleetingly, that lost harmony.

This belief that nature, if viewed from the correct
perspective, could provide one with a way of realign-
ing himself with the sources of beauty and harmony
was based on close and careful investigation, and
was the result of hard work as much as inspiration.
As the 1850s progressed, Thoreau focused increasingly on observing and recording the yearly natural
cycle of his local environment, with particular emphasis on the patterns of leafing and flowering, fruit-
ing, and seed dispersal in plants. One offshoot of these
larger studies was a discovery he outlined in "The
Succession of Forest Trees," his most sustained
treatment of what he termed a "purely scientific
subject." In it he describes a phase in the evolution
of a climax forest, dispelling still widely-held beliefs
that trees were propagated by spontaneous generation or by seeds that lay dormant in the ground for
many years. He also demonstrates that a naturalist
who believes in "a science which deals with the
higher law" can also produce accurate and useful
insights into the operations of nature — and does so
with a kind of self-deprecating humor that acknow-
ledges his "outside" position: "Every man is entitled
to come to a Cattle-show, even a transcendentalist."

Even in this discourse, however, meant to be in-

formative and useful to his audience of local farmers, Thoreau's habitual perspective is evident. Although he insists that trees do not spring up by
spontaneous generation or some other mysterious
process, he dispels this myth in order to call attention to a more fundamental and real mystery — the
seed: "Convince me that you have a seed there, and
I am prepared to accept wonders." A case in point
is the marvelous 186¼ pound squash — *"Poitrine
jaune grosse"* — he raised in his garden: "These
seeds were the bait I used to catch it, my ferrets
which I sent into its burrow, my brace of terriers
which unearthed it." Here, having just taken pains
to disprove the popular fallacies about the generation of plants and to prove that they spring from
seeds, Thoreau suddenly shifts the level of his argument to imply that the seed is not only related to
the mature fruit by material cause and effect but is
perhaps an organic principle in itself of yet another
order.

This sort of intermingling of "poetic" and "scientific" truth has led most twentieth century critics to
conclude that Thoreau was finally a poor naturalist
on the one hand, and, after *Walden*, a failed creative
artist as well, because he could not keep the elementary distinction between the two realms clear. But
it seems odd that Thoreau, who was after all thoroughly grounded in the objective natural science of
his day, should be so confused about such a fundamental point and find himself finally adrift somewhere between science and mysticism. Another possi-

bility is that our own implicit and unexamined assumption about the unbridgeable gap between scientific and imaginative truth simply makes it almost impossible to grasp the nature of his work from the inside. Its elements appear to be anomalous because contemporary thought is unconsciously the intellectual heir of that Association for the Advancement of Science, before whom Thoreau was already unlikely to receive an impartial hearing; it being no less true in science than in war that victors write the histories.

At any rate, enough prejudice, conscious or unconscious, has existed towards Thoreau's kind of natural history that the bulk of his late work in this field has not been considered important enough to be published yet. Toward the end of his life he worked on two long manuscripts, one on seeds and the other on fruits, which the progressive debilitation of tuberculosis did not permit him to complete, but which do survive in preliminary draft versions (in the Berg Collection of the New York Public Library). Fortunately, these manuscripts are at last scheduled for publication, in the Princeton Edition of Thoreau's *Writings* now in progress, but they have not yet been fully considered in the central debate over Thoreau's career — whether his late years form a record of declining power and a straying from the vision that led to *Walden*, or whether they furnish evidence of significant new directions and works which he did not live to complete.

Some necessarily tentative and provisional proposals, however, about the direction of this late work might be advanced on the basis of published works which were collateral with or part of these longer projects: two essays Thoreau was able to compile from lecture drafts before he died, "Autumnal Tints" and "Wild Apples," and a small portion of the manuscript on fruits, called "Huckleberries," edited by Professor Leo Stoller, which is made widely available for the first time in this volume. Although the circumstances of their composition and publication suggest that they may have undergone further refinement at Thoreau's hands, and although they form only a small portion of much longer and more ambitious projects, these works at least give some hints about the vision and the program of natural science toward which Thoreau was working.

"Autumnal Tints" treats the leaf as fruit, and displays the concern with ripeness that dominates the imagery of Thoreau's late work. At its basic level, of course, the essay is a catalogue of the different leaves and leaf-tints of a New England fall, bearing witness to Thoreau's long-standing interest in this phenomenon. One of his earliest literary projects, back in 1841, had been a work called "The Fall of the Leaf." Although the subject obviously admits of a popular treatment (Thoreau's essay is, after all, a kind of literary precursor to the fall foliage tour), the leaf held a high and very special place among nature's forms to Thoreau. He regarded it, in fact, as the archetypal organic form, a kind of ur-phenomenon expressive of creative life. In the "Spring" chapter of *Walden* it is the narrator's climactic meditation on the leaf-forms expressed in the flowing sand of the railroad cut which signals his discovery of a vital principle in nature: "The Maker of this earth but patented a leaf." The leaf is a sort of universal hieroglyph or symbol of creative energy, and thus its ripening and its fall are events to be attended to with care. These events take on an even greater significance when it is recalled that the essay was prepared by Thoreau on his death bed, and that his treatment of the subject closely reflects his own condition.

One expression of the law to be discerned in the fall foliage is that "Generally, every fruit, on ripening, and just before it falls, when it commences a more independent and individual existence . . . acquires a bright tint. So do leaves," The high color is a sign of ripeness, not decay, and the fall itself is a sort of individuation, the commencement of "a more independent and individual existence," and not a death. This notion is of course at odds with the scientific explanation of what happens when a leaf falls (which Thoreau knew perfectly well), but his slant on natural facts, as should be evident by now, is deeply opposed in principle to the customary assumptions about what constitutes organic life or even reality. He is "more interested in the rosy cheek" than in "the particular diet the maiden fed on"; which is to say that while Thoreau is cognizant of the physiologist's explanation, he knows that the phenomenon is greater than the sum of these parts, and has no use for an explanation which fails to take into account the perception which shapes the appearance itself.

This much is clear from the concluding portion of the essay, where Thoreau refers more than once to the "intention of the eye" as a determinant of reality. This principle, which Thoreau derives and illustrates from experience, means in essence that one must know what he is looking for before he can see it. "The astronomer," as he says, "knows where to go star-gathering, and sees one clearly in his mind before any have seen it with a glass." The history of science itself suggests the basic reasonableness of this proposition (think, for example, of the theoretical anticipation of the major discoveries of physics in this century). But the proposition undercuts at the same time the cherished and popular myth of a perfectly objective and quantifiable world which presupposes nature as matter independent of and anterior to any perceiving consciousness.

In effect, Thoreau found himself fighting a kind of rear-guard or guerilla action against scientific materialism, and he adopted as his favored rhetorical strategies "extreme statement," paradox, and the deliberate inversion of accepted wisdom, in order to try to startle his audience out of unexamined and merely habitual modes of thought. In the introduction to "Huckleberries," for example, the customary standards of littleness and greatness are reversed, not in order to allow Thoreau to deliver a few broadsides at politics and education but to try to induce in his auditors a new perspective on familiar objects and ideas. Thoreau's natural history would ultimately undermine the social as well as the philosophical conventions, for the humble huckleberry is the launching point for a radical critique — almost reminiscent of Marx at times — of entrepreneurial activity which robs the community of its natural birthright and promotes the division of labor and the alienation of the worker from his work. Elsewhere in "Huckleberries" he sounds what by now has become a familiar plea for cities and towns to set aside a portion of their wild and uninhabited lands as a resource for future generations. In his own country, though, Thoreau was a prophet without honor: even Emerson was unable at last to follow sympathetically or to grasp the nature of his work, and in regard to "Huckleberries," this long-buried and unknown work, there is a kind of consummate irony in the famous criticism of Thoreau leveled by Emerson in his funeral oration: "instead of engineering for all America, he was the captain of a huckleberry party."

"Wild Apples" is the most complete and most compelling of these late works, and furnishes perhaps the best evidence of the range of reference of Thoreau's detailed studies of his native ground. And portions of the essay are memorable in their own right for narrative and descriptive verve—the struggle of the apple tree against its bovine foes and its eventual triumph over them, for instance — independent of any historical or scientific context. The subject was perfectly suited to Thoreau. The wild apple was appealing to him because it was a forgotten and neglected fruit, one of the "least things" at which nature excelled, flourishing in the unfrequented corners of New England its chronicler instinctively sought; and because its situation and its qualities were so transparently suggestive of his own: a cultivated plant tending back to the wild, bearing its fruit late and unnoticed by most, crabbed and gnarled perhaps, but bracing if taken in the right spirit.

Yet it finally requires the sort of altered perspective on natural facts which Thoreau strove to induce in his audiences if "Wild Apples" is to be seen as a coherent whole, for without such a perspective (or the willingness, at least, to entertain it) crucial parts of the essay will seem at best to be unrelated to the descriptive body of the piece. What, for example, is the function of the very detailed philological and historical account of the apple which begins the essay? It is far too detailed merely to "introduce" the subject; and since "Wild Apples" was originally a lecture which Thoreau revised for publication during his final illness, it seems equally unlikely that this long recital of definitions and historical facts is mere padding.

The key to this section is the deceptively bland opening sentence: "It is remarkable how closely the history of the Apple-tree is connected with that of man." Thoreau does more here than establish the groundwork for a metaphorical connection between man and the apple tree. He suggests, rather, by tracing the significance of the apple in language and history, that it is a natural fact which can best be understood through an understanding of its evolution in human thought. By giving as his opening coordinates, so to speak, not merely the genus and species of the apple, but its meaning in history, poetry, mythology, religion, and folklore, Thoreau suggests an alternative approach to customary scientific description, which involves actively putting the history back in natural history. Since the reality of natural phenomena is in part dependent upon the perceiver, true natural history involves the historical evolution of this perception. What the apple tree means, finally, is the sum of its histories, of its relationship to man. Man and the apple tree have grown up together.

The frame Thoreau provides for his subject, then, in this introduction, seeks to establish an interconnectedness between supposedly independent and discrete phenomena and human thought. He deliberately reverses the path of normal science, which seeks for objectivity to isolate and separate the object studied.

This historical dimension opens even more far-reaching levels of significance. The word for apple, we learn, if traced back far enough once meant "riches in general," all the productions of nature which were at man's disposal. And, as Thoreau also points out in an understatement of epic proportions, "Some have thought that the first human pair were tempted by its fruit." Thus the apple embodies simultaneously man's dominion over nature and his

fall from harmony with it — the ultimate paradox
of human knowledge. If we understand the story of
the Fall at one level to represent the separation of
man from an original harmony with nature, a falling
into self-consciousness in which nature began to be
perceived as *other*, then the history of the apple tree
becomes the history of man's relation to nature.
How the apple tree is defined and perceived is at any
moment an index of our condition with respect to that
original harmony and our prospects for regaining it.

Hence Thoreau's glorification of the wild apple,
on the one hand, and his startling jeremiad at the
end of the essay over its disappearance. He cele-
brates the wild apple because it suggests the possibilities of reattachment and harmony with nature
without the sacrifice of knowledge. The apple tree has
grown cultivated and domestic with man, and now
aspires back to its original state without giving up
its fruitfulness. That fruitfulness is all the more
valuable because it is achieved after such a struggle.
It suggests, in its balance of the wild and the cultivated, the possibility of victory over both ignorance
and the tyranny of knowledge.

In this light the conclusion of the essay is a powerful and pertinent warning, and not merely a curious lapse into preaching, for it constitutes Thoreau's final plea against losing once and for all the
possibility of achieving the harmony the apple tree
suggests. "The era of the Wild Apple will soon be
past," given the spread of those assumptions and
habits of mind about nature which made his voice

more and more isolated even in his own day. The inevitable result will be a universal malaise arising from the final separation of man from nature. Thoreau's choice of biblical text is hauntingly appropriate to his plea, for it is the death of nature and the alienation of man which ensue from the denial of creative spirit working through both: " 'The vine is dried up, and the fig-tree languisheth; the pomegranate-tree, the palm-tree also, and the apple-tree, even all the trees of the field, are withered: because joy is withered away from the sons of man.' "

The naturalist's mission as Thoreau finally expressed it went far beyond the naming of the products of the New World garden. Up through the writing of *Walden* his imagination had centered on the Spring as an emblem of physical and spiritual rebirth, but in his later years he became more concerned with the Fall as season and as spiritual fact. If that Fall was to be a fortunate one, our way of knowing must lead us back to and not away from its great central life.

Robert Sattelmeyer

A NOTE ON THE TEXT

With the exception of "Huckleberries," the essays in this volume originally appeared in periodicals during or just after Thoreau's lifetime: "Natural History of Massachusetts" and "A Winter Walk" in *The Dial* for July 1842 and October 1843, respectively; "A Walk to Wachusett" in the *Boston Miscellany* in January 1843; "Walking," "Autumnal Tints," and "Wild Apples" in the June, October and November 1862 issues of the *Atlantic Monthly*, respectively; and "The Succession of Forest Trees" in the *Transactions of the Middlesex Agricultural Society* for 1860. They were then collected in the first posthumous volume of Thoreau's works, *Excursions* (1863), which was edited by Sophia Thoreau and Ellery Channing. A work by Thoreau called "Night and Moonlight" was also included in the 1863 *Excursions*, but recent scholarship has shown it to be non-authorial in its printed form, and it has not been included in the present volume. (See William L. Howarth, "Successor to *Walden?* Thoreau's 'Moonlight — An Intended Course of Lectures,'" *Proof*, 2 [1972], pp. 89-115.) The text in this collection is a reprinting of the standard 1906 Walden Edition of *Excursions*. A definitive scholarly edition of *Excursions* is in preparation for *The Writings of Henry D. Thoreau*, in progress at Princeton University Press.

"Huckleberries" was not prepared for publication by Thoreau, but exists in an intermediate draft form in a longer manuscript labelled "Notes on Fruits" in the New York Public Library's Berg Collection of English and American Literature. The present text was edited, with textual notes and an introduction, by the late Leo Stoller, as *Huckleberries* (The Windhover Press of the University of Iowa and The New York Public Library, 1970). A scholarly text will appear when the "Notes on Fruits" manuscript is edited for a forthcoming volume of the Princeton Edition of Thoreau's *Writings*.

BIBLIOGRAPHICAL NOTE

Thoreau's interest in nature has of course received a great deal of attention, even if his natural history writings have been relatively little studied. The following is a highly selective list of works on both Thoreau's natural history and on the development of natural history in America.

Consideration of Thoreau's attitude toward science and the practice of natural history include Raymond Adams, "Thoreau's Science," *Scientific Monthly*, 60 (1945), 379-382; Nina Baym, "Thoreau's View of Science," *Journal of the History of Ideas*, 26 (1965), 221-234; Leo Marx evaluated "Thoreau's Excursions" in the *Yale Review*, 51 (1962), 363-369; a full-length study is James McIntosh, *Thoreau as Romantic Naturalist* (Ithaca: Cornell University Press, 1974); a provocative study of the intellectual and philosophical tradition within which Thoreau was working (although not specifically concerned with him) is Owen Barfield, *What Coleridge Thought* (Middletown, Conn.: Wesleyan University Press, 1971); the most comprehensive account of the development of Thoreau's thought is Sherman Paul, *The Shores of America* (Urbana: University of Illinois Press, 1958); and the most detailed biography is Walter Harding, *The Days of Henry Thoreau* (New York: Alfred A. Knopf, 1965).

Scholarly studies of natural history in America, including its treatment in literary works, include Philip Marshal Hicks, *The Development of the Natural History Essay in American Literature* (Philadelphia, 1924); Norman Foerster, *Nature in American Literature* (New York: The Macmillan Company, 1923); Elizabeth Sewell, *Orphic Voice: Poetry and Natural History* (New Haven: Yale University Press, 1960); Thomas Smallwood, *Natural History and the American Mind* (New York: Columbia University Press, 1941); Roderick Nash, *Wilderness and the American Mind*, rev. ed. (New Haven: Yale University Press, 1973).

Some recent popular accounts of early naturalists in America are Robert Elman, *First in the Field: America's Pioneering Naturalists* (New York: Mason/Charter, 1977); Wayne Henley, *Natural History in America* (New York: Quadrangle/The New York Times Book Company, 1977); and Joseph Kastner, *A Species of Eternity* (New York: Knopf, 1978).

This engraving of a Scarlet Oak leaf, which appeared in the first publication of "Autumnal Tints" in the *Atlantic Monthly* in 1862, was requested by Thoreau to illustrate his discussion of the leaf on pages 166-168.

NATURAL HISTORY OF MASSACHUSETTS [1]

Books of natural history make the most cheerful winter reading. I read in Audubon with a thrill of delight, when the snow covers the ground, of the magnolia, and the Florida keys, and their warm sea-breezes; of the fence-rail, and the cotton-tree, and the migrations of the rice-bird; of the breaking up of winter in Labrador, and the melting of the snow on the forks of the Missouri; and owe an accession of health to these reminiscences of luxuriant nature.

> Within the circuit of this plodding life,
> There enter moments of an azure hue,
> Untarnished fair as is the violet
> Or anemone, when the spring strews them
> By some meandering rivulet, which make
> The best philosophy untrue that aims
> But to console man for his grievances.
> I have remembered, when the winter came,
> High in my chamber in the frosty nights,
> When in the still light of the cheerful moon,
> On every twig and rail and jutting spout,
> The icy spears were adding to their length
> Against the arrows of the coming sun,
> How in the shimmering noon of summer past
> Some unrecorded beam slanted across
> The upland pastures where the Johnswort grew;
> Or heard, amid the verdure of my mind,

[1] *Reports — on the Fishes, Reptiles, and Birds; the Herbaceous Plants and Quadrupeds; the Insects Injurious to Vegetation; and the Invertebrate Animals of Massachusetts.* Published agreeably to an Order of the Legislature, by the Commissioners on the Zoölogical and Botanical Survey of the State.

The bee's long smothered hum, on the blue flag
Loitering amidst the mead; or busy rill,
Which now through all its course stands still and dumb,
Its own memorial, — purling at its play
Along the slopes, and through the meadows next,
Until its youthful sound was hushed at last
In the staid current of the lowland stream;
Or seen the furrows shine but late upturned,
And where the fieldfare followed in the rear,
When all the fields around lay bound and hoar
Beneath a thick integument of snow.
So by God's cheap economy made rich
To go upon my winter's task again.

I am singularly refreshed in winter when I hear of
service-berries, poke-weed, juniper. Is not heaven made
up of these cheap summer glories? There is a singular
health in those words, Labrador and East Main, which
no desponding creed recognizes. How much more than
Federal are these States! If there were no other vicis-
situdes than the seasons, our interest would never tire.
Much more is adoing than Congress wots of. What
journal do the persimmon and the buckeye keep, and
the sharp-shinned hawk? What is transpiring from
summer to winter in the Carolinas, and the Great Pine
Forest, and the Valley of the Mohawk? The merely
political aspect of the land is never very cheering; men
are degraded when considered as the members of a
political organization. On this side all lands present
only the symptoms of decay. I see but Bunker Hill and
Sing-Sing, the District of Columbia and Sullivan's
Island, with a few avenues connecting them. But paltry
are they all beside one blast of the east or the south wind
which blows over them.

In society you will not find health, but in nature. Unless our feet at least stood in the midst of nature, all our faces would be pale and livid. Society is always diseased, and the best is the most so. There is no scent in it so wholesome as that of the pines, nor any fragrance so penetrating and restorative as the life-everlasting in high pastures. I would keep some book of natural history always by me as a sort of elixir, the reading of which should restore the tone of the system. To the sick, indeed, nature is sick, but to the well, a fountain of health. To him who contemplates a trait of natural beauty no harm nor disappointment can come. The doctrines of despair, of spiritual or political tyranny or servitude, were never taught by such as shared the serenity of nature. Surely good courage will not flag here on the Atlantic border, as long as we are flanked by the Fur Countries. There is enough in that sound to cheer one under any circumstances. The spruce, the hemlock, and the pine will not countenance despair. Methinks some creeds in vestries and churches do forget the hunter wrapped in furs by the Great Slave Lake, and that the Esquimaux sledges are drawn by dogs, and in the twilight of the northern night the hunter does not give over to follow the seal and walrus on the ice. They are of sick and diseased imaginations who would toll the world's knell so soon. Cannot these sedentary sects do better than prepare the shrouds and write the epitaphs of those other busy living men ? The practical faith of all men belies the preacher's consolation. What is any man's discourse to me, if I am not sensible of something in it as steady and cheery as the creak of crickets ? In it the woods must be relieved against the sky. Men tire me when I am not constantly greeted and refreshed as by the flux of sparkling streams. Surely joy is the condition of life. Think of the young fry that leap in ponds, the myriads of insects ushered into being on a summer evening, the incessant note of the hyla with which the woods ring in the spring, the nonchalance of the butterfly carrying accident and change painted in a thousand hues upon its wings, or the brook minnow stoutly stemming the current, the lustre of whose scales, worn bright by the attrition, is reflected upon the bank!

We fancy that this din of religion, literature, and philosophy, which is heard in pulpits, lyceums, and parlors, vibrates through the universe, and is as catholic a sound as the creaking of the earth's axle; but if a man sleep soundly, he will forget it all between sunset and dawn. It is the three-inch swing of a pendulum in a cupboard, which the great pulse of nature vibrates by and through each instant. When we lift our eyelids and open our ears, it disappears with smoke and rattle like the cars on a railroad. When I detect a beauty in any of the recesses of nature, I am reminded, by the serene and retired spirit in which it requires to be contemplated, of the inexpressible privacy of a life, — how silent and unambitious it is. The beauty there is in mosses must be considered from the holiest, quietest nook. What an admirable training is science for the more active warfare of life! Indeed, the unchallenged bravery which these studies imply, is far more impressive than the trumpeted valor of the warrior. I am pleased to learn that Thales was up and stirring by night not unfrequently, as his astronomical discoveries prove. Linnæus, setting out for Lapland, surveys his " comb " and " spare shirt," " leathern breeches " and " gauze cap to keep off gnats," with as much complacency as Bonaparte a park of artillery for the Russian campaign. The quiet bravery of the man is admirable. His eye is to take in fish, flower, and bird, quadruped and biped. Science is always brave; for to know is to know good; doubt and danger quail before her eye. What the coward overlooks in his hurry, she calmly scrutinizes, breaking ground like a pioneer for the array of arts that follow in her train. But cowardice is unscientific; for there cannot be a science of ignorance. There may be a science of bravery, for that advances; but a retreat is rarely well conducted; if it is, then is it an orderly advance in the face of circumstances.

But to draw a little nearer to our promised topics. Entomology extends the limits of being in a new direction, so that I walk in nature with a sense of greater space and freedom. It suggests besides, that the universe is not rough-hewn, but perfect in its details. Nature will bear the closest inspection; she invites us to lay our eye level with the smallest leaf, and take an insect view of its plain. She has no interstices; every part is full of life. I explore, too, with pleasure, the sources of the myriad sounds which crowd the summer noon, and which seem the very grain and stuff of which eternity is made. Who does not remember the shrill roll-call of the harvest-fly? There were ears for these sounds in Greece long ago, as Anacreon's ode will show.

"We pronounce thee happy, Cicada,
  For on the tops of the trees,
  Drinking a little dew,
  Like any king thou singest,
  For thine are they all,
  Whatever thou seest in the fields,
  And whatever the woods bear.
  Thou art the friend of the husbandmen,
  In no respect injuring any one;
  And thou art honored among men,
  Sweet prophet of summer.
  The Muses love thee,
  And Phœbus himself loves thee,
  And has given thee a shrill song;
  Age does not wrack thee,
  Thou skillful, earthborn, song-loving,
  Unsuffering, bloodless one;
  Almost thou art like the gods."

In the autumn days, the creaking of crickets is heard at noon over all the land, and as in summer they are heard chiefly at nightfall, so then by their incessant chirp they usher in the evening of the year. Nor can all the vanities that vex the world alter one whit the measure that night has chosen. Every pulse-beat is in exact time with the cricket's chant and the tickings of the death-watch in the wall. Alternate with these if you can.

About two hundred and eighty birds either reside permanently in the State, or spend the summer only, or make us a passing visit. Those which spend the winter with us have obtained our warmest sympathy. The nut-hatch and chickadee flitting in company through the dells of the wood, the one harshly scolding at the intruder, the other with a faint lisping note enticing him on; the jay screaming in the orchard; the crow cawing in unison with the storm; the partridge, like a russet link extended over from autumn to spring, preserving unbroken the chain of summers; the hawk with warrior-like firmness abiding the blasts of winter; the robin [1] and lark lurking by warm springs in the woods; the familiar snowbird culling a few seeds in the garden or a few crumbs in the yard; and occasionally the shrike, with heedless and unfrozen melody bringing back summer again: —

> His steady sails he never furls
> At any time o' year,
> And perching now on Winter's curls,
> He whistles in his ear.

As the spring advances, and the ice is melting in the river, our earliest and straggling visitors make their appearance. Again does the old Teian poet sing as well for New England as for Greece, in the

RETURN OF SPRING

> Behold, how, Spring appearing,
> The Graces send forth roses;
> Behold, how the wave of the sea
> Is made smooth by the calm;
> Behold, how the duck dives;
> Behold, how the crane travels;

[1] A white robin and a white quail have occasionally been seen. It is mentioned in Audubon as remarkable that the nest of a robin should be found on the ground; but this bird seems to be less particular than most in the choice of a building-spot. I have seen its nest placed under the thatched roof of a deserted barn, and in one instance, where the adjacent country was nearly destitute of trees, together with two of the phœbe, upon the end of a board in the loft of a sawmill, but a few feet from the saw, which vibrated several inches with the motion of the machinery.

And Titan shines constantly bright.
The shadows of the clouds are moving;
The works of man shine;
The earth puts forth fruits;
The fruit of the olive puts forth.
The cup of Bacchus is crowned,
Along the leaves, along the branches,
The fruit, bending them down, flourishes.

The ducks alight at this season in the still water, in company with the gulls, which do not fail to improve an east wind to visit our meadows, and swim about by twos and threes, pluming themselves, and diving to peck at the root of the lily, and the cranberries which the frost has not loosened. The first flock of geese is seen beating to north, in long harrows and waving lines; the jingle of the song sparrow salutes us from the shrubs and fences; the plaintive note of the lark comes clear and sweet from the meadow; and the bluebird, like an azure ray, glances past us in our walk. The fish hawk, too, is occasionally seen at this season sailing majestically over the water, and he who has once observed it will not soon forget the majesty of its flight. It sails the air like a ship of the line, worthy to struggle with the elements, falling back from time to time like a ship on its beam ends, and holding its talons up as if ready for the arrows, in the attitude of the national bird. It is a great presence, as of the master of river and forest. Its eye would not quail before the owner of the soil, but make him feel like an intruder on its domains. And then its retreat, sailing so steadily away, is a kind of advance. I have by me one of a pair of ospreys, which have for some years fished in this vicinity, shot by a neighboring pond, measuring more than two feet in length, and six in the stretch of its wings. Nuttall mentions that "the ancients, particularly Aristotle, pretended that the ospreys taught their young to gaze at the sun, and those who were unable to do so were destroyed. Linnæus even believed, on ancient authority, that one of the feet of this bird had all the toes divided, while the other was partly webbed, so that it could swim with one foot, and grasp a fish with the other." But that educated eye is now dim, and those talons are nerveless. Its shrill scream seems yet to linger in its throat, and the roar of the sea in its wings. There is the tyranny of Jove in its claws, and his wrath in the erectile feathers of the head and neck. It reminds me of the Argonautic expedition, and would inspire the dullest to take flight over Parnassus.

The booming of the bittern, described by Goldsmith and Nuttall, is frequently heard in our fens, in the morning and evening, sounding like a pump, or the chopping of wood in a frosty morning in some distant farm-yard. The manner in which this sound is produced I have not seen anywhere described. On one occasion, the bird has been seen by one of my neighbors to thrust its bill into the water, and suck up as much as it could hold, then, raising its head, it pumped it out again with four or five heaves of the neck, throwing it two or three feet, and making the sound each time.

At length the summer's eternity is ushered in by the cackle of the flicker among the oaks on the hillside, and a new dynasty begins with calm security.

In May and June the woodland quire is in full tune, and, given the immense spaces of hollow air, and this

curious human ear, one does not see how the void could
be better filled.

> Each summer sound
> Is a summer round.

As the season advances, and those birds which make
us but a passing visit depart, the woods become silent
again, and but few feathers ruffle the drowsy air. But
the solitary rambler may still find a response and
expression for every mood in the depths of the wood.

> Sometimes I hear the veery's [1] clarion,
> Or brazen trump of the impatient jay,
> And in secluded woods the chickadee
> Doles out her scanty notes, which sing the praise
> Of heroes, and set forth the loveliness
> Of virtue evermore.

The phœbe still sings in harmony with the sultry
weather by the brink of the pond, nor are the desultory
hours of noon in the midst of the village without their
minstrel.

> Upon the lofty elm-tree sprays
> The vireo rings the changes sweet,
> During the trivial summer days,
> Striving to lift our thoughts above the street.

With the autumn begins in some measure a new
spring. The plover is heard whistling high in the air
over the dry pastures, the finches flit from tree to tree,

[1] This bird, which is so well described by Nuttall, but is apparently
unknown by the author of the Report, is one of the most common in
the woods in this vicinity, and in Cambridge I have heard the college
yard ring with its trill. The boys call it "yorrick," from the sound of
its querulous and chiding note, as it flits near the traveler through the
underwood. The cowbird's egg is occasionally found in its nest, as
mentioned by Audubon.

the bobolinks and flickers fly in flocks, and the gold-finch rides on the earliest blast, like a winged hyla peeping amid the rustle of the leaves. The crows, too, begin now to congregate; you may stand and count them as they fly low and straggling over the landscape, singly or by twos and threes, at intervals of half a mile, until a hundred have passed.

I have seen it suggested somewhere that the crow was brought to this country by the white man; but I shall as soon believe that the white man planted these pines and hemlocks. He is no spaniel to follow our steps; but rather flits about the clearings like the dusky spirit of the Indian, reminding me oftener of Philip and Powhatan than of Winthrop and Smith. He is a relic of the dark ages. By just so slight, by just so lasting a tenure does superstition hold the world ever; there is the rook in England, and the crow in New England.

> Thou dusky spirit of the wood,
> Bird of an ancient brood,
> Flitting thy lonely way,
> A meteor in the summer's day,
> From wood to wood, from hill to hill,
> Low over forest, field, and rill,
> What wouldst thou say?
> Why shouldst thou haunt the day?
> What makes thy melancholy float?
> What bravery inspires thy throat,
> And bears thee up above the clouds,
> Over desponding human crowds,
> Which far below
> Lay thy haunts low?

The late walker or sailor, in the October evenings, may hear the murmurings of the snipe, circling over

the meadows, the most spirit-like sound in nature; and
still later in the autumn, when the frosts have tinged the
leaves, a solitary loon pays a visit to our retired ponds,
where he may lurk undisturbed till the season of moult-
ing is passed, making the woods ring with his wild
laughter. This bird, the Great Northern Diver, well
deserves its name; for when pursued with a boat, it
will dive, and swim like a fish under water, for sixty rods
or more, as fast as a boat can be paddled, and its pur-
suer, if he would discover his game again, must put
his ear to the surface to hear where it comes up. When
it comes to the surface, it throws the water off with one
shake of its wings, and calmly swims about until again
disturbed.

These are the sights and sounds which reach our
senses oftenest during the year. But sometimes one
hears a quite new note, which has for background other
Carolinas and Mexicos than the books describe, and
learns that his ornithology has done him no service.

It appears from the Report that there are about forty
quadrupeds belonging to the State, and among these
one is glad to hear of a few bears, wolves, lynxes, and
wildcats.

When our river overflows its banks in the spring,
the wind from the meadows is laden with a strong scent
of musk, and by its freshness advertises me of an unexplored wildness. Those backwoods are not far off then.
I am affected by the sight of the cabins of the muskrat,
made of mud and grass, and raised three or four feet
along the river, as when I read of the barrows of Asia.
The muskrat is the beaver of the settled States. Their

number has even increased within a few years in this
vicinity. Among the rivers which empty into the Merrimack, the Concord is known to the boatmen as a dead
stream. The Indians are said to have called it Musketaquid, or Prairie River. Its current being much more
sluggish and its water more muddy than the rest, it
abounds more in fish and game of every kind. According to the History of the town, " The fur-trade was here
once very important. As early as 1641, a company was
formed in the colony, of which Major Willard of Concord was superintendent, and had the exclusive right to
trade with the Indians in furs and other articles; and
for this right they were obliged to pay into the public
treasury one twentieth of all the furs they obtained."
There are trappers in our midst still, as well as on the
streams of the far West, who night and morning go
the round of their traps, without fear of the Indian.
One of these takes from one hundred and fifty to two
hundred muskrats in a year, and even thirty-six have
been shot by one man in a day. Their fur, which is not
nearly as valuable as formerly, is in good condition in
the winter and spring only; and upon the breaking up
of the ice, when they are driven out of their holes by the
water, the greatest number is shot from boats, either
swimming or resting on their stools, or slight supports
of grass and reeds, by the side of the stream. Though
they exhibit considerable cunning at other times, they
are easily taken in a trap, which has only to be placed
in their holes, or wherever they frequent, without any
bait being used, though it is sometimes rubbed with their
musk. In the winter the hunter cuts holes in the ice,

and shoots them when they come to the surface. Their
burrows are usually in the high banks of the river, with
the entrance under water, and rising within to above the
level of high water. Sometimes their nests, composed of
dried meadow-grass and flags, may be discovered where
the bank is low and spongy, by the yielding of the ground
under the feet. They have from three to seven or eight
young in the spring.

Frequently, in the morning or evening, a long ripple
is seen in the still water, where a muskrat is crossing
the stream, with only its nose above the surface, and
sometimes a green bough in its mouth to build its house
with. When it finds itself observed, it will dive and swim
five or six rods under water, and at length conceal itself
in its hole, or the weeds. It will remain under water for
ten minutes at a time, and on one occasion has been
seen, when undisturbed, to form an air-bubble under the
ice, which contracted and expanded as it breathed at
leisure. When it suspects danger on shore, it will stand
erect like a squirrel, and survey its neighborhood for
several minutes, without moving.

In the fall, if a meadow intervene between their burrows and the stream, they erect cabins of mud and
grass, three or four feet high, near its edge. These are
not their breeding-places, though young are sometimes
found in them in late freshets, but rather their hunting-
lodges, to which they resort in the winter with their
food, and for shelter. Their food consists chiefly of flags
and fresh-water mussels, the shells of the latter being left
in large quantities around their lodges in the spring.

The Penobscot Indian wears the entire skin of a muskrat, with the legs and tail dangling, and the head caught under his girdle, for a pouch, into which he puts his fishing-tackle, and essences to scent his traps with.

The bear, wolf, lynx, wildcat, deer, beaver, and marten have disappeared; the otter is rarely if ever seen here at present; and the mink is less common than formerly.

Perhaps of all our untamed quadrupeds, the fox has obtained the widest and most familiar reputation, from the time of Pilpay and Æsop to the present day. His recent tracks still give variety to a winter's walk. I tread in the steps of the fox that has gone before me by some hours, or which perhaps I have started, with such a tip-toe of expectation as if I were on the trail of the Spirit itself which resides in the wood, and expected soon to catch it in its lair. I am curious to know what has determined its graceful curvatures, and how surely they were coincident with the fluctuations of some mind. I know which way a mind wended, what horizon it faced, by the setting of these tracks, and whether it moved slowly or rapidly, by their greater or less intervals and distinctness; for the swiftest step leaves yet a lasting trace. Sometimes you will see the trails of many together, and where they have gamboled and gone through a hundred evolutions, which testify to a singular listlessness and leisure in nature.

When I see a fox run across the pond on the snow, with the carelessness of freedom, or at intervals trace his course in the sunshine along the ridge of a hill, I give up to him sun and earth as to their true proprietor. He does not go in the sun, but it seems to follow him, and there is a visible sympathy between him and it.

Sometimes, when the snow lies light and but five or six inches deep, you may give chase and come up with one on foot. In such a case he will show a remarkable presence of mind, choosing only the safest direction, though he may lose ground by it. Notwithstanding his fright, he will take no step which is not beautiful. His pace is a sort of leopard canter, as if he were in no wise impeded by the snow, but were husbanding his strength all the while. When the ground is uneven, the course is a series of graceful curves, conforming to the shape of the surface. He runs as though there were not a bone in his back. Occasionally dropping his muzzle to the ground for a rod or two, and then tossing his head aloft, when satisfied of his course. When he comes to a declivity, he will put his fore feet together, and slide swiftly down it, shoving the snow before him. He treads so softly that you would hardly hear it from any nearness, and yet with such expression that it would not be quite inaudible at any distance.

Of fishes, seventy-five genera and one hundred and seven species are described in the Report. The fisherman will be startled to learn that there are but about a dozen kinds in the ponds and streams of any inland town; and almost nothing is known of their habits. Only their names and residence make one love fishes. I would know even the number of their fin-rays, and how many scales compose the lateral line. I am the wiser in respect to all knowledges, and the better qualified for all fortunes, for knowing that there is a minnow in the brook. Methinks I have need even of his sympathy, and to be his fellow in a degree.

I have experienced such simple delight in the trivial matters of fishing and sporting, formerly, as might have inspired the muse of Homer or Shakespeare; and now, when I turn the pages and ponder the plates of the Angler's Souvenir, I am fain to exclaim, —

> "Can such things be,
> And overcome us like a summer's cloud?"

Next to nature, it seems as if man's actions were the most natural, they so gently accord with her. The small seines of flax stretched across the shallow and transparent parts of our river are no more intrusion than the cobweb in the sun. I stay my boat in mid-current, and look down in the sunny water to see the civil meshes of his nets, and wonder how the blustering people of the town could have done this elvish work. The twine looks like a new river-weed, and is to the river as a beautiful memento of man's presence in nature, discovered as silently and delicately as a footprint in the sand.

When the ice is covered with snow, I do not suspect the wealth under my feet; that there is as good as a mine under me wherever I go. How many pickerel are poised on easy fin fathoms below the loaded wain! The revolution of the seasons must be a curious phenomenon to them. At length the sun and wind brush aside their curtain, and they see the heavens again.

Early in the spring, after the ice has melted, is the time for spearing fish. Suddenly the wind shifts from northeast and east to west and south, and every icicle, which has tinkled on the meadow grass so long, trickles down its stem, and seeks its level unerringly with a million comrades. The steam curls up from every roof and fence.

I see the civil sun drying earth's tears,
Her tears of joy, which only faster flow.

In the brooks is heard the slight grating sound of small cakes of ice, floating with various speed, full of content and promise, and where the water gurgles under a natural bridge, you may hear these hasty rafts hold conversation in an undertone. Every rill is a channel for the juices of the meadow. In the ponds the ice cracks with a merry and inspiriting din, and down the larger streams is whirled grating hoarsely, and crashing its way along, which was so lately a highway for the woodman's team and the fox, sometimes with the tracks of the skaters still fresh upon it, and the holes cut for pickerel. Town committees anxiously inspect the bridges and causeways, as if by mere eye-force to intercede with the ice and save the treasury.

The river swelleth more and more,
Like some sweet influence stealing o'er
The passive town; and for a while
Each tussock makes a tiny isle,
Where, on some friendly Ararat,
Resteth the weary water-rat.

No ripple shows Musketaquid,
Her very current e'en is hid,
As deepest souls do calmest rest
When thoughts are swelling in the breast,
And she that in the summer's drought
Doth make a rippling and a rout,
Sleeps from Nahshawtuck to the Cliff,
Unruffled by a single skiff.
But by a thousand distant hills
The louder roar a thousand rills,

And many a spring which now is dumb,
And many a stream with smothered hum,
Doth swifter well and faster glide,
Though buried deep beneath the tide.
Our village shows a rural Venice,
Its broad lagoons where yonder fen is;
As lovely as the Bay of Naples
Yon placid cove amid the maples;
And in my neighbor's field of corn
I recognize the Golden Horn.

Here Nature taught from year to year,
When only red men came to hear, —
Methinks 't was in this school of art
Venice and Naples learned their part;
But still their mistress, to my mind,
Her young disciples leaves behind.

The fisherman now repairs and launches his boat. The best time for spearing is at this season, before the weeds have begun to grow, and while the fishes lie in the shallow water, for in summer they prefer the cool depths, and in the autumn they are still more or less concealed by the grass. The first requisite is fuel for your crate; and for this purpose the roots of the pitch pine are commonly used, found under decayed stumps, where the trees have been felled eight or ten years.

With a crate, or jack, made of iron hoops, to contain your fire, and attached to the bow of your boat about three feet from the water, a fish-spear with seven tines and fourteen feet long, a large basket or barrow to carry your fuel and bring back your fish, and a thick outer garment, you are equipped for a cruise. It should be a warm and still evening; and then, with a fire crackling merrily at the prow, you may launch forth like a cucullo

into the night. The dullest soul cannot go upon such an
expedition without some of the spirit of adventure; as
if he had stolen the boat of Charon and gone down the
Styx on a midnight expedition into the realms of Pluto.
And much speculation does this wandering star afford
to the musing night-walker, leading him on and on,
jack-o'-lantern-like, over the meadows; or, if he is wiser,
he amuses himself with imagining what of human life,
far in the silent night, is flitting moth-like round its candle. The silent navigator shoves his craft gently over
the water, with a smothered pride and sense of benefac-
tion, as if he were the phosphor, or light-bringer, to these
dusky realms, or some sister moon, blessing the spaces
with her light. The waters, for a rod or two on either
hand and several feet in depth, are lit up with more than
noonday distinctness, and he enjoys the opportunity
which so many have desired, for the roofs of a city are
indeed raised, and he surveys the midnight economy of
the fishes. There they lie in every variety of posture;
some on their backs, with their white bellies uppermost,
some suspended in mid-water, some sculling gently
along with a dreamy motion of the fins, and others quite
active and wide awake, — a scene not unlike what the
human city would present. Occasionally he will encounter a turtle selecting the choicest morsels, or a muskrat
resting on a tussock. He may exercise his dexterity, if
he sees fit, on the more distant and active fish, or fork
the nearer into his boat, as potatoes out of a pot, or even
take the sound sleepers with his hands. But these last
accomplishments he will soon learn to dispense with,
distinguishing the real object of his pursuit, and find

compensation in the beauty and never-ending novelty of his position. The pines growing down to the water's edge will show newly as in the glare of a conflagration; and as he floats under the willows with his light, the song sparrow will often wake on her perch, and sing that strain at midnight which she had meditated for the morning. And when he has done, he may have to steer his way home through the dark by the north star, and he will feel himself some degrees nearer to it for having lost his way on the earth.

The fishes commonly taken in this way are pickerel, suckers, perch, eels, pouts, breams, and shiners, — from thirty to sixty weight in a night. Some are hard to be recognized in the unnatural light, especially the perch, which, his dark bands being exaggerated, acquires a ferocious aspect. The number of these transverse bands, which the Report states to be seven, is, however, very variable, for in some of our ponds they have nine and ten even.

It appears that we have eight kinds of tortoises, twelve snakes, — but one of which is venomous, — nine frogs and toads, nine salamanders, and one lizard, for our neighbors.

I am particularly attracted by the motions of the serpent tribe. They make our hands and feet, the wings of the bird, and the fins of the fish seem very superfluous, as if Nature had only indulged her fancy in making them. The black snake will dart into a bush when pursued, and circle round and round with an easy and graceful motion, amid the thin and bare twigs, five or six feet from the ground, as a bird flits from bough to bough, or hang in festoons between the forks. Elasticity and flexibleness in the simpler forms of animal life are equivalent to a complex system of limbs in the higher; and we have only to be as wise and wily as the serpent, to perform as difficult feats without the vulgar assistance of hands and feet.

In May, the snapping turtle (*Emysaurus serpentina*) is frequently taken on the meadows and in the river. The fisherman, taking sight over the calm surface, discovers its snout projecting above the water, at the distance of many rods, and easily secures his prey through its unwillingness to disturb the water by swimming hastily away, for, gradually drawing its head under, it remains resting on some limb or clump of grass. Its eggs, which are buried at a distance from the water, in some soft place, as a pigeon-bed, are frequently devoured by the skunk. It will catch fish by daylight, as a toad catches flies, and is said to emit a transparent fluid from its mouth to attract them.

Nature has taken more care than the fondest parent for the education and refinement of her children. Consider the silent influence which flowers exert, no less upon the ditcher in the meadow than the lady in the bower. When I walk in the woods, I am reminded that a wise purveyor has been there before me; my most delicate experience is typified there. I am struck with the pleasing friendships and unanimities of nature, as when the lichen on the trees takes the form of their leaves. In the most stupendous scenes you will see delicate and fragile features, as slight wreaths of vapor, dew-lines, feathery sprays, which suggest a high refinement, a noble blood and breeding, as it were. It is not hard to account for elves and fairies; they represent this light grace, this ethereal gentility. Bring a spray from the wood, or a crystal from the brook, and place it on your mantel, and your household ornaments will seem plebeian beside its nobler fashion and bearing. It will wave superior there, as if used to a more refined and polished circle. It has a salute and a response to all your enthusiasm and heroism.

In the winter, I stop short in the path to admire how the trees grow up without forethought, regardless of the time and circumstances. They do not wait as man does, but now is the golden age of the sapling. Earth, air, sun, and rain are occasion enough; they were no better in primeval centuries. The "winter of *their* discontent" never comes. Witness the buds of the native poplar standing gayly out to the frost on the sides of its bare switches. They express a naked confidence. With cheerful heart one could be a sojourner in the wilderness, if he were sure to find there the catkins of the willow or the alder. When I read of them in the accounts of northern adventurers, by Baffin's Bay or Mackenzie's River, I see how even there, too, I could dwell. They are our little vegetable redeemers. Methinks our virtue will hold out till they come again. They are worthy to have had a greater than Minerva or Ceres for their inventor. Who was the benignant goddess that bestowed them on mankind?

Nature is mythical and mystical always, and works with the license and extravagance of genius. She has her luxurious and florid style as well as art. Having a pil-

grim's cup to make, she gives to the whole — stem, bowl,
handle, and nose — some fantastic shape, as if it were to
be the car of some fabulous marine deity, a Nereus or
Triton.

In the winter, the botanist need not confine himself
to his books and herbarium, and give over his outdoor
pursuits, but may study a new department of vegetable
physiology, what may be called crystalline botany, then.
The winter of 1837 was unusually favorable for this.
In December of that year, the Genius of vegetation
seemed to hover by night over its summer haunts with
unusual persistency. Such a hoar-frost as is very uncommon here or anywhere, and whose full effects can never
be witnessed after sunrise, occurred several times. As I
went forth early on a still and frosty morning, the trees
looked like airy creatures of darkness caught napping;
on this side huddled together, with their gray hairs
streaming, in a secluded valley which the sun had not
penetrated; on that, hurrying off in Indian file along
some watercourse, while the shrubs and grasses, like
elves and fairies of the night, sought to hide their diminished heads in the snow. The river, viewed from the
high bank, appeared of a yellowish-green color, though
all the landscape was white. Every tree, shrub, and spire
of grass, that could raise its head above the snow, was
covered with a dense ice-foliage, answering, as it were,
leaf for leaf to its summer dress. Even the fences had
put forth leaves in the night. The centre, diverging, and
more minute fibres were perfectly distinct, and the edges
regularly indented. These leaves were on the side of the
twig or stubble opposite to the sun, meeting it for the

most part at right angles, and there were others standing out at all possible angles upon these and upon one another, with no twig or stubble supporting them. When the first rays of the sun slanted over the scene, the grasses seemed hung with innumerable jewels, which jingled merrily as they were brushed by the foot of the traveler, and reflected all the hues of the rainbow, as he moved from side to side. It struck me that these ghost leaves, and the green ones whose forms they assume, were the creatures of but one law; that in obedience to the same law the vegetable juices swell gradually into the perfect leaf, on the one hand, and the crystalline particles troop to their standard in the same order, on the other. As if the material were indifferent, but the law one and invariable, and every plant in the spring but pushed up into and filled a permanent and eternal mould, which, summer and winter forever, is waiting to be filled.

This foliate structure is common to the coral and the plumage of birds, and to how large a part of animate and inanimate nature. The same independence of law on matter is observable in many other instances, as in the natural rhymes, when some animal form, color, or odor has its counterpart in some vegetable. As, indeed, all rhymes imply an eternal melody, independent of any particular sense.

As confirmation of the fact that vegetation is but a kind of crystallization, every one may observe how, upon the edge of the melting frost on the window, the needle-shaped particles are bundled together so as to resemble fields waving with grain, or shocks rising here and there from the stubble; on one side the vegetation of the torrid zone, high-towering palms and wide-spread banyans, such as are seen in pictures of oriental scenery; on the other, arctic pines stiff frozen, with downcast branches.

Vegetation has been made the type of all growth; but as in crystals the law is more obvious, their material being more simple, and for the most part more transient and fleeting, would it not be as philosophical as convenient to consider all growth, all filling up within the limits of nature, but a crystallization more or less rapid?

On this occasion, in the side of the high bank of the river, wherever the water or other cause had formed a cavity, its throat and outer edge, like the entrance to a citadel, bristled with a glistening ice-armor. In one place you might see minute ostrich-feathers, which seemed the waving plumes of the warriors filing into the fortress; in another, the glancing, fan-shaped banners of the Lilliputian host; and in another, the needle-shaped particles collected into bundles, resembling the plumes of the pine, might pass for a phalanx of spears. From the under side of the ice in the brooks, where there was a thicker ice below, depended a mass of crystallization, four or five inches deep, in the form of prisms, with their lower ends open, which, when the ice was laid on its smooth side, resembled the roofs and steeples of a Gothic city, or the vessels of a crowded haven under a press of canvas. The very mud in the road, where the ice had melted, was crystallized with deep rectilinear fissures, and the crystalline masses in the sides of the ruts resembled exactly asbestos in the disposition of their needles. Around the roots of the stubble and flower-stalks, the frost was gathered into the form of irregular conical shells, or fairy rings. In some places the ice-crystals were lying upon granite rocks, directly over crystals of quartz, the frostwork of a longer night, crystals of a longer period, but, to some eye unprejudiced by the short term of human life, melting as fast as the former.

In the Report on the Invertebrate Animals, this singular fact is recorded, which teaches us to put a new value on time and space: "The distribution of the marine shells is well worthy of notice as a geological fact. Cape Cod, the right arm of the Commonwealth, reaches out into the ocean, some fifty or sixty miles. It is nowhere many miles wide; but this narrow point of land has hitherto proved a barrier to the migrations of many species of Mollusca. Several genera and numerous species, which are separated by the intervention of only a few miles of land, are effectually prevented from mingling by the Cape, and do not pass from one side to the other. . . . Of the one hundred and ninety-seven marine species, eighty-three do not pass to the south shore, and fifty are not found on the north shore of the Cape."

That common mussel, the *Unio complanatus*, or more properly *fluviatilis*, left in the spring by the muskrat upon rocks and stumps, appears to have been an important article of food with the Indians. In one place, where they are said to have feasted, they are found in large quantities, at an elevation of thirty feet above the river, filling the soil to the depth of a foot, and mingled with ashes and Indian remains.

The works we have placed at the head of our chapter, with as much license as the preacher selects his text, are such as imply more labor than enthusiasm. The State wanted complete catalogues of its natural riches, with such additional facts merely as would be directly useful.

The reports on Fishes, Reptiles, Insects, and Invertebrate Animals, however, indicate labor and research, and have a value independent of the object of the legislature.

Those on Herbaceous Plants and Birds cannot be of much value, as long as Bigelow and Nuttall are accessible. They serve but to indicate, with more or less exactness, what species are found in the State. We detect several errors ourselves, and a more practiced eye would no doubt expand the list.

The Quadrupeds deserved a more final and instructive report than they have obtained.

These volumes deal much in measurements and minute descriptions, not interesting to the general reader, with only here and there a colored sentence to allure him, like those plants growing in dark forests, which bear only leaves without blossoms. But the ground was comparatively unbroken, and we will not complain of the pioneer, if he raises no flowers with his first crop. Let us not underrate the value of a fact; it will one day flower in a truth. It is astonishing how few facts of importance are added in a century to the natural history of any animal. The natural history of man himself is still being gradually written. Men are knowing enough after their fashion. Every countryman and dairy-maid knows that the coats of the fourth stomach of the calf will curdle milk, and what particular mushroom is a safe and nutritious diet. You cannot go into any field or wood, but it will seem as if every stone had been turned, and the bark on every tree ripped up. But, after all, it is much easier to discover than to see when the cover is off. It has been well said that "the attitude of inspection is prone." Wisdom does not inspect, but behold. We must look a long time before we can see. Slow are the beginnings of philosophy. He has something demoniacal in him, who can discern a law or couple two facts. We can imagine a time when "Water runs down hill" may have been taught in the schools. The true man of science will know nature better by his finer organization; he will smell, taste, see, hear, feel, better than other men. His will be a deeper and finer experience. We do not learn by inference and deduction and the application of mathematics to philosophy, but by direct intercourse and sympathy. It is with science as with ethics, — we cannot know truth by contrivance and method; the Baconian is as false as any other, and with all the helps of machinery and the arts, the most scientific will still be the healthiest and friendliest man, and possess a more perfect Indian wisdom.

A WALK TO WACHUSETT

Concord, July 19, 1842.

The needles of the pine
All to the west incline.

Summer and winter our eyes had rested on the dim outline of the mountains in our horizon, to which distance and indistinctness lent a grandeur not their own, so that they served equally to interpret all the allusions of poets and travelers; whether with Homer, on a spring morning, we sat down on the many-peaked Olympus, or with Virgil and his compeers roamed the Etrurian and Thessalian hills, or with Humboldt measured the more modern Andes and Teneriffe. Thus we spoke our mind to them, standing on the Concord cliffs: —

> With frontier strength ye stand your ground,
> With grand content ye circle round,
> Tumultuous silence for all sound,
> Ye distant nursery of rills,
> Monadnock, and the Peterboro' hills;
> Like some vast fleet,
> Sailing through rain and sleet,
> Through winter's cold and summer's heat;
> Still holding on, upon your high emprise,
> Until ye find a shore amid the skies;
> Not skulking close to land,
> With cargo contraband,
> For they who sent a venture out by ye
> Have set the sun to see
> Their honesty.
> Ships of the line, each one,
> Ye to the westward run,

Always before the gale,
Under a press of sail,
With weight of metal all untold.
I seem to feel ye, in my firm seat here,
Immeasurable depth of hold,
And breadth of beam, and length of running gear.

Methinks ye take luxurious pleasure
In your novel western leisure;
So cool your brows, and freshly blue,
As Time had nought for ye to do;
For ye lie at your length,
An unappropriated strength,
Unhewn primeval timber,
For knees so stiff, for masts so limber;
The stock of which new earths are made
One day to be our western trade,
Fit for the stanchions of a world
Which through the seas of space is hurled.

While we enjoy a lingering ray,
Ye still o'ertop the western day,
Reposing yonder, on God's croft,
Like solid stacks of hay.
Edged with silver, and with gold,
The clouds hang o'er in damask fold,
And with such depth of amber light
The west is dight,
Where still a few rays slant,
That even heaven seems extravagant.
On the earth's edge mountains and trees
Stand as they were on air graven,
Or as the vessels in a haven
Await the morning breeze.
I fancy even
Through your defiles windeth the way to heaven;
And yonder still, in spite of history's page,
Linger the golden and the silver age;
Upon the laboring gale

The news of future centuries is brought,
And of new dynasties of thought,
From your remotest vale.

But special I remember thee,
Wachusett, who like me
Standest alone without society.
Thy far blue eye,
A remnant of the sky,
Seen through the clearing or the gorge
Or from the windows of the forge,
Doth leaven all it passes by.
Nothing is true,
But stands 'tween me and you,
Thou western pioneer,
Who know'st not shame nor fear
By venturous spirit driven,
Under the eaves of heaven.
And canst expand thee there,
And breathe enough of air?
Upholding heaven, holding down earth,
Thy pastime from thy birth,
Not steadied by the one, nor leaning on the other;
May I approve myself thy worthy brother!

At length, like Rasselas, and other inhabitants of happy valleys, we resolved to scale the blue wall which bounded the western horizon, though not without misgivings that thereafter no visible fairyland would exist for us. But we will not leap at once to our journey's end, though near, but imitate Homer, who conducts his reader over the plain, and along the resounding sea, though it be but to the tent of Achilles. In the spaces of thought are the reaches of land and water, where men go and come. The landscape lies far and fair within, and the deepest thinker is the farthest traveled.

At a cool and early hour on a pleasant morning in July, my companion and I passed rapidly through Acton and Stow, stopping to rest and refresh us on the bank of a small stream, a tributary of the Assabet, in the latter town. As we traversed the cool woods of Acton, with stout staves in our hands, we were cheered by the song of the red-eye, the thrushes, the phœbe, and the cuckoo; and as we passed through the open country, we inhaled the fresh scent of every field, and all nature lay passive, to be viewed and traveled. Every rail, every farmhouse, seen dimly in the twilight, every tinkling sound told of peace and purity, and we moved happily along the dank roads, enjoying not such privacy as the day leaves when it withdraws, but such as it has not profaned. It was solitude with light; which is better than darkness. But anon, the sound of the mower's rifle was heard in the fields, and this, too, mingled with the lowing of kine.

This part of our route lay through the country of hops, which plant perhaps supplies the want of the vine in American scenery, and may remind the traveler of Italy and the South of France, whether he traverses the country when the hop-fields, as then, present solid and regular masses of verdure, hanging in graceful festoons from pole to pole, the cool coverts where lurk the gales which refresh the wayfarer; or in September, when the women and children, and the neighbors from far and near, are gathered to pick the hops into long troughs; or later still, when the poles stand piled in vast pyramids in the yards, or lie in heaps by the roadside.

The culture of the hop, with the processes of picking,

drying in the kiln, and packing for the market, as well as the uses to which it is applied, so analogous to the culture and uses of the grape, may afford a theme for future poets.

The mower in the adjacent meadow could not tell us the name of the brook on whose banks we had rested, or whether it had any, but his younger companion, perhaps his brother, knew that it was Great Brook. Though they stood very near together in the field, the things they knew were very far apart; nor did they suspect each other's reserved knowledge, till the stranger came by. In Bolton, while we rested on the rails of a cottage fence, the strains of music which issued from within, probably in compliment to us, sojourners, reminded us that thus far men were fed by the accustomed pleasures. So soon did we, wayfarers, begin to learn that man's life is rounded with the same few facts, the same simple relations everywhere, and it is vain to travel to find it new. The flowers grow more various ways than he. But coming soon to higher land, which afforded a prospect of the mountains, we thought we had not traveled in vain, if it were only to hear a truer and wilder pronunciation of their names from the lips of the inhabitants; not *Way*-tatic, *Way*-chusett, but *Wor*-tatic, *Wor*-chusett. It made us ashamed of our tame and civil pronunciation, and we looked upon them as born and bred farther west than we. Their tongues had a more generous accent than ours, as if breath was cheaper where they wagged. A countryman, who speaks but seldom, talks copiously, as it were, as his wife sets cream and cheese before you without stint. Before noon we

had reached the highlands overlooking the valley of
Lancaster (affording the first fair and open prospect into
the west), and there, on the top of a hill, in the shade of
some oaks, near to where a spring bubbled out from a
leaden pipe, we rested during the heat of the day, reading Virgil and enjoying the scenery. It was such a place
as one feels to be on the outside of the earth; for from
it we could, in some measure, see the form and structure
of the globe. There lay Wachusett, the object of our
journey, lowering upon us with unchanged proportions,
though with a less ethereal aspect than had greeted our
morning gaze, while further north, in successive order,
slumbered its sister mountains along the horizon.

We could get no further into the Æneid than

> — atque altae moenia Romae,
> — and the wall of high Rome,

before we were constrained to reflect by what myriad tests
a work of genius has to be tried; that Virgil, away in
Rome, two thousand years off, should have to unfold his
meaning, the inspiration of Italian vales, to the pilgrim
on New England hills. This life so raw and modern, that
so civil and ancient; and yet we read Virgil mainly to
be reminded of the identity of human nature in all ages,
and, by the poet's own account, we are both the children
of a late age, and live equally under the reign of Jupiter.

> "He shook honey from the leaves, and removed fire,
>   And stayed the wine, everywhere flowing in rivers;
>   That experience, by meditating, might invent various arts
>   By degrees, and seek the blade of corn in furrows,
>   And strike out hidden fire from the veins of the flint."

The old world stands serenely behind the new, as

one mountain yonder towers behind another, more dim and distant. Rome imposes her story still upon this late generation. The very children in the school we had that morning passed had gone through her wars, and recited her alarms, ere they had heard of the wars of neighboring Lancaster. The roving eye still rests inevitably on her hills, and she still holds up the skirts of the sky on that side, and makes the past remote.

The lay of the land hereabouts is well worthy the attention of the traveler. The hill on which we were resting made part of an extensive range, running from southwest to northeast, across the country, and separating the waters of the Nashua from those of the Concord, whose banks we had left in the morning, and by bearing in mind this fact, we could easily determine whither each brook was bound that crossed our path. Parallel to this, and fifteen miles further west, beyond the deep and broad valley in which lie Groton, Shirley, Lancaster, and Boylston, runs the Wachusett range, in the same general direction. The descent into the valley on the Nashua side is by far the most sudden; and a couple of miles brought us to the southern branch of the Nashua, a shallow but rapid stream, flowing between high and gravelly banks. But we soon learned that these were no *gelidae valles* into which we had descended, and, missing the coolness of the morning air, feared it had become the sun's turn to try his power upon us.

> " The sultry sun had gained the middle sky,
>   And not a tree, and not an herb was nigh,"

and with melancholy pleasure we echoed the melodious plaint of our fellow-traveler, Hassan, in the desert, —

"Sad was the hour, and luckless was the day,
	When first from Schiraz' walls I bent my way."

The air lay lifeless between the hills, as in a seething caldron, with no leaf stirring, and instead of the fresh odor of grass and clover, with which we had before been regaled, the dry scent of every herb seemed merely medicinal. Yielding, therefore, to the heat, we strolled into the woods, and along the course of a rivulet, on whose banks we loitered, observing at our leisure the products of these new fields. He who traverses the woodland paths, at this season, will have occasion to remember the small, drooping, bell-like flowers and slender red stem of the dogsbane, and the coarser stem and berry of the poke, which are both common in remoter and wilder scenes; and if "the sun casts such a reflecting heat from the sweet-fern" as makes him faint, when he is climbing the bare hills, as they complained who first penetrated into these parts, the cool fragrance of the swamp-pink restores him again, when traversing the valleys between.

As we went on our way late in the afternoon, we refreshed ourselves by bathing our feet in every rill that crossed the road, and anon, as we were able to walk in the shadows of the hills, recovered our morning elasticity. Passing through Sterling, we reached the banks of the Stillwater, in the western part of the town, at evening, where is a small village collected. We fancied that there was already a certain western look about this place, a smell of pines and roar of water, recently confined by dams, belying its name, which were exceedingly grateful. When the first inroad has been made, a few acres

leveled, and a few houses erected, the forest looks wilder
than ever. Left to herself, nature is always more or
less civilized, and delights in a certain refinement; but
where the axe has encroached upon the edge of the
forest, the dead and unsightly limbs of the pine, which
she had concealed with green banks of verdure, are
exposed to sight. This village had, as yet, no post-office,
nor any settled name. In the small villages which we
entered, the villagers gazed after us, with a complacent,
almost compassionate look, as if we were just making
our *début* in the world at a late hour. "Nevertheless,"
did they seem to say, "come and study us, and learn
men and manners." So is each one's world but a clearing in the forest, so much open and inclosed ground.
The landlord had not yet returned from the field with
his men, and the cows had yet to be milked. But we
remembered the inscription on the wall of the Swedish
inn, "You will find at Trolhate excellent bread, meat,
and wine, provided you bring them with you," and were
contented. But I must confess it did somewhat disturb
our pleasure, in this withdrawn spot, to have our own
village newspaper handed us by our host, as if the greatest charm the country offered to the traveler was the
facility of communication with the town. Let it recline
on its own everlasting hills, and not be looking out from
their summits for some petty Boston or New York in the
horizon.

At intervals we heard the murmuring of water, and
the slumberous breathing of crickets, throughout the
night; and left the inn the next morning in the gray
twilight, after it had been hallowed by the night air,

and when only the innocent cows were stirring, with a
kind of regret. It was only four miles to the base of the
mountain, and the scenery was already more picturesque. Our road lay along the course of the Stillwater,
which was brawling at the bottom of a deep ravine,
filled with pines and rocks, tumbling fresh from the
mountains, so soon, alas! to commence its career of
usefulness. At first, a cloud hung between us and the
summit, but it was soon blown away. As we gathered
the raspberries, which grew abundantly by the roadside,
we fancied that that action was consistent with a lofty
prudence; as if the traveler who ascends into a mountainous region should fortify himself by eating of such
light ambrosial fruits as grow there, and drinking of the
springs which gush out from the mountain-sides, as he
gradually inhales the subtler and purer atmosphere of
those elevated places, thus propitiating the mountain
gods by a sacrifice of their own fruits. The gross products of the plains and valleys are for such as dwell
therein; but it seemed to us that the juices of this berry
had relation to the thin air of the mountain-tops.

In due time we began to ascend the mountain, passing,
first, through a grand sugar maple wood, which bore
the marks of the auger, then a denser forest, which
gradually became dwarfed, till there were no trees whatever. We at length pitched our tent on the summit. It is
but nineteen hundred feet above the village of Princeton,
and three thousand above the level of the sea; but by
this slight elevation it is infinitely removed from the
plain, and when we reached it we felt a sense of remote-
ness, as if we had traveled into distant regions, to Arabia

Petræa, or the farthest East. A robin upon a staff was the highest object in sight. Swallows were flying about us, and the chewink and cuckoo were heard near at hand. The summit consists of a few acres, destitute of trees, covered with bare rocks, interspersed with blue-berry bushes, raspberries, gooseberries, strawberries, moss, and a fine, wiry grass. The common yellow lily and dwarf cornel grow abundantly in the crevices of the rocks. This clear space, which is gently rounded, is bounded a few feet lower by a thick shrubbery of oaks, with maples, aspens, beeches, cherries, and occasionally a mountain-ash intermingled, among which we found the bright blue berries of the Solomon's-seal, and the fruit of the pyrola. From the foundation of a wooden observatory, which was formerly erected on the highest point, forming a rude, hollow structure of stone, a dozen feet in diameter, and five or six in height, we could see Monadnock, in simple grandeur, in the northwest, rising nearly a thousand feet higher, still the "far blue moun-tain," though with an altered profile. The first day the weather was so hazy that it was in vain we endeav-ored to unravel the obscurity. It was like looking into the sky again, and the patches of forest here and there seemed to flit like clouds over a lower heaven. As to voyagers of an aerial Polynesia, the earth seemed like a larger island in the ether; on every side, even as low as we, the sky shutting down, like an unfathomable deep, around it, a blue Pacific island, where who knows what islanders inhabit? and as we sail near its shores we see the waving of trees and hear the lowing of kine.

We read Virgil and Wordsworth in our tent, with

new pleasure there, while waiting for a clearer atmosphere, nor did the weather prevent our appreciating the simple truth and beauty of Peter Bell: —

> "And he had lain beside his asses,
>   On lofty Cheviot Hills:

> "And he had trudged through Yorkshire dales,
>   Among the rocks and winding *scars;*
>   Where deep and low the hamlets lie
>   Beneath their little patch of sky
>   And little lot of stars."

Who knows but this hill may one day be a Helvellyn, or even a Parnassus, and the Muses haunt here, and other Homers frequent the neighboring plains?

> Not unconcerned Wachusett rears his head
>   Above the field, so late from nature won,
> With patient brow reserved, as one who read
>   New annals in the history of man.

The blueberries which the mountain afforded, added to the milk we had brought, made our frugal supper, while for entertainment the even-song of the wood thrush rang along the ridge. Our eyes rested on no painted ceiling nor carpeted hall, but on skies of Nature's painting, and hills and forests of her embroidery. Before sunset, we rambled along the ridge to the north, while a hawk soared still above us. It was a place where gods might wander, so solemn and solitary, and removed from all contagion with the plain. As the evening came on, the haze was condensed in vapor, and the landscape became more distinctly visible, and numerous sheets of water were brought to light.

> "Et jam summa procul villarum culmina fumant,
>   Majoresque cadunt altis de montibus umbrae."

And now the tops of the villas smoke afar off,
And the shadows fall longer from the high mountains.

As we stood on the stone tower while the sun was setting, we saw the shades of night creep gradually over
the valleys of the east; and the inhabitants went into
their houses, and shut their doors, while the moon
silently rose up, and took possession of that part. And
then the same scene was repeated on the west side, as far
as the Connecticut and the Green Mountains, and the
sun's rays fell on us two alone, of all New England men.

It was the night but one before the full of the moon,
so bright that we could see to read distinctly by moonlight, and in the evening strolled over the summit without danger. There was, by chance, a fire blazing on
Monadnock that night, which lighted up the whole
western horizon, and, by making us aware of a community of mountains, made our position seem less solitary. But at length the wind drove us to the shelter of
our tent, and we closed its door for the night, and fell
asleep.

It was thrilling to hear the wind roar over the rocks,
at intervals when we waked, for it had grown quite
cold and windy. The night was, in its elements, simple
even to majesty in that bleak place, — a bright moonlight and a piercing wind. It was at no time darker than
twilight within the tent, and we could easily see the
moon through its transparent roof as we lay; for there
was the moon still above us, with Jupiter and Saturn on
either hand, looking down on Wachusett, and it was a
satisfaction to know that they were our fellow-travelers
still, as high and out of our reach as our own destiny.

Truly the stars were given for a consolation to man. We should not know but our life were fated to be always groveling, but it is permitted to behold them, and surely they are deserving of a fair destiny. We see laws which never fail, of whose failure we never conceived; and their lamps burn all the night, too, as well as all day, — so rich and lavish is that nature which can afford this superfluity of light.

The morning twilight began as soon as the moon had set, and we arose and kindled our fire, whose blaze might have been seen for thirty miles around. As the daylight increased, it was remarkable how rapidly the wind went down. There was no dew on the summit, but coldness supplied its place. When the dawn had reached its prime, we enjoyed the view of a distinct horizon line, and could fancy ourselves at sea, and the distant hills the waves in the horizon, as seen from the deck of a vessel. The cherry-birds flitted around us, the nuthatch and flicker were heard among the bushes, the titmouse perched within a few feet, and the song of the wood thrush again rang along the ridge. At length we saw the run rise up out of the sea, and shine on Massachusetts; and from this moment the atmosphere grew more and more transparent till the time of our departure, and we began to realize the extent of the view, and how the earth, in some degree, answered to the heavens in breadth, the white villages to the constellations in the sky. There was little of the sublimity and grandeur which belong to mountain scenery, but an immense landscape to ponder on a summer's day. We could see how ample and roomy is nature. As far as the eye could

reach there was little life in the landscape; the few birds
that flitted past did not crowd. The travelers on the
remote highways, which intersect the country on every
side, had no fellow-travelers for miles, before or behind.
On every side, the eye ranged over successive circles of
towns, rising one above another, like the terraces of a
vineyard, till they were lost in the horizon. Wachusett
is, in fact, the observatory of the State. There lay Massachusetts, spread out before us in its length and
breadth, like a map. There was the level horizon which
told of the sea on the east and south, the well-known
hills of New Hampshire on the north, and the misty
summits of the Hoosac and Green Mountains, first
made visible to us the evening before, blue and unsub-
stantial, like some bank of clouds which the morning
wind would dissipate, on the northwest and west. These
last distant ranges, on which the eye rests unwearied,
commence with an abrupt boulder in the north, beyond
the Connecticut, and travel southward, with three or
four peaks dimly seen. But Monadnock, rearing its
masculine front in the northwest, is the grandest feature. As we beheld it, we knew that it was the height
of land between the two rivers, on this side the valley of
the Merrimack, on that of the Connecticut, fluctuating
with their blue seas of air, — these rival vales, already
teeming with Yankee men along their respective streams,
born to what destiny who shall tell? Watatic and the
neighboring hills, in this State and in New Hampshire,
are a continuation of the same elevated range on which
we were standing. But that New Hampshire bluff, —
that promontory of a State, — lowering day and night

on this our State of Massachusetts, will longest haunt
our dreams.

We could at length realize the place mountains occupy
on the land, and how they come into the general scheme
of the universe. When first we climb their summits and
observe their lesser irregularities, we do not give credit
to the comprehensive intelligence which shaped them;
but when afterward we behold their outlines in the
horizon, we confess that the hand which moulded their
opposite slopes, making one to balance the other,
worked round a deep centre, and was privy to the plan
of the universe. So is the least part of nature in its bear-
ings referred to all space. These lesser mountain ranges,
as well as the Alleghanies, run from northeast to southwest, and parallel with these mountain streams are the
more fluent rivers, answering to the general direction of
the coast, the bank of the great ocean stream itself.
Even the clouds, with their thin bars, fall into the same
direction by preference, and such even is the course of
the prevailing winds, and the migration of men and
birds. A mountain chain determines many things for
the statesman and philosopher. The improvements
of civilization rather creep along its sides than cross its
summit. How often is it a barrier to prejudice and fanaticism! In passing over these heights of land, through
their thin atmosphere, the follies of the plain are refined
and purified; and as many species of plants do not scale
their summits, so many species of folly, no doubt, do not
cross the Alleghanies; it is only the hardy mountain-
plant that creeps quite over the ridge, and descends into
the valley beyond.

We get a dim notion of the flight of birds, especially of such as fly high in the air, by having ascended a mountain. We can now see what landmarks mountains are to their migrations; how the Catskills and Highlands have hardly sunk to them, when Wachusett and Monadnock open a passage to the northeast; how they are guided, too, in their course by the rivers and valleys; and who knows but by the stars, as well as the mountain ranges, and not by the petty landmarks which we use. The bird whose eye takes in the Green Mountains on the one side, and the ocean on the other, need not be at a loss to find its way.

At noon we descended the mountain, and, having returned to the abodes of men, turned our faces to the east again; measuring our progress, from time to time, by the more ethereal hues which the mountain assumed. Passing swiftly through Stillwater and Sterling, as with a downward impetus, we found ourselves almost at home again in the green meadows of Lancaster, so like our own Concord, for both are watered by two streams which unite near their centres, and have many other features in common. There is an unexpected refinement about this scenery; level prairies of great extent, interspersed with elms and hop-fields and groves of trees, give it almost a classic appearance. This, it will be remembered, was the scene of Mrs. Rowlandson's capture, and of other events in the Indian wars, but from this July afternoon, and under that mild exterior, those times seemed as remote as the irruption of the Goths. They were the dark age of New England. On beholding a picture of a New England village as it then appeared, with a fair open prospect, and a light on trees and river, as if it were broad noon, we find we had not thought the sun shone in those days, or that men lived in broad daylight then. We do not imagine the sun shining on hill and valley during Philip's war, nor on the war-path of Paugus, or Standish, or Church, or Lovell, with serene summer weather, but a dim twilight or night did those events transpire in. They must have fought in the shade of their own dusky deeds.

At length, as we plodded along the dusty roads, our thoughts became as dusty as they; all thought indeed stopped, thinking broke down, or proceeded only passively in a sort of rhythmical cadence of the confused material of thought, and we found ourselves mechanically repeating some familiar measure which timed with our tread; some verse of the Robin Hood ballads, for instance, which one can recommend to travel by: —

> "Sweavens are swift, sayd lyttle John,
> As the wind blows over the hill;
> For if it be never so loud this night,
> To-morrow it may be still."

And so it went, up-hill and down, till a stone interrupted the line, when a new verse was chosen: —

> "His shoote it was but loosely shott,
> Yet flewe not the arrowe in vaine,
> For it mett one of the sheriffe's men,
> And William a Trent was slaine."

There is, however, this consolation to the most way-worn traveler, upon the dustiest road, that the path his feet describe is so perfectly symbolical of human life, — now climbing the hills, now descending into the vales.

From the summits he beholds the heavens and the horizon, from the vales he looks up to the heights again. He is treading his old lessons still, and though he may be very weary and travel-worn, it is yet sincere experience.

Leaving the Nashua, we changed our route a little, and arrived at Stillriver Village, in the western part of Harvard, just as the sun was setting. From this place, which lies to the northward, upon the western slope of the same range of hills on which we had spent the noon before, in the adjacent town, the prospect is beautiful, and the grandeur of the mountain outlines unsurpassed. There was such a repose and quiet here at this hour, as if the very hillsides were enjoying the scene; and as we passed slowly along, looking back over the country we had traversed, and listening to the evening song of the robin, we could not help contrasting the equanimity of Nature with the bustle and impatience of man. His words and actions presume always a crisis near at hand, but she is forever silent and unpretending.

And now that we have returned to the desultory life of the plain, let us endeavor to import a little of that mountain grandeur into it. We will remember within what walls we lie, and understand that this level life too has its summit, and why from the mountain-top the deepest valleys have a tinge of blue; that there is elevation in every hour, as no part of the earth is so low that the heavens may not be seen from, and we have only to stand on the summit of our hour to command an uninterrupted horizon.

We rested that night at Harvard, and the next morning, while one bent his steps to the nearer village of

Groton, the other took his separate and solitary way to the peaceful meadows of Concord; but let him not forget to record the brave hospitality of a farmer and his wife, who generously entertained him at their board, though the poor wayfarer could only congratulate the one on the continuance of hay weather, and silently accept the kindness of the other. Refreshed by this instance of generosity, no less than by the substantial viands set before him, he pushed forward with new vigor, and reached the banks of the Concord before the sun had climbed many degrees into the heavens.

A WINTER WALK

THE wind has gently murmured through the blinds, or puffed with feathery softness against the windows, and occasionally sighed like a summer zephyr lifting the leaves along, the livelong night. The meadow mouse has slept in his snug gallery in the sod, the owl has sat in a hollow tree in the depth of the swamp, the rabbit, the squirrel, and the fox have all been housed. The watch-dog has lain quiet on the hearth, and the cattle have stood silent in their stalls. The earth itself has slept, as it were its first, not its last sleep, save when some street-sign or wood-house door has faintly creaked upon its hinge, cheering forlorn nature at her midnight work, — the only sound awake 'twixt Venus and Mars, — advertising us of a remote inward warmth, a divine cheer and fellowship, where gods are met together, but where it is very bleak for men to stand. But while the earth has slumbered, all the air has been alive with feathery flakes descending, as if some northern Ceres reigned, showering her silvery grain over all the fields.

We sleep, and at length awake to the still reality of a winter morning. The snow lies warm as cotton or down upon the window-sill; the broadened sash and frosted panes admit a dim and private light, which enhances the snug cheer within. The stillness of the morning is impressive. The floor creaks under our feet as we move toward the window to look abroad through some clear space over the fields. We see the roofs stand under their snow burden. From the eaves and fences hang stalactites of snow, and in the yard stand stalagmites covering some concealed core. The trees and shrubs rear white arms to the sky on every side; and where were walls and fences, we see fantastic forms stretching in frolic gambols across the dusky landscape, as if Nature had strewn her fresh designs over the fields by night as models for man's art.

Silently we unlatch the door, letting the drift fall in, and step abroad to face the cutting air. Already the stars have lost some of their sparkle, and a dull, leaden mist skirts the horizon. A lurid brazen light in the east proclaims the approach of day, while the western landscape is dim and spectral still, and clothed in a sombre Tartarean light, like the shadowy realms. They are Infernal sounds only that you hear, — the crowing of cocks, the barking of dogs, the chopping of wood, the lowing of kine, all seem to come from Pluto's barnyard and beyond the Styx, — not for any melancholy they suggest, but their twilight bustle is too solemn and mysterious for earth. The recent tracks of the fox or otter, in the yard, remind us that each hour of the night is crowded with events, and the primeval nature is still working and making tracks in the snow. Opening the gate, we tread briskly along the lone country road, crunching the dry and crisped snow under our feet, or aroused by the sharp, clear creak of the wood-sled, just starting for the distant market, from the early farmer's door, where it has lain the summer long, dreaming amid the chips and stubble; while far through the drifts and powdered windows we see the farmer's early candle, like a paled star, emitting a lonely beam, as if some severe virtue were at its matins there. And one by one the smokes begin to ascend from the chimneys amid the trees and snows.

> The sluggish smoke curls up from some deep dell,
> The stiffened air exploring in the dawn,
> And making slow acquaintance with the day
> Delaying now upon its heavenward course,
> In wreathèd loiterings dallying with itself,
> With as uncertain purpose and slow deed
> As its half-wakened master by the hearth,
> Whose mind still slumbering and sluggish thoughts
> Have not yet swept into the onward current
> Of the new day; — and now it streams afar,
> The while the chopper goes with step direct,
> And mind intent to swing the early axe.
>   First in the dusky dawn he sends abroad
> His early scout, his emissary, smoke,
> The earliest, latest pilgrim from the roof,
> To feel the frosty air, inform the day;
> And while he crouches still beside the hearth,
> Nor musters courage to unbar the door,
> It has gone down the glen with the light wind,
> And o'er the plain unfurled its venturous wreath,
> Draped the tree-tops, loitered upon the hill,
> And warmed the pinions of the early bird;
> And now, perchance, high in the crispy air,
> Has caught sight of the day o'er the earth's edge,
> And greets its master's eye at his low door,
> As some refulgent cloud in the upper sky.

We hear the sound of wood-chopping at the farmers' doors, far over the frozen earth, the baying of the house-dog, and the distant clarion of the cock, — though the thin and frosty air conveys only the finer particles of sound to our ears, with short and sweet vibrations, as the waves subside soonest on the purest and lightest liquids, in which gross substances sink to the bottom. They come clear and bell-like, and from a greater distance in the horizon, as if there were fewer impediments than in summer to make them faint and ragged. The ground is sonorous, like seasoned wood, and even the ordinary rural sounds are melodious, and the jingling of the ice on the trees is sweet and liquid. There is the least possible moisture in the atmosphere, all being dried up or congealed, and it is of such extreme tenuity and elasticity that it becomes a source of delight. The withdrawn and tense sky seems groined like the aisles of a cathedral, and the polished air sparkles as if there were crystals of ice floating in it. As they who have resided in Greenland tell us that when it freezes "the sea smokes like burning turf-land, and a fog or mist arises, called frost-smoke," which "cutting smoke frequently raises blisters on the face and hands, and is very pernicious to the health." But this pure, stinging cold is an elixir to the lungs, and not so much a frozen mist as a crystallized midsummer haze, refined and purified by cold.

The sun at length rises through the distant woods, as if with the faint clashing, swinging sound of cymbals, melting the air with his beams, and with such rapid steps the morning travels, that already his rays are gilding the distant western mountains. Meanwhile we step hastily along through the powdery snow, warmed by an inward heat, enjoying an Indian summer still, in the increased glow of thought and feeling. Probably if our lives were more conformed to nature, we should not need to defend ourselves against her heats and colds, but find her our constant nurse and friend, as do plants and quadrupeds. If our bodies were fed with pure and simple elements, and not with a stimulating and heating diet, they would afford no more pasture for cold than a leafless twig, but thrive like the trees, which find even winter genial to their expansion.

The wonderful purity of nature at this season is a most pleasing fact. Every decayed stump and moss-grown stone and rail, and the dead leaves of autumn, are concealed by a clean napkin of snow. In the bare fields and tinkling woods, see what virtue survives. In the coldest and bleakest places, the warmest charities still maintain a foothold. A cold and searching wind drives away all contagion, and nothing can withstand it but what has a virtue in it, and accordingly, whatever we meet with in cold and bleak places, as the tops of mountains, we respect for a sort of sturdy innocence, a Puritan toughness. All things beside seem to be called in for shelter, and what stays out must be part of the original frame of the universe, and of such valor as God himself. It is invigorating to breathe the cleansed air. Its greater fineness and purity are visible to the eye, and we would fain stay out long and late, that the gales may sigh through us, too, as through the leafless trees, and fit us for the winter, — as if we hoped so to borrow some pure and steadfast virtue, which will stead us in all seasons.

There is a slumbering subterranean fire in nature which never goes out, and which no cold can chill. It finally melts the great snow, and in January or July is only buried under a thicker or thinner covering. In the coldest day it flows somewhere, and the snow melts around every tree. This field of winter rye, which sprouted late in the fall, and now speedily dissolves the snow, is where the fire is very thinly covered. We feel warmed by it. In the winter, warmth stands for all virtue, and we resort in thought to a trickling rill, with its bare stones shining in the sun, and to warm springs in the woods, with as much eagerness as rabbits and robins. The steam which rises from swamps and pools is as dear and domestic as that of our own kettle. What fire could ever equal the sunshine of a winter's day, when the meadow mice come out by the wall-sides, and the chickadee lisps in the defiles of the wood? The warmth comes directly from the sun, and is not radiated from the earth, as in summer; and when we feel his beams on our backs as we are treading some snowy dell, we are grateful as for a special kindness, and bless the sun which has followed us into that by-place.

This subterranean fire has its altar in each man's breast; for in the coldest day, and on the bleakest hill, the traveler cherishes a warmer fire within the folds of his cloak than is kindled on any hearth. A healthy man, indeed, is the complement of the seasons, and in winter, summer is in his heart. There is the south. Thither have all birds and insects migrated, and around the warm springs in his breast are gathered the robin and the lark.

At length, having reached the edge of the woods, and shut out the gadding town, we enter within their

covert as we go under the roof of a cottage, and cross
its threshold, all ceiled and banked up with snow. They
are glad and warm still, and as genial and cheery in
winter as in summer. As we stand in the midst of the
pines in the flickering and checkered light which strag-
gles but little way into their maze, we wonder if the
towns have ever heard their simple story. It seems to
us that no traveler has ever explored them, and notwithstanding the wonders which science is elsewhere
revealing every day, who would not like to hear their
annals? Our humble villages in the plain are their
contribution. We borrow from the forest the boards
which shelter and the sticks which warm us. How
important is their evergreen to the winter, that portion
of the summer which does not fade, the permanent
year, the unwithered grass! Thus simply, and with
little expense of altitude, is the surface of the earth diversified. What would human life be without forests,
those natural cities? From the tops of mountains they
appear like smooth-shaven lawns, yet whither shall we
walk but in this taller grass?

In this glade covered with bushes of a year's growth,
see how the silvery dust lies on every seared leaf and
twig, deposited in such infinite and luxurious forms
as by their very variety atone for the absence of color.
Observe the tiny tracks of mice around every stem,
and the triangular tracks of the rabbit. A pure elastic
heaven hangs over all, as if the impurities of the summer sky, refined and shrunk by the chaste winter's
cold, had been winnowed from the heavens upon the
earth.

Nature confounds her summer distinctions at this season. The heavens seem to be nearer the earth. The elements are less reserved and distinct. Water turns to ice, rain to snow. The day is but a Scandinavian night. The winter is an arctic summer.

How much more living is the life that is in nature, the furred life which still survives the stinging nights, and, from amidst fields and woods covered with frost and snow, sees the sun rise!

"The foodless wilds
Pour forth their brown inhabitants."

The gray squirrel and rabbit are brisk and playful in the remote glens, even on the morning of the cold Friday. Here is our Lapland and Labrador, and for our Esquimaux and Knistenaux, Dog-ribbed Indians, Novazemblaites, and Spitzbergeners, are there not the ice-cutter and woodchopper, the fox, muskrat, and mink?

Still, in the midst of the arctic day, we may trace the summer to its retreats, and sympathize with some contemporary life. Stretched over the brooks, in the midst of the frost-bound meadows, we may observe the submarine cottages of the caddis-worms, the larvæ of the Plicipennes; their small cylindrical cases built around themselves, composed of flags, sticks, grass, and withered leaves, shells, and pebbles, in form and color like the wrecks which strew the bottom, — now drifting along over the pebbly bottom, now whirling in tiny eddies and dashing down steep falls, or sweeping rapidly along with the current, or else swaying to and fro at the end of some grass-blade or root. Anon they

will leave their sunken habitations, and, crawling up
the stems of plants, or to the surface, like gnats, as perfect insects henceforth, flutter over the surface of the
water, or sacrifice their short lives in the flame of our
candles at evening. Down yonder little glen the shrubs
are drooping under their burden, and the red alder-
berries contrast with the white ground. Here are the
marks of a myriad feet which have already been abroad.
The sun rises as proudly over such a glen as over the
valley of the Seine or the Tiber, and it seems the residence of a pure and self-subsistent valor, such as they
never witnessed, — which never knew defeat nor fear.
Here reign the simplicity and purity of a primitive age,
and a health and hope far remote from towns and
cities. Standing quite alone, far in the forest, while the
wind is shaking down snow from the trees, and leaving
the only human tracks behind us, we find our reflections
of a richer variety than the life of cities. The chickadee and nuthatch are more inspiring society than statesmen and philosophers, and we shall return to these last
as to more vulgar companions. In this lonely glen, with
its brook draining the slopes, its creased ice and crystals
of all hues, where the spruces and hemlocks stand up
on either side, and the rush and sere wild oats in the
rivulet itself, our lives are more serene and worthy to
contemplate.

As the day advances, the heat of the sun is reflected
by the hillsides, and we hear a faint but sweet music,
where flows the rill released from its fetters, and the
icicles are melting on the trees; and the nuthatch and
partridge are heard and seen. The south wind melts

the snow at noon, and the bare ground appears with its withered grass and leaves, and we are invigorated by the perfume which exhales from it, as by the scent of strong meats.

Let us go into this deserted woodman's hut, and see how he has passed the long winter nights and the short and stormy days. For here man has lived under this south hillside, and it seems a civilized and public spot. We have such associations as when the traveler stands by the ruins of Palmyra or Hecatompolis. Singing birds and flowers perchance have begun to appear here, for flowers as well as weeds follow in the footsteps of man. These hemlocks whispered over his head, these hickory logs were his fuel, and these pitch pine roots kindled his fire; yonder fuming rill in the hollow, whose thin and airy vapor still ascends as busily as ever, though he is far off now, was his well. These hemlock boughs, and the straw upon this raised platform, were his bed, and this broken dish held his drink. But he has not been here this season, for the phœbes built their nest upon this shelf last summer. I find some embers left as if he had but just gone out, where he baked his pot of beans; and while at evening he smoked his pipe, whose stemless bowl lies in the ashes, chatted with his only companion, if perchance he had any, about the depth of the snow on the morrow, already falling fast and thick without, or disputed whether the last sound was the screech of an owl, or the creak of a bough, or imagination only; and through his broad chimney-throat, in the late winter evening, ere he stretched himself upon the straw, he looked up to learn the progress of the storm, and, seeing the bright stars of Cassiopeia's Chair shining brightly down upon him, fell contentedly asleep.

See how many traces from which we may learn the chopper's history! From this stump we may guess the sharpness of his axe, and from the slope of the stroke, on which side he stood, and whether he cut down the tree without going round it or changing hands; and, from the flexure of the splinters, we may know which way it fell. This one chip contains inscribed on it the whole history of the woodchopper and of the world. On this scrap of paper, which held his sugar or salt, perchance, or was the wadding of his gun, sitting on a log in the forest, with what interest we read the tattle of cities, of those larger huts, empty and to let, like this, in High Streets and Broadways. The eaves are dripping on the south side of this simple roof, while the titmouse lisps in the pine and the genial warmth of the sun around the door is somewhat kind and human.

After two seasons, this rude dwelling does not deform the scene. Already the birds resort to it, to build their nests, and you may track to its door the feet of many quadrupeds. Thus, for a long time, nature overlooks the encroachment and profanity of man. The wood still cheerfully and unsuspiciously echoes the strokes of the axe that fells it, and while they are few and seldom, they enhance its wildness, and all the elements strive to naturalize the sound.

Now our path begins to ascend gradually to the top of this high hill, from whose precipitous south side we can look over the broad country of forest and field and river, to the distant snowy mountains. See yonder thin column of smoke curling up through the woods from some invisible farmhouse, the standard raised over some rural homestead. There must be a warmer and more genial spot there below, as where we detect the vapor from a spring forming a cloud above the trees. What fine relations are established between the traveler who discovers this airy column from some eminence in the forest and him who sits below! Up goes the smoke as silently and naturally as the vapor exhales from the leaves, and as busy disposing itself in wreaths as the housewife on the hearth below. It is a hieroglyphic of man's life, and suggests more intimate and important things than the boiling of a pot. Where its fine column rises above the forest, like an ensign, some human life has planted itself, — and such is the beginning of Rome, the establishment of the arts, and the foundation of empires, whether on the prairies of America or the steppes of Asia.

And now we descend again, to the brink of this woodland lake, which lies in a hollow of the hills, as if it were their expressed juice, and that of the leaves which are annually steeped in it. Without outlet or inlet to the eye, it has still its history, in the lapse of its waves, in the rounded pebbles on its shore, and in the pines which grow down to its brink. It has not been idle, though sedentary, but, like Abu Musa, teaches that "sitting still at home is the heavenly way; the going out is the way of the world." Yet in its evaporation it travels as far as any. In summer it is the earth's liquid eye, a mirror in the breast of nature. The sins of the wood are washed out in it. See how the woods form an amphitheatre about it, and it is an arena for all the genialness of nature. All trees direct the traveler to its brink, all paths seek it out, birds fly to it, quadrupeds flee to it, and the very ground inclines toward it. It is nature's saloon, where she has sat down to her toilet. Consider her silent economy and tidiness; how the sun comes with his evaporation to sweep the dust from its surface each morning, and a fresh surface is constantly welling up; and annually, after whatever impurities have accumulated herein, its liquid transparency appears again in the spring. In summer a hushed music seems to sweep across its surface. But now a plain sheet of snow conceals it from our eyes, except where the wind has swept the ice bare, and the sere leaves are gliding from side to side, tacking and veering on their tiny voyages. Here is one just keeled up against a pebble on shore, a dry beech leaf, rocking still, as if it would start again. A skillful engineer, methinks, might project its course since it fell from the parent stem. Here are all the elements for such a calculation. Its present position, the direction of the wind, the level of the pond, and how much more is given. In its scarred edges and veins is its log rolled up.

We fancy ourselves in the interior of a larger house. The surface of the pond is our deal table or sanded floor, and the woods rise abruptly from its edge, like the walls of a cottage. The lines set to catch pickerel through the ice look like a larger culinary preparation, and the men stand about on the white ground like pieces of forest furniture. The actions of these men, at the distance of half a mile over the ice and snow, impress us as when we read the exploits of Alexander in history. They seem not unworthy of the scenery, and as momentous as the conquest of kingdoms.

Again we have wandered through the arches of the wood, until from its skirts we hear the distant booming of ice from yonder bay of the river, as if it were moved by some other and subtler tide than oceans know. To me it has a strange sound of home, thrilling as the voice of one's distant and noble kindred. A mild summer sun shines over forest and lake, and though there is but one green leaf for many rods, yet nature enjoys a serene health. Every sound is fraught with the same mysterious assurance of health, as well now the creaking of the boughs in January, as the soft sough of the wind in July.

When Winter fringes every bough
    With his fantastic wreath,
And puts the seal of silence now
    Upon the leaves beneath;

When every stream in its penthouse
    Goes gurgling on its way,
And in his gallery the mouse
    Nibbleth the meadow hay;

Methinks the summer still is nigh,
    And lurketh underneath,
As that same meadow mouse doth lie
    Snug in that last year's heath.

And if perchance the chickadee
    Lisp a faint note anon,
The snow is summer's canopy,
    Which she herself put on.

Fair blossoms deck the cheerful trees,
  And dazzling fruits depend;
The north wind sighs a summer breeze,
  The nipping frosts to fend,

Bringing glad tidings unto me,
  The while I stand all ear,
Of a serene eternity,
  Which need not winter fear.

Out on the silent pond straightway
  The restless ice doth crack,
And pond sprites merry gambols play
  Amid the deafening rack.

Eager I hasten to the vale,
  As if I heard brave news,
How nature held high festival,
  Which it were hard to lose.

I gambol with my neighbor ice,
  And sympathizing quake,
As each new crack darts in a trice
  Across the gladsome lake.

One with the cricket in the ground,
  And fagot on the hearth,
Resounds the rare domestic sound
  Along the forest path.

Before night we will take a journey on skates along
the course of this meandering river, as full of novelty
to one who sits by the cottage fire all the winter's day,
as if it were over the polar ice, with Captain Parry or
Franklin; following the winding of the stream, now
flowing amid hills, now spreading out into fair meadows,
and forming a myriad coves and bays where the pine

and hemlock overarch. The river flows in the rear of the
towns, and we see all things from a new and wilder side.
The fields and gardens come down to it with a frankness,
and freedom from pretension, which they do not wear on
the highway. It is the outside and edge of the earth.
Our eyes are not offended by violent contrasts. The last
rail of the farmer's fence is some swaying willow bough,
which still preserves its freshness, and here at length all
fences stop, and we no longer cross any road. We may
go far up within the country now by the most retired and
level road, never climbing a hill, but by broad levels
ascending to the upland meadows. It is a beautiful
illustration of the law of obedience, the flow of a river;
the path for a sick man, a highway down which an acorn
cup may float secure with its freight. Its slight occasional
falls, whose precipices would not diversify the landscape,
are celebrated by mist and spray, and attract the traveler
from far and near. From the remote interior, its current
conducts him by broad and easy steps, or by one gentler
inclined plane, to the sea. Thus by an early and constant
yielding to the inequalities of the ground it secures itself
the easiest passage.

No domain of nature is quite closed to man at all
times, and now we draw near to the empire of the fishes.
Our feet glide swiftly over unfathomed depths, where in
summer our line tempted the pout and perch, and where
the stately pickerel lurked in the long corridors formed
by the bulrushes. The deep, impenetrable marsh, where
the heron waded and bittern squatted, is made pervious
to our swift shoes, as if a thousand railroads had been
made into it. With one impulse we are carried to the

cabin of the muskrat, that earliest settler, and see him dart away under the transparent ice, like a furred fish, to his hole in the bank; and we glide rapidly over meadows where lately "the mower whet his scythe," through beds of frozen cranberries mixed with meadow-grass. We skate near to where the blackbird, the pewee, and the kingbird hung their nests over the water, and the hornets builded from the maple in the swamp. How many gay warblers, following the sun, have radiated from this nest of silver birch and thistle-down! On the swamp's outer edge was hung the supermarine village, where no foot penetrated. In this hollow tree the wood duck reared her brood, and slid away each day to forage in yonder fen.

In winter, nature is a cabinet of curiosities, full of dried specimens, in their natural order and position. The meadows and forests are a *hortus siccus*. The leaves and grasses stand perfectly pressed by the air without screw or gum, and the birds' nests are not hung on an artificial twig, but where they builded them. We go about dry-shod to inspect the summer's work in the rank swamp, and see what a growth have got the alders, the willows, and the maples; testifying to how many warm suns, and fertilizing dews and showers. See what strides their boughs took in the luxuriant summer, — and anon these dormant buds will carry them onward and upward another span into the heavens.

Occasionally we wade through fields of snow, under whose depths the river is lost for many rods, to appear again to the right or left, where we least expected; still holding on its way underneath, with a faint, stertorous, rumbling sound, as if, like the bear and marmot, it too had hibernated, and we had followed its faint summer trail to where it earthed itself in snow and ice. At first we should have thought that rivers would be empty and dry in midwinter, or else frozen solid till the spring thawed them; but their volume is not diminished even, for only a superficial cold bridges their surfaces. The thousand springs which feed the lakes and streams are flowing still. The issues of a few surface springs only are closed, and they go to swell the deep reservoirs. Nature's wells are below the frost. The summer brooks are not filled with snow-water, nor does the mower quench his thirst with that alone. The streams are swollen when the snow melts in the spring, because nature's work has been delayed, the water being turned into ice and snow, whose particles are less smooth and round, and do not find their level so soon.

Far over the ice, between the hemlock woods and snow-clad hills, stands the pickerel-fisher, his lines set in some retired cove, like a Finlander, with his arms thrust into the pouches of his dreadnaught; with dull, snowy, fishy thoughts, himself a finless fish, separated a few inches from his race; dumb, erect, and made to be enveloped in clouds and snows, like the pines on shore. In these wild scenes, men stand about in the scenery, or move deliberately and heavily, having sacrificed the sprightliness and vivacity of towns to the dumb sobriety of nature. He does not make the scenery less wild, more than the jays and muskrats, but stands there as a part of it, as the natives are represented in the voyages of early navigators, at Nootka Sound, and on the Northwest coast, with their furs about them, before they were tempted to loquacity by a scrap of iron. He belongs to the natural family of man, and is planted deeper in nature and has more root than the inhabitants of towns. Go to him, ask what luck, and you will learn that he too is a worshiper of the unseen. Hear with what sincere deference and waving gesture in his tone he speaks of the lake pickerel, which he has never seen, his primitive and ideal race of pickerel. He is connected with the shore still, as by a fish-line, and yet remembers the season when he took fish through the ice on the pond, while the peas were up in his garden at home.

But now, while we have loitered, the clouds have gathered again, and a few straggling snowflakes are beginning to descend. Faster and faster they fall, shutting out the distant objects from sight. The snow falls on every wood and field, and no crevice is forgotten; by the river and the pond, on the hill and in the valley. Quadrupeds are confined to their coverts and the birds sit upon their perches this peaceful hour. There is not so much sound as in fair weather, but silently and gradually every slope, and the gray walls and fences, and the polished ice, and the sere leaves, which were not buried before, are concealed, and the tracks of men and beasts are lost. With so little effort does nature reassert her rule and blot out the traces of men. Hear how Homer has described the same: "The snowflakes fall thick and fast on a winter's day. The winds are lulled, and the snow falls incessant, covering the tops of the mountains, and the hills, and the plains where the lotus-tree grows, and the cultivated fields, and they are falling by the inlets and shores of the foaming sea, but are silently dissolved by the waves." The snow levels all things, and infolds them deeper in the bosom of nature, as, in the slow summer, vegetation creeps up to the entablature of the temple, and the turrets of the castle, and helps her to prevail over art.

The surly night-wind rustles through the wood, and warns us to retrace our steps, while the sun goes down behind the thickening storm, and birds seek their roosts, and cattle their stalls.

> "Drooping the lab'rer ox
> Stands covered o'er with snow, and *now* demands
> The fruit of all his toil."

Though winter is represented in the almanac as an old man, facing the wind and sleet, and drawing his cloak about him, we rather think of him as a merry wood-chopper, and warm-blooded youth, as blithe as summer. The unexplored grandeur of the storm keeps up the spirits of the traveler. It does not trifle with us, but has a sweet earnestness. In winter we lead a more inward life. Our hearts are warm and cheery, like cottages under drifts, whose windows and doors are half concealed, but from whose chimneys the smoke cheerfully ascends. The imprisoning drifts increase the sense of comfort which the house affords, and in the coldest days we are content to sit over the hearth and see the sky through the chimney-top, enjoying the quiet and serene life that may be had in a warm corner by the chimney-side, or feeling our pulse by listening to the low of cattle in the street, or the sound of the flail in distant barns all the long afternoon. No doubt a skillful physician could determine our health by observing how these simple and natural sounds affected us. We enjoy now, not an Oriental, but a Boreal leisure, around warm stoves and fireplaces, and watch the shadow of motes in the sunbeams.

Sometimes our fate grows too homely and familiarly serious ever to be cruel. Consider how for three months the human destiny is wrapped in furs. The good Hebrew Revelation takes no cognizance of all this cheerful snow. Is there no religion for the temperate and frigid zones? We know of no scripture which records the pure benignity of the gods on a New England winter night. Their praises have never been sung, only their wrath deprecated. The best scripture, after all, records but a meagre faith. Its saints live reserved and austere. Let a brave, devout man spend the year in the woods of Maine or Labrador, and see if the Hebrew Scriptures speak adequately to his condition and experience, from the setting in of winter to the breaking up of the ice.

Now commences the long winter evening around the farmer's hearth, when the thoughts of the indwellers travel far abroad, and men are by nature and necessity charitable and liberal to all creatures. Now is the happy resistance to cold, when the farmer reaps his reward, and thinks of his preparedness for winter, and, through the glittering panes, sees with equanimity "the mansion of the northern bear," for now the storm is over, —

> "The full ethereal round,
> Infinite worlds disclosing to the view,
> Shines out intensely keen; and all one cope
> Of starry glitter glows from pole to pole."

THE SUCCESSION OF FOREST TREES [1]

Every man is entitled to come to Cattle-Show, even a transcendentalist; and for my part I am more interested in the men than in the cattle. I wish to see once more those old familiar faces, whose names I do not know, which for me represent the Middlesex country, and come as near being indigenous to the soil as a white man can; the men who are not above their business, whose coats are not too black, whose shoes do not shine very much, who never wear gloves to conceal their hands. It is true, there are some queer specimens of humanity attracted to our festival, but all are welcome. I am pretty sure to meet once more that weak-minded and whimsical fellow, generally weak-bodied too, who prefers a crooked stick for a cane; perfectly useless, you would say, only *bizarre*, fit for a cabinet, like a petrified snake. A ram's horn would be as convenient, and is yet more curiously twisted. He brings that much indulged bit of the country with him, from some town's end or other, and introduces it to Concord groves, as if he had promised it so much sometime. So some, it seems to me, elect their rulers for their crookedness. But I think that a straight stick makes the best cane, and an upright man the best ruler. Or why choose a man to do plain work who is distinguished for his oddity? However, I do not know

---

[1] An Address read to the Middlesex Agricultural Society in Concord, September, 1860.

but you will think that they have committed this mistake who invited me to speak to you to-day.

In my capacity of surveyor, I have often talked with some of you, my employers, at your dinner-tables, after having gone round and round and behind your farming, and ascertained exactly what its limits were. Moreover, taking a surveyor's and a naturalist's liberty, I have been in the habit of going across your lots much oftener than is usual, as many of you, perhaps to your sorrow, are aware. Yet many of you, to my relief, have seemed not to be aware of it; and, when I came across you in some out-of-the-way nook of your farms, have inquired, with an air of surprise, if I were not lost, since you had never seen me in that part of the town or county before; when, if the truth were known, and it had not been for betraying my secret, I might with more propriety have inquired if *you* were not lost, since I had never seen *you* there before. I have several times shown the proprietor the shortest way out of his wood-lot.

Therefore, it would seem that I have some title to speak to you to-day; and considering what that title is, and the occasion that has called us together, I need offer no apology if I invite your attention, for the few moments that are allotted me, to a purely scientific subject.

At those dinner-tables referred to, I have often been asked, as many of you have been, if I could tell how it happened, that when a pine wood was cut down an oak one commonly sprang up, and *vice versa*. To which I have answered, and now answer, that I can tell, — that it is no mystery to me. As I am not aware that this has been clearly shown by any one, I shall lay the more stress on this point. Let me lead you back into your wood-lots again.

When, hereabouts, a single forest tree or a forest springs up naturally where none of its kind grew before, I do not hesitate to say, though in some quarters still it may sound paradoxical, that it came from a seed. Of the various ways by which trees are *known* to be propagated, — by transplanting, cuttings, and the like, — this is the only supposable one under these circumstances. No such tree has ever been known to spring from anything else. If any one asserts that it sprang from something else, or from nothing, the burden of proof lies with him.

It remains, then, only to show how the seed is transported from where it grows to where it is planted. This is done chiefly by the agency of the wind, water, and animals. The lighter seeds, as those of pines and maples, are transported chiefly by wind and water; the heavier, as acorns and nuts, by animals.

In all the pines, a very thin membrane, in appearance much like an insect's wing, grows over and around the seed, and independent of it, while the latter is being developed within its base. Indeed this is often perfectly developed, though the seed is abortive; nature being, you would say, more sure to provide the means of transporting the seed, than to provide the seed to be transported. In other words, a beautiful thin sack is woven around the seed, with a handle to it such as the wind can take hold of, and it is then committed to the wind, expressly that it may transport the seed and extend the range of the species; and this it does, as effectually as when seeds are sent by mail in a different kind of sack from the Patent Office. There is a patent office at the seat of government of the universe, whose managers are as much interested in the dispersion of seeds as anybody at Washington can be, and their operations are infinitely more extensive and regular.

There is, then, no necessity for supposing that the pines have sprung up from nothing, and I am aware that I am not at all peculiar in asserting that they come from seeds, though the mode of their propagation *by nature* has been but little attended to. They are very extensively raised from the seed in Europe, and are beginning to be here.

When you cut down an oak wood, a pine wood will not *at once* spring up there unless there are, or have been quite recently, seed-bearing pines near enough for the seeds to be blown from them. But, adjacent to a forest of pines, if you prevent other crops from growing there, you will surely have an extension of your pine forest, provided the soil is suitable.

As for the heavy seeds and nuts which are not furnished with wings, the notion is still a very common one that, when the trees which bear these spring up where none of their kind were noticed before, they have come from seeds or other principles spontaneously generated there in an unusual manner, or which have lain dormant in the soil for centuries, or perhaps been called into activity by the heat of a burning. I do not believe these assertions, and I will state some of the ways in which, according to my observation, such forests are planted and raised.

Every one of these seeds, too, will be found to be winged or legged in another fashion. Surely it is not wonderful that cherry trees of all kinds are widely dispersed, since their fruit is well known to be the favorite food of various birds.   Many kinds are called bird cherries, and they appropriate many more kinds, which are not so called.   Eating cherries is a bird-like employment, and unless we disperse the seeds occasionally, as they do, I shall think that the birds have the best right to them.   See how artfully the seed of a cherry is placed in order that a bird may be compelled to transport it, — in the very midst of a tempting pericarp, so that the creature that would devour this must commonly take the stone also into its mouth or bill.   If you ever ate a cherry, and did not make two bites of it, you must have perceived it, — right in the centre of the luscious morsel, a large earthy residuum left on the tongue.   We thus take into our mouths cherry-stones as big as peas, a dozen at once, for Nature can persuade us to do almost anything when she would compass her ends.   Some wild men and children instinctively swallow these, as the birds do when in a hurry, it being the shortest way to get rid of them.   Thus, though these seeds are not provided with vegetable wings, Nature has impelled the thrush tribe to take them into their bills and fly away with them; and they are winged in another sense, and more effectually than the seeds of pines, for these are carried even against the wind.   The consequence is, that cherry trees grow not only here but there.   The same is true of a great many other seeds.

But to come to the observation which suggested these remarks.   As I have said, I suspect that I can throw some light on the fact that when hereabouts a dense pine wood is cut down, oaks and other hard woods may at once take its place. I have got only to show that the acorns and nuts, provided they are grown in the neighborhood, are regularly planted in such woods; for I assert that if an oak tree has not grown within ten miles, and man has not carried acorns thither, then an oak wood will not spring up *at once*, when a pine wood is cut down.

Apparently, there were only pines there before. They are cut off, and after a year or two you see oaks and other hard woods springing up there, with scarcely a pine amid them, and the wonder commonly is, how the seed could have lain in the ground so long without decaying. But the truth is, that it has not lain in the ground so long, but is regularly planted each year by various quadrupeds and birds.

In this neighborhood, where oaks and pines are about equally dispersed, if you look through the thickest pine wood, even the seemingly unmixed pitch pine ones, you will commonly detect many little oaks, birches, and other hard woods, sprung from seeds carried into the thicket by squirrels and other animals, and also blown thither, but which are overshadowed and choked by the pines. The denser the evergreen wood, the more likely it is to be well planted with these seeds, because the planters incline to resort with their forage to the closest covert. They also carry it into birch and other woods. This planting is carried on annually, and the oldest seedlings annually die; but when the pines are cleared off, the oaks, having got just the start they want, and now secured favorable conditions, immediately spring up to trees.

The shade of a dense pine wood is more unfavorable to the springing up of pines of the same species than of oaks within it, though the former may come up abundantly when the pines are cut, if there chance to be sound seed in the ground.

But when you cut off a lot of hard wood, very often the little pines mixed with it have a similar start, for the squirrels have carried off the nuts to the pines, and not to the more open wood, and they commonly make pretty clean work of it; and moreover, if the wood was old, the sprouts will be feeble or entirely fail; to say nothing about the soil being, in a measure, exhausted for this kind of crop.

If a pine wood is surrounded by a white oak one chiefly, white oaks may be expected to succeed when the pines are cut. If it is surrounded instead by an edging of shrub oaks, then you will probably have a dense shrub oak thicket.

I have no time to go into details, but will say, in a word, that while the wind is conveying the seeds of pines into hard woods and open lands, the squirrels and other animals are conveying the seeds of oaks and walnuts into the pine woods, and thus a rotation of crops is kept up.

I affirmed this confidently many years ago, and an occasional examination of dense pine woods confirmed me in my opinion. It has long been known to observers that squirrels bury nuts in the ground, but I am not aware that any one has thus accounted for the regular succession of forests.

On the 24th of September, in 1857, as I was paddling down the Assabet, in this town, I saw a red squirrel run along the bank under some herbage, with something large in its mouth. It stopped near the foot of a hemlock, within a couple of rods of me, and, hastily pawing a hole with its fore feet, dropped its booty into it, covered it up, and retreated part way up the trunk of the tree. As I approached the shore to examine the deposit, the squirrel, descending part way, betrayed no little anxiety about its treasure, and made two or three motions to recover it before it finally retreated. Digging there, I found two green pignuts joined together, with the thick husks on, buried about an inch and a half under the reddish soil of decayed hemlock leaves, — just the right depth to plant it. In short, this squirrel was then engaged in accomplishing two objects, to wit, laying up a store of winter food for itself, and planting a hickory wood for all creation. If the squirrel was killed, or neglected its deposit, a hickory would spring up. The nearest hickory tree was twenty rods distant. These nuts were there still just fourteen days later, but were gone when I looked again, November 21st, or six weeks later still.

I have since examined more carefully several dense woods, which are said to be, and are apparently, exclusively pine, and always with the same result. For instance, I walked the same day to a small but very dense and handsome white pine grove, about fifteen rods square, in the east part of this town. The trees are large for Concord, being from ten to twenty inches in diameter, and as exclusively pine as any wood that I know. Indeed, I selected this wood because I thought it the least likely to contain anything else. It stands on an open plain or pasture, except that it adjoins another small pine wood, which has a few little oaks in it, on the southeast side. On every other side, it was at least thirty rods from the nearest woods. Standing on the edge of this grove and looking through it, for it is quite level and free from underwood, for the most part bare, red-carpeted ground, you would have said that there was not a hardwood tree in it, young or old. But on looking carefully along over its floor I discovered, though it was not till my eye had got used to the search, that, alternating with thin ferns, and small blueberry bushes, there was, not merely here and there, but as often as every five feet and with a degree of regularity, a little oak, from three to twelve inches high, and in one place I found a green acorn dropped by the base of a pine.

I confess I was surprised to find my theory so perfectly proved in this case. One of the principal agents in this planting, the red squirrels, were all the while curiously inspecting me, while I was inspecting their plantation. Some of the little oaks had been browsed by cows, which resorted to this wood for shade.

After seven or eight years, the hard woods evidently find such a locality unfavorable to their growth, the pines being allowed to stand. As an evidence of this, I observed a diseased red maple twenty-five feet long, which had been recently prostrated, though it was still covered with green leaves, the only maple in any position in the wood.

But although these oaks almost invariably die if the pines are not cut down, it is probable that they do better for a few years under their shelter than they would anywhere else.

The very extensive and thorough experiments of the English have at length led them to adopt a method of raising oaks almost precisely like this which somewhat earlier had been adopted by Nature and her squirrels here; they have simply rediscovered the value of pines as nurses for oaks. The English experimenters seem, early and generally, to have found out the importance of using trees of some kind as nurse-plants for the young oaks. I quote from Loudon what he describes as "the ultimatum on the subject of planting and sheltering oaks," — "an abstract of the practice adopted by the government officers in the national forests" of England, prepared by Alexander Milne.

At first some oaks had been planted by themselves, and others mixed with Scotch pines; "but in all cases," says Mr. Milne, "where oaks were planted actually among the pines and surrounded by them [though the soil might be inferior], the oaks were found to be much the best." "For several years past, the plan pursued has been to plant the inclosures with Scotch pines only [a tree very similar to our pitch pine], and when the pines have got to the height of five or six feet, then to put in good strong oak plants of about four or five years' growth among the pines, — not cutting away any pines at first, unless they happen to be so strong and thick as to overshadow the oaks. In about two years it becomes necessary to shred the branches of the pines, to give light and air to the oaks, and in about two or three more years to begin gradually to remove the pines altogether, taking out a certain number each year, so that, at the end of twenty or twenty-five years, not a single Scotch pine shall be left; although, for the first ten or twelve years, the plantation may have appeared to contain nothing else but pine. The advantage of this mode of planting has been found to be that the pines dry and ameliorate the soil, destroying the coarse grass and brambles which frequently choke and injure oaks; and that no mending over is necessary, as scarcely an oak so planted is found to fail."

Thus much the English planters have discovered by patient experiment, and, for aught I know, they have taken out a patent for it; but they appear not to have discovered that it was discovered before, and that they are merely adopting the method of Nature, which she long ago made patent to all. She is all the while planting the oaks amid the pines without our knowledge, and at last, instead of government officers, we send a party of woodchoppers to cut down the pines, and so rescue an oak forest, at which we wonder as if it had dropped from the skies.

As I walk amid hickories, even in August, I hear the sound of green pignuts falling from time to time, cut off by the chickaree over my head. In the fall, I notice on the ground, either within or in the neighborhood of oak woods, on all sides of the town, stout oak twigs three or four inches long, bearing half a dozen empty acorn-cups, which twigs have been gnawed off by squirrels, on both sides of the nuts, in order to make them more portable. The jays scream and the red squirrels scold while you are clubbing and shaking the chestnut trees, for they are there on the same errand, and two of a trade never agree. I frequently see a red or gray squirrel cast down a green chestnut bur, as I am going through the woods, and I used to think, sometimes, that they were cast at me. In fact, they are so busy about it, in the midst of the chestnut season, that you cannot stand long in the woods without hearing one fall. A sportsman told me that he had, the day before, — that was in the middle of October, — seen a green chestnut bur dropped on our great river meadow, fifty rods from the nearest wood, and much further from the nearest chestnut tree, and he could not tell how it came there. Occasionally, when chestnutting in midwinter, I find thirty or forty nuts in a pile, left in its gallery, just under the leaves, by the common wood mouse (*Mus leucopus*).

But especially, in the winter, the extent to which this transportation and planting of nuts is carried on is made apparent by the snow. In almost every wood, you will see where the red or gray squirrels have pawed down through the snow in a hundred places, sometimes two feet deep, and almost always directly to a nut or a pine cone, as directly as if they had started from it and bored upward, — which you and I could not have done. It would be difficult for us to find one before the snow falls. Commonly, no doubt, they had deposited them there in the fall. You wonder if they remember the localities, or discover them by the scent. The red squirrel commonly has its winter abode in the earth under a thicket of evergreens, frequently under a small clump of evergreens in the midst of a deciduous wood. If there are any nut trees which still retain their nuts standing at a distance without the wood, their paths often lead directly to and from them. We therefore need not suppose an oak standing here and there *in* the wood in order to seed it, but if a few stand within twenty or thirty rods of it, it is sufficient.

I think that I may venture to say that every white pine cone that falls to the earth naturally in this town, before opening and losing its seeds, and almost every pitch pine one that falls at all, is cut off by a squirrel, and they begin to pluck them long before they are ripe, so that when the crop of white pine cones is a small one, as it commonly is, they cut off thus almost every one of these before it fairly ripens. I think, moreover, that their design, if I may so speak, in cutting them off green, is, partly, to prevent their opening and losing their seeds, for these are the ones for which they dig through the snow, and the only white pine cones which contain anything then. I have counted in one heap, within a diameter of four feet, the cores of 239 pitch pine cones which had been cut off and stripped by the red squirrel the previous winter.

The nuts thus left on the surface, or buried just beneath it, are placed in the most favorable circumstances for germinating. I have sometimes wondered how those which merely fell on the surface of the earth got planted; but, by the end of December, I find the chestnut of the same year partially mixed with the mould, as it were, under the decaying and mouldy leaves, where there is all the moisture and manure they want, for the nuts fall fast. In a plentiful year, a large proportion of the nuts are thus covered loosely an inch deep, and are, of course, somewhat concealed from squirrels. One winter, when the crop had been abundant, I got, with the aid of a rake, many quarts of these nuts as late as the tenth of January, and though some bought at the store the same day were more than half of them mouldy, I did not find a single mouldy one among these which I picked from under the wet and mouldy leaves, where they had been snowed on once or twice. Nature knows how to pack them best. They were still plump and tender. Apparently, they do not heat there, though wet. In the spring they were all sprouting.

Loudon says that "when the nut [of the common walnut of Europe] is to be preserved through the winter for the purpose of planting in the following spring, it should be laid in a rot-heap, as soon as gathered, with the husk on, and the heap should be turned over frequently in the course of the winter."

Here, again, he is stealing Nature's "thunder." How can a poor mortal do otherwise? for it is she that finds fingers to steal with, and the treasure to be stolen. In the planting of the seeds of most trees, the best gardeners do no more than follow Nature, though they may not know it. Generally, both large and small ones are most sure to germinate, and succeed best, when only beaten into the earth with the back of a spade, and then covered with leaves or straw. These results to which planters have arrived remind us of the experience of Kane and his companions at the north, who, when learning to live in that climate, were surprised to find themselves steadily adopting the customs of the natives, simply becoming Esquimaux. So, when we experiment in planting forests, we find ourselves at last doing as Nature does.

Would it not be well to consult with Nature in the outset? for she is the most extensive and experienced planter of us all, not excepting the Dukes of Athol.

In short, they who have not attended particularly to this subject are but little aware to what an extent quadrupeds and birds are employed, especially in the fall, in collecting, and so disseminating and planting, the seeds of trees. It is the almost constant employment of the squirrels at that season, and you rarely meet with one that has not a nut in its mouth, or is not just going to get one. One squirrel-hunter of this town told me that he knew of a walnut tree which bore particularly good nuts, but that on going to gather them one fall, he found that he had been anticipated by a family of a dozen red squirrels. He took out of the tree, which was hollow, one bushel and three pecks by measurement, without the husks, and they supplied him and his family for the winter. It would be easy to multiply instances of this kind. How commonly in the fall you see the cheek-pouches of the striped squirrel distended by a quantity of nuts! This species gets its scientific name, *Tamias*, or the steward, from its habit of storing up nuts and other seeds. Look under a nut tree a month after the nuts have fallen, and see what proportion of sound nuts to the abortive ones and shells you will find ordinarily. They have been already eaten, or dispersed far and wide. The ground looks like a platform before a grocery, where the gossips of the village sit to crack nuts and less savory jokes. You have come, you would say, after the feast was over, and are presented with the shells only.

Occasionally, when threading the woods in the fall, you will hear a sound as if some one had broken a twig, and, looking up, see a jay pecking at an acorn, or you will see a flock of them at once about it, in the top of an oak, and hear them break them off. They then fly to a suitable limb, and placing the acorn under one foot, hammer away at it busily, making a sound like a wood-pecker's tapping, looking round from time to time to see if any foe is approaching, and soon reach the meat, and nibble at it, holding up their heads to swallow, while they hold the remainder very firmly with their claws. Nevertheless it often drops to the ground before the bird has done with it. I can confirm what William Bartram wrote to Wilson, the ornithologist, that "the jay is one of the most useful agents in the economy of nature, for disseminating forest trees and other nuciferous and hard-seeded vegetables on which they feed. Their chief employment during the autumnal season is foraging to supply their winter stores. In performing this necessary duty they drop abundance of seed in their flight over fields, hedges, and by fences, where they alight to deposit them in the post-holes, etc. It is remarkable what numbers of young trees rise up in fields and pas-tures after a wet winter and spring. These birds alone are capable, in a few years' time, to replant all the cleared lands."

I have noticed that squirrels also frequently drop their nuts in open land, which will still further account for the oaks and walnuts which spring up in pastures, for, depend on it, every new tree comes from a seed. When I examine the little oaks, one or two years old, in such places, I invariably find the empty acorn from which they sprung.

So far from the seed having lain dormant in the soil since oaks grew there before, as many believe, it is well known that it is difficult to preserve the vitality of acorns long enough to transport them to Europe; and it is recommended in Loudon's "Arboretum," as the safest course, to sprout them in pots on the voyage. The same authority states that "very few acorns of any species will germinate after having been kept a year," that beech mast "only retains its vital properties one year," and the black walnut "seldom more than six months after it has ripened." I have frequently found that in November almost every acorn left on the ground had sprouted or decayed. What with frost, drouth, moisture, and worms, the greater part are soon destroyed. Yet it is stated by one botanical writer that "acorns that have lain for centuries, on being ploughed up, have soon vegetated."

Mr. George B. Emerson, in his valuable Report on the Trees and Shrubs of this State, says of the pines: "The tenacity of life of the seeds is remarkable. They will remain for many years unchanged in the ground, protected by the coolness and deep shade of the forest above them. But when the forest is removed, and the warmth of the sun admitted, they immediately vegetate." Since he does not tell us on what observation his remark is founded, I must doubt its truth. Besides, the experience of nursery-men makes it the more questionable.

The stories of wheat raised from seed buried with an ancient Egyptian, and of raspberries raised from seed found in the stomach of a man in England, who is supposed to have died sixteen or seventeen hundred years ago, are generally discredited, simply because the evidence is not conclusive.

Several men of science, Dr. Carpenter among them, have used the statement that beach plums sprang up in sand which was dug up forty miles inland in Maine, to prove that the seed had lain there a very long time, and some have inferred that the coast has receded so far. But it seems to me necessary to their argument to show, first, that beach plums grow only on a beach. They are not uncommon here, which is about half that distance from the shore; and I remember a dense patch a few miles north of us, twenty-five miles inland, from which the fruit was annually carried to market. How much further inland they grow, I know not. Dr. Charles T. Jackson speaks of finding " beach plums " (perhaps they were this kind) more than one hundred miles inland in Maine.

It chances that similar objections lie against all the more notorious instances of the kind on record.

Yet I am prepared to believe that some seeds, especially small ones, may retain their vitality for centuries under favorable circumstances. In the spring of 1859, the old Hunt house, so called, in this town, whose chimney bore the date 1703, was taken down. This stood on land which belonged to John Winthrop, the first governor of Massachusetts, and a part of the house was evidently much older than the above date, and belonged to the Winthrop family. For many years I have ransacked this neighborhood for plants, and I consider myself familiar with its productions. Thinking of the seeds which are said to be sometimes dug up at an unusual depth in the earth, and thus to reproduce long extinct plants, it occurred to me last fall that some new or rare plants might have sprung up in the cellar of this house, which had been covered from the light so long. Searching there on the 22d of September, I found, among other rank weeds, a species of nettle (*Urtica urens*) which I had not found before; dill, which I had not seen growing spontaneously; the Jerusalem oak (*Chenopodium Botrys*), which I had seen wild in but one place; black nightshade (*Solanum nigrum*), which is quite rare hereabouts, and common tobacco, which, though it was often cultivated here in the last century, has for fifty years been an unknown plant in this town, and a few months before this not even I had heard that one man, in the north part of the town, was cultivating a few plants for his own use. I have no doubt that some or all of these plants sprang from seeds which had long been buried under or about that house, and that that tobacco is an additional evidence that the plant was formerly cultivated here. The cellar has been filled up this year, and four of those plants, including the tobacco, are now again extinct in that locality.

It is true, I have shown that the animals consume a great part of the seeds of trees, and so, at least, effectually prevent their becoming trees; but in all these cases, as I have said, the consumer is compelled to be at the same time the disperser and planter, and this is the tax which he pays to Nature. I think it is Linnæus who says that while the swine is rooting for acorns he is planting acorns.

Though I do not believe that a plant will spring up where no seed has been, I have great faith in a seed,—a, to me, equally mysterious origin for it. Convince me that you have a seed there, and I am prepared to expect wonders. I shall even believe that the millennium is at hand, and that the reign of justice is about to commence, when the Patent Office, or Government, begins to distribute, and the people to plant, the seeds of these things.

In the spring of 1857 I planted six seeds sent to me from the Patent Office, and labeled, I think, *Poitrine jaune grosse*, large yellow squash. Two came up, and one bore a squash which weighed 123½ pounds, the other bore four, weighing together 186¼ pounds. Who would have believed that there was 310 pounds of *poitrine jaune grosse* in that corner of my garden? These seeds were the bait I used to catch it, my ferrets which I sent into its burrow, my brace of terriers which unearthed it. A little mysterious hoeing and manuring was all the *abracadabra presto-change* that I used, and lo! true to the label, they found for me 310 pounds of *poitrine jaune grosse* there, where it never was known to be, nor was before. These talismans had perchance sprung from America at first, and returned to it with unabated force. The big squash took a premium at your fair that fall, and I understood that the man who bought it, intended to sell the seeds for ten cents apiece. (Were they not cheap at that?) But I have more hounds of the same breed. I learn that one which I despatched to a distant town, true to its instincts, points to the large yellow squash there, too, where no hound ever found it before, as its ancestors did here and in France.

Other seeds I have which will find other things in that corner of my garden, in like fashion, almost any fruit you wish, every year for ages, until the crop more than fills the whole garden. You have but little more to do than throw up your cap for entertainment these American days. Perfect alchemists I keep who can transmute substances without end, and thus the corner of my garden is an inexhaustible treasure-chest. Here you can dig, not gold, but the value which gold merely represents; and there is no Signor Blitz about it. Yet farmers' sons will stare by the hour to see a juggler draw ribbons from his throat, though he tells them it is all deception. Surely, men love darkness rather than light.

WALKING

I wish to speak a word for Nature, for absolute freedom and wildness, as contrasted with a freedom and
culture merely civil, — to regard man as an inhabitant,
or a part and parcel of Nature, rather than a member
of society. I wish to make an extreme statement, if so
I may make an emphatic one, for there are enough
champions of civilization: the minister and the school
committee and every one of you will take care of that.

I have met with but one or two persons in the course
of my life who understood the art of Walking, that is,
of taking walks, — who had a genius, so to speak, for
sauntering, which word is beautifully derived "from
idle people who roved about the country, in the Middle
Ages, and asked charity, under pretense of going *à la
Sainte Terre*," to the Holy Land, till the children
exclaimed, "There goes a *Sainte-Terrer*," a Saunterer,
a Holy-Lander. They who never go to the Holy Land in
their walks, as they pretend, are indeed mere idlers and
vagabonds; but they who do go there are saunterers in
the good sense, such as I mean. Some, however, would
derive the word from *sans terre*, without land or a home,
which, therefore, in the good sense, will mean, having no
particular home, but equally at home everywhere. For
this is the secret of successful sauntering. He who sits
still in a house all the time may be the greatest vagrant
of all; but the saunterer, in the good sense, is no more

vagrant than the meandering river, which is all the while sedulously seeking the shortest course to the sea. But I prefer the first, which, indeed, is the most probable derivation. For every walk is a sort of crusade, preached by some Peter the Hermit in us, to go forth and reconquer this Holy Land from the hands of the Infidels.

It is true, we are but faint-hearted crusaders, even the walkers, nowadays, who undertake no persevering, never-ending enterprises. Our expeditions are but tours, and come round again at evening to the old hearth-side from which we set out. Half the walk is but retracing our steps. We should go forth on the shortest walk, perchance, in the spirit of undying adventure, never to return, — prepared to send back our embalmed hearts only as relics to our desolate kingdoms. If you are ready to leave father and mother, and brother and sister, and wife and child and friends, and never see them again, — if you have paid your debts, and made your will, and settled all your affairs, and are a free man, then you are ready for a walk.

To come down to my own experience, my companion and I, for I sometimes have a companion, take pleasure in fancying ourselves knights of a new, or rather an old, order, — not Equestrians or Chevaliers, not Ritters or Riders, but Walkers, a still more ancient and honorable class, I trust. The chivalric and heroic spirit which once belonged to the Rider seems now to reside in, or perchance to have subsided into, the Walker, — not the Knight, but Walker, Errant. He is a sort of fourth estate, outside of Church and State and People.

We have felt that we almost alone hereabouts practiced this noble art; though, to tell the truth, at least if their own assertions are to be received, most of my townsmen would fain walk sometimes, as I do, but they cannot. No wealth can buy the requisite leisure, freedom, and independence which are the capital in this profession. It comes only by the grace of God. It requires a direct dispensation from Heaven to become a walker. You must be born into the family of the Walkers. *Ambulator nascitur, non fit.* Some of my townsmen, it is true, can remember and have described to me some walks which they took ten years ago, in which they were so blessed as to lose themselves for half an hour in the woods; but I know very well that they have confined themselves to the highway ever since, whatever pretensions they may make to belong to this select class. No doubt they were elevated for a moment as by the reminiscence of a previous state of existence, when even they were foresters and outlaws.

"When he came to grene wode,
    In a mery mornynge,
There he herde the notes small
    Of byrdes mery syngynge.

"It is ferre gone, sayd Robyn,
    That I was last here;
Me lyste a lytell for to shote
    At the donne dere."

I think that I cannot preserve my health and spirits, unless I spend four hours a day at least — and it is commonly more than that — sauntering through the woods and over the hills and fields, absolutely free from all worldly engagements. You may safely say, A penny for your thoughts, or a thousand pounds. When sometimes I am reminded that the mechanics and shopkeepers stay in their shops not only all the forenoon, but all the afternoon too, sitting with crossed legs, so many of them, — as if the legs were made to sit upon, and not to stand or walk upon, — I think that they deserve some credit for not having all committed suicide long ago.

I, who cannot stay in my chamber for a single day without acquiring some rust, and when sometimes I have stolen forth for a walk at the eleventh hour, or four o'clock in the afternoon, too late to redeem the day, when the shades of night were already beginning to be mingled with the daylight, have felt as if I had committed some sin to be atoned for, — I confess that I am astonished at the power of endurance, to say nothing of the moral insensibility, of my neighbors who confine themselves to shops and offices the whole day for weeks and months, aye, and years almost together. I know not what manner of stuff they are of, — sitting there now at three o'clock in the afternoon, as if it were three o'clock in the morning. Bonaparte may talk of the three-o'clock-in-the-morning courage, but it is nothing to the courage which can sit down cheerfully at this hour in the afternoon over against one's self whom you have known all the morning, to starve out a garrison to whom you are bound by such strong ties of sympathy. I wonder that about this time, or say between four and five o'clock in the afternoon, too late for the morning papers and too early for the evening ones, there is not a general explosion heard up and down the street, scattering a legion of antiquated and house-bred notions and whims to the four winds for an airing, — and so the evil cure itself.

How womankind, who are confined to the house still more than men, stand it I do not know; but I have ground to suspect that most of them do not *stand* it at all. When, early in a summer afternoon, we have been shaking the dust of the village from the skirts of our garments, making haste past those houses with purely Doric or Gothic fronts, which have such an air of repose about them, my companion whispers that probably about these times their occupants are all gone to bed. Then it is that I appreciate the beauty and the glory of architecture, which itself never turns in, but forever stands out and erect, keeping watch over the slumberers.

No doubt temperament, and, above all, age, have a good deal to do with it. As a man grows older, his ability to sit still and follow indoor occupations increases. He grows vespertinal in his habits as the evening of life approaches, till at last he comes forth only just before sundown, and gets all the walk that he requires in half an hour.

But the walking of which I speak has nothing in it akin to taking exercise, as it is called, as the sick take medicine at stated hours, — as the swinging of dumb-bells or chairs; but is itself the enterprise and adventure of the day. If you would get exercise, go in search of the springs of life. Think of a man's swinging dumb-bells for his health, when those springs are bubbling up in far-off pastures unsought by him!

Moreover, you must walk like a camel, which is said to be the only beast which ruminates when walking. When a traveler asked Wordsworth's servant to show him her master's study, she answered, "Here is his library, but his study is out of doors."

Living much out of doors, in the sun and wind, will no doubt produce a certain roughness of character, — will cause a thicker cuticle to grow over some of the finer qualities of our nature, as on the face and hands, or as severe manual labor robs the hands of some of their delicacy of touch. So staying in the house, on the other hand, may produce a softness and smoothness, not to say thinness of skin, accompanied by an increased sensibility to certain impressions. Perhaps we should be more susceptible to some influences important to our intellectual and moral growth, if the sun had shone and the wind blown on us a little less; and no doubt it is a nice matter to proportion rightly the thick and thin skin. But methinks that is a scurf that will fall off fast enough, — that the natural remedy is to be found in the proportion which the night bears to the day, the winter to the summer, thought to experience. There will be so much the more air and sunshine in our thoughts. The callous palms of the laborer are conversant with finer tissues of self-respect and heroism, whose touch thrills the heart, than the languid fingers of idleness. That is mere sentimentality that lies abed by day and thinks itself white, far from the tan and callus of experience.

When we walk, we naturally go to the fields and woods: what would become of us, if we walked only

in a garden or a mall? Even some sects of philosophers
have felt the necessity of importing the woods to themselves, since they did not go to the woods. "They
planted groves and walks of Platanes," where they took
subdiales ambulationes in porticos open to the air. Of
course it is of no use to direct our steps to the woods,
if they do not carry us thither. I am alarmed when
it happens that I have walked a mile into the woods
bodily, without getting there in spirit. In my afternoon
walk I would fain forget all my morning occupations
and my obligations to society. But it sometimes happens
that I cannot easily shake off the village. The thought
of some work will run in my head and I am not where
my body is, — I am out of my senses. In my walks I
would fain return to my senses. What business have I
in the woods, if I am thinking of something out of the
woods? I suspect myself, and cannot help a shudder,
when I find myself so implicated even in what are called
good works, — for this may sometimes happen.

My vicinity affords many good walks; and though
for so many years I have walked almost every day, and
sometimes for several days together, I have not yet
exhausted them. An absolutely new prospect is a great
happiness, and I can still get this any afternoon. Two
or three hours' walking will carry me to as strange a
country as I expect ever to see. A single farmhouse
which I had not seen before is sometimes as good as the
dominions of the King of Dahomey. There is in fact
a sort of harmony discoverable between the capabilities
of the landscape within a circle of ten miles' radius,
or the limits of an afternoon walk, and the threescore

years and ten of human life. It will never become quite familiar to you.

Nowadays almost all man's improvements, so called, as the building of houses and the cutting down of the forest and of all large trees, simply deform the landscape, and make it more and more tame and cheap. A people who would begin by burning the fences and let the forest stand! I saw the fences half consumed, their ends lost in the middle of the prairie, and some worldly miser with a surveyor looking after his bounds, while heaven had taken place around him, and he did not see the angels going to and fro, but was looking for an old post-hole in the midst of paradise. I looked again, and saw him standing in the middle of a boggy Stygian fen, surrounded by devils, and he had found his bounds without a doubt, three little stones, where a stake had been driven, and looking nearer, I saw that the Prince of Darkness was his surveyor.

I can easily walk ten, fifteen, twenty, any number of miles, commencing at my own door, without going by any house, without crossing a road except where the fox and the mink do: first along by the river, and then the brook, and then the meadow and the woodside. There are square miles in my vicinity which have no inhabitant. From many a hill I can see civilization and the abodes of man afar. The farmers and their works are scarcely more obvious than woodchucks and their burrows. Man and his affairs, church and state and school, trade and commerce, and manufactures and agriculture, even politics, the most alarming of them all, — I am pleased to see how little space they occupy in the landscape. Politics is but a narrow field, and that still narrower highway yonder leads to it. I sometimes direct the traveler thither. If you would go to the political world, follow the great road, — follow that market-man, keep his dust in your eyes, and it will lead you straight to it; for it, too, has its place merely, and does not occupy all space. I pass from it as from a bean-field into the forest, and it is forgotten. In one half-hour I can walk off to some portion of the earth's surface where a man does not stand from one year's end to another, and there, consequently, politics are not, for they are but as the cigar-smoke of a man.

The village is the place to which the roads tend, a sort of expansion of the highway, as a lake of a river. It is the body of which roads are the arms and legs, — a trivial or quadrivial place, the thoroughfare and ordinary of travelers. The word is from the Latin *villa*, which together with *via*, a way, or more anciently *ved* and *vella*, Varro derives from *veho*, to carry, because the villa is the place to and from which things are carried. They who got their living by teaming were said *vellaturam facere*. Hence, too, the Latin word *vilis* and our vile, also *villain*. This suggests what kind of degeneracy villagers are liable to. They are wayworn by the travel that goes by and over them, without traveling themselves.

Some do not walk at all; others walk in the highways; a few walk across lots. Roads are made for horses and men of business. I do not travel in them much, comparatively, because I am not in a hurry to get to any tavern or grocery or livery-stable or depot to which they lead. I am a good horse to travel, but not from choice a roadster. The landscape-painter uses the figures of men to mark a road. He would not make that use of my figure. I walk out into a nature such as the old prophets and poets, Menu, Moses, Homer, Chaucer, walked in. You may name it America, but it is not America; neither Americus Vespucius, nor Columbus, nor the rest were the discoverers of it. There is a truer account of it in mythology than in any history of America, so called, that I have seen.

However, there are a few old roads that may be trodden with profit, as if they led somewhere now that they are nearly discontinued. There is the Old Marlborough Road, which does not go to Marlborough now, methinks, unless that is Marlborough where it carries me. I am the bolder to speak of it here, because I presume that there are one or two such roads in every town.

THE OLD MARLBOROUGH ROAD

Where they once dug for money,
But never found any;
Where sometimes Martial Miles
Singly files,
And Elijah Wood,
I fear for no good:
No other man,
Save Elisha Dugan, —
O man of wild habits,
Partridges and rabbits,
Who hast no cares
Only to set snares,
Who liv'st all alone,
Close to the bone,

And where life is sweetest
Constantly eatest.
When the spring stirs my blood
With the instinct to travel,
I can get enough gravel
On the Old Marlborough Road.
Nobody repairs it,
For nobody wears it;
It is a living way,
As the Christians say.
Not many there be
Who enter therein,
Only the guests of the
Irishman Quin.
What is it, what is it,
But a direction out there,
And the bare possibility
Of going somewhere?
Great guide-boards of stone,
But travelers none;
Cenotaphs of the towns
Named on their crowns.
It is worth going to see
Where you *might* be.
What king
Did the thing,
I am still wondering;
Set up how or when,
By what selectmen,
Gourgas or Lee,
Clark or Darby?
They 're a great endeavor
To be something forever;
Blank tablets of stone,
Where a traveler might groan,
And in one sentence
Grave all that is known;
Which another might read,
In his extreme need.

I know one or two
Lines that would do,
Literature that might stand
All over the land,
Which a man could remember
Till next December,
And read again in the spring,
After the thawing.
If with fancy unfurled
You leave your abode,
You may go round the world
By the Old Marlborough Road.

At present, in this vicinity, the best part of the land is not private property; the landscape is not owned, and the walker enjoys comparative freedom. But possibly the day will come when it will be partitioned off into so-called pleasure-grounds, in which a few will take a narrow and exclusive pleasure only,—when fences shall be multiplied, and man-traps and other engines invented to confine men to the *public* road, and walking over the surface of God's earth shall be construed to mean trespassing on some gentleman's grounds. To enjoy a thing exclusively is commonly to exclude yourself from the true enjoyment of it. Let us improve our opportunities, then, before the evil days come.

What is it that makes it so hard sometimes to determine whither we will walk? I believe that there is a subtle magnetism in Nature, which, if we unconsciously yield to it, will direct us aright. It is not indifferent to us which way we walk. There is a right way; but we are very liable from heedlessness and stupidity to take the wrong one. We would fain take that walk, never yet

taken by us through this actual world, which is perfectly symbolical of the path which we love to travel in
the interior and ideal world; and sometimes, no doubt,
we find it difficult to choose our direction, because it
does not yet exist distinctly in our idea.

When I go out of the house for a walk, uncertain as
yet whither I will bend my steps, and submit myself to
my instinct to decide for me, I find, strange and whimsical as it may seem, that I finally and inevitably settle
southwest, toward some particular wood or meadow or
deserted pasture or hill in that direction. My needle
is slow to settle, — varies a few degrees, and does not
always point due southwest, it is true, and it has good
authority for this variation, but it always settles between
west and south-southwest. The future lies that way to
me, and the earth seems more unexhausted and richer on
that side. The outline which would bound my walks
would be, not a circle, but a parabola, or rather like one
of those cometary orbits which have been thought to be
non-returning curves, in this case opening westward,
in which my house occupies the place of the sun. I turn
round and round irresolute sometimes for a quarter of
an hour, until I decide, for a thousandth time, that I will
walk into the southwest or west. Eastward I go only by
force; but westward I go free. Thither no business leads
me. It is hard for me to believe that I shall find fair
landscapes or sufficient wildness and freedom behind the
eastern horizon. I am not excited by the prospect of a
walk thither; but I believe that the forest which I see in
the western horizon stretches uninterruptedly toward
the setting sun, and there are no towns nor cities in it of

enough consequence to disturb me. Let me live where I will, on this side is the city, on that the wilderness, and ever I am leaving the city more and more, and withdrawing into the wilderness. I should not lay so much stress on this fact, if I did not believe that something like this is the prevailing tendency of my countrymen. I must walk toward Oregon, and not toward Europe. And that way the nation is moving, and I may say that mankind progress from east to west. Within a few years we have witnessed the phenomenon of a southeastward migration, in the settlement of Australia; but this affects us as a retrograde movement, and, judging from the moral and physical character of the first generation of Australians, has not yet proved a successful experiment. The eastern Tartars think that there is nothing west beyond Thibet. "The world ends there," say they; "beyond there is nothing but a shoreless sea." It is unmitigated East where they live.

We go eastward to realize history and study the works of art and literature, retracing the steps of the race; we go westward as into the future, with a spirit of enterprise and adventure. The Atlantic is a Lethean stream, in our passage over which we have had an opportunity to forget the Old World and its institutions. If we do not succeed this time, there is perhaps one more chance for the race left before it arrives on the banks of the Styx; and that is in the Lethe of the Pacific, which is three times as wide.

I know not how significant it is, or how far it is an evidence of singularity, that an individual should thus consent in his pettiest walk with the general movement of the race ; but I know that something akin to the migratory instinct in birds and quadrupeds, — which, in some instances, is known to have affected the squirrel tribe, impelling them to a general and mysterious movement, in which they were seen, say some, crossing the broadest rivers, each on its particular chip, with its tail raised for a sail, and bridging narrower streams with their dead, — that something like the *furor* which affects the domestic cattle in the spring, and which is referred to a worm in their tails, affects both nations and individuals, either perennially or from time to time. Not a flock of wild geese cackles over our town, but it to some extent unsettles the value of real estate here, and, if I were a broker, I should probably take that disturbance into account.

> " Than longen folk to gon on pilgrimages,
>   And palmeres for to seken strange strondes."

Every sunset which I witness inspires me with the desire to go to a West as distant and as fair as that into which the sun goes down. He appears to migrate westward daily, and tempt us to follow him. He is the Great Western Pioneer whom the nations follow. We dream all night of those mountain-ridges in the horizon, though they may be of vapor only, which were last gilded by his rays. The island of Atlantis, and the islands and gardens of the Hesperides, a sort of terrestrial paradise, appear to have been the Great West of the ancients, enveloped in mystery and poetry. Who has not seen in imagination, when looking into the sunset sky, the gardens of the Hesperides, and the foundation of all those fables ?

Columbus felt the westward tendency more strongly

than any before. He obeyed it, and found a New World
for Castile and Leon. The herd of men in those days
scented fresh pastures from afar.

> "And now the sun had stretched out all the hills,
> And now was dropped into the western bay;
> At last *he* rose, and twitched his mantle blue;
> To-morrow to fresh woods and pastures new."

Where on the globe can there be found an area of
equal extent with that occupied by the bulk of our
States, so fertile and so rich and varied in its productions, and at the same time so habitable by the European, as this is? Michaux, who knew but part of them,
says that "the species of large trees are much more
numerous in North America than in Europe; in the
United States there are more than one hundred and
forty species that exceed thirty feet in height; in France
there are but thirty that attain this size." Later botanists more than confirm his observations. Humboldt
came to America to realize his youthful dreams of a
tropical vegetation, and he beheld it in its greatest perfection in the primitive forests of the Amazon, the most
gigantic wilderness on the earth, which he has so eloquently described. The geographer Guyot, himself a
European, goes farther, — farther than I am ready to
follow him; yet not when he says: "As the plant is made
for the animal, as the vegetable world is made for the
animal world, America is made for the man of the Old
World. . . . The man of the Old World sets out upon
his way. Leaving the highlands of Asia, he descends
from station to station towards Europe. Each of his
steps is marked by a new civilization superior to the

preceding, by a greater power of development. Arrived at the Atlantic, he pauses on the shore of this unknown ocean, the bounds of which he knows not, and turns upon his footprints for an instant." When he has exhausted the rich soil of Europe, and reinvigorated himself, "then recommences his adventurous career westward as in the earliest ages." So far Guyot.

From this western impulse coming in contact with the barrier of the Atlantic sprang the commerce and enterprise of modern times. The younger Michaux, in his "Travels West of the Alleghanies in 1802," says that the common inquiry in the newly settled West was, "' From what part of the world have you come?' As if these vast and fertile regions would naturally be the place of meeting and common country of all the inhabitants of the globe."

To use an obsolete Latin word, I might say, *Ex Oriente lux; ex Occidente* FRUX. From the East light; from the West fruit.

Sir Francis Head, an English traveler and a Governor-General of Canada, tells us that "in both the northern and southern hemispheres of the New World, Nature has not only outlined her works on a larger scale, but has painted the whole picture with brighter and more costly colors than she used in delineating and in beautifying the Old World. . . . The heavens of America appear infinitely higher, the sky is bluer, the air is fresher, the cold is intenser, the moon looks larger, the stars are brighter, the thunder is louder, the lightning is vivider, the wind is stronger, the rain is heavier, the mountains are higher, the rivers longer, the forests bigger, the plains broader." This statement will do at least to set against Buffon's account of this part of the world and its productions.

Linnæus said long ago, "Nescio quae facies *laeta*, *glabra* plantis Americanis" (I know not what there is of joyous and smooth in the aspect of American plants); and I think that in this country there are no, or at most very few, *Africanae bestiae*, African beasts, as the Romans called them, and that in this respect also it is peculiarly fitted for the habitation of man. We are told that within three miles of the centre of the East-Indian city of Singapore, some of the inhabitants are annually carried off by tigers; but the traveler can lie down in the woods at night almost anywhere in North America without fear of wild beasts.

These are encouraging testimonies. If the moon looks larger here than in Europe, probably the sun looks larger also. If the heavens of America appear infinitely higher, and the stars brighter, I trust that these facts are symbolical of the height to which the philosophy and poetry and religion of her inhabitants may one day soar. At length, perchance, the immaterial heaven will appear as much higher to the American mind, and the intimations that star it as much brighter. For I believe that climate does thus react on man, — as there is something in the mountain air that feeds the spirit and inspires. Will not man grow to greater perfection intellectually as well as physically under these influences? Or is it unimportant how many foggy days there are in his life? I trust that we shall be more imaginative, that our thoughts will be clearer, fresher, and more ethereal,

as our sky, — our understanding more comprehensive
and broader, like our plains, — our intellect generally
on a grander scale, like our thunder and lightning, our
rivers and mountains and forests, — and our hearts
shall even correspond in breadth and depth and grandeur to our inland seas. Perchance there will appear to
the traveler something, he knows not what, of *laeta* and
glabra, of joyous and serene, in our very faces. Else
to what end does the world go on, and why was America
discovered?

To Americans I hardly need to say, —

"Westward the star of empire takes its way."

As a true patriot, I should be ashamed to think that Adam
in paradise was more favorably situated on the whole
than the backwoodsman in this country.

Our sympathies in Massachusetts are not confined
to New England; though we may be estranged from the
South, we sympathize with the West. There is the home
of the younger sons, as among the Scandinavians they
took to the sea for their inheritance. It is too late to be
studying Hebrew; it is more important to understand
even the slang of to-day.

Some months ago I went to see a panorama of the
Rhine. It was like a dream of the Middle Ages. I
floated down its historic stream in something more than
imagination, under bridges built by the Romans, and
repaired by later heroes, past cities and castles whose
very names were music to my ears, and each of which
was the subject of a legend. There were Ehrenbreitstein
and Rolandseck and Coblentz, which I knew only in

history. They were ruins that interested me chiefly. There seemed to come up from its waters and its vine-clad hills and valleys a hushed music as of Crusaders departing for the Holy Land. I floated along under the spell of enchantment, as if I had been transported to an heroic age, and breathed an atmosphere of chivalry.

Soon after, I went to see a panorama of the Mississippi, and as I worked my way up the river in the light of to-day, and saw the steamboats wooding up, counted the rising cities, gazed on the fresh ruins of Nauvoo, beheld the Indians moving west across the stream, and, as before I had looked up the Moselle, now looked up the Ohio and the Missouri and heard the legends of Dubuque and of Wenona's Cliff, — still thinking more of the future than of the past or present, — I saw that this was a Rhine stream of a different kind; that the foundations of castles were yet to be laid, and the famous bridges were yet to be thrown over the river; and I felt that *this was the heroic age itself*, though we know it not, for the hero is commonly the simplest and obscurest of men.

The West of which I speak is but another name for the Wild; and what I have been preparing to say is, that in Wildness is the preservation of the World. Every tree sends its fibres forth in search of the Wild. The cities import it at any price. Men plow and sail for it. From the forest and wilderness come the tonics and barks which brace mankind. Our ancestors were savages. The story of Romulus and Remus being suckled by a wolf is not a meaningless fable. The founders of every state which has risen to eminence have drawn their nourishment and vigor from a similar wild source. It was because the children of the Empire were not suckled by the wolf that they were conquered and displaced by the children of the northern forests who were.

I believe in the forest, and in the meadow, and in the night in which the corn grows. We require an infusion of hemlock spruce or arbor-vitæ in our tea. There is a difference between eating and drinking for strength and from mere gluttony. The Hottentots eagerly devour the marrow of the koodoo and other antelopes raw, as a matter of course. Some of our northern Indians eat raw the marrow of the Arctic reindeer, as well as various other parts, including the summits of the antlers, as long as they are soft. And herein, perchance, they have stolen a march on the cooks of Paris. They get what usually goes to feed the fire. This is probably better than stall-fed beef and slaughter-house pork to make a man of. Give me a wildness whose glance no civilization can endure, — as if we lived on the marrow of koodoos devoured raw.

There are some intervals which border the strain of the wood thrush, to which I would migrate, — wild lands where no settler has squatted; to which, methinks, I am already acclimated.

The African hunter Cumming tells us that the skin of the eland, as well as that of most other antelopes just killed, emits the most delicious perfume of trees and grass. I would have every man so much like a wild antelope, so much a part and parcel of nature, that his very person should thus sweetly advertise our senses of his presence, and remind us of those parts of nature which he most haunts. I feel no disposition to be satirical, when the trapper's coat emits the odor of musquash even; it is a sweeter scent to me than that which commonly exhales from the merchant's or the scholar's garments. When I go into their wardrobes and handle their vestments, I am reminded of no grassy plains and flowery meads which they have frequented, but of dusty merchants' exchanges and libraries rather.

A tanned skin is something more than respectable, and perhaps olive is a fitter color than white for a man, — a denizen of the woods. "The pale white man!" I do not wonder that the African pitied him. Darwin the naturalist says, "A white man bathing by the side of a Tahitian was like a plant bleached by the gardener's art, compared with a fine, dark green one, growing vigorously in the open fields."

Ben Jonson exclaims, —

> "How near to good is what is fair!"

So I would say, —

> How near to good is what is *wild!*

Life consists with wildness. The most alive is the wildest. Not yet subdued to man, its presence refreshes him. One who pressed forward incessantly and never rested from his labors, who grew fast and made infinite demands on life, would always find himself in a new country or wilderness, and surrounded by the raw material of life. He would be climbing over the prostrate stems of primitive forest-trees.

Hope and the future for me are not in lawns and cultivated fields, not in towns and cities, but in the imper-

vious and quaking swamps. When, formerly, I have
analyzed my partiality for some farm which I had contemplated purchasing, I have frequently found that I
was attracted solely by a few square rods of impermeable
and unfathomable bog, — a natural sink in one corner
of it. That was the jewel which dazzled me. I derive
more of my subsistence from the swamps which surround my native town than from the cultivated gardens
in the village. There are no richer parterres to my eyes
than the dense beds of dwarf andromeda (*Cassandra
calyculata*) which cover these tender places on the
earth's surface. Botany cannot go farther than tell me
the names of the shrubs which grow there, — the high
blueberry, panicled andromeda, lambkill, azalea, and
rhodora, — all standing in the quaking sphagnum. I
often think that I should like to have my house front on
this mass of dull red bushes, omitting other flower plots
and borders, transplanted spruce and trim box, even
graveled walks, — to have this fertile spot under my
windows, not a few imported barrowfuls of soil only to
cover the sand which was thrown out in digging the
cellar. Why not put my house, my parlor, behind this
plot, instead of behind that meagre assemblage of curiosities, that poor apology for a Nature and Art, which
I call my front yard? It is an effort to clear up and
make a decent appearance when the carpenter and mason
have departed, though done as much for the passer-by as
the dweller within. The most tasteful front-yard fence
was never an agreeable object of study to me; the most
elaborate ornaments, acorn tops, or what not, soon
wearied and disgusted me. Bring your sills up to the

very edge of the swamp, then (though it may not be the best place for a dry cellar), so that there be no access on that side to citizens. Front yards are not made to walk in, but, at most, through, and you could go in the back way.

Yes, though you may think me perverse, if it were proposed to me to dwell in the neighborhood of the most beautiful garden that ever human art contrived, or else of a Dismal Swamp, I should certainly decide for the swamp. How vain, then, have been all your labors, citizens, for me!

My spirits infallibly rise in proportion to the outward dreariness. Give me the ocean, the desert, or the wilderness! In the desert, pure air and solitude compensate for want of moisture and fertility. The traveler Burton says of it: "Your *morale* improves; you become frank and cordial, hospitable and single-minded. . . . In the desert, spirituous liquors excite only disgust. There is a keen enjoyment in a mere animal existence." They who have been traveling long on the steppes of Tartary say, "On reëntering cultivated lands, the agitation, perplexity, and turmoil of civilization oppressed and suffocated us; the air seemed to fail us, and we felt every moment as if about to die of asphyxia." When I would recreate myself, I seek the darkest wood, the thickest and most interminable and, to the citizen, most dismal, swamp. I enter a swamp as a sacred place, a *sanctum sanctorum*. There is the strength, the marrow, of Nature. The wildwood covers the virgin mould, and the same soil is good for men and for trees. A man's health requires as many acres of meadow to his prospect as his farm does loads of muck. There are the strong meats on which he feeds. A town is saved, not more by the righteous men in it than by the woods and swamps that surround it. A township where one primitive forest waves above while another primitive forest rots below, — such a town is fitted to raise not only corn and potatoes, but poets and philosophers for the coming ages. In such a soil grew Homer and Confucius and the rest, and out of such a wilderness comes the Reformer eating locusts and wild honey.

To preserve wild animals implies generally the creation of a forest for them to dwell in or resort to. So it is with man. A hundred years ago they sold bark in our streets peeled from our own woods. In the very aspect of those primitive and rugged trees there was, methinks, a tanning principle which hardened and consolidated the fibres of men's thoughts. Ah! already I shudder for these comparatively degenerate days of my native village, when you cannot collect a load of bark of good thickness, and we no longer produce tar and turpentine.

The civilized nations — Greece, Rome, England — have been sustained by the primitive forests which anciently rotted where they stand. They survive as long as the soil is not exhausted. Alas for human culture! little is to be expected of a nation, when the vegetable mould is exhausted, and it is compelled to make manure of the bones of its fathers. There the poet sustains himself merely by his own superfluous fat, and the philosopher comes down on his marrow-bones.

It is said to be the task of the American "to work

the virgin soil," and that "agriculture here already
assumes proportions unknown everywhere else."   I
think that the farmer displaces the Indian even because he redeems the meadow, and so makes himself
stronger and in some respects more natural.   I was
surveying for a man the other day a single straight
line one hundred and thirty-two rods long, through a
swamp at whose entrance might have been written the
words which Dante read over the entrance to the infernal regions, "Leave all hope, ye that enter," — that
is, of ever getting out again; where at one time I saw
my employer actually up to his neck and swimming
for his life in his property, though it was still winter.
He had another similar swamp which I could not survey at all, because it was completely under water, and
nevertheless, with regard to a third swamp, which I
did *survey* from a distance, he remarked to me, true
to his instincts, that he would not part with it for any
consideration, on account of the mud which it contained.   And that man intends to put a girdling ditch
round the whole in the course of forty months, and so
redeem it by the magic of his spade.   I refer to him
only as the type of a class.

The weapons with which we have gained our most
important victories, which should be handed down as
heirlooms from father to son, are not the sword and the
lance, but the bushwhack, the turf-cutter, the spade,
and the bog hoe, rusted with the blood of many a
meadow, and begrimed with the dust of many a hard-
fought field.   The very winds blew the Indian's corn-
field into the meadow, and pointed out the way which

he had not the skill to follow. He had no better implement with which to intrench himself in the land than a clamshell. But the farmer is armed with plow and spade.

In literature it is only the wild that attracts us. Dullness is but another name for tameness. It is the uncivilized free and wild thinking in Hamlet and the Iliad, in all the scriptures and mythologies, not learned in the schools, that delights us. As the wild duck is more swift and beautiful than the tame, so is the wild — the mallard — thought, which 'mid falling dews wings its way above the fens. A truly good book is something as natural, and as unexpectedly and unaccountably fair and perfect, as a wild-flower discovered on the prairies of the West or in the jungles of the East. Genius is a light which makes the darkness visible, like the lightning's flash, which perchance shatters the temple of knowledge itself, — and not a taper lighted at the hearth-stone of the race, which pales before the light of common day.

English literature, from the days of the minstrels to the Lake Poets, — Chaucer and Spenser and Milton, and even Shakespeare, included, — breathes no quite fresh and, in this sense, wild strain. It is an essentially tame and civilized literature, reflecting Greece and Rome. Her wilderness is a greenwood, her wild man a Robin Hood. There is plenty of genial love of Nature, but not so much of Nature herself. Her chronicles inform us when her wild animals, but not when the wild man in her, became extinct.

The science of Humboldt is one thing, poetry is another thing. The poet to-day, notwithstanding all the discoveries of science, and the accumulated learning of mankind, enjoys no advantage over Homer.

Where is the literature which gives expression to Nature? He would be a poet who could impress the winds and streams into his service, to speak for him; who nailed words to their primitive senses, as farmers drive down stakes in the spring, which the frost has heaved; who derived his words as often as he used them,.— transplanted them to his page with earth adhering to their roots; whose words were so true and fresh and natural that they would appear to expand like the buds at the approach of spring, though they lay half smothered between two musty leaves in a library, — aye, to bloom and bear fruit there, after their kind, annually, for the faithful reader, in sympathy with surrounding Nature.

I do not know of any poetry to quote which adequately expresses this yearning for the Wild. Approached from this side, the best poetry is tame. I do not know where to find in any literature, ancient or modern, any account which contents me of that Nature with which even I am acquainted. You will perceive that I demand something which no Augustan nor Elizabethan age, which no *culture*, in short, can give. Mythology comes nearer to it than anything. How much more fertile a Nature, at least, has Grecian mythology its root in than English literature! Mythology is the crop which the Old World bore before its soil was exhausted, before the fancy and imagination were affected with blight; and which it still bears,

wherever its pristine vigor is unabated. All other literatures endure only as the elms which overshadow
our houses; but this is like the great dragon-tree of
the Western Isles, as old as mankind, and, whether
that does or not, will endure as long; for the decay of
other literatures makes the soil in which it thrives.

The West is preparing to add its fables to those of
the East. The valleys of the Ganges, the Nile, and
the Rhine having yielded their crop, it remains to be
seen what the valleys of the Amazon, the Plate, the
Orinoco, the St. Lawrence, and the Mississippi will
produce. Perchance, when, in the course of ages,
American liberty has become a fiction of the past, — as
it is to some extent a fiction of the present, — the poets
of the world will be inspired by American mythology.

The wildest dreams of wild men, even, are not the
less true, though they may not recommend themselves
to the sense which is most common among Englishmen
and Americans to-day. It is not every truth that recom-
mends itself to the common sense. Nature has a place
for the wild clematis as well as for the cabbage. Some
expressions of truth are reminiscent, — others merely
sensible, as the phrase is, — others prophetic. Some
forms of disease, even, may prophesy forms of health.
The geologist has discovered that the figures of serpents,
griffins, flying dragons, and other fanciful embellish-
ments of heraldry, have their prototypes in the forms
of fossil species which were extinct before man was
created, and hence "indicate a faint and shadowy
knowledge of a previous state of organic existence."
The Hindoos dreamed that the earth rested on an ele-

phant, and the elephant on a tortoise, and the tortoise on a serpent; and though it may be an unimportant coincidence, it will not be out of place here to state, that a fossil tortoise has lately been discovered in Asia large enough to support an elephant. I confess that I am partial to these wild fancies, which transcend the order of time and development. They are the sublimest recreation of the intellect. The partridge loves peas, but not those that go with her into the pot.

In short, all good things are wild and free. There is something in a strain of music, whether produced by an instrument or by the human voice, — take the sound of a bugle in a summer night, for instance, — which by its wildness, to speak without satire, reminds me of the cries emitted by wild beasts in their native forests. It is so much of their wildness as I can understand. Give me for my friends and neighbors wild men, not tame ones. The wildness of the savage is but a faint symbol of the awful ferity with which good men and lovers meet.

I love even to see the domestic animals reassert their native rights, — any evidence that they have not wholly lost their original wild habits and vigor; as when my neighbor's cow breaks out of her pasture early in the spring and boldly swims the river, a cold, gray tide, twenty-five or thirty rods wide, swollen by the melted snow. It is the buffalo crossing the Mississippi. This exploit confers some dignity on the herd in my eyes, — already dignified. The seeds of instinct are preserved under the thick hides of cattle and horses, like seeds in the bowels of the earth, an indefinite period.

Any sportiveness in cattle is unexpected. I saw one day a herd of a dozen bullocks and cows running about and frisking in unwieldy sport, like huge rats, even like kittens. They shook their heads, raised their tails, and rushed up and down a hill, and I perceived by their horns, as well as by their activity, their relation to the deer tribe. But, alas! a sudden loud *Whoa!* would have damped their ardor at once, reduced them from venison to beef, and stiffened their sides and sinews like the locomotive. Who but the Evil One has cried " Whoa!" to mankind? Indeed, the life of cattle, like that of many men, is but a sort of locomotiveness; they move a side at a time, and man, by his machinery, is meeting the horse and the ox half-way. Whatever part the whip has touched is thenceforth palsied. Who would ever think of a *side* of any of the supple cat tribe, as we speak of a *side* of beef?

I rejoice that horses and steers have to be broken before they can be made the slaves of men, and that men themselves have some wild oats still left to sow before they become submissive members of society. Undoubtedly, all men are not equally fit subjects for civilization; and because the majority, like dogs and sheep, are tame by inherited disposition, this is no reason why the others should have their natures broken that they may be reduced to the same level. Men are in the main alike, but they were made several in order that they might be various. If a low use is to be served, one man will do nearly or quite as well as another; if a high one, individual excellence is to be regarded. Any man can stop a hole to keep the wind away, but no other man could serve so rare a use as the author of this illustration did.   Confucius says, "The skins of the tiger and the leopard, when they are tanned, are as the skins of the dog and the sheep tanned." But it is not the part of a true culture to tame tigers, any more than it is to make sheep ferocious; and tanning their skins for shoes is not the best use to which they can be put.

When looking over a list of men's names in a foreign language, as of military officers, or of authors who have written on a particular subject, I am reminded once more that there is nothing in a name. The name Menschikoff, for instance, has nothing in it to my ears more human than a whisker, and it may belong to a rat. As the names of the Poles and Russians are to us, so are ours to them. It is as if they had been named by the child's rigmarole, *Iery wiery ichery van, tittle-tol-tan.* I see in my mind a herd of wild creatures swarming over the earth, and to each the herdsman has affixed some barbarous sound in his own dialect. The names of men are, of course, as cheap and meaningless as *Bose* and *Tray,* the names of dogs.

Methinks it would be some advantage to philosophy if men were named merely in the gross, as they are known. It would be necessary only to know the genus and perhaps the race or variety, to know the individual. We are not prepared to believe that every private soldier in a Roman army had a name of his own, — because we have not supposed that he had a character of his own.

At present our only true names are nicknames.   I knew a boy who, from his peculiar energy, was called

"Buster" by his playmates, and this rightly supplanted his Christian name. Some travelers tell us that an Indian had no name given him at first, but earned it, and his name was his fame; and among some tribes he acquired a new name with every new exploit. It is pitiful when a man bears a name for convenience merely, who has earned neither name nor fame.

I will not allow mere names to make distinctions for me, but still see men in herds for all them. A familiar name cannot make a man less strange to me. It may be given to a savage who retains in secret his own wild title earned in the woods. We have a wild savage in us, and a savage name is perchance somewhere recorded as ours. I see that my neighbor, who bears the familiar epithet William or Edwin, takes it off with his jacket. It does not adhere to him when asleep or in anger, or aroused by any passion or inspiration. I seem to hear pronounced by some of his kin at such a time his original wild name in some jaw-breaking or else melodious tongue.

Here is this vast, savage, howling mother of ours, Nature, lying all around, with such beauty, and such affection for her children, as the leopard; and yet we are so early weaned from her breast to society, to that culture which is exclusively an interaction of man on man, — a sort of breeding in and in, which produces at most a merely English nobility, a civilization destined to have a speedy limit.

In society, in the best institutions of men, it is easy to detect a certain precocity. When we should still be growing children, we are already little men. Give me a culture which imports much muck from the meadows, and deepens the soil, — not that which trusts to heating manures, and improved implements and modes of culture only!

Many a poor sore-eyed student that I have heard of would grow faster, both intellectually and physically, if, instead of sitting up so very late, he honestly slumbered a fool's allowance.

There may be an excess even of informing light. Niepce, a Frenchman, discovered "actinism," that power in the sun's rays which produces a chemical effect; that granite rocks, and stone structures, and statues of metal "are all alike destructively acted upon during the hours of sunshine, and, but for provisions of Nature no less wonderful, would soon perish under the delicate touch of the most subtile of the agencies of the universe." But he observed that "those bodies which underwent this change during the daylight possessed the power of restoring themselves to their original conditions during the hours of night, when this excitement was no longer influencing them." Hence it has been inferred that "the hours of darkness are as necessary to the inorganic creation as we know night and sleep are to the organic kingdom." Not even does the moon shine every night, but gives place to darkness.

I would not have every man nor every part of a man cultivated, any more than I would have every acre of earth cultivated: part will be tillage, but the greater part will be meadow and forest, not only serving an immediate use, but preparing a mould against a distant future, by the annual decay of the vegetation which it supports.

There are other letters for the child to learn than those which Cadmus invented. The Spaniards have a good term to express this wild and dusky knowledge, *Gramática parda*, tawny grammar, a kind of mother-wit derived from that same leopard to which I have referred.

We have heard of a Society for the Diffusion of Useful Knowledge. It is said that knowledge is power, and the like. Methinks there is equal need of a Society for the Diffusion of Useful Ignorance, what we will call Beautiful Knowledge, a knowledge useful in a higher sense: for what is most of our boasted so-called knowledge but a conceit that we know something, which robs us of the advantage of our actual ignorance? What we call knowledge is often our positive ignorance; ignorance our negative knowledge. By long years of patient industry and reading of the newspapers, — for what are the libraries of science but files of newspapers? — a man accumulates a myriad facts, lays them up in his memory, and then when in some spring of his life he saunters abroad into the Great Fields of thought, he, as it were, goes to grass like a horse and leaves all his harness behind in the stable. I would say to the Society for the Diffusion of Useful Knowledge, sometimes, — Go to grass. You have eaten hay long enough. The spring has come with its green crop. The very cows are driven to their country pastures before the end of May; though I have heard of one unnatural farmer who kept his cow in the barn and fed her on hay all the year round. So, frequently, the Society for the Diffusion of Useful Knowledge treats its cattle.

A man's ignorance sometimes is not only useful, but
beautiful, — while his knowledge, so called, is oftentimes worse than useless, besides being ugly. Which is
the best man to deal with, — he who knows nothing
about a subject, and, what is extremely rare, knows that
he knows nothing, or he who really knows something
about it, but thinks that he knows all?

My desire for knowledge is intermittent, but my desire to bathe my head in atmospheres unknown to my
feet is perennial and constant. The highest that we
can attain to is not Knowledge, but Sympathy with
Intelligence. I do not know that this higher knowledge
amounts to anything more definite than a novel and
grand surprise on a sudden revelation of the insufficiency
of all that we called Knowledge before, — a discovery
that there are more things in heaven and earth than are
dreamed of in our philosophy. It is the lighting up of
the mist by the sun. Man cannot *know* in any higher
sense than this, any more than he can look serenely and
with impunity in the face of the sun: Ὡς τὶ νοῶν, οὐ κεῖνον
νοήσεις, "You will not perceive that, as perceiving a
particular thing," say the Chaldean Oracles.

There is something servile in the habit of seeking after
a law which we may obey. We may study the laws of
matter at and for our convenience, but a successful life
knows no law. It is an unfortunate discovery certainly,
that of a law which binds us where we did not know
before that we were bound. Live free, child of the mist,
— and with respect to knowledge we are all children
of the mist. The man who takes the liberty to live is
superior to all the laws, by virtue of his relation to the

lawmaker. "That is active duty," says the Vishnu Purana, "which is not for our bondage; that is knowledge which is for our liberation: all other duty is good only unto weariness; all other knowledge is only the cleverness of an artist."

It is remarkable how few events or crises there are in our histories, how little exercised we have been in our minds, how few experiences we have had. I would fain be assured that I am growing apace and rankly, though my very growth disturb this dull equanimity, — though it be with struggle through long, dark, muggy nights or seasons of gloom. It would be well if all our lives were a divine tragedy even, instead of this trivial comedy or farce. Dante, Bunyan, and others appear to have been exercised in their minds more than we: they were subjected to a kind of culture such as our district schools and colleges do not contemplate. Even Mahomet, though many may scream at his name, had a good deal more to live for, aye, and to die for, than they have commonly.

When, at rare intervals, some thought visits one, as perchance he is walking on a railroad, then, indeed, the cars go by without his hearing them. But soon, by some inexorable law, our life goes by and the cars return.

> "Gentle breeze, that wanderest unseen,
>   And bendest the thistles round Loira of storms,
>   Traveler of the windy glens,
>   Why hast thou left my ear so soon?"

While almost all men feel an attraction drawing them to society, few are attracted strongly to Nature. In their reaction to Nature men appear to me for the most part, notwithstanding their arts, lower than the animals. It is not often a beautiful relation, as in the case of the animals. How little appreciation of the beauty of the landscape there is among us! We have to be told that the Greeks called the world Κόσμος, Beauty, or Order, but we do not see clearly why they did so, and we esteem it at best only a curious philological fact.

For my part, I feel that with regard to Nature I live a sort of border life, on the confines of a world into which I make occasional and transient forays only, and my patriotism and allegiance to the state into whose territories I seem to retreat are those of a moss-trooper. Unto a life which I call natural I would gladly follow even a will-o'-the-wisp through bogs and sloughs unimaginable, but no moon nor firefly has shown me the causeway to it. Nature is a personality so vast and universal that we have never seen one of her features. The walker in the familiar fields which stretch around my native town sometimes finds himself in another land than is described in their owners' deeds, as it were in some faraway field on the confines of the actual Concord, where her jurisdiction ceases, and the idea which the word Concord suggests ceases to be suggested. These farms which I have myself surveyed, these bounds which I have set up, appear dimly still as through a mist; but they have no chemistry to fix them; they fade from the surface of the glass, and the picture which the painter painted stands out dimly from beneath. The world with which we are commonly acquainted leaves no trace, and it will have no anniversary.

I took a walk on Spaulding's Farm the other afternoon. I saw the setting sun lighting up the opposite side of a stately pine wood. Its golden rays straggled into the aisles of the wood as into some noble hall. I was impressed as if some ancient and altogether admirable and shining family had settled there in that part of the land called Concord, unknown to me, — to whom the sun was servant, — who had not gone into society in the village, — who had not been called on. I saw their park, their pleasure-ground, beyond through the wood, in Spaulding's cranberry-meadow. The pines furnished them with gables as they grew. Their house was not obvious to vision; the trees grew through it. I do not know whether I heard the sounds of a suppressed hilarity or not. They seemed to recline on the sunbeams. They have sons and daughters. They are quite well. The farmer's cart-path, which leads directly through their hall, does not in the least put them out, as the muddy bottom of a pool is sometimes seen through the reflected skies. They never heard of Spaulding, and do not know that he is their neighbor, — notwithstanding I heard him whistle as he drove his team through the house. Nothing can equal the serenity of their lives. Their coat-of-arms is simply a lichen. I saw it painted on the pines and oaks. Their attics were in the tops of the trees. They are of no politics. There was no noise of labor. I did not perceive that they were weaving or spinning. Yet I did detect, when the wind lulled and hearing was done away, the finest imaginable sweet musical hum, — as of a distant hive in May, — which perchance was the sound of their thinking. They had no idle thoughts, and no one without could see their work, for their industry was not as in knots and excrescences embayed.

But I find it difficult to remember them. They fade irrevocably out of my mind even now while I speak, and endeavor to recall them and recollect myself. It is only after a long and serious effort to recollect my best thoughts that I become again aware of their cohabitancy. If it were not for such families as this, I think I should move out of Concord.

We are accustomed to say in New England that few and fewer pigeons visit us every year. Our forests furnish no mast for them. So, it would seem, few and fewer thoughts visit each growing man from year to year, for the grove in our minds is laid waste, — sold to feed unnecessary fires of ambition, or sent to mill, — and there is scarcely a twig left for them to perch on. They no longer build nor breed with us. In some more genial season, perchance, a faint shadow flits across the landscape of the mind, cast by the *wings* of some thought in its vernal or autumnal migration, but, looking up, we are unable to detect the substance of the thought itself. Our winged thoughts are turned to poultry. They no longer soar, and they attain only to a Shanghai and Cochin-China grandeur. Those *gra-a-ate thoughts*, those *gra-a-ate men* you hear of!

We hug the earth, — how rarely we mount! Methinks we might elevate ourselves a little more. We might climb a tree, at least. I found my account in climbing

a tree once. It was a tall white pine, on the top of a
hill; and though I got well pitched, I was well paid
for it, for I discovered new mountains in the horizon
which I had never seen before, — so much more of the
earth and the heavens. I might have walked about the
foot of the tree for threescore years and ten, and yet
I certainly should never have seen them. But, above
all, I discovered around me, — it was near the end of
June, — on the ends of the topmost branches only,
a few minute and delicate red cone-like blossoms, the
fertile flower of the white pine looking heavenward.
I carried straightway to the village the topmost spire,
and showed it to stranger jurymen who walked the
streets, — for it was court week, — and to farmers
and lumber-dealers and woodchoppers and hunters,
and not one had ever seen the like before, but they
wondered as at a star dropped down. Tell of ancient
architects finishing their works on the tops of columns
as perfectly as on the lower and more visible parts!
Nature has from the first expanded the minute blossoms
of the forest only toward the heavens, above men's
heads and unobserved by them. We see only the flowers
that are under our feet in the meadows. The pines
have developed their delicate blossoms on the highest
twigs of the wood every summer for ages, as well over
the heads of Nature's red children as of her white ones;
yet scarcely a farmer or hunter in the land has ever seen
them.

Above all, we cannot afford not to live in the present.
He is blessed over all mortals who loses no moment of

the passing life in remembering the past. Unless our
philosophy hears the cock crow in every barn-yard
within our horizon, it is belated. That sound commonly reminds us that we are growing rusty and an-
tique in our employments and habits of thought. His
philosophy comes down to a more recent time than
ours. There is something suggested by it that is a
newer testament, — the gospel according to this moment. He has not fallen astern; he has got up early and
kept up early, and to be where he is is to be in season,
in the foremost rank of time. It is an expression of
the health and soundness of Nature, a brag for all the
world, — healthiness as of a spring burst forth, a new
fountain of the Muses, to celebrate this last instant of
time. Where he lives no fugitive slave laws are passed.
Who has not betrayed his master many times since last
he heard that note?

The merit of this bird's strain is in its freedom from
all plaintiveness. The singer can easily move us to tears
or to laughter, but where is he who can excite in us a
pure morning joy? When, in doleful dumps, breaking
the awful stillness of our wooden sidewalk on a Sunday,
or, perchance, a watcher in the house of mourning, I
hear a cockerel crow far or near, I think to myself,
"There is one of us well, at any rate," — and with a
sudden gush return to my senses.

We had a remarkable sunset one day last November.
I was walking in a meadow, the source of a small brook,
when the sun at last, just before setting, after a cold,
gray day, reached a clear stratum in the horizon, and

the softest, brightest morning sunlight fell on the dry grass and on the stems of the trees in the opposite horizon and on the leaves of the shrub oaks on the hillside, while our shadows stretched long over the meadow eastward, as if we were the only motes in its beams. It was such a light as we could not have imagined a moment before, and the air also was so warm and serene that nothing was wanting to make a paradise of that meadow. When we reflected that this was not a solitary phenomenon, never to happen again, but that it would happen forever and ever, an infinite number of evenings, and cheer and reassure the latest child that walked there, it was more glorious still.

The sun sets on some retired meadow, where no house is visible, with all the glory and splendor that it lavishes on cities, and perchance as it has never set before, — where there is but a solitary marsh hawk to have his wings gilded by it, or only a musquash looks out from his cabin, and there is some little black-veined brook in the midst of the marsh, just beginning to meander, winding slowly round a decaying stump. We walked in so pure and bright a light, gilding the withered grass and leaves, so softly and serenely bright, I thought I had never bathed in such a golden flood, without a ripple or a murmur to it. The west side of every wood and rising ground gleamed like the boundary of Elysium, and the sun on our backs seemed like a gentle herdsman driving us home at evening.

So we saunter toward the Holy Land, till one day the sun shall shine more brightly than ever he has done,

shall perchance shine into our minds and hearts, and
light up our whole lives with a great awakening light,
as warm and serene and golden as on a bankside in
autumn.

AUTUMNAL TINTS

Europeans coming to America are surprised by the
brilliancy of our autumnal foliage. There is no account
of such a phenomenon in English poetry, because the
trees acquire but few bright colors there. The most
that Thomson says on this subject in his "Autumn" is
contained in the lines, —

> "But see the fading many-colored woods
> Shade deepening over shade, the country round
> Imbrown; a crowded umbrage, dusk and dun,
> Of every hue, from wan declining green
> To sooty dark;"

and in the line in which he speaks of

> "Autumn beaming o'er the yellow woods."

The autumnal change of our woods has not made
a deep impression on our own literature yet. October
has hardly tinged our poetry.

A great many, who have spent their lives in cities,
and have never chanced to come into the country
at this season, have never seen this, the flower, or
rather the ripe fruit, of the year. I remember riding
with one such citizen, who, though a fortnight too late
for the most brilliant tints, was taken by surprise, and
would not believe that there had been any brighter. He
had never heard of this phenomenon before. Not only
many in our towns have never witnessed it, but it is
scarcely remembered by the majority from year to year.

Most appear to confound changed leaves with with-

ered ones, as if they were to confound ripe apples with
rotten ones.   I think that the change to some higher
color in a leaf is an evidence that it has arrived at a late
and perfect maturity, answering to the maturity of
fruits. It is generally the lowest and oldest leaves which
change first.   But as the perfect-winged and usually
bright-colored insect is short-lived, so the leaves ripen
but to fall.

Generally, every fruit, on ripening, and just before
it falls, when it commences a more independent and
individual existence, requiring less nourishment from
any source, and that not so much from the earth through
its stem as from the sun and air, acquires a bright tint.
So do leaves.   The physiologist says it is "due to an
increased absorption of oxygen." That is the scientific
account of the matter, — only a reassertion of the fact.
But I am more interested in the rosy cheek than I am
to know what particular diet the maiden fed on. The
very forest and herbage, the pellicle of the earth, must
acquire a bright color, an evidence of its ripeness, — as
if the globe itself were a fruit on its stem, with ever a
cheek toward the sun.

Flowers are but colored leaves, fruits but ripe ones.
The edible part of most fruits is, as the physiologist
says, "the parenchyma or fleshy tissue of the leaf," of
which they are formed.

Our appetites have commonly confined our views of
ripeness and its phenomena, color, mellowness, and
perfectness, to the fruits which we eat, and we are wont
to forget that an immense harvest which we do not eat,
hardly use at all, is annually ripened by Nature. At

our annual cattle-shows and horticultural exhibitions, we make, as we think, a great show of fair fruits, destined, however, to a rather ignoble end, fruits not valued for their beauty chiefly. But round about and within our towns there is annually another show of fruits, on an infinitely grander scale, fruits which address our taste for beauty alone.

October is the month for painted leaves. Their rich glow now flashes round the world. As fruits and leaves and the day itself acquire a bright tint just before they fall, so the year near its setting. October is its sunset sky; November the later twilight.

I formerly thought that it would be worth the while to get a specimen leaf from each changing tree, shrub, and herbaceous plant, when it had acquired its brightest characteristic color, in its transition from the green to the brown state, outline it, and copy its color exactly, with paint, in a book, which should be entitled "October, or Autumnal Tints," — beginning with the earliest reddening woodbine and the lake of radical leaves, and coming down through the maples, hickories, and sumachs, and many beautifully freckled leaves less generally known, to the latest oaks and aspens. What a memento such a book would be! You would need only to turn over its leaves to take a ramble through the autumn woods whenever you pleased. Or if I could preserve the leaves themselves, unfaded, it would be better still. I have made but little progress toward such a book, but I have endeavored, instead, to describe all these bright tints in the order in which they present themselves. The following are some extracts from my notes.

THE PURPLE GRASSES

By the twentieth of August, everywhere in woods and swamps we are reminded of the fall, both by the richly spotted sarsaparilla leaves and brakes, and the withering and blackened skunk-cabbage and hellebore, and, by the riverside, the already blackening pontederia.

The purple grass (*Eragrostis pectinacea*) is now in the height of its beauty. I remember still when I first noticed this grass particularly. Standing on a hillside near our river, I saw, thirty or forty rods off, a stripe of purple half a dozen rods long, under the edge of a wood, where the ground sloped toward a meadow. It was as high-colored and interesting, though not quite so bright, as the patches of rhexia, being a darker purple, like a berry's stain laid on close and thick. On going to and examining it, I found it to be a kind of grass in bloom, hardly a foot high, with but few green blades, and a fine spreading panicle of purple flowers, a shallow, purplish mist trembling around me. Close at hand it appeared but a dull purple, and made little impression on the eye; it was even difficult to detect; and if you plucked a single plant, you were surprised to find how thin it was, and how little color it had. But viewed at a distance in a favorable light, it was of a fine lively purple, flower-like, enriching the earth. Such puny causes combine to produce these decided effects. I was the more surprised and charmed because grass is commonly of a sober and humble color.

With its beautiful purple blush it reminds me, and

supplies the place, of the rhexia, which is now leaving off, and it is one of the most interesting phenomena of August. The finest patches of it grow on waste strips or selvages of land at the base of dry hills, just above the edge of the meadows, where the greedy mower does not deign to swing his scythe; for this is a thin and poor grass, beneath his notice. Or, it may be, because it is so beautiful he does not know that it exists; for the same eye does not see this and timothy. He carefully gets the meadow-hay and the more nutritious grasses which grow next to that, but he leaves this fine purple mist for the walker's harvest, — fodder for his fancy stock. Higher up the hill, perchance, grow also blackberries, John's-wort, and neglected, withered, and wiry June-grass. How fortunate that it grows in such places, and not in the midst of the rank grasses which are annually cut! Nature thus keeps use and beauty distinct. I know many such localities, where it does not fail to present itself annually, and paint the earth with its blush. It grows on the gentle slopes, either in a continuous patch or in scattered and rounded tufts a foot in diameter, and it lasts till it is killed by the first smart frosts.

In most plants the corolla or calyx is the part which attains the highest color, and is the most attractive; in many it is the seed-vessel or fruit; in others, as the red maple, the leaves; and in others still it is the very culm itself which is the principal flower or blooming part.

The last is especially the case with the poke or garget (*Phytolacca decandra*). Some which stand under our

cliffs quite dazzle me with their purple stems now and
early in September. They are as interesting to me as
most flowers, and one of the most important fruits of
our autumn. Every part is flower (or fruit), such is its
superfluity of color, — stem, branch, peduncle, pedicel,
petiole, and even the at length yellowish, purple-veined
leaves.   Its cylindrical racemes of berries of various
hues, from green to dark purple, six or seven inches
long, are gracefully drooping on all sides, offering re-
pasts to the birds; and even the sepals from which the
birds have picked the berries are a brilliant lake red,
with crimson flame-like reflections, equal to anything
of the kind, — all on fire with ripeness.   Hence the
lacca, from *lac*, lake. There are at the same time flower-
buds, flowers, green berries, dark-purple or ripe ones,
and these flower-like sepals, all on the same plant.

We love to see any redness in the vegetation of the
temperate zone. It is the color of colors. This plant
speaks to our blood. It asks a bright sun on it to make
it show to best advantage, and it must be seen at this
season of the year. On warm hillsides its stems are
ripe by the twenty-third of August. At that date I
walked through a beautiful grove of them, six or seven
feet high, on the side of one of our cliffs, where they
ripen early. Quite to the ground they were a deep,
brilliant purple, with a bloom contrasting with the still
clear green leaves. It appears a rare triumph of Nature
to have produced and perfected such a plant, as if this
were enough for a summer. What a perfect maturity it
arrives at! It is the emblem of a successful life concluded by a death not premature, which is an ornament

to Nature. What if we were to mature as perfectly, root
and branch, glowing in the midst of our decay, like the
poke! I confess that it excites me to behold them. I cut
one for a cane, for I would fain handle and lean on it.
I love to press the berries between my fingers, and see
their juice staining my hand. To walk amid these upright, branching casks of purple wine, which retain and
diffuse a sunset glow, tasting each one with your eye,
instead of counting the pipes on a London dock, what
a privilege! For Nature's vintage is not confined to
the vine. Our poets have sung of wine, the product of
a foreign plant which commonly they never saw, as if
our own plants had no juice in them more than the
singers. Indeed, this has been called by some the American grape, and, though a native of America, its juices
are used in some foreign countries to improve the color
of the wine; so that the poetaster may be celebrating
the virtues of the poke without knowing it. Here are
berries enough to paint afresh the western sky, and
play the bacchanal with, if you will. And what flutes
its ensanguined stems would make, to be used in such a
dance! It is truly a royal plant. I could spend the evening of the year musing amid the poke stems. And perchance amid these groves might arise at last a new school
of philosophy or poetry. It lasts all through September.

At the same time with this, or near the end of August,
a to me very interesting genus of grasses, andropogons,
or beard-grasses, is in its prime: *Andropogon furcatus*,
forked beard-grass, or call it purple-fingered grass;
Andropogon scoparius, purple wood-grass ; and *Andropogon* (now called *Sorghum*) *nutans*, Indian-grass.

The first is a very tall and slender-culmed grass, three to seven feet high, with four or five purple finger-like spikes raying upward from the top. The second is also quite slender, growing in tufts two feet high by one wide, with culms often somewhat curving, which, as the spikes go out of bloom, have a whitish, fuzzy look. These two are prevailing grasses at this season on dry and sandy fields and hillsides. The culms of both, not to mention their pretty flowers, reflect a purple tinge, and help to declare the ripeness of the year. Perhaps I have the more sympathy with them because they are despised by the farmer, and occupy sterile and neglected soil. They are high-colored, like ripe grapes, and express a maturity which the spring did not suggest. Only the August sun could have thus burnished these culms and leaves. The farmer has long since done his upland haying, and he will not condescend to bring his scythe to where these slender wild grasses have at length flowered thinly; you often see spaces of bare sand amid them. But I walk encouraged between the tufts of purple wood-grass over the sandy fields, and along the edge of the shrub oaks, glad to recognize these simple contemporaries. With thoughts cutting a broad swathe I "get" them, with horse-raking thoughts I gather them into windrows. The fine-eared poet may hear the whetting of my scythe. These two were almost the first grasses that I learned to distinguish, for I had not known by how many friends I was surrounded; I had seen them simply as grasses standing. The purple of their culms also excites me like that of the poke-weed stems.

Think what refuge there is for one, before August is over, from college commencements and society that isolates! I can skulk amid the tufts of purple wood-grass on the borders of the " Great Fields." Wherever I walk these afternoons, the purple-fingered grass also stands like a guide-board, and points my thoughts to more poetic paths than they have lately traveled.

A man shall perhaps rush by and trample down plants as high as his head, and cannot be said to know that they exist, though he may have cut many tons of them, littered his stables with them, and fed them to his cattle for years. Yet, if he ever favorably attends to them, he may be overcome by their beauty. Each humblest plant, or weed, as we call it, stands there to express some thought or mood of ours; and yet how long it stands in vain! I had walked over those Great Fields so many Augusts, and never yet distinctly recognized these purple companions that I had there. I had brushed against them and trodden on them, forsooth; and now, at last, they, as it were, rose up and blessed me. Beauty and true wealth are always thus cheap and despised. Heaven might be defined as the place which men avoid. Who can doubt that these grasses, which the farmer says are of no account to him, find some compensation in your appreciation of them? I may say that I never saw them before; though, when I came to look them face to face, there did come down to me a purple gleam from previous years; and now, wherever I go, I see hardly anything else. It is the reign and presidency of the andropogons.

Almost the very sands confess the ripening influence

of the August sun, and methinks, together with the slender grasses waving over them, reflect a purple tinge. The impurpled sands! Such is the consequence of all this sunshine absorbed into the pores of plants and of the earth. All sap or blood is now wine-colored. At last we have not only the purple sea, but the purple land.

The chestnut beard-grass, Indian-grass, or wood-grass, growing here and there in waste places, but more rare than the former (from two to four or five feet high), is still handsomer and of more vivid colors than its congeners, and might well have caught the Indian's eye. It has a long, narrow, one-sided, and slightly nodding panicle of bright purple and yellow flowers, like a banner raised above its reedy leaves. These bright standards are now advanced on the distant hillsides, not in large armies, but in scattered troops or single file, like the red men. They stand thus fair and bright, representative of the race which they are named after, but for the most part unobserved as they. The expression of this grass haunted me for a week, after I first passed and noticed it, like the glance of an eye. It stands like an Indian chief taking a last look at his favorite hunting-grounds.

THE RED MAPLE

By the twenty-fifth of September, the red maples generally are beginning to be ripe. Some large ones have been conspicuously changing for a week, and some single trees are now very brilliant. I notice a small one, half a mile off across a meadow, against the green woodside there, a far brighter red than the blossoms of any tree in summer, and more conspicuous. I have observed this tree for several autumns invariably changing earlier than its fellows, just as one tree ripens its fruit earlier than another. It might serve to mark the season, perhaps. I should be sorry if it were cut down. I know of two or three such trees in different parts of our town, which might, perhaps, be propagated from, as early ripeners or September trees, and their seed be advertised in the market, as well as that of radishes, if we cared as much about them.

At present these burning bushes stand chiefly along the edge of the meadows, or I distinguish them afar on the hillsides here and there. Sometimes you will see many small ones in a swamp turned quite crimson when all other trees around are still perfectly green, and the former appear so much the brighter for it. They take you by surprise, as you are going by on one side, across the fields, thus early in the season, as if it were some gay encampment of the red men, or other foresters, of whose arrival you had not heard.

Some single trees, wholly bright scarlet, seen against others of their kind still freshly green, or against evergreens, are more memorable than whole groves will be by and by. How beautiful, when a whole tree is like one great scarlet fruit full of ripe juices, every leaf, from lowest limb to topmost spire, all aglow, especially if you look toward the sun! What more remarkable object can there be in the landscape? Visible for miles, too fair to be believed. If such a phenomenon occurred but once, it would be handed down by tradition to posterity, and get into the mythology at last.

The whole tree thus ripening in advance of its fellows attains a singular preëminence, and sometimes maintains it for a week or two. I am thrilled at the sight of it, bearing aloft its scarlet standard for the regiment of green-clad foresters around, and I go half a mile out of my way to examine it. A single tree becomes thus the crowning beauty of some meadowy vale, and the expression of the whole surrounding forest is at once more spirited for it.

A small red maple has grown, perchance, far away at the head of some retired valley, a mile from any road, unobserved. It has faithfully discharged the duties of a maple there, all winter and summer, neglected none of its economies, but added to its stature in the virtue which belongs to a maple, by a steady growth for so many months, never having gone gadding abroad, and is nearer heaven than it was in the spring. It has faithfully husbanded its sap, and afforded a shelter to the wandering bird, has long since ripened its seeds and committed them to the winds, and has the satisfaction of knowing, perhaps, that a thousand little well-behaved maples are already settled in life somewhere. It deserves well of Mapledom. Its leaves have been asking it from time to time, in a whisper, "When shall we redden?" And now, in this month of September, this month of traveling, when men are hastening to the seaside, or the mountains, or the lakes, this modest maple, still without budging an inch, travels in its reputation, — runs up its scarlet flag on that hillside, which shows that it has finished its summer's work before all other trees, and withdraws from the

contest. At the eleventh hour of the year, the tree which
no scrutiny could have detected here when it was most
industrious is thus, by the tint of its maturity, by its
very blushes, revealed at last to the careless and distant traveler, and leads his thoughts away from the
dusty road into those brave solitudes which it inhab-
its. It flashes out conspicuous with all the virtue and
beauty of a maple, — *Acer rubrum*. We may now read
its title, or *rubric*, clear. Its *virtues*, not its sins, are as
scarlet.

Notwithstanding the red maple is the most intense
scarlet of any of our trees, the sugar maple has been
the most celebrated, and Michaux in his " Sylva " does
not speak of the autumnal color of the former. About
the second of October, these trees, both large and small,
are most brilliant, though many are still green. In
" sprout-lands " they seem to vie with one another,
and ever some particular one in the midst of the crowd
will be of a peculiarly pure scarlet, and by its more
intense color attract our eye even at a distance, and
carry off the palm. A large red maple swamp, when
at the height of its change, is the most obviously brilliant of all tangible things, where I dwell, so abundant
is this tree with us. It varies much both in form and
color. A great many are merely yellow; more, scarlet;
others, scarlet deepening into crimson, more red than
common. Look at yonder swamp of maples mixed
with pines, at the base of a pine-clad hill, a quarter
of a mile off, so that you get the full effect of the bright
colors, without detecting the imperfections of the leaves,
and see their yellow, scarlet, and crimson fires, of all

tints, mingled and contrasted with the green. Some maples are yet green, only yellow or crimson-tipped on the edges of their flakes, like the edges of a hazel-nut bur; some are wholly brilliant scarlet, raying out regularly and finely every way, bilaterally, like the veins of a leaf; others, of more irregular form, when I turn my head slightly, emptying out some of its earthi-ness and concealing the trunk of the tree, seem to rest heavily flake on flake, like yellow and scarlet clouds, wreath upon wreath, or like snow-drifts driving through the air, stratified by the wind. It adds greatly to the beauty of such a swamp at this season, that, even though there may be no other trees interspersed, it is not seen as a simple mass of color, but, different trees being of different colors and hues, the outline of each crescent treetop is distinct, and where one laps on to another. Yet a painter would hardly venture to make them thus distinct a quarter of a mile off.

As I go across a meadow directly toward a low rising ground this bright afternoon, I see, some fifty rods off toward the sun, the top of a maple swamp just appear-ing over the sheeny russet edge of the hill, a stripe ap-parently twenty rods long by ten feet deep, of the most intensely brilliant scarlet, orange, and yellow, equal to any flowers or fruits, or any tints ever painted. As I advance, lowering the edge of the hill which makes the firm foreground or lower frame of the picture, the depth of the brilliant grove revealed steadily increases, suggesting that the whole of the inclosed valley is filled with such color. One wonders that the tithing-men and fathers of the town are not out to see what the trees mean by their high colors and exuberance of spirits, fearing that some mischief is brewing. I do not see what the Puritans did at this season, when the maples blaze out in scarlet. They certainly could not have worshiped in groves then. Perhaps that is what they built meeting-houses and fenced them round with horse-sheds for.

THE ELM

Now too, the first of October, or later, the elms are at the height of their autumnal beauty, — great brownish-yellow masses, warm from their September oven, hanging over the highway. Their leaves are perfectly ripe. I wonder if there is any answering ripeness in the lives of the men who live beneath them. As I look down our street, which is lined with them, they remind me both by their form and color of yellowing sheaves of grain, as if the harvest had indeed come to the village itself, and we might expect to find some maturity and *flavor* in the thoughts of the villagers at last. Under those bright rustling yellow piles just ready to fall on the heads of the walkers, how can any crudity or greenness of thought or act prevail? When I stand where half a dozen large elms droop over a house, it is as if I stood within a ripe pumpkin-rind, and I feel as mellow as if I were the pulp, though I may be somewhat stringy and seedy withal. What is the late greenness of the English elm, like a cucumber out of season, which does not know when to have done, compared with the early and golden maturity of the American tree? The street is the scene of a great harvest-home. It would be worth the while to set out these trees, if only for their autumnal value. Think of these great yellow canopies or parasols held over our heads and houses by the mile together, making the village all one and compact, — an *ulmarium*, which is at the same time a nursery of men! And then how gently and unobserved they drop their burden and let in the sun when it is wanted, their leaves not heard when they fall on our roofs and in our streets; and thus the village parasol is shut up and put away! I see the market-man driving into the village, and disappearing under its canopy of elm-tops, with *his* crop, as into a great granary or barn-yard. I am tempted to go thither as to a husking of thoughts, now dry and ripe, and ready to be separated from their integuments; but, alas! I foresee that it will be chiefly husks and little thought, blasted pig-corn, fit only for cob-meal, — for, as you sow, so shall you reap.

FALLEN LEAVES

By the sixth of October the leaves generally begin to fall, in successive showers, after frost or rain; but the principal leaf-harvest, the acme of the *Fall*, is commonly about the sixteenth. Some morning at that date there is perhaps a harder frost than we have seen, and ice formed under the pump, and now, when the morning wind rises, the leaves come down in denser showers than ever. They suddenly form thick beds or carpets on the ground, in this gentle air, or even without wind, just the size and form of the tree above. Some trees, as small hickories, appear to have dropped their leaves instantaneously, as a soldier grounds arms at a signal;

and those of the hickory, being bright yellow still,
though withered, reflect a blaze of light from the ground
where they lie. Down they have come on all sides,
at the first earnest touch of autumn's wand, making a
sound like rain.

Or else it is after moist and rainy weather that we
notice how great a fall of leaves there has been in the
night, though it may not yet be the touch that loosens
the rock maple leaf. The streets are thickly strewn
with the trophies, and fallen elm leaves make a dark
brown pavement under our feet. After some remarkably warm Indian-summer day or days, I perceive that
it is the unusual heat which, more than anything,
causes the leaves to fall, there having been, perhaps, no
frost nor rain for some time. The intense heat suddenly
ripens and wilts them, just as it softens and ripens
peaches and other fruits, and causes them to drop.

The leaves of late red maples, still bright, strew
the earth, often crimson-spotted on a yellow ground,
like some wild apples, — though they preserve these
bright colors on the ground but a day or two, especially
if it rains. On causeways I go by trees here and there
all bare and smoke-like, having lost their brilliant clothing; but there it lies, nearly as bright as ever, on the
ground on one side, and making nearly as regular a
figure as lately on the tree. I would rather say that I
first observe the trees thus flat on the ground like a
permanent colored shadow, and they suggest to look
for the boughs that bore them. A queen might be proud
to walk where these gallant trees have spread their bright
cloaks in the mud. I see wagons roll over them as a

shadow or a reflection, and the drivers heed them just
as little as they did their shadows before.

Birds' nests, in the huckleberry and other shrubs,
and in trees, are already being filled with the withered
leaves. So many have fallen in the woods that a squirrel cannot run after a falling nut without being heard.
Boys are raking them in the streets, if only for the
pleasure of dealing with such clean, crisp substances.
Some sweep the paths scrupulously neat, and then stand
to see the next breath strew them with new trophies.
The swamp floor is thickly covered, and the *Lycopo-
dium lucidulum* looks suddenly greener amid them.
In dense woods they half cover pools that are three
or four rods long. The other day I could hardly find
a well-known spring, and even suspected that it had
dried up, for it was completely concealed by freshly
fallen leaves; and when I swept them aside and revealed it, it was like striking the earth, with Aaron's
rod, for a new spring. Wet grounds about the edges
of swamps look dry with them. At one swamp, where
I was surveying, thinking to step on a leafy shore from
a rail, I got into the water more than a foot deep.

When I go to the river the day after the principal fall
of leaves, the sixteenth, I find my boat all covered, bottom and seats, with the leaves of the golden willow
under which it is moored, and I set sail with a cargo of
them rustling under my feet. If I empty it, it will be
full again to-morrow. I do not regard them as litter,
to be swept out, but accept them as suitable straw or
matting for the bottom of my carriage. When I turn
up into the mouth of the Assabet, which is wooded,

large fleets of leaves are floating on its surface, as it were getting out to sea, with room to tack; but next the shore, a little farther up, they are thicker than foam, quite concealing the water for a rod in width, under and amid the alders, button-bushes, and maples, still perfectly light and dry, with fibre unrelaxed; and at a rocky bend where they are met and stopped by the morning wind, they sometimes form a broad and dense crescent quite across the river. When I turn my prow that way, and the wave which it makes strikes them, list what a pleasant rustling from these dry substances getting on one another! Often it is their undulation only which reveals the water beneath them. Also every motion of the wood turtle on the shore is betrayed by their rustling there. Or even in mid-channel, when the wind rises, I hear them blown with a rustling sound. Higher up they are slowly moving round and round in some great eddy which the river makes, as that at the "Leaning Hemlocks," where the water is deep, and the current is wearing into the bank.

Perchance, in the afternoon of such a day, when the water is perfectly calm and full of reflections, I paddle gently down the main stream, and, turning up the Assabet, reach a quiet cove, where I unexpectedly find myself surrounded by myriads of leaves, like fellow-voyagers, which seem to have the same purpose, or want of purpose, with myself. See this great fleet of scattered leaf-boats which we paddle amid, in this smooth river-bay, each one curled up on every side by the sun's skill, each nerve a stiff spruce knee, — like boats of hide, and of all patterns, — Charon's boat probably among the rest, — and some with lofty prows and poops, like the stately vessels of the ancients, scarcely moving in the sluggish current, — like the great fleets, the dense Chinese cities of boats, with which you mingle on entering some great mart, some New York or Canton, which we are all steadily approaching together. How gently each has been deposited on the water! No violence has been used towards them yet, though, perchance, palpitating hearts were present at the launching. And painted ducks, too, the splendid wood duck among the rest, often come to sail and float amid the painted leaves, — barks of a nobler model still!

What wholesome herb drinks are to be had in the swamps now! What strong medicinal but rich scents from the decaying leaves! The rain falling on the freshly dried herbs and leaves, and filling the pools and ditches into which they have dropped thus clean and rigid, will soon convert them into tea, — green, black, brown, and yellow teas, of all degrees of strength, enough to set all Nature a-gossiping. Whether we drink them or not, as yet, before their strength is drawn, these leaves, dried on great Nature's coppers, are of such various pure and delicate tints as might make the fame of Oriental teas.

How they are mixed up, of all species, oak and maple and chestnut and birch! But Nature is not cluttered with them; she is a perfect husbandman; she stores them all. Consider what a vast crop is thus annually shed on the earth! This, more than any mere grain or seed, is the great harvest of the year. The trees are now repaying the earth with interest what they have

taken from it. They are discounting. They are about
to add a leaf's thickness to the depth of the soil. This
is the beautiful way in which Nature gets her muck,
while I chaffer with this man and that, who talks to
me about sulphur and the cost of carting. We are all
the richer for their decay. I am more interested in this
crop than in the English grass alone or in the corn. It
prepares the virgin mould for future corn-fields and
forests, on which the earth fattens. It keeps our homestead in good heart.

For beautiful variety no crop can be compared with
this. Here is not merely the plain yellow of the grains,
but nearly all the colors that we know, the brightest
blue not excepted: the early blushing maple, the poison
sumach blazing its sins as scarlet, the mulberry ash,
the rich chrome yellow of the poplars, the brilliant red
huckleberry, with which the hills' backs are painted,
like those of sheep. The frost touches them, and, with
the slightest breath of returning day or jarring of earth's
axle, see in what showers they come floating down!
The ground is all parti-colored with them. But they
still live in the soil, whose fertility and bulk they increase, and in the forests that spring from it. They
stoop to rise, to mount higher in coming years, by
subtle chemistry, climbing by the sap in the trees; and
the sapling's first fruits thus shed, transmuted at last,
may adorn its crown, when, in after years, it has become the monarch of the forest.

It is pleasant to walk over the beds of these fresh,
crisp, and rustling leaves. How beautifully they go
to their graves! how gently lay themselves down and

turn to mould! — painted of a thousand hues, and fit to make the beds of us living. So they troop to their last resting-place, light and frisky. They put on no weeds, but merrily they go scampering over the earth, selecting the spot, choosing a lot, ordering no iron fence, whispering all through the woods about it, — some choosing the spot where the bodies of men are mouldering beneath, and meeting them half-way. How many flutterings before they rest quietly in their graves! They that soared so loftily, how contentedly they return to dust again, and are laid low, resigned to lie and decay at the foot of the tree, and afford nourishment to new generations of their kind, as well as to flutter on high! They teach us how to die. One wonders if the time will ever come when men, with their boasted faith in immortality, will lie down as gracefully and as ripe, — with such an Indian-summer serenity will shed their bodies, as they do their hair and nails.

When the leaves fall, the whole earth is a cemetery pleasant to walk in. I love to wander and muse over them in their graves. Here are no lying nor vain epitaphs. What though you own no lot at Mount Auburn? Your lot is surely cast somewhere in this vast cemetery, which has been consecrated from of old. You need attend no auction to secure a place. There is room enough here. The loosestrife shall bloom and the huckleberry-bird sing over your bones. The woodman and hunter shall be your sextons, and the children shall tread upon the borders as much as they will. Let us walk in the cemetery of the leaves; this is your true Greenwood Cemetery.

THE SUGAR MAPLE

But think not that the splendor of the year is over; for as one leaf does not make a summer, neither does one falling leaf make an autumn. The smallest sugar maples in our streets make a great show as early as the fifth of October, more than any other trees there. As I look up the main street, they appear like painted screens standing before the houses; yet many are green. But now, or generally by the seventeenth of October, when almost all red maples and some white maples are bare, the large sugar maples also are in their glory, glowing with yellow and red, and show unexpectedly bright and delicate tints. They are remarkable for the contrast they often afford of deep blushing red on one half and green on the other. They become at length dense masses of rich yellow with a deep scarlet blush, or more than blush, on the exposed surfaces. They are the brightest trees now in the street.

The large ones on our Common are particularly beautiful. A delicate but warmer than golden yellow is now the prevailing color, with scarlet cheeks. Yet, standing on the east side of the Common just before sundown, when the western light is transmitted through them, I see that their yellow even, compared with the pale lemon yellow of an elm close by, amounts to a scarlet, without noticing the bright scarlet portions. Generally, they are great regular oval masses of yellow and scarlet. All the sunny warmth of the season, the Indian summer, seems to be absorbed in their leaves. The lowest and inmost leaves next the bole are, as usual, of the most delicate yellow and green, like the complexion of young men brought up in the house. There is an auction on the Common to-day, but its red flag is hard to be discerned amid this blaze of color.

Little did the fathers of the town anticipate this brilliant success, when they caused to be imported from farther in the country some straight poles with their tops cut off, which they called sugar maples; and, as I remember, after they were set out, a neighboring merchant's clerk, by way of jest, planted beans about them. Those which were then jestingly called bean-poles are to-day far the most beautiful objects noticeable in our streets. They are worth all and more than they have cost, — though one of the selectmen, while setting them out, took the cold which occasioned his death, — if only because they have filled the open eyes of children with their rich color unstintedly so many Octobers. We will not ask them to yield us sugar in the spring, while they afford us so fair a prospect in the autumn. Wealth indoors may be the inheritance of few, but it is equally distributed on the Common. All children alike can revel in this golden harvest.

Surely trees should be set in our streets with a view to their October splendor, though I doubt whether this is ever considered by the "Tree Society." Do you not think it will make some odds to these children that they were brought up under the maples? Hundreds of eyes are steadily drinking in this color, and by these teachers even the truants are caught and educated the moment they step abroad. Indeed, neither the truant nor the studious is at present taught color in the schools.

These are instead of the bright colors in apothecaries' shops and city windows. It is a pity that we have no more *red* maples, and some hickories, in our streets as well. Our paint-box is very imperfectly filled. Instead of, or beside, supplying such paint-boxes as we do, we might supply these natural colors to the young. Where else will they study color under greater advantages? What School of Design can vie with this? Think how much the eyes of painters of all kinds, and of manufacturers of cloth and paper, and paper-stainers, and countless others, are to be educated by these autumnal colors. The stationer's envelopes may be of very various tints, yet not so various as those of the leaves of a single tree. If you want a different shade or tint of a particular color, you have only to look farther within or without the tree or the wood. These leaves are not many dipped in one dye, as at the dye-house, but they are dyed in light of infinitely various degrees of strength and left to set and dry there.

Shall the names of so many of our colors continue to be derived from those of obscure foreign localities, as Naples yellow, Prussian blue, raw Sienna, burnt Umber, Gamboge? (surely the Tyrian purple must have faded by this time), or from comparatively trivial articles of commerce, — chocolate, lemon, coffee, cinnamon, claret? (shall we compare our hickory to a lemon, or a lemon to a hickory?) or from ores and oxides which few ever see? Shall we so often, when describing to our neighbors the color of something we have seen, refer them, not to some natural object in our neighborhood, but perchance to a bit of earth fetched from the other side of the planet, which possibly they may find at the apothecary's, but which probably neither they nor we ever saw ? Have we not an *earth* under our feet, — aye, and a sky over our heads ? Or is the last *all* ultramarine ? What do we know of sapphire, amethyst, emerald, ruby, amber, and the like, — most of us who take these names in vain ? Leave these precious words to cabinet-keepers, virtuosos, and maids-of-honor, — to the Nabobs, Begums, and Chobdars of Hindostan, or wherever else. I do not see why, since America and her autumn woods have been discovered, our leaves should not compete with the precious stones in giving names to colors; and, indeed, I believe that in course of time the names of some of our trees and shrubs, as well as flowers, will get into our popular chromatic nomenclature.

But of much more importance than a knowledge of the names and distinctions of color is the joy and exhilaration which these colored leaves excite. Already these brilliant trees throughout the street, without any more variety, are at least equal to an annual festival and holiday, or a week of such. These are cheap and innocent gala-days, celebrated by one and all without the aid of committees or marshals, such a show as may safely be licensed, not attracting gamblers or rum-sellers, not requiring any special police to keep the peace. And poor indeed must be that New England village's October which has not the maple in its streets. This October festival costs no powder, nor ringing of bells, but every tree is a living liberty-pole on which a thousand bright flags are waving.

No wonder that we must have our annual cattle-show, and fall training, and perhaps cornwallis, our September courts, and the like. Nature herself holds her annual fair in October, not only in the streets, but in every hollow and on every hillside. When lately we looked into that red maple swamp all ablaze, where the trees were clothed in their vestures of most dazzling tints, did it not suggest a thousand gypsies beneath, — a race capable of wild delight, — or even the fabled fauns, satyrs, and wood-nymphs come back to earth? Or was it only a congregation of wearied woodchoppers, or of proprietors come to inspect their lots, that we thought of? Or, earlier still, when we paddled on the river through that fine-grained September air, did there not appear to be something new going on under the sparkling surface of the stream, a shaking of props, at least, so that we made haste in order to be up in time? Did not the rows of yellowing willows and button-bushes on each side seem like rows of booths, under which, perhaps, some fluviatile egg-pop equally yellow was effervescing? Did not all these suggest that man's spirits should rise as high as Nature's, — should hang out their flag, and the routine of his life be interrupted by an analogous expression of joy and hilarity?

No annual training or muster of soldiery, no celebration with its scarfs and banners, could import into the town a hundredth part of the annual splendor of our October. We have only to set the trees, or let them stand, and Nature will find the colored drapery, — flags of all her nations, some of whose private signals hardly the botanist can read, — while we walk under the triumphal arches of the elms. Leave it to Nature to appoint the days, whether the same as in neighboring States or not, and let the clergy read her proclamations, if they can understand them. Behold what a brilliant drapery is her woodbine flag! What public-spirited merchant, think you, has contributed this part of the show? There is no handsomer shingling and paint than this vine, at present covering a whole side of some houses. I do not believe that the ivy *never sere* is comparable to it. No wonder it has been extensively introduced into London. Let us have a good many maples and hickories and scarlet oaks, then, I say. Blaze away! Shall that dirty roll of bunting in the gun-house be all the colors a village can display? A village is not complete, unless it have these trees to mark the season in it. They are important, like the town clock. A village that has them not will not be found to work well. It has a screw loose, an essential part is wanting. Let us have willows for spring, elms for summer, maples and walnuts and tupeloes for autumn, evergreens for winter, and oaks for all seasons. What is a gallery in a house to a gallery in the streets, which every marketman rides through, whether he will or not? Of course, there is not a picture-gallery in the country which would be worth so much to us as is the western view at sunset under the elms of our main street. They are the frame to a picture which is daily painted behind them. An avenue of elms as large as our largest and three miles long would seem to lead to some admirable place, though only C—— were at the end of it.

A village needs these innocent stimulants of bright

and cheering prospects to keep off melancholy and superstition. Show me two villages, one embowered in trees and blazing with all the glories of October, the other a merely trivial and treeless waste, or with only a single tree or two for suicides, and I shall be sure that in the latter will be found the most starved and bigoted religionists and the most desperate drinkers. Every wash-tub and milk-can and gravestone will be exposed. The inhabitants will disappear abruptly behind their barns and houses, like desert Arabs amid their rocks, and I shall look to see spears in their hands. They will be ready to accept the most barren and forlorn doctrine, — as that the world is speedily coming to an end, or has already got to it, or that they themselves are turned wrong side outward. They will perchance crack their dry joints at one another and call it a spiritual communication.

But to confine ourselves to the maples. What if we were to take half as much pains in protecting them as we do in setting them out, — not stupidly tie our horses to our dahlia stems?

What meant the fathers by establishing this *perfectly living* institution before the church, — this institution which needs no repairing nor repainting, which is continually enlarged and repaired by its growth? Surely they

> "Wrought in a sad sincerity;
> Themselves from God they could not free;
> They *planted* better than they knew; —
> The conscious *trees* to beauty grew."

Verily these maples are cheap preachers, permanently

settled, which preach their half-century, and century, aye, and century-and-a-half sermons, with constantly increasing unction and influence, ministering to many generations of men; and the least we can do is to supply them with suitable colleagues as they grow infirm.

THE SCARLET OAK

Belonging to a genus which is remarkable for the beautiful form of its leaves, I suspect that some scarlet oak leaves surpass those of all other oaks in the rich and wild beauty of their outlines. I judge from an acquaintance with twelve species, and from drawings which I have seen of many others.

Stand under this tree and see how finely its leaves are cut against the sky, — as it were, only a few sharp points extending from a midrib. They look like double, treble, or quadruple crosses. They are far more ethereal than the less deeply scalloped oak leaves. They have so little leafy *terra firma* that they appear melting away in the light, and scarcely obstruct our view. The leaves of very young plants are, like those of full-grown oaks of other species, more entire, simple, and lumpish in their outlines, but these, raised high on old trees, have solved the leafy problem. Lifted higher and higher, and sublimated more and more, putting off some earthiness and cultivating more intimacy with the light each year, they have at length the least possible amount of earthy matter, and the greatest spread and grasp of skyey influences. There they dance, arm in arm with the light, — tripping it on fantastic points, fit partners in those aerial halls. So intimately mingled are they with it,

that, what with their slenderness and their glossy surfaces, you can hardly tell at last what in the dance is
leaf and what is light. And when no zephyr stirs, they
are at most but a rich tracery to the forest windows.

I am again struck with their beauty, when, a month
later, they thickly strew the ground in the woods, piled
one upon another under my feet. They are then brown
above, but purple beneath. With their narrow lobes
and their bold, deep scallops reaching almost to the
middle, they suggest that the material must be cheap, or
else there has been a lavish expense in their creation,
as if so much had been cut out. Or else they seem to us
the remnants of the stuff out of which leaves have been
cut with a die. Indeed, when they lie thus one upon
another, they remind me of a pile of scrap-tin.

Or bring one home, and study it closely at your leisure,
by the fireside. It is a type, not from any Oxford font,
not in the Basque nor the arrow-headed character, not
found on the Rosetta Stone, but destined to be copied
in sculpture one day, if they ever get to whittling stone
here. What a wild and pleasing outline, a combination
of graceful curves and angles! The eye rests with equal
delight on what is not leaf and on what is leaf, — on
the broad, free, open sinuses, and on the long, sharp,
bristle-pointed lobes. A simple oval outline would include it all, if you connected the points of the leaf; but
how much richer is it than that, with its half-dozen deep
scallops, in which the eye and thought of the beholder
are embayed! If I were a drawing-master, I would set
my pupils to copying these leaves, that they might
learn to draw firmly and gracefully.

Regarded as water, it is like a pond with half a dozen broad rounded promontories extending nearly to its middle, half from each side, while its watery bays extend far inland, like sharp friths, at each of whose heads several fine streams empty in, — almost a leafy archipelago.

But it oftener suggests land, and, as Dionysius and Pliny compared the form of the Morea to that of the leaf of the Oriental plane tree, so this leaf reminds me of some fair wild island in the ocean, whose extensive coast, alternate rounded bays with smooth strands, and sharp-pointed rocky capes, mark it as fitted for the habitation of man, and destined to become a centre of civilization at last. To the sailor's eye, it is a much indented shore. Is it not, in fact, a shore to the aerial ocean, on which the windy surf beats? At sight of this leaf we are all mariners, — if not vikings, buccaneers, and filibusters. Both our love of repose and our spirit of adventure are addressed. In our most casual glance, perchance, we think that if we succeed in doubling those sharp capes we shall find deep, smooth, and secure havens in the ample bays. How different from the white oak leaf, with its rounded headlands, on which no lighthouse need be placed! That is an England, with its long civil history, that may be read. This is some still unsettled New-found Island or Celebes. Shall we go and be rajahs there?

By the twenty-sixth of October the large scarlet oaks are in their prime, when other oaks are usually withered. They have been kindling their fires for a week past, and now generally burst into a blaze. This alone

of *our* indigenous deciduous trees (excepting the dog-
wood, of which I do not know half a dozen, and they are
but large bushes) is now in its glory. The two aspens
and the sugar maple come nearest to it in date, but they
have lost the greater part of their leaves. Of evergreens,
only the pitch pine is still commonly bright.

But it requires a particular alertness, if not devotion
to these phenomena, to appreciate the wide-spread, but
late and unexpected glory of the scarlet oaks. I do not
speak here of the small trees and shrubs, which are
commonly observed, and which are now withered, but
of the large trees. Most go in and shut their doors,
thinking that bleak and colorless November has already
come, when some of the most brilliant and memorable
colors are not yet lit.

This very perfect and vigorous one, about forty feet
high, standing in an open pasture, which was quite
glossy green on the twelfth, is now, the twenty-sixth,
completely changed to bright dark-scarlet, — every leaf,
between you and the sun, as if it had been dipped into a
scarlet dye. The whole tree is much like a heart in form,
as well as color. Was not this worth waiting for? Little
did you think, ten days ago, that that cold green tree
would assume such color as this. Its leaves are still
firmly attached, while those of other trees are falling
around it. It seems to say : " I am the last to blush,
but I blush deeper than any of ye. I bring up the rear in
my red coat. We scarlet ones, alone of oaks, have not
given up the fight."

The sap is now, and even far into November, frequently flowing fast in these trees, as in maples in the

spring; and apparently their bright tints, now that most
other oaks are withered, are connected with this phenomenon. They are full of life. It has a pleasantly
astringent, acorn-like taste, this strong oak wine, as
I find on tapping them with my knife.

Looking across this woodland valley, a quarter of a
mile wide, how rich those scarlet oaks embosomed in
pines, their bright red branches intimately intermingled
with them! They have their full effect there. The pine
boughs are the green calyx to their red petals. Or, as we
go along a road in the woods, the sun striking endwise
through it, and lighting up the red tents of the oaks,
which on each side are mingled with the liquid green of
the pines, makes a very gorgeous scene. Indeed, without
the evergreens for contrast, the autumnal tints would
lose much of their effect.

The scarlet oak asks a clear sky and the brightness
of late October days. These bring out its colors. If the
sun goes into a cloud they become comparatively indis-
tinct. As I sit on a cliff in the southwest part of our town,
the sun is now getting low, and the woods in Lincoln,
south and east of me, are lit up by its more level rays;
and in the scarlet oaks, scattered so equally over the
forest, there is brought out a more brilliant redness than
I had believed was in them. Every tree of this species
which is visible in those directions, even to the horizon,
now stands out distinctly red. Some great ones lift their
red backs high above the woods, in the next town, like
huge roses with a myriad of fine petals; and some more
slender ones, in a small grove of white pines on Pine
Hill in the east, on the very verge of the horizon, alter-

nating with the pines on the edge of the grove, and shouldering them with their red coats, look like soldiers in red amid hunters in green. This time it is Lincoln green, too. Till the sun got low, I did not believe that there were so many redcoats in the forest army. Theirs is an intense, burning red, which would lose some of its strength, methinks, with every step you might take toward them; for the shade that lurks amid their foliage does not report itself at this distance, and they are unanimously red. The focus of their reflected color is in the atmosphere far on this side. Every such tree becomes a nucleus of red, as it were, where, with the declining sun, that color grows and glows. It is partly borrowed fire, gathering strength from the sun on its way to your eye. It has only some comparatively dull red leaves for a rallying-point, or kindling-stuff, to start it, and it becomes an intense scarlet or red mist, or fire, which finds fuel for itself in the very atmosphere. So vivacious is redness. The very rails reflect a rosy light at this hour and season. You see a redder tree than exists.

If you wish to count the scarlet oaks, do it now. In a clear day stand thus on a hilltop in the woods, when the sun is an hour high, and every one within range of your vision, excepting in the west, will be revealed. You might live to the age of Methuselah and never find a tithe of them, otherwise. Yet sometimes even in a dark day I have thought them as bright as I ever saw them. Looking westward, their colors are lost in a blaze of light; but in other directions the whole forest is a flower-garden, in which these late roses burn, alternating with green, while the so-called "gardeners," walking here and there, perchance, beneath, with spade and water-pot, see only a few little asters amid withered leaves.

These are *my* China-asters, *my* late garden-flowers. It costs me nothing for a gardener. The falling leaves, all over the forest, are protecting the roots of my plants. Only look at what is to be seen, and you will have garden enough, without deepening the soil in your yard. We have only to elevate our view a little, to see the whole forest as a garden. The blossoming of the scarlet oak, — the forest-flower, surpassing all in splendor (at least since the maple)! I do not know but they interest me more than the maples, they are so widely and equally dispersed throughout the forest; they are so hardy, a nobler tree on the whole; our chief November flower, abiding the approach of winter with us, imparting warmth to early November prospects. It is remarkable that the latest bright color that is general should be this deep, dark scarlet and red, the intensest of colors. The ripest fruit of the year; like the cheek of a hard, glossy red apple, from the cold Isle of Orleans, which will not be mellow for eating till next spring! When I rise to a hilltop, a thousand of these great oak roses, distributed on every side, as far as the horizon! I admire them four or five miles off! This my unfailing prospect for a fort-night past! This late forest-flower surpasses all that spring or summer could do. Their colors were but rare and dainty specks comparatively (created for the near-sighted, who walk amid the humblest herbs and under-woods), and made no impression on a distant eye. Now it is an extended forest or a mountain-side, through or along which we journey from day to day, that bursts into bloom. Comparatively, our gardening is on a petty scale, — the gardener still nursing a few asters amid dead weeds, ignorant of the gigantic asters and roses which, as it were, overshadow him, and ask for none of his care. It is like a little red paint ground on a saucer, and held up against the sunset sky. Why not take more elevated and broader views, walk in the great garden; not skulk in a little "debauched" nook of it? consider the beauty of the forest, and not merely of a few impounded herbs?

Let your walks now be a little more adventurous; ascend the hills. If, about the last of October, you ascend any hill in the outskirts of our town, and probably of yours, and look over the forest, you may see — well, what I have endeavored to describe. All this you surely *will* see, and much more, if you are prepared to see it, — if you *look* for it. Otherwise, regular and universal as this phenomenon is, whether you stand on the hilltop or in the hollow, you will think for threescore years and ten that all the wood is, at this season, sere and brown. Objects are concealed from our view, not so much because they are out of the course of our visual ray as because we do not bring our minds and eyes to bear on them; for there is no power to see in the eye itself, any more than in any other jelly. We do not realize how far and widely, or how near and narrowly, we are to look. The greater part of the phenomena of Nature are for this reason concealed from us all our lives. The gardener sees only the gardener's garden. Here, too, as in political economy, the supply answers to the demand. Nature does not cast pearls before

swine. There is just as much beauty visible to us in the
landscape as we are prepared to appreciate, — not a
grain more. The actual objects which one man will see
from a particular hilltop are just as different from those
which another will see as the beholders are different.
The scarlet oak must, in a sense, be in your eye when
you go forth. We cannot see anything until we are possessed with the idea of it, take it into our heads, — and
then we can hardly see anything else. In my botanical
rambles I find that, first, the idea, or image, of a plant
occupies my thoughts, though it may seem very foreign
to this locality, — no nearer than Hudson's Bay, —
and for some weeks or months I go thinking of it, and
expecting it, unconsciously, and at length I surely see it.
This is the history of my finding a score or more of rare
plants which I could name. A man sees only what concerns him. A botanist absorbed in the study of grasses
does not distinguish the grandest pasture oaks. He, as
it were, tramples down oaks unwittingly in his walk,
or at most sees only their shadows. I have found that
it required a different intention of the eye, in the same
locality, to see different plants, even when they were
closely allied, as *Juncaceae* and *Gramineae:* when I was
looking for the former, I did not see the latter in the
midst of them. How much more, then, it requires different intentions of the eye and of the mind to attend to
different departments of knowledge! How differently
the poet and the naturalist look at objects!

Take a New England selectman, and set him on the
highest of our hills, and tell him to look, — sharpening
his sight to the utmost, and putting on the glasses that

suit him best (aye, using a spy-glass, if he likes), —
and make a full report. What, probably, will he *spy?* —
what will he *select* to look at? Of course, he will see a
Brocken spectre of himself. He will see several meeting-
houses, at least, and, perhaps, that somebody ought to
be assessed higher than he is, since he has so handsome
a wood-lot. Now take Julius Cæsar, or Emanuel Swe·
denborg, or a Fiji-Islander, and set him up there. Or
suppose all together, and let them compare notes afterward. Will it appear that they have enjoyed the same
prospect? What they will see will be as different as
Rome was from heaven or hell, or the last from the
Fiji Islands. For aught we know, as strange a man as
any of these is always at our elbow.

Why, it takes a sharpshooter to bring down even
such trivial game as snipes and woodcocks; he must
take very particular aim, and know what he is aiming
at. He would stand a very small chance, if he fired at
random into the sky, being told that snipes were flying
there. And so is it with him that shoots at beauty;
though he wait till the sky falls, he will not bag any, if
he does not already know its seasons and haunts, and
the color of its wing, — if he has not dreamed of it, so
that he can *anticipate* it; then, indeed, he flushes it at
every step, shoots double and on the wing, with both
barrels, even in corn-fields. The sportsman trains himself, dresses, and watches unweariedly, and loads and
primes for his particular game. He prays for it, and
offers sacrifices, and so he gets it. After due and long
preparation, schooling his eye and hand, dreaming
awake and asleep, with gun and paddle and boat, he

goes out after meadow-hens, which most of his towns-men never saw nor dreamed of, and paddles for miles against a head wind, and wades in water up to his knees, being out all day without his dinner, and *there-fore* he gets them. He had them half-way into his bag when he started, and has only to shove them down. The true sportsman can shoot you almost any of his game from his windows: what else has he windows or eyes for? It comes and perches at last on the barrel of his gun; but the rest of the world never see it *with the feathers on*. The geese fly exactly under his zenith, and honk when they get there, and he will keep himself supplied by firing up his chimney; twenty musquash have the refusal of each one of his traps before it is empty. If he lives, and his game spirit increases, heaven and earth shall fail him sooner than game; and when he dies, he will go to more extensive and, perchance, happier hunting-grounds. The fisherman, too, dreams of fish, sees a bobbing cork in his dreams, till he can almost catch them in his sink-spout. I knew a girl who, being sent to pick huckleberries, picked wild goose-berries by the quart, where no one else knew that there were any, because she was accustomed to pick them up-country where she came from. The astronomer knows where to go star-gathering, and sees one clearly in his mind before any have seen it with a glass. The hen scratches and finds her food right under where she stands; but such is not the way with the hawk.

These bright leaves which I have mentioned are not the exception, but the rule; for I believe that all leaves, even grasses and mosses, acquire brighter colors just before their fall. When you come to observe faithfully the changes of each humblest plant, you find that each has, sooner or later, its peculiar autumnal tint; and if you undertake to make a complete list of the bright tints, it will be nearly as long as a catalogue of the plants in your vicinity.

WILD APPLES

THE HISTORY OF THE APPLE TREE

I⊤ is remarkable how closely the history of the apple tree is connected with that of man. The geologist tells us that the order of the *Rosaceae*, which includes the apple, also the true grasses, and the *Labiatae*, or mints, were introduced only a short time previous to the appearance of man on the globe.

It appears that apples made a part of the food of that unknown primitive people whose traces have lately been found at the bottom of the Swiss lakes, supposed to be older than the foundation of Rome, so old that they had no metallic implements. An entire black and shriveled crab-apple has been recovered from their stores.

Tacitus says of the ancient Germans that they satisfied their hunger with wild apples (*agrestia poma*), among other things.

Niebuhr observes that "the words for a house, a field, a plow, plowing, wine, oil, milk, sheep, apples, and others relating to agriculture and the gentler way of life, agree in Latin and Greek, while the Latin words for all objects pertaining to war or the chase are utterly alien from the Greek." Thus the apple tree may be considered a symbol of peace no less than the olive.

The apple was early so important, and generally distributed, that its name traced to its root in many languages signifies fruit in general. Μῆλον, in Greek, means an apple, also the fruit of other trees, also a sheep and any cattle, and finally riches in general.

The apple tree has been celebrated by the Hebrews, Greeks, Romans, and Scandinavians. Some have thought that the first human pair were tempted by its fruit. Goddesses are fabled to have contended for it, dragons were set to watch it, and heroes were employed to pluck it.

The tree is mentioned in at least three places in the Old Testament, and its fruit in two or three more. Solomon sings, "As the apple-tree among the trees of the wood, so is my beloved among the sons." And again, "Stay me with flagons, comfort me with apples." The noblest part of man's noblest feature is named from this fruit, "the apple of the eye."

The apple tree is also mentioned by Homer and Herodotus. Ulysses saw in the glorious garden of Alcinoüs "pears and pomegranates, and apple trees bearing beautiful fruit" (καὶ μηλέαι ἀγλαόκαρποι). And according to Homer, apples were among the fruits which Tantalus could not pluck, the wind ever blowing their boughs away from him. Theophrastus knew and described the apple tree as a botanist.

According to the Prose Edda, "Iduna keeps in a box the apples which the gods, when they feel old age approaching, have only to taste of to become young again. It is in this manner that they will be kept in renovated youth until Ragnarök" (or the destruction of the gods).

I learn from Loudon that "the ancient Welsh bards were rewarded for excelling in song by the token of the apple-spray;" and "in the Highlands of Scotland the apple-tree is the badge of the clan Lamont."

The apple tree (*Pyrus malus*) belongs chiefly to the northern temperate zone. Loudon says that "it grows spontaneously in every part of Europe except the frigid zone, and throughout Western Asia, China, and Japan." We have also two or three varieties of the apple indigenous in North America. The cultivated apple tree was first introduced into this country by the earliest settlers, and is thought to do as well or better here than anywhere else. Probably some of the varieties which are now cultivated were first introduced into Britain by the Romans.

Pliny, adopting the distinction of Theophrastus, says, "Of trees there are some which are altogether wild (*sylvestres*), some more civilized (*urbaniores*)." Theophrastus includes the apple among the last; and, indeed, it is in this sense the most civilized of all trees. It is as harmless as a dove, as beautiful as a rose, and as valuable as flocks and herds. It has been longer cultivated than any other, and so is more humanized; and who knows but, like the dog, it will at length be no longer traceable to its wild original? It migrates with man, like the dog and horse and cow: first, perchance, from Greece to Italy, thence to England, thence to America; and our Western emigrant is still marching steadily toward the setting sun with the seeds of the apple in his pocket, or perhaps a few young trees strapped to his load. At least a million apple trees are thus set farther westward this year than any cultivated ones grew last year. Consider how the Blossom Week, like the Sabbath, is thus annually spreading over the prairies; for when man migrates, he carries with him not only his birds, quadrupeds, insects, vegetables, and his very sward, but his orchard also.

The leaves and tender twigs are an agreeable food to many domestic animals, as the cow, horse, sheep, and goat; and the fruit is sought after by the first, as well as by the hog. Thus there appears to have existed a natural alliance between these animals and this tree from the first. "The fruit of the crab in the forests of France" is said to be "a great resource for the wild boar."

Not only the Indian, but many indigenous insects, birds, and quadrupeds, welcomed the apple tree to these shores. The tent caterpillar saddled her eggs on the very first twig that was formed, and it has since shared her affections with the wild cherry; and the canker-worm also in a measure abandoned the elm to feed on it. As it grew apace, the bluebird, robin, cherry-bird, kingbird, and many more came with haste and built their nests and warbled in its boughs, and so became orchard-birds, and multiplied more than ever. It was an era in the history of their race. The downy woodpecker found such a savory morsel under its bark that he perforated it in a ring quite round the tree, before he left it, — a thing which he had never done before, to my knowledge. It did not take the partridge long to find out how sweet its buds were, and every winter eve she flew, and still flies, from the wood, to pluck them, much to the farmer's sorrow. The rabbit, too, was not slow to learn the taste of its twigs and bark;

and when the fruit was ripe, the squirrel half rolled,
half carried it to his hole; and even the musquash crept
up the bank from the brook at evening, and greedily
devoured it, until he had worn a path in the grass there;
and when it was frozen and thawed, the crow and the
jay were glad to taste it occasionally. The owl crept
into the first apple tree that became hollow, and fairly
hooted with delight, finding it just the place for him; so,
settling down into it, he has remained there ever since.

My theme being the Wild Apple, I will merely glance
at some of the seasons in the annual growth of the cultivated apple, and pass on to my special province.

The flowers of the apple are perhaps the most beautiful of any tree's, so copious and so delicious to both
sight and scent. The walker is frequently tempted to
turn and linger near some more than usually handsome
one, whose blossoms are two-thirds expanded. How
superior it is in these respects to the pear, whose blossoms are neither colored nor fragrant!

By the middle of July, green apples are so large as to
remind us of coddling, and of the autumn. The sward
is commonly strewed with little ones which fall still-
born, as it were, — Nature thus thinning them for
us. The Roman writer Palladius said, "If apples are
inclined to fall before their time, a stone placed in a
split root will retain them." Some such notion, still
surviving, may account for some of the stones which
we see placed, to be overgrown, in the forks of trees.
They have a saying in Suffolk, England, —

> "At Michaelmas time, or a little before,
> Half an apple goes to the core."

Early apples begin to be ripe about the first of August; but I think that none of them are so good to eat as some to smell. One is worth more to scent your handkerchief with than any perfume which they sell in the shops. The fragrance of some fruits is not to be forgotten, along with that of flowers. Some gnarly apple which I pick up in the road reminds me by its fragrance of all the wealth of Pomona, — carrying me forward to those days when they will be collected in golden and ruddy heaps in the orchards and about the cider-mills.

A week or two later, as you are going by orchards or gardens, especially in the evenings, you pass through a little region possessed by the fragrance of ripe apples, and thus enjoy them without price, and without robbing anybody.

There is thus about all natural products a certain volatile and ethereal quality which represents their highest value, and which cannot be vulgarized, or bought and sold. No mortal has ever enjoyed the perfect flavor of any fruit, and only the godlike among men begin to taste its ambrosial qualities. For nectar and ambrosia are only those fine flavors of every earthly fruit which our coarse palates fail to perceive, — just as we occupy the heaven of the gods without knowing it. When I see a particularly mean man carrying a load of fair and fragrant early apples to market, I seem to see a contest going on between him and his horse, on the one side, and the apples on the other, and, to my mind, the apples always gain it. Pliny says that apples are the heaviest of all things, and that the oxen begin to sweat at the mere sight of a load of them. Our driver begins to lose his load the moment he tries to transport them to where they do not belong, that is, to any but the most beautiful. Though he gets out from time to time, and feels of them, and thinks they are all there, I see the stream of their evanescent and celestial qualities going to heaven from his cart, while the pulp and skin and core only are going to market. They are not apples, but pomace. Are not these still Iduna's apples, the taste of which keeps the gods forever young? and think you that they will let Loki or Thjassi carry them off to Jötunheim, while they grow wrinkled and gray? No, for Ragnarök, or the destruction of the gods, is not yet.

There is another thinning of the fruit, commonly near the end of August or in September, when the ground is strewn with windfalls; and this happens especially when high winds occur after rain. In some orchards you may see fully three quarters of the whole crop on the ground, lying in a circular form beneath the trees, yet hard and green, or, if it is a hillside, rolled far down the hill. However, it is an ill wind that blows nobody any good. All the country over, people are busy picking up the windfalls, and this will make them cheap for early apple pies.

In October, the leaves falling, the apples are more distinct on the trees. I saw one year in a neighboring town some trees fuller of fruit than I remember to have ever seen before, small yellow apples hanging over the road. The branches were gracefully drooping with their weight, like a barberry bush, so that the whole tree acquired a new character. Even the topmost branches, instead of standing erect, spread and drooped in all directions; and there were so many poles supporting the lower ones that they looked like pictures of banyan trees. As an old English manuscript says, "The mo appelen the tree bereth the more sche boweth to the folk."

Surely the apple is the noblest of fruits. Let the most beautiful or the swiftest have it. That should be the "going" price of apples.

Between the 5th and 20th of October I see the barrels lie under the trees. And perhaps I talk with one who is selecting some choice barrels to fulfill an order. He turns a specked one over many times before he leaves it out. If I were to tell what is passing in my mind, I should say that every one was specked which he had handled; for he rubs off all the bloom, and those fugacious ethereal qualities leave it. Cool evenings prompt the farmers to make haste, and at length I see only the ladders here and there left leaning against the trees.

It would be well, if we accepted these gifts with more joy and gratitude, and did not think it enough simply to put a fresh load of compost about the tree. Some old English customs are suggestive at least. I find them described chiefly in Brand's "Popular Antiquities." It appears that "on Christmas Eve the farmers and their men in Devonshire take a large bowl of cider, with a toast in it, and carrying it in state to the orchard, they salute the apple-trees with much ceremony, in order to make them bear well the next season." This salutation consists in "throwing some of the cider about the roots of the tree, placing bits of the toast on

the branches," and then, "encircling one of the best
bearing trees in the orchard, they drink the following
toast three several times: —

> 'Here's to thee, old apple tree,
> Whence thou mayst bud, and whence thou mayst blow,
> And whence thou mayst bear apples enow!
> Hats-full! caps-full!
> Bushel, bushel, sacks-full!
> And my pockets full, too! Hurra!'"

Also what was called "apple-howling" used to be
practiced in various counties of England on New Year's
Eve. A troop of boys visited the different orchards,
and, encircling the apple trees, repeated the following
words: —

> "Stand fast, root! bear well, top!
> Pray God send us a good howling crop:
> Every twig, apples big;
> Every bough, apples enow!"

"They then shout in chorus, one of the boys accompanying them on a cow's horn. During this ceremony
they rap the trees with their sticks." This is called
"wassailing" the trees, and is thought by some to be
"a relic of the heathen sacrifice to Pomona."

Herrick sings, —

> "Wassaile the trees that they may beare
> You many a plum and many a peare;
> For more or less fruits they will bring
> As you so give them wassailing."

Our poets have as yet a better right to sing of cider
than of wine; but it behooves them to sing better than
English Phillips did, else they will do no credit to their
Muse.

THE WILD APPLE

So much for the more civilized apple trees (*urbani-ores*, as Pliny calls them). I love better to go through the old orchards of ungrafted appletrees, at what ever season of the year, — so irregularly planted: sometimes two trees standing close together; and the rows so devious that you would think that they not only had grown while the owner was sleeping, but had been set out by him in a somnambulic state. The rows of grafted fruit will never tempt me to wander amid them like these. But I now, alas, speak rather from memory than from any recent experience, such ravages have been made!

Some soils, like a rocky tract called the Easterbrooks Country in my neighborhood, are so suited to the apple, that it will grow faster in them without any care, or if only the ground is broken up once a year, than it will in many places with any amount of care. The owners of this tract allow that the soil is excellent for fruit, but they say that it is so rocky that they have not patience to plow it, and that, together with the distance, is the reason why it is not cultivated. There are, or were recently, extensive orchards there standing without order. Nay, they spring up wild and bear well there in the midst of pines, birches, maples, and oaks. I am often surprised to see rising amid these trees the rounded tops of apple trees glowing with red or yellow fruit, in harmony with the autumnal tints of the forest.

Going up the side of a cliff about the first of November, I saw a vigorous young apple tree, which, planted

by birds or cows, had shot up amid the rocks and open
woods there, and had now much fruit on it, uninjured
by the frosts, when all cultivated apples were gathered.
It was a rank, wild growth, with many green leaves on
it still, and made an impression of thorniness.   The
fruit was hard and green, but looked as if it would be
palatable in the winter. Some was dangling on the twigs,
but more half buried in the wet leaves under the tree,
or rolled far down the hill amid the rocks. The owner
knows nothing of it. The day was not observed when
it first blossomed, nor when it first bore fruit, unless by
the chickadee. There was no dancing on the green beneath it in its honor, and now there is no hand to pluck
its fruit, — which is only gnawed by squirrels, as I perceive. It has done double duty, — not only borne this
crop, but each twig has grown a foot into the air. And
this is *such* fruit! bigger than many berries, we must
admit, and carried home will be sound and palatable
next spring. What care I for Iduna's apples so long as
I can get these ?

When I go by this shrub thus late and hardy, and see
its dangling fruit, I respect the tree, and I am grateful
for Nature's bounty, even though I cannot eat it. Here
on this rugged and woody hillside has grown an apple
tree, not planted by man, no relic of a former orchard,
but a natural growth, like the pines and oaks. Most
fruits which we prize and use depend entirely on our
care. Corn and grain, potatoes, peaches, melons, etc.,
depend altogether on our planting; but the apple emu-
lates man's independence and enterprise. It is not simply carried, as I have said, but, like him, to some extent,

it has migrated to this New World, and is even, here and there, making its way amid the aboriginal trees; just as the ox and dog and horse sometimes run wild and maintain themselves.

Even the sourest and crabbedest apple, growing in the most unfavorable position, suggests such thoughts as these, it is so noble a fruit.

THE CRAB

Nevertheless, *our* wild apple is wild only like myself, perchance, who belong not to the aboriginal race here, but have strayed into the woods from the cultivated stock. Wilder still, as I have said, there grows elsewhere in this country a native and aboriginal crab-apple, *Malus coronaria*, "whose nature has not yet been modified by cultivation." It is found from western New York to Minnesota, and southward. Michaux says that its ordinary height "is fifteen or eighteen feet, but it is sometimes found twenty-five or thirty feet high," and that the large ones "exactly resemble the common apple tree." "The flowers are white mingled with rose color, and are collected in corymbs." They are remarkable for their delicious odor. The fruit, according to him, is about an inch and a half in diameter, and is intensely acid. Yet they make fine sweetmeats and also cider of them. He concludes that "if, on being cultivated, it does not yield new and palatable varieties, it will at least be celebrated for the beauty of its flowers, and for the sweetness of its perfume."

I never saw the crab-apple till May, 1861. I had heard of it through Michaux, but more modern botanists, so far as I know, have not treated it as of any peculiar importance. Thus it was a half-fabulous tree to me. I contemplated a pilgrimage to the "Glades," a portion of Pennsylvania where it was said to grow to perfection. I thought of sending to a nursery for it, but doubted if they had it, or would distinguish it from European varieties. At last I had occasion to go to Minnesota, and on entering Michigan I began to notice from the cars a tree with handsome rose-colored flowers. At first I thought it some variety of thorn; but it was not long before the truth flashed on me, that this was my long-sought crab-apple. It was the prevailing flowering shrub or tree to be seen from the cars at that season of the year, — about the middle of May. But the cars never stopped before one, and so I was launched on the bosom of the Mississippi without having touched one, experiencing the fate of Tantalus. On arriving at St. Anthony's Falls, I was sorry to be told that I was too far north for the crab-apple. Nevertheless I succeeded in finding it about eight miles west of the Falls; touched it and smelled it, and secured a lingering corymb of flowers for my herbarium. This must have been near its northern limit.

HOW THE WILD APPLE GROWS

But though these are indigenous, like the Indians, I doubt whether they are any hardier than those back-woodsmen among the apple trees, which, though descended from cultivated stocks, plant themselves in distant fields and forests, where the soil is favorable to them. I know of no trees which have more difficulties to contend with, and which more sturdily resist their foes. These are the ones whose story we have to tell. It oftentimes reads thus: —

Near the beginning of May, we notice little thickets of apple trees just springing up in the pastures where cattle have been, — as the rocky ones of our Easterbrooks Country, or the top of Nobscot Hill, in Sudbury. One or two of these, perhaps, survive the drought and other accidents, — their very birthplace defending them against the encroaching grass and some other dangers, at first.

> In two years' time 't had thus
>   Reached the level of the rocks,
> Admired the stretching world,
>   Nor feared the wandering flocks.
>
> But at this tender age
>   Its sufferings began:
> There came a browsing ox
>   And cut it down a span.

This time, perhaps, the ox does not notice it amid the grass; but the next year, when it has grown more stout, he recognizes it for a fellow-emigrant from the old country, the flavor of whose leaves and twigs he well knows; and though at first he pauses to welcome it, and express his surprise, and gets for answer, "The same cause that brought you here brought me," he nevertheless browses it again, reflecting, it may be, that he has some title to it.

Thus cut down annually, it does not despair; but, putting forth two short twigs for every one cut off, it spreads out low along the ground in the hollows or between the rocks, growing more stout and scrubby, until it forms, not a tree as yet, but a little pyramidal, stiff, twiggy mass, almost as solid and impenetrable as a rock. Some of the densest and most impenetrable clumps of bushes that I have ever seen, as well on account of the closeness and stubbornness of their branches as of their thorns, have been these wild apple scrubs. They are more like the scrubby fir and black spruce on which you stand, and sometimes walk, on the tops of mountains, where cold is the demon they contend with, than anything else. No wonder they are prompted to grow thorns at last, to defend themselves against such foes. In their thorniness, however, there is no malice, only some malic acid.

The rocky pastures of the tract I have referred to — for they maintain their ground best in a rocky field — are thickly sprinkled with these little tufts, reminding you often of some rigid gray mosses or lichens, and you see thousands of little trees just springing up between them, with the seed still attached to them.

Being regularly clipped all around each year by the cows, as a hedge with shears, they are often of a perfect conical or pyramidal form, from one to four feet high, and more or less sharp, as if trimmed by the gardener's art. In the pastures on Nobscot Hill and its spurs, they make fine dark shadows when the sun is low. They are also an excellent covert from hawks for many small birds that roost and build in them. Whole flocks perch in them at night, and I have seen three robins' nests in one which was six feet in diameter.

No doubt many of these are already old trees, if you

reckon from the day they were planted, but infants still when you consider their development and the long life before them. I counted the annual rings of some which were just one foot high, and as wide as high, and found that they were about twelve years old, but quite sound and thrifty! They were so low that they were unnoticed by the walker, while many of their contemporaries from the nurseries were already bearing considerable crops. But what you gain in time is perhaps in this case, too, lost in power, — that is, in the vigor of the tree. This is their pyramidal state.

The cows continue to browse them thus for twenty years or more, keeping them down and compelling them to spread, until at last they are so broad that they become their own fence, when some interior shoot, which their foes cannot reach, darts upward with joy: for it has not forgotten its high calling, and bears its own peculiar fruit in triumph.

Such are the tactics by which it finally defeats its bovine foes. Now, if you have watched the progress of a particular shrub, you will see that it is no longer a simple pyramid or cone, but that out of its apex there rises a sprig or two, growing more lustily perchance than an orchard-tree, since the plant now devotes the whole of its repressed energy to these upright parts. In a short time these become a small tree, an inverted pyramid resting on the apex of the other, so that the whole has now the form of a vast hour-glass. The spreading bottom, having served its purpose, finally disappears, and the generous tree permits the now harmless cows to come in and stand in its shade, and

rub against and redden its trunk, which has grown
in spite of them, and even to taste a part of its fruit, and
so disperse the seed.

Thus the cows create their own shade and food; and
the tree, its hour-glass being inverted, lives a second life,
as it were.

It is an important question with some nowadays,
whether you should trim young apple trees as high as
your nose or as high as your eyes. The ox trims them
up as high as he can reach, and that is about the right
height, I think.

In spite of wandering kine, and other adverse circumstances, that despised shrub, valued only by small
birds as a covert and shelter from hawks, has its blossom week at last, and in course of time its harvest, sincere, though small.

By the end of some October, when its leaves have
fallen, I frequently see such a central sprig, whose
progress I have watched, when I thought it had forgotten its destiny, as I had, bearing its first crop of small
green or yellow or rosy fruit, which the cows cannot get
at over the bushy and thorny hedge which surrounds it,
and I make haste to taste the new and undescribed variety. We have all heard of the numerous varieties of
fruit invented by Van Mons and Knight. This is the
system of Van Cow, and she has invented far more and
more memorable varieties than both of them.

Through what hardships it may attain to bear a
sweet fruit ! Though somewhat small, it may prove
equal, if not superior, in flavor to that which has grown
in a garden, — will perchance be all the sweeter and

more palatable for the very difficulties it has had to contend with. Who knows but this chance wild fruit, planted by a cow or a bird on some remote and rocky hillside, where it is as yet unobserved by man, may be the choicest of all its kind, and foreign potentates shall hear of it, and royal societies seek to propagate it, though the virtues of the perhaps truly crabbed owner of the soil may never be heard of, — at least, beyond the limits of his village? It was thus the Porter and the Baldwin grew.

Every wild apple shrub excites our expectation thus, somewhat as every wild child. It is, perhaps, a prince in disguise. What a lesson to man! So are human beings, referred to the highest standard, the celestial fruit which they suggest and aspire to bear, browsed on by fate; and only the most persistent and strongest genius defends itself and prevails, sends a tender scion upward at last, and drops its perfect fruit on the ungrateful earth. Poets and philosophers and statesmen thus spring up in the country pastures, and outlast the hosts of unoriginal men.

Such is always the pursuit of knowledge. The celestial fruits, the golden apples of the Hesperides, are ever guarded by a hundred-headed dragon which never sleeps, so that it is an Herculean labor to pluck them.

This is one, and the most remarkable way in which the wild apple is propagated; but commonly it springs up at wide intervals in woods and swamp, and by the sides of roads, as the soil may suit it, and grows with comparative rapidity. Those which grow in dense woods are very tall and slender. I frequently pluck from these trees a perfectly mild and tamed fruit. As Palladius says, "*Et injussu consternitur ubere mali:*" And the ground is strewn with the fruit of an unbidden apple tree.

It is an old notion that, if these wild trees do not bear a valuable fruit of their own, they are the best stocks by which to transmit to posterity the most highly prized qualities of others. However, I am not in search of stocks, but the wild fruit itself, whose fierce gust has suffered no "inteneration." It is not my

"highest plot
To plant the Bergamot."

THE FRUIT, AND ITS FLAVOR

The time for wild apples is the last of October and the first of November. They then get to be palatable, for they ripen late, and they are still perhaps as beautiful as ever. I make a great account of these fruits, which the farmers do not think it worth the while to gather, — wild flavors of the Muse, vivacious and inspiriting. The farmer thinks that he has better in his barrels, but he is mistaken, unless he has a walker's appetite and imagination, neither of which can he have.

Such as grow quite wild, and are left out till the first of November, I presume that the owner does not mean to gather. They belong to children as wild as themselves, — to certain active boys that I know, — to the wild-eyed woman of the fields, to whom nothing comes amiss, who gleans after all the world, and, moreover, to us walkers. We have met with them, and they are ours. These rights, long enough insisted upon, have come to be an institution in some old countries, where they have learned how to live. I hear that "the custom of grippling, which may be called apple-gleaning, is, or was formerly, practiced in Herefordshire. It consists in leaving a few apples, which are called the gripples, on every tree, after the general gathering, for the boys, who go with climbing-poles and bags to collect them."

As for those I speak of, I pluck them as a wild fruit, native to this quarter of the earth, — fruit of old trees that have been dying ever since I was a boy and are not yet dead, frequented only by the woodpecker and the squirrel, deserted now by the owner, who has not faith enough to look under their boughs. From the appearance of the tree-top, at a little distance, you would expect nothing but lichens to drop from it, but your faith is rewarded by finding the ground strewn with spirited fruit, — some of it, perhaps, collected at squirrel-holes, with the marks of their teeth by which they carried them, — some containing a cricket or two silently feeding within, and some, especially in damp days, a shell-less snail. The very sticks and stones lodged in the tree-top might have convinced you of the savoriness of the fruit which has been so eagerly sought after in past years.

I have seen no account of these among the "Fruits and Fruit-Trees of America," though they are more memorable to my taste than the grafted kinds; more racy and wild American flavors do they possess when October and November, when December and January, and perhaps February and March even, have assuaged them somewhat. An old farmer in my neighborhood, who always selects the right word, says that " they have a kind of bow-arrow tang."

Apples for grafting appear to have been selected commonly, not so much for their spirited flavor, as for their mildness, their size, and bearing qualities, — not so much for their beauty, as for their fairness and soundness. Indeed, I have no faith in the selected lists of pomological gentlemen. Their " Favorites " and " None-suches " and " Seek-no-farthers," when I have fruited them, commonly turn out very tame and forgettable. They are eaten with comparatively little zest, and have no real *tang* nor *smack* to them.

What if some of these wildings are acrid and puckery, genuine *verjuice*, do they not still belong to the *Pomaceæ*, which are uniformly innocent and kind to our race? I still begrudge them to the cider-mill. Perhaps they are not fairly ripe yet.

No wonder that these small and high-colored apples are thought to make the best cider. Loudon quotes from the " Herefordshire Report," that " apples of a small size are always, if equal in quality, to be preferred to those of a larger size, in order that the rind and kernel may bear the greatest proportion to the pulp, which affords the weakest and most watery juice." And he says that, " to prove this, Dr. Symonds, of Hereford, about the year 1800, made one hogshead of cider entirely from the rinds and cores of apples, and another from the pulp only, when the first was found of extraordinary strength and flavor, while the latter was sweet and insipid."

Evelyn says that the " Red-strake " was the favorite cider-apple in his day; and he quotes one Dr. Newburg as saying, " In Jersey 't is a general observation, as I hear, that the more of red any apple has in its rind, the more proper it is for this use. Pale-faced apples they exclude as much as may be from their cider-vat." This opinion still prevails.

All apples are good in November. Those which the farmer leaves out as unsalable and unpalatable to those who frequent the markets are choicest fruit to the walker. But it is remarkable that the wild apple, which I praise as so spirited and racy when eaten in the fields or woods, being brought into the house has frequently a harsh and crabbed taste. The Saunterer's Apple not even the saunterer can eat in the house. The palate rejects it there, as it does haws and acorns, and de-mands a tamed one; for there you miss the November air, which is the sauce it is to be eaten with. Accord-ingly, when Tityrus, seeing the lengthening shadows, invites Melibœus to go home and pass the night with him, he promises him *mild* apples and soft chestnuts, — *mitia poma, castaneœ molles.* I frequently pluck wild apples of so rich and spicy a flavor that I wonder all orchardists do not get a scion from that tree, and I fail not to bring home my pockets full. But perchance, when I take one out of my desk and taste it in my cham-ber, I find it unexpectedly crude, — sour enough to set a squirrel's teeth on edge and make a jay scream.

These apples have hung in the wind and frost and rain till they have absorbed the qualities of the weather or season, and thus are highly *seasoned*, and they *pierce* and *sting* and *permeate* us with their spirit. They must be eaten in *season*, accordingly, — that is, out-of-doors.

To appreciate the wild and sharp flavors of these October fruits, it is necessary that you be breathing the sharp October or November air. The outdoor air and exercise which the walker gets give a different tone to his palate, and he craves a fruit which the sedentary would call harsh and crabbed. They must be eaten in the fields, when your system is all aglow with exercise, when the frosty weather nips your fingers, the wind rattles the bare boughs or rustles the few remaining leaves, and the jay is heard screaming around. What is sour in the house a bracing walk makes sweet. Some of these apples might be labeled, " To be eaten in the wind."

Of course no flavors are thrown away; they are intended for the taste that is up to them. Some apples have two distinct flavors, and perhaps one half of them must be eaten in the house, the other outdoors. One Peter Whitney wrote from Northborough in 1782, for the Proceedings of the Boston Academy, describing an apple tree in that town " producing fruit of opposite qualities, part of the same apple being frequently sour and the other sweet;" also some all sour, and others all sweet, and this diversity on all parts of the tree.

There is a wild apple on Nawshawtuct Hill in my town which has to me a peculiarly pleasant bitter tang, not perceived till it is three-quarters tasted. It remains on the tongue. As you eat it, it smells exactly like a squash-bug. It is a sort of triumph to eat and relish it.

I hear that the fruit of a kind of plum tree in Provence is " called *Prunes sibarelles*, because it is impossible to whistle after having eaten them, from their sourness."

But perhaps they were only eaten in the house and in
summer, and if tried out-of-doors in a stinging atmosphere, who knows but you could whistle an octave
higher and clearer?

In the fields only are the sours and bitters of Nature
appreciated; just as the woodchopper eats his meal in
a sunny glade, in the middle of a winter day, with content, basks in a sunny ray there, and dreams of summer
in a degree of cold which, experienced in a chamber,
would make a student miserable. They who are at work
abroad are not cold, but rather it is they who sit shiver-
ing in houses. As with temperatures, so with flavors;
as with cold and heat, so with sour and sweet. This
natural raciness, the sours and bitters which the diseased
palate refuses, are the true condiments.

Let your condiments be in the condition of your
senses. To appreciate the flavor of these wild apples
requires vigorous and healthy senses, *papillæ* firm and
erect on the tongue and palate, not easily flattened and
tamed.

From my experience with wild apples, I can understand that there may be reason for a savage's preferring
many kinds of food which the civilized man rejects.
The former has the palate of an outdoor man. It takes
a savage or wild taste to appreciate a wild fruit.

What a healthy out-of-door appetite it takes to relish
the apple of life, the apple of the world, then!

"Nor is it every apple I desire,
  Nor that which pleases every palate best;
'T is not the lasting Deuxan I require,
  Nor yet the red-cheeked Greening I request,

Nor that which first beshrewed the name of wife,
Nor that whose beauty caused the golden strife:
No, no! bring me an apple from the tree of life."

So there is one *thought* for the field, another for the
house. I would have my thoughts, like wild apples, to
be food for walkers, and will not warrant them to be
palatable if tasted in the house.

THEIR BEAUTY

Almost all wild apples are handsome. They cannot
be too gnarly and crabbed and rusty to look at. The
gnarliest will have some redeeming traits even to the
eye. You will discover some evening redness dashed or
sprinkled on some protuberance or in some cavity. It is
rare that the summer lets an apple go without streaking
or spotting it on some part of its sphere. It will have
some red stains, commemorating the mornings and
evenings it has witnessed; some dark and rusty blotches,
in memory of the clouds and foggy, mildewy days that
have passed over it; and a spacious field of green reflecting the general face of nature, — green even as the
fields; or a yellow ground, which implies a milder flavor,
— yellow as the harvest, or russet as the hills.

Apples, these I mean, unspeakably fair, — apples not
of Discord, but of Concord! Yet not so rare but that the
homeliest may have a share. Painted by the frosts, some
a uniform clear bright yellow, or red, or crimson, as if
their spheres had regularly revolved, and enjoyed the
influence of the sun on all sides alike, — some with the
faintest pink blush imaginable, — some brindled with
deep red streaks like a cow, or with hundreds of fine

blood-red rays running regularly from the stem-dimple to the blossom end, like meridional lines, on a straw-colored ground, — some touched with a greenish rust, like a fine lichen, here and there, with crimson blotches or eyes more or less confluent and fiery when wet, — and others gnarly, and freckled or peppered all over on the stem side with fine crimson spots on a white ground, as if accidentally sprinkled from the brush of Him who paints the autumn leaves. Others, again, are sometimes red inside, perfused with a beautiful blush, fairy food, too beautiful to eat, — apple of the Hesperides, apple of the evening sky! But like shells and pebbles on the sea-shore, they must be seen as they sparkle amid the withering leaves in some dell in the woods, in the autumnal air, or as they lie in the wet grass, and not when they have wilted and faded in the house.

THE NAMING OF THEM

It would be a pleasant pastime to find suitable names for the hundred varieties which go to a single heap at the cider-mill. Would it not tax a man's invention, — no one to be named after a man, and all in the *lingua vernacula?* Who shall stand godfather at the christening of the wild apples? It would exhaust the Latin and Greek languages, if they were used, and make the *lingua vernacula* flag. We should have to call in the sunrise and the sunset, the rainbow and the autumn woods and the wild-flowers, and the woodpecker and the purple finch and the squirrel and the jay and the butterfly, the November traveler and the truant boy, to our aid.

In 1836 there were in the garden of the London Horticultural Society more than fourteen hundred distinct sorts. But here are species which they have not in their catalogue, not to mention the varieties which our crab might yield to cultivation.

Let us enumerate a few of these. I find myself compelled, after all, to give the Latin names of some for the benefit of those who live where English is not spoken, — for they are likely to have a world-wide reputation.

There is, first of all, the Wood Apple (*Malus sylvatica*); the Blue-Jay Apple; the Apple which grows in Dells in the Woods (*sylvestrivallis*), also in Hollows in Pastures (*campestrivallis*); the Apple that grows in an old Cellar-Hole (*Malus cellaris*); the Meadow Apple; the Partridge Apple; the Truant's Apple (*cessatoris*), which no boy will ever go by without knocking off some, however *late* it may be; the Saunterer's Apple, — you must lose yourself before you can find the way to that; the Beauty of the Air (*decus aëris*); December-Eating; the Frozen-Thawed (*gelato-soluta*), good only in that state; the Concord Apple, possibly the same with the *Musketaquidensis;* the Assabet Apple; the Brindled Apple; Wine of New England; the Chickaree Apple; the Green Apple (*Malus viridis*), — this has many synonyms: in an imperfect state, it is the *choleramorbifera aut dysenterifera, puerulis dilectissima;* the Apple which Atalanta stopped to pick up; the Hedge Apple (*Malus sepium*); the Slug Apple (*limacea*); the Railroad Apple, which perhaps came from a core thrown out of the cars; the Apple whose Fruit we tasted in our Youth; our Particular Apple, not to

be found in any catalogue; *pedestrium solatium;* also
the Apple where hangs the Forgotten Scythe; Iduna's
Apples, and the Apples which Loki found in the Wood;
and a great many more I have on my list, too numerous
to mention, — all of them good. As Bodæus exclaims,
referring to the cultivated kinds, and adapting Virgil to
his case, so I, adapting Bodæus, —

> "Not if I had a hundred tongues, a hundred mouths,
> An iron voice, could I describe all the forms
> And reckon up all the names of these *wild apples*."

THE LAST GLEANING

By the middle of November the wild apples have lost
some of their brilliancy, and have chiefly fallen. A great
part are decayed on the ground, and the sound ones are
more palatable than before. The note of the chickadee
sounds now more distinct, as you wander amid the old
trees, and the autumnal dandelion is half closed and
tearful. But still, if you are a skillful gleaner, you may
get many a pocketful even of grafted fruit, long after
apples are supposed to be gone out-of-doors. I know
a Blue Pearmain tree, growing within the edge of a
swamp, almost as good as wild. You would not suppose that there was any fruit left there, on the first survey, but you must look according to system. Those
which lie exposed are quite brown and rotten now, or
perchance a few still show one blooming cheek here and
there amid the wet leaves. Nevertheless, with experienced eyes, I explore amid the bare alders and the
huckleberry bushes and the withered sedge, and in the
crevices of the rocks, which are full of leaves, and pry

under the fallen and decaying ferns, which, with apple
and alder leaves, thickly strew the ground. For I know
that they lie concealed, fallen into hollows long since
and covered up by the leaves of the tree itself, — a
proper kind of packing. From these lurking-places,
anywhere within the circumference of the tree, I draw
forth the fruit, all wet and glossy, maybe nibbled by
rabbits and hollowed out by crickets, and perhaps with
a leaf or two cemented to it (as Curzon an old manuscript from a monastery's mouldy cellar), but still with
a rich bloom on it, and at least as ripe and well-kept,
if not better than those in barrels, more crisp and lively
than they. If these resources fail to yield anything, I
have learned to look between the bases of the suckers
which spring thickly from some horizontal limb, for
now and then one lodges there, or in the very midst of
an alder-clump, where they are covered by leaves, safe
from cows which may have smelled them out. If I am
sharp-set, for I do not refuse the Blue Pearmain, I fill
my pockets on each side; and as I retrace my steps in
the frosty eve, being perhaps four or five miles from
home, I eat one first from this side, and then from that,
to keep my balance.

I learn from Topsell's Gesner, whose authority appears to be Albertus, that the following is the way in
which the hedgehog collects and carries home his apples.
He says, — "His meat is apples, worms, or grapes:
when he findeth apples or grapes on the earth, he rolleth
himself upon them, until he have filled all his prickles,
and then carrieth them home to his den, never bearing
above one in his mouth; and if it fortune that one of

them fall off by the way, he likewise shaketh off all the residue, and walloweth upon them afresh, until they be all settled upon his back again. So, forth he goeth, making a noise like a cart-wheel; and if he have any young ones in his nest, they pull off his load wherewithal he is loaded, eating thereof what they please, and laying up the residue for the time to come."

THE "FROZEN-THAWED" APPLE

Toward the end of November, though some of the sound ones are yet more mellow and perhaps more edible, they have generally, like the leaves, lost their beauty, and are beginning to freeze. It is finger-cold, and prudent farmers get in their barreled apples, and bring you the apples and cider which they have engaged; for it is time to put them into the cellar. Perhaps a few on the ground show their red cheeks above the early snow, and occasionally some even preserve their color and soundness under the snow throughout the winter. But generally at the beginning of the winter they freeze hard, and soon, though undecayed, acquire the color of a baked apple.

Before the end of December, generally, they experience their first thawing. Those which a month ago were sour, crabbed, and quite unpalatable to the civilized taste, such at least as were frozen while sound, let a warmer sun come to thaw them, — for they are extremely sensitive to its rays, — are found to be filled with a rich, sweet cider, better than any bottled cider that I know of, and with which I am better acquainted than with wine. All apples are good in this state, and your jaws are the cider-press. Others, which have more substance, are a sweet and luscious food, — in my opinion of more worth than the pineapples which are imported from the West Indies. Those which lately even I tasted only to repent of it, — for I am semicivilized, — which the farmer willingly left on the tree, I am now glad to find have the property of hanging on like the leaves of the young oaks. It is a way to keep cider sweet without boiling. Let the frost come to freeze them first, solid as stones, and then the rain or a warm winter day to thaw them, and they will seem to have borrowed a flavor from heaven through the medium of the air in which they hang. Or perchance you find, when you get home, that those which rattled in your pocket have thawed, and the ice is turned to cider. But after the third or fourth freezing and thawing they will not be found so good.

What are the imported half-ripe fruits of the torrid south, to this fruit matured by the cold of the frigid north? These are those crabbed apples with which I cheated my companion, and kept a smooth face that I might tempt him to eat. Now we both greedily fill our pockets with them, — bending to drink the cup and save our lappets from the overflowing juice, — and grow more social with their wine. Was there one that hung so high and sheltered by the tangled branches that our sticks could not dislodge it?

It is a fruit never carried to market, that I am aware of, — quite distinct from the apple of the markets, as from dried apple and cider, — and it is not every winter that produces it in perfection.

The era of the Wild Apple will soon be past. It is a fruit which will probably become extinct in New England. You may still wander through old orchards of native fruit of great extent, which for the most part went to the cider-mill, now all gone to decay. I have heard of an orchard in a distant town, on the side of a hill, where the apples rolled down and lay four feet deep against a wall on the lower side, and this the owner cut down for fear they should be made into cider. Since the temperance reform and the general introduction of grafted fruit, no native apple trees, such as I see everywhere in deserted pastures, and where the woods have grown up around them, are set out. I fear that he who walks over these fields a century hence will not know the pleasure of knocking off wild apples. Ah, poor man, there are many pleasures which he will not know! Notwithstanding the prevalence of the Baldwin and the Porter, I doubt if so extensive orchards are set out to-day in my town as there were a century ago, when those vast straggling cider-orchards were planted, when men both ate and drank apples, when the pomace-heap was the only nursery, and trees cost nothing but the trouble of setting them out. Men could afford then to stick a tree by every wall-side and let it take its chance. I see nobody planting trees to-day in such out of the way places, along the lonely roads and lanes, and at the bottom of dells in the wood. Now that they have grafted trees, and pay a price for them, they collect them into a plat by their houses, and fence them in, — and the end of it all will be that we shall be compelled to look for our apples in a barrel.

This is "The word of the Lord that came to Joel the son of Pethuel.

"Hear this, ye old men, and give ear, all ye inhabitants of the land! Hath this been in your days, or even in the days of your fathers? . . .

"That which the palmerworm hath left hath the locust eaten; and that which the locust hath left hath the cankerworm eaten; and that which the cankerworm hath left hath the caterpillar eaten.

"Awake, ye drunkards, and weep; and howl, all ye drinkers of wine, because of the new wine; for it is cut off from your mouth.

"For a nation is come up upon my land, strong, and without number, whose teeth are the teeth of a lion, and he hath the cheek teeth of a great lion.

"He hath laid my vine waste, and barked my fig tree: he hath made it clean bare, and cast it away; the branches thereof are made white. . . .

"Be ye ashamed, O ye husbandmen; howl, O ye vinedressers. . . .

"The vine is dried up, and the fig tree languisheth; the pomegranate tree, the palm tree also, and the apple tree, even all the trees of the field, are withered: because joy is withered away from the sons of men."

HUCKLEBERRIES

Agrestem tenui meditabor arundine musam
I am going to play a rustic strain on my
slender reed —
non injussa cano —
but I trust that I do not sing unbidden things.

Many public speakers are accustomed, as I think
foolishly, to talk about what they call *little* things in
a patronising way sometimes, advising, perhaps, that
they be not wholly neglected; but in making this distinction they really use no juster measure than a
ten-foot pole, and their own ignorance. According to
this rule a small potatoe is a little thing, a big one a
great thing. A hogshead-full of anything — the big
cheese which it took so many oxen to draw — a national salute — a state-muster — a fat ox — the
horse Columbus — or Mr. Blank — the Oinan Boy
— there is no danger that any body will call these
little things. A cartwheel is a great thing — a snow
flake a little thing. The *Wellingtonia gigantea* — the
famous California tree, is a great thing — the seed

*The ornamental device (§) in the text marks those places
where Professor Leo Stoller determined the order of the text
by internal evidence—usually Thoreau's notes to himself about
placement of the manuscript. For a description of the manuscripts and the principles which governed their editing, see
Stoller's *Huckleberries* (The Windhover Press of the University of Iowa and The New York Public Library, 1970).

from which it sprang a little thing — scarcely one traveller has noticed the seed at all — and so with all the seeds or origins of things. But Pliny said — *In minimis Natura praestat* — Nature excels in the least things.

In this country a political speech, whether by Mr. Seward or Caleb Cushing, is a great thing, a ray of light a little thing. It would be felt to be a greater national calamity if you should take six inches from the corporeal bulk of one or two gentlemen in Congress, than if you should take a yard from their wisdom and manhood.

I have noticed that whatever is thought to be covered by the word *education* — whether reading, writing or 'rithmetick — is a great thing, but almost all that constitutes education is a little thing in the estimation of such speakers as I refer to. In short, whatever they know and care but *little* about is a little thing, and accordingly almost everything good or great is little in their sense, and is very slow to grow any bigger.

When the husk gets separated from the kernel, almost all men run after the husk and pay their respects to that. It is only the husk of Christianity that is so bruited and wide spread in this world, the kernel is still the very least and rarest of all things. There is not a single church founded on it. To obey the higher law is generally considered the last manifestation of littleness.

I have observed that many English naturalists have a pitiful habit of speaking of their proper pursuit as a sort of trifling or waste of time — a mere interruption to more important employments and 'severer studies' — for which they must ask pardon of the reader. As if they would have you believe that all the rest of their lives was consecrated to some truly great and serious enterprise. But it happens that we never hear more of this, as we certainly should, if it were only some great public or philanthropic service, and therefore conclude that they have been engaged in the heroic and magnanimous enterprise of feeding, clothing, housing and warming themselves and their dependents, the chief value of all which was that it enabled them to pursue just these studies of which they speak so slightingly. The 'severer study' they refer to was keeping their accounts. Comparatively speaking — what they call their graver pursuits and severer studies was the real trifling and misspense of life — and were they such fools as not to know it? It is, in effect at least, mere cant. All mankind have depended on them for this intellectual food.

I presume that every one of my audience knows what a huckleberry is — has seen a huckleberry — gathered a huckleberry — nay tasted a huckleberry — and that being the case, that you will not be averse to revisiting the huckleberry field in imagination this evening, though the pleasure of this excursion may fall as far short of the reality, as the flavor of a dried huckleberry is inferior to that of a fresh one. §*Huckleberries* begin to be ripe July third (or generally the thirteenth), are thick enough to pick about the twenty-second, at their height about the fifth of August, and last fresh till after the middle of that month.

This, as you know, is an upright shrub more or less stout depending on the exposure, with a spreading bushy top — a dark brown bark — red recent shoots and thick leaves. The flowers are smaller and much more red than those of the other species.

It is said to range from the Saskatchewan to the mountains of Georgia, and from the Atlantic to the Mississippi in this latitude — but it abounds over but a small part of this area, and there are large tracts where it is not found at all.

By botanists it is called of late, but I think without good reason, *Gaylussacia resinosa*, after the celebrated French chemist. If he had been the first to distil its juices and put them in this globular bag, he would deserve this honor, or if he had been a celebrated picker of huckleberries, perchance paid for his schooling so, or only notoriously a lover of them, we should not so much object. But it does not appear that he ever saw one. What if a committee of Parisian naturalists had been appointed to break this important news to an Indian maiden who had just filled her basket on the shore of Lake Huron! It is as if we should hear that the Daguerreotype had been *finally* named after the distinguished Chippeway conjurer, The-Wind-that-Blows. By another it has been called *Andromeda baccata*, the berry bearing andromeda — but he evidently lived far away from huckleberries and milk.

I observe green huckleberries by the nineteenth of June, and perhaps three weeks later, when I have forgotten them, I first notice on some hill side exposed to the light, some black or blue ones amid the green ones and the leaves, always sooner than I had expected, and though they may be manifestly premature, I make it a point to taste them, and so inaugurate the huckleberry season.

In a day or two the black are so thick among the green ones that they no longer incur the suspicion of being worm-eaten, and perhaps a day later I pluck a handful from one bush, and I do not fail to make report of it when I get home, though it is rarely believed, most people are so behind hand in their year's accounts.

Early in August, in a favorable year, the hills are black with them. At Nagog Pond I have seen a hundred bushels in one field — the bushes drooping over the rocks with the weight of them — and a very handsome sight they are, though you should not pluck one of them. They are of various forms, colors and flavors — some round — some pear-shaped — some glossy black — some dull black, some blue with a tough and thick skin (though they are never of the peculiar light blue of blueberries with a bloom) — some sweeter, some more insipid — etc., etc., more varieties than botanists take notice of.

To-day perhaps you gather some of those large, often pear-shaped, sweet blue ones which grow tall and thinly amid the rubbish where woods have been cut. They have not borne there before for a century

— being over-shadowed and stinted by the forest —
but they have the more concentrated their juices —
and profited by the new recipes which nature has
given them — and now they offer to you fruit of the
very finest flavor, like wine of the oldest vintage.

And tomorrow you come to a strong moist soil
where the black ones shine with such a gloss — every
one its eye on you, and the blue are so large and
firm, that you can hardly believe them to be huckleberries at all, or edible; but you seem to have travelled into a foreign country, or else are dreaming.

They are a firmer berry than most of the whortleberry family — and hence are the most marketable.

If you look closely at a huckleberry you will see
that it is dotted, as if sprinkled over with a yellow
dust or meal, which looks as if it could be rubbed
off. Through a microscope, it looks like a resin which
has exuded, and on the small green fruit is of a conspicuous light orange or lemon color, like small specks
of yellow lichens. It is apparently the same with that
shining resinous matter which so conspicuously covers the leaves when they are unfolding, making them
sticky to the touch — whence this species is called
resinosa or resinous.

§There is a variety growing in swamps — a very tall
and slender bush drooping or bent like grass to one
side — commonly three or four feet high, but often
seven feet — the berries, which are later than the
former, are round and glossy black — with resinous
dots as usual — and grow in flattish topped racemes
— sometimes ten or twelve together, though general-

ly more scattered. I call it the swamp-huckleberry.

But the most marked variety is the *red*-huckle-berry — the *white* of some, (for the less ripe are whitish) — which ripens at the same time with the black. It is red with a white cheek, often slightly pear-shaped, semitransparent with a luster, very fine-ly and indistinctly white dotted. It is as easily dis-tinguished from the common in the green state as when ripe. I know of but three or four places in the town where they grow. It might be called *Gaylussacia resinosa var. erythrocarpa.*

I once did some surveying for a man, who re-marked, but not till the job was nearly done, that he did not know when he should pay me. I did not at first pay much heed to this observation, though it was unusual, supposing that he meant to pay me within a reasonable time. Nevertheless it occurred to me that if he did not know when he should pay me still less did I know when I should be paid. He added, however, that I was perfectly secure, for there were the pigs in the stye (and as nice pigs as ever were seen) and there was his farm itself which I had sur-veyed, and knew was there as much as he. All this had its due influence in increasing my sense of secur-ity, as you may suppose. After many months he sent me a quart of red huckleberries, for they grew on his farm, and this I thought was ominous; he distin-guished me altogether too much by this gift, since I was not his particular friend. I saw that it was the first installment of my dues — and that it would go a great way toward being the last. In the course of years he paid a part of the debt in money, and that is the last that I have heard of it. I shall beware of red huckleberry gifts in the future.

§Then there is the Late Whortleberry — Dangleberry or Blue Tangles — whose fruit does not begin to be ripe until about a month after huckleberries begin, when these and blueberries are commonly shrivelled and spoiling — on about August seventh, and is in its prime near the end of August.

This is a tall and handsome bush about twice as high as a huckleberry bush, with altogether a glaucous aspect, growing in shady copses where it is rather moist, and to produce much fruit it seems to require wet weather.

The fruit is one of the handsomest of berries, smooth, round and blue, larger than most huckleberries and more transparent, on long stems dangling two or three inches, and more or less tangled. By the inexperienced it is suspected to be poisonous, and so avoided, and perhaps is the more fair and memorable to them on that account. Though quite good to eat, it has a peculiar, slightly astringent, and compared with most huckleberries, not altogether pleasant flavor, and a tough skin.

At the end of the first week of September, they are commonly the only edible Whortleberries which are quite fresh. They are rare hereabouts however, and it is only in certain years that you can find enough for a pudding.

There is still another kind of Huckleberry growing in this town, called the *Hairy Huckleberry*, which ripens about the same time with the last. It is quite rare, growing only in the wildest and most neglected places, such as cold sphagneous swamps where the *Andromeda polifolia* and *Kalmia glauca* are found, and in some almost equally neglected but firmer low ground. The berries are oblong and black, and, with us, roughened with short hairs. It is the only species of *Vaccinieae* that I know of in this town whose fruit is inedible; though I have seen another kind of Whortleberry, the *Deer-berry* or Squaw Huckleberry, growing in another part of the state, whose fruit is said to be equally inedible. The former is merely insipid however. Some which grow on firmer ground have a little more flavor, but the thick and shaggy-feeling coats of the berries left in the mouth are far from agreeable to the palate.

Both these and Dangleberries are placed in the same genus (or section) with the common huckleberry.

Huckleberries are very apt to dry up and not attain their proper size — unless rain comes to save them before the end of July. They will be dried quite hard and black by drought even before they have ripened. On the other hand they frequently burst open and are so spoiled in consequence of copious rains when they are fully ripe.

§They *begin* to be soft and wormy as early as the middle of August, and generally about the twentieth the children cease to carry them round to sell, as they are suspected by the purchasers.

How late when the huckleberries begin to be wormy

and the pickers are deserting the fields! The walker
feels very solitary now.

But in woods and other cool places they commonly last quite fresh a week or more longer, depending on the season. In some years when there are far
more berries than pickers or even worms, and the
birds appear to pass them by, I have found them
plump, fresh, and quite thick, though with a somewhat dried taste, the fourteenth of October, when the
bushes were mostly leafless, and the leaves that were
left, were all red, and they continued to hold on after
the leaves had all fallen, till they were softened and
spoiled by rain.

Sometimes they begin to dry up generally by the
middle of August — after they are ripe, but before
spoiling, and by the end of that month I have seen
the bushes so withered and brown owing to the
drought, that they appeared dead like those which
you see broken off by the pickers, or as if burnt.

I have seen the hills still black with them, though
hard and shrivelled as if dried in a pan, late in September. And one year I saw an abundance of them
still holding on the eleventh of December, they having dried ripe prematurely, but these had no sweetness left. The sight of them thus dried by nature
may have originally suggested to the Indians to dry
them artificially.

High-blueberries, the second kind of low-blueber-
ries, huckleberries and low-blackberries are all at their
height generally during the first week of August. In
the dog-days (or the first ten of them) they abound

and attain their full size.

Huckleberries are classed by botanists with the cranberries (both bog and mountain) — snowberry, bearberry — mayflower, checkerberry — the andromedas, clethra, laurels, azaleas, rhodora, ledum, pyrolas, prince's pine, Indian pipes, and many other plants, and they are called all together the Heath Family, they being in many respects similar to and occupying similar ground with the heaths of the Old World, which we have not. If the first botanists had been American this might have been called the Huckleberry Family including the heaths. Plants of this order (*Ericaceae*) are said to be among the earliest ones found in a fossil state, and one would say that they promised to last as long as any on this globe. George B. Emerson says that the whortleberry differs from the heath proper, 'essentially only in its juicy fruit surrounded by the calyx segments.'

The genus to which the whortleberries belong, is called by most botanists *Vaccinium*, which I am inclined to think is properly derived from *bacca*, a berry, as if these were the chief of all berries, though the etymology of this word is in dispute.

Whortle- or Hurtleberry, Bilberry, and Blae or Blea, that is *blue* berry are the names given in England originally to the fruit of the *Vaccinium myrtillus* which we have not in New England and also to the more scarce and local *Vaccinium uliginosum* which we have.

The word whortleberry is said to be derived from the Saxon *heortberg* (or *heorot-berg*), the hart's berry.

Hurts is an old English word used in heraldry, where, according to Bailey, it is 'certain balls resembling hurtleberries.'

The Germans say *Heidel-berre* — that is *heath berry.*

Huckleberry — this word is used by Lawson in 1709 — appears to be an American word derived from Whortleberry — and applied to fruits of the same family, but for the most part of different species from the English whortleberries. According to the Dictionary the word berry is from the Saxon *beria* — a grape or cluster of grapes. A French name of whortleberry is 'raisin des bois' — grape of the woods. It is evident that the word berry has a new significance in America.

We do not realize how rich our country is in berries. The ancient Greeks and Romans appear not to have made much account of strawberries, huckleberries, melons etc. because they had not got them.

The Englishman Lindley, in his *Natural System of Botany*, says that the *Vaccinieae* are 'Natives of North America, where they are found in great abundance as far as high northern latitudes; sparingly in Europe; and not uncommonly on high land in the Sandwich Islands.'

Or as George B. Emerson states it, they 'are found chiefly in the temperate, or on the mountains in the warmer regions of America. Some are found in Europe; some on the continent and islands of Asia, and on islands in the Atlantic, Pacific and Indian Oceans.' 'The whortleberries and cranberries,' says he, 'take the place, throughout the northern part of this continent, of the heaths of the corresponding climates of Europe; and fill it with no less of beauty, and incomparably more of use.'

According to the last arrangement of our plants, we have fourteen species of the Whortleberry Family (*Vaccinieae*) in New England, eleven of which bear edible berries, eight, berries which are eaten raw, and five of the last kind are abundant — to wit — the huckleberry — the bluet or Pennsylvania blueberry — the Canada blueberry (in the northern part of New England) — the second or common low blueberry — and the high or swamp-blueberry (not to mention the Dangleberry, which is common in some seasons and localities).

On the other hand I gather from London and others that there are only two species growing in England, which are eaten raw, answering to our eight — to wit, the Bilberry (*V. myrtillus*) and the Blea-berry or Bog Whortleberry (*V. uliginosum*), both of which are found in North America, and the last is the common one on the summit of the White Mountains, but in Great Britain it is found only in the northern part of England and in Scotland. This leaves only one in England to our five which are abundant.

In short, it chances that of the thirty-two species of *Vaccinium* which Loudon describes, all except the above two and four more are referred to North America alone, and only three or possibly four are found in Europe.

Yet the few Englishmen with whom I have spoken
on this subject love to think and to say that they
have as many huckleberries as we. I will therefore
quote the most which their own authorities say not
already quoted, about the abundance and value of
their only two kinds which are eaten raw.

Loudon says of the bog whortleberry (*V. uliginosum*), 'The berries are agreeable but inferior in flavor to those of *Vaccinium myrtillus* [the bilberry];
eaten in large quantities, they occasion giddiness,
and a slight headache.'

And of their common whortleberry (*V. myrtillus*)
he says, 'It is found in every country in Britain,
from Cornwall to Caithness, least frequently in the
south-eastern countries, and increases in quantity as
we advance northward.' It 'is an elegant and also a
fruit-bearing plant.' The berries 'are eaten in tarts
or with cream, or made into a jelly, in the northern
and western counties of England; and, in other parts
of the country they are made into pies and puddings.' They 'are very acceptable to children either
eaten by themselves, or with milk' or otherwise. They
'have an astringent quality.'

Coleman in his "Woodlands, Heaths, and Hedges,"
says 'The traveller in our upland and mountain districts can hardly have failed to notice, as his almost
constant companion, this cheerful little shrub, . . .
it flourishes best in a high airy situation, only the
summits of the very loftiest mountains of which this
country can boast being too elevated for this hardy
little mountaineer.' 'In Yorkshire, and many parts

of the north, large quantities of bilberries are brought into the market, being extensively used as an ingredient in pies and puddings, or preserved in the form of jam. . . . Much, however, of the relish of these wilding fruits must be set down to the exhilirating air, and those charms of scenery that form the accessories of a mountain feast; . . . One of the prettiest sights that greet one's eye in the districts where it abounds, is that of a party of rustic children "a-bilberrying" (for the greater portion of those that come to market are collected by children); there they may be seen, knee deep in the "wires," or clambering over the broken gray rocks to some rich nest of berries, their tanned faces glowing with health, and their picturesque dress (or undress) — with here and there bits of bright red, blue, or white — to the painter's eye contrasting beautifully with the purple, gray and brown of the moorland, and forming altogether rich pictorial subjects.'

These authorities tell us that children and others eat the fruit, just as they tell us that the birds do. It is evident from all this that whortleberries do not make an important part of the regular food of the Old English people in their season, as they do of the New Englanders. What should we think of a summer in which we did not taste a huckleberry pudding? That is to Jonathan what his plum pudding is to John Bull.

Yet Dr. Manassah Cutler, one of the earliest New England botanists, speaks of the huckleberry lightly as being merely a fruit which children love to eat with their milk. What ingratitude thus to shield himself behind the children! I should not wonder if it turned out that Dr. Manassah Cutler ate his huckleberry pudding or pie regularly through the season, as many his equals do. I should have pardoned him had he frankly put in his thumb and pulled out a plum, and cried 'What a Great Doctor am I?' But probably he was lead astray by reading English books or it may be that the Whites did not make so much use of them in his time.

Widely dispersed as their bilberry may still be in England, it was undoubtedly far more abundant there once. One botanist says that 'This is one of the species, that if allowed, would overrun Britain, and form, with *Culluna vulgaris* (heather) and *Empetrum nigrum* (crowberry, which grows on our White Mountains), much of the natural physiognomical character of its vegetation.'

The genus *Gaylussacia*, to which our huckleberry belongs, has no representative in Great Britain, nor does our species extend very far northward in this country.

So I might say of edible berries generally, that there are far fewer kinds in Old than in New England.

Take the *rubuses* or what you might call bramble berries, for instance, to which genus our raspberries, blackberries and thimbleberries belong. According to Loudon there are five kinds indigenous in Britain to our eight. But of these five only two appear to be at all common, while we have four kinds both very com-

mon and very good. The Englishman Coleman says
of their best, the English raspberry, which species
we also cultivate, that 'the wilding is not sufficiently
abundant to have much importance.'

And the same is true of wild fruits generally. Hips
and haws are much more important comparatively
there than here, where they have hardly got any popular name.

I state this to show how contented and thankful
we ought to be.

It is to be remembered that the vegetation in
Great Britain is that of a much more northern latitude than where we live, that some of our alpine
shrubs are found on the plain there and their two
whortleberries are alpine or extreme northern plants
with us.

If you look closely you will find blueberry and
huckleberry bushes under your feet, though they may
be feeble and barren, throughout all our woods, the
most persevering Native Americans, ready to shoot
up into place and power at the next election among
the plants, ready to reclothe the hills when man has
laid them bare and feed all kinds of pensioners. What
though the woods be cut down; it appears that this
emergency was long ago anticipated and provided
for by Nature, and the interregnum is not allowed
to be a barren one. She not only begins instantly to
heal that scar, but she compensates us for the loss
and refreshes us with fruits such as the forest did
not produce. As the sandal wood is said to diffuse
a perfume around the woodman who cuts it — so

in this case Nature rewards with unexpected fruits the hand that lays her waste.

I have only to remember each year where the woods have been cut just long enough to know where to look for them. It is to refresh us thus once in a century that they bide their time on the forest floor. If the farmer mows and burns over his overgrown pasture for the benefit of grass, or to keep the children out, the huckleberries spring up there more vigorous than ever, and the fresh blueberry shoots tinge the earth crimson. All our hills are, or have been, huckleberry hills, the three hills of Boston and no doubt Bunker Hill among the rest. My mother remembers a woman who went a-whortleberrying where Dr. Lowell's church now stands.

In short the whortleberry bushes in the Northern States and British America are a sort of miniature forest surviving under the great forest, and reappearing when the latter is cut, and also extending northward beyond it. The small berry-bearing shrubs of this family, as the crowberry, bilberry, and cranberry, are called by the Esquimaux in Greenland, 'berry grass,' and Crantz says that the Greenlanders cover their winter houses with 'bilberry bushes,' together with turf and earth. They also burn them; and I hear that somebody in this neighborhood has invented a machine for cutting up huckleberry bushes for fuel.

It is remarkable how universally, as it respects soil and exposure, the whortleberry family is distributed with us, almost we may say a new species for every thousand feet of elevation. One kind or another, of those of which I am speaking, fluorishing in every soil and locality.

There is the high blueberry in swamps — the second low blueberry, with the huckleberry, on almost all fields and hills — the Pennsylvanian and Canada blueberries especially in cool and airy places in openings in the woods and on hills and mountains, while we have two kinds confined to the alpine tops of our highest mountains — the family thus ranging from the lowest valleys to the highest mountain tops, and forming the prevailing small shrubbery of a great part of New England.

The same is true *hereabouts* of a single species of this family, the huckleberry proper. I do not know of a spot where any shrub grows in this neighborhood, but one or another variety of the huckleberry may also grow there. It is stated in Loudon that all the plants of this order 'require a peat soil, or a soil of a close cohesive nature,' but this is not the case with the huckleberry. It grows on the tops of our highest hills — no pasture is too rocky or barren for it — it grows in such deserts as we have, standing in pure sand — and at the same time it flourishes in the strongest and most fertile soil. One variety is peculiar to quaking bogs where there can hardly be said to be any soil beneath, to say nothing of another but unpalatable species, the hairy huckleberry, which is found there. It also extends through all our woods more or less thinly, and a distinct species, the dangle-berry, belongs especially to moist woods and thickets.

Such care has Nature taken to furnish to birds and quadrupeds, and to men, a palatable berry of this kind, slightly modified by soil and climate, wherever the consumer may chance to be. Corn and potatoes, apples and pears, have comparatively a narrow range, but we can fill our basket with whortleberries on the summit of Mount Washington, above almost all other shrubs with which we are familiar, the same kind which they have in Greenland, and again when we get home, with another species in our lowest swamps, such as the Greenlanders never dreamed of.

The berries *which I celebrate*, appear to have a range, most of them, very nearly coterminous with what has been called the Algonquin Family of Indians, whose territories embraced what are now the Eastern, Middle and Northwestern States — and the Canadas — and surrounded those of the Iroquois in what is now New York. These were the small fruits of the Algonquin and Iroquois Families.

Of course the Indians naturally made a much greater account of wild fruits than we do, and among the most important of these were huckleberries.

They taught us not only the use of corn and how to plant it, but also of whortleberries and how to dry them for winter. We should have hesitated long before we tasted some kinds if they had not set us the example, knowing by old experience that they were not only harmless but salutary. I have added a few to my number of edible berries, by walking behind an Indian in Maine, and observing that he ate some which I never thought of tasting before.

To convince you of the extensive use which the
Indians made of huckleberries, I will quote at length
the testimony of the most observing travellers, on this
subject, as nearly as possible in the order in which
it was given us; for it is only after listening patiently
to such reiterated and concurring testimony, of various dates — and respecting widely distant localities — that we come to realize the truth.

But little is said by the discoverers of the use
which the Indians made of the fresh berries in their
season — the hand to mouth use of them — because
there was little to be said — though in this form they
may have been much the most important to them.
We have volumes of recipes, called cookbooks — but
when a fruit or a tart is ready for the table, nothing
remains but to eat it without any more words. We
therefore have few or no accounts of Indians going
a-huckleberrying — though they had more than a six
weeks' vacation for that purpose, and probably
camped on the huckleberry field.

I will go far enough back for my authorities to
show that they did not learn the use of these berries
from us whites.

In the year 1615, Champlain, the founder of Quebec, being far up the Ottawa spying out the land
and taking notes among the Algonquins, on his way
to the Fresh Water Sea since called Lake Huron —
observed that the natives made a business of collecting and drying for winter use, a small berry which
he called blues, and also raspberries — the former
is the common blueberry of those regions, by some

considered a variety of our early low blueberry (*Vac-cinium Pennsylvanicum*) ; and again when near the lake he observes that the natives make a kind of bread of pounded corn sifted and mixed with mashed beans which have been boiled — and sometimes they put dried blueberries and raspberries into it.

This was five years before the Pilgrims crossed the Atlantic, and is the first account of huckleberry cake that I know of.

Gabriel Sagard, a Franciscan Friar, in the account of his visit to the Huron Country in 1624, says, 'There is so great a quantity of blues, which the Hurons call *Ohentaque*, and other little fruits which they call by a general name *Hahique*, that the savages regularly dry them for the winter, as we do prunes in the sun, and that serves them for comfits for the sick, and to give taste to their *sagamite* [or gruel, making a kind of plum porridge], and also to put into the little loaves (or cakes, *pains*) which they cook under the ashes.'

According to him they put not only blueberries and raspberries into their bread but strawberries, 'wild mulberries (*meures champestres*) and other little fruits dry and green.'

Indeed the gathering of blueberries by the savages is spoken of by the early French explorers as a regular and important harvest with them.

LeJeune, the Superior of the Jesuits in Canada — residing at Quebec — in his Relation for 1639 — says of the savages that 'Some figure to themselves a paradise full of *bluets*.'

Roger Williams, who knew the Indians well, in his account of those in his neighborhood — published in 1643 — tells us that '*Sautaash* are those currants (grapes and whortleberries) dried by the natives, and so preserved all the year, which they beat to powder and mingle it with their parched meal, and make a delicate dish which they call *Sautauthig*, which is as sweet to them as plum or spice cake to the English.'

But Nathaniel Morton, in his *New England's Memorial*, printed in 1669 — speaking of white men going to treat with Canonicus, a Narraghanset Indian, about Mr. Oldham's death in 1636 — says 'Boiled chestnuts is their white bread, and because they would be extraordinary in their feasting, they strove for variety after the English manner, boiling puddings made of beaten corn, putting therein great store of blackberries, somewhat like currants' — no doubt whortleberries. This *seems* to *imply* that the Indians imitated the English — or set before their guests dishes to which they themselves were not accustomed — or which were extra-ordinary. But we have seen that these dishes were not new or unusual to them and it was the whites who imitated the Indians rather.

John Josselyn — in his *New England Rarities*, published in 1672 — says under the fruits of New England, 'Bill-berries, two kinds, black and sky colored, which is more frequent. . . . The Indians dry them in the sun and sell them to the English by the bushel, who make use of them instead of currence, putting of them into puddens, both boyled and baked, and into water gruel.'

The largest Indian huckleberry party that I have heard of is mentioned in the life of Captain Church who, it is said, when in pursuit of King Phillip in the summer of 1676, came across a large body of Indians, chiefly squaws, gathering whortleberries on a plain near where New Bedford now is, and killed and took prisoner sixty-six of them — some throwing away their baskets and their berries in their flight. They told him that their husbands and brothers, a hundred of them, who with others had their rendezvous in a great cedar swamp nearby, had recently left them to gather whortleberries there, while they went to Sconticut Neck to kill cattle and horses for further and more substantial provisions.

La Hontan in 1689, writing from the Great Lakes, repeats what so many French travellers had said about the Indians drying and preserving blueberries — saying, 'The savages of the north make a great harvest of them in summer, which is a great resource especially when the chase fails them.' They were herein more provident than we commonly suppose.

Father Raslles — who was making a Dictionary of the Abenaki Language in 1691 (at Norridgewock?) — says that their word for blueberries was fresh *Satar*, dry *Sakisatar* — and the words in their name for July meant when the blueberries are ripe. This shows how important they were to them.

Father Hennepin — who writes in 1697 — says that his captors, Naudowessi (the Sioux!), near the falls of St. Anthony, feasted on wild-rice seasoned with blueberries, 'which they dry in the sun during the summer, and which are as good as raisins of Corinth' — [that is, the imported currants].

The Englishman John Lawson, who published an account of the Carolinas in 1709, says of North Carolina, 'The hurts, huckleberries or blues of this country are four sorts. . . . The first sort is the same blue or bilberry that grows plentifully in the North of England.' 'The second sort grows on a small bush,' the fruit being larger than the last. The third grows three or four feet high in low land. 'The fourth sort grows upon trees, some ten and twelve foot high, and the thickness of a man's arm; these are found in the runs and low grounds. . . . The Indians get many bushels, and dry them on mats, whereof they make plum bread, and many other eatables.' He is the first author that I remember who uses the word 'huckleberry.'

The well known natural botanist John Bartram, when returning to Philadelphia in 1743 from a Journey through what was then the wilderness of Pennsylvania and New York, to the Iroquois and Lake Ontario, says that he 'found [when in Pennsylvania] an Indian squaw drying huckleberries. This is done by setting four forked sticks in the ground, about three or four feet high, then others across, over them the stalks of our common *Jacea* or *Saratula*, on these lie the berries, as malt is spread on the hair cloth over the kiln. Underneath she had kindled a smoke fire, which one of her children was tending.'

Kalm, in his travels in this country in 1748-9,

writes, 'On my travels through the country of the Iroquois, they offered me, whenever they designed to treat me well, fresh maize bread, baked in an oblong shape, mixed with dried huckleberries, which lay as close in it as the raisins in a plumb pudding.'

The Moravian missionary Heckewelder, who spent a great part of his life among the Delawares toward the end of the last century, states that they mixed with their bread, which was six inches in diameter by one inch thick — 'whortleberries green or dry, but not boiled.'

Lewis and Clarke in 1805 found the Indians west of the Rocky Mountains using dried berries extensively.

And finally in Owen's Geological Survey of *Wisconsin, Iowa and Minnesota* — published in 1852 — occurs the following. '*Vaccinium Pennslvanicum* (*Lam.*) [that is, our early low blueberry] — Barrens on the upper St. Croix. This is the common Huckleberry, associated with the characteristic growth of the *Pinus Banksiana*, covering its sandy ridges with a verdant undergrowth, and an unsurpassed luxuriance of fruit. By the Indians these are collected and smoke dried in great quantities, and in this form constitute an agreeable article of food.'

Hence you see that the Indians from time immemorial, down to the present day, all over the northern part of America — have made far more extensive use of the whortleberry — at all seasons and in various ways — than we — and that they were far more important to them than to us.

It appears from the above evidence that the Indians used their dried berries commonly in the form of a cake, and also of huckleberry porridge or pudding.

What we call huckleberry cake made of Indian meal and huckleberries was evidently the principal cake of the aborigines — though they also used other berries and fruits in a similar manner and often put things into their cake which would not have been agreeable to our palates — though I do not hear that they ever put any soda or pearl ash or alum into it. We have no national cake so universal and well known as this was in all parts of the country where corn and huckleberries grew.

They enjoyed it all alone ages before our ancestors heard of their Indian corn — or their huckleberries — and probably if you had travelled here a thousand years ago it would have been offered you alike on the Connecticut, the Potomac, the Niagara, the Ottawa and the Mississippi.

The last Indian of Nantucket, who died a few years ago, was very properly represented in a painting which I saw there, with a basket full of huckleberries in his hand, as if to hint at the employment of his last days. I trust that I may not outlive the last of the huckleberries.

Tanner, who was taken captive by the Indians in 1789, and spent a good part of his life as an Indian, gives the Chippeway names of at least five kinds of whortleberries. He gives '*meen* — blue berry, *meen-un* — blue berries,' and says that 'this is a word that enters into the composition of almost all words which are used as the names of fruits,' that is as a terminal syllable. Hence this would appear to have been the typical berry — or berry of berries — among the Chippeway as it is among us.

I think that it would be well if the Indian names, were as far as possible restored and applied to the numerous species of huckleberries, by our botanists — instead of the very inadequate — Greek and Latin or English ones at present used. They might serve both a scientific and popular use. Certainly it is not the best point of view to look at this peculiarly American family as it were from the other side of the Atlantic. It is still in doubt whether the Latin word for the genus *Vaccinium* means a berry or a flower.

Botanists, on the look out for what they thought a respectable descent, have long been inclined to trace this family backward to Mount Ida. Tourneforte does not hestitate to give it the ancient name of *Vine of Mount Ida*. The common English Raspberry also is called *Rubus Idaea* or the Mount Ida bramble — from the old Greek name. The truth of it seems to be that blueberries and raspberries flourish best in cool and airy situations, on hills and mountains, and I can easily believe that something *like* these at least grows on Mount Ida. But Mount Monadnoc is as good as Mount Ida, and probably better for blueberries, though its name is said to mean *Bad Rock*. But the worst rocks are the best for poets' uses. Let us then exchange that oriental uncertainty for this western certainty.

We have in the northern states a few wild plums

and inedible crab apples — a few palatable grapes —
and many tolerable nuts — but I think that the various species of berries are our *wild fruits* which are
to be compared with the more celebrated ones of the
tropics, and for my part I would not exchange fruits
with them — for the object is not merely to get a
ship-load of something which you can eat or sell, but
the pleasure of gathering it is to be taken into the
account.

What is the pear crop as yet to the huckleberry
crop? Horticulturists make a great ado about their
pears, but how many families raise or buy a barrel
of pears in a year all told? They are comparatively
insignificant. I do not taste more than half a dozen
pears annually, and I suspect that the majority fare
worse even than I. (This was written before my
neighbor's pear-orchard began to bear. Now he frequently fills my own and others' pockets with the
fruit.) But Nature heaps the table with berries for
six weeks or more. Indeed the apple crop is not so
important as the huckleberry crop. Probably the
apples consumed in this town annually do not amount
to more than one barrel per family. But what is this
to a month or more of huckleberrying to every man,
woman and child, and the birds into the bargain.
Even the crop of oranges, lemons, nuts, raisins, figs,
quinces, etc, is of little importance to us compared
with these.

They are not unprofitable in a pecuniary sense;
I hear that some of the inhabitants of Ashby sold
$2000 worth of huckleberries in '56.

In May and June all our hills and fields are adorned with a profusion of the pretty little more or less bell-shaped flowers of this family, commonly turned toward the earth and more or less tinged with red or pink, and resounding with the hum of insects, each one the forerunner of a berry the most natural, wholesome and palatable that the soil can produce. I think to myself, these are the blossoms of the *Vaccinieae* or Whortleberry family, which affords so large a portion of our berries; the berry-promising flower of the *Vaccinieae*! This crop grows wild all over the country — wholesome, bountiful and free, a real ambrosia.   And yet men, the foolish demons that they are, devote themselves to the culture of tobacco, inventing slavery and a thousand other curses for that purpose — with infinite pains and inhumanity go raise tobacco all their lives, and that is the staple instead of huckleberries. Wreathes of tobacco smoke go up from this land, the only incense which its inhabitants burn in honor of their gods. With what authority can such as we distinguish between Christians and Mahometans? Almost every interest, as the codfish and mackerel interest, gets represented at the General Court — but not the huckleberry interest. The first discoverers and explorers of the land make report of this fruit — but the last make comparatively little account of them.

Blueberries and huckleberries are such simple, wholesome and universal fruits that they concern our race much. It is hard to imagine any country without this kind of berry, on which men live like birds.

Still covering our hills as when the red men lived here. Are they not the principal wild fruit?

What means this profusion of berries at this season only? Nature does her best to feed her children, and the broods of birds just matured find plenty to eat now. Every bush and vine does its part and offers a wholesome and palatable diet to the way-farer. He need not go out of the road to get as many berries as he wants — of various kinds and qualities according as his road leads him over high or low, wooded or open ground — huckleberries of different colors and flavors almost everywhere — the second kind of low blueberry largest in the moist ground — high blueberries with their agreeable acid when his way lies through a swamp, and low blackberries of two or more varieties on almost every sandy plain and bank and stone heap.

Man at length stands in such a relation to Nature as the animals which pluck and eat as they go. The fields and hills are a table constantly spread. Diet-drinks, cordials, wines of all kinds and qualities, are bottled up in the skins of countless berries for their refreshment, and they quaff them at every turn. They seem offered to us not so much for food as for sociality, inviting us to a pic-nic with Nature. We pluck and eat in remembrance of her. It is a sort of sacrament — a communion — the *not* forbidden fruits, which no serpent tempts us to eat. Slight and innocent savors which relate us to Nature, make us her guests, and entitle us to her regard and protection.

When I see, as now, in climbing one of our hills,

huckleberry and blueberry bushes bent to the ground with fruit, I think of them as fruits fit to grow on the most Olympian or heaven-pointing hills.

It does not occur to you at first that where such thoughts are suggested is Mount Olympus, and that you who taste these berries are a god. Why in his only royal moments should man abdicate his throne?

You eat these berries in the dry pastures where they grow not to gratify an appetite, but as simply and naturally as thoughts come into your mind, as if they were the food of thought, dry as itself, and surely they nourish the brain there.

Occasionally there is an unusual profusion of these fruits to compensate for the scarcity of a previous year. I remember some seasons when favorable moist weather had expanded the berries to their full size, so that the hill-sides were literally black with them. There were infinitely more of all kinds than any and all creatures could use.

One such year, on the side of Conantum Hill, they were literally five or six inches deep. First, if you searched low down in the shade under all, you found still fresh the great light blue earliest blueberries, bluets, in heavy clusters — that most Olympian fruit of all — delicate flavored, thin-skinned and cool — then, next above, the still denser masses or clusters of the second low blueberry of various varieties, firm and sweet food — and rising above these large blue and black huckleberries of various qualities — and over these ran rampant the low blackberry weighing down the thicket with its wreathes of black fruit, and binding it together in a trembling mass — while here and there the high blackberry, just beginning to be ripe, towered over all the rest. Thus, as it were, the berries hung up lightly in masses or heaps, separated by their leaves and twigs so that the air could circulate through and preserve them; and you went daintily wading through this thicket, picking perhaps only the finest of the high blackberries, as big as the end of your thumb, however big that may be, or clutching here and there a handful of huckleberries for variety, but never suspecting the delicious, cool blue-bloomed ones, which you were crushing with your feet under all. I have in such a case spread aside the bushes and revealed the last kind to those who had never in all their lives seen or heard of it before.

Each such patch, each bush — seems fuller and blacker than the last, as you proceed, and the huckleberries at length swell so big, as if aping the blackberries, that you mark the spot for future years.

There is all this profusion and yet you see neither birds nor beasts eating them — only ants and the huckleberry-bug. It seems fortunate for us that those cows in their pasture do not love them, but pass them by. We do not perceive that birds and quadrupeds make any use of them because they are so abundant we do not miss them, and they are not compelled to come when we are for them. Yet they are far more important to them than to us. We do not notice the robin when it plucks a huckleberry as we do when it visits our favorite cherry tree — and the fox pays his visits to the fields when we are not there.

I once carried my arms full of these bushes to my boat, and while I was rowing homeward two ladies, who were my companions, picked three pints from these alone, casting the bare bushes into the stream from time to time.

Even in ordinary years, when berries are comparatively scarce, I sometimes unexpectedly find so many in some distance and unfrequented part of the town, between and about the careless farmers' houses and walls, that the soil seems more fertile than where I live. Every bush and bramble bears its fruit. The very sides of the road are a fruit garden. The earth there teems with blackberries, huckleberries, thimbleberries, fresh and abundant — no signs of drought nor of pickers. Great shining black berries peep out at me from under the leaves upon the rocks. Do the rocks hold moisture? or are there no fingers to pluck these fruits? I seem to have wandered into a land of greater fertility — some up country Eden. These are the Delectable Hills. It is land flowing with milk and huckleberries, only they have not yet put the berries into the milk. *There* the herbage never withers, *there* are abundant dews. I ask myself, What are the virtues of the inhabitants that they are thus blessed?

A fortunatos nimium, sua si bona norint Agricolas—

O too fortunate husbandmen if they knew their own happiness.

These berries are further important as introducing children to the fields and woods. The season of

berrying is so far respected that the school children
have a vacation then — and many little fingers are
busy picking these small fruits. It is even a pastime,
not a drudgery — though it often pays well beside.
The First of August is to them the anniversary of
Emancipation in New England.

Women and children who never visit distant hills,
fields and swamps on any other errand are seen making haste thither now with half their domestic utensils
in their hands. The wood-chopper goes into the
swamp for fuel in the winter; his wife and children
for berries in the summer.

Now you will see who is the thorough country-
woman who does not go to the beach — conversant
with berries and nuts — a masculine wild-eyed woman
of the fields.

Now for a ride in the hay-rigging to that far off
Elysium that Zachariah See-all alighted on — but
has not mentioned to every person — in the hay-rigging without springs — trying to sensitive nerves
and to full pails, for all alike sit on the bottom —
such a ride is favorable to conversation for the incessant rumble hides all defects and fills the otherwise
aweful pauses — to be introduced to new scenes more
memorable than the berries— but to the old walker
the straggling party itself half concealed amid the
bushes is the most novel and interesting feature. If
hot the boys break up the bushes and carry them to
some shady place where the girls can pick them at
their ease. But this is a lazy and improvident way —
and gives an unsightly look to the hill. There are

many events not in the program. If you have an ear
for music — perhaps one is the sound of a cow bell
— never heard before — or a sudden thunder shower
putting you to flight — or a breakdown.

I served my apprenticeship and have since done
considerable journeywork in the huckleberry field.
Though I never paid for my schooling and clothing
in that way, it was some of the best schooling that
I got and paid for itself. Theodore Parker is not
the only New England boy who has got his education by picking huckleberries, though he may not
have gone to Harvard thereafter, nor to any school
more distant than the huckleberry field. *There* was
the university itself where you could learn the everlasting Laws, and Medicine and Theology, not under
Story, and Warren, and Ware, but far wiser professors than they. Why such haste to go from the
huckleberry field to the College yard?

As in old times they who dwelt on the heath, remote from towns, being backward to adopt the doctrines which prevailed in towns, were called heathen
in a bad sense, so I trust that we dwellers in the
huckleberry pastures, which are our heath-lands,
shall be slow to adopt the notions of large towns and
cities, though perchance we may be nicknamed huckleberry people. But the worst of it is that the emissaries of the towns come more for our berries than
they do for our salvation.

Occasionally, in still summer forenoons, when perhaps a mantua-maker was to be dined, and a huckleberry pudding had been decided on (by the authori-

ties), I a lad of ten was despatched to a neighboring hill alone. My scholastic education could be thus far tampered with, and an excuse might be found. No matter how scarce the berries on the near hills, the exact number necessary for a pudding could surely be collected by eleven o'clock — and all ripe ones too though I turned some round three times to be sure they were not premature. My rule in such cases was never to eat one till my dish was full; for going a-berrying implies more things than eating the berries. They at home got nothing but the pudding, a comparatively heavy affair — but I got the forenoon out of doors — to say nothing about the appetite for the pudding. They got only the plums that were in the pudding, but I got the far sweeter plums that never go into it.

At other times, when I had companions, some of them used to bring such remarkably shaped dishes, that I was often curious to see how the berries disposed of themselves in them. Some brought a coffeepot to the huckleberry field, and such a vessel possessed this advantage at least, that if a greedy boy had skimmed off a handful or two on his way home, he had only to close the lid and give his vessel a shake to have it full again. I have seen this done all round when the party got as far homeward as the Dutch House. It can probably be done with any vessel that has much side to it.

There was a Young America then, which has become Old America, but its principles and motives are still the same, only applied to other things. Sometimes, just before reaching the spot — every boy rushed to the hill side and hastily selecting a spot — shouted 'I speak for this place,' indicating its bounds, and another 'I speak for that,' and so on — and this was sometimes considered good law for the huckleberry field. At any rate it is a law similar to this by which we have taken possession of the territory of Indians and Mexicans.

I once met with a whole family, father, mother, and children, ravaging a huckleberry field in this wise. They cut up the bushes as they went and beat them over the edge of a bushel basket, till they had it full of berries, ripe and green, leaves, sticks etc., and so they passed along out of my sight like wild men.

I well remember with what a sense of freedom and spirit of adventure I used to take my way across the fields with my pail, some years later, toward some distant hill or swamp, when dismissed for all day, and I would not now exchange such an expansion of all my being for all the learning in the world. Liberation and enlargement — such is the fruit which all culture aims to secure. I suddenly knew more about my books than if I had never ceased studying them. I found myself in a schoolroom where I could not fail to see and hear things worth seeing and hearing — where I could not help getting my lesson — for my lesson came to me. Such experience often repeated, was the chief encouragement to go to the Academy and study a book at last.

But ah we have fallen on evil days! I hear of pickers ordered out of the huckleberry fields, and I see stakes set up with written notices forbidding any to pick them. Some let their fields or allow so much for the picking. *Sic transit gloria ruris*. I do not mean to blame any, but all —to bewail our fates generally. We are not grateful enough that we have lived a part of our lives before these things occurred. What becomes of the true value of country life — what, if you must go to market for it? It has come to this, that the butcher now brings round our huckleberries in his cart. Why, it is as if the hangman were to perform the marriage ceremony. Such is the inevitable tendency of our civilization, to reduce huckleberries to a level with beef-steaks — that is to blot out four fifths of it, or the going a-huckleberrying, and leave only a pudding, that part which is the fittest accompaniment to a beef-steak. You all know what it is to go a-beef-steaking. It is to knock your old fellow laborer Bright on the head to begin with — or possibly to cut a steak from him running in the Abyssinian fashion and wait for another to grow there. The butcher's item in chalk on the door is now 'Calf's head and huckleberries.'

I suspect that the inhabitants of England and the continent of Europe have thus lost in a measure their natural rights, with the increase of population and monopolies. The wild fruits of the earth disappear before civilization, or only the husks of them are to be found in large markets. The whole country becomes, as it were, a town or beaten common, and almost the only fruits left are a few hips and haws.

What sort of a country is that where the huckleberry fields are private property? When I pass such fields on the highway, my heart sinks within me. I see a blight on the land. Nature is under a veil there. I make haste away from the accursed spot. Nothing could deform her fair face more. I cannot think of it ever after but as the place where fair and palatable berries, are converted into money, where the huckleberry is desecrated.

It is true, we have as good a right to make berries private property, as to make wild grass and trees such — it is not worse than a thousand other practices which custom has sanctioned — but that is the worst of it, for it suggests how bad the rest are, and to what result our civilization and division of labor natually tend, to make all things venal.

A., a professional huckleberry picker, has hired B.'s field, and, we will suppose, is now gathering the crop, with a patent huckleberry horse rake.

C., a professed cook, is superintending the boiling of a pudding made of some of the berries.

While Professor D. — for whom the pudding is intended, sits in his library writing a book — a work on the *Vaccinieae* of course.

And now the result of this downward course will be seen in that work — which should be the ultimate fruit of the huckleberry field. It will be worthless. It will have none of the spirit of the huckleberry in it, and the reading of it will be a weariness of the flesh.

I believe in a different kind of division of labor — that Professor D. should be encouraged to divide himself freely between his library and the huckleberry field.

What I chiefly regret in this case, is the in effect dog-in-the-manger result; for at the same time that we exclude mankind from gathering berries in our field, we exclude them from gathering health and happiness and inspiration, and a hundred other far finer and nobler fruits than berries, which are found there, but which we have no notion of gathering and shall not gather ourselves, nor ever carry to market, for these is no market for them, but let them rot on the bushes.

We thus strike only one more blow at a simple and wholesome relation to nature. I do not know but this is the excuse of those who have lately taken to swinging bags of beans and ringing dumb bells. As long as the berries are free to all comers they are beautiful, though they may be few and small, but tell me that this is a blueberry swamp which somebody has hired, and I shall not want even to look at it. We so commit the berries to the wrong hands, that is to the hands of those who cannot appreciate them. This is proved by the fact that if we do not pay them some money, these parties will at once cease to pick them. They have no other interest in berries but a pecuniary one. Such is the constitution of our society that we make a compromise and permit the berries to be degraded, to be enslaved, as it were.

Accordingly in laying claim for the first time to the spontaneous fruit of our pastures, we are inevitably aware of a little meanness, and the merry berry party which we turn away naturally looks down on and despises us. If it were left to the berries to say who should have them, is it not likely that they would prefer to be gathered by the party of children in the hay-rigging, who have come to have a good time merely?

This is one of the taxes which we pay for having a rail-road. All our improvements, so called, tend to convert the country into the town. But I do not see clearly that these successive losses are ever quite made up to us. This suggests, as I have said, what origin and foundation many of our institutions have. I do not say this by way of complaining of this custom in particular, which is beginning to prevail — not that I love Caesar less but Rome more. It is my own way of living that I complain of as well as yours — and therefore I trust that my remarks will come home to you. I hope that I am not so poor a shot, like most clergymen, as to fire into a crowd of a thousand men without hitting somebody — though I do not aim at any one.

Thus we behave like oxen in a flower garden. The true fruit of Nature can only be plucked with a fluttering heart and a delicate hand, not bribed by any earthly reward. No hired man can help us to gather that crop.

Among the Indians, the earth and its productions generally were common and free to all the tribe, like the air and water — but among us who have supplanted the Indians, the public retain only a small yard or common in the middle of the village, with perhaps a grave-yard beside it, and the right of way, by sufferance, by a particular narrow route, which is annually becoming narrower, from one such yard to another. I doubt if you can ride out five miles in any direction without coming to where some individual is tolling in the road — and he expects the time when it will all revert to him or his heirs. This is the way we civilized men have arranged it.

I am not overflowing with respect and gratitude to the fathers who thus laid out our New England villages, whatever precedent they were influenced by, for I think that a 'prentice hand liberated from Old English prejudices could have done much better in this new world. If they were in earnest seeking thus far away 'freedom to worship God,' as some assure us — why did they not secure a little more of it, when it was so cheap and they were about it? At the same time that they built meeting-houses why did they not preserve from desecration and destruction far grander temples not made with hands?

What are the natural features which make a township handsome — and worth going far to dwell in? A river with its water-falls — meadows, lakes — hills, cliffs or individual rocks, a forest and single ancient trees — such things are beautiful. They have a high use which dollars and cents never represent. If the inhabitants of a town were wise they would seek to preserve these things though at a considerable expense. For such things educate far more than any hired teachers or preachers, or any at present recognized system of school education.

I do not think him fit to be the founder of a state or even of a town who does not foresee the use of these things, but legislates as it were, for oxen chiefly.

It would be worth the while if in each town there were a committee appointed, to see that the beauty of the town received no detriment. If here is the largest boulder in the country, then it should not belong to an individual nor be made into door-steps. In some countries precious metals belong to the crown — so here more precious objects of great natural beauty should belong to the public.

Let us try to keep the new world new, and while we make a wary use of the city, preserve as far as possible the advantages of living in the country.

I think of no natural feature which is a greater ornament and treasure to this town than the river. It is one of the things which determine whether a man will live here or in another place, and it is one of the first objects which we show to a stranger. In this respect we enjoy a great advantage over those neighboring towns which have no river. Yet the town, as a corporation, has never turned any but the most purely utilitarian eyes upon it — and has done nothing to preserve its natural beauty.

They who laid out the town should have made the river available as a common possession forever. The town collectively should at least have done as much as an individual of taste who owns an equal area commonly does in England. Indeed I think that not only the channel but one or both banks of every river should be a public highway — for a river is not useful merely to float on. In this case, one bank might have been reserved as a public walk and the trees that adorned it have been protected, and frequent avenues have been provided leading to it from the main street. This would have cost but a few acres of land and but little wood, and we should all have been gainers by it. Now it is accessible only at the bridges at points comparatively distant from the town, and there there is not a foot of shore to stand on unless you trespass on somebody's lot — and if you attempt a quiet stroll down the bank — you soon meet with fences built at right angles with the stream and projecting far over the water — where individuals, naturally enough, under the present arrangement — seek to monopolize the shore. At last we shall get our only view of the stream from the meeting house belfry.

As for the trees which fringed the shore within my remembrance — where are they? and where will the remnant of them be after ten years more?

So if there is any central and commanding hilltop, it should be reserved for the public use. Think of a mountain top in the township — even to the Indians a sacred place — only accessible through private grounds. A temple as it were which you cannot enter without trespassing — nay the temple itself private property and standing in a man's cow yard — for such is commonly the case. New Hampshire courts have lately been deciding, as if it was for them to decide, whether the top of Mount Washington belonged to A or B — and it being decided in favor of B, I hear that he went up one winter with the proper officers and took formal possession. That area should be left unappropriated for modesty and

reverence's sake — if only to suggest that the traveller who climbs thither in a degree rises above himself, as well as his native valley, and leaves some of
his grovelling habits behind.

I know it is a mere figure of speech to talk about
temples nowadays, when men recognize none and
associate the word with heathenism. Most men, it
appears to me, do not care for Nature, and would
sell their share in all her beauty, for as long as they
may live, for a stated and not very large sum. Thank
God they cannot yet fly and lay waste the sky as
well as the earth. We are safe on that side for the
present. It is for the very reason that some do not
care for these things that we need to combine to protect all from the vandalism of a few.

It is true, we as yet take liberties and go across
lots in most directions but we naturally take fewer
and fewer liberties every year, as we meet with more
resistance, and we shall soon be reduced to the same
straights they are in England, where going across
lots is out of the question — and we must ask leave
to walk in some lady's park.

There are a few hopeful signs. There is the growing *library* — and then the town does set trees along
the highways. But does not the broad landscape itself
deserve attention?

We cut down the few old oaks which witnessed the
transfer of the township from the Indian to the white
man, and perchance commence our museum with a
cartridge box taken from a British soldier in 1775.§
How little we insist on truly grand and beautiful nat-

ural features. There may be the most beautiful landscapes in the world within a dozen miles of us, for
aught we know — for their inhabitants do not value
nor perceive them — and so have not made them
known to others — but if a grain of gold were picked
up there, or a pearl found in a fresh-water clam, the
whole state would resound with the news.

Thousands annually seek the White Mountains to
be refreshed by their wild and primitive beauty —
but when the country was discovered a similar kind
of beauty prevailed all over it — and much of this
might have been preserved for our present refreshment if a little foresight and taste had been used.

I do not believe that there is a town in this country which realizes in what its true wealth consists.

I visited the town of Boxboro only eight miles west
of us last fall — and far the handsomest and most
memorable thing which I saw there, was its noble oak
wood. I doubt if there is a finer one in Massachusetts.
Let it stand fifty years longer and men will make pilgrimages to it from all parts of the country, and for
a worthier object than to shoot squirrels in it — and
yet I said to myself, Boxboro would be very like the
rest of New England, if she were ashamed of that
wood-land. Probably, if the history of this town is
written, the historian will have omitted to say a word
about this forest — the most interesting thing in it
— and lay all the stress on the history of the parish.

It turned out that I was not far from right — for
not long after I came across a very brief historical
notice of Stow — which then included Boxboro —

written by the Reverend John Gardiner in the *Massachusetts Historical Collections*, nearly a hundred years ago. In which Mr. Gardiner, after telling us who was his predecessor in the ministry, and when he himself was settled, goes on to say, 'As for any remarkables, I am of mind there have been the fewest of any town of our standing in the Province. . . . I can't call to mind above one thing worthy of public notice, and that is the grave of Mr. John Green' who it appears, when in England, 'was made clerk of the exchequer' by Cromwell. 'Whether he was excluded the act of oblivion or not I cannot tell,' says Mr. Gardiner. At any rate he returned to New England and as Gardiner tells us 'lived and died, and lies buried in this place.'

I can assure Mr. Gardiner that he was not excluded from the act of oblivion.

It is true Boxboro was less peculiar for its woods at that date — but they were not less interesting absolutely.

I remember talking a few years ago with a young man who had undertaken to write the history of his native town — a wild and mountainous town far up country, whose very name suggested a hundred things to me, and I almost wished I had the task to do myself — so few of the original settlers had been driven out — and not a single clerk of the exchequer buried in it. But to my chagrin I found that the author was complaining of want of materials, and that the crowning fact of his story was that the town had been the residence of General C — and the family mansion was still standing.

§I have since heard, however, that Boxboro is content to have that forest stand, instead of the houses and farms that might supplant it — not because of its beauty — but because the land pays a much larger tax now than it would then.

Nevertheless it is likely to be cut off within a few years for ship-timber and the like. It is too precious to be thus disposed of. I think that it would be wise for the state to purchase and preserve a few such forests.

If the people of Massachusetts are ready to found a professorship of Natural History — so they must see the importance of preserving some portions of nature herself unimpaired.

I find that the rising generation in this town do not know what an oak or a pine is, having seen only inferior specimens. Shall we hire a man to lecture on botany, on oaks for instance, our noblest plants — while we permit others to cut down the few best specimens of these trees that are left? It is like teaching children Latin and Greek while we burn the books printed in those languages.

I think that each town should have a park, or rather a primitive forest, of five hundred or a thousand acres, either in one body or several — where a stick should never be cut for fuel — nor for the navy, nor to make wagons, but stand and decay for higher uses — a common possession forever, for instruction and recreation.

All Walden wood might have been reserved, with

Walden in the midst of it, and the Easterbrooks country, an uncultivated area of some four square miles in the north of the town, might have been our huckleberry field. If any owners of these tracts are about to leave the world without natural heirs who need or deserve to be specially remembered, they will do wisely to abandon the possession to all mankind, and not will them to some individual who perhaps has enough already — and so correct the error that was made when the town was laid out. As some give to Harvard College or another Institution, so one might give a forest or a huckleberry field to Concord. This town surely is an institution which deserves to be remembered. Forget the heathen in foreign parts, and remember the pagans and salvages here.

We hear of cow commons and ministerial lots, but we want *men* commons and *lay* lots as well. There is meadow and pasture and woodlot for the town's poor, why not a forest and huckleberry field for the town's rich?

We boast of our system of education, but why stop at schoolmasters and schoolhouses? § We are all schoolmasters and our schoolhouse is the universe. To attend chiefly to the desk or schoolhouse, while we neglect the scenery in which it is placed, is absurd. If we do not look out we shall find our fine school-house standing in a cow yard at last.

It frequently happens that what the city prides itself on most is its park — those acres which require to be the least altered from their original condition.

Live in each season as it passes; breathe the air,

drink the drink, taste the fruit, and resign yourself to the influences of each. Let these be your only diet-drink and botanical medicines.

In August live on berries, not dried meats and pemmican as if you were on shipboard making your way through a waste ocean, or in the Darien Grounds, and so die of ship-fever and scurvy. Some will die of ship-fever and scurvy in an Illinois prairie, they lead such stifled and scurvy lives.

Be blown on by all the winds. Open all your pores and breathe in all the tides of nature, in all her streams and oceans, at all seasons. Miasma and infection are from within, not without. The invalid brought to the brink of the grave by an unnatural life, instead of imbibing the great influence that nature is — drinks only of the tea made of a particular herb — while he still continues his unnatural life — saves at the spile and wastes at the bung. He does not love nature or his life and so sickens and dies and no doctor can save him.

Grow green with spring — yellow and ripe with autumn. Drink of each season's influence as a vial, a true panacea of all remedies mixed for your especial use. The vials of summer never made a man sick, only those which he had stored in his cellar. Drink the wines not of your own but of nature's bottling — not kept in a goat- or pig-skin, but in the skins of a myriad fair berries.

Let Nature do your bottling, as also your pickling and preserving.

For all nature is doing her best each moment to

make us well. She exists for no other end. Do not resist her. With the least inclination to be well we should not be sick. Men have discovered, or think that they have discovered the salutariness of a few wild things only, and not of all nature. Why nature is but another name for health. Some men think that they are not well in Spring or Summer or Autumn or Winter, (if you will excuse the pun) it is only because they are not indeed *well*, that is fairly *in* those seasons.